$205.95 per copy (in United States)
Price is subject to change without prior notice.

0054

JUN -- 2014

RSMeans
Square Foot
Costs

35TH ANNUAL EDITION

2014

RSMeans
A division of Reed Construction Data, LLC
Construction Publishers & Consultants
700 Longwater Drive
Norwell, MA 02061
USA

1-800-334-3509
www.rsmeans.com

Copyright 2013 by RSMeans
A division of Reed Construction Data, LLC
All rights reserved.

Printed in the United States of America
ISSN 1540-6326
ISBN 978-1-940238-18-0

Senior Editor
Marilyn Phelan, AIA *(9, 10, 11, 12)**

Contributing Editors
Christopher Babbitt
Adrian C. Charest, PE *(26, 27, 28, 48)*
Gary W. Christensen
David G. Drain, PE *(33)*
Cheryl Elsmore
David Fiske
Robert Fortier, PE *(2, 31, 32, 34, 35, 46)*
Robert J. Kuchta *(8)*
Thomas Lane
Robert C. McNichols
Genevieve Medeiros
Melville J. Mossman, PE *(21, 22, 23)*
Jeannene D. Murphy
Stephen C. Plotner *(3, 5)*
Siobhan Soucie
Phillip R. Waier, PE *(1,13)*

Cover Design
Wendy McBay
Paul Robertson
Wayne Engebretson

Chief Operating Officer
Richard Remington

**Vice President,
Business Development**
Steven Ritchie

**Vice President,
Finance & Operations**
Renée Pinczes

Senior Director, Inside Sales
Derek F. Dean

Sales Manager
Reid Clanton

Director, Engineering
Bob Mewis, CCC *(4, 6, 7, 14, 41, 44)*

**Senior Director, Product
Management**
Jennifer Johnson

**Senior Product
Marketing Manager**
Andrea Sillah

**Senior Director,
Operations**
Rodney L. Sharples

Production Manager
Michael Kokernak

Production
Jill Goodman
Jonathan Forgit
Debbie Panarelli
Sara Rutan
Mary Lou Geary

Technical Support
Christopher Anderson
Gary L. Hoitt
Kathryn S. Rodriguez

** Numbers in italics are the divisional responsibilities for each editor.
Please contact the designated editor directly with any questions.*

Related RSMeans Products and Services

The residential section of this book is aimed at new residential construction projects valued at up to $1,000,000. The labor rate used in the calculations is open shop (non-union). The commercial/industrial/institutional section is aimed primarily at new construction projects valued at $1,500,00 and up. The labor rate in the calculations is union.

The engineers at RSMeans suggest the following products and services as companion information resources to *RSMeans Square Foot Costs*:

Construction Cost Data Books

Assemblies Cost Data 2014
Building Construction Cost Data 2014
Residential Cost Data 2014
Light Commercial Cost Data 2014

Reference Books

Estimating Building Costs
RSMeans Estimating Handbook
Green Building: Project Planning & Estimating
How to Estimate with RSMeans Data
Plan Reading & Material Takeoff
Project Scheduling & Management for Construction
Universal Design for Style, Comfort & Safety

Seminars and In-House Training

Conceptual Estimating Using RSMeans CostWorks® CD
RSMeans Online® Training
RSMeans Data for Job Order Contracting (JOC)
Plan Reading & Material Take-Off

RSMeans Online Bookstore

Visit RSMeans at **www.rsmeans.com** for a one-stop portal for the most reliable and current resources available on the market. Here you can learn about our more than 20 annual cost data books, also available on CD and online versions, as well as our libary of reference books and RSMeans seminars.

RSMeans Electronic Data

Get the information found in RSMeans cost books electronically at **RSMeansOnline.com**.

RSMeans Business Solutions

Cost engineers and analysts conduct facility life cycle and benchmark research studies and predictive cost modeling, as well as offer consultation services for conceptual estimating, real property management, and job order contracting. Research studies are designed with the application of proprietary cost and project data from Reed Construction Data and RSMeans' extensive North American databases. Analysts offer building product manufacturers qualitative and quantitative market research, as well as time/motion studies for new products, and Web-based dashboards for market opportunity analysis. Clients are from both the public and private sectors, including federal, state, and municipal agencies; corporations; institutions; construction management firms; hospitals; and associations.

RSMeans for Job Order Contracting (JOC)

Best practice job order contracting (JOC) services support the owner in the development of their program. RSMeans develops all required contracting documents, works with stakeholders, and develops qualified and experienced contractor lists. RSMeans JOCWorks® software is the best of class in the functional tools that meet JOC specific requirements. RSMeans data is organized to meet JOC cost estimating requirements.

Construction Costs for Software Applications

More than 25 unit price and assemblies cost databases are available through a number of leading estimating and facilities management software providers (listed below). For more information see the "Other RSMeans Products" pages at the back of this publication.

RSMeansData™ is also available to federal, state, and local government agencies as multi-year, multi-seat licenses.

- 4Clicks-Solutions, LLC
- Assetworks
- Beck Technology
- BSD – Building Systems Design, Inc.
- CMS – Construction Management Software
- Corecon Technologies, Inc.
- CorVet Systems
- Hard Dollar Corporation
- Maxwell Systems
- MC^2
- MOCA Systems
- Parsons Corporation
- ProEst
- Refined Data
- Sage Timberline Office
- UDA Technologies, Inc.
- US Cost, Inc.
- VFA – Vanderweil Facility Advisers
- WinEstimator, Inc.
- R & K Solutions
- Tririga

Table of Contents

Foreword | iv
How the Book Is Built: An Overview | v
Residential Models | 1
  Introduction | 3
  How to Use | 4
  Worksheets | 13
  Example | 15
  Economy | 18
  Average | 26
  Custom | 38
  Luxury | 48
  Adjustments | 58
Commercial/Industrial/Institutional Models | 65
  Introduction | 67
  How to Use | 68
  Examples | 73
  Building Types | 78
  Depreciation | 232
Green Commercial/Industrial/Institutional
  Models | 233
  Building Types | 234

Assemblies | 285
  Introduction | 289
  How to Use | 290
  Example | 294
  Substructure | 303
  Shell | 311
  Interiors | 395
  Services | 419
  Equipment & Furnishings | 491
  Special Construction | 501
  Building Sitework | 507
References | 517
  General Conditions | 518
  Location Factors | 519
  Historical Cost Indexes | 525
  Square Foot Costs | 533
  Glossary | 542
  Abbreviations | 546
  Estimating Forms | 550
Other RSMeans Products and Services | 571
Labor Trade Rates including
  Overhead & Profit | Inside Back Cover

Foreword

Our Mission

Since 1942, RSMeans has been actively engaged in construction cost publishing and consulting throughout North America.

Today, more than 70 years after RSMeans began, our primary objective remains the same: to provide you, the construction and facilities professional, with the most current and comprehensive construction cost data possible.

Whether you are a contractor, owner, architect, engineer, facilities manager, or anyone else who needs a reliable construction cost estimate, you'll find this publication to be a highly useful and necessary tool.

With the constant flow of new construction methods and materials today, it's difficult to find the time to look at and evaluate all the different construction cost possibilities. In addition, because labor and material costs keep changing, last year's cost information is not a reliable basis for today's estimate or budget.

That's why so many construction professionals turn to RSMeans. We keep track of the costs for you, along with a wide range of other key information, from city cost indexes . . . to productivity rates . . . to crew composition . . . to contractor's overhead and profit rates.

RSMeans performs these functions by collecting data from all facets of the industry and organizing it in a format that is instantly accessible to you. From the preliminary budget to the detailed unit price estimate, you'll find the data in this book useful for all phases of construction cost determination.

The Staff, the Organization, and Our Services

When you purchase one of RSMeans' publications, you are, in effect, hiring the services of a full-time staff of construction and engineering professionals.

Our thoroughly experienced and highly qualified staff works daily at collecting, analyzing, and disseminating comprehensive cost information for your needs. These staff members have years of practical construction experience and engineering training prior to joining the firm. As a result, you can count on them not only for accurate cost figures, but also for additional background reference information that will help you create a realistic estimate.

The RSMeans organization is always prepared to help you solve construction problems through its variety of data solutions, including online, CD, and print book formats, as well as cost estimating expertise available via our business solutions, training, and seminars.

Besides a full array of construction cost estimating books, RSMeans also publishes a number of other reference works for the construction industry. Subjects include construction estimating and project and business management, special topics such as green building and job order contracting, and a library of facility management references.

In addition, you can access all of our construction cost data electronically in convenient CD format or on the web. Visit **RSMeansonline.com** for more information on our 24/7 online cost data.

What's more, you can increase your knowledge and improve your construction estimating and management performance with an RSMeans construction seminar or in-house training program. These two-day seminar programs offer unparalleled opportunities for everyone in your organization to become updated on a wide variety of construction-related issues.

RSMeans is also a worldwide provider of construction cost management and analysis services for commercial and government owners.

In short, RSMeans can provide you with the tools and expertise for constructing accurate and dependable construction estimates and budgets in a variety of ways.

Robert Snow Means Established a Tradition of Quality That Continues Today

Robert Snow Means spent years building RSMeans, making certain he always delivered a quality product.

Today, at RSMeans, we do more than talk about the quality of our data and the usefulness of our books. We stand behind all of our data, from historical cost indexes to construction materials and techniques to current costs.

If you have any questions about our products or services, please call us toll-free at 1-800-334-3509. Our customer service representatives will be happy to assist you. You can also visit our website at **www.rsmeans.com**

How the Book is Built: An Overview

A Powerful Construction Tool

You have in your hands one of the most powerful construction tools available today. A successful project is built on the foundation of an accurate and dependable estimate. This book will enable you to construct just such an estimate.

For the casual user the book is designed to be:

- quickly and easily understood so you can get right to your estimate.
- filled with valuable information so you can understand the necessary factors that go into the cost estimate. For the regular user, the book is designed to be:
- a handy desk reference that can be quickly referred to for key costs.
- a comprehensive, fully reliable source of current construction costs for typical building structures when only minimum dimensions, specifications, and technical data are available. It is specifically useful in the conceptual or planning stage for preparing preliminary estimates which can be supported and developed into complete engineering estimates for construction.
- a source book for rapid estimating of replacement costs and preparing capital expenditure budgets.

To meet all of these requirements, we have organized the book into the following clearly defined sections.

How to Use the Book: The Details

This section contains an in-depth explanation of how the book is arranged and how you can use it to determine a reliable construction cost estimate. It includes information about how we develop our cost figures and how to completely prepare your estimate.

Residential Models

Model buildings for four classes of construction—economy, average, custom, and luxury—are developed and shown with complete costs per square foot.

Commercial, Industrial, Institutional Models

This section contains complete costs for 77 typical model buildings expressed as costs per square foot.

Green Commercial, Industrial, Institutional Models

This section contains complete costs for 25 green model buildings expressed as costs per square feet.

Assemblies

The cost data in this section has been organized in an "Assemblies" format. These assemblies are the functional elements of a building and are arranged according to the 7 divisions of the UNIFORMAT II classification system. The costs in this section include standard markups for the overhead and profit of the installing contractor. The assemblies costs are those used to calculate the total building costs in the Commercial/Industrial/Institutional section.

References

This section includes information on General Conditions, Location Factors, Historical Cost Indexes, a Glossary, Square Foot Costs, and a listing of Abbreviations used in this book.

Location Factors: You can adjust the total project costs to over 900 locations throughout the U.S. and Canada by using the data in this section.

Historical Cost Indexes: These indexes provide you with data to adjust construction costs over time.

Glossary: A listing of common terms related to construction and their definitions is included.

Square Foot Costs: This section contains costs for 59 different building types that allows you to make a rough estimate for the overall cost of a project or its major components.

Abbreviations: A listing of the abbreviations used throughout this book, along with the terms they represent, is included.

The Scope of This Book

This book is designed to be as comprehensive and as easy to use as possible. To that end we have made certain assumptions and limited its scope in two key ways:

1. We have established material prices based on a national average.
2. We have computed labor costs based on a 30-city national average of union wage rates.

All costs and adjustments in this manual were developed from the RSMeans Building Construction Cost Data, Assemblies Cost Data, Residential Cost Data, and Light Commercial Cost Data. Costs include labor, material, overhead and profit, and general conditions and architects' fees where specified. No allowance is made for sales tax, financing, premiums for material and labor, or unusual business and weather conditions.

What's Behind the Numbers? The Development of Cost Data

The staff at RSMeans continuously monitors developments in the construction industry in order to ensure reliable, thorough, and up-to-date cost information.

While overall construction costs may vary relative to general economic conditions, price fluctuations within the industry are dependent upon many factors. Individual price variations may, in fact, be opposite to overall economic trends. Therefore, costs are continually monitored and complete updates are published yearly. Also, new items are frequently added in response to changes in materials and methods.

Costs—$ (U.S.)

All costs represent U.S. national averages and are given in U.S. dollars. The RSMeans Location Factors can be used to adjust costs to a particular location. The Location Factors for Canada can be used to adjust U.S. national averages to local costs in Canadian dollars. No exchange rate conversion is necessary.

Factors Affecting Costs

Due to the almost limitless variation of building designs and combinations of construction methods and materials, costs in this book must be used with discretion. The editors have made every effort to develop costs for "typical" building types. By definition, a square foot estimate, due to the short time and limited amount of detail required, involves a relatively lower degree of accuracy than a detailed unit cost estimate, for example. The accuracy of an estimate will increase as the project is defined in more detailed components. The user should examine closely and compare the specific requirements of the project being estimated with the components included in the models in this book. Any differences should be accounted for in the estimate.

In many building projects, there may be factors that increase or decrease the cost beyond the range shown in this manual. Some of these factors are:

- Substitution of building materials or systems for those used in the model
- Custom-designed finishes, fixtures, and/or equipment
- Special structural qualities (allowance for earthquake, future expansion, high winds, long spans, and unusual shape)
- Special foundations and substructures to compensate for unusual soil conditions
- Inclusion of typical "owner-supplied" equipment in the building cost (special testing and monitoring equipment for hospitals, kitchen equipment for hotels, and offices that have cafeteria accommodations for employees, etc.)
- An abnormal shortage of labor or materials
- Isolated building site or rough terrain that would affect the transportation of personnel, material, or equipment
- Unusual climatic conditions during the construction process

We strongly urge that, for maximum accuracy, these factors be considered each time a structure is being evaluated.

If users require greater accuracy than this manual can provide, the editors recommend that the RSMeans Building Construction Cost Data or the RSMeans Assemblies Cost Data be consulted.

Final Checklist

Estimating can be a straightforward process provided you remember the basics. Here's a checklist of some of the steps you should remember to complete before finalizing your estimate.

Did you remember to . . .

- include the Location Factor for your city?
- mark up the entire estimate sufficiently for your purposes?
- include all components of your project in the final estimate?
- double check your figures for accuracy?
- call RSMeans if you have any questions about your estimate or the data you've found in our publications?

Remember, RSMeans stands behind its publications. If you have any questions about your estimate, about the costs you've used from our books, or even about the technical aspects of the job that may affect your estimate, feel free to call the RSMeans editors at 1-800-334-3509.

Free Quarterly Updates

Stay up-to-date throughout 2014 with RSMeans' free cost data updates four times a year. Sign up online to make sure you have access to the newest data. Every quarter we provide the city cost adjustment factors for hundreds of cities and key materials. Register at: **www.rsmeans2014updates.com**

Residential Section

Table of Contents

Page

Introduction

General	3
How to Use	4
Building Classes	6
Configurations	7
Building Types	8
Garage Types	10
Building Components	11
Exterior Wall Construction	12

Residential Cost Estimate Worksheets

Instructions	13
Model Residence Example	15

Page

Economy

Illustrations	18
Specifications	19
1 Story	20
1-1/2 Story	21
2 Story	22
Bi-Level	23
Tri-Level	24
Wings & Ells	25

Average

Illustrations	26
Specifications	27
1 Story	28
1-1/2 Story	29
2 Story	30
2-1/2 Story	31
3 Story	32
Bi-Level	33
Tri-Level	34
Solid Wall (log home) 1 Story	35
Solid Wall (log home) 2 Story	36
Wings & Ells	37

Custom

Illustrations	38
Specifications	39
1 Story	40
1-1/2 Story	41
2 Story	42
2-1/2 Story	43
3 Story	44
Bi-Level	45
Tri-Level	46
Wings & Ells	47

Page

Luxury

Illustrations	48
Specifications	49
1 Story	50
1-1/2 Story	51
2 Story	52
2-1/2 Story	53
3 Story	54
Bi-Level	55
Tri-Level	56
Wings & Ells	57

Residential Modifications

Kitchen Cabinets	58
Kitchen Countertops	58
Vanity Bases	59
Solid Surface Vanity Tops	59
Fireplaces & Chimneys	59
Windows & Skylights	59
Dormers	59
Appliances	60
Breezeway	60
Porches	60
Finished Attic	60
Alarm System	60
Sauna, Prefabricated	60
Garages	61
Swimming Pools	61
Wood & Coal Stoves	61
Sidewalks	61
Fencing	61
Carport	61
Insurance Exclusions	62
Architect/Designer Fees	62
Depreciation	63

Introduction to the Residential Section

The Residential Section of this manual contains costs per square foot for four classes of construction in seven building types. Costs are listed for various exterior wall materials which are typical of the class and building type. There are cost tables for Wings and Ells with modification tables to adjust the base cost of each class of building. Non-standard items can easily be added to the standard structures.

Cost estimating for a residence is a three-step process:

(1) Identification
(2) Listing dimensions
(3) Calculations

Guidelines and a sample cost estimating procedure are shown on the following pages.

Identification

To properly identify a residential building, the class of construction, type, and exterior wall material must be determined. Page 6 has drawings and guidelines for determining the class of construction. There are also detailed specifications and additional drawings at the beginning of each set of tables to further aid in proper building class and type identification.

Sketches for eight types of residential buildings and their configurations are shown on pages 8 and 9. Definitions of living area are next to each sketch. Sketches and definitions of garage types are on page 10.

Living Area

Base cost tables are prepared as costs per square foot of living area. The living area of a residence is that area which is suitable and normally designed for full time living. It does not include basement recreation rooms or finished attics, although these areas are often considered full time living areas by the owners.

Living area is calculated from the exterior dimensions without the need to adjust for exterior wall thickness. When calculating the living area of a 1-1/2 story, two story, three story or tri-level residence, overhangs and other differences in size and shape between floors must be considered.

Only the floor area with a ceiling height of seven feet or more in a 1-1/2 story residence is considered living area. In bi-levels and tri-levels, the areas that are below grade are considered living area, even when these areas may not be completely finished.

Base Tables and Modifications

Base cost tables show the base cost per square foot without a basement, with one full bath and one full kitchen for economy and average homes, and an additional half bath for custom and luxury models. Adjustments for finished and unfinished basements are part of the base cost tables. Adjustments for multi-family residences, additional bathrooms, townhouses, alternate roofs, and air conditioning and heating systems are listed in modification tables below the base cost tables.

Costs for other modifications, including garages, breezeways and site improvements, are in Modification, Adjustments, and Alternatives tables on pages 58 to 61.

Listing of Dimensions

To use this section of the manual, only the dimensions used to calculate the horizontal area of the building and additions and modifications are needed. The dimensions, normally the length and width, can come from drawings or field measurements. For ease in calculation, consider measuring in tenths of feet, i.e., 9 ft.6 in. = 9.5 ft., 9 ft. 4 in.= 9.3 ft.

In all cases, make a sketch of the building. Any protrusions or other variations in shape should be noted on the sketch with dimensions.

Calculations

The calculations portion of the estimate is a two-step activity:

(1) The selection of appropriate costs from the tables
(2) Computations

Selection of Appropriate Costs

To select the appropriate cost from the base tables, the following information is needed:

(1) Class of construction
    (a) Economy
    (b) Average
    (c) Custom
    (d) Luxury
(2) Type of residence
    (a) 1 story
    (b) 1-1/2 story
    (c) 2 story
    (d) 3 story
    (e) Bi-level
    (f) Tri-level
(3) Occupancy
    (a) One family
    (b) Two family
    (c) Three family
(4) Building configuration
    (a) Detached
    (b) Town/Row house
    (c) Semi-detached
(5) Exterior wall construction
    (a) Wood frame
    (b) Brick veneer
    (c) Solid masonry
(6) Living areas

Modifications are classified by class, type, and size.

Computations

The computation process should take the following sequence:

(1) Multiply the base cost by the area.
(2) Add or subtract the modifications, adjustments, and alternatives
(3) Apply the location modifier.

When selecting costs, interpolate or use the cost that most nearly matches the structure under study. This applies to size, exterior wall construction, and class.

How to Use the Residential Square Foot Cost Pages

The following is a detailed explanation of a sample entry in the Residential Square Foot Cost Section. Each bold number below corresponds to the item being described on the facing page with the appropriate component of the sample entry following in parentheses.

Prices listed are costs that include overhead and profit of the installing contractor. Total model costs include an additional markup for General Contractors' overhead and profit, and fees specific to class of construction.

RESIDENTIAL | Average **1** | 2 Story **2**

- Simple design from standard plans
- Single family — 1 full bath, 1 kitchen
- No basement
- Asphalt shingles on roof
- Hot air heat
- Gypsum wallboard interior finishes
- Materials and workmanship are average
- Detail specifications on p. 27

3

Note: The illustration shown may contain some optional components (for example: garages and/or fireplaces) whose costs are shown in the modifications, adjustments, & alternatives below or at the end of the square foot section.

Base cost per square foot of living area

5

Exterior Wall	1000	1200	1400	1600	1800	Living Area 2000	2200	2600	3000	3400	3800
Wood Siding - Wood Frame	133.80	121.10	115.25	111.15	106.95	102.40	99.45	93.75	88.30	85.85	83.50
Brick Veneer - Wood Frame	141.30	128.15	121.75	117.35	112.80	108.10	104.85	98.65	92.75	90.10	87.55
Stucco on Wood Frame	130.10	117.70	112.00	108.05	104.05	99.70	96.85	91.35	86.05	83.70	81.50
Solid Masonry	158.05	143.65	136.20	131.20	125.80	120.65	116.75	109.45	102.75	99.60	96.60

4 **6**

	1000	1200	1400	1600	1800	2000	2200	2600	3000	3400	3800
Finished Basement, Add	21.80	21.50	20.80	20.35	19.75	19.45	19.00	18.35	17.85	17.50	17.25
Unfinished Basement, Add	8.55	8.00	7.50	7.20	6.90	6.70	6.45	6.00	5.70	5.50	5.35

7 **8**

Modifications

9

Add to the total cost

Upgrade Kitchen Cabinets	$ + 4320
Solid Surface Countertops (Included)	
Full Bath - including plumbing, wall and floor finishes	+ 7120
Half Bath - including plumbing, wall and floor finishes	+ 4097
One Car Attached Garage	+ 13,653
One Car Detached Garage	+ 17,986
Fireplace & Chimney	+ 6660

Adjustments

For multi family - add to total cost

Additional Kitchen	$ + 8159
Additional Bath	+ 7120
Additional Entry & Exit	+ 1620
Separate Heating	+ 1392
Separate Electric	+ 1986

For Townhouse/Rowhouse - Multiply cost per square foot by

10

Inner Unit	.90
End Unit	.95

Alternatives

Add to or deduct from the cost per square foot of living area

Cedar Shake Roof	+ 1.55
Clay Tile Roof	+ 3.80
Slate Roof	+ 3.30
Upgrade Walls to Skim Coat Plaster	+ .50
Upgrade Ceilings to Textured Finish	+ .50
Air Conditioning, in Heating Ductwork	+ 2.86
In Separate Ductwork	+ 5.52
Heating Systems, Hot Water	+ 2
Heat Pump	+ 2.97
Electric Heat	– .37
Not Heated	– 2.93

11

Additional upgrades or components

Kitchen Cabinets & Countertops	Page 58
Bathroom Vanities	59
Fireplaces & Chimneys	59
Windows, Skylights & Dormers	59
Appliances	60
Breezeways & Porches	60
Finished Attic	60
Garages	61
Site Improvements	61
Wings & Ells	37

12

1 Class of Construction (Average)

The class of construction depends upon the design and specifications of the plan. The four classes are economy, average, custom, and luxury.

2 Type of Residence (2 Story)

The building type describes the number of stories or levels in the model. The seven building types are 1 story, 1-1/2 story, 2 story, 2-1/2 story, 3 story, bi-level, and tri-level.

3 Specification Highlights (Hot Air Heat)

These specifications include information concerning the components of the model, including the number of baths, roofing types, HVAC systems, and materials and workmanship. If the components listed are not appropriate, modifications can be made by consulting the information shown lower on the page or the Assemblies Section.

4 Exterior Wall System (Wood Siding -Wood Frame)

This section includes the types of exterior wall systems and the structural frame used. The exterior wall systems shown are typical of the class of construction and the building type shown.

5 Living Areas (2000 SF)

The living area is that area of the residence which is suitable and normally designed for full time living. It does not include basement recreation rooms or finished attics. Living area is calculated from the exterior dimensions without the need to adjust for exterior wall thickness. When calculating the living area of a 1-1/2 story, 2 story, 3 story or tri-level residence, overhangs and other differences in size and shape between floors must be considered. Only the floor area with a ceiling height of seven feet or more in a 1-1/2 story residence is considered living area. In bi-levels and tri-levels, the areas that are below grade are considered living area, even when these areas may not be completely finished. A range of various living areas for the residential model are shown to aid in selection of values from the matrix.

6 Base Costs per Square Foot of Living Area ($102.40)

Base cost tables show the cost per square foot of living area without a basement, with one full bath and one full kitchen for economy and average homes, and an additional half bath for custom and luxury models. When selecting costs, interpolate or use the cost that most nearly matches the residence under consideration

for size, exterior wall system, and class of construction. Prices listed are costs that include overhead and profit of the installing contractor, a general contractor markup, and an allowance for plans that vary by class of construction. For additional information on contractor overhead and architectural fees, see the Reference Section.

7 Basement Types (Finished)

The two types of basements are finished and unfinished. The specifications and components for both are shown on the Building Classes page in the Introduction to this section.

8 Additional Costs for Basements ($19.45 or $6.70)

These values indicate the additional cost per square foot of living area for either a finished or an unfinished basement.

9 Modifications and Adjustments (Upgrade Kitchen Cabinets $4320)

Modifications and Adjustments are costs added to or subtracted from the total cost of the residence. The total cost of the residence is equal to the cost per square foot of living area times the living area. Typical modifications and adjustments include kitchens, baths, garages and fireplaces.

10 Multiplier for Townhouse/ Rowhouse (Inner Unit .90)

The multipliers shown adjust the base costs per square foot of living area for the common wall condition encountered in townhouses or rowhouses.

11 Alternatives (Skim Coat Plaster $.50)

Alternatives are costs added to or subtracted from the base cost per square foot of living area. Typical alternatives include variations in kitchens, baths, roofing, and air conditioning and heating systems.

12 Additional Upgrades or Components (Wings & Ells page 37)

Costs for additional upgrades or components, including wings or ells, breezeways, porches, finished attics, and site improvements, are shown in other locations in the Residential Square Foot Cost Section.

Building Classes

Economy Class

An economy class residence is usually built from stock plans. The materials and workmanship are sufficient to satisfy building codes. Low construction cost is more important than distinctive features. The overall shape of the foundation and structure is seldom other than square or rectangular.

An unfinished basement includes 7' high 8" thick foundation wall composed of either concrete block or cast-in-place concrete.

Included in the finished basement cost are inexpensive paneling or drywall as the interior finish on the foundation walls, a low cost sponge backed carpeting adhered to the concrete floor, a drywall ceiling, and overhead lighting.

Custom Class

A custom class residence is usually built from plans and specifications with enough features to give the building a distinction of design. Materials and workmanship are generally above average with obvious attention given to construction details. Construction normally exceeds building code requirements.

An unfinished basement includes a 7'-6" high 10" thick cast-in-place concrete foundation wall or a 7'-6" high 12" thick concrete block foundation wall.

A finished basement includes painted drywall on insulated 2" x 4" wood furring as the interior finish to the concrete walls, a suspended ceiling, carpeting adhered to the concrete floor, overhead lighting and heating.

Average Class

An average class residence is a simple design and built from standard plans. Materials and workmanship are average, but often exceed minimum building codes. There are frequently special features that give the residence some distinctive characteristics.

An unfinished basement includes 7'-6" high 8" thick foundation wall composed of either cast-in-place concrete or concrete block.

Included in the finished basement are plywood paneling or drywall on furring that is fastened to the foundation walls, sponge backed carpeting adhered to the concrete floor, a suspended ceiling, overhead lighting and heating.

Luxury Class

A luxury class residence is built from an architect's plan for a specific owner. It is unique both in design and workmanship. There are many special features, and construction usually exceeds all building codes. It is obvious that primary attention is placed on the owner's comfort and pleasure. Construction is supervised by an architect.

An unfinished basement includes 8' high 12" thick foundation wall that is composed of cast-in-place concrete or concrete block.

A finished basement includes painted drywall on 2" x 4" wood furring as the interior finish, suspended ceiling, tackless carpet on wood subfloor with sleepers, overhead lighting and heating.

Configurations

Detached House

This category of residence is a free-standing separate building with or without an attached garage. It has four complete walls.

Semi-Detached House

This category of residence has two living units side-by-side. The common wall is a fireproof wall. Semi-detached residences can be treated as a row house with two end units. Semi-detached residences can be any of the building types.

Town/Row House

This category of residence has a number of attached units made up of inner units and end units. The units are joined by common walls. The inner units have only two exterior walls. The common walls are fireproof. The end units have three walls and a common wall. Town houses/row houses can be any of the building types.

Building Types

One Story

This is an example of a one-story dwelling. The living area of this type of residence is confined to the ground floor. The headroom in the attic is usually too low for use as a living area.

One-and-a-half Story

The living area in the upper level of this type of residence is 50% to 90% of the ground floor. This is made possible by a combination of this design's high-peaked roof and/or dormers. Only the upper level area with a ceiling height of 7 feet or more is considered living area. The living area of this residence is the sum of the ground floor area plus the area on the second level with a ceiling height of 7 feet or more.

One Story with Finished Attic

The main living area in this type of residence is the ground floor. The upper level or attic area has sufficient headroom for use as a living area. This is made possible by a high peaked roof. The living area in the attic is less than 50% of the ground floor. The living area of this type of residence is the ground floor area only. The finished attic is considered an adjustment.

Two Story

This type of residence has a second floor or upper level area which is equal or nearly equal to the ground floor area. The upper level of this type of residence can range from 90% to 110% of the ground floor area, depending on setbacks or overhangs. The living area is the sum of the ground floor area and the upper level floor area.

Two-and-one-half Story

This type of residence has two levels of equal or nearly equal area and a third level which has a living area that is 50% to 90% of the ground floor. This is made possible by a high peaked roof, extended wall heights and/or dormers. Only the upper level area with a ceiling height of 7 feet or more is considered living area. The living area of this residence is the sum of the ground floor area, the second floor area and the area on the third level with a ceiling height of 7 feet or more.

Bi-level

This type of residence has two living areas, one above the other. One area is about 4 feet below grade and the second is about 4 feet above grade. Both areas are equal in size. The lower level in this type of residence is originally designed and built to serve as a living area and not as a basement. Both levels have full ceiling heights. The living area is the sum of the lower level area and the upper level area.

Three Story

This type of residence has three levels which are equal or nearly equal. As in the 2 story residence, the second and third floor areas may vary slightly depending on setbacks or overhangs. The living area is the sum of the ground floor area and the two upper level floor areas.

Tri-level

This type of residence has three levels of living area: one at grade level, one about 4 feet below grade, and one about 4 feet above grade. All levels are originally designed to serve as living areas. All levels have full ceiling heights. The living area is a sum of the areas of each of the three levels.

9

Garage Types

Attached Garage

Shares a common wall with the dwelling. Access is typically through a door between dwelling and garage.

Basement Garage

Constructed under the roof of the dwelling but below the living area.

Built-In Garage

Constructed under the second floor living space and above basement level of dwelling. Reduces gross square feet of living area.

Detached Garage

Constructed apart from the main dwelling. Shares no common area or wall with the dwelling.

Building Components

1. Excavation	11. Collar Ties	21. Fascia	31. Backfill	41. Sub-floor
2. Sill Plate	12. Ridge Rafter	22. Downspout	32. Drainage Stone	42. Finish Floor
3. Basement Window	13. Roof Sheathing	23. Shutter	33. Drainage Tile	43. Attic Insulation
4. Floor Joist	14. Roof Felt	24. Window	34. Wall Footing	44. Soffit
5. Shoe Plate	15. Roof Shingles	25. Wall Shingles	35. Gravel	45. Ceiling Strapping
6. Studs	16. Flashing	26. Weather Barrier	36. Concrete Slab	46. Wall Insulation
7. Drywall	17. Flue Lining	27. Wall Sheathing	37. Column Footing	47. Cross Bridging
8. Plate	18. Chimney	28. Fire Stop	38. Pipe Column	48. Bulkhead Stairs
9. CeiHng Joists	19. Roof Shingles	29. Dampproofing	39. Expansion Joint	
10. Rafters	20. Gutter	30. Foundation Wall	40. Girder	

Exterior Wall Construction

Typical Frame Construction

Typical wood frame construction consists of wood studs with insulation between them. A typical exterior surface is made up of sheathing, building paper and exterior siding consisting of wood, vinyl, aluminum or stucco over the wood sheathing.

Brick Veneer

Typical brick veneer construction consists of wood studs with insulation between them. A typical exterior surface is sheathing, building paper and an exterior of brick tied to the sheathing, with metal strips.

Stone

Typical solid masonry construction consists of a stone or block wall covered on the exterior with brick, stone or other masonry.

Residential Cost Estimate Worksheet

Worksheet Instructions

The residential cost estimate worksheet can be used as an outline for developing a residential construction or replacement cost. It is also useful for insurance appraisals. The design of the worksheet helps eliminate errors and omissions. To use the worksheet, follow the example below.

1. Fill out the owner's name, residence address, the estimator or appraiser's name, some type of project identifying number or code, and the date.

2. Determine from the plans, specifications, owner's description, photographs or any other means possible the class of construction. The models in this book use economy, average, custom and luxury as classes. Fill in the appropriate box.

3. Fill in the appropriate box for the residence type, configuration, occupancy, and exterior wall. If you require clarification, the pages preceding this worksheet describe each of these.

4. Next, the living area of the residence must be established. The heated or air conditioned space of the residence, not including the basement, should be measured. It is easiest to break the structure up into separate components as shown in the example. The main house (A), a one-and-one-half story wing (B), and a one story wing (C). The breezeway (D), garage (E), and open covered porch (F) will be treated differently. Data entry blocks for the living area are included on the worksheet for your use. Keep each level of each component separate, and fill out the blocks as shown.

5. By using the information on the worksheet, find the model, wing or ell in the following square foot cost pages that best matches the class, type, exterior finish and size of the residence being estimated. Use the Modifications, Adjustments, and Alternatives to determine the adjusted cost per square foot of living area for each component.

6. For each component, multiply the cost per square foot by the living area square footage. If the residence is a townhouse/rowhouse, a multiplier should be applied based upon the configuration.

7. The second page of the residential cost estimate worksheet has space for the additional components of a house. The cost for additional bathrooms, finished attic space, breezeways, porches, fireplaces, appliance or cabinet upgrades, and garages should be added on this page. The information for each of these components is found with the model being used, or in the Modifications, Adjustments, and Alternatives pages.

8. Add the total from page one of the estimate worksheet and the items listed on page two. The sum is the adjusted total building cost.

9. Depending on the use of the final estimated cost, one of the remaining two boxes should be filled out. Any additional items or exclusions should be added or subtracted at this time. The data contained in this book is a national average. Construction costs are different throughout the country. To allow for this difference, a location factor based upon the first three digits of the residence's zip code must be applied. The location factor is a multiplier that increases or decreases the adjusted total building cost. Find the appropriate location factor and calculate the local cost. If depreciation is a concern, a dollar figure should be subtracted at this point.

10. No residence will match a model exactly. Many differences will be found. At this level of estimating, a variation of plus or minus 10% should be expected.

Adjustments Instructions

No residence matches a model exactly in shape, material, or specifications. The common differences are:

1. Two or more exterior wall systems:
   a. Partial basement
   b. Partly finished basement
2. Specifications or features that are between two classes
3. Crawl space instead of a basement

EXAMPLES

Below are quick examples. See pages 15–17 for complete examples of cost adjustments for these differences:

1. Residence "A" is an average one-story structure with 1,600 S.F. of living area and no basement. Three walls are wood siding on wood frame, and the fourth wall is brick veneer on wood frame. The brick veneer wall is 35% of the exterior wall area.

   Use page 28 to calculate the Base Cost per S.F. of Living Area.
   Wood Siding for 1,600 S.F. = $104.95 per S.F.
   Brick Veneer for 1,600 S.F. = $121.25 per S.F.

   .65 ($104.95) + .35 ($121.25) = $110.65 per S.F. of Living Area.

2. a. Residence "B" is the same as Residence "A"; However, it has an unfinished basement under 50% of the building. To adjust the $110.65 per S.F. of living area for this partial basement, use page 28.

   $110.65 + .50 ($10.85) = $116.08 per S.F. of Living Area.

   b. Residence "C" is the same as Residence "A"; However, it has a full basement under the entire building. 640 S.F. or 40% of the basement area is finished.

   Using Page 28:

   $110.65 + .40 ($31.30) + .60 ($10.85) = $129.68 per S.F. of Living Area.

3. When specifications or features of a building are between classes, estimate the percent deviation, and use two tables to calculate the cost per S.F.

   A two-story residence with wood siding and 1,800 S.F. of living area has features 30% better than Average, but 70% less than Custom.

   From pages 30 and 42:

   Custom 1,800 S.F. Base Cost   = $130.75 per S.F.
   Average 1,800 S.F. Base Cost   = $106.95 per S.F.
   DIFFERENCE   = $23.80 per S.F.

   Cost is $106.95 + .30 ($23.80) = $114.09 per S.F. of Living Area.

4. To add the cost of a crawl space, use the cost of an unfinished basement as a maximum. For specific costs of components to be added or deducted, such as vapor barrier, underdrain, and floor, see the "Assemblies" section, pages 285 to 516.

14

Model Residence Example

First Floor Plan

Second Floor Plan

A = Main House
B = 1-1/2 Story Wing
C = 1 Story Wing
D = Breezeway
E = Garage
F = Open Covered Porch

RESIDENTIAL
COST ESTIMATE

OWNERS NAME:	**Albert Westenberg**	APPRAISER:	**Nicole Wojtowicz**
RESIDENCE ADDRESS:	**300 Sygiel Road**	PROJECT:	**# 55**
CITY, STATE, ZIP CODE:	**Three Rivers, MA 01080**	DATE:	**Jan. 1, 2014**

CLASS OF CONSTRUCTION
- ☐ ECONOMY
- ☑ AVERAGE
- ☐ CUSTOM
- ☐ LUXURY

RESIDENCE TYPE
- ☐ 1 STORY
- ☐ 1 1/2 STORY
- ☑ 2 STORY
- ☐ 2 1/2 STORY
- ☐ 3 STORY
- ☐ BI-LEVEL
- ☐ TRI-LEVEL

CONFIGURATION
- ☑ DETACHED
- ☐ TOWN/ROW HOUSE
- ☐ SEMI-DETACHED

OCCUPANCY
- ☑ ONE FAMILY
- ☐ TWO FAMILY
- ☐ THREE FAMILY
- ☐ OTHER

EXTERIOR WALL SYSTEM
- ☑ WOOD SIDING - WOOD FRAME
- ☐ BRICK VENEER - WOOD FRAME
- ☐ STUCCO ON WOOD FRAME
- ☐ PAINTED CONCRETE BLOCK
- ☐ SOLID MASONRY (AVERAGE & CUSTOM)
- ☐ STONE VENEER - WOOD FRAME
- ☐ SOLID BRICK (LUXURY)
- ☐ SOLID STONE (LUXURY)

* LIVING AREA (Main Building)			* LIVING AREA (Wing or Ell)	(**B**)		* LIVING AREA (Wing or Ell)	(**C**)	
First Level	**1288**	S.F.	First Level	**360**	S.F.	First Level	**192**	S.F.
Second level	**1288**	S.F.	Second level	**310**	S.F.	Second level		S.F.
Third Level		S.F.	Third Level		S.F.	Third Level		S.F.
Total	**2576**	S.F.	Total	**670**	S.F.	Total	**192**	S.F.

lasement Area is not part of living area.

MAIN BUILDING		COSTS PER S.F. LIVING AREA	
Cost per Square Foot of Living Area, from Page	**30**	$	93.75
Basement Addition: _____ % Finished, **100** % Unfinished		+	6.00
Roof Cover Adjustment: **Cedar Shake** Type, Page **30** (Add or Deduct)		( )	1.55
Central Air Conditioning: ☐ Separate Ducts ☑ Heating Ducts, Page **30**		+	2.86
Heating System Adjustment: _____ Type, Page _____ (Add or Deduct)		( )	
Main Building: Adjusted Cost per S.F. of Living Area		$ # 104.16	

MAIN BUILDING TOTAL COST	$ 104.16 /S.F. x 2,576 S.F. x _____ = $ 268,316	
	Cost per S.F. Living Area Living Area Town/Row House Multiplier (Use 1 for Detached)	TOTAL COST

WING OR ELL (B) **1 - 1/2** STORY		COSTS PER S.F. LIVING AREA	
Cost per Square Foot of Living Area, from Page **37**		$	90.65
Basement Addition: **100** % Finished, _____ % Unfinished		+	28.25
Roof Cover Adjustment: _____ Type, Page _____ (Add or Deduct)		( )	—
Central Air Conditioning: ☐ Separate Ducts ☑ Heating Ducts, Page **30**		+	2.86
Heating System Adjustment: _____ Type, Page _____ (Add or Deduct)		( )	—
Wing or Ell (**B**): Adjusted Cost per S.F. of Living Area		$ # 121.76	

WING OR ELL (B) TOTAL COST	$ 121.76 /S.F. x 670 S.F. = $ 81,579	
	Cost per S.F. Living Area Living Area	TOTAL COST

WING OR ELL (C) **1** STORY		COSTS PER S.F. LIVING AREA	
Cost per Square Foot of Living Area, from Page **# 37** (WOOD SIDING)		$	153.15
Basement Addition: _____ % Finished, _____ % Unfinished		+	—
Roof Cover Adjustment: _____ Type, Page _____ (Add or Deduct)		( )	—
Central Air Conditioning: ☐ Separate Ducts ☐ Heating Ducts, Page _____		+	—
Heating System Adjustment: _____ Type, Page _____ (Add or Deduct)		( )	—
Wing or Ell (C) Adjusted Cost per S.F. of Living Area		$ 153.15	

WING OR ELL (C) TOTAL COST	$ 153.15 /S.F. x 192 S.F. = $ 29,405	
	Cost per S.F. Living Area Living Area	TOTAL COST

TOTAL THIS PAGE	379,300

Page 1 of 2

RESIDENTIAL

COST ESTIMATE

Total Page 1						$	379,300
			QUANTITY	**UNIT COST**			
Additional Bathrooms: __2__ Full, __1__ Half 2 @ 7120 1 @ 4097					+		18,337
Finished Attic: __N/A__ Ft. x _____ Ft.				S.F.			
Breezeway: ☑ Open ☐ closed __12__ Ft. x __12__ Ft.			144	S.F.	33.89	+	4,880
Covered Porch: ☑ Open ☐ Enclosed __18__ Ft. x __12__ Ft.			216	S.F.	35.51	+	7,670
Fireplace: ☑ Interior Chimney ☐ Exterior Chimney							
☑ No. of Flues (2) ☑ Additional Fireplaces **1 - 2nd Story**					+		11,167
Appliances:					+		—
Kitchen Cabinets Adjustments: (±)							—
☑ Garage ☐ Carport: __2__ Car(s) Description **Wood, Attached** (±)							23,160
Miscellaneous:					+		

ADJUSTED TOTAL BUILDING COST		$	444,514

REPLACEMENT COST		
ADJUSTED TOTAL BUILDING COST	$	444,514
Site Improvements		
(A) Paving & Sidewalks	$	
(B) Landscaping	$	
(C) Fences	$	
(D) Swimming Pools	$	
(E) Miscellaneous	$	
TOTAL	$	444,514
Location Factor	x	1.050
Location Replacement Cost	$	466,739
Depreciation	-$	46,674
LOCAL DEPRECIATED COST	$	420,065

INSURANCE COST		
ADJUSTED TOTAL BUILDING COST	$	
Insurance Exclusions		
(A) Footings, sitework, Underground Piping	-$	
(B) Architects Fees	-$	
Total Building Cost Less Exclusion	$	
Location Factor	x	
LOCAL INSURABLE REPLACEMENT COST	$	

SKETCH AND ADDITIONAL CALCULATIONS

1 Story

1-1/2 Story

2 Story

Bi-Level

Tri-Level

	Components
1 Site Work	Site preparation for slab or excavation for lower level; 4' deep trench excavation for foundation wall.
2 Foundations	Continuous reinforced concrete footing, 8" deep x 18" wide; dampproofed and insulated 8" thick reinforced concrete block foundation wall, 4' deep; 4" concrete slab on 4" crushed stone base and polyethylene vapor barrier, trowel finish.
3 Framing	Exterior walls—2 x 4 wood studs, 16" O.C.; 1/2" insulation board sheathing; wood truss roof 24" O.C. or 2 x 6 rafters 16" O.C. with 1/2" plywood sheathing, 4 in 12 or 8 in 12 roof pitch.
4 Exterior Walls	Beveled wood siding and #15 felt building paper on insulated wood frame walls; sliding sash or double hung wood windows; 2 flush solid core wood exterior doors. **Alternates:** • Brick veneer on wood frame, has 4" veneer of common brick. • Stucco on wood frame has 1" thick colored stucco finish. • Painted concrete block has 8" concrete block sealed and painted on exterior and furring on the interior for the drywall.
5 Roofing	20 year asphalt shingles; #15 felt building paper; aluminum gutters, downspouts, drip edge and flashings.
6 Interiors	Walls and ceilings—1/2" taped and finished drywall, primed and painted with 2 coats; painted baseboard and trim; rubber backed carpeting 80%, asphalt tile 20%; hollow core wood interior doors.
7 Specialties	Economy grade kitchen cabinets—6 L.F. wall and base with plastic laminate counter top and kitchen sink; 30 gallon electric water heater.
8 Mechanical	1 lavatory, white, wall hung; 1 water closet, white; 1 bathtub, enameled steel, white; gas fired warm air heat.
9 Electrical	100 Amp. service; romex wiring; incandescent lighting fixtures, switches, receptacles.
10 Overhead and Profit	General Contractor overhead and profit.

Adjustments

Unfinished Basement:
7' high 8" concrete block or cast-in-place concrete walls.

Finished Basement:
Includes inexpensive paneling or drywall on foundation walls. Inexpensive sponge backed carpeting on concrete floor, drywall ceiling, and lighting.

- **Mass produced from stock plans**
- **Single family — 1 full bath, 1 kitchen**
- **No basement**
- **Asphalt shingles on roof**
- **Hot air heat**
- **Gypsum wallboard interior finishes**
- **Materials and workmanship are sufficient to meet codes**
- **Detail specifications on page 19**

Note: The illustration shown may contain some optional components (for example: garages and/or fireplaces) whose costs are shown in the modifications, adjustments, & alternatives below or at the end of the square foot section.

©Home Planners, Inc.

Base cost per square foot of living area

Exterior Wall	Living Area										
	600	800	1000	1200	1400	1600	1800	2000	2400	2800	3200
Wood Siding - Wood Frame	124.80	112.85	103.70	96.45	90.00	85.95	83.90	81.20	75.60	71.60	68.90
Brick Veneer - Wood Frame	131.55	118.85	109.20	101.35	94.50	90.10	87.95	85.00	79.10	74.80	71.90
Stucco on Wood Frame	118.20	106.95	98.30	91.60	85.65	81.80	79.90	77.45	72.20	68.45	66.00
Painted Concrete Block	125.55	113.50	104.30	97.00	90.50	86.40	84.35	81.65	76.00	71.95	69.20
Finished Basement, Add	31.25	29.40	28.15	26.95	26.00	25.45	25.05	24.55	23.85	23.35	22.85
Unfinished Basement, Add	13.75	12.25	11.25	10.30	9.55	9.10	8.80	8.45	7.85	7.45	7.05

Modifications

Add to the total cost

Upgrade Kitchen Cabinets	$ + 920
Solid Surface Countertops	+ 661
Full Bath - including plumbing, wall and floor finishes	+ 5695
Half Bath - including plumbing, wall and floor finishes	+ 3277
One Car Attached Garage	+ 12,308
One Car Detached Garage	+ 15,837
Fireplace & Chimney	+ 5692

Adjustments

For multi family - add to total cost

Additional Kitchen	$ + 4618
Additional Bath	+ 5695
Additional Entry & Exit	+ 1620
Separate Heating	+ 1392
Separate Electric	+ 1115

For Townhouse/Rowhouse -
Multiply cost per square foot by

Inner Unit	.95
End Unit	.97

Alternatives

Add to or deduct from the cost per square foot of living area

Composition Roll Roofing	– 1.10
Cedar Shake Roof	+ 3.65
Upgrade Walls and Ceilings to Skim Coat Plaster	+ .68
Upgrade Ceilings to Textured Finish	+ .50
Air Conditioning, in Heating Ductwork	+ 4.57
In Separate Ductwork	+ 6.69
Heating Systems, Hot Water	+ 2.10
Heat Pump	+ 2.45
Electric Heat	– .85
Not Heated	– 3.76

Additional upgrades or components

Kitchen Cabinets & Countertops	Page 58
Bathroom Vanities	59
Fireplaces & Chimneys	59
Windows, Skylights & Dormers	59
Appliances	60
Breezeways & Porches	60
Finished Attic	60
Garages	61
Site Improvements	61
Wings & Ells	25

Important: See the Reference Section for Location Factors (to adjust for your city) and Estimating Forms.

- Mass produced from stock plans
- Single family — 1 full bath, 1 kitchen
- No basement
- Asphalt shingles on roof
- Hot air heat
- Gypsum wallboard interior finishes
- Materials and workmanship are sufficient to meet codes
- Detail specifications on page 19

Note: The illustration shown may contain some optional components (for example: garages and/or fireplaces) whose costs are shown in the modifications, adjustments, & alternatives below or at the end of the square foot section.

Base cost per square foot of living area

Exterior Wall	Living Area										
	600	800	1000	1200	1400	1600	1800	2000	2400	2800	3200
Wood Siding - Wood Frame	142.95	118.65	106.00	100.10	95.90	89.25	86.15	82.90	75.95	73.35	70.55
Brick Veneer - Wood Frame	152.40	125.50	112.30	106.05	101.50	94.40	91.00	87.45	80.05	77.25	74.15
Stucco on Wood Frame	133.75	111.95	99.80	94.25	90.35	84.25	81.40	78.35	72.00	69.60	67.05
Painted Concrete Block	144.00	119.40	106.70	100.75	96.55	89.85	86.70	83.35	76.40	73.80	70.95
Finished Basement, Add	23.95	20.35	19.45	18.75	18.30	17.60	17.20	16.85	16.05	15.75	15.35
Unfinished Basement, Add	12.10	9.30	8.55	7.95	7.55	7.00	6.70	6.45	5.85	5.55	5.25

Modifications

Add to the total cost

Upgrade Kitchen Cabinets	$ + 920
Solid Surface Countertops	+ 661
Full Bath - including plumbing, wall and floor finishes	+ 5695
Half Bath - including plumbing, wall and floor finishes	+ 3277
One Car Attached Garage	+ 12,308
One Car Detached Garage	+ 15,837
Fireplace & Chimney	+ 5692

Adjustments

For multi family - add to total cost

Additional Kitchen	$ + 4618
Additional Bath	+ 5695
Additional Entry & Exit	+ 1620
Separate Heating	+ 1392
Separate Electric	+ 1115

For Townhouse/Rowhouse -
Multiply cost per square foot by

Inner Unit	.95
End Unit	.97

Alternatives

Add to or deduct from the cost per square foot of living area

Composition Roll Roofing	– .75
Cedar Shake Roof	+ 2.60
Upgrade Walls and Ceilings to Skim Coat Plaster	+ .68
Upgrade Ceilings to Textured Finish	+ .50
Air Conditioning, in Heating Ductwork	+ 3.41
In Separate Ductwork	+ 5.88
Heating Systems, Hot Water	+ 2
Heat Pump	+ 2.70
Electric Heat	– .68
Not Heated	– 3.46

Additional upgrades or components

Kitchen Cabinets & Countertops	Page 58
Bathroom Vanities	59
Fireplaces & Chimneys	59
Windows, Skylights & Dormers	59
Appliances	60
Breezeways & Porches	60
Finished Attic	60
Garages	61
Site Improvements	61
Wings & Ells	25

Important: See the Reference Section for Location Factors (to adjust for your city) and Estimating Forms.

- **Mass produced from stock plans**
- **Single family — 1 full bath, 1 kitchen**
- **No basement**
- **Asphalt shingles on roof**
- **Hot air heat**
- **Gypsum wallboard interior finishes**
- **Materials and workmanship are sufficient to meet codes**
- **Detail specifications on page 19**

Note: The illustration shown may contain some optional components (for example: garages and/or fireplaces) whose costs are shown in the modifications, adjustments, & alternatives below or at the end of the square foot section.

Base cost per square foot of living area

Exterior Wall	Living Area										
	1000	1200	1400	1600	1800	2000	2200	2600	3000	3400	3800
Wood Siding - Wood Frame	112.85	101.90	96.95	93.45	89.95	85.90	83.30	78.40	73.50	71.35	69.35
Brick Veneer - Wood Frame	120.15	108.65	103.25	99.50	95.60	91.40	88.50	83.10	77.85	75.45	73.30
Stucco on Wood Frame	105.65	95.30	90.75	87.55	84.35	80.55	78.25	73.75	69.20	67.30	65.55
Painted Concrete Block	113.65	102.65	97.65	94.10	90.55	86.50	83.85	78.90	73.95	71.75	69.75
Finished Basement, Add	16.35	15.65	15.10	14.75	14.35	14.10	13.80	13.25	12.90	12.65	12.45
Unfinished Basement, Add	7.45	6.90	6.45	6.15	5.80	5.60	5.40	4.95	4.70	4.50	4.30

Modifications

Add to the total cost

Upgrade Kitchen Cabinets	$ + 920
Solid Surface Countertops	+ 661
Full Bath - including plumbing, wall and floor finishes	+ 5695
Half Bath - including plumbing, wall and floor finishes	+ 3277
One Car Attached Garage	+ 12,308
One Car Detached Garage	+ 15,837
Fireplace & Chimney	+ 6290

Adjustments

For multi family - add to total cost

Additional Kitchen	$ + 4618
Additional Bath	+ 5695
Additional Entry & Exit	+ 1620
Separate Heating	+ 1392
Separate Electric	+ 1115

For Townhouse/Rowhouse -
Multiply cost per square foot by

Inner Unit	.93
End Unit	.96

Alternatives

Add to or deduct from the cost per square foot of living area

Composition Roll Roofing	– .55
Cedar Shake Roof	+ 1.80
Upgrade Walls and Ceilings to Skim Coat Plaster	+ .69
Upgrade Ceilings to Textured Finish	+ .50
Air Conditioning, in Heating Ductwork	+ 2.77
In Separate Ductwork	+ 5.39
Heating Systems, Hot Water	+ 1.95
Heat Pump	+ 2.87
Electric Heat	– .59
Not Heated	– 3.27

Additional upgrades or components

Kitchen Cabinets & Countertops	Page 58
Bathroom Vanities	59
Fireplaces & Chimneys	59
Windows, Skylights & Dormers	59
Appliances	60
Breezeways & Porches	60
Finished Attic	60
Garages	61
Site Improvements	61
Wings & Ells	25

- **Mass produced from stock plans**
- **Single family — 1 full bath, 1 kitchen**
- **No basement**
- **Asphalt shingles on roof**
- **Hot air heat**
- **Gypsum wallboard interior finishes**
- **Materials and workmanship are sufficient to meet codes**
- **Detail specifications on page 19**

Note: The illustration shown may contain some optional components (for example: garages and/or fireplaces) whose costs are shown in the modifications, adjustments, & alternatives below or at the end of the square foot section.

Base cost per square foot of living area

Exterior Wall	Living Area										
	1000	1200	1400	1600	1800	2000	2200	2600	3000	3400	3800
Wood Siding - Wood Frame	104.50	94.20	89.65	86.60	83.40	79.65	77.40	73.00	68.55	66.60	64.80
Brick Veneer - Wood Frame	109.95	99.25	94.40	91.10	87.70	83.75	81.25	76.50	71.75	69.70	67.80
Stucco on Wood Frame	99.15	89.20	85.00	82.15	79.30	75.60	73.55	69.55	65.30	63.55	61.95
Painted Concrete Block	105.10	94.75	90.20	87.10	83.95	80.10	77.75	73.40	68.90	66.95	65.15
Finished Basement, Add	16.35	15.65	15.10	14.75	14.35	14.10	13.80	13.25	12.90	12.65	12.45
Unfinished Basement, Add	7.45	6.90	6.45	6.15	5.80	5.60	5.40	4.95	4.70	4.50	4.30

Modifications

Add to the total cost

Upgrade Kitchen Cabinets	$ + 920
Solid Surface Countertops	+ 661
Full Bath - including plumbing, wall and floor finishes	+ 5695
Half Bath - including plumbing, wall and floor finishes	+ 3277
One Car Attached Garage	+ 12,308
One Car Detached Garage	+ 15,837
Fireplace & Chimney	+ 5692

Adjustments

For multi family - add to total cost

Additional Kitchen	$ + 4618
Additional Bath	+ 5695
Additional Entry & Exit	+ 1620
Separate Heating	+ 1392
Separate Electric	+ 1115

For Townhouse/Rowhouse -
Multiply cost per square foot by

Inner Unit	.94
End Unit	.97

Alternatives

Add to or deduct from the cost per square foot of living area

Composition Roll Roofing	– .55
Cedar Shake Roof	+ 1.80
Upgrade Walls and Ceilings to Skim Coat Plaster	+ .65
Upgrade Ceilings to Textured Finish	+ .50
Air Conditioning, in Heating Ductwork	+ 2.77
In Separate Ductwork	+ 5.39
Heating Systems, Hot Water	+ 1.95
Heat Pump	+ 2.87
Electric Heat	– .59
Not Heated	– 3.27

Additional upgrades or components

Kitchen Cabinets & Countertops	Page 58
Bathroom Vanities	59
Fireplaces & Chimneys	59
Windows, Skylights & Dormers	59
Appliances	60
Breezeways & Porches	60
Finished Attic	60
Garages	61
Site Improvements	61
Wings & Ells	25

Important: See the Reference Section for Location Factors (to adjust for your city) and Estimating Forms.

- **Mass produced from stock plans**
- **Single family — 1 full bath, 1 kitchen**
- **No basement**
- **Asphalt shingles on roof**
- **Hot air heat**
- **Gypsum wallboard interior finishes**
- **Materials and workmanship are sufficient to meet codes**
- **Detail specifications on page 19**

Note: The illustration shown may contain some optional components (for example: garages and/or fireplaces) whose costs are shown in the modifications, adjustments, & alternatives below or at the end of the square foot section.

©Design Basics, Inc.

Base cost per square foot of living area

Exterior Wall	Living Area										
	1200	1500	1800	2000	2200	2400	2800	3200	3600	4000	4400
Wood Siding - Wood Frame	96.35	88.30	82.40	80.05	76.50	73.70	71.50	68.55	65.00	63.80	61.05
Brick Veneer - Wood Frame	101.40	92.85	86.55	83.95	80.20	77.25	74.90	71.65	67.90	66.65	63.70
Stucco on Wood Frame	91.40	83.80	78.35	76.20	72.80	70.25	68.20	65.50	62.20	61.05	58.50
Solid Masonry	96.90	88.75	82.85	80.45	76.90	74.10	71.85	68.90	65.35	64.10	61.35
Finished Basement, Add*	19.65	18.70	17.95	17.65	17.30	16.95	16.65	16.25	15.90	15.75	15.45
Unfinished Basement, Add*	8.20	7.45	6.90	6.60	6.35	6.05	5.85	5.55	5.25	5.10	4.90

*Basement under middle level only.

Modifications

Add to the total cost

Upgrade Kitchen Cabinets	$ + 920
Solid Surface Countertops	+ 661
Full Bath - including plumbing, wall and floor finishes	+ 5695
Half Bath - including plumbing, wall and floor finishes	+ 3277
One Car Attached Garage	+ 12,308
One Car Detached Garage	+ 15,837
Fireplace & Chimney	+ 5692

Adjustments

For multi family - add to total cost

Additional Kitchen	$ + 4618
Additional Bath	+ 5695
Additional Entry & Exit	+ 1620
Separate Heating	+ 1392
Separate Electric	+ 1115

For Townhouse/Rowhouse -
Multiply cost per square foot by

Inner Unit	.93
End Unit	.96

Alternatives

Add to or deduct from the cost per square foot of living area

Composition Roll Roofing	− .75
Cedar Shake Roof	+ 2.60
Upgrade Walls and Ceilings to Skim Coat Plaster	+ .59
Upgrade Ceilings to Textured Finish	+ .50
Air Conditioning, in Heating Ductwork	+ 2.37
In Separate Ductwork	+ 5.01
Heating Systems, Hot Water	+ 1.87
Heat Pump	+ 2.97
Electric Heat	− .51
Not Heated	− 3.17

Additional upgrades or components

Kitchen Cabinets & Countertops	Page 58
Bathroom Vanities	59
Fireplaces & Chimneys	59
Windows, Skylights & Dormers	59
Appliances	60
Breezeways & Porches	60
Finished Attic	60
Garages	61
Site Improvements	61
Wings & Ells	25

1 Story — Base cost per square foot of living area

Exterior Wall	Living Area							
	50	100	200	300	400	500	600	700
Wood Siding - Wood Frame	174.10	132.30	114.25	94.70	88.75	85.20	82.75	83.40
Brick Veneer - Wood Frame	191.10	144.50	124.40	101.40	94.80	90.85	88.20	88.60
Stucco on Wood Frame	157.35	120.40	104.30	88.00	82.75	79.60	77.50	78.30
Painted Concrete Block	175.90	133.65	115.35	95.40	89.40	85.80	83.40	84.00
Finished Basement, Add	47.45	38.75	35.20	29.20	27.95	27.25	26.80	26.40
Unfinished Basement, Add	26.15	19.40	16.60	11.90	11.00	10.45	10.10	9.85

1-1/2 Story — Base cost per square foot of living area

Exterior Wall	Living Area							
	100	200	300	400	500	600	700	800
Wood Siding - Wood Frame	137.50	110.45	93.80	83.65	78.65	76.20	73.10	72.20
Brick Veneer - Wood Frame	152.75	122.55	103.95	91.55	85.95	83.10	79.60	78.70
Stucco on Wood Frame	122.60	98.50	83.85	75.90	71.45	69.45	66.70	65.90
Painted Concrete Block	139.20	111.75	94.90	84.50	79.45	76.95	73.85	72.95
Finished Basement, Add	31.75	28.15	25.75	23.10	22.40	21.90	21.45	21.40
Unfinished Basement, Add	16.10	13.30	11.40	9.35	8.80	8.45	8.05	8.05

2 Story — Base cost per square foot of living area

Exterior Wall	Living Area							
	100	200	400	600	800	1000	1200	1400
Wood Siding - Wood Frame	140.70	104.30	88.50	72.60	67.45	64.35	62.25	63.10
Brick Veneer - Wood Frame	157.70	116.50	98.65	79.35	73.55	70.00	67.65	68.30
Stucco on Wood Frame	124.00	92.40	78.55	66.00	61.50	58.75	56.95	57.95
Painted Concrete Block	142.55	105.65	89.55	73.35	68.10	64.95	62.85	63.65
Finished Basement, Add	23.75	19.45	17.65	14.65	14.05	13.65	13.40	13.25
Unfinished Basement, Add	13.10	9.70	8.35	5.95	5.55	5.25	5.05	4.90

Base costs do not include bathroom or kitchen facilities. Use Modifications/Adjustments/Alternatives on pages 58-61 where appropriate.

Important: See the Reference Section for Location Factors (to adjust for your city) and Estimating Forms.

1 Story

1 - 1/2 Story

2 Story

2 - 1/2 Story

Bi-Level

Tri-Level

	Components
1 Site Work	Site preparation for slab or excavation for lower level; 4' deep trench excavation for foundation wall.
2 Foundations	Continuous reinforced concrete footing, 8" deep x 18" wide; dampproofed and insulated 8" thick reinforced concrete foundation wall, 4' deep; 4" concrete slab on 4" crushed stone base and polyethylene vapor barrier, trowel finish.
3 Framing	Exterior walls—2 x 4 wood studs, 16" O.C.; 1/2" plywood sheathing; 2 x 6 rafters 16" O.C. with 1/2" plywood sheathing, 4 in 12 or 8 in 12 roof pitch, 2 x 6 ceiling joists; 1/2" plywood subfloor on 1 x 2 wood sleepers 16" O.C.; 2 x 8 floor joists with 5/8" plywood subfloor on models with more than one level.
4 Exterior Walls	Beveled wood siding and #15 felt building paper on insulated wood frame walls; double hung windows; 3 flush solid core wood exterior doors with storms. **Alternates:** • Brick veneer on wood frame, has 4" veneer of common brick. • Stucco on wood frame has 1" thick colored stucco finish. • Solid masonry has a 6" concrete block load bearing wall with insulation and a brick or stone exterior. Also solid brick or stone walls.
5 Roofing	25 year asphalt shingles; #15 felt building paper; aluminum gutters, downspouts, drip edge and flashings.
6 Interiors	Walls and ceilings—1/2" taped and finished drywall, primed and painted with 2 coats; painted baseboard and trim, finished hardwood floor 40%, carpet with 1/2" underlayment 40%, vinyl tile with 1/2" underlayment 15%, ceramic tile with 1/2" underlayment 5%; hollow core and louvered interior doors.
7 Specialties	Average grade kitchen cabinets—14 L.F. wall and base with plastic laminate counter top and kitchen sink; 40 gallon electric water heater.
8 Mechanical	1 lavatory, white, wall hung; 1 water closet, white; 1 bathtub, enameled steel, white; gas fired warm air heat.
9 Electrical	100 Amp. service; romex wiring; incandescent lighting fixtures, switches, receptacles.
10 Overhead and Profit	General Contractor overhead and profit.

Adjustments

Unfinished Basement:
7'-6" high cast-in-place concrete walls 8" thick or 8" concrete block.

Finished Basement:
Includes plywood paneling or drywall on furring on foundation walls, sponge backed carpeting on concrete floor, suspended ceiling, lighting and heating.

- **Simple design from standard plans**
- **Single family — 1 full bath, 1 kitchen**
- **No basement**
- **Asphalt shingles on roof**
- **Hot air heat**
- **Gypsum wallboard interior finishes**
- **Materials and workmanship are average**
- **Detail specifications on p. 27**

Note: The illustration shown may contain some optional components (for example: garages and/or fireplaces) whose costs are shown in the modifications, adjustments, & alternatives below or at the end of the square foot section.

©Home Planners, Inc.

Base cost per square foot of living area

Exterior Wall	Living Area										
	600	800	1000	1200	1400	1600	1800	2000	2400	2800	3200
Wood Siding - Wood Frame	151.30	136.60	125.70	117.05	109.70	104.95	102.30	99.25	92.80	88.25	85.15
Brick Veneer - Wood Frame	170.30	154.80	143.30	134.10	126.25	121.25	118.50	115.15	108.35	103.50	100.15
Stucco on Wood Frame	159.85	145.50	134.90	126.50	119.35	114.75	112.20	109.25	103.05	98.55	95.60
Solid Masonry	185.80	168.70	155.90	145.40	136.60	130.90	127.80	123.90	116.40	110.90	107.00
Finished Basement, Add	37.90	36.65	34.95	33.40	32.15	31.30	30.80	30.15	29.25	28.55	27.85
Unfinished Basement, Add	15.60	14.15	13.10	12.10	11.30	10.85	10.55	10.15	9.55	9.15	8.75

Modifications

Add to the total cost

Upgrade Kitchen Cabinets	$ + 4320
Solid Surface Countertops (Included)	
Full Bath - including plumbing, wall and floor finishes	+ 7120
Half Bath - including plumbing, wall and floor finishes	+ 4097
One Car Attached Garage	+ 13,653
One Car Detached Garage	+ 17,986
Fireplace & Chimney	+ 6030

Adjustments

For multi family - add to total cost

Additional Kitchen	$ + 8159
Additional Bath	+ 7120
Additional Entry & Exit	+ 1620
Separate Heating	+ 1392
Separate Electric	+ 1986

For Townhouse/Rowhouse - Multiply cost per square foot by

Inner Unit	.92
End Unit	.96

Alternatives

Add to or deduct from the cost per square foot of living area

Cedar Shake Roof	+ 3.10
Clay Tile Roof	+ 7.55
Slate Roof	+ 6.60
Upgrade Walls to Skim Coat Plaster	+ .42
Upgrade Ceilings to Textured Finish	+ .50
Air Conditioning, in Heating Ductwork	+ 4.73
In Separate Ductwork	+ 6.95
Heating Systems, Hot Water	+ 2.14
Heat Pump	+ 2.55
Electric Heat	– .47
Not Heated	– 3.14

Additional upgrades or components

Kitchen Cabinets & Countertops	Page 58
Bathroom Vanities	59
Fireplaces & Chimneys	59
Windows, Skylights & Dormers	59
Appliances	60
Breezeways & Porches	60
Finished Attic	60
Garages	61
Site Improvements	61
Wings & Ells	37

- Simple design from standard plans
- Single family — 1 full bath, 1 kitchen
- No basement
- Asphalt shingles on roof
- Hot air heat
- Gypsum wallboard interior finishes
- Materials and workmanship are average
- Detail specifications on p. 27

Note: The illustration shown may contain some optional components (for example: garages and/or fireplaces) whose costs are shown in the modifications, adjustments, & alternatives below or at the end of the square foot section.

©By Designer

Base cost per square foot of living area

Exterior Wall	Living Area										
	600	800	1000	1200	1400	1600	1800	2000	2400	2800	3200
Wood Siding - Wood Frame	169.45	141.55	126.60	119.60	114.60	107.05	103.45	99.60	91.80	88.75	85.50
Brick Veneer - Wood Frame	179.20	148.65	133.15	125.75	120.45	112.35	108.45	104.35	96.05	92.75	89.15
Stucco on Wood Frame	164.70	138.10	123.45	116.60	111.75	104.45	100.95	97.25	89.70	86.75	83.65
Solid Masonry	200.85	164.35	147.70	139.40	133.45	124.15	119.60	114.95	105.40	101.65	97.40
Finished Basement, Add	30.90	26.95	25.75	24.90	24.25	23.35	22.75	22.30	21.35	20.85	20.35
Unfinished Basement, Add	13.50	10.60	9.80	9.25	8.85	8.25	7.95	7.65	7.05	6.75	6.50

Modifications

Add to the total cost

Upgrade Kitchen Cabinets	$ + 4320
Solid Surface Countertops (Included)	
Full Bath - including plumbing, wall and floor finishes	+ 7120
Half Bath - including plumbing, wall and floor finishes	+ 4097
One Car Attached Garage	+ 13,653
One Car Detached Garage	+ 17,986
Fireplace & Chimney	+ 6030

Adjustments

For multi family - add to total cost

Additional Kitchen	$ + 8159
Additional Bath	+ 7120
Additional Entry & Exit	+ 1620
Separate Heating	+ 1392
Separate Electric	+ 1986

For Townhouse/Rowhouse -
Multiply cost per square foot by

Inner Unit	.92
End Unit	.96

Alternatives

Add to or deduct from the cost per square foot of living area

Cedar Shake Roof	+ 2.25
Clay Tile Roof	+ 5.45
Slate Roof	+ 4.80
Upgrade Walls to Skim Coat Plaster	+ .48
Upgrade Ceilings to Textured Finish	+ .50
Air Conditioning, in Heating Ductwork	+ 3.59
In Separate Ductwork	+ 6.08
Heating Systems, Hot Water	+ 2.04
Heat Pump	+ 2.82
Electric Heat	− .43
Not Heated	− 3.02

Additional upgrades or components

Kitchen Cabinets & Countertops	Page 58
Bathroom Vanities	59
Fireplaces & Chimneys	59
Windows, Skylights & Dormers	59
Appliances	60
Breezeways & Porches	60
Finished Attic	60
Garages	61
Site Improvements	61
Wings & Ells	37

Important: See the Reference Section for Location Factors (to adjust for your city) and Estimating Forms.

- **Simple design from standard plans**
- **Single family — 1 full bath, 1 kitchen**
- **No basement**
- **Asphalt shingles on roof**
- **Hot air heat**
- **Gypsum wallboard interior finishes**
- **Materials and workmanship are average**
- **Detail specifications on p. 27**

Note: The illustration shown may contain some optional components (for example: garages and/or fireplaces) whose costs are shown in the modifications, adjustments, & alternatives below or at the end of the square foot section.

Base cost per square foot of living area

Exterior Wall	Living Area										
	1000	1200	1400	1600	1800	2000	2200	2600	3000	3400	3800
Wood Siding - Wood Frame	133.80	121.10	115.25	111.15	106.95	102.40	99.45	93.75	88.30	85.85	83.50
Brick Veneer - Wood Frame	141.30	128.15	121.75	117.35	112.80	108.10	104.85	98.65	92.75	90.10	87.55
Stucco on Wood Frame	130.10	117.70	112.00	108.05	104.05	99.70	96.85	91.35	86.05	83.70	81.50
Solid Masonry	158.05	143.65	136.20	131.20	125.80	120.65	116.75	109.45	102.75	99.60	96.60
Finished Basement, Add	21.80	21.50	20.80	20.35	19.75	19.45	19.00	18.35	17.85	17.50	17.25
Unfinished Basement, Add	8.55	8.00	7.50	7.20	6.90	6.70	6.45	6.00	5.70	5.50	5.35

Modifications

Add to the total cost

Upgrade Kitchen Cabinets	$ + 4320
Solid Surface Countertops (Included)	
Full Bath - including plumbing, wall and floor finishes	+ 7120
Half Bath - including plumbing, wall and floor finishes	+ 4097
One Car Attached Garage	+ 13,653
One Car Detached Garage	+ 17,986
Fireplace & Chimney	+ 6660

Adjustments

For multi family - add to total cost

Additional Kitchen	$ + 8159
Additional Bath	+ 7120
Additional Entry & Exit	+ 1620
Separate Heating	+ 1392
Separate Electric	+ 1986

For Townhouse/Rowhouse -
Multiply cost per square foot by

Inner Unit	.90
End Unit	.95

Alternatives

Add to or deduct from the cost per square foot of living area

Cedar Shake Roof	+ 1.55
Clay Tile Roof	+ 3.80
Slate Roof	+ 3.30
Upgrade Walls to Skim Coat Plaster	+ .50
Upgrade Ceilings to Textured Finish	+ .50
Air Conditioning, in Heating Ductwork	+ 2.86
In Separate Ductwork	+ 5.52
Heating Systems, Hot Water	+ 2
Heat Pump	+ 2.97
Electric Heat	− .37
Not Heated	− 2.93

Additional upgrades or components

Kitchen Cabinets & Countertops	Page 58
Bathroom Vanities	59
Fireplaces & Chimneys	59
Windows, Skylights & Dormers	59
Appliances	60
Breezeways & Porches	60
Finished Attic	60
Garages	61
Site Improvements	61
Wings & Ells	37

- **Simple design from standard plans**
- **Single family — 1 full bath, 1 kitchen**
- **No basement**
- **Asphalt shingles on roof**
- **Hot air heat**
- **Gypsum wallboard interior finishes**
- **Materials and workmanship are average**
- **Detail specifications on p. 27**

Note: The illustration shown may contain some optional components (for example: garages and/or fireplaces) whose costs are shown in the modifications, adjustments, & alternatives below or at the end of the square foot section.

Base cost per square foot of living area

Exterior Wall	Living Area										
	1200	1400	1600	1800	2000	2400	2800	3200	3600	4000	4400
Wood Siding - Wood Frame	132.65	124.60	113.60	111.60	107.60	101.20	96.10	91.00	88.35	83.70	82.20
Brick Veneer - Wood Frame	140.65	131.80	120.25	118.30	113.85	106.85	101.50	95.90	93.05	88.00	86.40
Stucco on Wood Frame	128.65	121.00	110.30	108.30	104.50	98.40	93.45	88.60	86.10	81.55	80.15
Solid Masonry	158.55	148.00	135.10	133.15	127.80	119.45	113.55	106.85	103.40	97.60	95.75
Finished Basement, Add	18.35	18.00	17.30	17.25	16.80	16.10	15.80	15.30	14.95	14.60	14.45
Unfinished Basement, Add	7.15	6.55	6.15	6.05	5.80	5.40	5.20	4.85	4.65	4.45	4.35

Modifications

Add to the total cost

Upgrade Kitchen Cabinets	$ + 4320
Solid Surface Countertops (Included)	
Full Bath - including plumbing, wall and floor finishes	+ 7120
Half Bath - including plumbing, wall and floor finishes	+ 4097
One Car Attached Garage	+ 13,653
One Car Detached Garage	+ 17,986
Fireplace & Chimney	+ 7307

Adjustments

For multi family - add to total cost

Additional Kitchen	$ + 8159
Additional Bath	+ 7120
Additional Entry & Exit	+ 1620
Separate Heating	+ 1392
Separate Electric	+ 1986

For Townhouse/Rowhouse -
Multiply cost per square foot by

Inner Unit	.90
End Unit	.95

Alternatives

Add to or deduct from the cost per square foot of living area

Cedar Shake Roof	+ 1.35
Clay Tile Roof	+ 3.25
Slate Roof	+ 2.85
Upgrade Walls to Skim Coat Plaster	+ .48
Upgrade Ceilings to Textured Finish	+ .50
Air Conditioning, in Heating Ductwork	+ 2.60
In Separate Ductwork	+ 5.33
Heating Systems, Hot Water	+ 1.80
Heat Pump	+ 3.06
Electric Heat	– .66
Not Heated	– 3.42

Additional upgrades or components

Kitchen Cabinets & Countertops	Page 58
Bathroom Vanities	59
Fireplaces & Chimneys	59
Windows, Skylights & Dormers	59
Appliances	60
Breezeways & Porches	60
Finished Attic	60
Garages	61
Site Improvements	61
Wings & Ells	37

Important: See the Reference Section for Location Factors (to adjust for your city) and Estimating Forms.

- **Simple design from standard plans**
- **Single family — 1 full bath, 1 kitchen**
- **No basement**
- **Asphalt shingles on roof**
- **Hot air heat**
- **Gypsum wallboard interior finishes**
- **Materials and workmanship are average**
- **Detail specifications on p. 27**

Note: The illustration shown may contain some optional components (for example: garages and/or fireplaces) whose costs are shown in the modifications, adjustments, & alternatives below or at the end of the square foot section.

Base cost per square foot of living area

Exterior Wall	Living Area										
	1500	1800	2100	2500	3000	3500	4000	4500	5000	5500	6000
Wood Siding - Wood Frame	123.05	111.65	106.65	102.70	95.30	92.05	87.50	82.60	81.10	79.20	77.45
Brick Veneer - Wood Frame	130.65	118.65	113.15	108.95	100.95	97.40	92.30	87.10	85.50	83.40	81.40
Stucco on Wood Frame	119.40	108.25	103.40	99.65	92.50	89.40	85.05	80.40	78.95	77.20	75.50
Solid Masonry	147.40	134.20	127.65	122.80	113.55	109.30	103.15	97.10	95.15	92.75	90.15
Finished Basement, Add	15.75	15.60	15.15	14.80	14.30	13.95	13.55	13.20	13.05	12.90	12.65
Unfinished Basement, Add	5.80	5.40	5.10	4.90	4.55	4.40	4.15	3.95	3.80	3.70	3.60

Modifications

Add to the total cost

Upgrade Kitchen Cabinets	$ + 4320
Solid Surface Countertops (Included)	
Full Bath - including plumbing, wall and floor finishes	+ 7120
Half Bath - including plumbing, wall and floor finishes	+ 4097
One Car Attached Garage	+ 13,653
One Car Detached Garage	+ 17,986
Fireplace & Chimney	+ 7307

Adjustments

For multi family - add to total cost

Additional Kitchen	$ + 8159
Additional Bath	+ 7120
Additional Entry & Exit	+ 1620
Separate Heating	+ 1392
Separate Electric	+ 1986

For Townhouse/Rowhouse -
Multiply cost per square foot by

Inner Unit	.88
End Unit	.94

Alternatives

Add to or deduct from the cost per square foot of living area

Cedar Shake Roof	+ 1.05
Clay Tile Roof	+ 2.50
Slate Roof	+ 2.20
Upgrade Walls to Skim Coat Plaster	+ .50
Upgrade Ceilings to Textured Finish	+ .50
Air Conditioning, in Heating Ductwork	+ 2.60
In Separate Ductwork	+ 5.33
Heating Systems, Hot Water	+ 1.80
Heat Pump	+ 3.06
Electric Heat	– .51
Not Heated	– 3.18

Additional upgrades or components

Kitchen Cabinets & Countertops	Page 58
Bathroom Vanities	59
Fireplaces & Chimneys	59
Windows, Skylights & Dormers	59
Appliances	60
Breezeways & Porches	60
Finished Attic	60
Garages	61
Site Improvements	61
Wings & Ells	37

- **Simple design from standard plans**
- **Single family — 1 full bath, 1 kitchen**
- **No basement**
- **Asphalt shingles on roof**
- **Hot air heat**
- **Gypsum wallboard interior finishes**
- **Materials and workmanship are average**
- **Detail specifications on p. 27**

Note: The illustration shown may contain some optional components (for example: garages and/or fireplaces) whose costs are shown in the modifications, adjustments, & alternatives below or at the end of the square foot section.

Base cost per square foot of living area

Exterior Wall	Living Area										
	1000	1200	1400	1600	1800	2000	2200	2600	3000	3400	3800
Wood Siding - Wood Frame	124.75	112.70	107.40	103.60	99.90	95.60	93.00	87.90	82.85	80.70	78.65
Brick Veneer - Wood Frame	130.40	118.00	112.25	108.30	104.30	99.85	97.00	91.60	86.30	83.90	81.70
Stucco on Wood Frame	121.95	110.15	104.95	101.30	97.75	93.55	91.00	86.10	81.25	79.10	77.15
Solid Masonry	143.00	129.60	123.20	118.70	114.10	109.30	105.95	99.70	93.80	91.00	88.45
Finished Basement, Add	21.80	21.50	20.80	20.35	19.75	19.45	19.00	18.35	17.85	17.50	17.25
Unfinished Basement, Add	8.55	8.00	7.50	7.20	6.90	6.70	6.45	6.00	5.70	5.50	5.35

Modifications
Add to the total cost
Upgrade Kitchen Cabinets	$ + 4320
Solid Surface Countertops (Included)	
Full Bath - including plumbing, wall and floor finishes	+ 7120
Half Bath - including plumbing, wall and floor finishes	+ 4097
One Car Attached Garage	+ 13,653
One Car Detached Garage	+ 17,986
Fireplace & Chimney	+ 6030

Adjustments
For multi family - add to total cost
Additional Kitchen	$ + 8159
Additional Bath	+ 7120
Additional Entry & Exit	+ 1620
Separate Heating	+ 1392
Separate Electric	+ 1986

For Townhouse/Rowhouse - Multiply cost per square foot by
Inner Unit	.91
End Unit	.96

Alternatives
Add to or deduct from the cost per square foot of living area
Cedar Shake Roof	+ 1.55
Clay Tile Roof	+ 3.80
Slate Roof	+ 3.30
Upgrade Walls to Skim Coat Plaster	+ .46
Upgrade Ceilings to Textured Finish	+ .50
Air Conditioning, in Heating Ductwork	+ 2.86
In Separate Ductwork	+ 5.52
Heating Systems, Hot Water	+ 2
Heat Pump	+ 2.97
Electric Heat	- .37
Not Heated	- 2.93

Additional upgrades or components
Kitchen Cabinets & Countertops	Page 58
Bathroom Vanities	59
Fireplaces & Chimneys	59
Windows, Skylights & Dormers	59
Appliances	60
Breezeways & Porches	60
Finished Attic	60
Garages	61
Site Improvements	61
Wings & Ells	37

Important: See the Reference Section for Location Factors (to adjust for your city) and Estimating Forms.

- **Simple design from standard plans**
- **Single family — 1 full bath, 1 kitchen**
- **No basement**
- **Asphalt shingles on roof**
- **Hot air heat**
- **Gypsum wallboard interior finishes**
- **Materials and workmanship are average**
- **Detail specifications on p. 27**

Note: The illustration shown may contain some optional components (for example: garages and/or fireplaces) whose costs are shown in the modifications, adjustments, & alternatives below or at the end of the square foot section.

©Design Basics, Inc.

Base cost per square foot of living area

Exterior Wall	Living Area										
	1200	1500	1800	2100	2400	2700	3000	3400	3800	4200	4600
Wood Siding - Wood Frame	118.40	109.05	102.15	96.10	92.30	90.00	87.60	85.35	81.50	78.40	76.85
Brick Veneer - Wood Frame	123.60	113.75	106.40	100.00	95.90	93.50	90.85	88.50	84.45	81.20	79.50
Stucco on Wood Frame	115.85	106.70	100.05	94.25	90.50	88.35	86.00	83.80	80.05	77.05	75.55
Solid Masonry	135.15	124.25	115.85	108.65	103.95	101.30	98.20	95.55	91.05	87.30	85.45
Finished Basement, Add*	25.05	24.60	23.55	22.75	22.15	21.85	21.45	21.15	20.70	20.30	20.10
Unfinished Basement, Add*	9.50	8.80	8.20	7.65	7.35	7.15	6.85	6.70	6.45	6.20	6.10

*Basement under middle level only.

Modifications

Add to the total cost

Upgrade Kitchen Cabinets	$ + 4320
Solid Surface Countertops (Included)	
Full Bath - including plumbing, wall and floor finishes	+ 7120
Half Bath - including plumbing, wall and floor finishes	+ 4097
One Car Attached Garage	+ 13,653
One Car Detached Garage	+ 17,986
Fireplace & Chimney	+ 6030

Adjustments

For multi family - add to total cost

Additional Kitchen	$ + 8159
Additional Bath	+ 7120
Additional Entry & Exit	+ 1620
Separate Heating	+ 1392
Separate Electric	+ 1986

For Townhouse/Rowhouse - Multiply cost per square foot by

Inner Unit	.90
End Unit	.95

Alternatives

Add to or deduct from the cost per square foot of living area

Cedar Shake Roof	+ 2.25
Clay Tile Roof	+ 5.45
Slate Roof	+ 4.80
Upgrade Walls to Skim Coat Plaster	+ .40
Upgrade Ceilings to Textured Finish	+ .50
Air Conditioning, in Heating Ductwork	+ 2.41
In Separate Ductwork	+ 5.20
Heating Systems, Hot Water	+ 1.93
Heat Pump	+ 3.10
Electric Heat	– .31
Not Heated	– 2.82

Additional upgrades or components

Kitchen Cabinets & Countertops	Page 58
Bathroom Vanities	59
Fireplaces & Chimneys	59
Windows, Skylights & Dormers	59
Appliances	60
Breezeways & Porches	60
Finished Attic	60
Garages	61
Site Improvements	61
Wings & Ells	37

- Post and beam frame
- Log exterior walls
- Simple design from standard plans
- Single family — 1 full bath, 1 kitchen
- No basement
- Asphalt shingles on roof
- Hot air heat
- Gypsum wallboard interior finishes
- Materials and workmanship are average
- Detail specification on page 27

Note: The illustration shown may contain some optional components (for example: garages and/or fireplaces) whose costs are shown in the modifications, adjustments, & alternatives below or at the end of the square foot section.

Base cost per square foot of living area

Exterior Wall	Living Area										
	600	800	1000	1200	1400	1600	1800	2000	2400	2800	3200
6" Log - Solid Wall	168.40	152.75	140.95	131.55	123.60	118.40	115.60	112.15	105.30	100.30	96.85
8" Log - Solid Wall	158.15	143.50	132.60	124.00	116.75	112.00	109.45	106.35	99.95	95.45	92.35
Finished Basement, Add	37.90	36.65	34.95	33.40	32.15	31.30	30.80	30.15	29.25	28.55	27.85
Unfinished Basement, Add	15.60	14.15	13.10	12.10	11.30	10.85	10.55	10.15	9.55	9.15	8.75

Modifications

Add to the total cost

Upgrade Kitchen Cabinets	$ + 4320
Solid Surface Countertops (Included)	
Full Bath - including plumbing, wall and floor finishes	+ 7120
Half Bath - including plumbing, wall and floor finishes	+ 4097
One Car Attached Garage	+ 13,653
One Car Detached Garage	+ 17,986
Fireplace & Chimney	+ 6030

Adjustments

For multi family - add to total cost

Additional Kitchen	$ + 8159
Additional Bath	+ 7120
Additional Entry & Exit	+ 1620
Separate Heating	+ 1392
Separate Electric	+ 1986

For Townhouse/Rowhouse -
Multiply cost per square foot by

Inner Unit	.92
End Unit	.96

Alternatives

Add to or deduct from the cost per square foot of living area

Cedar Shake Roof	+ 3.10
Air Conditioning, in Heating Ductwork	+ 4.73
In Separate Ductwork	+ 6.94
Heating Systems, Hot Water	+ 2.14
Heat Pump	+ 2.54
Electric Heat	– .49
Not Heated	– 3.14

Additional upgrades or components

Kitchen Cabinets & Countertops	Page 58
Bathroom Vanities	59
Fireplaces & Chimneys	59
Windows, Skylights & Dormers	59
Appliances	60
Breezeways & Porches	60
Finished Attic	60
Garages	61
Site Improvements	61
Wings & Ells	37

- **Post and beam frame**
- **Log exterior walls**
- **Simple design from standard plans**
- **Single family — 1 full bath, 1 kitchen**
- **No basement**
- **Asphalt shingles on roof**
- **Hot air heat**
- **Gypsum wallborad interior finishes**
- **Materials and workmanship are average**
- **Detail specification on page 27**

Note: The illustration shown may contain some optional components (for example: garages and/or fireplaces) whose costs are shown in the modifications, adjustments, & alternatives below or at the end of the square foot section.

Base cost per square foot of living area

	Living Area										
Exterior Wall	**1000**	**1200**	**1400**	**1600**	**1800**	**2000**	**2200**	**2600**	**3000**	**3400**	**3800**
6" Log - Solid Wall	149.25	135.90	129.30	124.80	120.15	115.35	112.00	105.60	99.60	96.85	94.20
8" Log - Solid Wall	138.15	125.60	119.70	115.60	111.50	107.00	104.05	98.45	92.95	90.50	88.25
Finished Basement, Add	21.80	21.50	20.80	20.35	19.75	19.45	19.00	18.35	17.85	17.50	17.25
Unfinished Basement, Add	8.55	8.00	7.50	7.20	6.90	6.70	6.45	6.00	5.70	5.50	5.35

Modifications

Add to the total cost

Upgrade Kitchen Cabinets	$	+ 4320
Solid Surface Countertops (Included)		
Full Bath - including plumbing, wall and floor finishes		+ 7120
Half Bath - including plumbing, wall and floor finishes		+ 4097
One Car Attached Garage		+ 13,653
One Car Detached Garage		+ 17,986
Fireplace & Chimney		+ 6660

Adjustments

For multi family - add to total cost

Additional Kitchen	$	+ 8159
Additional Bath		+ 7120
Additional Entry & Exit		+ 1620
Separate Heating		+ 1392
Separate Electric		+ 1986

For Townhouse/Rowhouse - Multiply cost per square foot by

Inner Unit	.92
End Unit	.96

Alternatives

Add to or deduct from the cost per square foot of living area

Cedar Shake Roof	+ 1.55
Air Conditioning, in Heating Ductwork	+ 2.86
In Separate Ductwork	+ 5.52
Heating Systems, Hot Water	+ 2
Heat Pump	+ 2.97
Electric Heat	- .37
Not Heated	- 2.93

Additional upgrades or components

Kitchen Cabinets & Countertops	Page 58
Bathroom Vanities	59
Fireplaces & Chimneys	59
Windows, Skylights & Dormers	59
Appliances	60
Breezeways & Porches	60
Finished Attic	60
Garages	61
Site Improvements	61
Wings & Ells	37

1 Story — Base cost per square foot of living area

Exterior Wall	Living Area							
	50	100	200	300	400	500	600	700
Wood Siding - Wood Frame	198.95	153.15	133.20	112.40	105.85	101.90	99.35	100.20
Brick Veneer - Wood Frame	204.55	153.75	131.75	107.40	100.20	95.85	92.95	93.65
Stucco on Wood Frame	190.05	146.70	127.80	108.70	102.55	98.80	96.30	97.35
Solid Masonry	255.65	193.65	167.00	134.90	126.10	120.80	118.95	119.00
Finished Basement, Add	60.60	50.20	45.25	36.80	35.20	34.15	33.50	33.05
Unfinished Basement, Add	28.35	21.45	18.60	13.80	12.85	12.25	11.90	11.60

1-1/2 Story — Base cost per square foot of living area

Exterior Wall	Living Area							
	100	200	300	400	500	600	700	800
Wood Siding - Wood Frame	159.85	128.70	110.00	99.05	93.35	90.65	87.25	86.15
Brick Veneer - Wood Frame	215.90	161.50	133.90	117.30	108.95	104.50	99.70	97.85
Stucco on Wood Frame	192.45	142.70	118.30	105.10	97.75	93.95	89.65	87.95
Solid Masonry	250.85	189.45	157.25	135.50	125.70	120.40	114.65	112.70
Finished Basement, Add	40.85	37.00	33.60	29.95	28.90	28.25	27.70	27.55
Unfinished Basement, Add	17.80	14.95	13.00	10.90	10.30	9.95	9.60	9.50

2 Story — Base cost per square foot of living area

Exterior Wall	Living Area							
	100	200	400	600	800	1000	1200	1400
Wood Siding - Wood Frame	160.05	119.95	102.35	85.35	79.60	76.15	73.90	74.95
Brick Veneer - Wood Frame	220.10	153.70	123.40	99.45	91.20	86.25	83.00	83.45
Stucco on Wood Frame	193.80	134.95	107.80	89.00	81.85	77.50	74.70	75.40
Solid Masonry	259.20	181.70	146.75	115.00	105.20	99.30	95.45	95.40
Finished Basement, Add	32.30	27.15	24.60	20.45	19.60	19.10	18.75	18.45
Unfinished Basement, Add	14.35	10.90	9.45	7.05	6.55	6.25	6.10	5.95

Base costs do not include bathroom or kitchen facilities. Use Modifications/Adjustments/Alternatives on pages 58-61 where appropriate.

Important: See the Reference Section for Location Factors (to adjust for your city) and Estimating Forms.

1 Story

1-1/2 Story

2 Story

2-1/2 Story

Bi-Level

Tri-Level

	Components
1 Site Work	Site preparation for slab or excavation for lower level; 4' deep trench excavation for foundation wall.
2 Foundations	Continuous reinforced concrete footing, 8" deep x 18" wide; dampproofed and insulated 8" thick reinforced concrete foundation wall, 4' deep; 4" concrete slab on 4" crushed stone base and polyethylene vapor barrier, trowel finish.
3 Framing	Exterior walls—2 x 6 wood studs, 16" O.C.; 1/2" plywood sheathing; 2 x 8 rafters 16" O.C. with 1/2" plywood sheathing, 4 in 12, 6 in 12 or 8 in 12 roof pitch, 2 x 6 or 2 x 8 ceiling joists; 1/2" plywood subfloor on 1 x 3 wood sleepers 16" O.C.; 2 x 10 floor joists with 5/8" plywood subfloor on models with more than one level.
4 Exterior Walls	Horizontal beveled wood siding and #15 felt building paper on insulated wood frame walls; double hung windows; 3 flush solid core wood exterior doors with storms. **Alternates:** • Brick veneer on wood frame, has 4" veneer high quality face brick or select common brick. • Stone veneer on wood frame has exterior veneer of field stone or 2" thick limestone. • Solid masonry has an 8" concrete block wall with insulation and a brick or stone facing. It may be a solid brick or stone structure.
5 Roofing	30 year asphalt shingles; #15 felt building paper; aluminum gutters, downspouts and drip edge; copper flashings.
6 Interiors	Walls and ceilings—5/8" drywall, skim coat plaster, primed and painted with 2 coats; hardwood baseboard and trim; sanded and finished, hardwood floor 70%, ceramic tile with 1/2" underlayment 20%, vinyl tile with 1/2" underlayment 10%; wood panel interior doors, primed and painted with 2 coats.
7 Specialties	Custom grade kitchen cabinets—20 L.F. wall and base with plastic laminate counter top and kitchen sink; 4 L.F. bathroom vanity; 75 gallon electric water heater; medicine cabinet.
8 Mechanical	Gas fired warm air heat/air conditioning; one full bath including bathtub, corner shower, built in lavatory and water closet; one 1/2 bath including built in lavatory and water closet.
9 Electrical	100 Amp. service; romex wiring; incandescent lighting fixtures, switches, receptacles.
10 Overhead and Profit	General Contractor overhead and profit.

Adjustments

Unfinished Basement:
7'-6" high cast-in-place concrete walls 10" thick or 12" concrete block.

Finished Basement:
Includes painted drywall on 2 x 4 wood furring with insulation, suspended ceiling, carpeting on concrete floor, heating and lighting.

- **A distinct residence from designer's plans**
- **Single family — 1 full bath, 1 half bath, 1 kitchen**
- **No basement**
- **Asphalt shingles on roof**
- **Forced hot air heat/air conditioning**
- **Gypsum wallboard interior finishes**
- **Materials and workmanship are above average**
- **Detail specifications on page 39**

Note: The illustration shown may contain some optional components (for example: garages and/or fireplaces) whose costs are shown in the modifications, adjustments, & alternatives below or at the end of the square foot section.

©Design Basics, Inc.

Base cost per square foot of living area

Exterior Wall	Living Area										
	800	1000	1200	1400	1600	1800	2000	2400	2800	3200	3600
Wood Siding - Wood Frame	181.05	163.25	149.50	138.40	130.80	126.55	121.55	112.35	105.65	101.05	96.15
Brick Veneer - Wood Frame	202.25	183.65	169.10	157.40	149.35	144.85	139.50	129.80	122.75	117.85	112.60
Stone Veneer - Wood Frame	209.85	190.55	175.30	163.05	154.65	150.00	144.30	134.25	126.80	121.55	116.15
Solid Masonry	214.05	194.45	178.80	166.20	157.65	152.80	147.05	136.65	129.10	123.65	118.10
Finished Basement, Add	56.80	56.70	54.30	52.35	51.10	50.40	49.35	47.95	46.85	45.85	44.95
Unfinished Basement, Add	24.05	22.75	21.50	20.45	19.85	19.50	18.95	18.20	17.60	17.15	16.65

Modifications

Add to the total cost

Upgrade Kitchen Cabinets	$ + 1315
Solid Surface Countertops (Included)	
Full Bath - including plumbing, wall and floor finishes	+ 8543
Half Bath - including plumbing, wall and floor finishes	+ 4916
Two Car Attached Garage	+ 26,684
Two Car Detached Garage	+ 30,391
Fireplace & Chimney	+ 6305

Adjustments

For multi family - add to total cost

Additional Kitchen	$ + 16,589
Additional Full Bath & Half Bath	+ 13,459
Additional Entry & Exit	+ 1620
Separate Heating & Air Conditioning	+ 6803
Separate Electric	+ 1986

For Townhouse/Rowhouse -
Multiply cost per square foot by

Inner Unit	.90
End Unit	.95

Alternatives

Add to or deduct from the cost per square foot of living area

Cedar Shake Roof	+ 2.05
Clay Tile Roof	+ 6.50
Slate Roof	+ 5.50
Upgrade Ceilings to Textured Finish	+ .50
Air Conditioning, in Heating Ductwork	Base System
Heating Systems, Hot Water	+ 2.20
Heat Pump	+ 2.53
Electric Heat	– 1.38
Not Heated	– 3.94

Additional upgrades or components

Kitchen Cabinets & Countertops	Page 58
Bathroom Vanities	59
Fireplaces & Chimneys	59
Windows, Skylights & Dormers	59
Appliances	60
Breezeways & Porches	60
Finished Attic	60
Garages	61
Site Improvements	61
Wings & Ells	47

- **A distinct residence from designer's plans**
- **Single family — 1 full bath, 1 half bath, 1 kitchen**
- **No basement**
- **Asphalt shingles on roof**
- **Forced hot air heat/air conditioning**
- **Gypsum wallboard interior finishes**
- **Materials and workmanship are above average**
- **Detail specifications on page 39**

Note: The illustration shown may contain some optional components (for example: garages and/or fireplaces) whose costs are shown in the modifications, adjustments, & alternatives below or at the end of the square foot section.

●Donald A. Gardner Architects, inc.

Base cost per square foot of living area

Exterior Wall	Living Area										
	1000	1200	1400	1600	1800	2000	2400	2800	3200	3600	4000
Wood Siding - Wood Frame	163.10	151.45	143.10	133.10	127.40	121.80	111.30	106.45	102.00	98.60	93.75
Brick Veneer - Wood Frame	172.30	160.05	151.30	140.55	134.45	128.45	117.20	112.05	107.15	103.55	98.45
Stone Veneer - Wood Frame	180.30	167.55	158.45	147.05	140.60	134.35	122.40	116.95	111.70	107.95	102.50
Solid Masonry	184.75	171.70	162.45	150.70	144.05	137.55	125.30	119.65	114.20	110.35	104.70
Finished Basement, Add	37.60	37.90	36.90	35.40	34.60	33.85	32.30	31.65	30.85	30.40	29.75
Unfinished Basement, Add	16.20	15.50	14.95	14.20	13.75	13.40	12.60	12.25	11.85	11.65	11.30

Modifications

Add to the total cost

Upgrade Kitchen Cabinets	$ + 1315
Solid Surface Countertops (Included)	
Full Bath - including plumbing, wall and floor finishes	+ 8543
Half Bath - including plumbing, wall and floor finishes	+ 4916
Two Car Attached Garage	+ 26,684
Two Car Detached Garage	+ 30,391
Fireplace & Chimney	+ 6305

Adjustments

For multi family - add to total cost

Additional Kitchen	$ + 16,589
Additional Full Bath & Half Bath	+ 13,459
Additional Entry & Exit	+ 1620
Separate Heating & Air Conditioning	+ 6803
Separate Electric	+ 1986

For Townhouse/Rowhouse -
Multiply cost per square foot by

Inner Unit	.90
End Unit	.95

Alternatives

Add to or deduct from the cost per square foot of living area

Cedar Shake Roof	+ 1.45
Clay Tile Roof	+ 4.65
Slate Roof	+ 4
Upgrade Ceilings to Textured Finish	+ .50
Air Conditioning, in Heating Ductwork	Base System
Heating Systems, Hot Water	+ 2.10
Heat Pump	+ 2.64
Electric Heat	− 1.22
Not Heated	− 3.63

Additional upgrades or components

Kitchen Cabinets & Countertops	Page 58
Bathroom Vanities	59
Fireplaces & Chimneys	59
Windows, Skylights & Dormers	59
Appliances	60
Breezeways & Porches	60
Finished Attic	60
Garages	61
Site Improvements	61
Wings & Ells	47

- **A distinct residence from designer's plans**
- **Single family — 1 full bath, 1 half bath, 1 kitchen**
- **No basement**
- **Asphalt shingles on roof**
- **Forced hot air heat/air conditioning**
- **Gypsum wallboard interior finishes**
- **Materials and workmanship are above average**
- **Detail specifications on page 39**

Note: The illustration shown may contain some optional components (for example: garages and/or fireplaces) whose costs are shown in the modifications, adjustments, & alternatives below or at the end of the square foot section.

Base cost per square foot of living area

Exterior Wall	Living Area										
	1200	1400	1600	1800	2000	2400	2800	3200	3600	4000	4400
Wood Siding - Wood Frame	152.65	143.35	136.65	130.75	124.45	115.40	107.75	102.80	99.75	96.55	93.90
Brick Veneer - Wood Frame	162.45	152.50	145.40	138.95	132.40	122.60	114.30	108.90	105.70	102.10	99.25
Stone Veneer - Wood Frame	170.95	160.45	153.00	146.10	139.30	128.80	119.95	114.20	110.80	106.95	103.90
Solid Masonry	175.70	164.90	157.20	150.15	143.15	132.30	123.10	117.20	113.65	109.60	106.55
Finished Basement, Add	30.25	30.50	29.75	28.95	28.40	27.15	26.25	25.60	25.25	24.70	24.45
Unfinished Basement, Add	13.00	12.45	12.05	11.65	11.40	10.75	10.25	9.95	9.75	9.50	9.35

Modifications

Add to the total cost

Upgrade Kitchen Cabinets	$ + 1315
Solid Surface Countertops (Included)	
Full Bath - including plumbing, wall and floor finishes	+ 8543
Half Bath - including plumbing, wall and floor finishes	+ 4916
Two Car Attached Garage	+ 26,684
Two Car Detached Garage	+ 30,391
Fireplace & Chimney	+ 7116

Adjustments

For multi family - add to total cost

Additional Kitchen	$ + 16,589
Additional Full Bath & Half Bath	+ 13,459
Additional Entry & Exit	+ 1620
Separate Heating & Air Conditioning	+ 6803
Separate Electric	+ 1986

For Townhouse/Rowhouse -
Multiply cost per square foot by

Inner Unit	.87
End Unit	.93

Alternatives

Add to or deduct from the cost per square foot of living area

Cedar Shake Roof	+ 1
Clay Tile Roof	+ 3.25
Slate Roof	+ 2.75
Upgrade Ceilings to Textured Finish	+ .50
Air Conditioning, in Heating Ductwork	Base System
Heating Systems, Hot Water	+ 2.04
Heat Pump	+ 2.95
Electric Heat	– 1.22
Not Heated	– 3.43

Additional upgrades or components

Kitchen Cabinets & Countertops	Page 58
Bathroom Vanities	59
Fireplaces & Chimneys	59
Windows, Skylights & Dormers	59
Appliances	60
Breezeways & Porches	60
Finished Attic	60
Garages	61
Site Improvements	61
Wings & Ells	47

- **A distinct residence from designer's plans**
- **Single family — 1 full bath, 1 half bath, 1 kitchen**
- **No basement**
- **Asphalt shingles on roof**
- **Forced hot air heat/air conditioning**
- **Gypsum wallboard interior finishes**
- **Materials and workmanship are above average**
- **Detail specifications on page 39**

Note: The illustration shown may contain some optional components (for example: garages and/or fireplaces) whose costs are shown in the modifications, adjustments, & alternatives below or at the end of the square foot section.

Base cost per square foot of living area

Exterior Wall	Living Area										
	1500	1800	2100	2400	2800	3200	3600	4000	4500	5000	5500
Wood Siding - Wood Frame	149.95	134.75	125.80	120.40	113.40	106.70	103.15	97.40	94.30	91.60	88.90
Brick Veneer - Wood Frame	160.15	144.15	134.20	128.40	121.00	113.65	109.65	103.45	100.10	97.05	94.10
Stone Veneer - Wood Frame	169.05	152.30	141.55	135.30	127.65	119.60	115.40	108.75	105.10	101.85	98.60
Solid Masonry	174.05	156.90	145.60	139.20	131.35	123.00	118.55	111.65	107.90	104.55	101.10
Finished Basement, Add	24.00	24.00	22.80	22.20	21.70	20.85	20.35	19.85	19.45	19.10	18.80
Unfinished Basement, Add	10.40	9.85	9.20	8.95	8.70	8.25	8.00	7.75	7.55	7.40	7.20

Modifications

Add to the total cost

Upgrade Kitchen Cabinets	$ + 1315
Solid Surface Countertops (Included)	
Full Bath - including plumbing, wall and floor finishes	+ 8543
Half Bath - including plumbing, wall and floor finishes	+ 4916
Two Car Attached Garage	+ 26,684
Two Car Detached Garage	+ 30,391
Fireplace & Chimney	+ 8036

Adjustments

For multi family - add to total cost

Additional Kitchen	$ + 16,589
Additional Full Bath & Half Bath	+ 13,459
Additional Entry & Exit	+ 1620
Separate Heating & Air Conditioning	+ 6803
Separate Electric	+ 1986

For Townhouse/Rowhouse -
Multiply cost per square foot by

Inner Unit	.87
End Unit	.94

Alternatives

Add to or deduct from the cost per square foot of living area

Cedar Shake Roof	+ .90
Clay Tile Roof	+ 2.80
Slate Roof	+ 2.40
Upgrade Ceilings to Textured Finish	+ .50
Air Conditioning, in Heating Ductwork	Base System
Heating Systems, Hot Water	+ 1.84
Heat Pump	+ 3.06
Electric Heat	– 2.14
Not Heated	– 3.43

Additional upgrades or components

Kitchen Cabinets & Countertops	Page 58
Bathroom Vanities	59
Fireplaces & Chimneys	59
Windows, Skylights & Dormers	59
Appliances	60
Breezeways & Porches	60
Finished Attic	60
Garages	61
Site Improvements	61
Wings & Ells	47

Important: See the Reference Section for Location Factors (to adjust for your city) and Estimating Forms.

- **A distinct residence from designer's plans**
- **Single family — 1 full bath, 1 half bath, 1 kitchen**
- **No basement**
- **Asphalt shingles on roof**
- **Forced hot air heat/air conditioning**
- **Gypsum wallboard interior finishes**
- **Materials and workmanship are above average**
- **Detail specifications on page 39**

Note: The illustration shown may contain some optional components (for example: garages and/or fireplaces) whose costs are shown in the modifications, adjustments, & alternatives below or at the end of the square foot section.

Base cost per square foot of living area

Exterior Wall	Living Area										
	1500	1800	2100	2500	3000	3500	4000	4500	5000	5500	6000
Wood Siding - Wood Frame	149.45	134.40	127.05	120.95	111.45	106.80	101.10	95.20	93.00	90.65	88.30
Brick Veneer - Wood Frame	160.05	144.25	136.20	129.70	119.40	114.35	107.90	101.50	99.15	96.50	93.85
Stone Veneer - Wood Frame	169.25	152.70	144.15	137.35	126.30	120.85	113.85	107.00	104.45	101.60	98.65
Solid Masonry	174.35	157.50	148.60	141.55	130.15	124.50	117.25	110.05	107.40	104.50	101.35
Finished Basement, Add	21.05	21.05	20.30	19.70	18.90	18.40	17.70	17.25	17.00	16.75	16.40
Unfinished Basement, Add	9.15	8.65	8.25	8.00	7.55	7.30	6.95	6.75	6.60	6.50	6.30

Modifications

Add to the total cost

Upgrade Kitchen Cabinets	$ + 1315
Solid Surface Countertops (Included)	
Full Bath - including plumbing, wall and floor finishes	+ 8543
Half Bath - including plumbing, wall and floor finishes	+ 4916
Two Car Attached Garage	+ 26,684
Two Car Detached Garage	+ 30,391
Fireplace & Chimney	+ 8036

Adjustments

For multi family - add to total cost

Additional Kitchen	$ + 16,589
Additional Full Bath & Half Bath	+ 13,459
Additional Entry & Exit	+ 1620
Separate Heating & Air Conditioning	+ 6803
Separate Electric	+ 1986

For Townhouse/Rowhouse -
Multiply cost per square foot by

Inner Unit	.85
End Unit	.93

Alternatives

Add to or deduct from the cost per square foot of living area

Cedar Shake Roof	+ .70
Clay Tile Roof	+ 2.15
Slate Roof	+ 1.85
Upgrade Ceilings to Textured Finish	+ .50
Air Conditioning, in Heating Ductwork	Base System
Heating Systems, Hot Water	+ 1.84
Heat Pump	+ 3.06
Electric Heat	- 2.14
Not Heated	- 3.32

Additional upgrades or components

Kitchen Cabinets & Countertops	Page 58
Bathroom Vanities	59
Fireplaces & Chimneys	59
Windows, Skylights & Dormers	59
Appliances	60
Breezeways & Porches	60
Finished Attic	60
Garages	61
Site Improvements	61
Wings & Ells	47

- **A distinct residence from designer's plans**
- **Single family — 1 full bath, 1 half bath, 1 kitchen**
- **No basement**
- **Asphalt shingles on roof**
- **Forced hot air heat/air conditioning**
- **Gypsum wallboard interior finishes**
- **Materials and workmanship are above average**
- **Detail specifications on page 39**

Note: The illustration shown may contain some optional components (for example: garages and/or fireplaces) whose costs are shown in the modifications, adjustments, & alternatives below or at the end of the square foot section.

Base cost per square foot of living area

Exterior Wall	Living Area										
	1200	1400	1600	1800	2000	2400	2800	3200	3600	4000	4400
Wood Siding - Wood Frame	144.20	135.45	129.10	123.70	117.65	109.25	102.15	97.55	94.70	91.85	89.30
Brick Veneer - Wood Frame	151.55	142.30	135.70	129.90	123.55	114.65	107.00	102.10	99.15	96.00	93.30
Stone Veneer - Wood Frame	157.95	148.35	141.45	135.25	128.75	119.35	111.30	106.10	102.95	99.60	96.75
Solid Masonry	161.50	151.70	144.60	138.25	131.65	121.95	113.65	108.30	105.10	101.60	98.75
Finished Basement, Add	30.25	30.50	29.75	28.95	28.40	27.15	26.25	25.60	25.25	24.70	24.45
Unfinished Basement, Add	13.00	12.45	12.05	11.65	11.40	10.75	10.25	9.95	9.75	9.50	9.35

Modifications

Add to the total cost

Upgrade Kitchen Cabinets	$ + 1315
Solid Surface Countertops (Included)	
Full Bath - including plumbing, wall and floor finishes	+ 8543
Half Bath - including plumbing, wall and floor finishes	+ 4916
Two Car Attached Garage	+ 26,684
Two Car Detached Garage	+ 30,391
Fireplace & Chimney	+ 6305

Adjustments

For multi family - add to total cost

Additional Kitchen	$ + 16,589
Additional Full Bath & Half Bath	+ 13,459
Additional Entry & Exit	+ 1620
Separate Heating & Air Conditioning	+ 6803
Separate Electric	+ 1986

For Townhouse/Rowhouse -
Multiply cost per square foot by

Inner Unit	.89
End Unit	.95

Alternatives

Add to or deduct from the cost per square foot of living area

Cedar Shake Roof	+ 1
Clay Tile Roof	+ 3.25
Slate Roof	+ 2.75
Upgrade Ceilings to Textured Finish	+ .50
Air Conditioning, in Heating Ductwork	Base System
Heating Systems, Hot Water	+ 2.04
Heat Pump	+ 2.95
Electric Heat	− 1.22
Not Heated	− 3.32

Additional upgrades or components

Kitchen Cabinets & Countertops	Page 58
Bathroom Vanities	59
Fireplaces & Chimneys	59
Windows, Skylights & Dormers	59
Appliances	60
Breezeways & Porches	60
Finished Attic	60
Garages	61
Site Improvements	61
Wings & Ells	47

Important: See the Reference Section for Location Factors (to adjust for your city) and Estimating Forms.

- **A distinct residence from designer's plans**
- **Single family — 1 full bath, 1 half bath, 1 kitchen**
- **No basement**
- **Asphalt shingles on roof**
- **Forced hot air heat/air conditioning**
- **Gypsum wallboard interior finishes**
- **Materials and workmanship are above average**
- **Detail specifications on page 39**

Note: The illustration shown may contain some optional components (for example: garages and/or fireplaces) whose costs are shown in the modifications, adjustments, & alternatives below or at the end of the square foot section.

eDesign Basics, Inc.

Base cost per square foot of living area

Exterior Wall	Living Area										
	1200	1500	1800	2100	2400	2800	3200	3600	4000	4500	5000
Wood Siding - Wood Frame	148.25	134.30	123.90	115.20	109.45	105.20	100.30	95.05	92.85	87.85	85.25
Brick Veneer - Wood Frame	155.55	140.85	129.85	120.60	114.55	110.05	104.85	99.25	96.90	91.60	88.75
Stone Veneer - Wood Frame	161.90	146.65	135.05	125.35	119.00	114.35	108.80	102.95	100.45	94.90	91.85
Solid Masonry	165.45	149.85	137.90	128.00	121.45	116.70	110.95	105.00	102.40	96.70	93.60
Finished Basement, Add*	37.90	37.85	36.20	34.95	34.10	33.50	32.75	31.95	31.60	30.95	30.45
Unfinished Basement, Add*	16.05	15.20	14.35	13.65	13.20	12.95	12.50	12.15	11.95	11.60	11.35

*Basement under middle level only.

Modifications

Add to the total cost

Upgrade Kitchen Cabinets	$ + 1315
Solid Surface Countertops (Included)	
Full Bath - including plumbing, wall and floor finishes	+ 8543
Half Bath - including plumbing, wall and floor finishes	+ 4916
Two Car Attached Garage	+ 26,684
Two Car Detached Garage	+ 30,391
Fireplace & Chimney	+ 6305

Adjustments

For multi family - add to total cost

Additional Kitchen	$ + 16,589
Additional Full Bath & Half Bath	+ 13,459
Additional Entry & Exit	+ 1620
Separate Heating & Air Conditioning	+ 6803
Separate Electric	+ 1986

For Townhouse/Rowhouse -
Multiply cost per square foot by

Inner Unit	.87
End Unit	.94

Alternatives

Add to or deduct from the cost per square foot of living area

Cedar Shake Roof	+ 1.45
Clay Tile Roof	+ 4.65
Slate Roof	+ 4
Upgrade Ceilings to Textured Finish	+ .50
Air Conditioning, in Heating Ductwork	Base System
Heating Systems, Hot Water	+ 1.97
Heat Pump	+ 3.08
Electric Heat	− 1.08
Not Heated	− 3.32

Additional upgrades or components

Kitchen Cabinets & Countertops	Page 58
Bathroom Vanities	59
Fireplaces & Chimneys	59
Windows, Skylights & Dormers	59
Appliances	60
Breezeways & Porches	60
Finished Attic	60
Garages	61
Site Improvements	61
Wings & Ells	47

1 Story — Base cost per square foot of living area

Exterior Wall	Living Area							
	50	100	200	300	400	500	600	700
Wood Siding - Wood Frame	235.80	184.10	161.65	137.75	130.40	125.90	123.00	123.95
Brick Veneer - Wood Frame	260.50	201.80	176.35	147.60	139.20	134.20	130.85	131.55
Stone Veneer - Wood Frame	282.05	217.15	189.20	156.05	146.90	141.30	137.70	138.15
Solid Masonry	294.00	225.75	196.30	160.85	151.20	145.35	141.50	141.80
Finished Basement, Add	90.60	77.55	70.35	58.35	55.95	54.50	53.55	52.85
Unfinished Basement, Add	66.25	45.70	36.20	27.80	25.60	24.25	23.35	22.70

1-1/2 Story — Base cost per square foot of living area

Exterior Wall	Living Area							
	100	200	300	400	500	600	700	800
Wood Siding - Wood Frame	189.00	155.70	135.45	123.40	117.35	114.40	110.65	109.60
Brick Veneer - Wood Frame	211.05	173.35	150.15	134.85	127.95	124.40	120.10	118.95
Stone Veneer - Wood Frame	230.20	188.70	162.95	144.85	137.15	133.10	128.35	127.15
Solid Masonry	240.95	197.30	170.15	150.45	142.30	137.95	132.90	131.70
Finished Basement, Add	60.75	56.30	51.50	46.15	44.75	43.80	42.90	42.80
Unfinished Basement, Add	39.55	30.05	25.60	21.75	20.45	19.55	18.80	18.55

2 Story — Base cost per square foot of living area

Exterior Wall	Living Area							
	100	200	400	600	800	1000	1200	1400
Wood Siding - Wood Frame	188.85	145.15	126.00	107.60	101.40	97.55	95.05	96.40
Brick Veneer - Wood Frame	213.50	162.75	140.65	117.45	110.15	105.80	102.95	103.95
Stone Veneer - Wood Frame	235.00	178.15	153.50	125.95	117.85	112.95	109.80	110.50
Solid Masonry	247.05	186.75	160.65	130.70	122.15	116.95	113.60	114.20
Finished Basement, Add	45.40	38.80	35.15	29.25	28.00	27.30	26.80	26.45
Unfinished Basement, Add	33.15	22.85	18.15	13.95	12.80	12.15	11.65	11.40

Base costs do not include bathroom or kitchen facilities. Use Modifications/Adjustments/Alternatives on pages 58-61 where appropriate.

1 Story

1-1/2 Story

2 Story

2-1/2 Story

Bi-Level

Tri-Level

Components

#	Component	Description
1	**Site Work**	Site preparation for slab or excavation for lower level; 4' deep trench excavation for foundation wall.
2	**Foundations**	Continuous reinforced concrete footing, 8" deep x 18" wide; dampproofed and insulated 12" thick reinforced concrete foundation wall, 4' deep; 4" concrete slab on 4" crushed stone base and polyethylene vapor barrier, trowel finish.
3	**Framing**	Exterior walls—2 x 6 wood studs, 16" O.C.; 1/2" plywood sheathing; 2 x 8 rafters 16" O.C. with 1/2" plywood sheathing, 4 in 12, 6 in 12 or 8 in 12 roof pitch, 2 x 6 or 2 x 8 ceiling joists; 1/2" plywood subfloor on 1 x 3 wood sleepers 16" O.C.; 2 x 10 floor joists with 5/8" plywood subfloor on models with more than one level.
4	**Exterior Walls**	Face brick veneer and #15 felt building paper on insulated wood frame walls; double hung windows; 3 flush solid core wood exterior doors with storms. **Alternates:** • Wood siding on wood frame, has top quality cedar or redwood siding or hand split cedar shingles or shakes. • Solid brick may have solid brick exterior wall or brick on concrete block. • Solid stone concrete block with selected fieldstone or limestone exterior.
5	**Roofing**	Red cedar shingles; #15 felt building paper; aluminum gutters, downspouts and drip edge; copper flashings.
6	**Interiors**	Walls and ceilings—5/8" drywall, skim coat plaster, primed and painted with 2 coats; hardwood baseboard and trim; sanded and finished, hardwood floor 70%, ceramic tile with 1/2" underlayment 20%, vinyl tile with 1/2" underlayment 10%; wood panel interior doors, primed and painted with 2 coats.
7	**Specialties**	Luxury grade kitchen cabinets—25 L.F. wall and base with plastic laminate counter top and kitchen sink; 6 L.F. bathroom vanity; 75 gallon electric water heater; medicine cabinet.
8	**Mechanical**	Gas fired warm air heat/air conditioning; one full bath including bathtub, corner shower, built in lavatory and water closet; one 1/2 bath including built in lavatory and water closet.
9	**Electrical**	100 Amp. service; romex wiring; incandescent lighting fixtures, switches, receptacles.
10	**Overhead and Profit**	General Contractor overhead and profit.

Adjustments

Unfinished Basement:
8" high cast-in-place concrete walls 12" thick or 12" concrete block.

Finished Basement:
Includes painted drywall on 2 x 4 wood furring with insulation, suspended ceiling, carpeting on subfloor with sleepers, heating and lighting.

- **Unique residence built from an architect's plan**
- **Single family — 1 full bath, 1 half bath, 1 kitchen**
- **No basement**
- **Cedar shakes on roof**
- **Forced hot air heat/air conditioning**
- **Gypsum wallboard interior finishes**
- **Many special features**
- **Extraordinary materials and workmanship**
- **Detail specifications on page 49**

Note: The illustration shown may contain some optional components (for example: garages and/or fireplaces) whose costs are shown in the modifications, adjustments, & alternatives below or at the end of the square foot section.

©Home Planners, Inc.

Base cost per square foot of living area

Exterior Wall	Living Area										
	1000	1200	1400	1600	1800	2000	2400	2800	3200	3600	4000
Wood Siding - Wood Frame	208.10	191.70	178.60	169.60	164.40	158.60	147.90	140.10	134.75	129.00	124.40
Brick Veneer - Wood Frame	217.20	199.90	186.05	176.60	171.20	164.90	153.65	145.45	139.65	133.60	128.75
Solid Brick	232.35	213.55	198.55	188.20	182.40	175.45	163.35	154.35	147.95	141.30	135.95
Solid Stone	236.15	217.05	201.65	191.20	185.25	178.15	165.80	156.60	150.05	143.25	137.75
Finished Basement, Add	54.90	59.00	56.65	55.10	54.25	52.85	51.15	49.75	48.55	47.45	46.55
Unfinished Basement, Add	24.45	22.95	21.75	21.00	20.55	19.85	19.00	18.25	17.65	17.10	16.65

Modifications

Add to the total cost

Upgrade Kitchen Cabinets	$ + 1735
Solid Surface Countertops (Included)	
Full Bath - including plumbing, wall and floor finishes	+ 10,251
Half Bath - including plumbing, wall and floor finishes	+ 5900
Two Car Attached Garage	+ 30,537
Two Car Detached Garage	+ 34,570
Fireplace & Chimney	+ 9032

Adjustments

For multi family - add to total cost

Additional Kitchen	$ + 21,242
Additional Full Bath & Half Bath	+ 16,151
Additional Entry & Exit	+ 2306
Separate Heating & Air Conditioning	+ 6803
Separate Electric	+ 1986

For Townhouse/Rowhouse -
Multiply cost per square foot by

Inner Unit	.90
End Unit	.95

Alternatives

Add to or deduct from the cost per square foot of living area

Heavyweight Asphalt Shingles	– 2.05
Clay Tile Roof	+ 4.45
Slate Roof	+ 3.50
Upgrade Ceilings to Textured Finish	+ .50
Air Conditioning, in Heating Ductwork	Base System
Heating Systems, Hot Water	+ 2.37
Heat Pump	+ 2.73
Electric Heat	– 1.22
Not Heated	– 4.29

Additional upgrades or components

Kitchen Cabinets & Countertops	Page 58
Bathroom Vanities	59
Fireplaces & Chimneys	59
Windows, Skylights & Dormers	59
Appliances	60
Breezeways & Porches	60
Finished Attic	60
Garages	61
Site Improvements	61
Wings & Ells	57

- **Unique residence built from an architect's plan**
- **Single family — 1 full bath, 1 half bath, 1 kitchen**
- **No basement**
- **Cedar shakes on roof**
- **Forced hot air heat/air conditioning**
- **Gypsum wallboard interior finishes**
- **Many special features**
- **Extraordinary materials and workmanship**
- **Detail specifications on page 49**

Note: The illustration shown may contain some optional components (for example: garages and/or fireplaces) whose costs are shown in the modifications, adjustments, & alternatives below or at the end of the square foot section.

©Larry E. Belk Designs

Base cost per square foot of living area

Exterior Wall	Living Area										
	1000	1200	1400	1600	1800	2000	2400	2800	3200	3600	4000
Wood Siding - Wood Frame	193.45	179.35	169.20	157.45	150.60	144.05	131.85	126.00	120.80	116.70	111.20
Brick Veneer - Wood Frame	203.95	189.15	178.60	166.00	158.75	151.75	138.60	132.45	126.70	122.45	116.50
Solid Brick	221.45	205.60	194.20	180.20	172.30	164.60	149.90	143.15	136.65	131.95	125.40
Solid Stone	225.90	209.75	198.20	183.80	175.65	167.75	152.75	145.85	139.20	134.35	127.65
Finished Basement, Add	38.55	41.85	40.60	38.75	37.75	36.85	34.95	34.10	33.10	32.55	31.80
Unfinished Basement, Add	17.65	16.80	16.20	15.30	14.80	14.35	13.40	12.95	12.45	12.15	11.80

Modifications

Add to the total cost

Upgrade Kitchen Cabinets	$ + 1735
Solid Surface Countertops (Included)	
Full Bath - including plumbing, wall and floor finishes	+ 10,251
Half Bath - including plumbing, wall and floor finishes	+ 5900
Two Car Attached Garage	+ 30,537
Two Car Detached Garage	+ 34,570
Fireplace & Chimney	+ 9032

Adjustments

For multi family - add to total cost

Additional Kitchen	$ + 21,242
Additional Full Bath & Half Bath	+ 16,151
Additional Entry & Exit	+ 2306
Separate Heating & Air Conditioning	+ 6803
Separate Electric	+ 1986

For Townhouse/Rowhouse -
Multiply cost per square foot by

Inner Unit	.90
End Unit	.95

Alternatives

Add to or deduct from the cost per square foot of living area

Heavyweight Asphalt Shingles	– 1.45
Clay Tile Roof	+ 3.20
Slate Roof	+ 2.55
Upgrade Ceilings to Textured Finish	+ .50
Air Conditioning, in Heating Ductwork	Base System
Heating Systems, Hot Water	+ 2.27
Heat Pump	+ 3.04
Electric Heat	– 1.22
Not Heated	– 3.96

Additional upgrades or components

Kitchen Cabinets & Countertops	Page 58
Bathroom Vanities	59
Fireplaces & Chimneys	59
Windows, Skylights & Dormers	59
Appliances	60
Breezeways & Porches	60
Finished Attic	60
Garages	61
Site Improvements	61
Wings & Ells	57

Important: See the Reference Section for Location Factors (to adjust for your city) and Estimating Forms.

- **Unique residence built from an architect's plan**
- **Single family — 1 full bath, 1 half bath, 1 kitchen**
- **No basement**
- **Cedar shakes on roof**
- **Forced hot air heat/air conditioning**
- **Gypsum wallboard interior finishes**
- **Many special features**
- **Extraordinary materials and workmanship**
- **Detail specifications on page 49**

Note: The illustration shown may contain some optional components (for example: garages and/or fireplaces) whose costs are shown in the modifications, adjustments, & alternatives below or at the end of the square foot section.

Base cost per square foot of living area

Exterior Wall	Living Area										
	1200	1400	1600	1800	2000	2400	2800	3200	3600	4000	4400
Wood Siding - Wood Frame	178.85	167.80	159.80	152.85	145.55	134.95	126.10	120.30	116.70	113.05	109.95
Brick Veneer - Wood Frame	190.10	178.30	169.85	162.30	154.60	143.15	133.55	127.30	123.40	119.40	116.05
Solid Brick	208.85	195.75	186.60	178.05	169.80	156.85	146.00	138.90	134.65	129.95	126.30
Solid Stone	213.50	200.20	190.75	182.00	173.65	160.30	149.15	141.90	137.45	132.60	128.90
Finished Basement, Add	31.00	33.60	32.75	31.75	31.05	29.55	28.40	27.60	27.15	26.50	26.15
Unfinished Basement, Add	14.15	13.50	13.10	12.55	12.20	11.50	10.85	10.50	10.25	9.95	9.75

Modifications

Add to the total cost

Upgrade Kitchen Cabinets	$ + 1735
Solid Surface Countertops (Included)	
Full Bath - including plumbing, wall and floor finishes	+ 10,251
Half Bath - including plumbing, wall and floor finishes	+ 5900
Two Car Attached Garage	+ 30,537
Two Car Detached Garage	+ 34,570
Fireplace & Chimney	+ 9900

Adjustments

For multi family - add to total cost

Additional Kitchen	$ + 21,242
Additional Full Bath & Half Bath	+ 16,151
Additional Entry & Exit	+ 2306
Separate Heating & Air Conditioning	+ 6803
Separate Electric	+ 1986

For Townhouse/Rowhouse -
Multiply cost per square foot by

Inner Unit	.86
End Unit	.93

Alternatives

Add to or deduct from the cost per square foot of living area

Heavyweight Asphalt Shingles	– 1
Clay Tile Roof	+ 2.25
Slate Roof	+ 1.75
Upgrade Ceilings to Textured Finish	+ .50
Air Conditioning, in Heating Ductwork	Base System
Heating Systems, Hot Water	+ 2.20
Heat Pump	+ 3.20
Electric Heat	– 1.10
Not Heated	– 3.74

Additional upgrades or components

Kitchen Cabinets & Countertops	Page 58
Bathroom Vanities	59
Fireplaces & Chimneys	59
Windows, Skylights & Dormers	59
Appliances	60
Breezeways & Porches	60
Finished Attic	60
Garages	61
Site Improvements	61
Wings & Ells	57

- Unique residence built from an architect's plan
- Single family — 1 full bath, 1 half bath, 1 kitchen
- No basement
- Cedar shakes on roof
- Forced hot air heat/air conditioning
- Gypsum wallboard interior finishes
- Many special features
- Extraordinary materials and workmanship
- Detail specifications on page 49

Note: The illustration shown may contain some optional components (for example: garages and/or fireplaces) whose costs are shown in the modifications, adjustments, & alternatives below or at the end of the square foot section.

©Larry W. Garnett & Associates, Inc

Base cost per square foot of living area

Exterior Wall	Living Area										
	1500	1800	2100	2500	3000	3500	4000	4500	5000	5500	6000
Wood Siding - Wood Frame	173.75	156.15	145.70	137.95	127.50	119.95	112.70	109.15	106.00	102.85	99.35
Brick Veneer - Wood Frame	185.45	166.90	155.40	147.05	135.80	127.45	119.65	115.70	112.25	108.85	105.05
Solid Brick	204.90	184.80	171.40	162.20	149.55	140.05	131.25	126.70	122.75	118.80	114.60
Solid Stone	209.90	189.35	175.45	166.00	153.05	143.20	134.15	129.40	125.40	121.30	117.00
Finished Basement, Add	24.70	26.55	25.10	24.25	23.15	22.15	21.50	21.00	20.50	20.15	19.90
Unfinished Basement, Add	11.40	10.75	10.00	9.65	9.05	8.55	8.20	7.95	7.75	7.60	7.40

Modifications

Add to the total cost

Upgrade Kitchen Cabinets	$ + 1735
Solid Surface Countertops (Included)	
Full Bath - including plumbing, wall and floor finishes	+ 10,251
Half Bath - including plumbing, wall and floor finishes	+ 5900
Two Car Attached Garage	+ 30,537
Two Car Detached Garage	+ 34,570
Fireplace & Chimney	+ 10,835

Adjustments

For multi family - add to total cost

Additional Kitchen	$ + 21,242
Additional Full Bath & Half Bath	+ 16,151
Additional Entry & Exit	+ 2306
Separate Heating & Air Conditioning	+ 6803
Separate Electric	+ 1986

For Townhouse/Rowhouse -
Multiply cost per square foot by

Inner Unit	.86
End Unit	.93

Alternatives

Add to or deduct from the cost per square foot of living area

Heavyweight Asphalt Shingles	– .90
Clay Tile Roof	+ 1.90
Slate Roof	+ 1.50
Upgrade Ceilings to Textured Finish	+ .50
Air Conditioning, in Heating Ductwork	Base System
Heating Systems, Hot Water	+ 1.99
Heat Pump	+ 3.29
Electric Heat	– 2.16
Not Heated	– 3.74

Additional upgrades or components

Kitchen Cabinets & Countertops	Page 58
Bathroom Vanities	59
Fireplaces & Chimneys	59
Windows, Skylights & Dormers	59
Appliances	60
Breezeways & Porches	60
Finished Attic	60
Garages	61
Site Improvements	61
Wings & Ells	57

Important: See the Reference Section for Location Factors (to adjust for your city) and Estimating Forms.

- **Unique residence built from an architect's plan**
- **Single family — 1 full bath, 1 half bath, 1 kitchen**
- **No basement**
- **Cedar shakes on roof**
- **Forced hot air heat/air conditioning**
- **Gypsum wallboard interior finishes**
- **Many special features**
- **Extraordinary materials and workmanship**
- **Detail specifications on page 49**

Note: The illustration shown may contain some optional components (for example: garages and/or fireplaces) whose costs are shown in the modifications, adjustments, & alternatives below or at the end of the square foot section.

Base cost per square foot of living area

Exterior Wall	Living Area										
	1500	1800	2100	2500	3000	3500	4000	4500	5000	5500	6000
Wood Siding - Wood Frame	172.65	155.25	146.65	139.40	128.50	122.95	116.40	109.55	107.05	104.30	101.55
Brick Veneer - Wood Frame	184.80	166.50	157.10	149.40	137.55	131.60	124.25	116.80	114.10	111.05	107.85
Solid Brick	205.10	185.20	174.60	166.15	152.75	146.00	137.30	128.80	125.70	122.25	118.40
Solid Stone	210.15	189.90	179.05	170.35	156.60	149.55	140.60	131.90	128.70	125.05	121.10
Finished Basement, Add	21.70	23.40	22.35	21.70	20.70	20.05	19.25	18.65	18.35	18.05	17.65
Unfinished Basement, Add	10.00	9.45	8.95	8.65	8.15	7.85	7.40	7.15	7.00	6.85	6.60

Modifications

Add to the total cost

Upgrade Kitchen Cabinets	$ + 1735
Solid Surface Countertops (Included)	
Full Bath - including plumbing, wall and floor finishes	+ 10,251
Half Bath - including plumbing, wall and floor finishes	+ 5900
Two Car Attached Garage	+ 30,537
Two Car Detached Garage	+ 34,570
Fireplace & Chimney	+ 10,835

Adjustments

For multi family - add to total cost

Additional Kitchen	$ + 21,242
Additional Full Bath & Half Bath	+ 16,151
Additional Entry & Exit	+ 2306
Separate Heating & Air Conditioning	+ 6803
Separate Electric	+ 1986

For Townhouse/Rowhouse -
Multiply cost per square foot by

Inner Unit	.84
End Unit	.92

Alternatives

Add to or deduct from the cost per square foot of living area

Heavyweight Asphalt Shingles	– .70
Clay Tile Roof	+ 1.50
Slate Roof	+ 1.15
Upgrade Ceilings to Textured Finish	+ .50
Air Conditioning, in Heating Ductwork	Base System
Heating Systems, Hot Water	+ 1.99
Heat Pump	+ 3.29
Electric Heat	– 2.16
Not Heated	– 3.63

Additional upgrades or components

Kitchen Cabinets & Countertops	Page 58
Bathroom Vanities	59
Fireplaces & Chimneys	59
Windows, Skylights & Dormers	59
Appliances	60
Breezeways & Porches	60
Finished Attic	60
Garages	61
Site Improvements	61
Wings & Ells	57

- **Unique residence built from an architect's plan**
- **Single family — 1 full bath, 1 half bath, 1 kitchen**
- **No basement**
- **Cedar shakes on roof**
- **Forced hot air heat/air conditioning**
- **Gypsum wallboard interior finishes**
- **Many special features**
- **Extraordinary materials and workmanship**
- **Detail specifications on page 49**

Note: The illustration shown may contain some optional components (for example: garages and/or fireplaces) whose costs are shown in the modifications, adjustments, & alternatives below or at the end of the square foot section.

Base cost per square foot of living area

Exterior Wall	Living Area										
	1200	1400	1600	1800	2000	2400	2800	3200	3600	4000	4400
Wood Siding - Wood Frame	169.40	159.00	151.45	144.95	137.95	128.15	119.85	114.40	111.00	107.75	104.75
Brick Veneer - Wood Frame	177.80	166.90	159.00	152.00	144.75	134.25	125.45	119.65	116.10	112.50	109.35
Solid Brick	191.95	180.00	171.55	163.85	156.15	144.55	134.75	128.40	124.55	120.40	117.05
Solid Stone	195.45	183.30	174.75	166.85	159.00	147.15	137.15	130.65	126.65	122.40	118.95
Finished Basement, Add	31.00	33.60	32.75	31.75	31.05	29.55	28.40	27.60	27.15	26.50	26.15
Unfinished Basement, Add	14.15	13.50	13.10	12.55	12.20	11.50	10.85	10.50	10.25	9.95	9.75

Modifications

Add to the total cost

Upgrade Kitchen Cabinets	$ + 1735
Solid Surface Countertops (Included)	
Full Bath - including plumbing, wall and floor finishes	+ 10,251
Half Bath - including plumbing, wall and floor finishes	+ 5900
Two Car Attached Garage	+ 30,537
Two Car Detached Garage	+ 34,570
Fireplace & Chimney	+ 9032

Adjustments

For multi family - add to total cost

Additional Kitchen	$ + 21,242
Additional Full Bath & Half Bath	+ 16,151
Additional Entry & Exit	+ 2306
Separate Heating & Air Conditioning	+ 6803
Separate Electric	+ 1986

For Townhouse/Rowhouse -
Multiply cost per square foot by

Inner Unit	.89
End Unit	.94

Alternatives

Add to or deduct from the cost per square foot of living area

Heavyweight Asphalt Shingles	– 1
Clay Tile Roof	+ 2.25
Slate Roof	+ 1.75
Upgrade Ceilings to Textured Finish	+ .50
Air Conditioning, in Heating Ductwork	Base System
Heating Systems, Hot Water	+ 2.20
Heat Pump	+ 3.20
Electric Heat	– 1.10
Not Heated	– 3.74

Additional upgrades or components

Kitchen Cabinets & Countertops	Page 58
Bathroom Vanities	59
Fireplaces & Chimneys	59
Windows, Skylights & Dormers	59
Appliances	60
Breezeways & Porches	60
Finished Attic	60
Garages	61
Site Improvements	61
Wings & Ells	57

Important: See the Reference Section for Location Factors (to adjust for your city) and Estimating Forms.

- **Unique residence built from an architect's plan**
- **Single family — 1 full bath, 1 half bath, 1 kitchen**
- **No basement**
- **Cedar shakes on roof**
- **Forced hot air heat/air conditioning**
- **Gypsum wallboard interior finishes**
- **Many special features**
- **Extraordinary materials and workmanship**
- **Detail specifications on page 49**

Note: The illustration shown may contain some optional components (for example: garages and/or fireplaces) whose costs are shown in the modifications, adjustments, & alternatives below or at the end of the square foot section.

©Home Planners, Inc.

Base cost per square foot of living area

Exterior Wall	Living Area										
	1500	1800	2100	2400	2800	3200	3600	4000	4500	5000	5500
Wood Siding - Wood Frame	158.95	146.85	136.70	129.90	124.85	119.10	113.00	110.40	104.80	101.65	98.10
Brick Veneer - Wood Frame	166.60	153.60	142.90	135.75	130.45	124.30	117.80	115.10	109.10	105.70	101.95
Solid Brick	179.20	165.00	153.30	145.45	139.75	132.90	125.85	122.90	116.25	112.50	108.40
Solid Stone	182.40	167.90	155.90	147.95	142.10	135.10	127.90	124.85	118.05	114.20	110.05
Finished Basement, Add*	36.55	39.35	37.75	36.70	35.95	34.95	34.05	33.65	32.75	32.15	31.65
Unfinished Basement, Add*	16.25	15.25	14.45	13.95	13.65	13.15	12.65	12.45	12.00	11.65	11.40

Basement under middle level only.

Modifications

Add to the total cost

Upgrade Kitchen Cabinets	$ + 1735
Solid Surface Countertops (Included)	
Full Bath - including plumbing, wall and floor finishes	+ 10,251
Half Bath - including plumbing, wall and floor finishes	+ 5900
Two Car Attached Garage	+ 30,537
Two Car Detached Garage	+ 34,570
Fireplace & Chimney	+ 9032

Adjustments

For multi family - add to total cost

Additional Kitchen	$ + 21,242
Additional Full Bath & Half Bath	+ 16,151
Additional Entry & Exit	+ 2306
Separate Heating & Air Conditioning	+ 6803
Separate Electric	+ 1986

For Townhouse/Rowhouse -
Multiply cost per square foot by

Inner Unit	.86
End Unit	.93

Alternatives

Add to or deduct from the cost per square foot of living area

Heavyweight Asphalt Shingles	− 1.45
Clay Tile Roof	+ 3.20
Slate Roof	+ 2.55
Upgrade Ceilings to Textured Finish	+ .50
Air Conditioning, in Heating Ductwork	Base System
Heating Systems, Hot Water	+ 2.13
Heat Pump	+ 3.32
Electric Heat	− .97
Not Heated	− 3.63

Additional upgrades or components

Kitchen Cabinets & Countertops	Page 58
Bathroom Vanities	59
Fireplaces & Chimneys	59
Windows, Skylights & Dormers	59
Appliances	60
Breezeways & Porches	60
Finished Attic	60
Garages	61
Site Improvements	61
Wings & Ells	57

1 Story — Base cost per square foot of living area

Exterior Wall	Living Area							
	50	100	200	300	400	500	600	700
Wood Siding - Wood Frame	252.90	195.25	170.10	143.40	135.25	130.20	127.00	128.00
Brick Veneer - Wood Frame	281.20	215.50	186.95	154.65	145.35	139.65	136.00	136.70
Solid Brick	328.40	249.15	215.05	173.35	162.20	155.40	150.95	151.15
Solid Stone	340.30	257.65	222.15	178.05	166.45	159.35	154.70	154.75
Finished Basement, Add	98.10	88.90	79.80	64.60	61.50	59.65	58.45	57.65
Unfinished Basement, Add	50.90	39.20	34.35	26.30	24.70	23.70	23.10	22.60

1-1/2 Story — Base cost per square foot of living area

Exterior Wall	Living Area							
	100	200	300	400	500	600	700	800
Wood Siding - Wood Frame	200.85	163.80	141.15	127.70	120.90	117.70	113.45	112.25
Brick Veneer - Wood Frame	226.10	184.00	158.05	140.85	133.05	129.15	124.30	123.00
Solid Brick	268.30	217.70	186.15	162.80	153.30	148.25	142.35	140.90
Solid Stone	278.95	226.25	193.15	168.30	158.35	153.10	146.90	145.45
Finished Basement, Add	64.60	63.85	57.80	51.05	49.20	48.00	46.85	46.75
Unfinished Basement, Add	32.35	27.55	24.30	20.70	19.75	19.10	18.50	18.40

2 Story — Base cost per square foot of living area

Exterior Wall	Living Area							
	100	200	400	600	800	1000	1200	1400
Wood Siding - Wood Frame	198.00	149.20	127.85	107.30	100.40	96.10	93.40	94.75
Brick Veneer - Wood Frame	226.25	169.45	144.75	118.55	110.50	105.55	102.40	103.45
Solid Brick	273.50	203.15	172.80	137.30	127.35	121.30	117.35	117.85
Solid Stone	285.35	211.65	179.85	141.95	131.65	125.20	121.10	121.50
Finished Basement, Add	49.10	44.50	39.95	32.30	30.80	29.90	29.25	28.85
Unfinished Basement, Add	25.45	19.60	17.20	13.15	12.35	11.85	11.55	11.30

Base costs do not include bathroom or kitchen facilities. Use Modifications/Adjustments/Alternatives on pages 58-61 where appropriate.

Important: See the Reference Section for Location Factors (to adjust for your city) and Estimating Forms.

Kitchen cabinets - Base units, hardwood (Cost per Unit)

	Economy	Average	Custom	Luxury
24" deep, 35" high,				
One top drawer,				
One door below				
12" wide	$ 236	$ 315	$ 419	$ 551
15" wide	244	325	432	569
18" wide	263	350	466	613
21" wide	274	365	485	639
24" wide	319	425	565	744
Four drawers				
12" wide	248	330	439	578
15" wide	251	335	446	586
18" wide	274	365	485	639
24" wide	300	400	532	700
Two top drawers,				
Two doors below				
27" wide	341	455	605	796
30" wide	368	490	652	858
33" wide	379	505	672	884
36" wide	394	525	698	919
42" wide	416	555	738	971
48" wide	443	590	785	1033
Range or sink base				
(Cost per unit)				
Two doors below				
30" wide	308	410	545	718
33" wide	330	440	585	770
36" wide	345	460	612	805
42" wide	364	485	645	849
48" wide	379	505	672	884
Corner Base Cabinet				
(Cost per unit)				
36" wide	533	710	944	1243
Lazy Susan (Cost per unit)				
With revolving door	705	940	1250	1645

Kitchen cabinets - Wall cabinets, hardwood (Cost per Unit)

	Economy	Average	Custom	Luxury
12" deep, 2 doors				
12" high				
30" wide	$ 214	$ 285	$ 379	$ 499
36" wide	251	335	446	586
15" high				
30" wide	218	290	386	508
33" wide	263	350	466	613
36" wide	266	355	472	621
24" high				
30" wide	281	375	499	656
36" wide	311	415	552	726
42" wide	353	470	625	823
30" high, 1 door				
12" wide	200	267	355	467
15" wide	221	295	392	516
18" wide	240	320	426	560
24" wide	278	370	492	648
30" high, 2 doors				
27" wide	300	400	532	700
30" wide	319	425	565	744
36" wide	356	475	632	831
42" wide	383	510	678	893
48" wide	431	575	765	1006
Corner wall, 30" high				
24" wide	319	425	565	744
30" wide	338	450	599	788
36" wide	379	505	672	884
Broom closet				
84" high, 24" deep				
18" wide	578	770	1024	1348
Oven Cabinet				
84" high, 24" deep				
27" wide	863	1150	1530	2013

Kitchen countertops (Cost per L.F.)

	Economy	Average	Custom	Luxury
Solid Surface				
24" wide, no backsplash	108	144	192	252
with backsplash	117	156	207	273
Stock plastic laminate, 24" wide				
with backsplash	25	33	44	58
Custom plastic laminate, no splash				
7/8" thick, alum. molding	35	47	63	82
1-1/4" thick, no splash	40	53	71	94
Marble				
1/2" - 3/4" thick w/splash	53	70	93	123
Maple, laminated				
1-1/2" thick w/splash	84	112	149	196
Stainless steel				
(per S.F.)	137	183	243	320
Cutting blocks, recessed				
16" x 20" x 1" (each)	115	153	203	268

Vanity bases (Cost per Unit)

2 door, 30" high, 21" deep	Economy	Average	Custom	Luxury
24" wide	278	370	492	648
30" wide	334	445	592	779
36" wide	334	445	592	779
48" wide	428	570	758	998

Solid surface vanity tops (Cost Each)

Center bowl	Economy	Average	Custom	Luxury
22" x 25"	$ 420	$ 454	$ 490	$ 529
22" x 31"	480	518	559	604
22" x 37"	555	599	647	699
22" x 49"	685	740	799	863

Fireplaces & Chimneys (Cost per Unit)

	1-1/2 Story	2 Story	3 Story
Economy (prefab metal)			
Exterior chimney & 1 fireplace	$ 5691	$ 6288	$ 6898
Interior chimney & 1 fireplace	5453	6063	6343
Average (masonry)			
Exterior chimney & 1 fireplace	6029	6661	7307
Interior chimney & 1 fireplace	5777	6422	6719
For more than 1 flue, add	410	698	1170
For more than 1 fireplace, add	4045	4045	4045
Custom (masonry)			
Exterior chimney & 1 fireplace	6304	7115	8035
Interior chimney & 1 fireplace	5910	6690	7211
For more than 1 flue, add	494	856	1432
For more than 1 fireplace, add	4528	4528	4528
Luxury (masonry)			
Exterior chimney & 1 fireplace	9032	9900	10834
Interior chimney & 1 fireplace	8617	9421	9972
For more than 1 flue, add	745	1244	1737
For more than 1 fireplace, add	7119	7119	7119

Windows and Skylights (Cost Each)

	Economy	Average	Custom	Luxury
Fixed Picture Windows				
3'-6" x 4'-0"	$ 347	$ 462	$ 615	$ 809
4'-0" x 6'-0"	620	827	1100	1447
5'-0" x 6'-0"	691	921	1225	1612
6'-0" x 6'-0"	691	921	1225	1612
Bay/Bow Windows				
8'-0" x 5'-0"	860	1146	1525	2007
10'-0" x 5'-0"	930	1240	1650	2171
10'-0" x 6'-0"	1466	1954	2600	3421
12'-0" x 6'-0"	1903	2537	3375	4441
Palladian Windows				
3'-2" x 6'-4"		1466	1950	2566
4'-0" x 6'-0"		1729	2300	3026
5'-5" x 6'-10"		2255	3000	3947
8'-0" x 6'-0"		2650	3525	4638
Skylights				
46" x 21-1/2"	592	910	1115	1227
46" x 28"	614	945	1170	1287
57" x 44"	673	1035	1150	1265

Dormers (Cost/S.F. of plan area)

	Economy	Average	Custom	Luxury
Framing and Roofing Only				
Gable dormer, 2" x 6" roof frame	$ 29	$ 33	$ 35	$ 58
2" x 8" roof frame	30	34	36	61
Shed dormer, 2" x 6" roof frame	18	21	24	37
2" x 8" roof frame	20	22	25	38
2" x 10" roof frame	21	24	26	39

Appliances (Cost per Unit)

	Economy	Average	Custom	Luxury
Range				
30" free standing, 1 oven	$ 545	$ 1448	$ 1899	$ 2350
2 oven	1400	2125	2488	2850
30" built-in, 1 oven	820	1360	1630	1900
2 oven	1650	1898	2022	2145
21" free standing				
1 oven	560	605	628	650
Counter Top Ranges				
4 burner standard	400	988	1282	1575
As above with griddle	1425	2800	3488	4175
Microwave Oven	248	494	617	740
Compactor				
4 to 1 compaction	790	1020	1135	1250
Deep Freeze				
15 to 23 C.F.	730	878	952	1025
30 C.F.	845	1023	1112	1200
Dehumidifier, portable, auto.				
15 pint	282	325	346	367
30 pint	228	262	279	296
Washing Machine, automatic	690	1420	1785	2150
Water Heater				
Electric, glass lined				
30 gal.	595	728	794	860
80 gal.	1650	2063	2269	2475
Water Heater, Gas, glass lined				
30 gal.	1075	1313	1432	1550
50 gal.	1325	1638	1794	1950
Dishwasher, built-in				
2 cycles	415	598	689	780
4 or more cycles	565	700	1100	1500
Dryer, automatic	670	1560	2005	2450
Garage Door Opener	525	628	679	730
Garbage Disposal	157	229	265	300
Heater, Electric, built-in				
1250 watt ceiling type	233	289	317	345
1250 watt wall type	305	330	343	355
Wall type w/blower				
1500 watt	305	351	374	397
3000 watt	540	621	662	702
Hood For Range, 2 speed				
30" wide	187	606	816	1025
42" wide	293	1334	1855	2375
Humidifier, portable				
7 gal. per day	144	166	177	187
15 gal. per day	229	264	281	298
Ice Maker, automatic				
13 lb. per day	1050	1208	1287	1365
51 lb. per day	1975	2272	2420	2568
Refrigerator, no frost				
10-12 C.F.	525	558	574	590
14-16 C.F.	620	713	759	805
18-20 C.F.	765	1233	1467	1700
21-29 C.F.	1150	2525	3213	3900
Sump Pump, 1/3 H.P.	315	443	507	570

Breezeway (Cost per S.F.)

Class	Type	Area (S.F.)			
		50	100	150	200
Economy	Open	$ 43.99	$ 36.73	$ 32.38	$ 30.20
	Enclosed	160.11	113.89	93.91	80.85
Average	Open	52.20	42.61	37.48	34.91
	Enclosed	164.65	119.19	99.02	88.70
Custom	Open	62.68	51.55	45.49	42.47
	Enclosed	220.43	159.28	131.86	117.90
Luxury	Open	70.40	58.09	51.64	48.41
	Enclosed	259.21	184.60	151.41	134.58

Porches (Cost per S.F.)

Class	Type	Area (S.F.)				
		25	50	100	200	300
Economy	Open	$ 78.79	$ 59.29	$ 44.68	$ 34.33	$ 30.99
	Enclosed	168.38	133.94	88.07	66.76	58.38
Average	Open	83.11	63.99	47.03	35.51	31.77
	Enclosed	182.81	145.86	93.44	68.86	59.38
Custom	Open	133.43	97.43	74.77	56.21	54.91
	Enclosed	224.21	181.21	119.18	90.17	96.76
Luxury	Open	150.96	110.24	83.50	61.07	55.40
	Enclosed	262.68	237.45	152.55	111.21	92.19

Finished attic (Cost per S.F.)

Class	Area (S.F.)				
	400	500	600	800	1000
Economy	$ 19.93	$ 19.27	$ 18.46	$ 18.15	$ 17.48
Average	31.05	30.37	29.63	29.26	28.44
Custom	39.69	38.81	37.92	37.34	36.58
Luxury	50.65	49.43	48.27	47.12	46.35

Alarm system (Cost per System)

	Burglar Alarm	Smoke Detector
Economy	$ 415	$ 71
Average	475	86
Custom	820	196
Luxury	1200	255

Sauna, prefabricated
(Cost per unit, including heater and controls—7' high)

Size	Cost
6' x 4'	$ 5975
6' x 5'	6250
6' x 6'	6975
6' x 9'	8450
8' x 10'	11,200
8' x 12'	12,600
10' x 12'	13,200

Garages *

(Costs include exterior wall systems comparable with the quality of the residence. Included in the cost is an allowance for one personnel door, manual overhead door(s) and electrical fixture.)

Class	Type									
	Detached			Attached			Built-in		Basement	
	One Car	Two Car	Three Car	One Car	Two Car	Three Car	One Car	Two Car	One Car	Two Car
Economy										
Wood	$15,837	$24,288	$32,739	$12,308	$21,275	$29,726	$-1583	$-3166	$1720	$2384
Masonry	21,936	31,921	41,906	16,125	26,625	36,610	-2332	-4664		
Average										
Wood	17,986	26,978	35,969	13,653	23,160	32,152	-1847	-3694	1947	2839
Masonry	21,977	31,972	41,968	16,150	26,661	36,656	-2337	-3828		
Custom										
Wood	19,740	30,391	41,041	15,360	26,684	37,335	-3104	-2848	2923	4789
Masonry	24,116	35,867	47,618	18,098	30,523	42,274	-3642	-3923		
Luxury										
Wood	22,156	34,570	46,983	17,449	30,537	42,950	-3212	-3062	3864	6229
Masonry	28,630	42,672	56,713	21,500	36,216	50,257	-4007	-4652		

*See the Introduction to this section for definitions of garage types.

Swimming pools *(Cost per S.F.)*

Residential	
In-ground	$ 34.00 - 83.50
Deck equipment	1.30
Paint pool, preparation & 3 coats (epoxy)	5.25
Rubber base paint	4.62
Pool Cover	.92
Swimming Pool Heaters	
(not including wiring, external piping, base or pad)	
Gas	
155 MBH	$ 2975.00
190 MBH	3550.00
500 MBH	12,600.
Electric	
15 KW 7200 gallon pool	2825.00
24 KW 9600 gallon pool	3250.00
54 KW 24,000 gallon pool	5075.00

Wood and coal stoves

Wood Only	
Free Standing (minimum)	$ 1750
Fireplace Insert (minimum)	1961
Coal Only	
Free Standing	$ 2216
Fireplace Insert	2426
Wood and Coal	
Free Standing	$ 4559
Fireplace Insert	4672

Sidewalks *(Cost per S.F.)*

Concrete, 3000 psi with wire mesh	4" thick	$ 3.74
	5" thick	4.53
	6" thick	5.08
Precast concrete patio blocks (natural)	2" thick	6.50
Precast concrete patio blocks (colors)	2" thick	6.90
Flagstone, bluestone	1" thick	16.50
Flagstone, bluestone	1-1/2" thick	21.75
Slate (natural, irregular)	3/4" thick	18.40
Slate (random rectangular)	1/2" thick	29.35
Seeding		
Fine grading & seeding includes lime, fertilizer & seed per S.Y.		2.94
Lawn Sprinkler System	per S.F.	1.09

Fencing *(Cost per L.F.)*

Chain Link, 4' high, galvanized	$ 15.85
Gate, 4' high (each)	198.00
Cedar Picket, 3' high, 2 rail	14.50
Gate (each)	228.00
3 Rail, 4' high	17.90
Gate (each)	248.00
Cedar Stockade, 3 Rail, 6' high	17.75
Gate (each)	249.00
Board & Battens, 2 sides 6' high, pine	26.00
6' high, cedar	35.00
No. 1 Cedar, basketweave, 6' high	36.00
Gate, 6' high (each)	255.00

Carport *(Cost per S.F.)*

Economy	$ 9.12
Average	13.72
Custom	20.09
Luxury	23.36

Insurance Exclusions

Insurance exclusions are a matter of policy coverage and are not standard or universal. When making an appraisal for insurance purposes, it is recommended that some time be taken in studying the insurance policy to determine the specific items to be excluded. Most homeowners insurance policies have, as part of their provisions, statements that read "the policy permits the insured to exclude from value, in determining whether the amount of the insurance equals or exceeds 80% of its replacement cost, such items as building excavation, basement footings, underground piping and wiring, piers and other supports which are below the undersurface of the lowest floor or where there is no basement below the ground." Loss to any of these items, however, is covered.

Costs for Excavation, Spread and Strip Footings and Underground Piping

This chart shows excluded items expressed as a percentage of total building cost.

Class	Number of Stories			
	1	1-1/2	2	3
Luxury	3.4%	2.7%	2.4%	1.9%
Custom	3.5%	2.7%	2.4%	1.9%
Average	5.0%	4.3%	3.8%	3.3%
Economy	5.0%	4.4%	4.1%	3.5%

Architect/Designer Fees

Architect/designer fees as presented in the following chart are typical ranges for 4 classes of residences. Factors affecting these ranges include economic conditions, size and scope of project, site selection, and standardization. Where superior quality and detail is required or where closer supervision is required, fees may run higher than listed. Lower quality or simplicity may dictate lower fees.

The editors have included architect/designer fees from the "mean" column in calculating costs.

Listed below are average costs expressed as a range and mean of total building cost for 4 classes of residences.

Class		Range	Mean
Luxury	— Architecturally designed and supervised	5%–15%	10%
Custom	— Architecturally modified designer plans	$2000–$3500	$2500
Average	— Designer plans	$800–$1500	$1100
Economy	— Stock plans	$100–$500	$300

Depreciation as generally defined is "the loss of value due to any cause." Specifically, depreciation can be broken down into three categories: **Physical Depreciation, Functional Obsolescence,** and **Economic Obsolescence.**

Physical Depreciation is the loss of value from the wearing out of the building's components. Such causes may be decay, dry rot, cracks, or structural defects.

Functional Obsolescence is the loss of value from features which render the residence less useful or desirable. Such features may be higher than normal ceilings, design and/or style changes, or outdated mechanical systems.

Economic Obsolescence is the loss of value from external features which render the residence less useful or desirable. These features may be changes in neighborhood socio-economic grouping, zoning changes, legislation, etc.

Depreciation as it applies to the residential portion of this manual deals with the observed physical condition of the residence being appraised. It is in essence *"the cost to cure."*

The ultimate method to arrive at *"the cost to cure"* is to analyze each component of the residence.

For example:

> Component, Roof Covering – Cost = $2400
> Average Life = 15 years
> Actual Life = 5 years
> Depreciation = 5 ÷ 15 = .33 or 33%
>
> $2400 × 33% = $792 = Amount of Depreciation

The following table, however, can be used as a guide in estimating the % depreciation using the actual age and general condition of the residence.

Depreciation Table — Residential

Age in Years	Good	Average	Poor
2	2%	3%	10%
5	4	6	20
10	7	10	25
15	10	15	30
20	15	20	35
25	18	25	40
30	24	30	45
35	28	35	50
40	32	40	55
45	36	45	60
50	40	50	65

Commercial/Industrial/Institutional Models

Table of Contents

Table No.	Page
Introduction	
General	67
How To Use	68
Examples	
Example 1	73
Example 2	75
Standard Models	
Building Types	
M.010 Apartment, 1-3 Story	78
M.020 Apartment, 4-7 Story	80
M.030 Apartment, 8-24 Story	82
M.035 Assisted - Senior Living	84
M.040 Auditorium	86
M.050 Bank	88
M.060 Bowling Alley	90
M.070 Bus Terminal	92
M.080 Car Wash	94
M.090 Church	96
M.100 Club, Country	98
M.110 Club, Social	100
M.120 College, Classroom, 2-3 Story	102
M.130 College, Dorm., 2-3 Story	104
M.140 College, Dorm., 4-8 Story	106
M.150 College, Laboratory	108
M.160 College, Student Union	110
M.170 Community Center	112
M.175 Computer Data Center	114
M.180 Courthouse, 1 Story	116
M.190 Courthouse, 2-3 Story	118

Table No.	Page
M.195 Day Care Center	120
M.200 Factory, 1 Story	122
M.210 Factory, 3 Story	124
M.220 Fire Station, 1 Story	126
M.230 Fire Station, 2 Story	128
M.240 Fraternity/Sorority House	130
M.250 Funeral Home	132
M.260 Garage, Auto Sales	134
M.270 Garage, Parking	136
M.280 Garage, Underground Parking	138
M.290 Garage, Repair	140
M.300 Garage, Service Station	142
M.310 Gymnasium	144
M.320 Hangar, Aircraft	146
M.330 Hospital, 2-3 Story	148
M.340 Hospital, 4-8 Story	150
M.350 Hotel, 4-7 Story	152
M.360 Hotel, 8-24 Story	154
M.370 Jail	156
M.380 Laundromat	158
M.390 Library	160
M.400 Medical Office, 1 Story	162
M.410 Medical Office, 2 Story	164
M.420 Motel, 1 Story	166
M.430 Motel, 2-3 Story	168
M.440 Movie Theatre	170
M.450 Nursing Home	172
M.455 Office, 1 Story	174

Table No.	Page
M.460 Office, 2-4 Story	176
M.470 Office, 5-10 Story	178
M.480 Office, 11-20 Story	180
M.485 Outpatient Surgery Center	182
M.490 Police Station	184
M.495 Post Frame Barn	186
M.500 Post Office	188
M.510 Racquetball Court	190
M.520 Religious Education	192
M.530 Restaurant	194
M.540 Restaurant, Fast Food	196
M.550 Rink, Hockey/Indoor Soccer	198
M.560 School, Elementary	200
M.570 School, High, 2-3 Story	202
M.580 School, Jr. High, 2-3 Story	204
M.590 School, Vocational	206
M.600 Store, Convenience	208
M.610 Store, Department, 1 Story	210
M.620 Store, Department, 3 Story	212
M.630 Store, Retail	214
M.640 Supermarket	216
M.650 Swimming Pool, Enclosed	218
M.660 Telephone Exchange	220
M.670 Town Hall, 1 Story	222
M.680 Town Hall, 2-3 Story	224
M.685 Veterinary Hospital	226
M.690 Warehouse	228
M.700 Warehouse, Self Storage	230
Depreciation	232

Introduction to the Commercial/Industrial/Institutional Section

General

The Commercial/Industrial/Institutional section of this manual contains base building costs per square foot of floor area for 75 model buildings. Each model has a table of square foot costs for combinations of exterior wall and framing systems. This table is supplemented by a list of common additives and their unit costs. A breakdown of the component costs used to develop the base cost for the model is on the opposite page. The total cost derived from the base cost and additives must be modified using the appropriate location factor from the Reference Section.

This section may be used directly to estimate the construction cost of most types of buildings knowing only the floor area, exterior wall construction and framing systems. To adjust the base cost for components which are different than the model, use the tables from the Assemblies Section.

Building Identification & Model Selection

The building models in this section represent structures by use. Occupancy, however, does not necessarily identify the building, i.e., a restaurant could be a converted warehouse. In all instances, the building should be described and identified by its own physical characteristics. The model selection should also be guided by comparing specifications with the model. In the case of converted use, data from one model may be used to supplement data from another.

Green Models

Consistent with expanding green trends in the design and construction industry, RSMeans introduced 25 new green building models. Although similar to our standard models in building type and structural system, the new green models meet or exceed Energy Star requirements and address many of the items necessary to obtain LEED certification. Although our models do not include site-specific information, our design assumption is that they are located in climate zone 5. DOE's eQuest software was used to perform an energy analysis of the model buildings. By reducing energy use, we were able to reduce the size of the service entrances, switchgear, power feeds, and generators. Each of the following building systems was researched and analyzed: building envelope, HVAC, plumbing fixtures, lighting, and electrical service. These systems were targeted because of their impact on energy usage and green building.

Wall and roof insulation was increased to reduce heat loss and a recycled vapor barrier was added to the foundation. White roofs were specified for models with flat roofs. Interior finishes include materials with recycled content and low VOC paint. Stainless steel toilet partitions were selected because it is a recycled material and is easy to maintain. Plumbing fixtures were selected to conserve water. Water closets are low-flow and equipped with auto-sensor valves. Waterless urinals are specified throughout. Faucets use auto-sensor flush valves and are powered by a hydroelectric power unit inside the faucet. Energy efficient, low flow water coolers were specified to reduce energy consumption and water usage throughout each building model.

Lighting efficiency was achieved by specifying LED fixtures in place of standard fluorescents. Daylight on/off lighting control systems were incorporated into the models. These controls are equipped with sensors that automatically turn off the lights when sufficient daylight is available. Energy monitoring systems were also included in all green models.

Adjustments

The base cost tables represent the base cost per square foot of floor area for buildings without a basement and without unusual special features. Basement costs and other common additives are listed below the base cost table. Cost adjustments can also be made to the model by using the tables from the Assemblies Section. This table is for example only.

Dimensions

All base cost tables are developed so that measurement can be readily made during the inspection process. Areas are calculated from exterior dimensions and story heights are measured from the top surface of one floor to the top surface of the floor above. Roof areas are measured by horizontal area covered and costs related to inclines are converted with appropriate factors. The precision of measurement is a matter of the user's choice and discretion. For ease in calculation, consideration should be given to measuring in tenths of a foot, i.e., 9 ft. 6 in. = 9.5 ft., 9 ft. 4 in. = 9.3 ft.

Floor Area

The term "Floor Area" as used in this section includes the sum of floor plate at grade level and above. This dimension is measured from the outside face of the foundation wall. Basement costs are calculated separately. The user must exercise his/her own judgment, where the lowest level floor is slightly below grade, whether to consider it at grade level or make the basement adjustment.

How to Use the Commercial/Industrial/Institutional Section

The following is a detailed explanation of a sample entry in the Commercial/Industrial/Institutional Square Foot Cost Section. Each bold number below corresponds to the described item on the following page with the appropriate component or cost of the sample entry following in parentheses.

Prices listed are costs that include overhead and profit of the installing contractor and additional markups for General Conditions and Architects' Fees.

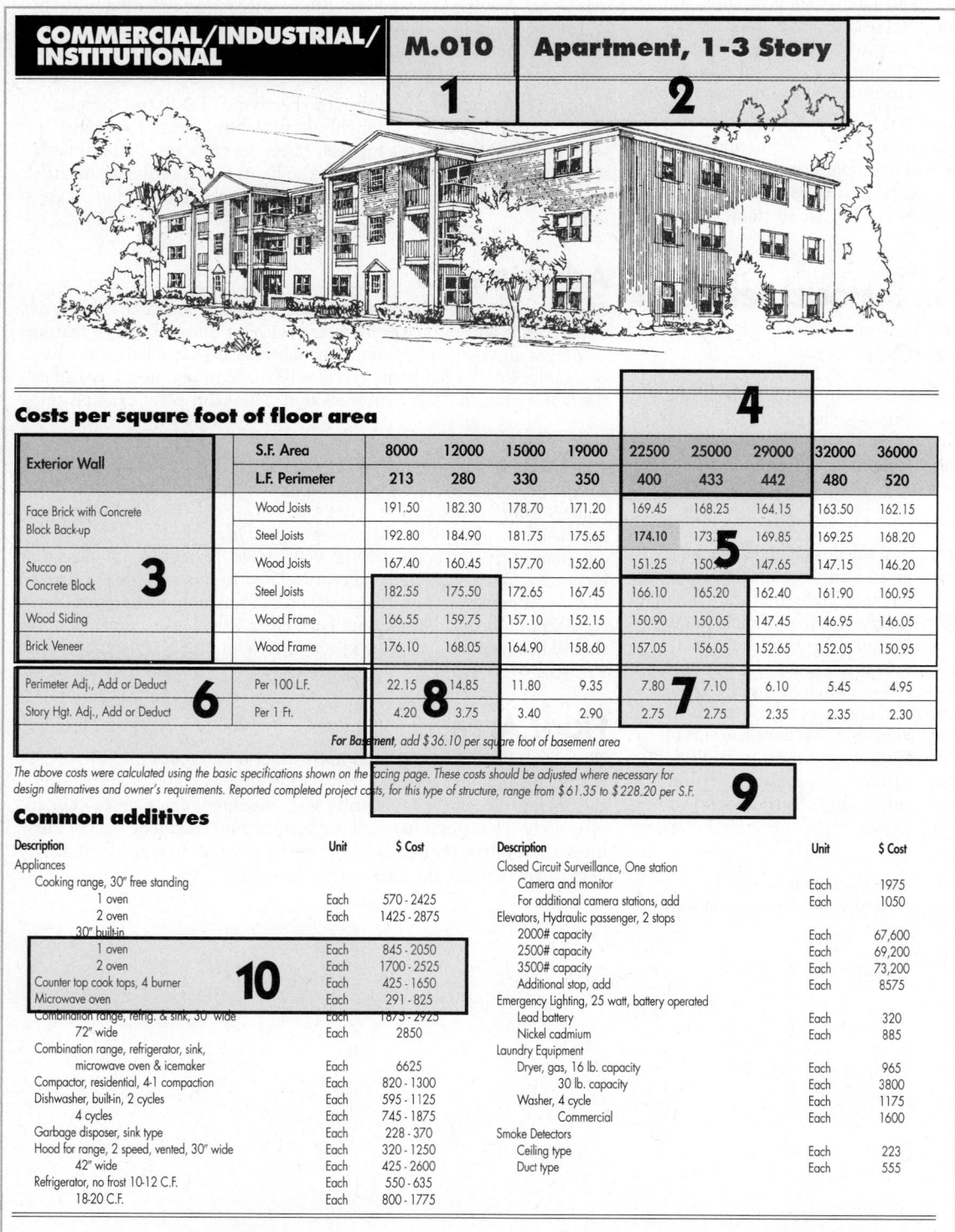

COMMERCIAL/INDUSTRIAL/INSTITUTIONAL   **M.010** **1**   **Apartment, 1-3 Story** **2**

Costs per square foot of floor area

Exterior Wall **3**		S.F. Area	8000	12000	15000	19000	22500	25000	29000	32000	36000
		L.F. Perimeter	213	280	330	350	400	433	442	480	520
Face Brick with Concrete Block Back-up		Wood Joists	191.50	182.30	178.70	171.20	169.45	168.25	164.15	163.50	162.15
		Steel Joists	192.80	184.90	181.75	175.65	**174.10**	173.	169.85	169.25	168.20
Stucco on Concrete Block		Wood Joists	167.40	160.45	157.70	152.60	151.25	150.	147.65	147.15	146.20
		Steel Joists	182.55	175.50	172.65	167.45	166.10	165.20	162.40	161.90	160.95
Wood Siding		Wood Frame	166.55	159.75	157.10	152.15	150.90	150.05	147.45	146.95	146.05
Brick Veneer		Wood Frame	176.10	168.05	164.90	158.60	157.05	156.05	152.65	152.05	150.95
Perimeter Adj., Add or Deduct **6**		Per 100 L.F.	22.15	14.85	11.80	9.35	7.80	7.10	6.10	5.45	4.95
Story Hgt. Adj., Add or Deduct		Per 1 Ft.	4.20	3.75	3.40	2.90	2.75	2.75	2.35	2.35	2.30
		For Basement, add $36.10 per square foot of basement area									

The above costs were calculated using the basic specifications shown on the facing page. These costs should be adjusted where necessary for design alternatives and owner's requirements. Reported completed project costs, for this type of structure, range from $61.35 to $228.20 per S.F. **9**

Common additives

Description	Unit	$ Cost	Description	Unit	$ Cost
Appliances			Closed Circuit Surveillance, One station		
Cooking range, 30" free standing			Camera and monitor	Each	1975
1 oven	Each	570 - 2425	For additional camera stations, add	Each	1050
2 oven	Each	1425 - 2875	Elevators, Hydraulic passenger, 2 stops		
30" built-in			2000# capacity	Each	67,600
1 oven	Each	845 - 2050	2500# capacity	Each	69,200
2 oven	Each	1700 - 2525	3500# capacity	Each	73,200
Counter top cook tops, 4 burner **10**	Each	425 - 1650	Additional stop, add	Each	8575
Microwave oven	Each	291 - 825	Emergency Lighting, 25 watt, battery operated		
Combination range, refrig. & sink, 30" wide	Each	1875 - 2925	Lead battery	Each	320
72" wide	Each	2850	Nickel cadmium	Each	885
Combination range, refrigerator, sink,			Laundry Equipment		
microwave oven & icemaker	Each	6625	Dryer, gas, 16 lb. capacity	Each	965
Compactor, residential, 4-1 compaction	Each	820 - 1300	30 lb. capacity	Each	3800
Dishwasher, built-in, 2 cycles	Each	595 - 1125	Washer, 4 cycle	Each	1175
4 cycles	Each	745 - 1875	Commercial	Each	1600
Garbage disposer, sink type	Each	228 - 370	Smoke Detectors		
Hood for range, 2 speed, vented, 30" wide	Each	320 - 1250	Ceiling type	Each	223
42" wide	Each	425 - 2600	Duct type	Each	555
Refrigerator, no frost 10-12 C.F.	Each	550 - 635			
18-20 C.F.	Each	800 - 1775			

1 Model Number (M.010)

"M" distinguishes this section of the book and stands for model. The number designation is a sequential number. Our newest models are green and are designated with the letter "G" followed by the building type number.

2 Type of Building (Apartment, 1–3 Story)

There are 50 different types of commercial/industrial/institutional buildings highlighted in this section.

3 Exterior Wall Construction and Building Framing Options (Face Brick with Concrete Block Back-up and Open Web Steel Bar Joists)

Three or more commonly used exterior walls and, in most cases, two typical building framing systems are presented for each type of building. The model selected should be based on the actual characteristics of the building being estimated.

4 Total Square Foot of Floor Area and Base Perimeter Used to Compute Base Costs (22,500 Square Feet and 400 Linear Feet)

Square foot of floor area is the total gross area of all floors at grade, and above, and does not include a basement. The perimeter in linear feet used for the base cost is generally for a rectangular, economical building shape.

5 Cost per Square Foot of Floor Area ($174.10)

The highlighted cost is for a building of the selected exterior wall and framing system and floor area. Costs for buildings with floor areas other than those calculated may be interpolated between the costs shown.

6 Building Perimeter and Story Height Adjustments

Square-foot costs for a building with a perimeter or floor-to-floor story height significantly different from the model used to calculate the base cost may be adjusted (add or deduct) to reflect the actual building geometry.

7 Cost per Square Foot of Floor Area for the Perimeter and/or Height Adjustment ($7.80 for Perimeter Difference and $2.75 for Story Height Difference)

Add (or deduct) $7.05 to the base square-foot cost for each 100 feet of perimeter difference between the model and the actual building. Add (or deduct) $2.55 to the base square-foot cost for each 1 foot of story height difference between the model and the actual building.

8 Optional Cost per Square Foot of Basement Floor Area ($36.10)

The cost of an unfinished basement for the building being estimated is $30.45 times the gross floor area of the basement.

9 Range of Cost per Square Foot of Floor Area for Similar Buildings ($61.35 to $228.20)

Many different buildings of the same type have been built using similar materials and systems. RSMeans historical cost data of actual construction projects indicates a range of $59.60 to $221.65 for this type of building.

10 Common Additives

Common components and/or systems used in this type of building are listed. These costs should be added to the total building cost. Additional selections may be found in the Assemblies Section.

The following is a detailed explanation of the specification and costs for a model building in the Commercial/Industrial/Institutional Square Foot Cost Section. Each bold number below corresponds to the described item on the following page with the appropriate component of the sample entry following in parentheses.

Prices listed are costs that include overhead and profit of the installing contractor.

Model costs calculated for a 3 story building with 10' story height and 22,500 square feet of floor area **1**	**2** Apartment, 1-3 Story			
	Unit	Unit Cost	Cost Per S.F.	% Of Sub-Total

A. SUBSTRUCTURE

1010	Standard Foundations	Poured concrete; strip and spread footings		S.F. Ground	6.30	2.10	
1020	Special Foundations	N/A		–	–	–	
1030	Slab on Grade	4" reinforced concrete with vapor barrier and granular base		S.F. Slab	5.31	1.77	4.3%
2010	Basement Excavation	Site preparation for slab and trench for foundation wall and footing		S.F. Ground	.18	.06	
2020	Basement Walls	4' foundation wall		L.F. Wall	77	1.57	

B. SHELL

B10 Superstructure

1010	Floor Construction	Open web steel joists, slab form, concrete, interior steel columns		S.F. Floor	20.07	13.38	13.0%
1020	Roof Construction	Open web steel joists with rib metal deck, interior steel columns		S.F. Roof	10.32	3.44	

B20 Exterior Enclosure

2010	Exterior Walls	Face brick with concrete block backup	88% of wall	S.F. Wall	23.84	11.19	
2020	Exterior Windows	Aluminum horizontal sliding	12% of wall	Each	525	2.24	10.7%
2030	Exterior Doors	Aluminum and glass		Each	2010	.36	

B30 Roofing

3010	Roof Coverings	Built-up tar and gravel with flashing; perlite/EPS composite insulation		S.F. Roof	6.54	2.18	1.7%
3020	Roof Openings	N/A		–	–	–	

C. INTERIORS

1010	Partitions	Gypsum board and sound deadening board on metal studs	10 S.F. of Floor/L.F. Partition	S.F. Partition	6.87	6.11	
1020	Interior Doors	15% solid core wood, 85% hollow core wood	80 S.F. Floor/Door	Each	569	7.12	
1030	Fittings	Kitchen cabinets		S.F. Floor	3.16	3.16	
2010	Stair Construction	Concrete filled metal pan		Flight	14,450	3.21	24.4%
3010	Wall Finishes	70% paint, 25% vinyl wall covering, 5% ceramic tile		S.F. Surface	1.44	2.56	
3020	Floor Finishes	60% carpet, 30% vinyl composition tile, 10% ceramic tile		S.F. Floor	5.50	5.50	
3030	Ceiling Finishes	Painted gypsum board on resilient channels		S.F. Ceiling	3.83	3.83	

D. SERVICES

D10 Conveying

1010	Elevators & Lifts	One hydraulic passenger elevator		Each	109,575	4.87	3.8%
1020	Escalators & Moving Walks	N/A		–	–	–	

D20 Plumbing

2010	Plumbing Fixtures	Kitchen, bathroom and service fixtures, supply and drainage	1 Fixture/200 S.F. Floor	Each	3050	15.25	
2020	Domestic Water Distribution	Gas fired water heater		S.F. Floor	4.90	4.90	16.0%
2040	Rain Water Drainage	Roof drains		S.F. Roof	1.44	.48	

D30 HVAC

3010	Energy Supply	Oil fired hot water, baseboard radiation		S.F. Floor	9.01	9.01	
3020	Heat Generating Systems	N/A		–	–	–	
3030	Cooling Generating Systems	Chilled water, air cooled condenser system		S.F. Floor	10	10	14.7%
3050	Terminal & Package Units	N/A		–	–	–	
3090	Other HVAC Sys. & Equipment	N/A		–	–	–	

D40 Fire Protection

4010	Sprinklers	Wet pipe sprinkler system		S.F. Floor	3.44	3.44	2.7%
4020	Standpipes	N/A		–	–	–	

D50 Electrical

5010	Electrical Service/Distribution	600 ampere service, panel board and feeders		S.F. Floor	2.16	2.16	
5020	Lighting & Branch Wiring	Incandescent fixtures, receptacles, switches, A.C. and misc. power		S.F. Floor	7.13	7.13	8.7%
5030	Communications & Security	Addressable alarm systems, internet wiring, and emergency lighting		S.F. Floor	1.77	1.77	
5090	Other Electrical Systems	Emergency generator, 11.5 kW		S.F. Floor	.19	.19	

E. EQUIPMENT & FURNISHINGS

1010	Commercial Equipment	N/A		–	–	–	
1020	Institutional Equipment	N/A		–	–	–	0.0%
1030	Vehicular Equipment	N/A		–	–	–	
1090	Other Equipment	N/A		–	–	–	

F. SPECIAL CONSTRUCTION

1020	Integrated Construction	N/A		–	–	–	0.0%
1040	Special Facilities	N/A		–	–	–	

G. BUILDING SITEWORK   N/A

	Sub-Total	128.98	100%
CONTRACTOR FEES (General Requirements: 10%, Overhead: 5%, Profit: 10%)	25%	32.22	
ARCHITECT FEES	8%	12.90	
Total Building Cost		174.10	

1 **Building Description**
(Model costs are calculated for a 3-story apartment building with 10' story height and 22,500 square feet of floor area)
The model highlighted is described in terms of building type, number of stories, typical story height, and square footage.

2 **Type of Building**
(Apartment, 1–3 Story)

3 **Division C Interiors**
(C1020 Interior Doors)
System costs are presented in divisions according to the 7-division UNIFORMAT II classifications. Each of the component systems is listed.

4 **Specification Highlights**
(15% solid core wood; 85% hollow core wood)
All systems in each subdivision are described with the material and proportions used.

5 **Quantity Criteria**
(80 S.F. Floor/Door)
The criteria used in determining quantities for the calculations are shown.

6 **Unit (Each)**
The unit of measure shown in this column is the unit of measure of the particular system shown that corresponds to the unit cost.

7 **Unit Cost ($569)**
The cost per unit of measure of each system subdivision.

8 **Cost per Square Foot ($7.12)**
The cost per square foot for each system is the unit cost of the system times the total number of units, divided by the total square feet of building area.

9 **% of Sub-Total (24.4%)**
The percent of sub-total is the total cost per square foot of all systems in the division divided by the sub-total cost per square foot of the building.

10 **Sub-Total ($128.98)**
The sub-total is the total of all the system costs per square foot.

11 **Project Fees**
(Contractor Fees) (25%)
(Architects' Fees) (8%)
Contractor Fees to cover the general requirements, overhead, and profit of the General Contractor are added as a percentage of the sub-total. An Architect's Fee, also as a percentage of the sub-total, is also added. These values vary with the building type.

12 **Total Building Cost ($174.10)**
The total building cost per square foot of building area is the sum of the square foot costs of all the systems, the General Contractor's general requirements, overhead and profit, and the Architect's fee. The total building cost is the amount which appears shaded in the Cost per Square Foot of Floor Area table shown previously.

Examples

Example 1

This example illustrates the use of the base cost tables. The base cost is adjusted for different exterior wall systems, different story height and a partial basement.

Example 1 (continued)

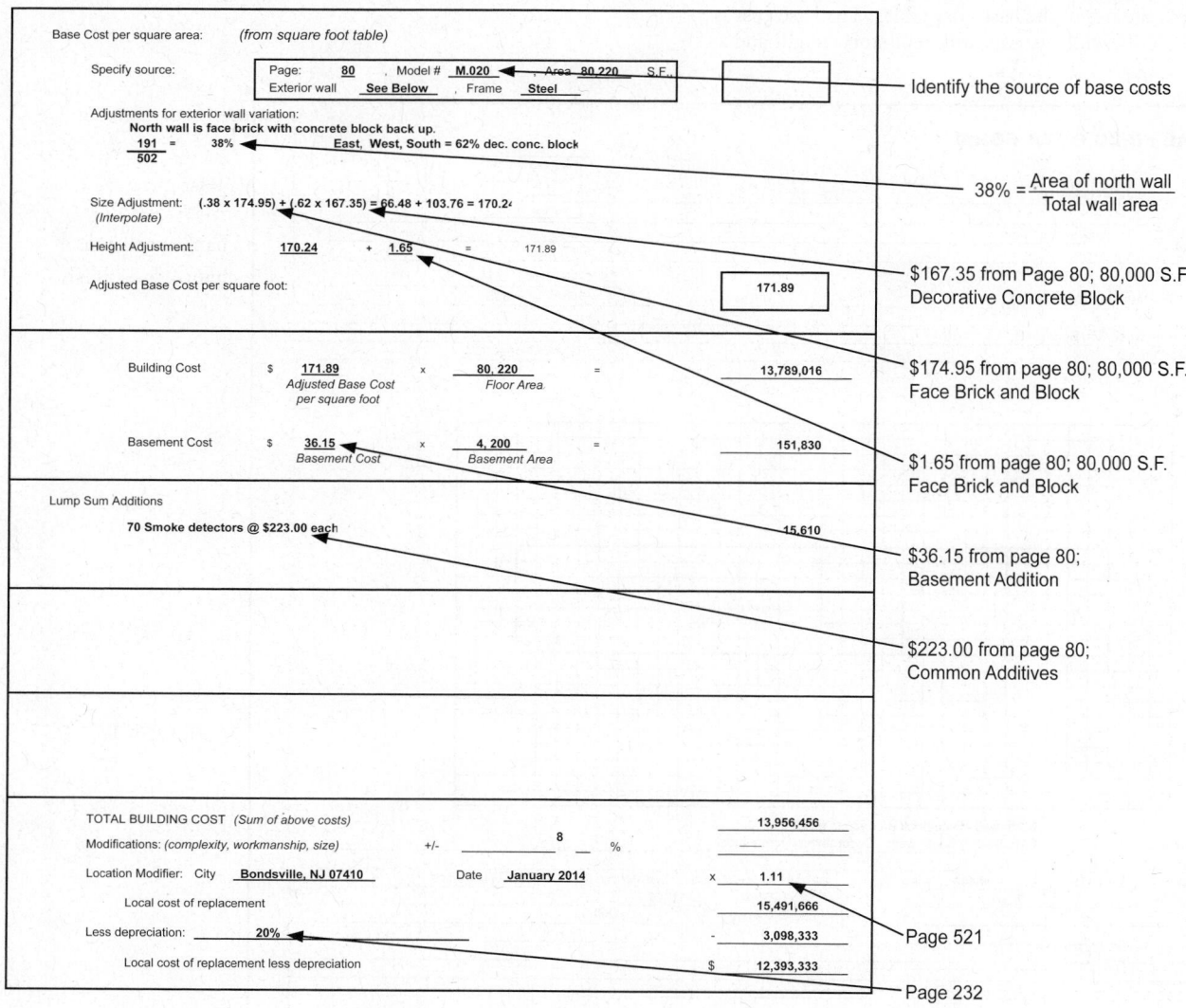

Base Cost per square area: *(from square foot table)*

Specify source:

Page: **80**	Model # **M.020**	Area **80,220** S.F.	
Exterior wall **See Below**	Frame **Steel**		

→ Identify the source of base costs

Adjustments for exterior wall variation:
North wall is face brick with concrete block back up.

$$\frac{191}{502} = 38\%$$ **East, West, South = 62% dec. conc. block**

$38\% = \dfrac{\text{Area of north wall}}{\text{Total wall area}}$

Size Adjustment: (.38 x 174.95) + (.62 x 167.35) = 66.48 + 103.76 = 170.2
(Interpolate)

Height Adjustment: **170.24**   +   **1.65**   =   171.89

Adjusted Base Cost per square foot: | 171.89 |

$167.35 from Page 80; 80,000 S.F.
Decorative Concrete Block

Building Cost $ **171.89**   x   **80,220**   =   13,789,016
Adjusted Base Cost per square foot   Floor Area

$174.95 from page 80; 80,000 S.F.
Face Brick and Block

Basement Cost $ **36.15**   x   **4,200**   =   151,830
Basement Cost   Basement Area

$1.65 from page 80; 80,000 S.F.
Face Brick and Block

Lump Sum Additions

70 Smoke detectors @ $223.00 each   15,610

$36.15 from page 80;
Basement Addition

$223.00 from page 80;
Common Additives

TOTAL BUILDING COST *(Sum of above costs)*   13,956,456

Modifications: *(complexity, workmanship, size)*   +/- _____ **8** __ %   ____

Location Modifier: City **Bondsville, NJ 07410**   Date **January 2014**   x **1.11**

Local cost of replacement   15,491,666

Less depreciation: **20%**   - 3,098,333   Page 521

Local cost of replacement less depreciation $ 12,393,333   Page 232

Example 2

This example shows how to modify a model building.

Model #M.020, 4–7 Story Apartment, page 80, matches the example quite closely. The model specifies a 6-story building with a 10' story height.

The following adjustments must be made:

- add stone ashlar wall
- adjust model to a 5-story building
- change partitions
- change floor finish

CII APPRAISAL

1. SUBJECT PROPERTY: **Westernberg Holdings, Inc.**

5. DATE: **Jan. 1, 2014**

6. APPRAISER: **SJS**

2. BUILDING: **#623**

3. ADDRESS: **55 Pine Wood Rd., Bondsville, N.J. 07410**

4. BUILDING USE: **Apartments**

7. YEAR BUILT: **1991**

```
                    N
                   170 '

 W                                                    E
64.7'

                    S
```

Two exterior wall types

8. EXTERIOR WALL CONSTRUCTION: **North wall - 4" stone Ashlar w/8" block back-up (split Face)**
East, West & South walls - 12" Decorative concrete block

9. FRAME: **Steel**

10. GROUND FLOOR AREA: **11,000**

11. GROSS FLOOR AREA (EXCL. BASEMENT):   **55,000**   S.F.

12. NUMBER OF STORIES: **5**

13. STORY HEIGHT: **11' Ft.**

14. PERIMETER: **469.4**

15. BASEMENT AREA: S.F.

16. GENERAL COMMENTS:

Example 2 (continued)

Square foot area (excluding basement) from item 11 ___55,000___ S.F.
Perimeter from item 14 ___469.4___ Lin. Ft.
Item 17-Model square foot costs (from model sub-total) ___$132.39___

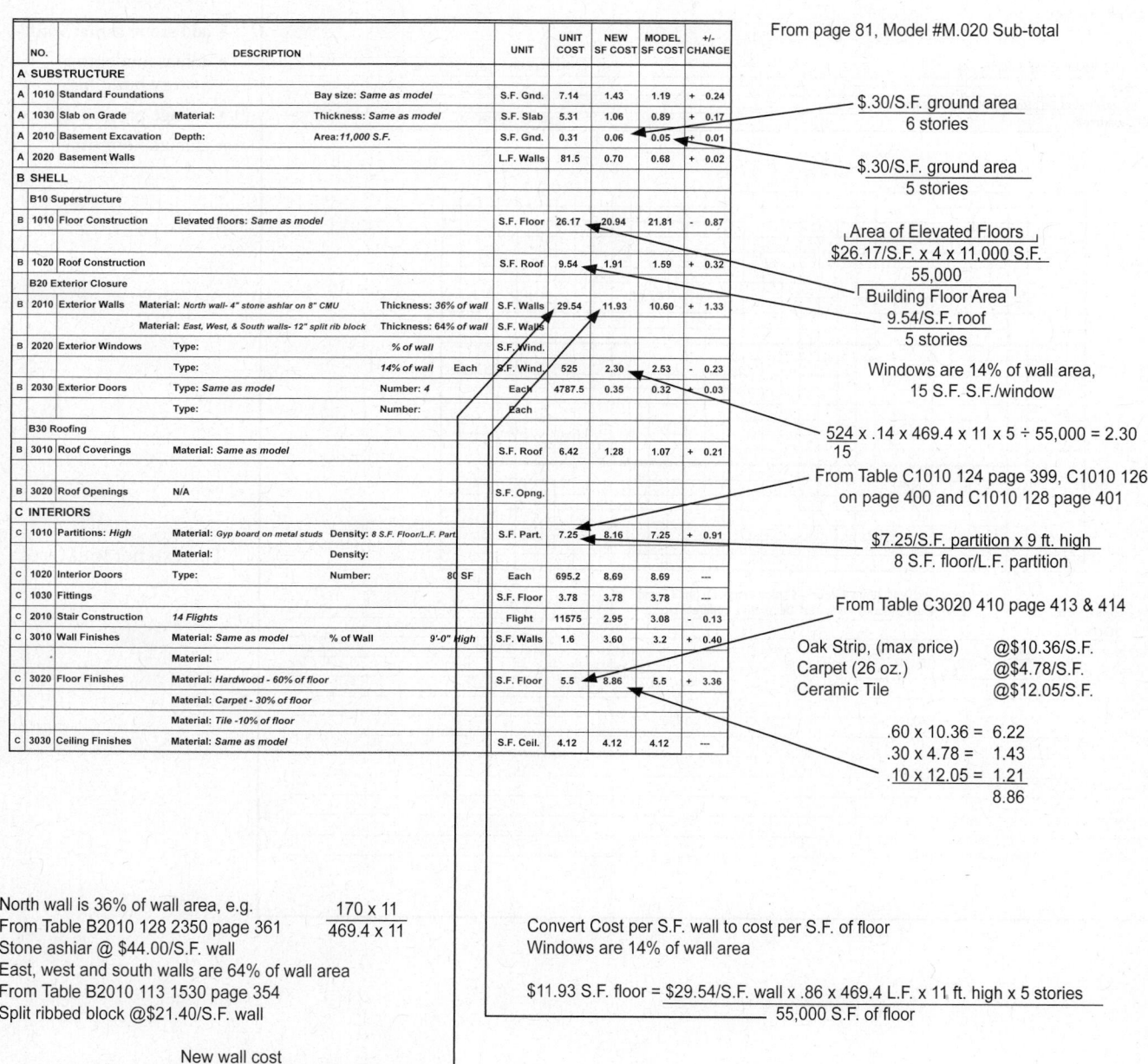

NO.		DESCRIPTION		UNIT	UNIT COST	NEW SF COST	MODEL SF COST	+/- CHANGE
A SUBSTRUCTURE								
A	1010	Standard Foundations	Bay size: *Same as model*	S.F. Gnd.	7.14	1.43	1.19	+ 0.24
A	1030	Slab on Grade	Material: Thickness: *Same as model*	S.F. Slab	5.31	1.06	0.89	+ 0.17
A	2010	Basement Excavation	Depth: Area:*11,000 S.F.*	S.F. Gnd.	0.31	0.06	0.05	+ 0.01
A	2020	Basement Walls		L.F. Walls	81.5	0.70	0.68	+ 0.02
B SHELL								
	B10 Superstructure							
B	1010	Floor Construction	Elevated floors: *Same as model*	S.F. Floor	26.17	20.94	21.81	- 0.87
B	1020	Roof Construction		S.F. Roof	9.54	1.91	1.59	+ 0.32
	B20 Exterior Closure							
B	2010	Exterior Walls	Material: *North wall- 4" stone ashlar on 8" CMU* Thickness: *36% of wall*	S.F. Walls	29.54	11.93	10.60	+ 1.33
			Material: *East, West, & South walls- 12" split rib block* Thickness: *64% of wall*	S.F. Walls				
B	2020	Exterior Windows	Type: % of wall	S.F. Wind.				
			Type: 14% of wall Each	S.F. Wind.	525	2.30	2.53	- 0.23
B	2030	Exterior Doors	Type: *Same as model* Number: 4	Each	4787.5	0.35	0.32	+ 0.03
			Type: Number:	Each				
	B30 Roofing							
B	3010	Roof Coverings	Material: *Same as model*	S.F. Roof	6.42	1.28	1.07	+ 0.21
B	3020	Roof Openings	N/A	S.F. Opng.				
C INTERIORS								
C	1010	Partitions: *High*	Material: *Gyp board on metal studs* Density: *8 S.F. Floor/L.F. Part.*	S.F. Part.	7.25	8.16	7.25	+ 0.91
			Material: Density:					
C	1020	Interior Doors	Type: Number: 80 SF	Each	695.2	8.69	8.69	---
C	1030	Fittings		S.F. Floor	3.78	3.78	3.78	---
C	2010	Stair Construction	*14 Flights*	Flight	11575	2.95	3.08	- 0.13
C	3010	Wall Finishes	Material: *Same as model* % of Wall 9'-0" High	S.F. Walls	1.6	3.60	3.2	+ 0.40
			Material:					
C	3020	Floor Finishes	Material: *Hardwood - 60% of floor*	S.F. Floor	5.5	8.86	5.5	+ 3.36
			Material: *Carpet - 30% of floor*					
			Material: *Tile -10% of floor*					
C	3030	Ceiling Finishes	Material: *Same as model*	S.F. Ceil.	4.12	4.12	4.12	---

From page 81, Model #M.020 Sub-total

$.30/S.F. ground area
6 stories

$.30/S.F. ground area
5 stories

Area of Elevated Floors
$26.17/S.F. x 4 x 11,000 S.F.
55,000
Building Floor Area
9.54/S.F. roof
5 stories

Windows are 14% of wall area,
15 S.F. S.F./window

524 x .14 x 469.4 x 11 x 5 ÷ 55,000 = 2.30
15

From Table C1010 124 page 399, C1010 126
on page 400 and C1010 128 page 401

$7.25/S.F. partition x 9 ft. high
8 S.F. floor/L.F. partition

From Table C3020 410 page 413 & 414

Oak Strip, (max price)   @$10.36/S.F.
Carpet (26 oz.)   @$4.78/S.F.
Ceramic Tile   @$12.05/S.F.

.60 x 10.36 = 6.22
.30 x 4.78 = 1.43
.10 x 12.05 = 1.21
8.86

North wall is 36% of wall area, e.g.   170 x 11
From Table B2010 128 2350 page 361   ―――――
Stone ashlar @ $44.00/S.F. wall   469.4 x 11
East, west and south walls are 64% of wall area
From Table B2010 113 1530 page 354
Split ribbed block @$21.40/S.F. wall

New wall cost
(.36 x $44.00/S.F.) + (.64 x $21.40/S.F.) = $29.54/S.F. wall

Convert Cost per S.F. wall to cost per S.F. of floor
Windows are 14% of wall area

$11.93 S.F. floor = $29.54/S.F. wall x .86 x 469.4 L.F. x 11 ft. high x 5 stories
―――――――――――――――――――――――――――――――――――――――
55,000 S.F. of floor

Example 2 (continued)

	NO.	SYSTEM/COMPONENT	DESCRIPTION		UNIT	UNIT COST	NEW S.F. COST	MODEL S.F. COST	+/- CHANGE
D SERVICES									
	D10 Conveying								
D	1010	Elevators & Lifts 2	Type: *Same as model*	Capacity: Stops:	Each	233,100	8.48	7.77	+ 0.71
D	1020	Escalators & Moving Walks	Type:		Each				
	D20 Plumbing								
D	2010	Plumbing *Kitchen, bath, + service fixtures*	*1 Fixture/215 S.F. Floor*		Each	2990.65	13.91	13.91	---
D	2020	Domestic Water Distribution			S.F. Floor	4.72	4.72	4.72	---
D	2040	Rain Water Drainage			S.F. Roof	1.38	0.28	0.23	+ 0.05
	D30 HVAC								
D	3010	Energy Supply			S.F. Floor	7.92	7.92	7.92	---
D	3020	Heat Generating Systems	Type: *Same as model*		S.F. Floor				
D	3030	Cooling Generating Systems	Type: *Same as model*		S.F. Floor	9.66	9.66	9.66	---
D	3090	Other HVAC Sys. & Equipment			Each				
	D40 Fire Protection								
D	4010	Sprinklers	*Same as model*		S.F. Floor	2.78	2.78	2.78	---
D	4020	Standpipes	*Same as model*		S.F. Floor	0.90	0.90	0.90	---
	D50 Electrical								
D	5010	Electrical Service/Distribution	*Same as model*		S.F. Floor	1.97	1.97	1.97	---
D	5020	Lighting & Branch Wiring			S.F. Floor	7.10	7.10	7.10	---
D	5030	Communications & Security			S.F. Floor	1.68	1.68	1.68	---
D	5090	Other Electrical Systems			S.F. Floor	0.18	0.18	0.18	---
E EQUIPMENT & FURNISHINGS									
E	1010	Commercial Equipment			Each				
E	1020	Institutional Equipment			Each				
E	1030	Vehicular Equipment			Each				
E	1090	Other Equipment			Each				
F SPECIAL CONSTRUCTION									
F	1020	Integrated Construction	N/A		S.F.				
F	1040	Special Facilities	N/A		S.F.				
G BUILDING SITEWORK									

ITEM			Total Change	+ 6.53
17	Model 020 total	$ 135.17		
18	Adjusted S.F. cost $ 141.70 item 17 +/- changes			
19	Building area - from item 11 **55,000** S.F. x adjusted S.F. cost	$	7,793,500	
20	Basement area - from item 15 S.F. x S.F. cost $	$		
21	Base building sub-total - item 20 + item 19	$	7,793,500	
22	Miscellaneous addition (quality, etc.)	$		
23	Sub-total - item 22 + 21	$	7,793,500	
24	General conditions -25 % of item 23	$	1,948,375	
25	Sub-total - item 24 + item 23	$	9,741,875	
26	Architects fees **5.5** % of item 25	$	535,803	
27	Sub-total - item 26 + item 27	$	10,277,678	
28	Location modifier **zip code 07410**	x	1.11	← From page 521
29	Local replacement cost - item 28 x item 27	$	11,408,223	
30	Depreciation **20** % of item 29	$	2,281,645	
31	Depreciated local replacement cost - item 29 less item 30	$	9,126,578	
32	Exclusions	$		
33	Net depreciated replacement cost - item 31 less item 32	$	9,126,578	

Use table on page 232

Costs per square foot of floor area

Exterior Wall	S.F. Area	8000	12000	15000	19000	22500	25000	29000	32000	36000
	L.F. Perimeter	213	280	330	350	400	433	442	480	520
Face Brick with Concrete Block Back-up	Wood Joists	191.50	182.30	178.70	171.20	169.45	168.25	164.15	163.50	162.15
	Steel Joists	192.80	184.90	181.75	175.65	174.10	173.20	169.85	169.25	168.20
Stucco on Concrete Block	Wood Joists	167.40	160.45	157.70	152.60	151.25	150.40	147.65	147.15	146.20
	Steel Joists	182.55	175.50	172.65	167.45	166.10	165.20	162.40	161.90	160.95
Wood Siding	Wood Frame	166.55	159.75	157.10	152.15	150.90	150.05	147.45	146.95	146.05
Brick Veneer	Wood Frame	176.10	168.05	164.90	158.60	157.05	156.05	152.65	152.05	150.95
Perimeter Adj., Add or Deduct	Per 100 L.F.	22.15	14.85	11.80	9.35	7.80	7.10	6.10	5.45	4.95
Story Hgt. Adj., Add or Deduct	Per 1 Ft.	4.20	3.75	3.40	2.90	2.75	2.75	2.35	2.35	2.30

For Basement, add $36.10 per square foot of basement area

The above costs were calculated using the basic specifications shown on the facing page. These costs should be adjusted where necessary for design alternatives and owner's requirements. Reported completed project costs, for this type of structure, range from $61.35 to $228.20 per S.F.

Common additives

Description	Unit	$ Cost
Appliances		
Cooking range, 30" free standing		
1 oven	Each	570 - 2425
2 oven	Each	1425 - 2875
30" built-in		
1 oven	Each	845 - 2050
2 oven	Each	1700 - 2525
Counter top cook tops, 4 burner	Each	425 - 1650
Microwave oven	Each	291 - 825
Combination range, refrig. & sink, 30" wide	Each	1875 - 2925
72" wide	Each	2850
Combination range, refrigerator, sink,		
microwave oven & icemaker	Each	6625
Compactor, residential, 4-1 compaction	Each	820 - 1300
Dishwasher, built-in, 2 cycles	Each	595 - 1125
4 cycles	Each	745 - 1875
Garbage disposer, sink type	Each	228 - 370
Hood for range, 2 speed, vented, 30" wide	Each	320 - 1250
42" wide	Each	425 - 2600
Refrigerator, no frost 10-12 C.F.	Each	550 - 635
18-20 C.F.	Each	800 - 1775

Description	Unit	$ Cost
Closed Circuit Surveillance, One station		
Camera and monitor	Each	1975
For additional camera stations, add	Each	1050
Elevators, Hydraulic passenger, 2 stops		
2000# capacity	Each	67,600
2500# capacity	Each	69,200
3500# capacity	Each	73,200
Additional stop, add	Each	8575
Emergency Lighting, 25 watt, battery operated		
Lead battery	Each	320
Nickel cadmium	Each	885
Laundry Equipment		
Dryer, gas, 16 lb. capacity	Each	965
30 lb. capacity	Each	3800
Washer, 4 cycle	Each	1175
Commercial	Each	1600
Smoke Detectors		
Ceiling type	Each	223
Duct type	Each	555

Important: See the Reference Section for Location Factors.

Model costs calculated for a 3 story building with 10′ story height and 22,500 square feet of floor area

Apartment, 1-3 Story

				Unit	Unit Cost	Cost Per S.F.	% Of Sub-Total
A.	**SUBSTRUCTURE**						
1010	Standard Foundations	Poured concrete; strip and spread footings		S.F. Ground	6.30	2.10	
1020	Special Foundations	N/A		—	—	—	
1030	Slab on Grade	4″ reinforced concrete with vapor barrier and granular base		S.F. Slab	5.31	1.77	4.3%
2010	Basement Excavation	Site preparation for slab and trench for foundation wall and footing		S.F. Ground	.18	.06	
2020	Basement Walls	4′ foundation wall		L.F. Wall	77	1.57	
B.	**SHELL**						
	B10 Superstructure						
1010	Floor Construction	Open web steel joists, slab form, concrete, interior steel columns		S.F. Floor	20.07	13.38	13.0%
1020	Roof Construction	Open web steel joists with rib metal deck, interior steel columns		S.F. Roof	10.32	3.44	
	B20 Exterior Enclosure						
2010	Exterior Walls	Face brick with concrete block backup	88% of wall	S.F. Wall	23.84	11.19	
2020	Exterior Windows	Aluminum horizontal sliding	12% of wall	Each	525	2.24	10.7%
2030	Exterior Doors	Aluminum and glass		Each	2010	.36	
	B30 Roofing						
3010	Roof Coverings	Built-up tar and gravel with flashing; perlite/EPS composite insulation		S.F. Roof	6.54	2.18	1.7%
3020	Roof Openings	N/A		—	—	—	
C.	**INTERIORS**						
1010	Partitions	Gypsum board and sound deadening board on metal studs	10 S.F. of Floor/L.F. Partition	S.F. Partition	6.87	6.11	
1020	Interior Doors	15% solid core wood, 85% hollow core wood	80 S.F. Floor/Door	Each	569	7.12	
1030	Fittings	Kitchen Cabinets		S.F. Floor	3.16	3.16	
2010	Stair Construction	Concrete filled metal pan		Flight	14,450	3.21	24.4%
3010	Wall Finishes	70% paint, 25% vinyl wall covering, 5% ceramic tile		S.F. Surface	1.44	2.56	
3020	Floor Finishes	60% carpet, 30% vinyl composition tile, 10% ceramic tile		S.F. Floor	5.50	5.50	
3030	Ceiling Finishes	Painted gypsum board on resilient channels		S.F. Ceiling	3.83	3.83	
D.	**SERVICES**						
	D10 Conveying						
1010	Elevators & Lifts	One hydraulic passenger elevator		Each	109,575	4.87	3.8%
1020	Escalators & Moving Walks	N/A		—	—	—	
	D20 Plumbing						
2010	Plumbing Fixtures	Kitchen, bathroom and service fixtures, supply and drainage	1 Fixture/200 S.F. Floor	Each	3050	15.25	
2020	Domestic Water Distribution	Gas fired water heater		S.F. Floor	4.90	4.90	16.0%
2040	Rain Water Drainage	Roof drains		S.F. Roof	1.44	.48	
	D30 HVAC						
3010	Energy Supply	Oil fired hot water, baseboard radiation		S.F. Floor	9.01	9.01	
3020	Heat Generating Systems	N/A		—	—	—	
3030	Cooling Generating Systems	Chilled water, air cooled condenser system		S.F. Floor	10	10	14.7%
3050	Terminal & Package Units	N/A		—	—	—	
3090	Other HVAC Sys. & Equipment	N/A		—	—	—	
	D40 Fire Protection						
4010	Sprinklers	Wet pipe sprinkler system		S.F. Floor	3.44	3.44	2.7%
4020	Standpipes	N/A		—	—	—	
	D50 Electrical						
5010	Electrical Service/Distribution	600 ampere service, panel board and feeders		S.F. Floor	2.16	2.16	
5020	Lighting & Branch Wiring	Incandescent fixtures, receptacles, switches, A.C. and misc. power		S.F. Floor	7.13	7.13	8.7%
5030	Communications & Security	Addressable alarm systems, internet wiring, and emergency lighting		S.F. Floor	1.77	1.77	
5090	Other Electrical Systems	Emergency generator, 11.5 kW		S.F. Floor	.19	.19	
E.	**EQUIPMENT & FURNISHINGS**						
1010	Commercial Equipment	N/A		—	—	—	
1020	Institutional Equipment	N/A		—	—	—	0.0%
1030	Vehicular Equipment	N/A		—	—	—	
1090	Other Equipment	N/A		—	—	—	
F.	**SPECIAL CONSTRUCTION**						
1020	Integrated Construction	N/A		—	—	—	0.0%
1040	Special Facilities	N/A		—	—	—	
G.	**BUILDING SITEWORK**	**N/A**					

	Sub-Total	128.98	100%
CONTRACTOR FEES (General Requirements: 10%, Overhead: 5%, Profit: 10%)	25%	32.22	
ARCHITECT FEES	8%	12.90	
Total Building Cost		**174.10**	

79

Costs per square foot of floor area

Exterior Wall	S.F. Area	40000	45000	50000	55000	60000	70000	80000	90000	100000
	L.F. Perimeter	366	400	433	466	500	510	530	550	594
Face Brick with Concrete Block Back-up	Steel Frame	185.10	183.65	182.50	181.55	180.80	177.25	174.95	173.25	172.45
	R/Conc. Frame	191.20	189.65	188.35	187.25	186.45	182.20	179.55	177.45	176.65
Decorative Concrete Block	Steel Frame	176.05	174.80	173.80	172.90	172.25	169.25	167.35	165.85	165.20
	R/Conc. Frame	175.90	174.55	173.55	172.70	172.00	168.95	167.05	165.50	164.85
Precast Concrete Panels	Steel Frame	189.85	188.20	186.85	185.70	184.80	180.25	177.30	175.10	174.20
	R/Conc. Frame	189.35	187.65	186.35	185.15	184.25	179.70	176.75	174.50	173.60
Perimeter Adj., Add or Deduct	Per 100 L.F.	6.95	6.15	5.60	5.00	4.65	3.90	3.45	3.05	2.80
Story Hgt. Adj., Add or Deduct	Per 1 Ft.	2.25	2.25	2.25	2.05	2.05	1.80	1.65	1.45	1.50

For Basement, add $36.15 per square foot of basement area

The above costs were calculated using the basic specifications shown on the facing page. These costs should be adjusted where necessary for design alternatives and owner's requirements. Reported completed project costs, for this type of structure, range from $73.50 to $208.95 per S.F.

Common additives

Description	Unit	$ Cost	Description	Unit	$ Cost
Appliances			Closed Circuit Surveillance, One station		
Cooking range, 30" free standing			Camera and monitor	Each	1975
1 oven	Each	570 - 2425	For additional camera stations, add	Each	1050
2 oven	Each	1425 - 2875	Elevators, Electric passenger, 5 stops		
30" built-in			2000# capacity	Each	167,200
1 oven	Each	845 - 2050	3500# capacity	Each	173,200
2 oven	Each	1700 - 2525	5000# capacity	Each	179,200
Counter top cook tops, 4 burner	Each	425 - 1650	Additional stop, add	Each	12,700
Microwave oven	Each	291 - 825	Emergency Lighting, 25 watt, battery operated		
Combination range, refrig. & sink, 30" wide	Each	1875 - 2925	Lead battery	Each	320
72" wide	Each	2850	Nickel cadmium	Each	885
Combination range, refrigerator, sink,			Laundry Equipment		
microwave oven & icemaker	Each	6625	Dryer, gas, 16 lb. capacity	Each	965
Compactor, residential, 4-1 compaction	Each	820 - 1300	30 lb. capacity	Each	3800
Dishwasher, built-in, 2 cycles	Each	595 - 1125	Washer, 4 cycle	Each	1175
4 cycles	Each	745 - 1875	Commercial	Each	1600
Garbage disposer, sink type	Each	228 - 370	Smoke Detectors		
Hood for range, 2 speed, vented, 30" wide	Each	320 - 1250	Ceiling type	Each	223
42" wide	Each	425 - 2600	Duct type	Each	555
Refrigerator, no frost 10-12 C.F.	Each	550 - 635			
18-20 C.F.	Each	800 - 1775			

Important: See the Reference Section for Location Factors.

Model costs calculated for a 6 story building with 10'-4" story height and 60,000 square feet of floor area

				Unit	Unit Cost	Cost Per S.F.	% Of Sub-Total
A. SUBSTRUCTURE							
1010	Standard Foundations	Poured concrete; strip and spread footings and 4' foundation wall		S.F. Ground	7.14	1.19	
1020	Special Foundations	N/A		—	—	—	
1030	Slab on Grade	4" reinforced concrete with vapor barrier and granular base		S.F. Slab	5.31	.89	2.1%
2010	Basement Excavation	Site preparation for slab and trench for foundation wall and footing		S.F. Ground	.31	.05	
2020	Basement Walls	4' foundation wall		L.F. Wall	82	.68	
B. SHELL							
	B10 Superstructure						
1010	Floor Construction	Open web steel joists, slab form, concrete, steel columns		S.F. Floor	26.17	21.81	17.3%
1020	Roof Construction	Open web steel joists with rib metal deck, steel columns		S.F. Roof	9.54	1.59	
	B20 Exterior Enclosure						
2010	Exterior Walls	Face brick with concrete block backup	86% of wall	S.F. Wall	23.86	10.60	
2020	Exterior Windows	Aluminum horizontal sliding	14% of wall	Each	525	2.53	10.0%
2030	Exterior Doors	Aluminum and glass		Each	4788	.32	
	B30 Roofing						
3010	Roof Coverings	Built-up tar and gravel with flashing; perlite/EPS composite insulation		S.F. Roof	6.42	1.07	0.8%
3020	Roof Openings	N/A		—	—	—	
C. INTERIORS							
1010	Partitions	Gypsum board and sound deadening board on metal studs	8 S.F. Floor/L.F. Partitions	S.F. Partition	7.25	7.25	
1020	Interior Doors	15% solid core wood, 85% hollow core wood	80 S.F Floor/Door	Each	695	8.69	
1030	Fittings	Kitchen cabinets		S.F. Floor	3.78	3.78	
2010	Stair Construction	Concrete filled metal pan		Flight	11,575	3.08	26.4%
3010	Wall Finishes	70% paint, 25% vinyl wall covering, 5% ceramic tile		S.F. Surface	1.60	3.20	
3020	Floor Finishes	60% carpet, 30% vinyl composition tile, 10% ceramic tile		S.F. Floor	5.50	5.50	
3030	Ceiling Finishes	Painted gypsum board on resilient channels		S.F. Ceiling	4.12	4.12	
D. SERVICES							
	D10 Conveying						
1010	Elevators & Lifts	Two geared passenger elevators		Each	233,100	7.77	5.7%
1020	Escalators & Moving Walks	N/A		—	—	—	
	D20 Plumbing						
2010	Plumbing Fixtures	Kitchen, bathroom and service fixtures, supply and drainage	1 Fixture/215 S.F. Floor	Each	2991	13.91	
2020	Domestic Water Distribution	Gas fired water heater		S.F. Floor	4.72	4.72	14.0%
2040	Rain Water Drainage	Roof drains		S.F. Roof	1.38	.23	
	D30 HVAC						
3010	Energy Supply	Oil fired hot water, baseboard radiation		S.F. Floor	7.92	7.92	
3020	Heat Generating Systems	N/A		—	—	—	
3030	Cooling Generating Systems	Chilled water, air cooled condenser system		S.F. Floor	9.66	9.66	13.0%
3050	Terminal & Package Units	N/A		—	—	—	
3090	Other HVAC Sys. & Equipment	N/A		—	—	—	
	D40 Fire Protection						
4010	Sprinklers	Wet pipe sprinkler system		S.F. Floor	2.78	2.78	2.7%
4020	Standpipes	Standpipe, fire pump		S.F. Floor	.90	.90	
	D50 Electrical						
5010	Electrical Service/Distribution	1600 ampere service, panel board and feeders		S.F. Floor	1.97	1.97	
5020	Lighting & Branch Wiring	Incandescent fixtures, receptacles, switches, A.C. and misc. power		S.F. Floor	7.10	7.10	8.1%
5030	Communications & Security	Addressable alarm system, internet wiring, emergency lighting, and intercom		S.F. Floor	1.68	1.68	
5090	Other Electrical Systems	Emergency generator, 30 kW		S.F. Floor	.18	.18	
E. EQUIPMENT & FURNISHINGS							
1010	Commercial Equipment	N/A		—	—	—	
1020	Institutional Equipment	N/A		—	—	—	
1030	Vehicular Equipment	N/A		—	—	—	0.0 %
1090	Other Equipment	N/A		—	—	—	
F. SPECIAL CONSTRUCTION							
1020	Integrated Construction	N/A		—	—	—	
1040	Special Facilities	N/A		—	—	—	0.0 %
G. BUILDING SITEWORK	**N/A**						

			Sub-Total	135.17	100%
CONTRACTOR FEES (General Requirements: 10%, Overhead: 5%, Profit: 10%)			25%	33.80	
ARCHITECT FEES			7%	11.83	

Total Building Cost   **180.80**

Costs per square foot of floor area

Exterior Wall	S.F. Area	95000	112000	129000	145000	170000	200000	275000	400000	600000
	L.F. Perimeter	345	386	406	442	480	510	530	570	630
Ribbed Precast Concrete Panel	Steel Frame	239.55	236.35	232.20	230.45	227.30	223.60	215.55	209.15	204.35
	R/Conc. Frame	230.35	227.40	223.45	221.85	218.85	215.40	208.00	202.05	197.60
Face Brick with Concrete Block Back-up	Steel Frame	213.10	210.50	207.20	205.80	203.30	200.55	194.50	189.65	186.00
	R/Conc. Frame	222.30	219.75	216.45	215.00	212.55	209.70	203.70	198.85	195.25
Stucco on Concrete Block	Steel Frame	202.10	200.05	197.70	196.60	194.80	192.80	188.65	185.35	182.80
	R/Conc. Frame	211.30	209.30	206.90	205.80	203.95	201.95	197.90	194.55	192.05
Perimeter Adj., Add or Deduct	Per 100 L.F.	11.85	10.10	8.70	7.80	6.55	5.60	4.10	2.85	1.90
Story Hgt. Adj., Add or Deduct	Per 1 Ft.	3.80	3.55	3.25	3.15	2.90	2.60	2.05	1.50	1.15
For Basement, add $37.00 per square foot of basement area										

The above costs were calculated using the basic specifications shown on the facing page. These costs should be adjusted where necessary for design alternatives and owner's requirements. Reported completed project costs, for this type of structure, range from $94.10 to $220.75 per S.F.

Common additives

Description	Unit	$ Cost	Description	Unit	$ Cost
Appliances			Closed Circuit Surveillance, One station		
Cooking range, 30" free standing			Camera and monitor	Each	1975
1 oven	Each	570 - 2425	For additional camera stations, add	Each	1050
2 oven	Each	1425 - 2875	Elevators, Electric passenger, 10 stops		
30" built-in			3000# capacity	Each	420,000
1 oven	Each	845 - 2050	4000# capacity	Each	422,500
2 oven	Each	1700 - 2525	5000# capacity	Each	427,500
Counter top cook tops, 4 burner	Each	425 - 1650	Additional stop, add	Each	12,700
Microwave oven	Each	291 - 825	Emergency Lighting, 25 watt, battery operated		
Combination range, refrig. & sink, 30" wide	Each	1875 - 2925	Lead battery	Each	320
72" wide	Each	2850	Nickel cadmium	Each	885
Combination range, refrigerator, sink,			Laundry Equipment		
microwave oven & icemaker	Each	6625	Dryer, gas, 16 lb. capacity	Each	965
Compactor, residential, 4-1 compaction	Each	820 - 1300	30 lb. capacity	Each	3800
Dishwasher, built-in, 2 cycles	Each	595 - 1125	Washer, 4 cycle	Each	1175
4 cycles	Each	745 - 1875	Commercial	Each	1600
Garbage disposer, sink type	Each	228 - 370	Smoke Detectors		
Hood for range, 2 speed, vented, 30" wide	Each	320 - 1250	Ceiling type	Each	223
42" wide	Each	425 - 2600	Duct type	Each	555
Refrigerator, no frost 10-12 C.F.	Each	550 - 635			
18-20 C.F.	Each	800 - 1775			

Model costs calculated for a 15 story building with 10'-6" story height and 145,000 square feet of floor area

Apartment, 8-24 Story

				Unit	Unit Cost	Cost Per S.F.	% Of Sub-Total
A. SUBSTRUCTURE							
1010	Standard Foundations	CIP concrete pile caps		S.F. Ground	9.45	.63	
1020	Special Foundations	Steel H-piles, concrete grade beams		S.F. Ground	196	13.07	
1030	Slab on Grade	4" reinforced concrete with vapor barrier and granular base		S.F. Slab	5.31	.36	8.3%
2010	Basement Excavation	Site preparation for slab, piles and grade beam		S.F. Ground	.31	.02	
2020	Basement Walls	4' Foundation wall		L.F. Wall	77	.28	
B. SHELL							
B10 Superstructure							
1010	Floor Construction	Open web steel joists, slab form, concrete, interior steel columns		S.F. Floor	22.45	20.95	12.3%
1020	Roof Construction	Open web steel joists with rib metal deck, interior steel columns		S.F. Roof	7.20	.48	
B20 Exterior Enclosure							
2010	Exterior Walls	Ribbed precast concrete panel	87% of wall	S.F. Wall	46.23	19.31	
2020	Exterior Windows	Aluminum horizontal sliding	13% of wall	Each	525	2.19	13.9%
2030	Exterior Doors	Aluminum and glass		Each	3227	2.76	
B30 Roofing							
3010	Roof Coverings	Built-up tar and gravel with flashing; perlite/EPS composite insulation		S.F. Roof	6.15	.41	0.2%
3020	Roof Openings	N/A		—	—	—	
C. INTERIORS							
1010	Partitions	Gypsum board on concrete block and metal studs	10 S.F. of Floor/L.F. Partition	S.F. Partition	14.46	14.46	
1020	Interior Doors	15% solid core wood, 85% hollow core wood	80 S.F. Floor/Door	Each	710	8.87	
1030	Fittings	Kitchen cabinets		S.F. Floor	3.92	3.92	
2010	Stair Construction	Concrete filled metal pan		Flight	11,575	3.43	25.0%
3010	Wall Finishes	70% paint, 25% vinyl wall covering, 5% ceramic tile		S.F. Surface	1.58	3.16	
3020	Floor Finishes	60% carpet, 30% vinyl composition tile, 10% ceramic tile		S.F. Floor	5.50	5.50	
3030	Ceiling Finishes	Painted gypsum board on resilient channels		S.F. Ceiling	4.12	4.12	
D. SERVICES							
D10 Conveying							
1010	Elevators & Lifts	Four geared passenger elevators		Each	498,800	13.76	7.9%
1020	Escalators & Moving Walks	N/A		—	—	—	
D20 Plumbing							
2010	Plumbing Fixtures	Kitchen, bathroom and service fixtures, supply and drainage	1 Fixture/210 S.F. Floor	Each	3339	15.90	
2020	Domestic Water Distribution	Gas fired water heater		S.F. Floor	5.42	5.42	12.4%
2040	Rain Water Drainage	Roof drains		S.F. Roof	2.55	.17	
D30 HVAC							
3010	Energy Supply	Oil fired hot water, baseboard radiation		S.F. Floor	7.92	7.92	
3020	Heat Generating Systems	N/A		—	—	—	
3030	Cooling Generating Systems	Chilled water, air cooled condenser system		S.F. Floor	9.66	9.66	10.1%
3050	Terminal & Package Units	N/A		—	—	—	
3090	Other HVAC Sys. & Equipment	N/A		—	—	—	
D40 Fire Protection							
4010	Sprinklers	Wet pipe sprinkler system		S.F. Floor	2.82	2.82	2.6%
4020	Standpipes	Standpipe, fire pumps		S.F. Floor	1.70	1.70	
D50 Electrical							
5010	Electrical Service/Distribution	4000 ampere service, panel board and feeders		S.F. Floor	1.70	1.70	
5020	Lighting & Branch Wiring	Incandescent fixtures, receptacles, switches, A.C. and misc. power		S.F. Floor	7.64	7.64	7.3%
5030	Communications & Security	Addressable alarm systems, internet wiring, em. lighting, intercom & security TV		S.F. Floor	3.12	3.12	
5090	Other Electrical Systems	Emergency generator, 30 kW		S.F. Floor	.19	.19	
E. EQUIPMENT & FURNISHINGS							
1010	Commercial Equipment	N/A		—	—	—	
1020	Institutional Equipment	N/A		—	—	—	
1030	Vehicular Equipment	N/A		—	—	—	0.0%
1090	Other Equipment	N/A		—	—	—	
F. SPECIAL CONSTRUCTION							
1020	Integrated Construction	N/A		—	—	—	0.0%
1040	Special Facilities	N/A		—	—	—	
G. BUILDING SITEWORK	**N/A**						

			Sub-Total	173.92	100%
CONTRACTOR FEES (General Requirements: 10%, Overhead: 5%, Profit: 10%)		25%	43.49		
ARCHITECT FEES		6%	13.04		

Total Building Cost	**230.45**

Costs per square foot of floor area

Exterior Wall	S.F. Area	2000	3000	4000	5000	7500	10000	15000	25000	50000
	L.F. Perimeter	188	224	260	300	356	400	504	700	1200
Brick Veneer	Wood Frame	239.85	213.20	199.85	192.40	178.70	171.20	164.30	158.50	154.25
	Steel Frame	266.30	239.95	226.75	219.40	205.95	198.50	191.75	186.00	181.90
Brick Veneer on Block	Wood Truss	243.10	215.15	201.20	193.40	178.85	170.85	163.45	157.35	152.80
	Bearing Wall	277.05	249.10	235.10	227.35	212.80	204.70	197.35	191.20	186.65
Wood Siding	Wood Frame	224.65	200.80	188.85	182.10	170.15	163.65	157.65	152.55	148.90
Vinyl Siding	Wood Frame	224.30	200.85	189.10	182.45	170.85	164.55	158.75	153.85	150.30
Perimeter Adj., Add or Deduct	Per 100 L.F.	30.85	20.60	15.45	12.30	8.25	6.15	4.10	2.45	1.20
Story Hgt. Adj., Add or Deduct	Per 1 Ft.	3.85	3.05	2.65	2.40	1.90	1.55	1.35	1.15	0.95

For Basement, add $32.55 per square foot of basement area

The above costs were calculated using the basic specifications shown on the facing page. These costs should be adjusted where necessary for design alternatives and owner's requirements. Reported completed project costs, for this type of structure, range from $92.40 to $231.75 per S.F.

Common additives

Description	Unit	$ Cost
Appliances		
Cooking range, 30" free standing		
1 oven	Each	570 - 2425
2 oven	Each	1425 - 2875
30" built-in		
1 oven	Each	845 - 2050
2 oven	Each	1700 - 2525
Counter top cook tops, 4 burner	Each	425 - 1650
Microwave oven	Each	291 - 825
Combination range, refrig. & sink, 30" wide	Each	1875 - 2925
60" wide	Each	2625
72" wide	Each	2850
Combination range, refrigerator, sink,		
microwave oven & icemaker	Each	6625
Compactor, residential, 4-1 compaction	Each	820 - 1300
Dishwasher, built-in, 2 cycles	Each	595 - 1125
4 cycles	Each	745 - 1875
Garbage disposer, sink type	Each	228 - 370
Hood for range, 2 speed, vented, 30" wide	Each	320 - 1250
42" wide	Each	425 - 2600

Description	Unit	$ Cost
Appliances, cont.		
Refrigerator, no frost 10-12 C.F.	Each	550 - 635
14-16 C.F.	Each	650 - 855
18-20 C.F.	Each	800 - 1775
Laundry Equipment		
Dryer, gas, 16 lb. capacity	Each	965
30 lb. capacity	Each	3800
Washer, 4 cycle	Each	1175
Commercial	Each	1600
Sound System		
Amplifier, 250 watts	Each	2025
Speaker, ceiling or wall	Each	208
Trumpet	Each	400

Important: See the Reference Section for Location Factors.

Model costs calculated for a 1 story building with 10' story height and 10,000 square feet of floor area

					Unit	Unit Cost	Cost Per S.F.	% Of Sub-Total
A.	**SUBSTRUCTURE**							
1010	Standard Foundations	Poured concrete strip footings			S.F. Ground	2.04	2.04	
1020	Special Foundations	N/A			—	—	—	
1030	Slab on Grade	4" reinforced concrete with vapor barrier and granular base			S.F. Slab	5.31	5.31	9.1%
2010	Basement Excavation	Site preparation for slab and trench for foundation wall and footing			S.F. Ground	.57	.57	
2020	Basement Walls	4' foundation wall			L.F. Wall	82	3.26	
B.	**SHELL**							
	B10 Superstructure							
1010	Floor Construction	N/A			—	—	—	6.0 %
1020	Roof Construction	Plywood on wood trusses (pitched); fiberglass batt insulation			S.F. Roof	7.42	7.42	
	B20 Exterior Enclosure							
2010	Exterior Walls	Brick veneer on wood studs, insulated		80% of wall	S.F. Wall	24.44	7.82	
2020	Exterior Windows	Double hung wood		20% of wall	Each	637	3.19	10.1%
2030	Exterior Doors	Aluminum and glass; 18 ga. steel flush			Each	2446	1.48	
	B30 Roofing							
3010	Roof Coverings	Asphalt shingles with flashing (pitched); al. gutters & downspouts			S.F. Roof	2.90	2.90	2.4%
3020	Roof Openings	N/A			—	—	—	
C.	**INTERIORS**							
1010	Partitions	Gypsum board on wood studs		6 S.F. Floor/L.F. Partition	S.F. Partition	5.27	7.03	
1020	Interior Doors	Single leaf wood		80 S.F. Floor/Door	Each	636	7.48	
1030	Fittings	N/A			—	—	—	
2010	Stair Construction	N/A			—	—	—	26.9%
3010	Wall Finishes	Paint on drywall			S.F. Surface	.84	2.24	
3020	Floor Finishes	80% carpet, 20% ceramic tile			S.F. Floor	7.65	7.65	
3030	Ceiling Finishes	Gypsum board on wood furring, painted			S.F. Ceiling	8.82	8.82	
D.	**SERVICES**							
	D10 Conveying							
1010	Elevators & Lifts	N/A			—	—	—	0.0 %
1020	Escalators & Moving Walks	N/A			—	—	—	
	D20 Plumbing							
2010	Plumbing Fixtures	Kitchen, toilet and service fixtures, supply and drainage		1 Fixture/200 S.F. Floor	Each	3164	15.82	
2020	Domestic Water Distribution	Gas water heater			S.F. Floor	2.36	2.36	14.7%
2040	Rain Water Drainage	N/A			—	—	—	
	D30 HVAC							
3010	Energy Supply	N/A			—	—	—	
3020	Heat Generating Systems	N/A			—	—	—	
3030	Cooling Generating Systems	N/A			—	—	—	3.1 %
3050	Terminal & Package Units	Gas fired hot water boiler; terminal package heat/A/C units			S.F. Floor	3.81	3.81	
3090	Other HVAC Sys. & Equipment	N/A			—	—	—	
	D40 Fire Protection							
4010	Sprinklers	Wet pipe sprinkler system			S.F. Floor	3.56	3.56	3.6%
4020	Standpipes	Standpipes			S.F. Floor	.83	.83	
	D50 Electrical							
5010	Electrical Service/Distribution	600 ampere service, panel board, feeders and branch wiring			S.F. Floor	8.50	8.50	
5020	Lighting & Branch Wiring	Fuorescent & incandescent fixtures, receptacles, switches, A.C. and misc. power			S.F. Floor	11.29	11.29	22.9%
5030	Communications & Security	Addressable alarm, fire detection and command center, communication system			S.F. Floor	8.22	8.22	
5090	Other Electrical Systems	Emergency generator, 7.5 kW			S.F. Floor	.19	.19	
E.	**EQUIPMENT & FURNISHINGS**							
1010	Commercial Equipment	Residential washers and dryers			S.F. Floor	.44	.44	
1020	Institutional Equipment	N/A			—	—	—	1.3%
1030	Vehicular Equipment	N/A			—	—	—	
1090	Other Equipment	Residential ranges & refrigerators			S.F. Floor	1.14	1.14	
F.	**SPECIAL CONSTRUCTION**							
1020	Integrated Construction	N/A			—	—	—	0.0 %
1040	Special Facilities	N/A			—	—	—	
G.	**BUILDING SITEWORK**	**N/A**						

						Sub-Total	123.37	100%
	CONTRACTOR FEES (General Requirements: 10%, Overhead: 5%, Profit: 10%)					25%	30.87	
	ARCHITECT FEES					11%	16.96	

Total Building Cost 171.20

Costs per square foot of floor area

Exterior Wall	S.F. Area	12000	15000	18000	21000	24000	27000	30000	33000	36000
	L.F. Perimeter	440	500	540	590	640	665	700	732	770
Face Brick with Concrete Block Back-up	Steel Frame	198.00	192.30	186.70	183.50	181.05	177.70	175.50	173.60	172.30
	Bearing Wall	191.40	186.30	181.35	178.45	176.30	173.30	171.35	169.65	168.40
Precast Concrete	Steel Frame	203.00	196.90	190.90	187.45	184.90	181.25	178.95	176.90	175.45
Decorative Concrete Block	Bearing Wall	172.95	169.50	166.10	164.20	162.70	160.70	159.40	158.25	157.45
Concrete Block	Steel Frame	181.75	179.00	176.35	174.80	173.60	172.05	171.00	170.10	169.45
	Bearing Wall	168.75	165.65	162.70	160.95	159.60	157.85	156.75	155.70	155.00
Perimeter Adj., Add or Deduct	Per 100 L.F.	13.55	10.80	9.00	7.70	6.75	6.00	5.45	4.90	4.50
Story Hgt. Adj., Add or Deduct	Per 1 Ft.	2.10	1.90	1.80	1.65	1.60	1.40	1.35	1.30	1.20

For Basement, add $29.55 per square foot of basement area

The above costs were calculated using the basic specifications shown on the facing page. These costs should be adjusted where necessary for design alternatives and owner's requirements. Reported completed project costs, for this type of structure, range from $93.15 to $235.75 per S.F.

Common additives

Description	Unit	$ Cost
Closed Circuit Surveillance, One station		
Camera and monitor	Each	1975
For additional camera stations, add	Each	1050
Emergency Lighting, 25 watt, battery operated		
Lead battery	Each	320
Nickel cadmium	Each	885
Seating		
Auditorium chair, all veneer	Each	300
Veneer back, padded seat	Each	315
Upholstered, spring seat	Each	315
Classroom, movable chair & desk	Set	81 - 171
Lecture hall, pedestal type	Each	258 - 610
Smoke Detectors		
Ceiling type	Each	223
Duct type	Each	555
Sound System		
Amplifier, 250 watts	Each	2025
Speaker, ceiling or wall	Each	208
Trumpet	Each	400

Important: See the Reference Section for Location Factors.

Model costs calculated for a 1 story building with 24' story height and 24,000 square feet of floor area

Auditorium

				Unit	Unit Cost	Cost Per S.F.	% Of Sub-Total
A. SUBSTRUCTURE							
1010	Standard Foundations	Poured concrete; strip and spread footings		S.F. Ground	1.45	1.45	
1020	Special Foundations	N/A		—	—	—	
1030	Slab on Grade	6" reinforced concrete with vapor barrier and granular base		S.F. Slab	6.29	6.29	7.5%
2010	Basement Excavation	Site preparation for slab and trench for foundation wall and footing		S.F. Ground	.18	.18	
2020	Basement Walls	4' foundation wall		L.F. Wall	91	2.41	
B. SHELL							
	B10 Superstructure						
1010	Floor Construction	Open web steel joists, slab form, concrete	(balcony)	S.F. Floor	25.20	3.15	9.3%
1020	Roof Construction	Metal deck on steel truss		S.F. Roof	9.66	9.66	
	B20 Exterior Enclosure						
2010	Exterior Walls	Precast concrete panel	80% of wall (adjusted for end walls)	S.F. Wall	44.53	22.80	
2020	Exterior Windows	Glass curtain wall	20% of wall	Each	43.10	5.52	22.0%
2030	Exterior Doors	Double aluminum and glass and hollow metal		Each	4145	2.07	
	B30 Roofing						
3010	Roof Coverings	Built-up tar and gravel with flashing; perlite/EPS composite insulation		S.F. Roof	6.01	6.01	4.5%
3020	Roof Openings	Roof hatches		S.F. Roof	.24	.24	
C. INTERIORS							
1010	Partitions	Concrete Block and toilet partitions	40 S.F. Floor/L.F. Partition	S.F. Partition	9.38	3.75	
1020	Interior Doors	Single leaf hollow metal	400 S.F. Floor/Door	Each	1152	2.89	
1030	Fittings	N/A		—	—	—	
2010	Stair Construction	Concrete filled metal pan		Flight	17,250	2.16	18.5%
3010	Wall Finishes	70% paint, 30% epoxy coating		S.F. Surface	5.64	4.51	
3020	Floor Finishes	70% vinyl tile, 30% carpet		S.F. Floor	7.75	7.75	
3030	Ceiling Finishes	Fiberglass board, suspended		S.F. Ceiling	4.57	4.57	
D. SERVICES							
	D10 Conveying						
1010	Elevators & Lifts	One hydraulic passenger elevator		Each	91,920	3.83	2.8%
1020	Escalators & Moving Walks	N/A		—	—	—	
	D20 Plumbing						
2010	Plumbing Fixtures	Toilet and service fixtures, supply and drainage	1 Fixture/800 S.F. Floor	Each	6536	8.17	
2020	Domestic Water Distribution	Gas fired water heater		S.F. Floor	3.86	3.86	9.5%
2040	Rain Water Drainage	Roof drains		S.F. Roof	1.10	1.10	
	D30 HVAC						
3010	Energy Supply	N/A		—	—	—	
3020	Heat Generating Systems	Included in D3050		—	—	—	
3030	Cooling Generating Systems	N/A		—	—	—	9.3 %
3050	Terminal & Package Units	Single zone rooftop unit, gas heating, electric cooling		S.F. Floor	12.85	12.85	
3090	Other HVAC Sys. & Equipment	N/A		—	—	—	
	D40 Fire Protection						
4010	Sprinklers	Wet pipe sprinkler system		S.F. Floor	3.56	3.56	2.8%
4020	Standpipes	Standpipe		S.F. Floor	.34	.34	
	D50 Electrical						
5010	Electrical Service/Distribution	800 ampere service, panel board and feeders		S.F. Floor	1.92	1.92	
5020	Lighting & Branch Wiring	Fluorescent fixtures, receptacles, switches, A.C. and misc. power		S.F. Floor	11.94	11.94	13.8%
5030	Communications & Security	Addressable alarm systems, emergency lighting and public address system		S.F. Floor	4.04	4.04	
5090	Other Electrical Systems	Emergency generator, 100 kW		S.F. Floor	1.20	1.20	
E. EQUIPMENT & FURNISHINGS							
1010	Commercial Equipment	N/A		—	—	—	
1020	Institutional Equipment	N/A		—	—	—	0.0 %
1030	Vehicular Equipment	N/A		—	—	—	
1090	Other Equipment	N/A		—	—	—	
F. SPECIAL CONSTRUCTION							
1020	Integrated Construction	N/A		—	—	—	0.0 %
1040	Special Facilities	N/A		—	—	—	
G. BUILDING SITEWORK	**N/A**						

	Sub-Total	138.22	**100%**
CONTRACTOR FEES (General Requirements: 10%, Overhead: 5%, Profit: 10%)	25%	34.59	
ARCHITECT FEES	7%	12.09	
	Total Building Cost	**184.90**	

Costs per square foot of floor area

Exterior Wall	S.F. Area	2000	2700	3400	4100	4800	5500	6200	6900	7600
	L.F. Perimeter	180	208	236	256	280	303	317	337	357
Face Brick with Concrete Block Back-up	Steel Frame	269.10	253.15	243.85	235.65	230.70	226.95	222.50	219.90	217.70
	R/Conc. Frame	284.85	268.90	259.65	251.45	246.50	242.70	238.25	235.65	233.45
Precast Concrete Panel	Steel Frame	273.90	257.25	247.40	238.85	233.70	229.65	225.00	222.20	219.90
	R/Conc. Frame	294.45	275.60	264.60	255.15	249.40	244.95	239.90	236.90	234.35
Limestone with Concrete Block Back-up	Steel Frame	309.10	287.40	274.70	263.40	256.70	251.40	245.20	241.55	238.55
	R/Conc. Frame	324.80	303.20	290.45	279.15	272.45	267.20	261.00	257.30	254.35
Perimeter Adj., Add or Deduct	Per 100 L.F.	49.65	36.80	29.15	24.20	20.75	18.00	16.05	14.35	13.00
Story Hgt. Adj., Add or Deduct	Per 1 Ft.	4.70	4.05	3.60	3.25	3.15	2.85	2.70	2.55	2.40

For Basement, add $34.20 per square foot of basement area

The above costs were calculated using the basic specifications shown on the facing page. These costs should be adjusted where necessary for design alternatives and owner's requirements. Reported completed project costs, for this type of structure, range from $142.00 to $349.50 per S.F.

Common additives

Description	Unit	$ Cost	Description	Unit	$ Cost
Bulletproof Teller Window, 44" x 60"	Each	5100	Service Windows, Pass thru, steel		
60" x 48"	Each	6975	24" x 36"	Each	3800
Closed Circuit Surveillance, One station			48" x 48"	Each	4125
Camera and monitor	Each	1975	72" x 40"	Each	6425
For additional camera stations, add	Each	1050	Smoke Detectors		
Counters, Complete	Station	6200	Ceiling type	Each	223
Door & Frame, 3' x 6'-8", bullet resistant steel			Duct type	Each	555
with vision panel	Each	7350 - 9500	Twenty-four Hour Teller		
Drive-up Window, Drawer & micr., not incl. glass	Each	8950 - 12,900	Automatic deposit cash & memo	Each	53,500
Emergency Lighting, 25 watt, battery operated			Vault Front, Door & frame		
Lead battery	Each	320	1 hour test, 32"x 78"	Opening	8200
Nickel cadmium	Each	885	2 hour test, 32" door	Opening	10,000
Night Depository	Each	9650 - 14,600	40" door	Opening	11,600
Package Receiver, painted	Each	1950	4 hour test, 32" door	Opening	10,600
stainless steel	Each	3000	40" door	Opening	12,500
Partitions, Bullet resistant to 8' high	L.F.	330 - 530	Time lock, two movement, add	Each	2800
Pneumatic Tube Systems, 2 station	Each	33,300			
With TV viewer	Each	61,000			

Important: See the Reference Section for Location Factors.

Model costs calculated for a 1 story building with 14' story height and 4,100 square feet of floor area

				Unit	Unit Cost	Cost Per S.F.	% Of Sub-Total
A. SUBSTRUCTURE							
1010	Standard Foundations	Poured concrete; strip and spread footings		S.F. Ground	4.21	4.21	
1020	Special Foundations	N/A		—	—	—	
1030	Slab on Grade	4" reinforced concrete with vapor barrier and granular base		S.F. Slab	5.31	5.31	8.8%
2010	Basement Excavation	Site preparation for slab and trench for foundation wall and footing		S.F. Ground	.32	.32	
2020	Basement Walls	4' Foundation wall		L.F. Wall	82	6.11	
B. SHELL							
B10 Superstructure							
1010	Floor Construction	Cast-in-place columns		L.F. Column	122	5.95	12.0%
1020	Roof Construction	Cast-in-place concrete flat plate		S.F. Roof	15.75	15.75	
B20 Exterior Enclosure							
2010	Exterior Walls	Face brick with concrete block backup	80% of wall	S.F. Wall	32.89	23	
2020	Exterior Windows	Horizontal aluminum sliding	20% of wall	Each	585	6.81	17.3%
2030	Exterior Doors	Double aluminum and glass and hollow metal		Each	3298	1.61	
B30 Roofing							
3010	Roof Coverings	Built-up tar and gravel with flashing; perlite/EPS composite insulation		S.F. Roof	7.53	7.53	4.2%
3020	Roof Openings	N/A		—	—	—	
C. INTERIORS							
1010	Partitions	Gypsum board on metal studs	20 S.F. of Floor/L.F. Partition	S.F. Partition	10.50	5.25	
1020	Interior Doors	Single leaf hollow metal	200 S.F. Floor/Door	Each	1152	5.76	
1030	Fittings	N/A		—	—	—	
2010	Stair Construction	N/A		—	—	—	13.8%
3010	Wall Finishes	50% vinyl wall covering, 50% paint		S.F. Surface	1.43	1.43	
3020	Floor Finishes	50% carpet tile, 40% vinyl composition tile, 10% quarry tile		S.F. Floor	5.69	5.69	
3030	Ceiling Finishes	Mineral fiber tile on concealed zee bars		S.F. Ceiling	6.89	6.89	
D. SERVICES							
D10 Conveying							
1010	Elevators & Lifts	N/A		—	—	—	0.0 %
1020	Escalators & Moving Walks	N/A		—	—	—	
D20 Plumbing							
2010	Plumbing Fixtures	Toilet and service fixtures, supply and drainage	1 Fixture/580 S.F. Floor	Each	5487	9.46	
2020	Domestic Water Distribution	Gas fired water heater		S.F. Floor	1.36	1.36	6.8%
2040	Rain Water Drainage	Roof drains		S.F. Roof	1.54	1.54	
D30 HVAC							
3010	Energy Supply	N/A		—	—	—	
3020	Heat Generating Systems	Included in D3050		—	—	—	
3030	Cooling Generating Systems	N/A		—	—	—	6.8 %
3050	Terminal & Package Units	Single zone rooftop unit, gas heating, electric cooling		S.F. Floor	12.30	12.30	
3090	Other HVAC Sys. & Equipment	N/A		—	—	—	
D40 Fire Protection							
4010	Sprinklers	Wet pipe sprinkler system		S.F. Floor	4.76	4.76	4.2%
4020	Standpipes	Standpipe		S.F. Floor	2.83	2.83	
D50 Electrical							
5010	Electrical Service/Distribution	200 ampere service, panel board and feeders		S.F. Floor	2.68	2.68	
5020	Lighting & Branch Wiring	Fluorescent fixtures, receptacles, switches, A.C. and misc. power		S.F. Floor	9.34	9.34	12.9%
5030	Communications & Security	Alarm systems, internet and phone wiring, emergency lighting, and security television		S.F. Floor	10.81	10.81	
5090	Other Electrical Systems	Emergency generator, 15 kW, Uninterruptible power supply		S.F. Floor	.63	.63	
E. EQUIPMENT & FURNISHINGS							
1010	Commercial Equipment	Automatic teller, drive up window, night depository		S.F. Floor	7.93	7.93	
1020	Institutional Equipment	Closed circuit TV monitoring system		S.F. Floor	2.85	2.85	5.9%
1030	Vehicular Equipment	N/A		—	—	—	
1090	Other Equipment	N/A		—	—	—	
F. SPECIAL CONSTRUCTION							
1020	Integrated Construction	N/A		—	—	—	7.2 %
1040	Special Facilities	Security vault door		S.F. Floor	13.09	13.09	
G. BUILDING SITEWORK	**N/A**						

			Sub-Total	181.20	100%
CONTRACTOR FEES (General Requirements: 10%, Overhead: 5%, Profit: 10%)		25%	45.33		
ARCHITECT FEES		11%	24.92		
	Total Building Cost		**251.45**		

Costs per square foot of floor area

Exterior Wall	S.F. Area	12000	14000	16000	18000	20000	22000	24000	26000	28000
	L.F. Perimeter	460	491	520	540	566	593	620	645	670
Concrete Block	Steel Roof Deck	171.55	168.40	165.95	163.75	162.20	160.90	159.80	158.90	158.10
Decorative Concrete Block	Steel Roof Deck	176.15	172.65	169.85	167.40	165.60	164.10	162.90	161.85	160.95
Face Brick on Concrete Block	Steel Roof Deck	184.50	180.25	176.90	173.90	171.75	170.00	168.55	167.30	166.20
Jumbo Brick on Concrete Block	Steel Roof Deck	180.85	176.95	173.90	171.00	169.10	167.40	166.10	164.95	163.95
Stucco on Concrete Block	Steel Roof Deck	175.05	171.55	168.90	166.45	164.75	163.30	162.15	161.15	160.30
Precast Concrete Panel	Steel Roof Deck	180.30	176.40	173.35	170.60	168.65	167.00	165.70	164.55	163.55
Perimeter Adj., Add or Deduct	Per 100 L.F.	5.20	4.50	3.95	3.50	3.15	2.85	2.65	2.45	2.25
Story Hgt. Adj., Add or Deduct	Per 1 Ft.	1.20	1.10	1.00	0.95	0.90	0.80	0.80	0.75	0.70

For Basement, add $33.70 per square foot of basement area

The above costs were calculated using the basic specifications shown on the facing page. These costs should be adjusted where necessary for design alternatives and owner's requirements. Reported completed project costs, for this type of structure, range from $62.80 to $165.40 per S.F.

Common additives

Description	Unit	$ Cost
Bowling Alleys, Incl. alley, pinsetter,		
scorer, counter & misc. supplies, average	Lane	62,500
For automatic scorer, add (maximum)	Lane	10,900
Emergency Lighting, 25 watt, battery operated		
Lead battery	Each	320
Nickel cadmium	Each	885
Lockers, Steel, Single tier, 60" or 72"	Opening	218 - 365
2 tier, 60" or 72" total	Opening	113 - 156
5 tier, box lockers	Opening	71.50 - 85
Locker bench, lam., maple top only	L.F.	26.50
Pedestals, steel pipe	Each	74
Seating		
Auditorium chair, all veneer	Each	300
Veneer back, padded seat	Each	315
Upholstered, spring seat	Each	315
Sound System		
Amplifier, 250 watts	Each	2025
Speaker, ceiling or wall	Each	208
Trumpet	Each	400

Important: See the Reference Section for Location Factors.

Model costs calculated for a 1 story building with 14' story height and 20,000 square feet of floor area

Bowling Alley

				Unit	Unit Cost	Cost Per S.F.	% Of Sub-Total
A. SUBSTRUCTURE							
1010	Standard Foundations	Poured concrete; strip and spread footings		S.F. Ground	1.23	1.23	
1020	Special Foundations	N/A		—	—	—	
1030	Slab on Grade	4" reinforced concrete with vapor barrier and granular base		S.F. Slab	5.31	5.31	7.8%
2010	Basement Excavation	Site preparation for slab and trench for foundation wall and footing		S.F. Ground	.57	.57	
2020	Basement Walls	4' Foundation wall		L.F. Wall	82	2.31	
B. SHELL							
B10 Superstructure							
1010	Floor Construction	N/A		—	—	—	8.0 %
1020	Roof Construction	Metal deck on open web steel joists with columns and beams		S.F. Roof	9.76	9.76	
B20 Exterior Enclosure							
2010	Exterior Walls	Concrete block	90% of wall	S.F. Wall	12.87	4.59	
2020	Exterior Windows	Horizontal pivoted	10% of wall	Each	2015	3.32	7.0%
2030	Exterior Doors	Double aluminum and glass and hollow metal		Each	2441	.61	
B30 Roofing							
3010	Roof Coverings	Built-up tar and gravel with flashing; perlite/EPS composite insulation		S.F. Roof	5.76	5.76	4.9%
3020	Roof Openings	Roof hatches		S.F. Roof	.17	.17	
C. INTERIORS							
1010	Partitions	Concrete block	50 S.F. Floor/L.F. Partition	S.F. Partition	10.45	2.09	
1020	Interior Doors	Hollow metal single leaf	1000 S.F. Floor/Door	Each	1152	1.15	
1030	Fittings	N/A		—	—	—	
2010	Stair Construction	N/A		—	—	—	6.2%
3010	Wall Finishes	Paint and block filler		S.F. Surface	6.23	2.49	
3020	Floor Finishes	Vinyl tile	25% of floor	S.F. Floor	2.68	.67	
3030	Ceiling Finishes	Suspended fiberglass board	25% of area	S.F. Ceiling	4.57	1.14	
D. SERVICES							
D10 Conveying							
1010	Elevators & Lifts	N/A		—	—	—	0.0 %
1020	Escalators & Moving Walks	N/A		—	—	—	
D20 Plumbing							
2010	Plumbing Fixtures	Toilet and service fixtures, supply and drainage	1 Fixture/2200 S.F. Floor	Each	3388	1.54	
2020	Domestic Water Distribution	Gas fired water heater		S.F. Floor	.25	.25	2.0%
2040	Rain Water Drainage	Roof drains		S.F. Roof	.68	.68	
D30 HVAC							
3010	Energy Supply	N/A		—	—	—	
3020	Heat Generating Systems	Included in D3050		—	—	—	
3030	Cooling Generating Systems	N/A		—	—	—	12.0 %
3050	Terminal & Package Units	Single zone rooftop unit, gas heating, electric cooling		S.F. Floor	14.55	14.55	
3090	Other HVAC Sys. & Equipment	N/A		—	—	—	
D40 Fire Protection							
4010	Sprinklers	Sprinklers, light hazard		S.F. Floor	3.56	3.56	3.4%
4020	Standpipes	Standpipe, wet, Class III		S.F. Floor	.58	.58	
D50 Electrical							
5010	Electrical Service/Distribution	800 ampere service, panel board and feeders		S.F. Floor	2.32	2.32	
5020	Lighting & Branch Wiring	High efficiency fluorescent fixtures, receptacles, switches, A.C. and misc. power		S.F. Floor	10.86	10.86	12.0%
5030	Communications & Security	Addressable alarm systems and emergency lighting		S.F. Floor	1.32	1.32	
5090	Other Electrical Systems	Emergency generator, 7.5 kW		S.F. Floor	.08	.08	
E. EQUIPMENT & FURNISHINGS							
1010	Commercial Equipment	N/A		—	—	—	
1020	Institutional Equipment	N/A		—	—	—	36.6 %
1030	Vehicular Equipment	N/A		—	—	—	
1090	Other Equipment	Bowling Alley, ballrack, automatic scorers		S.F. Floor	44.36	44.36	
F. SPECIAL CONSTRUCTION							
1020	Integrated Construction	N/A		—	—	—	0.0 %
1040	Special Facilities	N/A		—	—	—	
G. BUILDING SITEWORK	**N/A**						

	Sub-Total	121.27	**100%**
CONTRACTOR FEES (General Requirements: 10%, Overhead: 5%, Profit: 10%)	25%	30.32	
ARCHITECT FEES	7%	10.61	
Total Building Cost		**162.20**	

91

Costs per square foot of floor area

Exterior Wall	S.F. Area	6000	8000	10000	12000	14000	16000	18000	20000	22000
	L.F. Perimeter	320	386	453	520	540	597	610	660	710
Face Brick with Concrete Block Back-up	Bearing Walls	177.95	171.75	168.10	165.65	161.05	159.55	156.35	155.30	154.50
	Steel Frame	181.10	174.95	171.35	168.95	164.35	162.90	159.75	158.75	157.90
Decorative Concrete Block	Bearing Walls	168.95	163.60	160.45	158.35	154.50	153.25	150.60	149.75	149.00
	Steel Frame	172.05	166.80	163.65	161.65	157.85	156.60	154.05	153.20	152.50
Precast Concrete Panels	Bearing Walls	177.05	170.95	167.35	164.95	160.35	158.90	155.80	154.75	153.95
	Steel Frame	180.20	174.15	170.60	168.20	163.70	162.30	159.20	158.15	157.40
Perimeter Adj., Add or Deduct	Per 100 L.F.	14.25	10.65	8.55	7.15	6.15	5.35	4.80	4.30	3.90
Story Hgt. Adj., Add or Deduct	Per 1 Ft.	2.35	2.10	2.00	1.95	1.65	1.65	1.45	1.50	1.45
Basement—Not Applicable										

The above costs were calculated using the basic specifications shown on the facing page. These costs should be adjusted where necessary for design alternatives and owner's requirements. Reported completed project costs, for this type of structure, range from $75.90 to $182.95 per S.F.

Common additives

Description	Unit	$ Cost
Directory Boards, Plastic, glass covered		
30" x 20"	Each	630
36" x 48"	Each	1500
Aluminum, 24" x 18"	Each	630
36" x 24"	Each	735
48" x 32"	Each	1050
48" x 60"	Each	2200
Emergency Lighting, 25 watt, battery operated		
Lead battery	Each	320
Nickel cadmium	Each	885
Benches, Hardwood	L.F.	132 - 242
Ticket Printer	Each	7675
Turnstiles, One way		
4 arm, 46" dia., manual	Each	2075
Electric	Each	3200
High security, 3 arm		
65" dia., manual	Each	7525
Electric	Each	10,800
Gate with horizontal bars		
65" dia., 7' high transit type	Each	7250

Important: See the Reference Section for Location Factors.

Model costs calculated for a 1 story building with 14' story height and 12,000 square feet of floor area

					Unit	Unit Cost	Cost Per S.F.	% Of Sub-Total
A.	**SUBSTRUCTURE**							
1010	Standard Foundations	Poured concrete; strip and spread footings			S.F. Ground	2.58	2.58	
1020	Special Foundations	N/A			—	—	—	
1030	Slab on Grade	6" reinforced concrete with vapor barrier and granular base			S.F. Slab	7.82	7.82	11.6%
2010	Basement Excavation	Site preparation for slab and trench for foundation wall and footing			S.F. Ground	.32	.32	
2020	Basement Walls	4' Foundation wall			L.F. Wall	84	3.62	
B.	**SHELL**							
	B10 Superstructure							
1010	Floor Construction	N/A			—	—	—	5.4 %
1020	Roof Construction	Metal deck on open web steel joists with columns and beams			S.F. Roof	6.70	6.70	
	B20 Exterior Enclosure							
2010	Exterior Walls	Face brick with concrete block backup	70% of wall		S.F. Wall	32.92	13.98	
2020	Exterior Windows	Store front	30% of wall		Each	31.55	5.74	17.5%
2030	Exterior Doors	Double aluminum and glass			Each	5700	1.90	
	B30 Roofing							
3010	Roof Coverings	Built-up tar and gravel with flashing; perlite/EPS composite insulation			S.F. Roof	6.73	6.73	5.4%
3020	Roof Openings	N/A			—	—	—	
C.	**INTERIORS**							
1010	Partitions	Lightweight concrete block	15 S.F. Floor/L.F. Partition		S.F. Partition	10.47	6.98	
1020	Interior Doors	Hollow metal	150 S.F. Floor/Door		Each	1152	7.68	
1030	Fittings	N/A			—	—	—	
2010	Stair Construction	N/A			—	—	—	27.0%
3010	Wall Finishes	Glazed coating			S.F. Surface	1.97	2.63	
3020	Floor Finishes	Quarry tile and vinyl composition tile			S.F. Floor	9.32	9.32	
3030	Ceiling Finishes	Mineral fiber tile on concealed zee bars			S.F. Ceiling	6.89	6.89	
D.	**SERVICES**							
	D10 Conveying							
1010	Elevators & Lifts	N/A			—	—	—	0.0 %
1020	Escalators & Moving Walks	N/A			—	—	—	
	D20 Plumbing							
2010	Plumbing Fixtures	Toilet and service fixtures, supply and drainage	1 Fixture/850 S.F. Floor		Each	7021	8.26	
2020	Domestic Water Distribution	Electric water heater			S.F. Floor	1.56	1.56	8.9%
2040	Rain Water Drainage	Roof drains			S.F. Roof	1.18	1.18	
	D30 HVAC							
3010	Energy Supply	N/A			—	—	—	
3020	Heat Generating Systems	Included in D3050			—	—	—	
3030	Cooling Generating Systems	N/A			—	—	—	8.9 %
3050	Terminal & Package Units	Single zone rooftop unit, gas heating, electric cooling			S.F. Floor	11.05	11.05	
3090	Other HVAC Sys. & Equipment	N/A			—	—	—	
	D40 Fire Protection							
4010	Sprinklers	Wet pipe sprinkler system			S.F. Floor	4.55	4.55	4.5%
4020	Standpipes	Standpipe			S.F. Floor	.97	.97	
	D50 Electrical							
5010	Electrical Service/Distribution	400 ampere service, panel board and feeders			S.F. Floor	1.84	1.84	
5020	Lighting & Branch Wiring	Fluorescent fixtures, receptacles, switches, A.C. and misc. power			S.F. Floor	9.16	9.16	10.8%
5030	Communications & Security	Alarm systems and emergency lighting			S.F. Floor	2.03	2.03	
5090	Other Electrical Systems	Emergency generator, 7.5 kW			S.F. Floor	.39	.39	
E.	**EQUIPMENT & FURNISHINGS**							
1010	Commercial Equipment	N/A			—	—	—	
1020	Institutional Equipment	N/A			—	—	—	0.0 %
1030	Vehicular Equipment	N/A			—	—	—	
1090	Other Equipment	N/A			—	—	—	
F.	**SPECIAL CONSTRUCTION**							
1020	Integrated Construction	N/A			—	—	—	0.0 %
1040	Special Facilities	N/A			—	—	—	
G.	**BUILDING SITEWORK**	**N/A**						

				Sub-Total	123.88	100%
CONTRACTOR FEES (General Requirements: 10%, Overhead: 5%, Profit: 10%)				25%	30.93	
ARCHITECT FEES				7%	10.84	

Total Building Cost	**165.65**

Costs per square foot of floor area

Exterior Wall	S.F. Area	600	800	1000	1200	1600	2000	2400	3000	4000
	L.F. Perimeter	100	114	128	139	164	189	214	250	314
Brick with Concrete Block Back-up	Steel Frame	361.65	347.10	338.35	331.05	323.00	318.20	315.00	311.45	308.55
	Bearing Walls	355.55	340.95	332.20	324.90	316.90	312.05	308.90	305.30	302.45
Concrete Block	Steel Frame	318.70	310.30	305.35	301.20	296.60	293.85	292.00	290.00	288.30
	Bearing Walls	312.55	304.20	299.20	295.05	290.45	287.70	285.85	283.85	282.20
Galvanized Steel Siding	Steel Frame	319.90	312.70	308.35	304.70	300.70	298.30	296.70	294.95	293.50
Metal Sandwich Panel	Steel Frame	317.65	308.50	303.05	298.45	293.40	290.40	288.35	286.10	284.30
Perimeter Adj., Add or Deduct	Per 100 L.F.	100.30	75.20	60.20	50.15	37.65	30.05	25.10	20.10	15.10
Story Hgt. Adj., Add or Deduct	Per 1 Ft.	6.10	5.20	4.70	4.30	3.75	3.45	3.25	3.05	2.90
Basement—Not Applicable										

The above costs were calculated using the basic specifications shown on the facing page. These costs should be adjusted where necessary for design alternatives and owner's requirements. Reported completed project costs, for this type of structure, range from $136.20 to $386.80 per S.F.

Common additives

Description	Unit	$ Cost	Description	Unit	$ Cost
Air Compressors, Electric			Lockers, Steel, single tier, 60" or 72"	Opening	218 - 365
1-1/2 H.P., standard controls	Each	1575	2 tier, 60" or 72" total	Opening	113 - 156
Dual controls	Each	1950	5 tier, box lockers	Opening	71.50 - 85
5 H.P., 115/230 volt, standard control	Each	4400	Locker bench, lam. maple top only	L.F.	26.50
Dual controls	Each	5000	Pedestals, steel pipe	Each	74
Emergency Lighting, 25 watt, battery operated			Paving, Bituminous		
Lead battery	Each	320	Wearing course plus base course	S.Y.	7.50
Nickel cadmium	Each	885	Safe, Office type, 1 hour rating		
Fence, Chain link, 6' high			30" x 18" x 18"	Each	2500
9 ga. wire, galvanized	L.F.	28	60" x 36" x 18", double door	Each	8075
6 ga. wire	L.F.	30	Sidewalks, Concrete 4" thick	S.F.	4.39
Gate	Each	375	Yard Lighting,		
Product Dispenser with vapor recovery			20' aluminum pole		
for 6 nozzles	Each	26,900	with 400 watt		
Laundry Equipment			high pressure sodium		
Dryer, gas, 16 lb. capacity	Each	965	fixture	Each	3150
30 lb. capacity	Each	3800			
Washer, 4 cycle	Each	1175			
Commercial	Each	1600			

Model costs calculated for a 1 story building with 12' story height and 800 square feet of floor area

Car Wash

				Unit	Unit Cost	Cost Per S.F.	% Of Sub-Total
A. SUBSTRUCTURE							
1010	Standard Foundations	Poured concrete; strip and spread footings		S.F. Ground	3.17	3.17	
1020	Special Foundations	N/A		—	—	—	
1030	Slab on Grade	5" reinforced concrete with vapor barrier and granular base		S.F. Slab	6.93	6.93	8.3%
2010	Basement Excavation	Site preparation for slab and trench for foundation wall and footing		S.F. Ground	1.04	1.04	
2020	Basement Walls	4' Foundation wall		L.F. Wall	73	10.34	
B. SHELL							
	B10 Superstructure						
1010	Floor Construction	N/A		—	—	—	3.5 %
1020	Roof Construction	Metal deck, open web steel joists, beams, columns		S.F. Roof	9.04	9.04	
	B20 Exterior Enclosure						
2010	Exterior Walls	Face brick with concrete block backup	70% of wall	S.F. Wall	32.90	39.38	
2020	Exterior Windows	Horizontal pivoted steel	5% of wall	Each	787	7.48	24.9%
2030	Exterior Doors	Steel overhead hollow metal		Each	3530	17.66	
	B30 Roofing						
3010	Roof Coverings	Built-up tar and gravel with flashing; perlite/EPS composite insulation		S.F. Roof	8.62	8.62	3.3%
3020	Roof Openings	N/A		—	—	—	
C. INTERIORS							
1010	Partitions	Concrete block	20 S.F. Floor/S.F. Partition	S.F. Partition	9.96	4.98	
1020	Interior Doors	Hollow metal	600 S.F. Floor/Door	Each	1152	1.92	
1030	Fittings	N/A		—	—	—	
2010	Stair Construction	N/A		—	—	—	3.2%
3010	Wall Finishes	Paint		S.F. Surface	1.30	1.30	
3020	Floor Finishes	N/A		—	—	—	
3030	Ceiling Finishes	N/A		—	—	—	
D. SERVICES							
	D10 Conveying						
1010	Elevators & Lifts	N/A		—	—	—	0.0 %
1020	Escalators & Moving Walks	N/A		—	—	—	
	D20 Plumbing						
2010	Plumbing Fixtures	Toilet and service fixtures, supply and drainage	1 Fixture/160 S.F. Floor	Each	2882	18.01	
2020	Domestic Water Distribution	Gas fired water heater		S.F. Floor	37.19	37.19	22.9%
2040	Rain Water Drainage	Roof drains		S.F. Roof	4.15	4.15	
	D30 HVAC						
3010	Energy Supply	N/A		—	—	—	
3020	Heat Generating Systems	Unit heaters		Each	21.20	21.20	
3030	Cooling Generating Systems	N/A		—	—	—	8.2 %
3050	Terminal & Package Units	N/A		—	—	—	
3090	Other HVAC Sys. & Equipment	N/A		—	—	—	
	D40 Fire Protection						
4010	Sprinklers	N/A		—	—	—	0.0 %
4020	Standpipes	N/A		—	—	—	
	D50 Electrical						
5010	Electrical Service/Distribution	400 ampere service, panel board and feeders		S.F. Floor	24.56	24.56	
5020	Lighting & Branch Wiring	Fluorescent fixtures, receptacles, switches and misc. power		S.F. Floor	40.84	40.84	25.9%
5030	Communications & Security	N/A		—	—	—	
5090	Other Electrical Systems	Emergency generator, 7.5 kW		S.F. Floor	1.69	1.69	
E. EQUIPMENT & FURNISHINGS							
1010	Commercial Equipment	N/A		—	—	—	
1020	Institutional Equipment	N/A		—	—	—	0.0 %
1030	Vehicular Equipment	N/A		—	—	—	
1090	Other Equipment	N/A		—	—	—	
F. SPECIAL CONSTRUCTION							
1020	Integrated Construction	N/A		—	—	—	0.0 %
1040	Special Facilities	N/A		—	—	—	
G. BUILDING SITEWORK	**N/A**						

		Sub-Total	259.50	100%
CONTRACTOR FEES (General Requirements: 10%, Overhead: 5%, Profit: 10%)		25%	64.89	
ARCHITECT FEES		7%	22.71	

Total Building Cost	**347.10**

Costs per square foot of floor area

Exterior Wall	S.F. Area	2000	7000	12000	17000	22000	27000	32000	37000	42000
	L.F. Perimeter	180	340	470	540	640	740	762	793	860
Decorative Concrete Block	Wood Arch	263.30	195.25	180.55	169.80	165.75	163.20	158.20	154.85	153.50
	Steel Truss	264.95	196.90	182.20	171.40	167.40	164.80	159.85	156.50	155.15
Stone with Concrete Block Back-up	Wood Arch	326.20	229.20	207.95	192.00	186.15	182.35	174.85	169.85	167.80
	Steel Truss	320.80	223.85	202.60	186.60	180.70	176.95	169.50	164.45	162.45
Face Brick with Concrete Block Back-up	Wood Arch	294.60	212.15	194.20	180.85	175.90	172.75	166.50	162.35	160.65
	Steel Truss	289.25	206.80	188.80	175.45	170.50	167.35	161.10	156.90	155.25
Perimeter Adj., Add or Deduct	Per 100 L.F.	66.90	19.15	11.15	7.90	6.15	4.95	4.20	3.60	3.15
Story Hgt. Adj., Add or Deduct	Per 1 Ft.	3.90	2.10	1.75	1.40	1.30	1.20	1.00	0.95	0.90

For Basement, add $35.20 per square foot of basement area

The above costs were calculated using the basic specifications shown on the facing page. These costs should be adjusted where necessary for design alternatives and owner's requirements. Reported completed project costs, for this type of structure, range from $86.90 to $355.45 per S.F.

Common additives

Description	Unit	$ Cost
Altar, Wood, custom design, plain	Each	3175
Deluxe	Each	16,200
Granite or marble, average	Each	16,600
Deluxe	Each	46,500
Ark, Prefabricated, plain	Each	12,000
Deluxe	Each	156,000
Baptistry, Fiberglass, incl. plumbing	Each	7700 - 12,200
Bells & Carillons, 48 bells	Each	1,082,500
24 bells	Each	509,500
Confessional, Prefabricated wood		
Single, plain	Each	4400
Deluxe	Each	10,900
Double, plain	Each	8350
Deluxe	Each	23,400
Emergency Lighting, 25 watt, battery operated		
Lead battery	Each	320
Nickel cadmium	Each	885
Lecterns, Wood, plain	Each	1025
Deluxe	Each	6925

Description	Unit	$ Cost
Pews/Benches, Hardwood	L.F.	132 - 242
Pulpits, Prefabricated, hardwood	Each	1900 - 11,400
Railing, Hardwood	L.F.	249
Steeples, translucent fiberglass		
30" square, 15' high	Each	10,900
25' high	Each	12,600
Painted fiberglass, 24" square, 14' high	Each	9375
28' high	Each	8925
Aluminum		
20' high, 3'- 6" base	Each	10,400
35' high, 8'- 0" base	Each	39,900
60' high, 14'- 0" base	Each	84,000

Model costs calculated for a 1 story building with 24' story height and 17,000 square feet of floor area

Church

				Unit	Unit Cost	Cost Per S.F.	% Of Sub-Total
A.	**SUBSTRUCTURE**						
1010	Standard Foundations	Poured concrete; strip and spread footings		S.F. Ground	4	4	
1020	Special Foundations	N/A		—	—	—	
1030	Slab on Grade	4" reinforced concrete with vapor barrier and granular base		S.F. Slab	5.31	5.31	10.3%
2010	Basement Excavation	Site preparation for slab and trench for foundation wall and footing		S.F. Ground	.18	.18	
2020	Basement Walls	4' Foundation wall		L.F. Wall	82	3.88	
B.	**SHELL**						
	B10 Superstructure						
1010	Floor Construction	N/A		—	—	—	15.4 %
1020	Roof Construction	Wood deck on laminated wood arches		S.F. Roof	18.77	20.03	
	B20 Exterior Enclosure						
2010	Exterior Walls	Face brick with concrete block backup	80% of wall (adjusted for end walls)	S.F. Wall	39.07	23.83	
2020	Exterior Windows	Aluminum, top hinged, in-swinging and curtain wall panels	20% of wall	S.F. Window	32.14	4.90	22.4%
2030	Exterior Doors	Double hollow metal swinging, single hollow metal		Each	1460	.52	
	B30 Roofing						
3010	Roof Coverings	Asphalt shingles with flashing; polystyrene insulation		S.F. Roof	6.12	6.12	4.7%
3020	Roof Openings	N/A		—	—	—	
C.	**INTERIORS**						
1010	Partitions	Plaster on metal studs	40 S.F. Floor/L.F. Partitions	S.F. Partition	14.62	8.77	
1020	Interior Doors	Hollow metal	400 S.F. Floor/Door	Each	1152	2.89	
1030	Fittings	N/A		—	—	—	
2010	Stair Construction	N/A		—	—	—	14.6%
3010	Wall Finishes	Paint		S.F. Surface	1.18	1.41	
3020	Floor Finishes	Carpet		S.F. Floor	5.92	5.92	
3030	Ceiling Finishes	N/A		—	—	—	
D.	**SERVICES**						
	D10 Conveying						
1010	Elevators & Lifts	N/A		—	—	—	0.0 %
1020	Escalators & Moving Walks	N/A		—	—	—	
	D20 Plumbing						
2010	Plumbing Fixtures	Kitchen, toilet and service fixtures, supply and drainage	1 Fixture/2430 S.F. Floor	Each	8481	3.49	
2020	Domestic Water Distribution	Gas fired hot water heater		S.F. Floor	.32	.32	2.9%
2040	Rain Water Drainage	N/A		—	—	—	
	D30 HVAC						
3010	Energy Supply	Oil fired hot water, wall fin radiation		S.F. Floor	10.34	10.34	
3020	Heat Generating Systems	N/A		—	—	—	
3030	Cooling Generating Systems	N/A		—	—	—	16.8%
3050	Terminal & Package Units	Split systems with air cooled condensing units		S.F. Floor	11.60	11.60	
3090	Other HVAC Sys. & Equipment	N/A		—	—	—	
	D40 Fire Protection						
4010	Sprinklers	Wet pipe sprinkler system		S.F. Floor	3.56	3.56	3.6%
4020	Standpipes	Standpipe		S.F. Floor	1.16	1.16	
	D50 Electrical						
5010	Electrical Service/Distribution	400 ampere service, panel board and feeders		S.F. Floor	.81	.81	
5020	Lighting & Branch Wiring	Fluorescent fixtures, receptacles, switches, A.C. and misc. power		S.F. Floor	8.22	8.22	9.3%
5030	Communications & Security	Alarm systems, sound system and emergency lighting		S.F. Floor	2.98	2.98	
5090	Other Electrical Systems	Emergency generator, 7.5 kW		S.F. Floor	.11	.11	
E.	**EQUIPMENT & FURNISHINGS**						
1010	Commercial Equipment	N/A		—	—	—	
1020	Institutional Equipment	N/A		—	—	—	0.0 %
1030	Vehicular Equipment	N/A		—	—	—	
1090	Other Equipment	N/A		—	—	—	
F.	**SPECIAL CONSTRUCTION**						
1020	Integrated Construction	N/A		—	—	—	0.0 %
1040	Special Facilities	N/A		—	—	—	
G.	**BUILDING SITEWORK**	**N/A**					

		Sub-Total	130.35	**100%**
CONTRACTOR FEES (General Requirements: 10%, Overhead: 5%, Profit: 10%)		25%	32.58	
ARCHITECT FEES		11%	17.92	

Total Building Cost	**180.85**

Costs per square foot of floor area

Exterior Wall	S.F. Area	2000	4000	6000	8000	12000	15000	18000	20000	22000
	L.F. Perimeter	180	280	340	386	460	535	560	600	640
Stone Ashlar Veneer On Concrete Block	Wood Truss	265.40	236.45	220.30	210.55	199.35	196.20	191.30	190.05	188.95
	Steel Joists	262.20	233.25	217.10	207.40	196.15	193.00	188.15	186.85	185.80
Stucco on Concrete Block	Wood Truss	236.90	214.30	202.35	195.30	187.25	184.90	181.45	180.55	179.75
	Steel Joists	234.25	211.65	199.70	192.65	184.55	182.20	178.75	177.85	177.10
Brick Veneer	Wood Frame	269.10	227.15	208.10	197.20	185.15	181.40	176.70	175.30	174.05
Wood Shingles	Wood Frame	256.75	217.60	200.30	190.60	179.95	176.50	172.45	171.15	170.10
Perimeter Adj., Add or Deduct	Per 100 L.F.	48.40	24.20	16.15	12.15	8.15	6.40	5.35	4.80	4.45
Story Hgt. Adj., Add or Deduct	Per 1 Ft.	5.40	4.20	3.45	2.95	2.30	2.20	1.90	1.80	1.80

For Basement, add $30.85 per square foot of basement area

The above costs were calculated using the basic specifications shown on the facing page. These costs should be adjusted where necessary for design alternatives and owner's requirements. Reported completed project costs, for this type of structure, range from $86.00 to $286.05 per S.F.

Common additives

Description	Unit	$ Cost
Bar, Front bar	L.F.	415
Back bar	L.F.	330
Booth, Upholstered, custom, straight	L.F.	241 - 440
"L" or "U" shaped	L.F.	249 - 425
Fireplaces, Brick not incl. chimney or foundation, 30" x 24" opening	Each	3125
Chimney, standard brick		
Single flue 16" x 20"	V.L.F.	106
20" x 20"	V.L.F.	128
2 flue, 20" x 32"	V.L.F.	198
Lockers, Steel, single tier, 60" or 72"	Opening	218 - 365
2 tier, 60" or 72" total	Opening	113 - 156
5 tier, box lockers	Opening	71.50 - 85
Locker bench, lam. maple top only	L.F.	26.50
Pedestals, steel pipe	Each	74
Refrigerators, Prefabricated, walk-in		
7'-6" High, 6' x 6'	S.F.	195
10' x 10'	S.F.	154
12' x 14'	S.F.	136
12' x 20'	S.F.	119

Description	Unit	$ Cost
Sauna, Prefabricated, complete, 6' x 4'	Each	6800
6' x 9'	Each	9725
8' x 8'	Each	11,500
10' x 12'	Each	15,400
Smoke Detectors		
Ceiling type	Each	223
Duct type	Each	555
Sound System		
Amplifier, 250 watts	Each	2025
Speaker, ceiling or wall	Each	208
Trumpet	Each	400
Steam Bath, Complete, to 140 C.F.	Each	2175
To 300 C.F.	Each	2325
To 800 C.F.	Each	8850
To 2500 C.F.	Each	10,900
Swimming Pool Complete, gunite	S.F.	90.50 - 113
Tennis Court, Complete with fence		
Bituminous	Each	46,400 - 83,000
Clay	Each	48,200 - 79,500

Club, Country

				Unit	Unit Cost	Cost Per S.F.	% Of Sub-Total
A. SUBSTRUCTURE							
1010	Standard Foundations	Poured concrete; strip and spread footings		S.F. Ground	2.88	2.88	
1020	Special Foundations	N/A		—	—	—	
1030	Slab on Grade	4" reinforced concrete with vapor barrier and granular base		S.F. Slab	5.31	5.31	9.1%
2010	Basement Excavation	Site preparation for slab and trench for foundation wall and footing		S.F. Ground	.32	.32	
2020	Basement Walls	4' Foundation wall		L.F. Wall	82	6	
B. SHELL							
B10 Superstructure							
1010	Floor Construction	N/A		—	—	—	4.3 %
1020	Roof Construction	Wood truss with plywood sheathing		S.F. Roof	6.85	6.85	
B20 Exterior Enclosure							
2010	Exterior Walls	Stone ashlar veneer on concrete block	65% of wall	S.F. Wall	43.98	19.44	
2020	Exterior Windows	Aluminum horizontal sliding	35% of wall	Each	525	8.33	19.3%
2030	Exterior Doors	Double aluminum and glass, hollow metal		Each	2822	2.82	
B30 Roofing							
3010	Roof Coverings	Asphalt shingles		S.F. Roof	18.46	3.48	2.2%
3020	Roof Openings	N/A		—	—	—	
C. INTERIORS							
1010	Partitions	Gypsum board on metal studs, load bearing	14 S.F. Floor/L.F. Partition	S.F. Partition	8.01	5.72	
1020	Interior Doors	Single leaf wood	140 S.F. Floor/Door	Each	636	4.55	
1030	Fittings	N/A		—	—	—	
2010	Stair Construction	N/A		—	—	—	16.6%
3010	Wall Finishes	40% vinyl wall covering, 40% paint, 20% ceramic tile		S.F. Surface	2.56	3.66	
3020	Floor Finishes	50% carpet, 30% hardwood tile, 20% ceramic tile		S.F. Floor	8.03	8.03	
3030	Ceiling Finishes	Gypsum plaster on wood furring		S.F. Ceiling	4.39	4.39	
D. SERVICES							
D10 Conveying							
1010	Elevators & Lifts	N/A		—	—	—	0.0 %
1020	Escalators & Moving Walks	N/A		—	—	—	
D20 Plumbing							
2010	Plumbing Fixtures	Kitchen, toilet and service fixtures, supply and drainage	1 Fixture/125 S.F. Floor	Each	2219	17.75	
2020	Domestic Water Distribution	Gas fired hot water		S.F. Floor	8.21	8.21	16.4%
2040	Rain Water Drainage	N/A		—	—	—	
D30 HVAC							
3010	Energy Supply	N/A		—	—	—	
3020	Heat Generating Systems	Included in D3050		—	—	—	
3030	Cooling Generating Systems	N/A		—	—	—	18.6 %
3050	Terminal & Package Units	Multizone rooftop unit, gas heating, electric cooling		S.F. Floor	29.61	29.61	
3090	Other HVAC Sys. & Equipment	N/A		—	—	—	
D40 Fire Protection							
4010	Sprinklers	Wet pipe sprinkler system		S.F. Floor	5.66	5.66	4.6%
4020	Standpipes	Standpipe		S.F. Floor	1.66	1.66	
D50 Electrical							
5010	Electrical Service/Distribution	400 ampere service, panel board and feeders		S.F. Floor	3.58	3.58	
5020	Lighting & Branch Wiring	High efficiency fluorescent fixtures, receptacles, switches, A.C. and misc. power		S.F. Floor	8.36	8.36	8.9%
5030	Communications & Security	Addressable alarm systems and emergency lighting		S.F. Floor	1.95	1.95	
5090	Other Electrical Systems	Emergency generator, 11.5 kW		S.F. Floor	.21	.21	
E. EQUIPMENT & FURNISHINGS							
1010	Commercial Equipment	N/A		—	—	—	
1020	Institutional Equipment	N/A		—	—	—	0.0 %
1030	Vehicular Equipment	N/A		—	—	—	
1090	Other Equipment	N/A		—	—	—	
F. SPECIAL CONSTRUCTION							
1020	Integrated Construction	N/A		—	—	—	0.0 %
1040	Special Facilities	N/A		—	—	—	
G. BUILDING SITEWORK	**N/A**						

	Sub-Total	158.77	**100%**
CONTRACTOR FEES (General Requirements: 10%, Overhead: 5%, Profit: 10%)		25%	39.70
ARCHITECT FEES		11%	21.83
	Total Building Cost	**220.30**	

Costs per square foot of floor area

Exterior Wall	S.F. Area	4000	8000	12000	17000	22000	27000	32000	37000	42000
	L.F. Perimeter	280	386	520	585	640	740	840	940	940
Stone Ashlar on Concrete Block	Steel Joists	219.95	185.70	176.75	164.95	157.95	155.35	153.65	152.40	148.80
	Wood Joists	209.65	180.15	172.75	162.00	155.65	153.40	151.85	150.75	147.40
Face Brick on Concrete Block	Steel Joists	205.30	177.55	170.60	160.50	154.60	152.50	151.05	150.05	146.95
	Wood Joists	201.60	174.55	167.70	158.00	152.30	150.20	148.85	147.85	144.80
Decorative Concrete Block	Steel Joists	195.90	171.05	164.70	155.85	150.70	148.80	147.55	146.65	143.90
	Wood Joists	190.45	166.35	160.20	151.70	146.70	144.85	143.60	142.75	140.10
Perimeter Adj., Add or Deduct	Per 100 L.F.	27.35	13.60	9.10	6.45	5.05	4.15	3.45	2.95	2.60
Story Hgt. Adj., Add or Deduct	Per 1 Ft.	4.55	3.10	2.85	2.15	1.90	1.85	1.75	1.65	1.50
For Basement, add $31.45 per square foot of basement area										

The above costs were calculated using the basic specifications shown on the facing page. These costs should be adjusted where necessary for design alternatives and owner's requirements. Reported completed project costs, for this type of structure, range from $87.90 to $252.65 per S.F.

Common additives

Description	Unit	$ Cost	Description	Unit	$ Cost
Bar, Front bar	L.F.	415	Kitchen Equipment, cont.		
Back bar	L.F.	330	Freezer, 44 C.F., reach-in	Each	5125
Booth, Upholstered, custom, straight	L.F.	241 - 440	Ice cube maker, 50 lb. per day	Each	1950
"L" or "U" shaped	L.F.	249 - 425	Lockers, Steel, single tier, 60" or 72"	Opening	218 - 365
Emergency Lighting, 25 watt, battery operated			2 tier, 60" or 72" total	Opening	113 - 156
Lead battery	Each	320	5 tier, box lockers	Opening	71.50 - 85
Nickel cadmium	Each	885	Locker bench, lam. maple top only	L.F.	26.50
Flagpoles, Complete			Pedestals, steel pipe	Each	74
Aluminum, 20' high	Each	1775	Refrigerators, Prefabricated, walk-in		
40' High	Each	3925	7'-6" High, 6' x 6'	S.F.	195
70' High	Each	10,800	10' x 10'	S.F.	154
Fiberglass, 23' High	Each	1325	12' x 14'	S.F.	136
39'-5" High	Each	3575	12' x 20'	S.F.	119
59' High	Each	7275	Smoke Detectors		
Kitchen Equipment			Ceiling type	Each	223
Broiler	Each	4000	Duct type	Each	555
Coffee urn, twin 6 gallon	Each	2975	Sound System		
Cooler, 6 ft. long, reach-in	Each	4100	Amplifier, 250 watts	Each	2025
Dishwasher, 10-12 racks per hr.	Each	4225	Speaker, ceiling or wall	Each	208
Food warmer, counter 1.2 kw	Each	725	Trumpet	Each	400

Important: See the Reference Section for Location Factors.

Model costs calculated for a 1 story building with 12' story height and 22,000 square feet of floor area

Club, Social

				Unit	Unit Cost	Cost Per S.F.	% Of Sub-Total
A. SUBSTRUCTURE							
1010	Standard Foundations	Poured concrete; strip and spread footings		S.F. Ground	1.82	1.82	
1020	Special Foundations	N/A		—	—	—	
1030	Slab on Grade	4" reinforced concrete with vapor barrier and granular base		S.F. Slab	5.31	5.31	9.4%
2010	Basement Excavation	Site preparation for slab and trench for foundation wall and footing		S.F. Ground	.18	.18	
2020	Basement Walls	4' Foundation wall		L.F. Wall	82	3.79	
B. SHELL							
B10 Superstructure							
1010	Floor Construction	N/A		—	—	—	5.8 %
1020	Roof Construction	Metal deck on open web steel joists		S.F. Roof	6.87	6.87	
B20 Exterior Enclosure							
2010	Exterior Walls	Stone, ashlar veneer on concrete block	65% of wall	S.F. Wall	44.03	9.99	
2020	Exterior Windows	Window wall	35% of wall	Each	47.80	5.84	14.1%
2030	Exterior Doors	Double aluminum and glass doors		Each	2822	.77	
B30 Roofing							
3010	Roof Coverings	Built-up tar and gravel with flashing; perlite/EPS composite insulation		S.F. Roof	6.12	6.12	5.2%
3020	Roof Openings	N/A		—	—	—	
C. INTERIORS							
1010	Partitions	Lightweight concrete block	14 S.F. Floor/L.F. Partition	S.F. Partition	11.55	8.25	
1020	Interior Doors	Single leaf wood	140 S.F. Floor/Door	Each	636	4.55	
1030	Fittings	N/A		—	—	—	
2010	Stair Construction	N/A		—	—	—	25.1%
3010	Wall Finishes	65% paint, 25% vinyl wall covering, 10% ceramic tile		S.F. Surface	1.76	2.52	
3020	Floor Finishes	60% carpet, 35% hardwood, 15% ceramic tile		S.F. Floor	7.44	7.44	
3030	Ceiling Finishes	Mineral fiber tile on concealed zee bars		S.F. Ceiling	6.89	6.89	
D. SERVICES							
D10 Conveying							
1010	Elevators & Lifts	N/A		—	—	—	0.0 %
1020	Escalators & Moving Walks	N/A		—	—	—	
D20 Plumbing							
2010	Plumbing Fixtures	Kitchen, toilet and service fixtures, supply and drainage	1 Fixture/1050 S.F. Floor	Each	8642	8.23	
2020	Domestic Water Distribution	Gas fired hot water heater		S.F. Floor	.30	.30	7.9%
2040	Rain Water Drainage	Roof drains		S.F. Roof	.78	.78	
D30 HVAC							
3010	Energy Supply	N/A		—	—	—	
3020	Heat Generating Systems	Included in D3050		—	—	—	
3030	Cooling Generating Systems	N/A		—	—	—	18.7 %
3050	Terminal & Package Units	Multizone rooftop unit, gas heating, electric cooling		S.F. Floor	22.10	22.10	
3090	Other HVAC Sys. & Equipment	N/A		—	—	—	
D40 Fire Protection							
4010	Sprinklers	Wet pipe sprinkler system		S.F. Floor	4.91	4.91	4.5%
4020	Standpipes	Standpipe		S.F. Floor	.45	.45	
D50 Electrical							
5010	Electrical Service/Distribution	400 ampere service, panel board and feeders		S.F. Floor	1.23	1.23	
5020	Lighting & Branch Wiring	High efficiency fluorescent fixtures, receptacles, switches, A.C. and misc. power		S.F. Floor	8.19	8.19	9.3%
5030	Communications & Security	Addressable alarm systems and emergency lighting		S.F. Floor	1.48	1.48	
5090	Other Electrical Systems	Emergency generator, 11.5 kW		S.F. Floor	.11	.11	
E. EQUIPMENT & FURNISHINGS							
1010	Commercial Equipment	N/A		—	—	—	
1020	Institutional Equipment	N/A		—	—	—	0.0 %
1030	Vehicular Equipment	N/A		—	—	—	
1090	Other Equipment	N/A		—	—	—	
F. SPECIAL CONSTRUCTION							
1020	Integrated Construction	N/A		—	—	—	0.0 %
1040	Special Facilities	N/A		—	—	—	
G. BUILDING SITEWORK	**N/A**						

			Sub-Total		118.12	**100%**
	CONTRACTOR FEES (General Requirements: 10%, Overhead: 5%, Profit: 10%)			25%	29.49	
	ARCHITECT FEES			7%	10.34	
			Total Building Cost		**157.95**	

Costs per square foot of floor area

Exterior Wall	S.F. Area	15000	20000	28000	38000	50000	65000	85000	100000	150000
	L.F. Perimeter	350	400	480	550	630	660	750	825	1035
Face Brick with Concrete Block Back-up	Steel Frame	227.25	217.95	210.00	203.75	199.35	194.60	191.70	190.40	187.60
	Bearing Walls	225.95	215.40	206.35	199.05	193.95	188.25	184.80	183.35	180.00
Decorative Concrete Block	Steel Frame	219.10	211.00	204.10	198.70	195.00	191.10	188.65	187.55	185.20
	Bearing Walls	217.85	208.40	200.40	193.95	189.60	184.70	181.75	180.45	177.60
Stucco on Concrete Block	Steel Frame	218.40	210.35	203.55	198.20	194.60	190.80	188.35	187.25	185.00
	Bearing Walls	217.15	207.85	199.90	193.55	189.20	184.40	181.50	180.20	177.40
Perimeter Adj., Add or Deduct	Per 100 L.F.	9.55	7.20	5.15	3.65	2.85	2.15	1.70	1.45	0.95
Story Hgt. Adj., Add or Deduct	Per 1 Ft.	2.35	2.00	1.75	1.45	1.25	1.05	0.90	0.80	0.70

For Basement, add $ 36.70 per square foot of basement area

The above costs were calculated using the basic specifications shown on the facing page. These costs should be adjusted where necessary for design alternatives and owner's requirements. Reported completed project costs, for this type of structure, range from $ 127.20 to $ 298.95 per S.F.

Common additives

Description	Unit	$ Cost
Carrels Hardwood	Each	960 - 2300
Clock System		
20 Room	Each	19,500
50 Room	Each	45,700
Elevators, Hydraulic passenger, 2 stops		
1500# capacity	Each	66,100
2500# capacity	Each	69,200
3500# capacity	Each	73,200
Additional stop, add	Each	8575
Emergency Lighting, 25 watt, battery operated		
Lead battery	Each	320
Nickel cadmium	Each	885
Flagpoles, Complete		
Aluminum, 20' high	Each	1775
40' High	Each	3925
70' High	Each	10,800
Fiberglass, 23' High	Each	1325
39'-5" High	Each	3575
59' High	Each	7275

Description	Unit	$ Cost
Lockers, Steel, single tier, 60" or 72"	Opening	218 - 365
2 tier, 60" or 72" total	Opening	113 - 156
5 tier, box lockers	Opening	71.50 - 85
Locker bench, lam. maple top only	L.F.	26.50
Pedestals, steel pipe	Each	74
Seating		
Auditorium chair, all veneer	Each	300
Veneer back, padded seat	Each	315
Upholstered, spring seat	Each	315
Classroom, movable chair & desk	Set	81 - 171
Lecture hall, pedestal type	Each	258 - 610
Smoke Detectors		
Ceiling type	Each	223
Duct type	Each	555
Sound System		
Amplifier, 250 watts	Each	2025
Speaker, ceiling or wall	Each	208
Trumpet	Each	400
TV Antenna, Master system, 12 outlet	Outlet	280
30 outlet	Outlet	218
100 outlet	Outlet	206

Important: See the Reference Section for Location Factors.

Model costs calculated for a 2 story building with 12' story height and 50,000 square feet of floor area

				Unit	Unit Cost	Cost Per S.F.	% Of Sub-Total
A. SUBSTRUCTURE							
1010	Standard Foundations	Poured concrete; strip and spread footings		S.F. Ground	1.32	.66	
1020	Special Foundations	N/A		—	—	—	
1030	Slab on Grade	4" reinforced concrete with vapor barrier and granular base		S.F. Slab	5.31	2.66	3.6%
2010	Basement Excavation	Site preparation for slab and trench for foundation wall and footing		S.F. Ground	.31	.16	
2020	Basement Walls	4' Foundation wall		L.F. Wall	77	1.57	
B. SHELL							
	B10 Superstructure						
1010	Floor Construction	Open web steel joists, slab form, concrete		S.F. Floor	17.06	8.53	9.5%
1020	Roof Construction	Metal deck on open web steel joists, columns		S.F. Roof	9.90	4.95	
	B20 Exterior Enclosure						
2010	Exterior Walls	Decorative concrete block	65% of wall	S.F. Wall	16.23	3.19	
2020	Exterior Windows	Window wall	35% of wall	Each	40.45	4.29	5.8%
2030	Exterior Doors	Double glass and aluminum with transom		Each	5700	.69	
	B30 Roofing						
3010	Roof Coverings	Built-up tar and gravel with flashing; perlite/EPS composite insulation		S.F. Roof	5.98	2.99	2.1%
3020	Roof Openings	N/A		—	—	—	
C. INTERIORS							
1010	Partitions	Concrete block	20 S.F. Floor/L.F. Partition	S.F. Partition	15.30	7.65	
1020	Interior Doors	Single leaf hollow metal	200 S.F. Floor/Door	Each	1152	5.76	
1030	Fittings	Chalkboards, counters, cabinets		S.F. Floor	6.02	6.02	
2010	Stair Construction	Concrete filled metal pan		Flight	17,250	3.45	27.0%
3010	Wall Finishes	95% paint, 5% ceramic tile		S.F. Surface	4.13	4.13	
3020	Floor Finishes	70% vinyl composition tile, 25% carpet, 5% ceramic tile		S.F. Floor	4.31	4.31	
3030	Ceiling Finishes	Mineral fiber tile on concealed zee bars		S.F. Ceiling	6.89	6.89	
D. SERVICES							
	D10 Conveying						
1010	Elevators & Lifts	Two hydraulic passenger elevators		Each	83,500	3.34	2.4%
1020	Escalators & Moving Walks	N/A		—	—	—	
	D20 Plumbing						
2010	Plumbing Fixtures	Toilet and service fixtures, supply and drainage	1 Fixture/455 S.F. Floor	Each	8490	18.66	
2020	Domestic Water Distribution	Oil fired hot water heater		S.F. Floor	2.84	2.84	15.6%
2040	Rain Water Drainage	Roof drains		S.F. Roof	1.34	.67	
	D30 HVAC						
3010	Energy Supply	N/A		—	—	—	
3020	Heat Generating Systems	Included in D3050		—	—	—	
3030	Cooling Generating Systems	N/A		—	—	—	14.4 %
3050	Terminal & Package Units	Multizone unit, gas heating, electric cooling		S.F. Floor	20.45	20.45	
3090	Other HVAC Sys. & Equipment	N/A		—	—	—	
	D40 Fire Protection						
4010	Sprinklers	Sprinklers, light hazard		S.F. Floor	3.11	3.11	2.4%
4020	Standpipes	Standpipe, dry, Class III		S.F. Floor	.34	.34	
	D50 Electrical						
5010	Electrical Service/Distribution	2000 ampere service, panel board and feeders		S.F. Floor	3.85	3.85	
5020	Lighting & Branch Wiring	High efficiency fluorescent fixtures, receptacles, switches, A.C. and misc. power		S.F. Floor	12.87	12.87	17.2%
5030	Communications & Security	Addressable alarm systems, internet wiring, communications systems and emergency lighting		S.F. Floor	7.07	7.07	
5090	Other Electrical Systems	Emergency generator, 100 kW		S.F. Floor	.64	.64	
E. EQUIPMENT & FURNISHINGS							
1010	Commercial Equipment	N/A		—	—	—	
1020	Institutional Equipment	N/A		—	—	—	
1030	Vehicular Equipment	N/A		—	—	—	0.0 %
1090	Other Equipment	N/A		—	—	—	
F. SPECIAL CONSTRUCTION							
1020	Integrated Construction	N/A		—	—	—	
1040	Special Facilities	N/A		—	—	—	0.0 %
G. BUILDING SITEWORK	**N/A**						

					Sub-Total	141.74	100%
	CONTRACTOR FEES (General Requirements: 10%, Overhead: 5%, Profit: 10%)				25%	35.46	
	ARCHITECT FEES				7%	12.40	

	Total Building Cost	**189.60**

Costs per square foot of floor area

Exterior Wall	S.F. Area	10000	15000	25000	40000	55000	70000	80000	90000	100000
	L.F. Perimeter	260	320	400	476	575	628	684	721	772
Face Brick with Concrete Block Back-up	R/Conc. Frame	233.05	216.15	199.65	188.20	183.85	180.10	178.90	177.45	176.65
	Steel Frame	245.85	229.00	212.50	201.00	196.70	192.90	191.65	190.25	189.45
Decorative Concrete Block	R/Conc. Frame	216.30	202.40	189.35	180.55	177.15	174.35	173.35	172.30	171.70
	Steel Frame	229.10	215.25	202.20	193.40	189.95	187.10	186.20	185.10	184.50
Precast Concrete Panels	R/Conc. Frame	239.00	221.05	203.30	190.95	186.25	182.10	180.85	179.30	178.45
	Steel Frame	251.85	233.90	216.15	203.80	199.10	194.95	193.65	192.10	191.25
Perimeter Adj., Add or Deduct	Per 100 L.F.	19.15	12.85	7.70	4.80	3.50	2.70	2.40	2.10	1.95
Story Hgt. Adj., Add or Deduct	Per 1 Ft.	3.65	3.05	2.25	1.70	1.50	1.25	1.20	1.15	1.10

For Basement, add $35.70 per square foot of basement area

The above costs were calculated using the basic specifications shown on the facing page. These costs should be adjusted where necessary for design alternatives and owner's requirements. Reported completed project costs, for this type of structure, range from $82.15 to $242.10 per S.F.

Common additives

Description	Unit	$ Cost
Carrels Hardwood	Each	960 - 2300
Closed Circuit Surveillance, One station		
Camera and monitor	Each	1975
For additional camera stations, add	Each	1050
Elevators, Hydraulic passenger, 2 stops		
2000# capacity	Each	67,600
2500# capacity	Each	69,200
3500# capacity	Each	73,200
Additional stop, add	Each	8575
Emergency Lighting, 25 watt, battery operated		
Lead battery	Each	320
Nickel cadmium	Each	885
Furniture	Student	2800 - 5350
Intercom System, 25 station capacity		
Master station	Each	3175
Intercom outlets	Each	184
Handset	Each	505

Description	Unit	$ Cost
Kitchen Equipment		
Broiler	Each	4000
Coffee urn, twin 6 gallon	Each	2975
Cooler, 6 ft. long	Each	4100
Dishwasher, 10-12 racks per hr.	Each	4225
Food warmer	Each	725
Freezer, 44 C.F., reach-in	Each	5125
Ice cube maker, 50 lb. per day	Each	1950
Range with 1 oven	Each	3000
Laundry Equipment		
Dryer, gas, 16 lb. capacity	Each	965
30 lb. capacity	Each	3800
Washer, 4 cycle	Each	1175
Commercial	Each	1600
Smoke Detectors		
Ceiling type	Each	223
Duct type	Each	555
TV Antenna, Master system, 12 outlet	Outlet	280
30 outlet	Outlet	218
100 outlet	Outlet	206

Important: See the Reference Section for Location Factors.

Model costs calculated for a 3 story building with 12' story height and 25,000 square feet of floor area

College, Dormitory, 2-3 Story

				Unit	Unit Cost	Cost Per S.F.	% Of Sub-Total
A.	**SUBSTRUCTURE**						
1010	Standard Foundations	Poured concrete; strip and spread footings		S.F. Ground	6.18	2.06	
1020	Special Foundations	N/A		—	—	—	
1030	Slab on Grade	4" reinforced concrete with vapor barrier and granular base		S.F. Slab	5.31	1.77	3.5%
2010	Basement Excavation	Site preparation for slab and trench for foundation wall and footing		S.F. Ground	.18	.06	
2020	Basement Walls	4' Foundation wall		L.F. Wall	82	1.30	
B.	**SHELL**						
	B10 Superstructure						
1010	Floor Construction	Concrete flat plate		S.F. Floor	25.08	16.72	14.2%
1020	Roof Construction	Concrete flat plate		S.F. Roof	13.56	4.52	
	B20 Exterior Enclosure						
2010	Exterior Walls	Face brick with concrete block backup	80% of wall	S.F. Wall	32.90	15.16	
2020	Exterior Windows	Aluminum horizontal sliding	20% of wall	Each	736	3.68	13.6%
2030	Exterior Doors	Double glass & aluminum doors		Each	5925	1.42	
	B30 Roofing						
3010	Roof Coverings	Single ply membrane, loose laid and ballasted; perlite/EPS composite insulation		S.F. Roof	5.55	1.85	1.2%
3020	Roof Openings	N/A		—	—	—	
C.	**INTERIORS**						
1010	Partitions	Gypsum board on metal studs, concrete block	9 S.F. Floor/L.F. Partition	S.F. Partition	6.37	7.08	
1020	Interior Doors	Single leaf wood	90 S.F. Floor/Door	Each	636	7.06	
1030	Fittings	Closet shelving, mirrors, bathroom accessories		S.F. Floor	1.95	1.95	
2010	Stair Construction	Cast in place concrete		Flight	5250	2.73	20.8%
3010	Wall Finishes	95% paint, 5% ceramic tile		S.F. Surface	1.89	4.21	
3020	Floor Finishes	80% carpet, 10% vinyl composition tile, 10% ceramic tile		S.F. Floor	6.95	6.95	
3030	Ceiling Finishes	90% paint, 10% suspended fiberglass board		S.F. Ceiling	1.03	1.02	
D.	**SERVICES**						
	D10 Conveying						
1010	Elevators & Lifts	One hydraulic passenger elevator		Each	115,000	4.60	3.1%
1020	Escalators & Moving Walks	N/A		—	—	—	
	D20 Plumbing						
2010	Plumbing Fixtures	Toilet and service fixtures, supply and drainage	1 Fixture/455 S.F. Floor	Each	10,056	22.10	
2020	Domestic Water Distribution	Electric water heater		S.F. Floor	3.56	3.56	17.5%
2040	Rain Water Drainage	Roof drains		S.F. Roof	1.32	.44	
	D30 HVAC						
3010	Energy Supply	N/A		—	—	—	
3020	Heat Generating Systems	Included in D3050		—	—	—	
3030	Cooling Generating Systems	N/A		—	—	—	8.6 %
3050	Terminal & Package Units	Rooftop multizone unit system		S.F. Floor	12.85	12.85	
3090	Other HVAC Sys. & Equipment	N/A		—	—	—	
	D40 Fire Protection						
4010	Sprinklers	Wet pipe sprinkler system		S.F. Floor	2.95	2.95	2.5%
4020	Standpipes	Standpipe, dry, Class III		S.F. Floor	.85	.85	
	D50 Electrical						
5010	Electrical Service/Distribution	800 ampere service, panel board and feeders		S.F. Floor	2.06	2.06	
5020	Lighting & Branch Wiring	High efficiency fluorescent fixtures, receptacles, switches, A.C. and misc. power		S.F. Floor	9.67	9.67	12.8%
5030	Communications & Security	Alarm systems, internet and phone wiring, communications systems and emergency lighting		S.F. Floor	7.32	7.32	
5090	Other Electrical Systems	Emergency generator, 7.5 kW		S.F. Floor	.08	.08	
E.	**EQUIPMENT & FURNISHINGS**						
1010	Commercial Equipment	N/A		—	—	—	
1020	Institutional Equipment	N/A		—	—	—	2.2 %
1030	Vehicular Equipment	N/A		—	—	—	
2020	Moveable Furnishings	Dormitory furniture		S.F. Floor	3.25	3.25	
F.	**SPECIAL CONSTRUCTION**						
1020	Integrated Construction	N/A		—	—	—	0.0 %
1040	Special Facilities	N/A		—	—	—	
G.	**BUILDING SITEWORK**	**N/A**					

	Sub-Total	149.27	100%
CONTRACTOR FEES (General Requirements: 10%, Overhead: 5%, Profit: 10%)	25%	37.32	
ARCHITECT FEES	7%	13.06	
Total Building Cost		**199.65**	

Costs per square foot of floor area

Exterior Wall	S.F. Area	20000	35000	45000	65000	85000	110000	135000	160000	200000
	L.F. Perimeter	260	340	400	440	500	540	560	590	640
Face Brick with Concrete Block Back-up	R/Conc. Frame	229.30	213.40	209.30	200.25	196.30	192.30	189.10	187.20	185.25
	Steel Frame	243.25	227.40	223.30	214.20	210.30	206.30	203.10	201.20	199.25
Decorative Concrete Block	R/Conc. Frame	214.25	202.20	199.05	192.45	189.55	186.65	184.35	183.00	181.55
	Steel Frame	228.25	216.15	213.00	206.45	203.55	200.65	198.35	197.00	195.55
Precast Concrete Panels With Exposed Aggregate	R/Conc. Frame	233.90	216.85	212.50	202.65	198.45	194.00	190.60	188.55	186.35
	Steel Frame	247.75	230.80	226.35	216.55	212.35	207.95	204.55	202.50	200.30
Perimeter Adj., Add or Deduct	Per 100 L.F.	18.65	10.75	8.30	5.80	4.45	3.45	2.85	2.40	1.85
Story Hgt. Adj., Add or Deduct	Per 1 Ft.	3.70	2.85	2.60	1.95	1.80	1.45	1.25	1.10	0.90

For Basement, add $35.70 per square foot of basement area

The above costs were calculated using the basic specifications shown on the facing page. These costs should be adjusted where necessary for design alternatives and owner's requirements. Reported completed project costs, for this type of structure, range from $116.75 to $281.60 per S.F.

Common additives

Description	Unit	$ Cost
Carrels Hardwood	Each	960 - 2300
Closed Circuit Surveillance, One station		
Camera and monitor	Each	1975
For additional camera stations, add	Each	1050
Elevators, Electric passenger, 5 stops		
2000# capacity	Each	167,200
2500# capacity	Each	171,200
3500# capacity	Each	171,700
Additional stop, add	Each	12,700
Emergency Lighting, 25 watt, battery operated		
Lead battery	Each	320
Nickel cadmium	Each	885
Furniture	Student	2800 - 5350
Intercom System, 25 station capacity		
Master station	Each	3175
Intercom outlets	Each	184
Handset	Each	505

Description	Unit	$ Cost
Kitchen Equipment		
Broiler	Each	4000
Coffee urn, twin, 6 gallon	Each	2975
Cooler, 6 ft. long	Each	4100
Dishwasher, 10-12 racks per hr.	Each	4225
Food warmer	Each	725
Freezer, 44 C.F., reach-in	Each	5125
Ice cube maker, 50 lb. per day	Each	1950
Range with 1 oven	Each	3000
Laundry Equipment		
Dryer, gas, 16 lb. capacity	Each	965
30 lb. capacity	Each	3800
Washer, 4 cycle	Each	1175
Commercial	Each	1600
Smoke Detectors		
Ceiling type	Each	223
Duct type	Each	555
TV Antenna, Master system, 12 outlet	Outlet	280
30 outlet	Outlet	218
100 outlet	Outlet	206

Important: See the Reference Section for Location Factors.

Model costs calculated for a 6 story building with 12' story height and 85,000 square feet of floor area

College, Dormitory, 4-8 Story

				Unit	Unit Cost	Cost Per S.F.	% Of Sub-Total
A. SUBSTRUCTURE							
1010	Standard Foundations	Poured concrete; strip and spread footings		S.F. Ground	9.06	1.51	
1020	Special Foundations	N/A		—	—	—	
1030	Slab on Grade	4" reinforced concrete with vapor barrier and granular base		S.F. Slab	5.31	.89	2.0%
2010	Basement Excavation	Site preparation for slab and trench for foundation wall and footing		S.F. Ground	.31	.05	
2020	Basement Walls	4' foundation wall		L.F. Wall	77	.66	
B. SHELL							
B10 Superstructure							
1010	Floor Construction	Concrete slab with metal deck and beams		S.F. Floor	29.39	24.49	18.5%
1020	Roof Construction	Concrete slab with metal deck and beams		S.F. Roof	21.96	3.66	
B20 Exterior Enclosure							
2010	Exterior Walls	Decorative concrete block	80% of wall	S.F. Wall	17.91	6.07	
2020	Exterior Windows	Aluminum horizontal sliding	20% of wall	Each	525	2.96	6.2%
2030	Exterior Doors	Double glass & aluminum doors		Each	3619	.34	
B30 Roofing							
3010	Roof Coverings	Single ply membrane, loose laid and ballasted; perlite/EPS composite insulation		S.F. Roof	5.04	.84	0.6%
3020	Roof Openings	N/A		—	—	—	
C. INTERIORS							
1010	Partitions	Concrete block	9 S.F. Floor/L.F. Partition	S.F. Partition	10.47	11.63	
1020	Interior Doors	Single leaf wood	90 S.F. Floor/Door	Each	636	7.06	
1030	Fittings	Closet shelving, mirrors, bathroom accessories		S.F. Floor	1.60	1.60	
2010	Stair Construction	Concrete filled metal pan		Flight	17,250	3.65	24.8%
3010	Wall Finishes	95% paint, 5% ceramic tile		S.F. Surface	2.60	5.78	
3020	Floor Finishes	80% carpet, 10% vinyl composition tile, 10% ceramic tile		S.F. Floor	6.95	6.95	
3030	Ceiling Finishes	Mineral fiber tile on concealed zee bars, paint		S.F. Ceiling	1.03	1.02	
D. SERVICES							
D10 Conveying							
1010	Elevators & Lifts	Four geared passenger elevators		Each	247,563	11.65	7.7%
1020	Escalators & Moving Walks	N/A		—	—	—	
D20 Plumbing							
2010	Plumbing Fixtures	Toilet and service fixtures, supply and drainage	1 Fixture/390 S.F. Floor	Each	8576	21.99	
2020	Domestic Water Distribution	Oil fired water heater		S.F. Floor	1.81	1.81	15.9%
2040	Rain Water Drainage	Roof drains		S.F. Roof	2.10	.35	
D30 HVAC							
3010	Energy Supply	Oil fired hot water, wall fin radiation		S.F. Floor	4.43	4.43	
3020	Heat Generating Systems	N/A		—	—	—	
3030	Cooling Generating Systems	Chilled water, air cooled condenser system		S.F. Floor	9.66	9.66	9.3%
3050	Terminal & Package Units	N/A		—	—	—	
3090	Other HVAC Sys. & Equipment	N/A		—	—	—	
D40 Fire Protection							
4010	Sprinklers	Sprinklers, light hazard		S.F. Floor	2.88	2.88	2.3%
4020	Standpipes	Standpipe, dry, Class III		S.F. Floor	.64	.64	
D50 Electrical							
5010	Electrical Service/Distribution	1200 ampere service, panel board and feeders		S.F. Floor	.99	.99	
5020	Lighting & Branch Wiring	High efficiency fluorescent fixtures, receptacles, switches, A.C. and misc. power		S.F. Floor	9.46	9.46	11.1%
5030	Communications & Security	Alarm systems, internet and phone wiring, communications systems and emergency lighting		S.F. Floor	6.30	6.30	
5090	Other Electrical Systems	Emergency generator, 30 kW		S.F. Floor	.20	.20	
E. EQUIPMENT & FURNISHINGS							
1010	Commercial Equipment	N/A		—	—	—	
1020	Institutional Equipment	N/A		—	—	—	
1030	Vehicular Equipment	N/A		—	—	—	1.7%
2020	Moveable Furnishings	Built-in dormitory furnishings		S.F. Floor	2.66	2.66	
F. SPECIAL CONSTRUCTION							
1020	Integrated Construction	N/A		—	—	—	0.0%
1040	Special Facilities	N/A		—	—	—	
G. BUILDING SITEWORK	**N/A**						

	Sub-Total	152.18	**100%**
CONTRACTOR FEES (General Requirements: 10%, Overhead: 5%, Profit: 10%)	25%	38.05	
ARCHITECT FEES	7%	13.32	
Total Building Cost		**203.55**	

Costs per square foot of floor area

Exterior Wall	S.F. Area	12000	20000	28000	37000	45000	57000	68000	80000	92000
	L.F. Perimeter	470	600	698	793	900	1060	1127	1200	1320
Face Brick with Concrete Brick Back-up	Steel Frame	338.60	271.35	240.95	222.05	212.15	202.55	195.20	189.45	185.90
	Bearing Walls	333.15	265.90	235.50	216.60	206.70	197.05	189.70	184.00	180.40
Decorative Concrete Block	Steel Frame	331.35	265.80	236.35	218.05	208.40	199.10	192.10	186.70	183.20
	Bearing Walls	326.10	260.55	231.10	212.80	203.15	193.85	186.85	181.45	177.95
Stucco on Concrete Block	Steel Frame	329.85	264.65	235.35	217.25	207.65	198.35	191.50	186.10	182.70
	Bearing Walls	324.60	259.45	230.15	212.05	202.40	193.15	186.25	180.90	177.45
Perimeter Adj., Add or Deduct	Per 100 L.F.	11.05	6.60	4.80	3.50	2.95	2.30	1.95	1.65	1.45
Story Hgt. Adj., Add or Deduct	Per 1 Ft.	2.00	1.55	1.30	1.05	1.00	0.95	0.85	0.80	0.70
For Basement, add $23.10 per square foot of basement area										

The above costs were calculated using the basic specifications shown on the facing page. These costs should be adjusted where necessary for design alternatives and owner's requirements. Reported completed project costs, for this type of structure, range from $168.20 to $314.05 per S.F.

Common additives

Description	Unit	$ Cost
Cabinets, Base, door units, metal	L.F.	315
Drawer units	L.F.	625
Tall storage cabinets, open	L.F.	590
With doors	L.F.	860
Wall, metal 12-1/2" deep, open	L.F.	238
With doors	L.F.	430
Carrels Hardwood	Each	960 - 2300
Countertops, not incl. base cabinets, acid proof	S.F.	58 - 70.50
Stainless steel	S.F.	156
Fume Hood, Not incl. ductwork	L.F.	750 - 1575
Ductwork	Hood	5750 - 9500
Glassware Washer, Distilled water rinse	Each	7625 - 15,700
Seating		
Auditorium chair, all veneer	Each	300
Veneer back, padded seat	Each	315
Upholstered, spring seat	Each	315
Classroom, movable chair & desk	Set	81 - 171
Lecture hall, pedestal type	Each	258 - 610

Description	Unit	$ Cost
Safety Equipment, Eye wash, hand held	Each	445
Deluge shower	Each	840
Sink, One piece plastic		
Flask wash, freestanding	Each	2550
Tables, acid resist. top, drawers	L.F.	216
Titration Unit, Four 2000 ml reservoirs	Each	6050

Important: See the Reference Section for Location Factors.

Model costs calculated for a 1 story building with 12' story height and 45,000 square feet of floor area

College, Laboratory

				Unit	Unit Cost	Cost Per S.F.	% Of Sub-Total
A. SUBSTRUCTURE							
1010	Standard Foundations	Poured concrete; strip and spread footings		S.F. Ground	3.13	3.13	
1020	Special Foundations	N/A		—	—	—	
1030	Slab on Grade	4" reinforced concrete with vapor barrier and granular base		S.F. Slab	5.31	5.31	10.0%
2010	Basement Excavation	Site preparation for slab and trench for foundation wall and footing		S.F. Ground	.18	.18	
2020	Basement Walls	4' foundation wall		L.F. Wall	77	6.34	
B. SHELL							
B10 Superstructure							
1010	Floor Construction	Metal deck on open web steel joists	(5680 S.F.)	S.F. Floor	17.08	2.22	4.8%
1020	Roof Construction	Metal deck on open web steel joists		S.F. Roof	5.03	5.03	
B20 Exterior Enclosure							
2010	Exterior Walls	Face brick with concrete block backup	75% of wall	S.F. Wall	32.89	5.92	
2020	Exterior Windows	Window wall	25% of wall	Each	40.45	2.43	7.0%
2030	Exterior Doors	Glass and metal doors and entrances with transom		Each	4904	2.19	
B30 Roofing							
3010	Roof Coverings	Built-up tar and gravel with flashing; perlite/EPS composite insulation		S.F. Roof	5.72	5.72	4.0%
3020	Roof Openings	Skylight		S.F. Roof	.35	.35	
C. INTERIORS							
1010	Partitions	Concrete block	10 S.F. Floor/L.F. Partition	S.F. Partition	12.11	12.11	
1020	Interior Doors	Single leaf-kalamein fire doors	820 S.F. Floor/Door	Each	1265	1.54	
1030	Fittings	Lockers		S.F. Floor	.05	.05	
2010	Stair Construction	N/A		—	—	—	21.8%
3010	Wall Finishes	60% paint, 40% epoxy coating		S.F. Surface	3.05	6.09	
3020	Floor Finishes	60% epoxy, 20% carpet, 20% vinyl composition tile		S.F. Floor	6.10	6.10	
3030	Ceiling Finishes	Mineral fiber tile on concealed zee runners		S.F. Ceiling	6.89	6.89	
D. SERVICES							
D10 Conveying							
1010	Elevators & Lifts	N/A		—	—	—	0.0 %
1020	Escalators & Moving Walks	N/A		—	—	—	
D20 Plumbing							
2010	Plumbing Fixtures	Toilet and service fixtures, supply and drainage	1 Fixture/260 S.F. Floor	Each	8746	33.64	
2020	Domestic Water Distribution	Gas fired water heater		S.F. Floor	3.15	3.15	25.0%
2040	Rain Water Drainage	Roof drains		S.F. Roof	.72	.72	
D30 HVAC							
3010	Energy Supply	N/A		—	—	—	
3020	Heat Generating Systems	Included in D3050		—	—	—	
3030	Cooling Generating Systems	N/A		—	—	—	13.6 %
3050	Terminal & Package Units	Multizone unit, gas heating, electric cooling		S.F. Floor	20.45	20.45	
3090	Other HVAC Sys. & Equipment	N/A		—	—	—	
D40 Fire Protection							
4010	Sprinklers	Sprinklers, light hazard		S.F. Floor	2.85	2.85	2.1%
4020	Standpipes	Standpipe, wet, Class III		S.F. Floor	.31	.31	
D50 Electrical							
5010	Electrical Service/Distribution	1000 ampere service, panel board and feeders		S.F. Floor	1.63	1.63	
5020	Lighting & Branch Wiring	High efficiency fluorescent fixtures, receptacles, switches, A.C. and misc. power		S.F. Floor	10.84	10.84	10.8%
5030	Communications & Security	Addressable alarm systems, internet wiring, and emergency lighting		S.F. Floor	3.50	3.50	
5090	Other Electrical Systems	Emergency generator, 11.5 kW, Uninterruptible power supply		S.F. Floor	.22	.22	
E. EQUIPMENT & FURNISHINGS							
1010	Commercial Equipment	N/A		—	—	—	
1020	Institutional Equipment	Cabinets, fume hoods, lockers, glassware washer		S.F. Floor	1.39	1.39	0.9 %
1030	Vehicular Equipment	N/A		—	—	—	
1090	Other Equipment	N/A		—	—	—	
F. SPECIAL CONSTRUCTION							
1020	Integrated Construction	N/A		—	—	—	0.0 %
1040	Special Facilities	N/A		—	—	—	
G. BUILDING SITEWORK	**N/A**						

		Sub-Total	150.30	**100%**
CONTRACTOR FEES (General Requirements: 10%, Overhead: 5%, Profit: 10%)		25%	37.61	
ARCHITECT FEES		10%	18.79	
		Total Building Cost	206.70	

109

Costs per square foot of floor area

Exterior Wall	S.F. Area	15000	20000	25000	30000	35000	40000	45000	50000	55000
	L.F. Perimeter	354	425	457	513	568	583	629	644	683
Brick Face with Concrete Block Back-up	Steel Frame	189.00	183.30	177.60	175.00	173.05	170.25	168.95	167.15	166.15
	R/Conc. Frame	178.00	172.30	166.60	164.00	162.05	159.25	158.00	156.10	155.20
Precast Concrete Panel	Steel Frame	194.75	188.60	182.25	179.35	177.20	174.05	172.65	170.45	169.40
	R/Conc. Frame	184.50	178.15	171.65	168.70	166.50	163.30	161.85	159.70	158.60
Limestone Face Concrete Block Back-up	Steel Frame	205.25	197.90	190.20	186.75	184.20	180.30	178.60	175.95	174.75
	R/Conc. Frame	194.20	186.90	179.20	175.80	173.25	169.30	167.60	165.00	163.75
Perimeter Adj., Add or Deduct	Per 100 L.F.	9.55	7.15	5.75	4.80	4.15	3.60	3.20	2.80	2.65
Story Hgt. Adj., Add or Deduct	Per 1 Ft.	2.35	2.15	1.85	1.70	1.60	1.45	1.45	1.25	1.30

For Basement, add $38.25 per square foot of basement area

The above costs were calculated using the basic specifications shown on the facing page. These costs should be adjusted where necessary for design alternatives and owner's requirements. Reported completed project costs, for this type of structure, range from $137.80 to $281.10 per S.F.

Common additives

Description	Unit	$ Cost
Carrels Hardwood	Each	960 - 2300
Elevators, Hydraulic passenger, 2 stops		
2000# capacity	Each	67,600
2500# capacity	Each	69,200
3500# capacity	Each	73,200
Emergency Lighting, 25 watt, battery operated		
Lead battery	Each	320
Nickel cadmium	Each	885
Escalators, Metal		
32" wide, 10' story height	Each	147,500
20' story height	Each	180,500
48" wide, 10' Story height	Each	155,500
20' story height	Each	189,500
Glass		
32" wide, 10' story height	Each	140,500
20' story height	Each	172,000
48" wide, 10' story height	Each	147,500
20' story height	Each	180,500

Description	Unit	$ Cost
Lockers, Steel, Single tier, 60" or 72"	Opening	218 - 365
2 tier, 60" or 72" total	Opening	113 - 156
5 tier, box lockers	Opening	71.50 - 85
Locker bench, lam. maple top only	L.F.	26.50
Pedestals, steel pipe	Each	74
Sound System		
Amplifier, 250 watts	Each	2025
Speaker, ceiling or wall	Each	208
Trumpet	Each	400

Important: See the Reference Section for Location Factors.

Model costs calculated for a 2 story building with 12' story height and 25,000 square feet of floor area

College, Student Union

				Unit	Unit Cost	Cost Per S.F.	% Of Sub-Total
A. SUBSTRUCTURE							
1010	Standard Foundations	Poured concrete; strip and spread footings		S.F. Ground	4.60	2.30	
1020	Special Foundations	N/A		—	—	—	
1030	Slab on Grade	4" reinforced concrete with vapor barrier and granular base		S.F. Slab	5.31	2.66	5.3%
2010	Basement Excavation	Site preparation for slab and trench for foundation wall and footing		S.F. Ground	.18	.09	
2020	Basement Walls	4' foundation wall		L.F. Wall	82	1.49	
B. SHELL							
	B10 Superstructure						
1010	Floor Construction	Concrete flat plate		S.F. Floor	26.80	13.40	16.8%
1020	Roof Construction	Concrete flat plate		S.F. Roof	15.16	7.58	
	B20 Exterior Enclosure						
2010	Exterior Walls	Face brick with concrete block backup	75% of wall	S.F. Wall	32.88	10.82	
2020	Exterior Windows	Window wall	25% of wall	Each	40.45	4.44	12.6%
2030	Exterior Doors	Double aluminum and glass		Each	2650	.42	
	B30 Roofing						
3010	Roof Coverings	Built-up tar and gravel with flashing; perlite/EPS composite insulation		S.F. Roof	6.44	3.22	2.6%
3020	Roof Openings	Roof hatches		S.F. Roof	.12	.06	
C. INTERIORS							
1010	Partitions	Gypsum board on metal studs	14 S.F. Floor/L.F. Partition	S.F. Partition	6.26	4.47	
1020	Interior Doors	Single leaf hollow metal	140 S.F. Floor/Door	Each	1152	8.23	
1030	Fittings	N/A		—	—	—	
2010	Stair Construction	Cast in place concrete		Flight	8025	1.29	22.1%
3010	Wall Finishes	50% paint, 50% vinyl wall covering		S.F. Surface	2.43	3.47	
3020	Floor Finishes	50% carpet, 50% vinyl composition tile		S.F. Floor	5.47	5.47	
3030	Ceiling Finishes	Suspended fiberglass board		S.F. Ceiling	4.57	4.57	
D. SERVICES							
	D10 Conveying						
1010	Elevators & Lifts	One hydraulic passenger elevator		Each	83,500	3.34	2.7%
1020	Escalators & Moving Walks	N/A		—	—	—	
	D20 Plumbing						
2010	Plumbing Fixtures	Toilet and service fixtures, supply and drainage	1 Fixture/1040 S.F. Floor	Each	3432	3.30	
2020	Domestic Water Distribution	Gas fired water heater		S.F. Floor	.93	.93	3.8%
2040	Rain Water Drainage	Roof drains		S.F. Roof	1.12	.56	
	D30 HVAC						
3010	Energy Supply	N/A		—	—	—	
3020	Heat Generating Systems	Included in D3050		—	—	—	
3030	Cooling Generating Systems	N/A		—	—	—	16.4 %
3050	Terminal & Package Units	Multizone unit, gas heating, electric cooling		S.F. Floor	20.45	20.45	
3090	Other HVAC Sys. & Equipment	N/A		—	—	—	
	D40 Fire Protection						
4010	Sprinklers	Wet pipe sprinkler system		S.F. Floor	3.11	3.11	3.2%
4020	Standpipes	Standpipe, wet, Class III		S.F. Floor	.86	.86	
	D50 Electrical						
5010	Electrical Service/Distribution	600 ampere service, panel board and feeders		S.F. Floor	1.83	1.83	
5020	Lighting & Branch Wiring	High efficiency fluorescent fixtures, receptacles, switches, A.C. and misc. power		S.F. Floor	12.55	12.55	14.5%
5030	Communications & Security	Addressable alarm systems, internet wiring, communications systems and emergency lighting		S.F. Floor	3.50	3.50	
5090	Other Electrical Systems	Emergency generator, 11.5 kW		S.F. Floor	.15	.15	
E. EQUIPMENT & FURNISHINGS							
1010	Commercial Equipment	N/A		—	—	—	
1020	Institutional Equipment	N/A		—	—	—	0.0 %
1030	Vehicular Equipment	N/A		—	—	—	
1090	Other Equipment	N/A		—	—	—	
F. SPECIAL CONSTRUCTION							
1020	Integrated Construction	N/A		—	—	—	0.0 %
1040	Special Facilities	N/A		—	—	—	
G. BUILDING SITEWORK	**N/A**						

		Unit	Cost Per S.F.	%
	Sub-Total		124.56	100%
CONTRACTOR FEES (General Requirements: 10%, Overhead: 5%, Profit: 10%)		25%	31.14	
ARCHITECT FEES		7%	10.90	
	Total Building Cost		**166.60**	

Costs per square foot of floor area

Exterior Wall	S.F. Area	4000	6000	8000	10000	12000	14000	16000	18000	20000
	L.F. Perimeter	260	340	420	453	460	510	560	610	600
Face Brick with Concrete Block Back-up	Bearing Walls	176.55	167.45	162.95	155.90	149.15	147.15	145.70	144.55	140.95
	Steel Frame	171.95	164.05	160.10	153.95	148.25	146.60	145.25	144.25	141.15
Decorative Concrete Block	Bearing Walls	155.20	148.05	144.50	139.05	133.90	132.35	131.25	130.35	127.60
	Steel Frame	157.80	151.65	148.60	144.05	139.85	138.60	137.60	136.90	134.60
Tilt Up Concrete Wall Panels	Bearing Walls	157.90	151.20	147.85	142.85	138.15	136.75	135.65	134.85	132.30
	Steel Frame	153.30	147.75	145.00	141.00	137.20	136.10	135.20	134.55	132.55
Perimeter Adj., Add or Deduct	Per 100 L.F.	23.15	15.45	11.60	9.20	7.70	6.65	5.85	5.20	4.60
Story Hgt. Adj., Add or Deduct	Per 1 Ft.	2.90	2.55	2.35	2.00	1.70	1.65	1.55	1.55	1.35
For Basement, add $33.50 per square foot of basement area										

The above costs were calculated using the basic specifications shown on the facing page. These costs should be adjusted where necessary for design alternatives and owner's requirements. Reported completed project costs, for this type of structure, range from $84.10 to $265.65 per S.F.

Common additives

Description	Unit	$ Cost		Description	Unit	$ Cost
Bar, Front bar	L.F.	415		Movie Equipment		
Back bar	L.F.	330		Projector, 35mm	Each	12,200 - 16,700
Booth, Upholstered, custom straight	L.F.	241 - 440		Screen, wall or ceiling hung	S.F.	8.70 - 13.20
"L" or "U" shaped	L.F.	249 - 425		Partitions, Folding leaf, wood		
Bowling Alleys, incl. alley, pinsetter				Acoustic type	S.F.	81.50 - 134
Scorer, counter & misc. supplies, average	Lane	62,500		Seating		
For automatic scorer, add	Lane	10,900		Auditorium chair, all veneer	Each	300
Emergency Lighting, 25 watt, battery operated				Veneer back, padded seat	Each	315
Lead battery	Each	320		Upholstered, spring seat	Each	315
Nickel cadmium	Each	885		Classroom, movable chair & desk	Set	81 - 171
Kitchen Equipment				Lecture hall, pedestal type	Each	258 - 610
Broiler	Each	4000		Sound System		
Coffee urn, twin 6 gallon	Each	2975		Amplifier, 250 watts	Each	2025
Cooler, 6 ft. long	Each	4100		Speaker, ceiling or wall	Each	208
Dishwasher, 10-12 racks per hr.	Each	4225		Trumpet	Each	400
Food warmer	Each	725		Stage Curtains, Medium weight	S.F.	10.60 - 39
Freezer, 44 C.F., reach-in	Each	5125		Curtain Track, Light duty	L.F.	86.50
Ice cube maker, 50 lb. per day	Each	1950		Swimming Pools, Complete, gunite	S.F.	90.50 - 113
Range with 1 oven	Each	3000				

Important: See the Reference Section for Location Factors.

Model costs calculated for a 1 story building with 12' story height and 10,000 square feet of floor area

				Unit	Unit Cost	Cost Per S.F.	% Of Sub-Total
A. SUBSTRUCTURE							
1010	Standard Foundations	Poured concrete; strip and spread footings		S.F. Ground	2.30	2.30	
1020	Special Foundations	N/A		—	—	—	
1030	Slab on Grade	4" reinforced concrete with vapor barrier and granular base		S.F. Slab	5.31	5.31	14.0%
2010	Basement Excavation	Site preparation for slab and trench for foundation wall and footing		S.F. Ground	.32	.32	
2020	Basement Walls	4' foundation wall		L.F. Wall	77	8.09	
B. SHELL							
B10 Superstructure							
1010	Floor Construction	N/A		—	—	—	
1020	Roof Construction	Metal deck on open web steel joists		S.F. Roof	6.86	6.86	6.0 %
B20 Exterior Enclosure							
2010	Exterior Walls	Face brick with concrete block backup	80% of wall	S.F. Wall	32.88	14.30	
2020	Exterior Windows	Aluminum sliding	20% of wall	Each	626	2.13	15.3%
2030	Exterior Doors	Double aluminum and glass and hollow metal		Each	2584	1.04	
B30 Roofing							
3010	Roof Coverings	Built-up tar and gravel with flashing; perlite/EPS composite insulation		S.F. Roof	7.40	7.40	6.5%
3020	Roof Openings	Roof hatches		S.F. Roof	.09	.09	
C. INTERIORS							
1010	Partitions	Gypsum board on metal studs	14 S.F. Floor/L.F. Partition	S.F. Partition	8.50	6.07	
1020	Interior Doors	Single leaf hollow metal	140 S.F. Floor/Door	Each	1152	8.23	
1030	Fittings	Toilet partitions, directory board, mailboxes		S.F. Floor	1.69	1.69	
2010	Stair Construction	N/A		—	—	—	26.9%
3010	Wall Finishes	Paint		S.F. Surface	1.84	2.63	
3020	Floor Finishes	50% carpet, 50% vinyl tile		S.F. Floor	5.22	5.22	
3030	Ceiling Finishes	Mineral fiber tile on concealed zee bars		S.F. Ceiling	6.89	6.89	
D. SERVICES							
D10 Conveying							
1010	Elevators & Lifts	N/A		—	—	—	0.0 %
1020	Escalators & Moving Walks	N/A		—	—	—	
D20 Plumbing							
2010	Plumbing Fixtures	Kitchen, toilet and service fixtures, supply and drainage	1 Fixture/910 S.F. Floor	Each	3458	3.80	
2020	Domestic Water Distribution	Electric water heater		S.F. Floor	6.64	6.64	9.6%
2040	Rain Water Drainage	Roof drains		S.F. Roof	.54	.54	
D30 HVAC							
3010	Energy Supply	N/A		—	—	—	
3020	Heat Generating Systems	Included in D3050		—	—	—	
3030	Cooling Generating Systems	N/A		—	—	—	8.9 %
3050	Terminal & Package Units	Single zone rooftop unit, gas heating, electric cooling		S.F. Floor	10.18	10.18	
3090	Other HVAC Sys. & Equipment	N/A		—	—	—	
D40 Fire Protection							
4010	Sprinklers	Wet pipe sprinkler system		S.F. Floor	3.56	3.56	3.1%
4020	Standpipes	N/A		—	—	—	
D50 Electrical							
5010	Electrical Service/Distribution	200 ampere service, panel board and feeders		S.F. Floor	1.11	1.11	
5020	Lighting & Branch Wiring	High efficiency fluorescent fixtures, receptacles, switches, A.C. and misc. power		S.F. Floor	5.72	5.72	7.4%
5030	Communications & Security	Addressable alarm systems and emergency lighting		S.F. Floor	1.49	1.49	
5090	Other Electrical Systems	Emergency generator, 15 kW		S.F. Floor	.16	.16	
E. EQUIPMENT & FURNISHINGS							
1010	Commercial Equipment	Freezer, chest type		S.F. Floor	.93	.93	
1020	Institutional Equipment	N/A		—	—	—	2.3%
1030	Vehicular Equipment	N/A		—	—	—	
1090	Other Equipment	Kitchen equipment, directory board, mailboxes, built-in coat racks		S.F. Floor	1.70	1.70	
F. SPECIAL CONSTRUCTION							
1020	Integrated Construction	N/A		—	—	—	0.0 %
1040	Special Facilities	N/A		—	—	—	
G. BUILDING SITEWORK	**N/A**						

			Sub-Total	114.40	100%
CONTRACTOR FEES (General Requirements: 10%, Overhead: 5%, Profit: 10%)		25%	28.63		
ARCHITECT FEES		9%	12.87		
	Total Building Cost		**155.90**		

113

Costs per square foot of floor area

Exterior Wall	S.F. Area	10000	12500	15000	17500	20000	22500	25000	30000	40000
	L.F. Perimeter	400	450	500	550	600	625	650	700	800
Brick Veneer	Steel Frame	315.55	312.15	309.80	308.20	306.95	305.10	303.60	301.35	298.50
	Bearing Wall	329.50	324.65	321.45	319.20	317.45	314.80	312.70	309.55	305.60
Tilt Up Concrete	Steel Frame	307.25	303.85	301.55	299.90	298.70	296.85	295.35	293.05	290.25
Concrete Panels	Bearing Wall	337.30	331.75	328.00	325.35	323.40	320.35	317.90	314.20	309.60
E.I.F.S. System on Metal Studs	Steel Frame	311.70	308.90	307.05	305.75	304.75	303.20	301.95	300.15	297.85
	Bearing Wall	311.90	308.90	306.85	305.40	304.30	302.65	301.35	299.40	296.90
Perimeter Adj., Add or Deduct	Per 100 L.F.	8.45	6.70	5.65	4.80	4.30	3.75	3.35	2.80	2.10
Story Hgt. Adj., Add or Deduct	Per 1 Ft.	1.50	1.30	1.35	1.15	1.10	1.05	0.95	0.85	0.80

For Basement, add $36.80 per square foot of basement area

The above costs were calculated using the basic specifications shown on the facing page. These costs should be adjusted where necessary for design alternatives and owner's requirements. Reported completed project costs, for this type of structure, range from $173.50 to $352.10 per S.F.

Common additives

Description	Unit	$ Cost
Clock System		
20 room	Ea.	19,500
50 room	Ea.	45,700
Closed Circuit Surveillance, one station		
Camera and monitor	Total	1975
For additional camera stations, add	Ea.	1050
For zoom lens - remote control, add	Ea.	3075 - 10,300
For automatic iris for low light, add	Ea.	2725
Directory Boards, plastic, glass covered		
30" x 20"	Ea.	630
36" x 48"	Ea.	1500
Aluminum, 24" x 18"	Ea.	630
36" x 24"	Ea.	735
48" x 32"	Ea.	1050
48" x 60"	Ea.	2200
Emergency Lighting, 25 watt, battery operated		
Lead battery	Ea.	320
Nickel cadmium	Ea.	885

Description	Unit	$ Cost
Smoke Detectors		
Ceiling type	Ea.	223
Duct type	Ea.	555
Sound System		
Amplifier, 250 watts	Ea.	2025
Speakers, ceiling or wall	Ea.	208
Trumpets	Ea.	400

Important: See the Reference Section for Location Factors.

Model costs calculated for a 1 story building with 16'-6" story height and 22,500 square feet of floor area

Computer Data Center

				Unit	Unit Cost	Cost Per S.F.	% Of Sub-Total
A. SUBSTRUCTURE							
1010	Standard Foundations	Poured concrete; strip and spread footings		S.F. Ground	1.66	1.66	
1020	Special Foundations	N/A		—	—	—	
1030	Slab on Grade	4" concrete with vapor barrier and granular base		S.F. Slab	5.31	5.31	4.1%
2010	Basement Excavation	Site preparation for slab and trench for foundation wall and footing		S.F. Ground	.18	.20	
2020	Basement Walls	4' foundation wall		L.F. Wall	82	2.27	
B. SHELL							
	B10 Superstructure						
1010	Floor Construction	N/A		—	—	—	4.3 %
1020	Roof Construction	Steel joist, girders & deck on columns		S.F. Roof	9.83	9.83	
	B20 Exterior Enclosure						
2010	Exterior Walls	Brick veneer on metal studs		S.F. Wall	24.46	10.65	
2020	Exterior Windows	Aluminum sliding	5% of Wall	Each	585	.89	5.5%
2030	Exterior Doors	Aluminum and glass		Each	3833	1.02	
	B30 Roofing						
3010	Roof Coverings	Single ply membrane, loose laid and ballasted; polyisocyanurate insulation		S.F. Roof	5.88	5.88	2.6%
3020	Roof Openings	Roof hatch		S.F. Roof	.11	.11	
C. INTERIORS							
1010	Partitions	Gypsum board on metal studs	13 S.F. Floor/L.F. Partition	S.F. Partition	4.92	4.54	
1020	Interior Doors	Solid core wood, metal frame	370 S.F. Floor/Door	Each	765	2.07	
1030	Fittings	Toilet partitions		S.F. Floor	.48	.48	
2010	Stair Construction	N/A		—	—	—	10.5%
3010	Wall Finishes	90% paint, 10% ceramic tile		S.F. Surface	2.05	3.79	
3020	Floor Finishes	65% carpet tile, 10% ceramic tile, 10% quarry tile		S.F. Floor	6.11	6.11	
3030	Ceiling Finishes	Mineral fiber tile on concealed zee bars		S.F. Ceiling	6.89	6.89	
D. SERVICES							
	D10 Conveying						
1010	Elevators & Lifts	N/A		—	—	—	0.0 %
1020	Escalators & Moving Walks	N/A		—	—	—	
	D20 Plumbing						
2010	Plumbing Fixtures	Toilet and service fixtures, supply and drainage	1 fixture/1180 S.F. Floor	Each	4991	4.23	
2020	Domestic Water Distribution	Gas fired water heater		S.F. Floor	.72	.72	2.7%
2040	Rain Water Drainage	Roof drains		S.F. Floor	1.11	1.11	
	D30 HVAC						
3010	Energy Supply	Hot water reheat		S.F. Floor	6.56	6.56	
3020	Heat Generating Systems	Boiler, oil fired hot water		Each	49,250	9.48	
3030	Cooling Generating Systems	Cooling tower		S.F. Floor	9.41	9.41	39.3%
3050	Terminal & Package Units	N/A		—	—	—	
3090	Other HVAC Sys. & Equipment	Heat exchanger, ductwork, air handling units, VAV terminals		S.F. Floor	64	64.11	
	D40 Fire Protection						
4010	Sprinklers	85% wet pipe sprinkler system, 15% preaction sprinkler system		S.F. Floor	4.22	4.22	2.1%
4020	Standpipes	Standpipes and hose systems		S.F. Floor	.63	.63	
	D50 Electrical						
5010	Electrical Service/Distribution	1200 ampere service, panel board and feeders		S.F. Floor	3.77	3.77	
5020	Lighting & Branch Wiring	High efficiency fluorescent fixtures, receptacles, A.C. and misc. power		S.F. Floor	16.27	16.27	27.9%
5030	Communications & Security	Addressable alarm & telephone systems, internet wiring and emergency lighting		S.F. Floor	31.12	31.12	
5090	Other Electrical Systems	Emergency generator, 350 kW; UPS system		S.F. Floor	12.50	12.50	
E. EQUIPMENT & FURNISHINGS							
1010	Commercial Equipment	N/A		—	—	—	
1020	Institutional Equipment	N/A		—	—	—	0.0 %
1030	Vehicular Equipment	N/A		—	—	—	
1090	Other Equipment	N/A		—	—	—	
F. SPECIAL CONSTRUCTION & DEMOLITION							
1020	Integrated Construction	Pedestal access floor	15% of Floor	S.F. Floor	2.30	2.30	1.0%
1040	Special Facilities	N/A		—	—	—	
G. BUILDING SITEWORK	**N/A**						

			Sub-Total	228.13	**100%**
CONTRACTOR FEES (General Requirements: 10%, Overhead: 5%, Profit: 10%)		25%	57.01		
ARCHITECT FEES		7%	19.96		

Total Building Cost	**305.10**

Costs per square foot of floor area

Exterior Wall	S.F. Area	16000	23000	30000	37000	44000	51000	58000	65000	72000
	L.F. Perimeter	597	763	821	968	954	1066	1090	1132	1220
Limestone with Concrete Block Back-up	R/Conc. Frame	226.55	217.35	207.40	204.55	197.50	195.85	192.50	190.20	189.30
	Steel Frame	228.45	219.20	209.25	206.45	199.40	197.70	194.40	192.10	191.20
Face Brick with Concrete Block Back-up	R/Conc. Frame	208.20	201.00	193.85	191.65	186.85	185.55	183.20	181.60	180.95
	Steel Frame	210.10	202.85	195.80	193.50	188.70	187.40	185.10	183.50	182.85
Stone with Concrete Block Back-up	R/Conc. Frame	213.95	206.05	198.05	195.65	190.10	188.70	186.05	184.25	183.50
	Steel Frame	215.90	208.05	200.00	197.60	192.10	190.65	188.00	186.25	185.45
Perimeter Adj., Add or Deduct	Per 100 L.F.	8.70	6.05	4.65	3.80	3.15	2.70	2.35	2.20	1.95
Story Hgt. Adj., Add or Deduct	Per 1 Ft.	3.20	2.75	2.25	2.20	1.85	1.75	1.55	1.50	1.45

For Basement, add $31.65 per square foot of basement area

The above costs were calculated using the basic specifications shown on the facing page. These costs should be adjusted where necessary for design alternatives and owner's requirements. Reported completed project costs, for this type of structure, range from $148.05 to $275.80 per S.F.

Common additives

Description	Unit	$ Cost
Benches, Hardwood	L.F.	132 - 242
Clock System		
20 room	Each	19,500
50 room	Each	45,700
Closed Circuit Surveillance, One station		
Camera and monitor	Each	1975
For additional camera stations, add	Each	1050
Directory Boards, Plastic, glass covered		
30" x 20"	Each	630
36" x 48"	Each	1500
Aluminum, 24" x 18"	Each	630
36" x 24"	Each	735
48" x 32"	Each	1050
48" x 60"	Each	2200
Emergency Lighting, 25 watt, battery operated		
Lead battery	Each	320
Nickel cadmium	Each	885

Description	Unit	$ Cost
Flagpoles, Complete		
Aluminum, 20' high	Each	1775
40' high	Each	3925
70' high	Each	10,800
Fiberglass, 23' high	Each	1325
39'-5" high	Each	3575
59' high	Each	7275
Intercom System, 25 station capacity		
Master station	Each	3175
Intercom outlets	Each	184
Handset	Each	505
Safe, Office type, 1 hour rating		
30" x 18" x 18"	Each	2500
60" x 36" x 18", double door	Each	8075
Smoke Detectors		
Ceiling type	Each	223
Duct type	Each	555

Important: See the Reference Section for Location Factors.

Model costs calculated for a 1 story building with 14' story height and 30,000 square feet of floor area

				Unit	Unit Cost	Cost Per S.F.	% Of Sub-Total
A. SUBSTRUCTURE							
1010	Standard Foundations	Poured concrete; strip and spread footings		S.F. Ground	1.73	1.73	
1020	Special Foundations	N/A		—	—	—	
1030	Slab on Grade	4" reinforced concrete with vapor barrier and granular base		S.F. Slab	5.31	5.31	6.2%
2010	Basement Excavation	Site preparation for slab and trench for foundation wall and footing		S.F. Ground	.18	.18	
2020	Basement Walls	4' foundation wall		L.F. Wall	82	2.39	
B. SHELL							
B10 Superstructure							
1010	Floor Construction	Cast-in-place columns		L.F. Column	73	1.83	13.8%
1020	Roof Construction	Cast-in-place concrete waffle slab		S.F. Roof	19.60	19.60	
B20 Exterior Enclosure							
2010	Exterior Walls	Limestone panels with concrete block backup	75% of wall	S.F. Wall	68	19.54	
2020	Exterior Windows	Aluminum with insulated glass	25% of wall	Each	736	3.07	14.9%
2030	Exterior Doors	Double wood		Each	1904	.44	
B30 Roofing							
3010	Roof Coverings	Built-up tar and gravel with flashing; perlite/EPS composite insulation		S.F. Roof	5.74	5.74	3.8%
3020	Roof Openings	Roof hatches		S.F. Roof	.09	.09	
C. INTERIORS							
1010	Partitions	Plaster on metal studs	10 S.F. Floor/L.F. Partition	S.F. Partition	13.15	15.78	
1020	Interior Doors	Single leaf wood	100 S.F. Floor/Door	Each	636	6.36	
1030	Fittings	Toilet partitions		S.F. Floor	.48	.48	
2010	Stair Construction	N/A		—	—	—	33.0%
3010	Wall Finishes	70% paint, 20% wood paneling, 10% vinyl wall covering		S.F. Surface	2.13	5.12	
3020	Floor Finishes	60% hardwood, 20% carpet, 20% terrazzo		S.F. Floor	13.37	13.37	
3030	Ceiling Finishes	Gypsum plaster on metal lath, suspended		S.F. Ceiling	10	10	
D. SERVICES							
D10 Conveying							
1010	Elevators & Lifts	N/A		—	—	—	0.0 %
1020	Escalators & Moving Walks	N/A		—	—	—	
D20 Plumbing							
2010	Plumbing Fixtures	Toilet and service fixtures, supply and drainage	1 Fixture/1110 S.F. Floor	Each	4695	4.23	
2020	Domestic Water Distribution	Electric hot water heater		S.F. Floor	2.38	2.38	5.0%
2040	Rain Water Drainage	Roof drains		S.F. Roof	1.11	1.11	
D30 HVAC							
3010	Energy Supply	N/A		—	—	—	
3020	Heat Generating Systems	Included in D3050		—	—	—	
3030	Cooling Generating Systems	N/A		—	—	—	13.2 %
3050	Terminal & Package Units	Multizone unit, gas heating, electric cooling		S.F. Floor	20.45	20.45	
3090	Other HVAC Sys. & Equipment	N/A		—	—	—	
D40 Fire Protection							
4010	Sprinklers	Wet pipe sprinkler system		S.F. Floor	2.85	2.85	2.1%
4020	Standpipes	Standpipe, wet, Class III		S.F. Floor	.47	.47	
D50 Electrical							
5010	Electrical Service/Distribution	400 ampere service, panel board and feeders		S.F. Floor	1.02	1.02	
5020	Lighting & Branch Wiring	High efficiency fluorescent fixtures, receptacles, switches, A.C. and misc. power		S.F. Floor	9.70	9.70	8.1%
5030	Communications & Security	Addressable alarm systems, internet wiring, and emergency lighting		S.F. Floor	1.68	1.68	
5090	Other Electrical Systems	Emergency generator, 11.5 kW		S.F. Floor	.12	.12	
E. EQUIPMENT & FURNISHINGS							
1010	Commercial Equipment	N/A		—	—	—	
1020	Institutional Equipment	N/A		—	—	—	0.0 %
1030	Vehicular Equipment	N/A		—	—	—	
1090	Other Equipment	N/A		—	—	—	
F. SPECIAL CONSTRUCTION							
1020	Integrated Construction	N/A		—	—	—	0.0 %
1040	Special Facilities	N/A		—	—	—	
G. BUILDING SITEWORK	**N/A**						

		Sub-Total	155.04	**100%**
CONTRACTOR FEES (General Requirements: 10%, Overhead: 5%, Profit: 10%)		25%	38.79	
ARCHITECT FEES		7%	13.57	

Total Building Cost	**207.40**

Costs per square foot of floor area

Exterior Wall	S.F. Area	30000	40000	45000	50000	60000	70000	80000	90000	100000
	L.F. Perimeter	410	493	535	533	600	666	733	800	795
Limestone with Concrete Block Back-up	R/Conc. Frame	246.20	235.65	232.20	225.95	221.35	217.85	215.40	213.45	209.10
	Steel Frame	250.30	239.80	236.30	230.10	225.50	222.00	219.50	217.55	213.25
Face Brick with Concrete Block Back-up	R/Conc. Frame	228.80	220.00	217.00	212.40	208.65	205.80	203.70	202.10	199.00
	Steel Frame	232.95	224.20	221.20	216.55	212.85	209.95	207.85	206.30	203.20
Stone with Concrete Block Back-up	R/Conc. Frame	234.35	225.00	221.85	216.75	212.70	209.65	207.45	205.75	202.20
	Steel Frame	238.45	229.10	226.00	220.85	216.80	213.75	211.55	209.90	206.35
Perimeter Adj., Add or Deduct	Per 100 L.F.	12.90	9.70	8.55	7.75	6.45	5.65	4.80	4.35	3.90
Story Hgt. Adj., Add or Deduct	Per 1 Ft.	4.15	3.80	3.60	3.30	3.05	2.90	2.75	2.75	2.45

For Basement, add $32.30 per square foot of basement area

The above costs were calculated using the basic specifications shown on the facing page. These costs should be adjusted where necessary for design alternatives and owner's requirements. Reported completed project costs, for this type of structure, range from $148.70 to $277.40 per S.F.

Common additives

Description	Unit	$ Cost	Description	Unit	$ Cost
Benches, Hardwood	L.F.	132 - 242	Emergency Lighting, 25 watt, battery operated		
Clock System			Lead battery	Each	320
20 room	Each	19,500	Nickel cadmium	Each	885
50 room	Each	45,700	Flagpoles, Complete		
Closed Circuit Surveillance, One station			Aluminum, 20' high	Each	1775
Camera and monitor	Each	1975	40' high	Each	3925
For additional camera stations, add	Each	1050	70' high	Each	10,800
Directory Boards, Plastic, glass covered			Fiberglass, 23' high	Each	1325
30" x 20"	Each	630	39'-5" high	Each	3575
36" x 48"	Each	1500	59' high	Each	7275
Aluminum, 24" x 18"	Each	630	Intercom System, 25 station capacity		
36" x 24"	Each	735	Master station	Each	3175
48" x 32"	Each	1050	Intercom outlets	Each	184
48" x 60"	Each	2200	Handset	Each	505
Elevators, Hydraulic passenger, 2 stops			Safe, Office type, 1 hour rating		
1500# capacity	Each	66,100	30" x 18" x 18"	Each	2500
2500# capacity	Each	69,200	60" x 36" x 18", double door	Each	8075
3500# capacity	Each	73,200	Smoke Detectors		
Additional stop, add	Each	8575	Ceiling type	Each	223
			Duct type	Each	555

Important: See the Reference Section for Location Factors.

Model costs calculated for a 3 story building with 12' story height and 60,000 square feet of floor area

Courthouse, 2-3 Story

				Unit	Unit Cost	Cost Per S.F.	% Of Sub-Total
A.	**SUBSTRUCTURE**						
1010	Standard Foundations	Poured concrete; strip and spread footings		S.F. Ground	3.90	1.30	
1020	Special Foundations	N/A		—	—	—	
1030	Slab on Grade	4" reinforced concrete with vapor barrier and granular base		S.F. Slab	5.31	1.77	2.6%
2010	Basement Excavation	Site preparation for slab and trench for foundation wall and footing		S.F. Ground	.18	.06	
2020	Basement Walls	4' foundation wall		L.F. Wall	77	.94	
B.	**SHELL**						
	B10 Superstructure						
1010	Floor Construction	Concrete slab with metal deck and beams		S.F. Floor	30.36	20.24	16.9%
1020	Roof Construction	Concrete slab with metal deck and beams		S.F. Roof	19.98	6.66	
	B20 Exterior Enclosure						
2010	Exterior Walls	Face brick with concrete block backup	75% of wall	S.F. Wall	35.48	9.58	
2020	Exterior Windows	Horizontal pivoted steel	25% of wall	Each	755	7.55	11.0%
2030	Exterior Doors	Double aluminum and glass and hollow metal		Each	3522	.34	
	B30 Roofing						
3010	Roof Coverings	Built-up tar and gravel with flashing; perlite/EPS composite insulation		S.F. Roof	6.18	2.06	1.3%
3020	Roof Openings	N/A		—	—	—	
C.	**INTERIORS**						
1010	Partitions	Plaster on metal studs	10 S.F. Floor/L.F. Partition	S.F. Partition	13.31	13.31	
1020	Interior Doors	Single leaf wood	100 S.F. Floor/Door	Each	636	6.36	
1030	Fittings	Toilet partitions		S.F. Floor	.25	.25	
2010	Stair Construction	Concrete filled metal pan		Flight	20,150	3.36	32.0%
3010	Wall Finishes	70% paint, 20% wood paneling, 10% vinyl wall covering		S.F. Surface	2.14	4.27	
3020	Floor Finishes	60% hardwood, 20% terrazzo, 20% carpet		S.F. Floor	13.37	13.37	
3030	Ceiling Finishes	Gypsum plaster on metal lath, suspended		S.F. Ceiling	10	10	
D.	**SERVICES**						
	D10 Conveying						
1010	Elevators & Lifts	Five hydraulic passenger elevators		Each	156,960	13.08	8.2%
1020	Escalators & Moving Walks	N/A		—	—	—	
	D20 Plumbing						
2010	Plumbing Fixtures	Toilet and service fixtures, supply and drainage	1 Fixture/665 S.F. Floor	Each	3172	4.77	
2020	Domestic Water Distribution	Electric water heater		S.F. Floor	2.73	2.73	5.1%
2040	Rain Water Drainage	Roof drains		S.F. Roof	2.04	.68	
	D30 HVAC						
3010	Energy Supply	N/A		—	—	—	
3020	Heat Generating Systems	Included in D3050		—	—	—	
3030	Cooling Generating Systems	N/A		—	—	—	12.9 %
3050	Terminal & Package Units	Multizone unit, gas heating, electric cooling		S.F. Floor	20.45	20.45	
3090	Other HVAC Sys. & Equipment	N/A		—	—	—	
	D40 Fire Protection						
4010	Sprinklers	Wet pipe sprinkler system		S.F. Floor	3.02	3.02	2.2%
4020	Standpipes	Standpipe, wet, Class III		S.F. Floor	.43	.43	
	D50 Electrical						
5010	Electrical Service/Distribution	800 ampere service, panel board and feeders		S.F. Floor	.97	.97	
5020	Lighting & Branch Wiring	High efficiency fluorescent fixtures, receptacles, switches, A.C. and misc. power		S.F. Floor	9.84	9.84	7.9%
5030	Communications & Security	Addressable alarm systems, internet wiring, and emergency lighting		S.F. Floor	1.53	1.53	
5090	Other Electrical Systems	Emergency generator, 15 kW		S.F. Floor	.20	.20	
E.	**EQUIPMENT & FURNISHINGS**						
1010	Commercial Equipment	N/A		—	—	—	
1020	Institutional Equipment	N/A		—	—	—	0.0 %
1030	Vehicular Equipment	N/A		—	—	—	
1090	Other Equipment	N/A		—	—	—	
F.	**SPECIAL CONSTRUCTION**						
1020	Integrated Construction	N/A		—	—	—	0.0 %
1040	Special Facilities	N/A		—	—	—	
G.	**BUILDING SITEWORK**	**N/A**					

	Sub-Total	159.12	**100%**
CONTRACTOR FEES (General Requirements: 10%, Overhead: 5%, Profit: 10%)	25%	39.81	
ARCHITECT FEES	7%	13.92	
Total Building Cost		**212.85**	

Costs per square foot of floor area

Exterior Wall	S.F. Area	2000	5000	7000	10000	12000	15000	18000	21000	25000
	L.F. Perimeter	200	310	360	440	480	520	560	600	660
Tiltup Concrete Panel	Steel Joists	210.40	180.45	172.95	167.60	164.90	161.55	159.25	157.60	156.20
Decorative Concrete Block	Bearing Walls	208.60	177.80	170.05	164.50	161.70	158.20	155.80	154.10	152.65
Brick on Block	Steel Joists	253.15	215.05	205.05	197.95	194.30	189.60	186.40	184.10	182.20
Stucco on Concrete Block	Wood Truss	210.85	180.50	172.85	167.40	164.65	161.25	158.90	157.20	155.85
Brick Veneer	Wood Frame	218.80	186.90	178.65	172.80	169.80	165.95	163.30	161.45	159.90
Wood Siding	Wood Frame	200.65	176.50	170.30	166.00	163.75	161.00	159.10	157.70	156.55
Perimeter Adj., Add or Deduct	Per 100 L.F.	26.85	10.75	7.65	5.35	4.50	3.60	2.95	2.55	2.20
Story Hgt. Adj., Add or Deduct	Per 1 Ft.	2.70	1.65	1.40	1.15	1.05	0.90	0.75	0.80	0.70

For Basement, add $31.40 per square foot of basement area

The above costs were calculated using the basic specifications shown on the facing page. These costs should be adjusted where necessary for design alternatives and owner's requirements. Reported completed project costs, for this type of structure, range from $64.10 to $233.70 per S.F.

Common additives

Description	Unit	$ Cost	Description	Unit	$ Cost
Emergency Lighting, 25 watt, battery operated			Lockers, Steel, single tier, 60" to 72"	Opening	218 - 365
Lead battery	Each	320	2 tier, 60" to 72" total	Opening	113 - 156
Nickel cadmium	Each	885	5 tier, box lockers	Opening	71.50 - 85
Flagpoles, Complete			Locker bench, lam. maple top only	L.F.	26.50
Aluminum, 20' high	Each	1775	Pedestals, steel pipe	Each	74
40' high	Each	3925	Smoke Detectors		
70' high	Each	10,800	Ceiling type	Each	223
Fiberglass, 23' high	Each	1325	Duct type	Each	555
39'-5" high	Each	3575	Sound System		
59' high	Each	7275	Amplifier, 250 watts	Each	2025
Gym Floor, Incl. sleepers and finish, maple	S.F.	14.30	Speaker, ceiling or wall	Each	208
Intercom System, 25 Station capacity			Trumpet	Each	400
Master station	Each	3175			
Intercom outlets	Each	184			
Handset	Each	505			

Important: See the Reference Section for Location Factors.

Model costs calculated for a 1 story building with 12' story height and 10,000 square feet of floor area

				Unit	Unit Cost	Cost Per S.F.	% Of Sub-Total
A.	**SUBSTRUCTURE**						
1010	Standard Foundations	Poured concrete; strip and spread footings		S.F. Ground	2.11	2.11	
1020	Special Foundations	N/A		—	—	—	
1030	Slab on Grade	4" concrete with vapor barrier and granular base		S.F. Slab	4.78	4.78	8.5%
2010	Basement Excavation	Site preparation for slab and trench for foundation wall and footing		S.F. Ground	.32	.32	
2020	Basement Walls	4' foundation wall		L.F. Wall	82	3.59	
B.	**SHELL**						
	B10 Superstructure						
1010	Floor Construction	Wood beams on columns		S.F. Floor	.15	.15	6.7%
1020	Roof Construction	Wood trusses		S.F. Roof	8.36	8.36	
	B20 Exterior Enclosure						
2010	Exterior Walls	Brick veneer on wood studs	85% of wall	S.F. Wall	24.80	11.13	
2020	Exterior Windows	Window wall	15% of wall	Each	47.80	3.78	15.5%
2030	Exterior Doors	Aluminum and glass; steel		Each	2505	4.76	
	B30 Roofing						
3010	Roof Coverings	Asphalt shingles, 9" fiberglass batt insulation, gutters and downspouts		S.F. Roof	4.47	4.47	3.5%
3020	Roof Openings	N/A		—	—	—	
C.	**INTERIORS**						
1010	Partitions	Gypsum board on wood studs	8 S.F. Floor/S.F. Partition	S.F. Partition	7.85	5.23	
1020	Interior Doors	Single leaf hollow metal	700 S.F. Floor/Door	Each	1152	3.07	
1030	Fittings	Toilet partitions		S.F. Floor	.43	.43	
2010	Stair Construction	N/A		—	—	—	14.2%
3010	Wall Finishes	Paint		S.F. Surface	1.58	2.10	
3020	Floor Finishes	5% quarry tile, 95% vinyl composition tile		S.F. Floor	2.56	2.56	
3030	Ceiling Finishes	Fiberglass tile on tee grid		S.F. Ceiling	4.57	4.57	
D.	**SERVICES**						
	D10 Conveying						
1010	Elevators & Lifts	N/A		—	—	—	0.0 %
1020	Escalators & Moving Walks	N/A		—	—	—	
	D20 Plumbing						
2010	Plumbing Fixtures	Toilet and service fixtures, supply and drainage	1 Fixture/455 S.F. Floor	Each	3106	17.45	
2020	Domestic Water Distribution	Electric water heater		S.F. Floor	2.05	2.05	15.4%
2040	Rain Water Drainage	N/A		—	—	—	
	D30 HVAC						
3010	Energy Supply	Oil fired hot water, wall fin radiation		S.F. Floor	11.38	11.38	
3020	Heat Generating Systems	N/A		—	—	—	
3030	Cooling Generating Systems	N/A		—	—	—	20.6%
3050	Terminal & Package Units	Split systems with air cooled condensing units		S.F. Floor	14.69	14.69	
3090	Other HVAC Sys. & Equipment	N/A		—	—	—	
	D40 Fire Protection						
4010	Sprinklers	Sprinkler, light hazard		S.F. Floor	3.56	3.56	3.5%
4020	Standpipes	Standpipe		S.F. Floor	.83	.83	
	D50 Electrical						
5010	Electrical Service/Distribution	200 ampere service, panel board and feeders		S.F. Floor	1.11	1.11	
5020	Lighting & Branch Wiring	High efficiency fluorescent fixtures, receptacles, switches, A.C. and misc. power		S.F. Floor	8.09	8.09	8.5%
5030	Communications & Security	Addressable alarm systems and emergency lighting		S.F. Floor	1.51	1.51	
5090	Other Electrical Systems	Emergency generator, 15 kW		S.F. Floor	.08	.08	
E.	**EQUIPMENT & FURNISHINGS**						
1010	Commercial Equipment	N/A		—	—	—	
1020	Institutional Equipment	Cabinets and countertop		S.F. Floor	4.67	4.67	3.7 %
1030	Vehicular Equipment	N/A		—	—	—	
1090	Other Equipment	N/A		—	—	—	
F.	**SPECIAL CONSTRUCTION**						
1020	Integrated Construction	N/A		—	—	—	0.0 %
1040	Special Facilities	N/A		—	—	—	
G.	**BUILDING SITEWORK**	**N/A**					

			Sub-Total	126.83	100%
CONTRACTOR FEES (General Requirements: 10%, Overhead: 5%, Profit: 10%)			25%	31.70	
ARCHITECT FEES			9%	14.27	

Total Building Cost	**172.80**

Costs per square foot of floor area

Exterior Wall	S.F. Area	12000	18000	24000	30000	36000	42000	48000	54000	60000
	L.F. Perimeter	460	580	713	730	826	880	965	1006	1045
Concrete Block	Steel Frame	142.35	135.25	132.15	127.60	126.00	124.35	123.40	122.20	121.15
	Bearing Walls	139.40	132.30	129.15	124.65	123.05	121.35	120.40	119.20	118.20
Precast Concrete Panels	Steel Frame	150.05	141.75	138.10	132.50	130.65	128.55	127.45	125.95	124.70
Insulated Metal Panels	Steel Frame	144.75	137.30	134.00	129.15	127.45	125.65	124.65	123.35	122.25
Face Brick on Common Brick	Steel Frame	161.10	151.05	146.65	139.50	137.25	134.60	133.25	131.25	129.70
Tilt-up Concrete Panel	Steel Frame	144.15	136.80	133.55	128.80	127.15	125.35	124.35	123.10	122.00
Perimeter Adj., Add or Deduct	Per 100 L.F.	5.55	3.75	2.75	2.25	1.90	1.55	1.40	1.20	1.20
Story Hgt. Adj., Add or Deduct	Per 1 Ft.	0.80	0.70	0.60	0.50	0.50	0.40	0.40	0.40	0.35

For Basement, add $ 32.00 per square foot of basement area

The above costs were calculated using the basic specifications shown on the facing page. These costs should be adjusted where necessary for design alternatives and owner's requirements. Reported completed project costs, for this type of structure, range from $ 47.60 to $ 184.20 per S.F.

Common additives

Description	Unit	$ Cost
Clock System		
20 room	Each	19,500
50 room	Each	45,700
Dock Bumpers, Rubber blocks		
4-1/2" thick, 10" high, 14" long	Each	91.50
24" long	Each	130
36" long	Each	113
12" high, 14" long	Each	133
24" long	Each	151
36" long	Each	174
6" thick, 10" high, 14" long	Each	139
24" long	Each	165
36" long	Each	248
20" high, 11" long	Each	205
Dock Boards, Heavy		
60" x 60" Aluminum, 5,000# cap.	Each	1600
9000# cap.	Each	1750
15,000# cap.	Each	1900

Description	Unit	$ Cost
Dock Levelers, Hinged 10 ton cap.		
6' x 8'	Each	6975
7' x 8'	Each	8000
Partitions, Woven wire, 10 ga., 1-1/2" mesh		
4' wide x 7' high	Each	202
8' high	Each	227
10' High	Each	273
Platform Lifter, Portable, 6'x 6'		
3000# cap.	Each	10,100
4000# cap.	Each	12,400
Fixed, 6' x 8', 5000# cap.	Each	13,100

Important: See the Reference Section for Location Factors.

Model costs calculated for a 1 story building with 20' story height and 30,000 square feet of floor area

Factory, 1 Story

				Unit	Unit Cost	Cost Per S.F.	% Of Sub-Total
A.	**SUBSTRUCTURE**						
1010	Standard Foundations	Poured concrete; strip and spread footings		S.F. Ground	1.43	1.43	
1020	Special Foundations	N/A		—	—	—	
1030	Slab on Grade	4" reinforced concrete with vapor barrier and granular base		S.F. Slab	6.93	6.93	11.4%
2010	Basement Excavation	Site preparation for slab and trench for foundation wall and footing		S.F. Ground	.18	.18	
2020	Basement Walls	4' foundation wall		L.F. Wall	82	2.38	
B.	**SHELL**						
	B10 Superstructure						
1010	Floor Construction	N/A		—	—	—	10.2 %
1020	Roof Construction	Metal deck, open web steel joists, beams and columns		S.F. Roof	9.69	9.69	
	B20 Exterior Enclosure						
2010	Exterior Walls	Concrete block	75% of wall	S.F. Wall	8.52	3.11	
2020	Exterior Windows	Industrial horizontal pivoted steel	25% of wall	Each	861	3.28	8.0%
2030	Exterior Doors	Double aluminum and glass, hollow metal, steel overhead		Each	2464	1.24	
	B30 Roofing						
3010	Roof Coverings	Built-up tar and gravel with flashing; perlite/EPS composite insulation		S.F. Roof	5.91	5.91	6.6%
3020	Roof Openings	Roof hatches		S.F. Roof	.36	.36	
C.	**INTERIORS**						
1010	Partitions	Concrete block	60 S.F. Floor/L.F. Partition	S.F. Partition	8.75	1.75	
1020	Interior Doors	Single leaf hollow metal and fire doors	600 S.F. Floor/Door	Each	1152	1.92	
1030	Fittings	Toilet partitions		S.F. Floor	.97	.97	
2010	Stair Construction	N/A		—	—	—	8.0%
3010	Wall Finishes	Paint		S.F. Surface	4.83	1.93	
3020	Floor Finishes	Vinyl composition tile	10% of floor	S.F. Floor	3.50	.35	
3030	Ceiling Finishes	Fiberglass board on exposed grid system	10% of area	S.F. Ceiling	6.89	.69	
D.	**SERVICES**						
	D10 Conveying						
1010	Elevators & Lifts	N/A		—	—	—	0.0 %
1020	Escalators & Moving Walks	N/A		—	—	—	
	D20 Plumbing						
2010	Plumbing Fixtures	Toilet and service fixtures, supply and drainage	1 Fixture/1000 S.F. Floor	Each	9230	9.23	
2020	Domestic Water Distribution	Gas fired water heater		S.F. Floor	.61	.61	11.3%
2040	Rain Water Drainage	Roof drains		S.F. Roof	.95	.95	
	D30 HVAC						
3010	Energy Supply	Oil fired hot water, unit heaters		S.F. Floor	9.79	9.79	
3020	Heat Generating Systems	N/A		—	—	—	
3030	Cooling Generating Systems	Chilled water, air cooled condenser system		S.F. Floor	12.40	12.40	23.3%
3050	Terminal & Package Units	N/A		—	—	—	
3090	Other HVAC Sys. & Equipment	N/A		—	—	—	
	D40 Fire Protection						
4010	Sprinklers	Sprinklers, ordinary hazard		S.F. Floor	4.02	4.02	4.8%
4020	Standpipes	Standpipe, wet, Class III		S.F. Floor	.60	.60	
	D50 Electrical						
5010	Electrical Service/Distribution	600 ampere service, panel board and feeders		S.F. Floor	1.07	1.07	
5020	Lighting & Branch Wiring	High intensity discharge fixtures, receptacles, switches, A.C. and misc. power		S.F. Floor	13.15	13.15	16.4%
5030	Communications & Security	Addressable alarm systems and emergency lighting		S.F. Floor	1.46	1.46	
5090	Other Electrical Systems	N/A		—	—	—	
E.	**EQUIPMENT & FURNISHINGS**						
1010	Commercial Equipment	N/A		—	—	—	
1020	Institutional Equipment	N/A		—	—	—	0.0 %
1030	Vehicular Equipment	N/A		—	—	—	
1090	Other Equipment	N/A		—	—	—	
F.	**SPECIAL CONSTRUCTION**						
1020	Integrated Construction	N/A		—	—	—	0.0 %
1040	Special Facilities	N/A		—	—	—	
G.	**BUILDING SITEWORK**	**N/A**					

		Sub-Total	95.40	100%
CONTRACTOR FEES (General Requirements: 10%, Overhead: 5%, Profit: 10%)		25%	23.85	
ARCHITECT FEES		7%	8.35	
	Total Building Cost		**127.60**	

Costs per square foot of floor area

Exterior Wall	S.F. Area	20000	30000	40000	50000	60000	70000	80000	90000	100000
	L.F. Perimeter	362	410	493	576	600	628	660	700	744
Face Brick Common Brick Back-up	Steel Frame	176.45	162.05	157.10	154.15	149.65	146.60	144.40	142.95	141.90
	Concrete Frame	168.80	154.45	149.50	146.55	142.05	138.95	136.75	135.30	134.25
Face Brick Concrete Block Back-up	Steel Frame	175.40	161.25	156.40	153.45	149.05	146.05	143.95	142.45	141.40
	Concrete Frame	167.75	153.60	148.80	145.85	141.45	138.40	136.30	134.85	133.80
Stucco on Concrete Block	Steel Frame	164.45	153.00	148.95	146.45	143.00	140.60	138.95	137.75	136.90
	Concrete Frame	156.80	145.35	141.35	138.90	135.40	133.00	131.30	130.15	129.30
Perimeter Adj., Add or Deduct	Per 100 L.F.	12.75	8.55	6.45	5.10	4.25	3.60	3.15	2.80	2.45
Story Hgt. Adj., Add or Deduct	Per 1 Ft.	3.55	2.65	2.45	2.25	1.95	1.70	1.60	1.50	1.40

For Basement, add $34.90 per square foot of basement area

The above costs were calculated using the basic specifications shown on the facing page. These costs should be adjusted where necessary for design alternatives and owner's requirements. Reported completed project costs, for this type of structure, range from $47.60 to $184.25 per S.F.

Common additives

Description	Unit	$ Cost
Clock System		
20 room	Each	19,500
50 room	Each	45,700
Dock Bumpers, Rubber blocks		
4-1/2" thick, 10" high, 14" long	Each	91.50
24" long	Each	130
36" long	Each	113
12" high, 14" long	Each	133
24" long	Each	151
36" long	Each	174
6" thick, 10" high, 14" long	Each	139
24" long	Each	165
36" long	Each	248
20" high, 11" long	Each	205
Dock Boards, Heavy		
60" x 60" Aluminum, 5,000# cap.	Each	1600
9000# cap.	Each	1750
15,000# cap.	Each	1900

Description	Unit	$ Cost
Dock Levelers, Hinged 10 ton cap.		
6' x 8'	Each	6975
7' x 8'	Each	8000
Elevator, Hydraulic freight, 2 stops		
3500# capacity	Each	141,700
4000# capacity	Each	148,700
Additional stop, add	Each	10,300
Partitions, Woven wire, 10 ga., 1-1/2" mesh		
4' Wide x 7" high	Each	202
8' High	Each	227
10' High	Each	273
Platform Lifter, Portable, 6'x 6'		
3000# cap.	Each	10,100
4000# cap.	Each	12,400
Fixed, 6'x 8', 5000# cap.	Each	13,100

Important: See the Reference Section for Location Factors.

Model costs calculated for a 3 story building with 12' story height and 90,000 square feet of floor area

Factory, 3 Story

				Unit	Unit Cost	Cost Per S.F.	% Of Sub-Total
A.	**SUBSTRUCTURE**						
1010	Standard Foundations	Poured concrete; strip and spread footings		S.F. Ground	6.60	2.20	
1020	Special Foundations	N/A		—	—	—	
1030	Slab on Grade	4" reinforced concrete with vapor barrier and granular base		S.F. Slab	10.78	3.59	6.4%
2010	Basement Excavation	Site preparation for slab and trench for foundation wall and footing		S.F. Ground	.18	.06	
2020	Basement Walls	4' foundation wall		L.F. Wall	82	.64	
B.	**SHELL**						
	B10 Superstructure						
1010	Floor Construction	Concrete flat slab		S.F. Floor	23.93	15.95	20.7%
1020	Roof Construction	Concrete flat slab		S.F. Roof	15.66	5.22	
	B20 Exterior Enclosure						
2010	Exterior Walls	Face brick with common brick backup	70% of wall	S.F. Wall	34.64	6.79	
2020	Exterior Windows	Industrial, horizontal pivoted steel	30% of wall	Each	1333	6.99	13.9%
2030	Exterior Doors	Double aluminum & glass, hollow metal, overhead doors		Each	2337	.44	
	B30 Roofing						
3010	Roof Coverings	Built-up tar and gravel with flashing; perlite/EPS composite insulation		S.F. Roof	5.73	1.91	2.0%
3020	Roof Openings	Roof hatches		S.F. Roof	.36	.12	
C.	**INTERIORS**						
1010	Partitions	Gypsum board on metal studs	50 S.F. Floor/L.F. Partition	S.F. Partition	4.20	.84	
1020	Interior Doors	Single leaf fire doors	500 S.F. Floor/Door	Each	1265	2.53	
1030	Fittings	Toilet partitions		S.F. Floor	.48	.48	
2010	Stair Construction	Concrete		Flight	8025	.71	8.9%
3010	Wall Finishes	Paint		S.F. Surface	.83	.33	
3020	Floor Finishes	90% metallic hardener, 10% vinyl composition tile		S.F. Floor	3.73	3.73	
3030	Ceiling Finishes	Fiberglass board on exposed grid systems	10% of area	S.F. Ceiling	4.57	.45	
D.	**SERVICES**						
	D10 Conveying						
1010	Elevators & Lifts	Two hydraulic freight elevators		Each	208,800	4.64	4.5%
1020	Escalators & Moving Walks	N/A		—	—	—	
	D20 Plumbing						
2010	Plumbing Fixtures	Toilet and service fixtures, supply and drainage	1 Fixture/1345 S.F. Floor	Each	14,418	10.72	
2020	Domestic Water Distribution	Gas fired water heater		S.F. Floor	.37	.37	11.3%
2040	Rain Water Drainage	Roof drains		S.F. Roof	1.23	.41	
	D30 HVAC						
3010	Energy Supply	Oil fired hot water, unit heaters		S.F. Floor	4.68	4.68	
3020	Heat Generating Systems	N/A		—	—	—	
3030	Cooling Generating Systems	Chilled water, air cooled condenser system		S.F. Floor	12.40	12.40	16.7%
3050	Terminal & Package Units	N/A		—	—	—	
3090	Other HVAC Sys. & Equipment	N/A		—	—	—	
	D40 Fire Protection						
4010	Sprinklers	Wet pipe sprinkler system		S.F. Floor	3.53	3.53	4.0%
4020	Standpipes	Standpipe, wet, Class III		S.F. Floor	.58	.58	
	D50 Electrical						
5010	Electrical Service/Distribution	800 ampere service, panel board and feeders		S.F. Floor	.65	.65	
5020	Lighting & Branch Wiring	High intensity discharge fixtures, switches, A.C. and misc. power		S.F. Floor	9.78	9.78	11.6%
5030	Communications & Security	Addressable alarm systems and emergency lighting		S.F. Floor	1.19	1.19	
5090	Other Electrical Systems	Emergency generator, 30 kW		S.F. Floor	.18	.18	
E.	**EQUIPMENT & FURNISHINGS**						
1010	Commercial Equipment	N/A		—	—	—	
1020	Institutional Equipment	N/A		—	—	—	
1030	Vehicular Equipment	N/A		—	—	—	0.0 %
1090	Other Equipment	N/A		—	—	—	
F.	**SPECIAL CONSTRUCTION**						
1020	Integrated Construction	N/A		—	—	—	0.0 %
1040	Special Facilities	N/A		—	—	—	
G.	**BUILDING SITEWORK**	**N/A**					

					Sub-Total	102.11	100%
	CONTRACTOR FEES (General Requirements: 10%, Overhead: 5%, Profit: 10%)				25%	25.53	
	ARCHITECT FEES				6%	7.66	

Total Building Cost 135.30

125

Costs per square foot of floor area

Exterior Wall	S.F. Area	4000	4500	5000	5500	6000	6500	7000	7500	8000
	L.F. Perimeter	260	280	300	310	320	336	353	370	386
Face Brick Concrete Block Back-up	Steel Joists	189.70	185.95	183.00	179.00	175.75	173.70	172.10	170.75	169.40
	Bearing Walls	182.35	178.55	175.70	171.65	168.35	166.35	164.75	163.40	162.05
Decorative Concrete Block	Steel Joists	174.50	171.45	169.10	165.90	163.35	161.75	160.40	159.25	158.20
	Bearing Walls	167.15	164.10	161.70	158.55	156.05	154.40	153.05	151.95	150.85
Limestone with Concrete Block Back-up	Steel Joists	216.25	211.40	207.60	202.10	197.60	194.95	192.80	190.95	189.20
	Bearing Walls	208.90	204.10	200.25	194.75	190.25	187.55	185.45	183.60	181.80
Perimeter Adj., Add or Deduct	Per 100 L.F.	21.10	18.80	16.95	15.40	14.15	13.05	12.15	11.25	10.50
Story Hgt. Adj., Add or Deduct	Per 1 Ft.	2.75	2.65	2.55	2.40	2.25	2.20	2.15	2.10	2.05

For Basement, add $39.15 per square foot of basement area

The above costs were calculated using the basic specifications shown on the facing page. These costs should be adjusted where necessary for design alternatives and owner's requirements. Reported completed project costs, for this type of structure, range from $77.05 to $227.90 per S.F.

Common additives

Description	Unit	$ Cost
Appliances		
Cooking range, 30" free standing		
1 oven	Each	570 - 2425
2 oven	Each	1425 - 2875
30" built-in		
1 oven	Each	845 - 2050
2 oven	Each	1700 - 2525
Counter top cook tops, 4 burner	Each	425 - 1650
Microwave oven	Each	291 - 825
Combination range, refrig. & sink, 30" wide	Each	1875 - 2925
60" wide	Each	2625
72" wide	Each	2850
Combination range refrigerator, sink		
microwave oven & icemaker	Each	6625
Compactor, residential, 4-1 compaction	Each	820 - 1300
Dishwasher, built-in, 2 cycles	Each	595 - 1125
4 cycles	Each	745 - 1875
Garbage disposer, sink type	Each	228 - 370
Hood for range, 2 speed, vented, 30" wide	Each	320 - 1250
42" wide	Each	425 - 2600

Description	Unit	$ Cost
Appliances, cont.		
Refrigerator, no frost 10-12 C.F.	Each	550 - 635
14-16 C.F.	Each	650 - 855
18-20 C.F.	Each	800 - 1775
Lockers, Steel, single tier, 60" or 72"	Opening	218 - 365
2 tier, 60" or 72" total	Opening	113 - 156
5 tier, box lockers	Opening	71.50 - 85
Locker bench, lam. maple top only	L.F.	26.50
Pedestals, steel pipe	Each	74
Sound System		
Amplifier, 250 watts	Each	2025
Speaker, ceiling or wall	Each	208
Trumpet	Each	400

Important: See the Reference Section for Location Factors.

Model costs calculated for a 1 story building with 14' story height and 6,000 square feet of floor area

Fire Station, 1 Story

				Unit	Unit Cost	Cost Per S.F.	% Of Sub-Total
A. SUBSTRUCTURE							
1010	Standard Foundations	Poured concrete; strip and spread footings		S.F. Ground	3.34	3.34	
1020	Special Foundations	N/A		—	—	—	
1030	Slab on Grade	6" reinforced concrete with vapor barrier and granular base		S.F. Slab	6.93	6.93	11.7%
2010	Basement Excavation	Site preparation for slab and trench for foundation wall and footing		S.F. Ground	.57	.57	
2020	Basement Walls	4' foundation wall		L.F. Wall	82	4.34	
B. SHELL							
B10 Superstructure							
1010	Floor Construction	N/A		—	—	—	7.9 %
1020	Roof Construction	Metal deck, open web steel joists, beams on columns		S.F. Roof	10.30	10.30	
B20 Exterior Enclosure							
2010	Exterior Walls	Face brick with concrete block backup	75% of wall	S.F. Wall	32.89	18.42	
2020	Exterior Windows	Aluminum insulated glass	10% of wall	Each	861	2.01	19.1%
2030	Exterior Doors	Single aluminum and glass, overhead, hollow metal	15% of wall	S.F. Door	40	4.48	
B30 Roofing							
3010	Roof Coverings	Built-up tar and gravel with flashing; perlite/EPS composite insulation		S.F. Roof	7.15	7.15	5.6%
3020	Roof Openings	Skylights, roof hatches		S.F. Roof	.16	.16	
C. INTERIORS							
1010	Partitions	Concrete block	17 S.F. Floor/L.F. Partition	S.F. Partition	9.37	5.51	
1020	Interior Doors	Single leaf hollow metal	500 S.F. Floor/Door	Each	1152	2.30	
1030	Fittings	Toilet partitions		S.F. Floor	.48	.48	
2010	Stair Construction	N/A		—	—	—	13.0%
3010	Wall Finishes	Paint		S.F. Surface	2.13	2.51	
3020	Floor Finishes	50% vinyl tile, 50% paint		S.F. Floor	2.67	2.67	
3030	Ceiling Finishes	Fiberglass board on exposed grid, suspended	50% of area	S.F. Ceiling	6.89	3.45	
D. SERVICES							
D10 Conveying							
1010	Elevators & Lifts	N/A		—	—	—	0.0 %
1020	Escalators & Moving Walks	N/A		—	—	—	
D20 Plumbing							
2010	Plumbing Fixtures	Kitchen, toilet and service fixtures, supply and drainage	1 Fixture/375 S.F. Floor	Each	4103	10.94	
2020	Domestic Water Distribution	Gast fired water heater		S.F. Floor	3.09	3.09	11.8%
2040	Rain Water Drainage	Roof drains		S.F. Roof	1.30	1.30	
D30 HVAC							
3010	Energy Supply	N/A		—	—	—	
3020	Heat Generating Systems	Included in D3050		—	—	—	
3030	Cooling Generating Systems	N/A		—	—	—	18.3 %
3050	Terminal & Package Units	Rooftop multizone unit system		S.F. Floor	23.88	23.88	
3090	Other HVAC Sys. & Equipment	N/A		—	—	—	
D40 Fire Protection							
4010	Sprinklers	Wet pipe sprinkler system		S.F. Floor	4.76	4.76	4.7%
4020	Standpipes	Standpipe, wet, Class III		S.F. Floor	1.38	1.38	
D50 Electrical							
5010	Electrical Service/Distribution	200 ampere service, panel board and feeders		S.F. Floor	1.60	1.60	
5020	Lighting & Branch Wiring	High efficiency fluorescent fixtures, receptacles, switches, A.C. and misc. power		S.F. Floor	6.66	6.66	7.8%
5030	Communications & Security	Addressable alarm systems		S.F. Floor	1.95	1.95	
5090	Other Electrical Systems	N/A		—	—	—	
E. EQUIPMENT & FURNISHINGS							
1010	Commercial Equipment	N/A		—	—	—	
1020	Institutional Equipment	N/A		—	—	—	0.0 %
1030	Vehicular Equipment	N/A		—	—	—	
1090	Other Equipment	N/A		—	—	—	
F. SPECIAL CONSTRUCTION							
1020	Integrated Construction	N/A		—	—	—	0.0 %
1040	Special Facilities	N/A		—	—	—	
G. BUILDING SITEWORK	**N/A**						

		Sub-Total	130.18	100%
CONTRACTOR FEES (General Requirements: 10%, Overhead: 5%, Profit: 10%)		25%	32.55	
ARCHITECT FEES		8%	13.02	

Total Building Cost 175.75

Costs per square foot of floor area

Exterior Wall	S.F. Area	6000	7000	8000	9000	10000	11000	12000	13000	14000
	L.F. Perimeter	220	240	260	280	286	303	320	336	353
Face Brick with Concrete Block Back-up	Steel Joists	196.25	189.85	185.05	181.35	176.30	173.65	171.45	169.45	167.90
	Precast Conc.	204.70	198.35	193.60	189.95	184.95	182.25	180.15	178.15	176.60
Decorative Concrete Block	Steel Joists	182.85	177.30	173.20	170.00	165.85	163.55	161.70	160.00	158.65
	Precast Conc.	191.30	185.85	181.75	178.60	174.45	172.20	170.40	168.75	167.40
Limestone with Concrete Block Back-up	Steel Joists	225.95	217.60	211.40	206.60	199.50	195.95	193.10	190.45	188.35
	Precast Conc.	234.25	226.00	219.80	215.00	207.95	204.40	201.60	198.95	196.85
Perimeter Adj., Add or Deduct	Per 100 L.F.	24.45	20.90	18.35	16.25	14.60	13.30	12.20	11.30	10.45
Story Hgt. Adj., Add or Deduct	Per 1 Ft.	3.20	2.95	2.80	2.70	2.50	2.40	2.30	2.25	2.15

For Basement, add $38.00 per square foot of basement area

The above costs were calculated using the basic specifications shown on the facing page. These costs should be adjusted where necessary for design alternatives and owner's requirements. Reported completed project costs, for this type of structure, range from $76.85 to $227.90 per S.F.

Common additives

Description	Unit	$ Cost
Appliances		
Cooking range, 30" free standing		
1 oven	Each	570 - 2425
2 oven	Each	1425 - 2875
30" built-in		
1 oven	Each	845 - 2050
2 oven	Each	1700 - 2525
Counter top cook tops, 4 burner	Each	425 - 1650
Microwave oven	Each	291 - 825
Combination range, refrig. & sink, 30" wide	Each	1875 - 2925
60" wide	Each	2625
72" wide	Each	2850
Combination range, refrigerator, sink, microwave oven & icemaker	Each	6625
Compactor, residential, 4-1 compaction	Each	820 - 1300
Dishwasher, built-in, 2 cycles	Each	595 - 1125
4 cycles	Each	745 - 1875
Garbage diposer, sink type	Each	228 - 370
Hood for range, 2 speed, vented, 30" wide	Each	320 - 1250
42" wide	Each	425 - 2600

Description	Unit	$ Cost
Appliances, cont.		
Refrigerator, no frost 10-12 C.F.	Each	550 - 635
14-16 C.F.	Each	650 - 855
18-20 C.F.	Each	800 - 1775
Elevators, Hydraulic passenger, 2 stops		
1500# capacity	Each	66,100
2500# capacity	Each	69,200
3500# capacity	Each	73,200
Lockers, Steel, single tier, 60" or 72"	Opening	218 - 365
2 tier, 60" or 72" total	Opening	113 - 156
5 tier, box lockers	Opening	71.50 - 85
Locker bench, lam. maple top only	L.F.	26.50
Pedestals, steel pipe	Each	74
Sound System		
Amplifier, 250 watts	Each	2025
Speaker, ceiling or wall	Each	208
Trumpet	Each	400

Important: See the Reference Section for Location Factors.

Model costs calculated for a 2 story building with 14' story height and 10,000 square feet of floor area

Fire Station, 2 Story

					Unit	Unit Cost	Cost Per S.F.	% Of Sub-Total
A. SUBSTRUCTURE								
1010	Standard Foundations	Poured concrete; strip and spread footings			S.F. Ground	3.14	1.57	
1020	Special Foundations	N/A			—	—	—	
1030	Slab on Grade	6" reinforced concrete with vapor barrier and granular base			S.F. Slab	6.93	3.47	6.4%
2010	Basement Excavation	Site preparation for slab and trench for foundation wall and footing			S.F. Ground	.57	.29	
2020	Basement Walls	4' foundation wall			L.F. Wall	91	2.58	
B. SHELL								
B10 Superstructure								
1010	Floor Construction	Open web steel joists, slab form, concrete			S.F. Floor	14.58	7.29	8.0%
1020	Roof Construction	Metal deck on open web steel joists			S.F. Roof	5.04	2.52	
B20 Exterior Enclosure								
2010	Exterior Walls	Decorative concrete block	75% of wall		S.F. Wall	20	12.01	
2020	Exterior Windows	Aluminum insulated glass	10% of wall		Each	736	2.56	14.9%
2030	Exterior Doors	Single aluminum and glass, steel overhead, hollow metal	15% of wall		S.F. Door	30.72	3.69	
B30 Roofing								
3010	Roof Coverings	Built-up tar and gravel with flashing; perlite/EPS composite insulation			S.F. Roof	7.34	3.67	3.0%
3020	Roof Openings	N/A			—	—	—	
C. INTERIORS								
1010	Partitions	Concrete block	10 S.F. Floor/L.F. Partition		S.F. Partition	9.37	5.51	
1020	Interior Doors	Single leaf hollow metal	500 S.F. Floor/Door		Each	1265	2.53	
1030	Fittings	Toilet partitions			S.F. Floor	.43	.43	
2010	Stair Construction	Concrete filled metal pan			Flight	20,150	4.03	17.7%
3010	Wall Finishes	Paint			S.F. Surface	3.61	4.25	
3020	Floor Finishes	50% vinyl tile, 50% paint			S.F. Floor	2.67	2.67	
3030	Ceiling Finishes	Fiberglass board on exposed grid, suspended	50% of area		S.F. Ceiling	4.57	2.29	
D. SERVICES								
D10 Conveying								
1010	Elevators & Lifts	One hydraulic passenger elevator			Each	83,400	8.34	6.8%
1020	Escalators & Moving Walks	N/A			—	—	—	
D20 Plumbing								
2010	Plumbing Fixtures	Kitchen toilet and service fixtures, supply and drainage	1 Fixture/400 S.F. Floor		Each	4172	10.43	
2020	Domestic Water Distribution	Gas fired water heater			S.F. Floor	2.50	2.50	11.2%
2040	Rain Water Drainage	Roof drains			S.F. Roof	1.66	.83	
D30 HVAC								
3010	Energy Supply	N/A			—	—	—	
3020	Heat Generating Systems	Included in D3050			—	—	—	
3030	Cooling Generating Systems	N/A			—	—	—	19.4 %
3050	Terminal & Package Units	Rooftop multizone unit system			S.F. Floor	23.88	23.88	
3090	Other HVAC Sys. & Equipment	N/A			—	—	—	
D40 Fire Protection								
4010	Sprinklers	Wet pipe sprinkler system			S.F. Floor	3.79	3.79	4.2%
4020	Standpipes	Standpipe, wet, Class III			S.F. Floor	1.42	1.42	
D50 Electrical								
5010	Electrical Service/Distribution	400 ampere service, panel board and feeders			S.F. Floor	1.67	1.67	
5020	Lighting & Branch Wiring	High efficiency fluorescent fixtures, receptacles, switches, A.C. and misc. power			S.F. Floor	6.88	6.88	8.4%
5030	Communications & Security	Addressable alarm systems and emergency lighting			S.F. Floor	1.51	1.51	
5090	Other Electrical Systems	Emergency generator, 15 kW			S.F. Floor	.23	.23	
E. EQUIPMENT & FURNISHINGS								
1010	Commercial Equipment	N/A			—	—	—	
1020	Institutional Equipment	N/A			—	—	—	
1030	Vehicular Equipment	N/A			—	—	—	0.0 %
1090	Other Equipment	N/A			—	—	—	
F. SPECIAL CONSTRUCTION								
1020	Integrated Construction	N/A			—	—	—	
1040	Special Facilities	N/A			—	—	—	0.0 %
G. BUILDING SITEWORK	**N/A**							

		Sub-Total	122.84	100%
CONTRACTOR FEES (General Requirements: 10%, Overhead: 5%, Profit: 10%)		25%	30.73	
ARCHITECT FEES		8%	12.28	

Total Building Cost	**165.85**

Costs per square foot of floor area

Exterior Wall	S.F. Area	4000	5000	6000	8000	10000	12000	14000	16000	18000
	L.F. Perimeter	180	205	230	260	300	340	353	386	420
Cedar Beveled Siding	Wood Frame	192.35	183.75	178.05	169.25	164.60	161.55	158.00	156.25	154.95
Aluminum Siding	Wood Frame	191.15	182.60	176.85	168.05	163.45	160.35	156.85	155.05	153.75
Board and Batten	Wood Frame	188.20	181.00	176.20	168.55	164.60	162.00	158.80	157.25	156.10
Face Brick on Block	Bearing Wall	223.85	213.60	206.75	195.50	189.80	186.00	181.20	178.95	177.30
Stucco on Block	Bearing Wall	206.35	197.60	191.75	182.75	178.05	174.95	171.30	169.45	168.10
Decorative Block	Wood Joists	197.10	188.05	182.05	172.70	167.75	164.50	160.70	158.75	157.40
Perimeter Adj., Add or Deduct	Per 100 L.F.	16.65	13.35	11.10	8.35	6.65	5.55	4.80	4.20	3.65
Story Hgt. Adj., Add or Deduct	Per 1 Ft.	2.10	1.90	1.75	1.50	1.40	1.30	1.20	1.10	1.10

For Basement, add $24.15 per square foot of basement area

The above costs were calculated using the basic specifications shown on the facing page. These costs should be adjusted where necessary for design alternatives and owner's requirements. Reported completed project costs, for this type of structure, range from $111.70 to $244.35 per S.F.

Common additives

Description	Unit	$ Cost
Appliances		
Cooking range, 30" free standing		
1 oven	Each	570 - 2425
2 oven	Each	1425 - 2875
30" built-in		
1 oven	Each	845 - 2050
2 oven	Each	1700 - 2525
Counter top cook tops, 4 burner	Each	425 - 1650
Microwave oven	Each	291 - 825
Combination range, refrig. & sink, 30" wide	Each	1875 - 2925
60" wide	Each	2625
72" wide	Each	2850
Combination range, refrigerator, sink,		
microwave oven & icemaker	Each	6625
Compactor, residential, 4-1 compaction	Each	820 - 1300
Dishwasher, built-in, 2 cycles	Each	595 - 1125
4 cycles	Each	745 - 1875
Garbage disposer, sink type	Each	228 - 370
Hood for range, 2 speed, vented, 30" wide	Each	320 - 1250
42" wide	Each	425 - 2600

Description	Unit	$ Cost
Appliances, cont.		
Refrigerator, no frost 10-12 C.F.	Each	550 - 635
14-16 C.F.	Each	650 - 855
18-20 C.F.	Each	800 - 1775
Elevators, Hydraulic passenger, 2 stops		
1500# capacity	Each	66,100
2500# capacity	Each	69,200
3500# capacity	Each	73,200
Laundry Equipment		
Dryer, gas, 16 lb. capacity	Each	965
30 lb. capacity	Each	3800
Washer, 4 cycle	Each	1175
Commercial	Each	1600
Sound System		
Amplifier, 250 watts	Each	2025
Speaker, ceiling or wall	Each	208
Trumpet	Each	400

Important: See the Reference Section for Location Factors.

Model costs calculated for a 2 story building with 10' story height and 10,000 square feet of floor area

Fraternity/Sorority House

				Unit	Unit Cost	Cost Per S.F.	% Of Sub-Total
A. SUBSTRUCTURE							
1010	Standard Foundations	Poured concrete; strip and spread footings		S.F. Ground	3.06	1.53	
1020	Special Foundations	N/A		—	—	—	
1030	Slab on Grade	4" reinforced concrete with vapor barrier and granular base		S.F. Slab	5.31	2.66	5.5%
2010	Basement Excavation	Site preparation for slab and trench for foundation wall and footing		S.F. Ground	.57	.29	
2020	Basement Walls	4' foundation wall		L.F. Wall	73	2.18	
B. SHELL							
B10 Superstructure							
1010	Floor Construction	Plywood on wood joists		S.F. Floor	3.94	1.97	
1020	Roof Construction	Plywood on wood rafters (pitched)		S.F. Roof	3.48	1.95	3.2%
B20 Exterior Enclosure							
2010	Exterior Walls	Cedar bevel siding on wood studs, insulated	80% of wall	S.F. Wall	13.06	6.27	
2020	Exterior Windows	Double hung wood	20% of wall	Each	637	3.05	9.1%
2030	Exterior Doors	Solid core wood		Each	2354	1.66	
B30 Roofing							
3010	Roof Coverings	Asphalt shingles with flashing (pitched); rigid fiberglass insulation		S.F. Roof	5.12	2.56	2.1%
3020	Roof Openings	N/A		—	—	—	
C. INTERIORS							
1010	Partitions	Gypsum board on wood studs	25 S.F. Floor/L.F. Partition	S.F. Partition	8.25	2.64	
1020	Interior Doors	Single leaf wood	200 S.F. Floor/Door	Each	636	3.19	
1030	Fittings	N/A		—	—	—	
2010	Stair Construction	Wood		Flight	2294	.92	16.3%
3010	Wall Finishes	Paint		S.F. Surface	.83	.53	
3020	Floor Finishes	10% hardwood, 70% carpet, 20% ceramic tile		S.F. Floor	8.03	8.03	
3030	Ceiling Finishes	Gypsum board on wood furring		S.F. Ceiling	4.39	4.39	
D. SERVICES							
D10 Conveying							
1010	Elevators & Lifts	One hydraulic passenger elevator		Each	83,400	8.34	6.9%
1020	Escalators & Moving Walks	N/A		—	—	—	
D20 Plumbing							
2010	Plumbing Fixtures	Kitchen toilet and service fixtures, supply and drainage	1 Fixture/150 S.F. Floor	Each	2303	15.35	
2020	Domestic Water Distribution	Gas fired water heater		S.F. Floor	3.42	3.42	15.5%
2040	Rain Water Drainage	N/A		—	—	—	
D30 HVAC							
3010	Energy Supply	Oil fired hot water, baseboard radiation		S.F. Floor	8.13	8.13	
3020	Heat Generating Systems	N/A		—	—	—	
3030	Cooling Generating Systems	N/A		—	—	—	13.8%
3050	Terminal & Package Units	Split system with air cooled condensing unit		S.F. Floor	8.49	8.49	
3090	Other HVAC Sys. & Equipment	N/A		—	—	—	
D40 Fire Protection							
4010	Sprinklers	Wet pipe sprinkler system		S.F. Floor	3.79	3.79	4.0%
4020	Standpipes	Standpipe		S.F. Floor	1.01	1.01	
D50 Electrical							
5010	Electrical Service/Distribution	600 ampere service, panel board and feeders		S.F. Floor	4.04	4.04	
5020	Lighting & Branch Wiring	High efficiency fluorescent fixtures, receptacles, switches, A.C. and misc. power		S.F. Floor	9.96	9.96	23.6%
5030	Communications & Security	Addressable alarm, communication system, internet and phone wiring, and generator set		S.F. Floor	14.26	14.26	
5090	Other Electrical Systems	Emergency generator, 7.5 kW		S.F. Floor	.19	.19	
E. EQUIPMENT & FURNISHINGS							
1010	Commercial Equipment	N/A		—	—	—	
1020	Institutional Equipment	N/A		—	—	—	
1030	Vehicular Equipment	N/A		—	—	—	0.0 %
1090	Other Equipment	N/A		—	—	—	
F. SPECIAL CONSTRUCTION							
1020	Integrated Construction	N/A		—	—	—	
1040	Special Facilities	N/A		—	—	—	0.0 %
G. BUILDING SITEWORK	**N/A**						

		Sub-Total	120.80	100%
CONTRACTOR FEES (General Requirements: 10%, Overhead: 5%, Profit: 10%)		25%	30.21	
ARCHITECT FEES		9%	13.59	
	Total Building Cost		**164.60**	

131

Costs per square foot of floor area

Exterior Wall	S.F. Area	4000	6000	8000	10000	12000	14000	16000	18000	20000
	L.F. Perimeter	260	320	384	424	460	484	510	540	576
Vertical Redwood Siding	Wood Frame	160.00	147.05	140.90	135.95	132.50	129.60	127.45	126.00	124.95
Brick Veneer	Wood Frame	194.55	172.45	161.75	153.65	148.10	143.50	140.10	137.70	135.95
Aluminum Siding	Wood Frame	179.85	160.40	150.95	144.05	139.45	135.70	132.90	130.95	129.45
Brick on Block	Wood Truss	203.65	180.25	168.95	160.30	154.25	149.20	145.60	142.95	141.05
Limestone on Block	Wood Truss	235.55	206.35	192.40	180.95	172.90	166.00	161.00	157.45	155.00
Stucco on Block	Wood Truss	186.85	166.45	156.55	149.35	144.30	140.30	137.35	135.20	133.60
Perimeter Adj., Add or Deduct	Per 100 L.F.	12.45	8.35	6.20	4.95	4.15	3.55	3.15	2.75	2.50
Story Hgt. Adj., Add or Deduct	Per 1 Ft.	1.50	1.30	1.10	0.95	0.90	0.85	0.80	0.70	0.65

For Basement, add $32.25 per square foot of basement area

The above costs were calculated using the basic specifications shown on the facing page. These costs should be adjusted where necessary for design alternatives and owner's requirements. Reported completed project costs, for this type of structure, range from $109.40 to $336.30 per S.F.

Common additives

Description	Unit	$ Cost	Description	Unit	$ Cost
Autopsy Table, Standard	Each	11,300	Planters, Precast concrete		
Deluxe	Each	17,600	48" diam., 24" high	Each	740
Directory Boards, Plastic, glass covered			7" diam., 36" high	Each	1800
30" x 20"	Each	630	Fiberglass, 36" diam., 24" high	Each	840
36" x 48"	Each	1500	60" diam., 24" high	Each	1300
Aluminum, 24" x 18"	Each	630	Smoke Detectors		
36" x 24"	Each	735	Ceiling type	Each	223
48" x 32"	Each	1050	Duct type	Each	555
48" x 60"	Each	2200			
Emergency Lighting, 25 watt, battery operated					
Lead battery	Each	320			
Nickel cadmium	Each	885			
Mortuary Refrigerator, End operated					
Two capacity	Each	13,400			
Six capacity	Each	24,100			

Important: See the Reference Section for Location Factors.

Model costs calculated for a 1 story building with 12' story height and 10,000 square feet of floor area

Funeral Home

					Unit	Unit Cost	Cost Per S.F.	% Of Sub-Total
A.	**SUBSTRUCTURE**							
1010	Standard Foundations	Poured concrete; strip and spread footings			S.F. Ground	1.82	1.82	
1020	Special Foundations	N/A			—	—	—	
1030	Slab on Grade	4" reinforced concrete with vapor barrier and granular base			S.F. Slab	5.31	5.31	10.9%
2010	Basement Excavation	Site preparation for slab and trench for foundation wall and footing			S.F. Ground	.32	.32	
2020	Basement Walls	4' foundation wall			L.F. Wall	73	3.38	
B.	**SHELL**							
	B10 Superstructure							
1010	Floor Construction	N/A			—	—	—	
1020	Roof Construction	Plywood on wood truss			S.F. Roof	4.93	4.93	4.9 %
	B20 Exterior Enclosure							
2010	Exterior Walls	1" x 4" vertical T & G redwood siding on wood studs	90% of wall		S.F. Wall	12.25	5.61	
2020	Exterior Windows	Double hung wood	10% of wall		Each	510	2.16	9.0%
2030	Exterior Doors	Wood swinging double doors, single leaf hollow metal			Each	1978	1.19	
	B30 Roofing							
3010	Roof Coverings	Single ply membrane, fully adhered; polyisocyanurate sheets			S.F. Roof	6.68	6.68	6.7%
3020	Roof Openings	N/A			—	—	—	
C.	**INTERIORS**							
1010	Partitions	Gypsum board on wood studs with sound deadening board	15 S.F. Floor/L.F. Partition		S.F. Partition	9.45	5.04	
1020	Interior Doors	Single leaf wood	150 S.F. Floor/Door		Each	636	4.24	
1030	Fittings	N/A			—	—	—	
2010	Stair Construction	N/A			—	—	—	26.3%
3010	Wall Finishes	50% wallpaper, 25% wood paneling, 25% paint			S.F. Surface	3.34	3.56	
3020	Floor Finishes	70% carpet, 30% ceramic tile			S.F. Floor	8.81	8.81	
3030	Ceiling Finishes	Fiberglass board on exposed grid, suspended			S.F. Ceiling	4.57	4.57	
D.	**SERVICES**							
	D10 Conveying							
1010	Elevators & Lifts	N/A			—	—	—	0.0 %
1020	Escalators & Moving Walks	N/A			—	—	—	
	D20 Plumbing							
2010	Plumbing Fixtures	Toilet and service fixtures, supply and drainage	1 Fixture/770 S.F. Floor		Each	3196	4.15	
2020	Domestic Water Distribution	Electric water heater			S.F. Floor	3.33	3.33	8.5%
2040	Rain Water Drainage	Roof drain			S.F. Roof	1	1	
	D30 HVAC							
3010	Energy Supply	N/A			—	—	—	
3020	Heat Generating Systems	Included in D3030			—	—	—	
3030	Cooling Generating Systems	Multizone rooftop unit, gas heating, electric cooling			S.F. Floor	18.95	18.95	19.0 %
3050	Terminal & Package Units	N/A			—	—	—	
3090	Other HVAC Sys. & Equipment	N/A			—	—	—	
	D40 Fire Protection							
4010	Sprinklers	Wet pipe sprinkler system			S.F. Floor	3.56	3.56	4.4%
4020	Standpipes	Standpipe, wet, Class III			S.F. Floor	.83	.83	
	D50 Electrical							
5010	Electrical Service/Distribution	400 ampere service, panel board and feeders			S.F. Floor	1.92	1.92	
5020	Lighting & Branch Wiring	High efficiency fluorescent fixtures, receptacles, switches, A.C. and misc. power			S.F. Floor	6.82	6.82	10.4%
5030	Communications & Security	Addressable alarm systems and emergency lighting			S.F. Floor	1.51	1.51	
5090	Other Electrical Systems	Emergency generator, 15 kW			S.F. Floor	.08	.08	
E.	**EQUIPMENT & FURNISHINGS**							
1010	Commercial Equipment	N/A			—	—	—	
1020	Institutional Equipment	N/A			—	—	—	0.0 %
1030	Vehicular Equipment	N/A			—	—	—	
1090	Other Equipment	N/A			—	—	—	
F.	**SPECIAL CONSTRUCTION**							
1020	Integrated Construction	N/A			—	—	—	0.0 %
1040	Special Facilities	N/A			—	—	—	
G.	**BUILDING SITEWORK**	**N/A**						

		Sub-Total	99.77	100%
CONTRACTOR FEES (General Requirements: 10%, Overhead: 5%, Profit: 10%)		25%	24.96	
ARCHITECT FEES		9%	11.22	
	Total Building Cost		**135.95**	

Costs per square foot of floor area

Exterior Wall	S.F. Area	12000	14000	16000	19000	21000	23000	26000	28000	30000
	L.F. Perimeter	440	474	510	556	583	607	648	670	695
E.I.F.S. on Concrete Block	Steel Frame	129.80	126.90	124.80	122.05	120.60	119.20	117.75	116.80	116.00
Tilt-up Concrete Wall	Steel Frame	126.40	123.80	121.80	119.40	118.10	116.80	115.45	114.55	113.85
Face Brick with Concrete Block Back-up	Bearing Walls	131.00	127.55	125.05	121.85	120.10	118.40	116.60	115.50	114.50
	Steel Frame	136.60	133.15	130.65	127.45	125.70	124.05	122.20	121.10	120.15
Stucco on Concrete Block	Bearing Walls	122.30	119.50	117.45	114.85	113.40	112.10	110.70	109.75	109.00
	Steel Frame	128.45	125.65	123.60	121.00	119.60	118.25	116.85	115.90	115.15
Perimeter Adj., Add or Deduct	Per 100 L.F.	7.25	6.20	5.40	4.65	4.15	3.85	3.35	3.10	2.85
Story Hgt. Adj., Add or Deduct	Per 1 Ft.	1.70	1.55	1.50	1.40	1.35	1.25	1.10	1.10	1.10

For Basement, add $36.65 per square foot of basement area

The above costs were calculated using the basic specifications shown on the facing page. These costs should be adjusted where necessary for design alternatives and owner's requirements. Reported completed project costs, for this type of structure, range from $58.20 to $169.30 per S.F.

Common additives

Description	Unit	$ Cost
Emergency Lighting, 25 watt, battery operated		
Lead battery	Each	320
Nickel cadmium	Each	885
Smoke Detectors		
Ceiling type	Each	223
Duct type	Each	555
Sound System		
Amplifier, 250 watts	Each	2025
Speaker, ceiling or wall	Each	208
Trumpet	Each	400

Model costs calculated for a 1 story building with 14' story height and 21,000 square feet of floor area

				Unit	Unit Cost	Cost Per S.F.	% Of Sub-Total

A. SUBSTRUCTURE

1010	Standard Foundations	Poured concrete; strip and spread footings		S.F. Ground	1.45	1.45	
1020	Special Foundations	N/A		—	—	—	
1030	Slab on Grade	4" reinforced concrete with vapor barrier and granular base		S.F. Slab	7.82	7.82	13.2%
2010	Basement Excavation	Site preparation for slab and trench for foundation wall and footing		S.F. Ground	.32	.32	
2020	Basement Walls	4' foundation wall		L.F. Wall	82	2.27	

B. SHELL

B10 Superstructure

1010	Floor Construction	N/A		—	—	—	11.6%
1020	Roof Construction	Metal deck, open web steel joists, beams, columns		S.F. Roof	10.49	10.49	

B20 Exterior Enclosure

2010	Exterior Walls	E.I.F.S.	70% of wall	S.F. Wall	26.32	7.16	
2020	Exterior Windows	Window wall	30% of wall	Each	55	6.42	19.0%
2030	Exterior Doors	Double aluminum and glass, hollow metal, steel overhead		Each	4116	3.54	

B30 Roofing

3010	Roof Coverings	Built-up tar and gravel with flashing; perlite/EPS composite insulation		S.F. Roof	5.91	5.91	6.6%
3020	Roof Openings	N/A		—	—	—	

C. INTERIORS

1010	Partitions	Gypsum board on metal studs	28 S.F. Floor/L.F. Partition	S.F. Partition	4.43	1.90	
1020	Interior Doors	Hollow metal	280 S.F. Floor/Door	Each	1152	4.11	
1030	Fittings	N/A		—	—	—	
2010	Stair Construction	N/A		—	—	—	13.0%
3010	Wall Finishes	Paint		S.F. Surface	.84	.72	
3020	Floor Finishes	50% vinyl tile, 50% paint		S.F. Floor	2.67	2.67	
3030	Ceiling Finishes	Fiberglass board on exposed grid, suspended	50% of area	S.F. Ceiling	4.57	2.29	

D. SERVICES

D10 Conveying

1010	Elevators & Lifts	N/A		—	—	—	0.0%
1020	Escalators & Moving Walks	N/A		—	—	—	

D20 Plumbing

2010	Plumbing Fixtures	Toilet and service fixtures, supply and drainage	1 Fixture/1500 S.F. Floor	Each	3210	2.14	
2020	Domestic Water Distribution	Gas fired water heater		S.F. Floor	2.07	2.07	7.6%
2040	Rain Water Drainage	Roof drains		S.F. Roof	2.66	2.66	

D30 HVAC

3010	Energy Supply	N/A		—	—	—	
3020	Heat Generating Systems	N/A		—	—	—	
3030	Cooling Generating Systems	N/A		—	—	—	10.4%
3050	Terminal & Package Units	Single zone rooftop unit, gas heating, electric cooling		S.F. Floor	8.74	8.74	
3090	Other HVAC Sys. & Equipment	Underfloor garage exhaust system		S.F. Floor	.65	.65	

D40 Fire Protection

4010	Sprinklers	Wet pipe sprinkler system		S.F. Floor	4.55	4.55	5.5%
4020	Standpipes	Standpipe		S.F. Floor	.43	.43	

D50 Electrical

5010	Electrical Service/Distribution	200 ampere service, panel board and feeders		S.F. Floor	.48	.48	
5020	Lighting & Branch Wiring	T-8 fluorescent fixtures, receptacles, switches, A.C. and misc. power		S.F. Floor	6.60	6.60	11.6%
5030	Communications & Security	Addressable alarm systems, partial internet wiring and emergency lighting		S.F. Floor	3.31	3.31	
5090	Other Electrical Systems	Emergency generator, 7.5 kW		S.F. Floor	.06	.06	

E. EQUIPMENT & FURNISHINGS

1010	Commercial Equipment	N/A		—	—	—	
1020	Institutional Equipment	N/A		—	—	—	1.6%
1030	Vehicular Equipment	Hoists, compressor, fuel pump		S.F. Floor	1.41	1.41	
1090	Other Equipment	N/A		—	—	—	

F. SPECIAL CONSTRUCTION

1020	Integrated Construction	N/A		—	—	—	0.0%
1040	Special Facilities	N/A		—	—	—	

G. BUILDING SITEWORK   N/A

Sub-Total		90.17	**100%**

CONTRACTOR FEES (General Requirements: 10%, Overhead: 5%, Profit: 10%)	25%	22.54	
ARCHITECT FEES	7%	7.89	

Total Building Cost	**120.60**

Costs per square foot of floor area

Exterior Wall	S.F. Area	85000	115000	145000	175000	205000	235000	265000	295000	325000
	L.F. Perimeter	529	638	723	823	923	951	1037	1057	1132
Face Brick with Concrete Block Back-up	Steel Frame	86.60	85.10	83.90	83.30	82.90	82.10	81.80	81.30	81.10
	Precast Concrete	67.60	66.10	64.90	64.35	63.90	63.10	62.80	62.30	62.05
Precast Concrete	Steel Frame	91.45	89.45	88.00	87.15	86.55	85.50	85.10	84.35	84.10
	Precast Concrete	71.65	69.65	68.20	67.35	66.75	65.70	65.35	64.55	64.35
Reinforced Concrete	Steel Frame	86.00	84.60	83.70	83.10	82.70	82.05	81.80	81.40	81.20
	R/Conc. Frame	70.90	69.50	68.55	68.05	67.60	66.95	66.75	66.30	66.15
Perimeter Adj., Add or Deduct	Per 100 L.F.	1.60	1.15	0.95	0.80	0.65	0.55	0.50	0.40	0.40
Story Hgt. Adj., Add or Deduct	Per 1 Ft.	0.60	0.50	0.50	0.45	0.35	0.35	0.35	0.25	0.30
Basement—Not Applicable										

The above costs were calculated using the basic specifications shown on the facing page. These costs should be adjusted where necessary for design alternatives and owner's requirements. Reported completed project costs, for this type of structure, range from $35.70 to $138.15 per S.F.

Common additives

Description	Unit	$ Cost
Elevators, Electric passenger, 5 stops		
2000# capacity	Each	167,200
3500# capacity	Each	173,200
5000# capacity	Each	179,200
Barrier gate w/programmable controller	Each	4100
Booth for attendant, average	Each	13,500
Fee computer	Each	15,800
Ticket spitter with time/date stamp	Each	7675
Mag strip encoding	Each	21,000
Collection station, pay on foot	Each	127,000
Parking control software	Each	27,200 - 116,500
Painting, Parking stalls	Stall	8.80
Parking Barriers		
Timber with saddles, 4" x 4"	L.F.	7.45
Precast concrete, 6" x 10" x 6'	Each	62
Traffic Signs, directional, 12" x 18", high density	Each	96.50

Important: See the Reference Section for Location Factors.

Model costs calculated for a 5 story building with 10' story height and 145,000 square feet of floor area

			Unit	Unit Cost	Cost Per S.F.	% Of Sub-Total
A. SUBSTRUCTURE						
1010	Standard Foundations	Poured concrete; strip and spread footings	S.F. Ground	6.95	1.39	
1020	Special Foundations	N/A	—	—	—	
1030	Slab on Grade	6" reinforced concrete with vapor barrier and granular base	S.F. Slab	6.80	1.36	8.7%
2010	Basement Excavation	Site preparation for slab and trench for foundation wall and footing	S.F. Ground	.18	.04	
2020	Basement Walls	4' foundation wall	L.F. Wall	73	1.45	
B. SHELL						
B10 Superstructure						
1010	Floor Construction	Double tee precast concrete slab, precast concrete columns	S.F. Floor	27.30	21.84	44.6%
1020	Roof Construction	N/A	—	—	—	
B20 Exterior Enclosure						
2010	Exterior Walls	Face brick with concrete block backup 40% of story height	S.F. Wall	32.89	3.28	
2020	Exterior Windows	N/A	—	—	—	6.7%
2030	Exterior Doors	N/A	—	—	—	
B30 Roofing						
3010	Roof Coverings	N/A	—	—	—	0.0%
3020	Roof Openings	N/A	—	—	—	
C. INTERIORS						
1010	Partitions	Concrete block	S.F. Partition	33.02	1.27	
1020	Interior Doors	Hollow metal	Each	23,040	.16	
1030	Fittings	N/A	—	—	—	
2010	Stair Construction	Concrete	Flight	4175	.29	13.7%
3010	Wall Finishes	Paint	S.F. Surface	1.82	.14	
3020	Floor Finishes	Parking deck surface coating	S.F. Floor	4.87	4.87	
3030	Ceiling Finishes	N/A	—	—	—	
D. SERVICES						
D10 Conveying						
1010	Elevators & Lifts	Two hydraulic passenger elevators	Each	167,475	2.31	4.7%
1020	Escalators & Moving Walks	N/A	—	—	—	
D20 Plumbing						
2010	Plumbing Fixtures	Toilet and service fixtures, supply and drainage 1 Fixture/18,125 S.F. Floor	Each	725	.04	
2020	Domestic Water Distribution	Electric water heater	S.F. Floor	.07	.07	3.4%
2040	Rain Water Drainage	Roof drains	S.F. Roof	7.90	1.58	
D30 HVAC						
3010	Energy Supply	N/A	—	—	—	
3020	Heat Generating Systems	N/A	—	—	—	
3030	Cooling Generating Systems	N/A	—	—	—	0.0%
3050	Terminal & Package Units	N/A	—	—	—	
3090	Other HVAC Sys. & Equipment	N/A	—	—	—	
D40 Fire Protection						
4010	Sprinklers	Dry pipe sprinkler system	S.F. Floor	4.11	4.11	8.6%
4020	Standpipes	Standpipes and hose systems	S.F. Floor	.09	.09	
D50 Electrical						
5010	Electrical Service/Distribution	400 ampere service, panel board and feeders	S.F. Floor	.25	.25	
5020	Lighting & Branch Wiring	T-8 fluorescent fixtures, receptacles, switches and misc. power	S.F. Floor	2.99	2.99	7.0%
5030	Communications & Security	Addressable alarm systems and emergency lighting	S.F. Floor	.12	.12	
5090	Other Electrical Systems	Emergency generator, 7.5 kW	S.F. Floor	.05	.05	
E. EQUIPMENT & FURNISHINGS						
1010	Commercial Equipment	N/A	—	—	—	
1020	Institutional Equipment	N/A	—	—	—	2.7%
1030	Vehicular Equipment	Ticket dispensers, booths, automatic gates	S.F. Floor	1.31	1.31	
1090	Other Equipment	N/A	—	—	—	
F. SPECIAL CONSTRUCTION						
1020	Integrated Construction	N/A	—	—	—	0.0%
1040	Special Facilities	N/A	—	—	—	
G. BUILDING SITEWORK	**N/A**					
			Sub-Total		49.01	**100%**
CONTRACTOR FEES (General Requirements: 10%, Overhead: 5%, Profit: 10%)				25%	12.21	
ARCHITECT FEES				6%	3.68	
			Total Building Cost		**64.90**	

Costs per square foot of floor area

Exterior Wall	S.F. Area	20000	30000	40000	50000	75000	100000	125000	150000	175000
	L.F. Perimeter	400	500	600	650	775	900	1000	1100	1185
Reinforced Concrete	R/Conc. Frame	99.55	92.85	89.50	86.40	82.10	80.05	78.55	77.55	76.70
Perimeter Adj., Add or Deduct	Per 100 L.F.	5.75	3.90	2.90	2.30	1.60	1.15	0.90	0.75	0.65
Story Hgt. Adj., Add or Deduct	Per 1 Ft.	2.15	1.85	1.70	1.45	1.15	1.00	0.90	0.80	0.75
Basement—Not Applicable										

The above costs were calculated using the basic specifications shown on the facing page. These costs should be adjusted where necessary for design alternatives and owner's requirements. Reported completed project costs, for this type of structure, range from $51.90 to $123.70 per S.F.

Common additives

Description	Unit	$ Cost
Elevators, Hydraulic passenger, 2 stops		
1500# capacity	Each	66,100
2500# capacity	Each	69,200
3500# capacity	Each	73,200
Barrier gate w/programmable controller	Each	4100
Booth for attendant, average	Each	13,500
Fee computer	Each	15,800
Ticket spitter with time/date stamp	Each	7675
Mag strip encoding	Each	21,000
Collection station, pay on foot	Each	127,000
Parking control software	Each	27,200 - 116,500
Painting, Parking stalls	Stall	8.80
Parking Barriers		
Timber with saddles, 4" x 4"	L.F.	7.45
Precast concrete, 6" x 10" x 6'	Each	62
Traffic Signs, directional, 12" x 18"	Each	96.50

Important: See the Reference Section for Location Factors.

Model costs calculated for a 2 story building with 10' story height and 100,000 square feet of floor area

Garage, Underground Parking

				Unit	Unit Cost	Cost Per S.F.	% Of Sub-Total
A. SUBSTRUCTURE							
1010	Standard Foundations	Poured concrete; strip and spread footings and waterproofing		S.F. Ground	8.28	4.14	
1020	Special Foundations	N/A		—	—	—	
1030	Slab on Grade	5" reinforced concrete with vapor barrier and granular base		S.F. Slab	6.93	3.47	22.0%
2010	Basement Excavation	Excavation 24' deep		S.F. Ground	10.85	5.43	
2020	Basement Walls	N/A		—	—	—	
B. SHELL							
B10 Superstructure							
1010	Floor Construction	Cast-in-place concrete beam and slab, concrete columns		S.F. Floor	27.66	13.83	44.9%
1020	Roof Construction	Cast-in-place concrete beam and slab, concrete columns		S.F. Roof	25.56	12.78	
B20 Exterior Enclosure							
2010	Exterior Walls	Cast-in place concrete		S.F. Wall	22.22	4	
2020	Exterior Windows	N/A		—	—	—	7.1%
2030	Exterior Doors	Steel overhead, hollow metal		Each	4473	.18	
B30 Roofing							
3010	Roof Coverings	Neoprene membrane traffic deck		S.F. Roof	5.08	2.54	4.3%
3020	Roof Openings	N/A		—	—	—	
C. INTERIORS							
1010	Partitions	Concrete block		S.F. Partition	43.16	.83	
1020	Interior Doors	Hollow metal		Each	9216	.09	
1030	Fittings	N/A		—	—	—	
2010	Stair Construction	Concrete		Flight	6625	.34	2.3%
3010	Wall Finishes	Paint		S.F. Surface	2.60	.10	
3020	Floor Finishes	N/A		—	—	—	
3030	Ceiling Finishes	N/A		—	—	—	
D. SERVICES							
D10 Conveying							
1010	Elevators & Lifts	Two hydraulic passenger elevators		Each	83,500	1.67	2.8%
1020	Escalators & Moving Walks	N/A		—	—	—	
D20 Plumbing							
2010	Plumbing Fixtures	Drainage in parking areas, toilets, & service fixtures	1 Fixture/5000 S.F. Floor	Each	.06	.06	
2020	Domestic Water Distribution	Electric water heater		S.F. Floor	.11	.11	2.4%
2040	Rain Water Drainage	Roof drains		S.F. Roof	2.52	1.26	
D30 HVAC							
3010	Energy Supply	N/A		—	—	—	
3020	Heat Generating Systems	N/A		—	—	—	
3030	Cooling Generating Systems	N/A		—	—	—	0.3 %
3050	Terminal & Package Units	Exhaust fans		S.F. Floor	.17	.17	
3090	Other HVAC Sys. & Equipment	N/A		—	—	—	
D40 Fire Protection							
4010	Sprinklers	Dry pipe sprinkler system		S.F. Floor	4.12	4.12	7.2%
4020	Standpipes	Dry standpipe system, class 3		S.F. Floor	.15	.15	
D50 Electrical							
5010	Electrical Service/Distribution	200 ampere service, panel board and feeders		S.F. Floor	.14	.14	
5020	Lighting & Branch Wiring	T-8 fluorescent fixtures, receptacles, switches and misc. power		S.F. Floor	3.23	3.23	6.1%
5030	Communications & Security	Addressable alarm systems and emergency lighting		S.F. Floor	.18	.18	
5090	Other Electrical Systems	Emergency generator, 11.5 kW		S.F. Floor	.06	.06	
E. EQUIPMENT & FURNISHINGS							
1010	Commercial Equipment	N/A		—	—	—	
1020	Institutional Equipment	N/A		—	—	—	
1030	Vehicular Equipment	Ticket dispensers, booths, automatic gates		S.F. Floor	.41	.41	0.7 %
1090	Other Equipment	N/A		—	—	—	
F. SPECIAL CONSTRUCTION							
1020	Integrated Construction	N/A		—	—	—	0.0 %
1040	Special Facilities	N/A		—	—	—	
G. BUILDING SITEWORK	**N/A**						
				Sub-Total		59.29	**100%**
	CONTRACTOR FEES (General Requirements: 10%, Overhead: 5%, Profit: 10%)				25%	14.83	
	ARCHITECT FEES				8%	5.93	
				Total Building Cost		**80.05**	

Costs per square foot of floor area

Exterior Wall	S.F. Area	2000	4000	6000	8000	10000	12000	14000	16000	18000
	L.F. Perimeter	180	260	340	420	500	580	586	600	610
Concrete Block	Wood Joists	159.10	136.80	129.35	125.60	123.35	121.90	117.95	115.25	113.10
	Steel Joists	160.30	138.85	131.70	128.10	125.90	124.50	120.60	117.90	115.80
Cast in Place Concrete	Wood Joists	170.05	145.05	136.75	132.55	130.05	128.40	123.55	120.25	117.65
	Steel Joists	172.75	147.70	139.40	135.20	132.70	131.05	126.25	122.95	120.35
Stucco	Wood Frame	165.10	139.60	131.05	126.75	124.20	122.50	117.50	114.10	111.45
Insulated Metal Panels	Steel Frame	181.00	155.00	146.25	141.90	139.30	137.55	132.45	129.00	126.25
Perimeter Adj., Add or Deduct	Per 100 L.F.	27.15	13.50	9.05	6.80	5.50	4.50	3.85	3.40	3.05
Story Hgt. Adj., Add or Deduct	Per 1 Ft.	2.05	1.50	1.30	1.20	1.20	1.15	0.95	0.90	0.75
For Basement, add $34.45 per square foot of basement area										

The above costs were calculated using the basic specifications shown on the facing page. These costs should be adjusted where necessary for design alternatives and owner's requirements. Reported completed project costs, for this type of structure, range from $74.45 to $223.65 per S.F.

Common additives

Description	Unit	$ Cost
Air Compressors		
Electric 1-1/2 H.P., standard controls	Each	1575
Dual controls	Each	1950
5 H.P. 115/230 Volt, standard controls	Each	4400
Dual controls	Each	5000
Product Dispenser		
with vapor recovery for 6 nozzles	Each	26,900
Lifts, Single post		
8000# cap., swivel arm	Each	10,100
Two post, adjustable frames, 12,000# cap.	Each	5300
24,000# cap.	Each	11,200
30,000# cap.	Each	51,500
Four post, roll on ramp, 25,000# cap.	Each	20,600
Lockers, Steel, single tier, 60" or 72"	Opening	218 - 365
2 tier, 60" or 72" total	Opening	113 - 156
5 tier, box lockers	Opening	71.50 - 85
Locker bench, lam. maple top only	L.F.	26.50
Pedestals, steel pipe	Each	74
Lube Equipment		
3 reel type, with pumps, no piping	Each	12,800
Spray Painting Booth, 26' long, complete	Each	21,800

Important: See the Reference Section for Location Factors.

Model costs calculated for a 1 story building with 14' story height and 10,000 square feet of floor area

Garage, Repair

				Unit	Unit Cost	Cost Per S.F.	% Of Sub-Total
A. SUBSTRUCTURE							
1010	Standard Foundations	Poured concrete; strip and spread footings		S.F. Ground	2.25	2.25	
1020	Special Foundations	N/A		—	—	—	
1030	Slab on Grade	6" reinforced concrete with vapor barrier and granular base		S.F. Slab	7.82	7.82	15.5%
2010	Basement Excavation	Site preparation for slab and trench for foundation wall and footing		S.F. Ground	.32	.32	
2020	Basement Walls	4' foundation wall		L.F. Wall	82	4.08	
B. SHELL							
B10 Superstructure							
1010	Floor Construction	N/A		—	—	—	
1020	Roof Construction	Metal deck on open web steel joists		S.F. Roof	5.60	5.60	6.0 %
B20 Exterior Enclosure							
2010	Exterior Walls	Concrete block	80% of wall	S.F. Wall	12.86	7.20	
2020	Exterior Windows	Hopper type commercial steel	5% of wall	Each	525	1.22	11.4%
2030	Exterior Doors	Steel overhead and hollow metal	15% of wall	S.F. Door	20.76	2.18	
B30 Roofing							
3010	Roof Coverings	Built-up tar and gravel; perlite/EPS composite insulation		S.F. Roof	6.75	6.75	7.3%
3020	Roof Openings	Skylight		S.F. Roof	.02	.02	
C. INTERIORS							
1010	Partitions	Concrete block	50 S.F. Floor/L.F. Partition	S.F. Partition	7.75	1.55	
1020	Interior Doors	Single leaf hollow metal	3000 S.F. Floor/Door	Each	1152	.38	
1030	Fittings	Toilet partitions		S.F. Floor	.15	.15	
2010	Stair Construction	N/A		—	—	—	7.4%
3010	Wall Finishes	Paint		S.F. Surface	7.90	3.16	
3020	Floor Finishes	90% metallic floor hardener, 10% vinyl composition tile		S.F. Floor	1.25	1.25	
3030	Ceiling Finishes	Gypsum board on wood joists in office and washrooms	10% of area	S.F. Ceiling	3.82	.38	
D. SERVICES							
D10 Conveying							
1010	Elevators & Lifts	N/A		—	—	—	0.0 %
1020	Escalators & Moving Walks	N/A		—	—	—	
D20 Plumbing							
2010	Plumbing Fixtures	Toilet and service fixtures, supply and drainage	1 Fixture/500 S.F. Floor	Each	1670	3.34	
2020	Domestic Water Distribution	Gas fired water heater		S.F. Floor	.56	.56	6.9%
2040	Rain Water Drainage	Roof drains		S.F. Roof	2.54	2.54	
D30 HVAC							
3010	Energy Supply	N/A		—	—	—	
3020	Heat Generating Systems	N/A		—	—	—	
3030	Cooling Generating Systems	N/A		—	—	—	10.6 %
3050	Terminal & Package Units	Single zone AC unit		S.F. Floor	8.95	8.95	
3090	Other HVAC Sys. & Equipment	Garage exhaust system		S.F. Floor	.92	.92	
D40 Fire Protection							
4010	Sprinklers	Sprinklers, ordinary hazard		S.F. Floor	4.55	4.55	5.9%
4020	Standpipes	Standpipe		S.F. Floor	.91	.91	
D50 Electrical							
5010	Electrical Service/Distribution	200 ampere service, panel board and feeders		S.F. Floor	.50	.50	
5020	Lighting & Branch Wiring	T-8 fluorescent fixtures, receptacles, switches, A.C. and misc. power		S.F. Floor	8.02	8.02	13.0%
5030	Communications & Security	Addressable alarm systems, partial internet wiring and emergency lighting		S.F. Floor	3.51	3.51	
5090	Other Electrical Systems	Emergency generator, 15 kW		S.F. Floor	.08	.08	
E. EQUIPMENT & FURNISHINGS							
1010	Commercial Equipment	N/A		—	—	—	
1020	Institutional Equipment	N/A		—	—	—	16.2 %
1030	Vehicular Equipment	Hoists		S.F. Floor	15.08	15.08	
1090	Other Equipment	N/A		—	—	—	
F. SPECIAL CONSTRUCTION							
1020	Integrated Construction	N/A		—	—	—	0.0 %
1040	Special Facilities	N/A		—	—	—	
G. BUILDING SITEWORK	**N/A**						

	Sub-Total	93.27	**100%**
CONTRACTOR FEES (General Requirements: 10%, Overhead: 5%, Profit: 10%)	25%	23.30	
ARCHITECT FEES	8%	9.33	
	Total Building Cost	**125.90**	

141

Costs per square foot of floor area

Exterior Wall	S.F. Area	600	800	1000	1200	1400	1600	1800	2000	2200
	L.F. Perimeter	100	120	126	140	153	160	170	180	190
Face Brick with Concrete Block Back-up	Wood Truss	280.60	263.20	242.80	233.90	227.05	219.25	214.35	210.45	207.30
	Steel Joists	282.10	264.70	244.30	235.40	228.55	220.80	215.95	212.00	208.80
Enameled Sandwich Panel	Steel Frame	261.90	246.65	229.35	221.65	215.80	209.20	205.00	201.65	198.95
Tile on Concrete Block	Steel Joists	300.10	280.85	257.95	248.00	240.35	231.60	226.10	221.65	218.15
Aluminum Siding	Wood Frame	242.60	229.00	214.05	207.30	202.15	196.50	192.90	189.95	187.65
Wood Siding	Wood Frame	243.75	230.05	214.95	208.10	202.90	197.15	193.50	190.55	188.20
Perimeter Adj., Add or Deduct	Per 100 L.F.	118.80	89.10	71.25	59.40	50.95	44.60	39.60	35.65	32.40
Story Hgt. Adj., Add or Deduct	Per 1 Ft.	7.80	7.00	5.90	5.40	5.05	4.70	4.50	4.20	4.05
Basement—Not Applicable										

The above costs were calculated using the basic specifications shown on the facing page. These costs should be adjusted where necessary for design alternatives and owner's requirements. Reported completed project costs, for this type of structure, range from $53.65 to $270.90 per S.F.

Common additives

Description	Unit	$ Cost
Air Compressors		
Electric 1-1/2 H.P., standard controls	Each	1575
Dual controls	Each	1950
5 H.P. 115/230 volt, standard controls	Each	4400
Dual controls	Each	5000
Product Dispenser		
with vapor recovery for 6 nozzles	Each	26,900
Lifts, Single post		
8000# cap. swivel arm	Each	10,100
Two post, adjustable frames, 12,000# cap.	Each	5300
24,000# cap.	Each	11,200
30,000# cap.	Each	51,500
Four post, roll on ramp, 25,000# cap.	Each	20,600
Lockers, Steel, single tier, 60" or 72"	Opening	218 - 365
2 tier, 60" or 72" total	Opening	113 - 156
5 tier, box lockers	Each	71.50 - 85
Locker bench, lam. maple top only	L.F.	26.50
Pedestals, steel pipe	Each	74
Lube Equipment		
3 reel type, with pumps, no piping	Each	12,800

Important: See the Reference Section for Location Factors.

Model costs calculated for a 1 story building with 12' story height and 1,400 square feet of floor area

				Unit	Unit Cost	Cost Per S.F.	% Of Sub-Total
A. SUBSTRUCTURE							
1010	Standard Foundations	Poured concrete; strip and spread footings		S.F. Ground	4.27	4.27	
1020	Special Foundations	N/A		—	—	—	
1030	Slab on Grade	6" reinforced concrete with vapor barrier and granular base		S.F. Slab	7.82	7.82	12.5%
2010	Basement Excavation	Site preparation for slab and trench for foundation wall and footing		S.F. Ground	1.04	1.04	
2020	Basement Walls	4' foundation wall		L.F. Wall	73	7.93	
B. SHELL							
	B10 Superstructure						
1010	Floor Construction	N/A		—	—	—	4.1%
1020	Roof Construction	Plywood on wood trusses		S.F. Roof	6.85	6.85	
	B20 Exterior Enclosure						
2010	Exterior Walls	Face brick with concrete block backup	60% of wall	S.F. Wall	32.89	25.88	
2020	Exterior Windows	Store front and metal top hinged outswinging	20% of wall	Each	40.45	10.62	28.6%
2030	Exterior Doors	Steel overhead, aluminum & glass and hollow metal	20% of wall	Each	44.34	11.63	
	B30 Roofing						
3010	Roof Coverings	Asphalt shingles with flashing; perlite/EPS composite insulation		S.F. Roof	3.86	3.86	2.3%
3020	Roof Openings	N/A		—	—	—	
C. INTERIORS							
1010	Partitions	Concrete block	25 S.F. Floor/L.F. Partition	S.F. Partition	7.72	2.47	
1020	Interior Doors	Single leaf hollow metal	700 S.F. Floor/Door	Each	1152	1.65	
1030	Fittings	Toilet partitions		S.F. Floor	2.08	2.08	
2010	Stair Construction	N/A		—	—	—	7.6%
3010	Wall Finishes	Paint		S.F. Surface	5.88	3.76	
3020	Floor Finishes	Vinyl composition tile	35% of floor area	S.F. Floor	3.49	1.22	
3030	Ceiling Finishes	Painted gypsum board on furring in sales area & washrooms	35% of floor area	S.F. Ceiling	4.39	1.54	
D. SERVICES							
	D10 Conveying						
1010	Elevators & Lifts	N/A		—	—	—	0.0%
1020	Escalators & Moving Walks	N/A		—	—	—	
	D20 Plumbing						
2010	Plumbing Fixtures	Toilet and service fixtures, supply and drainage	1 Fixture/235 S.F. Floor	Each	2834	12.06	
2020	Domestic Water Distribution	Gas fired water heater		S.F. Floor	3.98	3.98	9.5%
2040	Rain Water Drainage	N/A		—	—	—	
	D30 HVAC						
3010	Energy Supply	N/A		—	—	—	
3020	Heat Generating Systems	N/A		—	—	—	
3030	Cooling Generating Systems	N/A		—	—	—	15.7%
3050	Terminal & Package Units	Single zone AC unit		S.F. Floor	20.95	20.95	
3090	Other HVAC Sys. & Equipment	Underfloor exhaust system		S.F. Floor	5.47	5.47	
	D40 Fire Protection						
4010	Sprinklers	Wet pipe sprinkler system		S.F. Floor	9.11	9.11	7.8%
4020	Standpipes	Standpipe		S.F. Floor	4.02	4.02	
	D50 Electrical						
5010	Electrical Service/Distribution	200 ampere service, panel board and feeders		S.F. Floor	4.91	4.91	
5020	Lighting & Branch Wiring	High efficiency fluorescent fixtures, receptacles, switches, A.C. and misc. power		S.F. Floor	6.02	6.02	11.9%
5030	Communications & Security	Addressable alarm systems and emergency lighting		S.F. Floor	8.45	8.45	
5090	Other Electrical Systems	Emergency generator		S.F. Floor	.58	.58	
E. EQUIPMENT & FURNISHINGS							
1010	Commercial Equipment	N/A		—	—	—	
1020	Institutional Equipment	N/A		—	—	—	0.0%
1030	Vehicular Equipment	N/A		—	—	—	
1090	Other Equipment	N/A		—	—	—	
F. SPECIAL CONSTRUCTION							
1020	Integrated Construction	N/A		—	—	—	0.0%
1040	Special Facilities	N/A		—	—	—	
G. BUILDING SITEWORK	**N/A**						

		Sub-Total	168.17	100%
CONTRACTOR FEES (General Requirements: 10%, Overhead: 5%, Profit: 10%)		25%	42.06	
ARCHITECT FEES		8%	16.82	

Total Building Cost	**227.05**

Costs per square foot of floor area

Exterior Wall	S.F. Area	12000	16000	20000	25000	30000	35000	40000	45000	50000
	L.F. Perimeter	440	520	600	700	708	780	841	910	979
Reinforced Concrete Block	Lam. Wood Arches	171.35	166.45	163.60	161.25	156.90	155.40	154.15	153.20	152.55
	Rigid Steel Frame	175.35	170.45	167.55	165.20	160.85	159.35	158.05	157.20	156.45
Face Brick with Concrete Block Back-up	Lam. Wood Arches	198.45	190.50	185.75	181.90	174.35	171.90	169.65	168.15	166.95
	Rigid Steel Frame	202.65	194.70	189.95	186.10	178.50	176.05	173.85	172.35	171.15
Metal Sandwich Panels	Lam. Wood Arches	183.50	177.25	173.55	170.50	164.75	162.75	161.10	159.95	159.00
	Rigid Steel Frame	187.70	181.45	177.75	174.70	168.90	166.95	165.30	164.10	163.20
Perimeter Adj., Add or Deduct	Per 100 L.F.	7.50	5.65	4.45	3.55	3.00	2.65	2.20	2.00	1.80
Story Hgt. Adj., Add or Deduct	Per 1 Ft.	1.10	0.95	0.85	0.80	0.65	0.65	0.55	0.60	0.55
Basement—Not Applicable										

The above costs were calculated using the basic specifications shown on the facing page. These costs should be adjusted where necessary for design alternatives and owner's requirements. Reported completed project costs, for this type of structure, range from $81.35 to $242.80 per S.F.

Common additives

Description	Unit	$ Cost
Bleachers, Telescoping, manual		
To 15 tier	Seat	135 - 187
16-20 tier	Seat	277 - 340
21-30 tier	Seat	295 - 385
For power operation, add	Seat	54.50 - 84.50
Gym Divider Curtain, Mesh top		
Manual roll-up	S.F.	13
Gym Mats		
2" naugahyde covered	S.F.	4.04
2" nylon	S.F.	8.70
1-1/2" wall pads	S.F.	8.55
1" wrestling mats	S.F.	6.10
Scoreboard		
Basketball, one side	Each	3475 - 9650
Basketball Backstop		
Wall mtd., 6' extended, fixed	Each	2500 - 3075
Swing up, wall mtd.	Each	2575 - 4100

Description	Unit	$ Cost
Lockers, Steel, single tier, 60" or 72"	Opening	218 - 365
2 tier, 60" or 72" total	Opening	113 - 156
5 tier, box lockers	Opening	71.50 - 85
Locker bench, lam. maple top only	L.F.	26.50
Pedestals, steel pipe	Each	74
Sound System		
Amplifier, 250 watts	Each	2025
Speaker, ceiling or wall	Each	208
Trumpet	Each	400
Emergency Lighting, 25 watt, battery operated		
Lead battery	Each	320
Nickel cadmium	Each	885

Important: See the Reference Section for Location Factors.

Model costs calculated for a 1 story building with 25' story height and 20,000 square feet of floor area

				Unit	Unit Cost	Cost Per S.F.	% Of Sub-Total
A. SUBSTRUCTURE							
1010	Standard Foundations	Poured concrete; strip and spread footings		S.F. Ground	1.76	1.76	
1020	Special Foundations	N/A		—	—	—	
1030	Slab on Grade	4" reinforced concrete with vapor barrier and granular base		S.F. Slab	5.31	5.31	8.0%
2010	Basement Excavation	Site preparation for slab and trench for foundation wall and footing		S.F. Ground	.18	.18	
2020	Basement Walls	4' foundation wall		L.F. Wall	73	2.55	
B. SHELL							
B10 Superstructure							
1010	Floor Construction	N/A		—	—	—	
1020	Roof Construction	Wood deck on laminated wood arches		S.F. Roof	18.45	18.45	15.1%
B20 Exterior Enclosure							
2010	Exterior Walls	Reinforced concrete block (end walls included)	90% of wall	S.F. Wall	13.47	9.09	
2020	Exterior Windows	Metal horizontal pivoted	10% of wall	Each	674	5.06	12.1%
2030	Exterior Doors	Aluminum and glass, hollow metal, steel overhead		Each	2111	.62	
B30 Roofing							
3010	Roof Coverings	EPDM, 60 mils, fully adhered; polyisocyanurate insulation		S.F. Roof	5.36	5.36	4.4%
3020	Roof Openings	N/A		—	—	—	
C. INTERIORS							
1010	Partitions	Concrete block	50 S.F. Floor/L.F. Partition	S.F. Partition	9.35	1.87	
1020	Interior Doors	Single leaf hollow metal	500 S.F. Floor/Door	Each	1152	2.30	
1030	Fittings	Toilet partitions		S.F. Floor	.30	.30	
2010	Stair Construction	N/A		—	—	—	20.1%
3010	Wall Finishes	50% paint, 50% ceramic tile		S.F. Surface	10.03	4.01	
3020	Floor Finishes	90% hardwood, 10% ceramic tile		S.F. Floor	15.03	15.03	
3030	Ceiling Finishes	Mineral fiber tile on concealed zee bars	15% of area	S.F. Ceiling	6.89	1.03	
D. SERVICES							
D10 Conveying							
1010	Elevators & Lifts	N/A		—	—	—	0.0%
1020	Escalators & Moving Walks	N/A		—	—	—	
D20 Plumbing							
2010	Plumbing Fixtures	Toilet and service fixtures, supply and drainage	1 Fixture/515 S.F. Floor	Each	4604	8.94	
2020	Domestic Water Distribution	Electric water heater		S.F. Floor	4.93	4.93	11.3%
2040	Rain Water Drainage	N/A		—	—	—	
D30 HVAC							
3010	Energy Supply	N/A		—	—	—	
3020	Heat Generating Systems	Included in D3050		—	—	—	
3030	Cooling Generating Systems	N/A		—	—	—	9.0%
3050	Terminal & Package Units	Single zone rooftop unit, gas heating, electric cooling		S.F. Floor	11.05	11.05	
3090	Other HVAC Sys. & Equipment	N/A		—	—	—	
D40 Fire Protection							
4010	Sprinklers	Wet pipe sprinkler system		S.F. Floor	3.56	3.56	3.7%
4020	Standpipes	Standpipe		S.F. Floor	.99	.99	
D50 Electrical							
5010	Electrical Service/Distribution	400 ampere service, panel board and feeders		S.F. Floor	1.11	1.11	
5020	Lighting & Branch Wiring	High efficiency fluorescent fixtures, receptacles, switches, A.C. and misc. power		S.F. Floor	9.13	9.13	10.9%
5030	Communications & Security	Addressable alarm systems, sound system and emergency lighting		S.F. Floor	2.87	2.87	
5090	Other Electrical Systems	Emergency generator, 7.5 kW		S.F. Floor	.19	.19	
E. EQUIPMENT & FURNISHINGS							
1010	Commercial Equipment	N/A		—	—	—	
1020	Institutional Equipment	N/A		—	—	—	5.4%
1030	Vehicular Equipment	N/A		—	—	—	
1090	Other Equipment	Bleachers, sauna, weight room		S.F. Floor	6.62	6.62	
F. SPECIAL CONSTRUCTION							
1020	Integrated Construction	N/A		—	—	—	0.0%
1040	Special Facilities	N/A		—	—	—	
G. BUILDING SITEWORK	**N/A**						

			Sub-Total	122.31	100%
CONTRACTOR FEES (General Requirements: 10%, Overhead: 5%, Profit: 10%)		25%	30.59	
ARCHITECT FEES		7%	10.70	

	Total Building Cost	**163.60**

Costs per square foot of floor area

Exterior Wall	S.F. Area	5000	10000	15000	20000	30000	40000	50000	75000	100000
	L.F. Perimeter	300	410	500	580	710	830	930	1150	1300
Concrete Block Reinforced	Steel Frame	171.75	140.20	128.45	122.20	115.00	111.15	108.45	104.55	101.95
	Bearing Walls	175.60	144.10	132.40	126.05	118.90	115.10	112.40	108.50	105.95
Precast Concrete	Steel Frame	197.70	157.95	142.80	134.65	125.20	120.10	116.45	111.15	107.55
	Bearing Walls	201.80	162.10	147.00	138.85	129.35	124.25	120.60	115.30	111.65
Galv. Steel Siding	Steel Frame	170.90	139.65	128.00	121.75	114.60	110.80	108.15	104.30	101.70
Metal Sandwich Panel	Steel Frame	181.60	146.30	133.10	126.05	118.00	113.70	110.65	106.35	103.45
Perimeter Adj., Add or Deduct	Per 100 L.F.	18.10	9.10	6.05	4.50	3.05	2.20	1.80	1.25	0.90
Story Hgt. Adj., Add or Deduct	Per 1 Ft.	1.85	1.30	1.05	0.85	0.70	0.65	0.55	0.50	0.40
Basement—Not Applicable										

The above costs were calculated using the basic specifications shown on the facing page. These costs should be adjusted where necessary for design alternatives and owner's requirements. Reported completed project costs, for this type of structure, range from $46.70 to $213.00 per S.F.

Common additives

Description	Unit	$ Cost
Closed Circuit Surveillance, One station		
Camera and monitor	Each	1975
For additional camera stations, add	Each	1050
Emergency Lighting, 25 watt, battery operated		
Lead battery	Each	320
Nickel cadmium	Each	885
Lockers, Steel, single tier, 60" or 72"	Opening	218 - 365
2 tier, 60" or 72" total	Opening	113 - 156
5 tier, box lockers	Opening	71.50 - 85
Locker bench, lam. maple top only	L.F.	26.50
Pedestals, steel pipe	Each	74
Safe, Office type, 1 hour rating		
30" x 18" x 18"	Each	2500
60" x 36" x 18", double door	Each	8075
Sound System		
Amplifier, 250 watts	Each	2025
Speaker, ceiling or wall	Each	208
Trumpet	Each	400

Important: See the Reference Section for Location Factors.

Model costs calculated for a 1 story building with 24' story height and 20,000 square feet of floor area

Hangar, Aircraft

				Unit	Unit Cost	Cost Per S.F.	% Of Sub-Total
A. SUBSTRUCTURE							
1010	Standard Foundations	Poured concrete; strip and spread footings and		S.F. Ground	1.93	1.93	
1020	Special Foundations	N/A		—	—	—	
1030	Slab on Grade	6" reinforced concrete with vapor barrier and granular base		S.F. Slab	7.82	7.82	13.7%
2010	Basement Excavation	Site preparation for slab and trench for foundation wall and footing		S.F. Ground	.32	.32	
2020	Basement Walls	4' foundation wall		L.F. Wall	82	2.37	
B. SHELL							
	B10 Superstructure						
1010	Floor Construction	N/A		—	—	—	10.8 %
1020	Roof Construction	Metal deck, open web steel joists, beams, columns		S.F. Roof	9.83	9.83	
	B20 Exterior Enclosure						
2010	Exterior Walls	Galvanized steel siding		S.F. Wall	11.03	3.84	
2020	Exterior Windows	Industrial horizontal pivoted steel	20% of wall	Each	2015	11.69	26.7%
2030	Exterior Doors	Steel overhead and sliding	30% of wall	Each	42.10	8.79	
	B30 Roofing						
3010	Roof Coverings	Elastomeric membrane; fiberboard insulation		S.F. Roof	4.56	4.56	5.2%
3020	Roof Openings	Roof hatches		S.F. Roof	.14	.14	
C. INTERIORS							
1010	Partitions	Concrete block	200 S.F. Floor/L.F. Partition	S.F. Partition	10	.50	
1020	Interior Doors	Single leaf hollow metal	5000 S.F. Floor/Door	Each	1152	.23	
1030	Fittings	Toilet partitions		S.F. Floor	.26	.26	
2010	Stair Construction	N/A		—	—	—	1.2%
3010	Wall Finishes	Paint		S.F. Surface	1.30	.13	
3020	Floor Finishes	N/A		—	—	—	
3030	Ceiling Finishes	N/A		—	—	—	
D. SERVICES							
	D10 Conveying						
1010	Elevators & Lifts	N/A		—	—	—	0.0 %
1020	Escalators & Moving Walks	N/A		—	—	—	
	D20 Plumbing						
2010	Plumbing Fixtures	Toilet and service fixtures, supply and drainage	1 Fixture/1000 S.F. Floor	Each	2870	2.87	
2020	Domestic Water Distribution	Gas fired water heater		S.F. Floor	2.47	2.47	5.9%
2040	Rain Water Drainage	N/A		—	—	—	
	D30 HVAC						
3010	Energy Supply	N/A		—	—	—	
3020	Heat Generating Systems	Unit heaters		Each	7.43	7.43	
3030	Cooling Generating Systems	N/A		—	—	—	8.5 %
3050	Terminal & Package Units	Exhaust fan		S.F. Floor	.28	.28	
3090	Other HVAC Sys. & Equipment	N/A		—	—	—	
	D40 Fire Protection						
4010	Sprinklers	Sprinklers, extra hazard, deluge system		S.F. Floor	7.70	7.70	13.9%
4020	Standpipes	Standpipe and fire pump		S.F. Floor	4.99	4.99	
	D50 Electrical						
5010	Electrical Service/Distribution	200 ampere service, panel board and feeders		S.F. Floor	.99	.99	
5020	Lighting & Branch Wiring	High intensity discharge fixtures, receptacles, switches and misc. power		S.F. Floor	10.42	10.42	14.1%
5030	Communications & Security	Addressable alarm systems and emergency lighting		S.F. Floor	1.32	1.32	
5090	Other Electrical Systems	Emergency generator, 7.5 kW		S.F. Floor	.13	.13	
E. EQUIPMENT & FURNISHINGS							
1010	Commercial Equipment	N/A		—	—	—	
1020	Institutional Equipment	N/A		—	—	—	0.0 %
1030	Vehicular Equipment	N/A		—	—	—	
1090	Other Equipment	N/A		—	—	—	
F. SPECIAL CONSTRUCTION							
1020	Integrated Construction	N/A		—	—	—	0.0 %
1040	Special Facilities	N/A		—	—	—	
G. BUILDING SITEWORK	**N/A**						

	Sub-Total	91.01	100%
CONTRACTOR FEES (General Requirements: 10%, Overhead: 5%, Profit: 10%)	25%	22.78	
ARCHITECT FEES	7%	7.96	

Total Building Cost	**121.75**

Costs per square foot of floor area

Exterior Wall	S.F. Area	25000	40000	55000	70000	85000	100000	115000	130000	145000
	L.F. Perimeter	388	520	566	666	766	866	878	962	1045
Face Brick with Structural Facing Tile	Steel Frame	350.30	341.85	334.20	331.65	330.10	328.90	326.25	325.55	324.90
	R/Conc. Frame	357.00	348.50	340.80	338.30	336.75	335.60	332.90	332.20	331.60
Face Brick with Concrete Block Back-up	Steel Frame	341.65	334.55	328.40	326.30	325.05	324.10	322.00	321.40	320.85
	R/Conc. Frame	341.10	334.10	327.90	325.85	324.50	323.55	321.50	320.90	320.40
Precast Concrete Panels	Steel Frame	356.10	346.75	338.00	335.20	333.45	332.15	329.10	328.30	327.65
	R/Conc. Frame	362.75	353.40	344.70	341.90	340.15	338.80	335.80	335.00	334.35
Perimeter Adj., Add or Deduct	Per 100 L.F.	9.70	6.00	4.35	3.45	2.85	2.40	2.10	1.85	1.65
Story Hgt. Adj., Add or Deduct	Per 1 Ft.	2.80	2.35	1.85	1.70	1.60	1.60	1.40	1.35	1.35
For Basement, add $36.00 per square foot of basement area										

The above costs were calculated using the basic specifications shown on the facing page. These costs should be adjusted where necessary for design alternatives and owner's requirements. Reported completed project costs, for this type of structure, range from $179.55 to $453.50 per S.F.

Common additives

Description	Unit	$ Cost	Description	Unit	$ Cost
Cabinet, Base, door units, metal	L.F.	315	Nurses Call Station		
Drawer units	L.F.	625	Single bedside call station	Each	330
Tall storage cabinets, 7' high, open	L.F.	590	Ceiling speaker station	Each	154
With doors	L.F.	860	Emergency call station	Each	159
Wall, metal 12-1/2" deep, open	L.F.	238	Pillow speaker	Each	273
With doors	L.F.	430	Double bedside call station	Each	315
Closed Circuit TV (Patient monitoring)			Duty station	Each	320
One station camera & monitor	Each	1975	Standard call button	Each	175
For additional camera, add	Each	1050	Master control station for 20 stations	Each	6300
For automatic iris for low light, add	Each	2725	Sound System		
Hubbard Tank, with accessories			Amplifier, 250 watts	Each	2025
Stainless steel, 125 GPM 45 psi	Each	29,500	Speaker, ceiling or wall	Each	208
For electric hoist, add	Each	3225	Trumpet	Each	400
Mortuary Refrigerator, End operated			Station, Dietary with ice	Each	18,200
2 capacity	Each	13,400	Sterilizers		
6 capacity	Each	24,100	Single door, steam	Each	133,000
			Double door, steam	Each	224,000
			Portable, countertop, steam	Each	3850 - 4700
			Gas	Each	43,200
			Automatic washer/sterilizer	Each	59,500

Model costs calculated for a 3 story building with 12' story height and 55,000 square feet of floor area

					Unit	Unit Cost	Cost Per S.F.	% Of Sub-Total

A. SUBSTRUCTURE

				Unit	Unit Cost	Cost Per S.F.	% Of Sub-Total
1010	Standard Foundations	Poured concrete; strip and spread footings		S.F. Ground	5.55	1.85	
1020	Special Foundations	N/A		—	—	—	
1030	Slab on Grade	4" reinforced concrete with vapor barrier and granular base		S.F. Slab	5.31	1.77	1.8%
2010	Basement Excavation	Site preparation for slab and trench for foundation wall and footing		S.F. Ground	.18	.06	
2020	Basement Walls	4' foundation wall		L.F. Wall	82	.84	

B. SHELL

B10 Superstructure

				Unit	Unit Cost	Cost Per S.F.	% Of Sub-Total
1010	Floor Construction	Cast-in-place concrete beam and slab		S.F. Floor	23.78	15.85	8.9%
1020	Roof Construction	Cast-in-place concrete beam and slab		S.F. Roof	19.14	6.38	

B20 Exterior Enclosure

				Unit	Unit Cost	Cost Per S.F.	% Of Sub-Total
2010	Exterior Walls	Face brick and structural facing tile	85% of wall	S.F. Wall	46.30	14.58	
2020	Exterior Windows	Aluminum sliding	15% of wall	Each	736	1.78	6.7%
2030	Exterior Doors	Double aluminum and glass and sliding doors		Each	3240	.35	

B30 Roofing

				Unit	Unit Cost	Cost Per S.F.	% Of Sub-Total
3010	Roof Coverings	Built-up tar and gravel with flashing; perlite/EPS composite insulation		S.F. Roof	6.18	2.06	0.8%
3020	Roof Openings	Roof hatches		S.F. Roof	.03	.01	

C. INTERIORS

				Unit	Unit Cost	Cost Per S.F.	% Of Sub-Total
1010	Partitions	Concrete block, gypsum board on metal studs	9 S.F. Floor/L.F. Partition	S.F. Partition	8.88	9.87	
1020	Interior Doors	Single leaf hollow metal	90 S.F. Floor/Door	Each	1198	13.31	
1030	Fittings	Hospital curtains		S.F. Floor	1.05	1.05	
2010	Stair Construction	Concrete filled metal pan		Flight	6225	1.47	20.5%
3010	Wall Finishes	40% vinyl wall covering, 35% ceramic tile, 25% epoxy coating		S.F. Surface	3.58	7.95	
3020	Floor Finishes	60% vinyl tile, 20% ceramic, 20% terrazzo		S.F. Floor	10.69	10.69	
3030	Ceiling Finishes	Plaster on suspended metal lath		S.F. Ceiling	6.89	6.89	

D. SERVICES

D10 Conveying

				Unit	Unit Cost	Cost Per S.F.	% Of Sub-Total
1010	Elevators & Lifts	Two hydraulic hospital elevators		Each	121,550	4.42	1.8%
1020	Escalators & Moving Walks	N/A		—	—	—	

D20 Plumbing

				Unit	Unit Cost	Cost Per S.F.	% Of Sub-Total
2010	Plumbing Fixtures	Medical, patient & specialty fixtures, supply and drainage	1 Fixture/224 S.F. Floor	Each	7186	32.08	
2020	Domestic Water Distribution	Electric water heater		S.F. Floor	11.75	11.75	17.7%
2040	Rain Water Drainage	Roof drains		S.F. Roof	1.71	.57	

D30 HVAC

				Unit	Unit Cost	Cost Per S.F.	% Of Sub-Total
3010	Energy Supply	Conditioned air with hot water reheat system		S.F. Floor	4.99	4.99	
3020	Heat Generating Systems	Boiler		Each	122,125	3.49	
3030	Cooling Generating Systems	Conditioned air, chillers, cooling towers		S.F. Floor	6.77	6.77	22.3%
3050	Terminal & Package Units	N/A		—	—	—	
3090	Other HVAC Sys. & Equipment	Conditioned air, ductwork, surgery air curtain		S.F. Floor	40.56	40.56	

D40 Fire Protection

				Unit	Unit Cost	Cost Per S.F.	% Of Sub-Total
4010	Sprinklers	Wet pipe sprinkler system		S.F. Floor	3.03	3.03	1.5%
4020	Standpipes	Standpipe		S.F. Floor	.76	.76	

D50 Electrical

				Unit	Unit Cost	Cost Per S.F.	% Of Sub-Total
5010	Electrical Service/Distribution	1200 ampere service, panel board and feeders		S.F. Floor	1.54	1.54	
5020	Lighting & Branch Wiring	High efficiency hospital grade light fixtures, receptacles, switches, A.C. and misc. power		S.F. Floor	16.53	16.53	11.1%
5030	Communications & Security	Addressable alarm systems, internet wiring, communications systems, emergency lighting		S.F. Floor	5.34	5.34	
5090	Other Electrical Systems	Emergency generator, 200 kW with fuel tank, Uninterruptible power supply		S.F. Floor	4.47	4.47	

E. EQUIPMENT & FURNISHINGS

				Unit	Unit Cost	Cost Per S.F.	% Of Sub-Total
1010	Commercial Equipment	N/A		—	—	—	
1020	Institutional Equipment	Medical gas system, kitchen equip, lab equip., curtain partitions		S.F. Floor	11.36	11.36	6.8%
1030	Vehicular Equipment	N/A		—	—	—	
2020	Moveable Furnishings	Patient wall systems		S.F. Floor	5.73	5.73	

F. SPECIAL CONSTRUCTION

				Unit	Unit Cost	Cost Per S.F.	% Of Sub-Total
1020	Integrated Construction	N/A		—	—	—	0.0%
1040	Special Facilities	N/A		—	—	—	

G. BUILDING SITEWORK   N/A

	Sub-Total	250.15	**100%**
CONTRACTOR FEES (General Requirements: 10%, Overhead: 5%, Profit: 10%)	25%	62.51	
ARCHITECT FEES	9%	28.14	
	Total Building Cost	**340.80**	

Costs per square foot of floor area

Exterior Wall	S.F. Area	100000	125000	150000	175000	200000	225000	250000	275000	300000
	L.F. Perimeter	594	705	816	783	866	950	1033	1116	1200
Face Brick with Structural Facing Tile	Steel Frame	306.70	303.35	301.10	295.45	294.05	293.00	292.15	291.40	290.85
	R/Conc. Frame	311.25	307.80	305.45	299.75	298.35	297.25	296.35	295.60	295.05
Face Brick with Concrete Block Back-up	Steel Frame	301.20	297.95	295.80	291.00	289.75	288.75	287.90	287.25	286.75
	R/Conc. Frame	305.85	302.65	300.40	295.65	294.35	293.35	292.55	291.85	291.35
Precast Concrete Panels With Exposed Aggregate	Steel Frame	304.80	301.35	299.10	293.75	292.30	291.25	290.40	289.65	289.15
	R/Conc. Frame	309.40	306.00	303.70	298.35	296.95	295.85	295.00	294.30	293.75
Perimeter Adj., Add or Deduct	Per 100 L.F.	4.85	3.85	3.20	2.80	2.45	2.20	1.95	1.80	1.65
Story Hgt. Adj., Add or Deduct	Per 1 Ft.	2.20	2.05	1.95	1.65	1.55	1.50	1.45	1.55	1.50
For Basement, add $37.10 per square foot of basement area										

The above costs were calculated using the basic specifications shown on the facing page. These costs should be adjusted where necessary for design alternatives and owner's requirements. Reported completed project costs, for this type of structure, range from $183.65 to $447.85 per S.F.

Common additives

Description	Unit	$ Cost	Description	Unit	$ Cost
Cabinets, Base, door units, metal	L.F.	315	Nurses Call Station		
Drawer units	L.F.	625	Single bedside call station	Each	330
Tall storage cabinets, 7' high, open	L.F.	590	Ceiling speaker station	Each	154
With doors	L.F.	860	Emergency call station	Each	159
Wall, metal 12-1/2" deep, open	L.F.	238	Pillow speaker	Each	273
With doors	L.F.	430	Double bedside call station	Each	315
Closed Circuit TV (Patient monitoring)			Duty station	Each	320
One station camera & monitor	Each	1975	Standard call button	Each	175
For additional camera add	Each	1050	Master control station for 20 stations	Each	6300
For automatic iris for low light add	Each	2725	Sound System		
Hubbard Tank, with accessories			Amplifier, 250 watts	Each	2025
Stainless steel, 125 GPM 45 psi	Each	29,500	Speaker, ceiling or wall	Each	208
For electric hoist, add	Each	3225	Trumpet	Each	400
Mortuary Refrigerator, End operated			Station, Dietary with ice	Each	18,200
2 capacity	Each	13,400	Sterilizers		
6 capacity	Each	24,100	Single door, steam	Each	133,000
			Double door, steam	Each	224,000
			Portable, counter top, steam	Each	3850 - 4700
			Gas	Each	43,200
			Automatic washer/sterilizer	Each	59,500

Important: See the Reference Section for Location Factors.

Model costs calculated for a 6 story building with 12' story height and 200,000 square feet of floor area

				Unit	Unit Cost	Cost Per S.F.	% Of Sub-Total
A. SUBSTRUCTURE							
1010	Standard Foundations	Poured concrete; strip and spread footings		S.F. Ground	14.34	2.39	
1020	Special Foundations	N/A		—	—	—	
1030	Slab on Grade	4" reinforced concrete with vapor barrier and granular base		S.F. Slab	7.82	1.31	1.9%
2010	Basement Excavation	Site preparation for slab and trench for foundation wall and footing		S.F. Ground	.18	.03	
2020	Basement Walls	4' foundation wall		L.F. Wall	82	.35	
B. SHELL							
	B10 Superstructure						
1010	Floor Construction	Concrete slab with metal deck and beams, steel columns		S.F. Floor	22.15	18.46	9.3%
1020	Roof Construction	Metal deck, open web steel joists, beams, interior columns		S.F. Roof	9.24	1.54	
	B20 Exterior Enclosure						
2010	Exterior Walls	Face brick and structural facing tile	70% of wall	S.F. Wall	46.28	10.10	
2020	Exterior Windows	Aluminum sliding	30% of wall	Each	585	3.65	6.7%
2030	Exterior Doors	Double aluminum and glass and sliding doors		Each	5787	.81	
	B30 Roofing						
3010	Roof Coverings	Built-up tar and gravel with flashing; perlite/EPS composite insulation		S.F. Roof	7.56	1.26	0.6%
3020	Roof Openings	Roof hatches		S.F. Roof	.18	.03	
C. INTERIORS							
1010	Partitions	Gypsum board on metal studs with sound deadening board	9 S.F. Floor/L.F. Partition	S.F. Partition	7.95	8.83	
1020	Interior Doors	Single leaf hollow metal	90 S.F. Floor/Door	Each	1198	13.31	
1030	Fittings	Hospital curtains		S.F. Floor	1.16	1.16	
2010	Stair Construction	Concrete filled metal pan		Flight	11,575	1.50	24.3%
3010	Wall Finishes	40% vinyl wall covering, 35% ceramic tile, 25% epoxy coating		S.F. Surface	3.57	7.94	
3020	Floor Finishes	60% vinyl tile, 20% ceramic, 20% terrazzo		S.F. Floor	11.59	11.59	
3030	Ceiling Finishes	Plaster on suspended metal lath		S.F. Ceiling	8.06	8.07	
D. SERVICES							
	D10 Conveying						
1010	Elevators & Lifts	Six geared hospital elevators		Each	217,667	6.53	3.0%
1020	Escalators & Moving Walks	N/A		—	—	—	
	D20 Plumbing						
2010	Plumbing Fixtures	Kitchen, toilet and service fixtures, supply and drainage	1 Fixture/416S.F. Floor	Each	6144	14.77	
2020	Domestic Water Distribution	Electric water heater		S.F. Floor	4.99	4.99	9.4%
2040	Rain Water Drainage	Roof drains		S.F. Floor	3.78	.63	
	D30 HVAC						
3010	Energy Supply	Oil fired hot water, wall fin radiation		S.F. Floor	4.28	4.28	
3020	Heat Generating Systems	Hot water boilers, steam boiler for services		Each	43,175	.54	
3030	Cooling Generating Systems	Chilled water units		S.F. Floor	3.04	3.04	20.7%
3050	Terminal & Package Units	N/A		—	—	—	
3090	Other HVAC Sys. & Equipment	Conditioned air with reheat, operating room air curtains		S.F. Floor	36.88	36.88	
	D40 Fire Protection						
4010	Sprinklers	Wet pipe sprinkler system		S.F. Floor	2.85	2.85	1.6%
4020	Standpipes	Standpipe		S.F. Floor	.51	.51	
	D50 Electrical						
5010	Electrical Service/Distribution	4000 ampere service, panel board and feeders		S.F. Floor	3.32	3.32	
5020	Lighting & Branch Wiring	High efficiency hospital grade light fixtures, receptacles, switches, A.C. and misc. power		S.F. Floor	19.28	19.28	13.7%
5030	Communications & Security	Addressable alarm systems, internet wiring, communications system, emergency lighting		S.F. Slab	2.45	2.45	
5090	Other Electrical Systems	Emergency generator, 800 kW with fuel tank, uninterruptible power supply		S.F. Floor	4.50	4.50	
E. EQUIPMENT & FURNISHINGS							
1010	Commercial Equipment	N/A		—	—	—	
1020	Institutional Equipment	Medical gases, curtain partitions		S.F. Floor	15.14	15.14	8.8 %
1030	Vehicular Equipment	N/A		—	—	—	
2020	Moveable Furnishings	Patient wall systems		S.F. Floor	3.78	3.78	
F. SPECIAL CONSTRUCTION							
1020	Integrated Construction	N/A		—	—	—	0.0 %
1040	Special Facilities	N/A		—	—	—	
G. BUILDING SITEWORK	**N/A**						

			Sub-Total	215.82	100%
CONTRACTOR FEES (General Requirements: 10%, Overhead: 5%, Profit: 10%)		25%	53.95		
ARCHITECT FEES		9%	24.28		

Total Building Cost	**294.05**

Costs per square foot of floor area

Exterior Wall	S.F. Area	35000	55000	75000	95000	115000	135000	155000	175000	195000
	L.F. Perimeter	314	401	497	555	639	722	754	783	850
Face Brick with Concrete Block Back-up	Steel Frame	203.45	194.55	190.80	187.25	185.65	184.60	182.55	181.00	180.40
	R/Conc. Frame	203.50	194.60	190.85	187.30	185.70	184.65	182.65	181.05	180.50
Glass and Metal Curtain Walls	Steel Frame	217.95	206.05	201.10	196.20	194.15	192.65	189.90	187.70	186.85
	R/Conc. Frame	218.30	206.35	201.40	196.50	194.45	192.95	190.20	188.00	187.20
Precast Concrete Panels	Steel Frame	214.10	202.90	198.20	193.70	191.70	190.35	187.80	185.75	185.00
	R/Conc. Frame	215.60	204.20	199.40	194.75	192.75	191.30	188.75	186.65	185.85
Perimeter Adj., Add or Deduct	Per 100 L.F.	10.15	6.45	4.75	3.75	3.15	2.60	2.35	2.00	1.80
Story Hgt. Adj., Add or Deduct	Per 1 Ft.	2.85	2.30	2.10	1.80	1.80	1.65	1.60	1.45	1.40

For Basement, add $35.35 per square foot of basement area

The above costs were calculated using the basic specifications shown on the facing page. These costs should be adjusted where necessary for design alternatives and owner's requirements. Reported completed project costs, for this type of structure, range from $121.15 to $232.55 per S.F.

Common additives

Description	Unit	$ Cost
Bar, Front bar	L.F.	415
Back bar	L.F.	330
Booth, Upholstered, custom, straight	L.F.	241 - 440
"L" or "U" shaped	L.F.	249 - 425
Closed Circuit Surveillance, One station		
Camera and monitor	Each	1975
For additional camera stations, add	Each	1050
Directory Boards, Plastic, glass covered		
30" x 20"	Each	630
36" x 48"	Each	1500
Aluminum, 24" x 18"	Each	630
48" x 32"	Each	1050
48" x 60"	Each	2200
Elevators, Electric passenger, 5 stops		
3500# capacity	Each	173,200
5000# capacity	Each	179,200
Additional stop, add	Each	12,700
Emergency Lighting, 25 watt, battery operated		
Lead battery	Each	320
Nickel cadmium	Each	885

Description	Unit	$ Cost
Laundry Equipment		
Folders, blankets & sheets, king size	Each	71,500
Ironers, 110" single roll	Each	38,100
Combination washer extractor 50#	Each	13,300
125#	Each	36,500
Sauna, Prefabricated, complete		
6' x 4'	Each	6800
6' x 6'	Each	7950
6' x 9'	Each	9725
8' x 8'	Each	11,500
10' x 12'	Each	15,400
Smoke Detectors		
Ceiling type	Each	223
Duct type	Each	555
Sound System		
Amplifier, 250 watts	Each	2025
Speaker, ceiling or wall	Each	208
Trumpet	Each	400
TV Antenna, Master system, 12 outlet	Outlet	280
30 outlet	Outlet	218
100 outlet	Outlet	206

Important: See the Reference Section for Location Factors.

Model costs calculated for a 6 story building with 10' story height and 135,000 square feet of floor area

			Unit	Unit Cost	Cost Per S.F.	% Of Sub-Total
A. SUBSTRUCTURE						
1010	Standard Foundations	Poured concrete; strip and spread footings	S.F. Ground	6.24	1.04	
1020	Special Foundations	N/A	—	—	—	
1030	Slab on Grade	4" reinforced concrete with vapor barrier and granular base	S.F. Slab	5.31	.89	2.0%
2010	Basement Excavation	Site preparation for slab and trench for foundation wall and footing	S.F. Ground	.18	.03	
2020	Basement Walls	4' foundation wall	L.F. Wall	82	.87	
B. SHELL						
	B10 Superstructure					
1010	Floor Construction	Concrete slab with metal deck, beams, columns	S.F. Floor	21.44	17.87	14.1%
1020	Roof Construction	Metal deck, open web steel joists, beams, columns	S.F. Roof	10.74	1.79	
	B20 Exterior Enclosure					
2010	Exterior Walls	Face brick with concrete block backup	80% of wall	S.F. Wall	32.92	8.45	
2020	Exterior Windows	Window wall	20% of wall	Each	51	3.26	8.6%
2030	Exterior Doors	Glass amd metal doors and entrances	Each	3583	.27	
	B30 Roofing					
3010	Roof Coverings	Built-up tar and gravel with flashing; perlite/EPS composite insulation	S.F. Roof	6.24	1.04	0.8%
3020	Roof Openings	Roof hatches	S.F. Roof	.06	.01	
C. INTERIORS						
1010	Partitions	Gypsum board and sound deadening board, steel studs	9 S.F. Floor/L.F. Partition	S.F. Partition	7.32	6.51	
1020	Interior Doors	Single leaf hollow metal	90 S.F. Floor/Door	Each	1152	12.80	
1030	Fittings	N/A	—	—	—	
2010	Stair Construction	Concrete filled metal pan	Flight	14,450	1.50	24.7%
3010	Wall Finishes	20% paint, 75% vinyl cover, 5% ceramic tile	S.F. Surface	2.04	3.62	
3020	Floor Finishes	80% carpet, 10% vinyl composition tile, 10% ceramic tile	S.F. Floor	5.54	5.54	
3030	Ceiling Finishes	Mineral fiber tile applied with adhesive	S.F. Ceiling	4.37	4.37	
D. SERVICES						
	D10 Conveying					
1010	Elevators & Lifts	Four geared passenger elevators	Each	233,213	6.91	5.0%
1020	Escalators & Moving Walks	N/A	—	—	—	
	D20 Plumbing					
2010	Plumbing Fixtures	Kitchen, toilet and service fixtures, supply and drainage	1 Fixture/155 S.F. Floor	Each	3956	25.52	
2020	Domestic Water Distribution	Oil fired water heater	S.F. Floor	.64	.64	19.0%
2040	Rain Water Drainage	Roof drains	S.F. Roof	1.56	.26	
	D30 HVAC					
3010	Energy Supply	Gas fired hot water, wall fin radiation	S.F. Floor	4.88	4.88	
3020	Heat Generating Systems	N/A	—	—	—	
3030	Cooling Generating Systems	Chilled water, fan coil units	S.F. Floor	13.80	13.80	13.4%
3050	Terminal & Package Units	N/A	—	—	—	
3090	Other HVAC Sys. & Equipment	N/A	—	—	—	
	D40 Fire Protection					
4010	Sprinklers	Sprinkler system, light hazard	S.F. Floor	2.86	2.86	2.3%
4020	Standpipes	Standpipes and hose systems	S.F. Floor	.38	.38	
	D50 Electrical					
5010	Electrical Service/Distribution	2000 ampere service, panel board and feeders	S.F. Floor	1.08	1.08	
5020	Lighting & Branch Wiring	High efficiency fluorescent fixtures, receptacles, switches, A.C. and misc. power	S.F. Floor	8.50	8.50	10.2%
5030	Communications & Security	Addressable alarm systems, internet wiring, communications systems and emergency lighting	S.F. Floor	4.19	4.19	
5090	Other Electrical Systems	Emergency generator, 250 kW	S.F. Floor	.42	.42	
E. EQUIPMENT & FURNISHINGS						
1010	Commercial Equipment	N/A	—	—	—	
1020	Institutional Equipment	N/A	—	—	—	0.0 %
1030	Vehicular Equipment	N/A	—	—	—	
1090	Other Equipment	N/A	—	—	—	
F. SPECIAL CONSTRUCTION						
1020	Integrated Construction	N/A	—	—	—	0.0 %
1040	Special Facilities	N/A	—	—	—	
G. BUILDING SITEWORK	**N/A**					

			Sub-Total	139.30	**100%**
CONTRACTOR FEES (General Requirements: 10%, Overhead: 5%, Profit: 10%)			25%	34.85	
ARCHITECT FEES			6%	10.45	

Total Building Cost	**184.60**

Costs per square foot of floor area

Exterior Wall	S.F. Area	140000	243000	346000	450000	552000	655000	760000	860000	965000
	L.F. Perimeter	403	587	672	800	936	1073	1213	1195	1312
Face Brick with Concrete Block Back-up	Steel Frame	184.40	178.00	172.95	171.10	170.05	169.35	168.75	166.90	166.60
	R/Conc. Frame	187.40	180.95	175.95	174.00	173.00	172.25	171.75	169.90	169.50
Face Brick Veneer On Steel Studs	Steel Frame	181.00	175.15	170.70	169.00	168.05	167.40	166.90	165.30	164.95
	R/Conc. Frame	186.90	181.05	176.60	174.90	173.95	173.30	172.80	171.20	170.85
Glass and Metal Curtain Walls	Steel Frame	231.90	217.80	208.50	204.70	202.50	201.05	199.90	197.00	196.30
	R/Conc. Frame	226.00	212.05	202.95	199.15	196.95	195.50	194.40	191.45	190.80
Perimeter Adj., Add or Deduct	Per 100 L.F.	6.05	3.45	2.45	1.90	1.50	1.30	1.15	1.00	0.90
Story Hgt. Adj., Add or Deduct	Per 1 Ft.	2.35	1.95	1.60	1.40	1.35	1.30	1.30	1.10	1.10

For Basement, add $36.70 per square foot of basement area

The above costs were calculated using the basic specifications shown on the facing page. These costs should be adjusted where necessary for design alternatives and owner's requirements. Reported completed project costs, for this type of structure, range from $134.45 to $235.10 per S.F.

Common additives

Description	Unit	$ Cost	Description	Unit	$ Cost
Bar, Front bar	L.F.	415	Laundry Equipment		
Back bar	L.F.	330	Folders, blankets & sheets, king size	Each	71,500
Booth, Upholstered, custom, straight	L.F.	241 - 440	Ironers, 110" single roll	Each	38,100
"L" or "U" shaped	L.F.	249 - 425	Combination washer & extractor 50#	Each	13,300
Closed Circuit Surveillance, One station			125#	Each	36,500
Camera and monitor	Each	1975	Sauna, Prefabricated, complete		
For additional camera stations, add	Each	1050	6' x 4'	Each	6800
Directory Boards, Plastic, glass covered			6' x 6'	Each	7950
30" x 20"	Each	630	6' x 9'	Each	9725
36" x 48"	Each	1500	8' x 8'	Each	11,500
Aluminum, 24" x 18"	Each	630	10' x 12'	Each	15,400
48" x 32"	Each	1050	Smoke Detectors		
48" x 60"	Each	2200	Ceiling type	Each	223
Elevators, Electric passenger, 10 stops			Duct type	Each	555
3500# capacity	Each	420,000	Sound System		
5000# capacity	Each	427,500	Amplifier, 250 watts	Each	2025
Additional stop, add	Each	12,700	Speaker, ceiling or wall	Each	208
Emergency Lighting, 25 watt, battery operated			Trumpet	Each	400
Lead battery	Each	320	TV Antenna, Master system, 12 outlet	Outlet	280
Nickel cadmium	Each	885	30 outlet	Outlet	218
			100 outlet	Outlet	206

Important: See the Reference Section for Location Factors.

Model costs calculated for a 15 story building with 10' story height and 450,000 square feet of floor area

Hotel, 8-24 Story

				Unit	Unit Cost	Cost Per S.F.	% Of Sub-Total
A. SUBSTRUCTURE							
1010	Standard Foundations	CIP concrete pile caps		S.F. Ground	6	.40	
1020	Special Foundations	Steel H-piles, concrete grade beams		S.F. Ground	110	7.32	
1030	Slab on Grade	4" reinforced concrete with vapor barrier and granular base		S.F. Slab	5.31	.36	5.4%
2010	Basement Excavation	Site preparation for slab, piles and grade beams		S.F. Ground	.18	.01	
2020	Basement Walls	4' foundation wall		L.F. Wall	82	.18	
B. SHELL							
	B10 Superstructure						
1010	Floor Construction	Open web steel joists, slab form, concrete, columns		S.F. Floor	21.43	20	13.4%
1020	Roof Construction	Metal deck, open web steel joists, beams, columns		S.F. Roof	9.45	.63	
	B20 Exterior Enclosure						
2010	Exterior Walls	N/A		—	—	—	
2020	Exterior Windows	Glass and metal curtain walls	100% of wall	Each	56	14.81	9.7 %
2030	Exterior Doors	Glass and metal doors and entrances		Each	3263	.23	
	B30 Roofing						
3010	Roof Coverings	Built-up tar and gravel with flashing; perlite/EPS composite insulation		S.F. Roof	6	.40	0.3%
3020	Roof Openings	N/A		—	—	—	
C. INTERIORS							
1010	Partitions	Gypsum board and sound deadening board, steel studs	9 S.F. Floor/L.F. Partition	S.F. Partition	7.10	6.31	
1020	Interior Doors	Single leaf hollow metal	90 S.F. Floor/Door	Each	1152	12.80	
1030	Fittings	N/A					
2010	Stair Construction	Concrete filled metal pan		Flight	14,450	2.93	22.8%
3010	Wall Finishes	20% paint, 75% vinyl cover, 5% ceramic tile		S.F. Surface	2.01	3.58	
3020	Floor Finishes	80% carpet tile, 10% vinyl composition tile, 10% ceramic tile		S.F. Floor	5.54	5.54	
3030	Ceiling Finishes	Gypsum board on resilient channel		S.F. Ceiling	4.12	4.12	
D. SERVICES							
	D10 Conveying						
1010	Elevators & Lifts	One geared freight, six geared passenger elevators		Each	509,250	6.79	4.4%
1020	Escalators & Moving Walks	N/A		—	—	—	
	D20 Plumbing						
2010	Plumbing Fixtures	Kitchen, toilet and service fixtures, supply and drainage	1 Fixture/165 S.F. Floor	Each	4359	26.42	
2020	Domestic Water Distribution	Electric water heater		S.F. Floor	3.39	3.39	19.4%
2040	Rain Water Drainage	Roof drains		S.F. Roof	2.10	.14	
	D30 HVAC						
3010	Energy Supply	Gas fired hot water, wall fin radiation		S.F. Floor	2.62	2.62	
3020	Heat Generating Systems	N/A		—	—	—	
3030	Cooling Generating Systems	Chilled water, fan coil units		S.F. Floor	13.80	13.80	10.6%
3050	Terminal & Package Units	N/A		—	—	—	
3090	Other HVAC Sys. & Equipment	N/A		—	—	—	
	D40 Fire Protection						
4010	Sprinklers	Sprinkler system, light hazard		S.F. Floor	3.99	3.99	4.9%
4020	Standpipes	Standpipes, fire pump and hose systems		S.F. Floor	3.60	3.60	
	D50 Electrical						
5010	Electrical Service/Distribution	6000 ampere service, panel board and feeders		S.F. Floor	1.23	1.23	
5020	Lighting & Branch Wiring	High efficiency fluorescent fixtures, receptacles, switches, A.C. and misc. power		S.F. Floor	8.39	8.39	9.1%
5030	Communications & Security	Addressable alarm systems, internet wiring, communications systems and emergency lighting		S.F. Floor	4.17	4.17	
5090	Other Electrical Systems	Emergency generator, 500 kW		S.F. Floor	.31	.31	
E. EQUIPMENT & FURNISHINGS							
1010	Commercial Equipment	N/A		—	—	—	
1020	Institutional Equipment	N/A		—	—	—	0.0 %
1030	Vehicular Equipment	N/A		—	—	—	
1090	Other Equipment	N/A		—	—	—	
F. SPECIAL CONSTRUCTION							
1020	Integrated Construction	N/A		—	—	—	0.0 %
1040	Special Facilities	N/A		—	—	—	
G. BUILDING SITEWORK	**N/A**						

			Sub-Total	154.47	100%
CONTRACTOR FEES (General Requirements: 10%, Overhead: 5%, Profit: 10%)		25%	38.64		
ARCHITECT FEES		6%	11.59		

Total Building Cost	**204.70**

155

Costs per square foot of floor area

Exterior Wall	S.F. Area	5500	12000	20000	30000	40000	60000	80000	100000	145000
	L.F. Perimeter	310	330	400	490	530	590	680	760	920
Face Brick with Concrete Block Back-up	Steel Frame	484.30	365.85	332.20	315.65	303.85	291.00	285.70	282.25	277.45
	R/Conc. Frame	483.80	365.35	331.65	315.15	303.35	290.45	285.15	281.70	276.90
Stucco on Concrete Block	Steel Frame	452.40	350.40	321.05	306.60	296.55	285.65	281.00	278.10	274.05
	R/Conc. Frame	451.60	349.65	320.30	305.80	295.75	284.85	280.25	277.35	273.30
Reinforced Concrete	Steel Frame	459.70	354.00	323.65	308.70	298.25	286.85	282.15	279.10	274.85
	R/Conc. Frame	458.90	353.20	322.85	307.90	297.45	286.10	281.35	278.30	274.10
Perimeter Adj., Add or Deduct	Per 100 L.F.	51.75	23.70	14.30	9.50	7.10	4.75	3.50	2.85	1.95
Story Hgt. Adj., Add or Deduct	Per 1 Ft.	12.35	6.05	4.45	3.60	2.90	2.15	1.85	1.70	1.40

For Basement, add $50.75 per square foot of basement area

The above costs were calculated using the basic specifications shown on the facing page. These costs should be adjusted where necessary for design alternatives and owner's requirements. Reported completed project costs, for this type of structure, range from $195.65 to $519.60 per S.F.

Common additives

Description	Unit	$ Cost	Description	Unit	$ Cost
Clock System			Emergency Lighting, 25 watt, battery operated		
20 room	Each	19,500	Nickel cadmium	Each	885
50 room	Each	45,700	Flagpoles, Complete		
Closed Circuit Surveillance, One station			Aluminum, 20' high	Each	1775
Camera and monitor	Each	1975	40' High	Each	3925
For additional camera stations, add	Each	1050	70' High	Each	10,800
Elevators, Hydraulic passenger, 2 stops			Fiberglass, 23' High	Each	1325
1500# capacity	Each	66,100	39'-5" High	Each	3575
2500# capacity	Each	69,200	59' High	Each	7275
3500# capacity	Each	73,200	Laundry Equipment		
Additional stop, add	Each	8575	Folders, blankets, & sheets	Each	71,500
Emergency Generators, Complete system, gas			Ironers, 110" single roll	Each	38,100
15 KW	Each	16,200	Combination washer & extractor, 50#	Each	13,300
70 KW	Each	30,500	125#	Each	36,500
85 KW	Each	33,900	Safe, Office type, 1 hour rating		
115 KW	Each	64,500	30" x 18" x 18"	Each	2500
170 KW	Each	84,500	60" x 36" x 18", double door	Each	8075
Diesel, 50 KW	Each	25,500	Sound System		
100 KW	Each	36,400	Amplifier, 250 watts	Each	2025
150 KW	Each	44,000	Speaker, ceiling or wall	Each	208
350 KW	Each	69,000	Trumpet	Each	400

Important: See the Reference Section for Location Factors.

Model costs calculated for a 3 story building with 12' story height and 40,000 square feet of floor area

Jail

				Unit	Unit Cost	Cost Per S.F.	% Of Sub-Total
A. SUBSTRUCTURE							
1010	Standard Foundations	Poured concrete; strip and spread footings		S.F. Ground	2.16	.72	
1020	Special Foundations	N/A		—	—	—	
1030	Slab on Grade	4" reinforced concrete with vapor barrier and granular base		S.F. Slab	5.31	1.77	1.6%
2010	Basement Excavation	Site preparation for slab and trench for foundation wall and footing		S.F. Ground	.32	.11	
2020	Basement Walls	4' foundation wall		L.F. Wall	73	.96	
B. SHELL							
B10 Superstructure							
1010	Floor Construction	Concrete slab with metal deck and beams		S.F. Floor	29.91	19.94	12.2%
1020	Roof Construction	Concrete slab with metal deck and beams		S.F. Roof	23.37	7.79	
B20 Exterior Enclosure							
2010	Exterior Walls	Face brick with reinforced concrete block backup	85% of wall	S.F. Wall	32.90	13.34	
2020	Exterior Windows	Bullet resisting and metal horizontal pivoted	15% of wall	Each	160	11.42	11.0%
2030	Exterior Doors	Metal		Each	6450	.16	
B30 Roofing							
3010	Roof Coverings	Built-up tar and gravel with flashing; perlite/EPS composite insulation		S.F. Roof	6.36	2.12	0.9%
3020	Roof Openings	Roof hatches		S.F. Roof	.09	.03	
C. INTERIORS							
1010	Partitions	Concrete block	45 S.F. of Floor/L.F. Partition	S.F. Partition	10.46	2.79	
1020	Interior Doors	Hollow metal fire doors	930 S.F. Floor/Door	Each	1152	1.24	
1030	Fittings	N/A		—	—	—	
2010	Stair Construction	Concrete filled metal pan		Flight	17,250	2.16	6.1%
3010	Wall Finishes	Paint		S.F. Surface	4.33	2.31	
3020	Floor Finishes	70% vinyl composition tile, 20% carpet, 10% ceramic tile		S.F. Floor	3.35	3.35	
3030	Ceiling Finishes	Mineral tile on zee runners	30% of area	S.F. Ceiling	6.89	2.07	
D. SERVICES							
D10 Conveying							
1010	Elevators & Lifts	One hydraulic passenger elevator		Each	167,200	4.18	1.8%
1020	Escalators & Moving Walks	N/A		—	—	—	
D20 Plumbing							
2010	Plumbing Fixtures	Toilet and service fixtures, supply and drainage	1 Fixture/78 S.F. Floor	Each	4110	52.69	
2020	Domestic Water Distribution	Electric water heater		S.F. Floor	4.16	4.16	25.5%
2040	Rain Water Drainage	Roof drains		S.F. Roof	2.97	.99	
D30 HVAC							
3010	Energy Supply	N/A		—	—	—	
3020	Heat Generating Systems	Included in D3050		—	—	—	
3030	Cooling Generating Systems	N/A		—	—	—	7.1%
3050	Terminal & Package Units	Rooftop multizone unit systems		S.F. Floor	16.07	16.07	
3090	Other HVAC Sys. & Equipment	N/A		—	—	—	
D40 Fire Protection							
4010	Sprinklers	Sprinkler system, light hazard		S.F. Floor	2.95	2.95	1.6%
4020	Standpipes	Standpipes and hose systems		S.F. Floor	.59	.59	
D50 Electrical							
5010	Electrical Service/Distribution	600 ampere service, panel board and feeders		S.F. Floor	1.03	1.03	
5020	Lighting & Branch Wiring	Fluorescent fixtures, receptacles, switches, A.C. and misc. power		S.F. Floor	9.78	9.78	7.0%
5030	Communications & Security	Addressable alarm systems, intercom, and emergency lighting		S.F. Floor	4.35	4.35	
5090	Other Electrical Systems	Emergency generator, 80 kW		S.F. Floor	.67	.67	
E. EQUIPMENT & FURNISHINGS							
1010	Commercial Equipment	N/A		—	—	—	
1020	Institutional Equipment	Prefabricated cells, visitor cubicles		S.F. Floor	57	57.43	25.3%
1030	Vehicular Equipment	N/A		—	—	—	
1090	Other Equipment	N/A		—	—	—	
F. SPECIAL CONSTRUCTION							
1020	Integrated Construction	N/A		—	—	—	0.0%
1040	Special Facilities	N/A		—	—	—	
G. BUILDING SITEWORK	**N/A**						

Sub-Total		227.17	**100%**
CONTRACTOR FEES (General Requirements: 10%, Overhead: 5%, Profit: 10%)	25%	56.80	
ARCHITECT FEES	7%	19.88	
Total Building Cost		**303.85**	

Costs per square foot of floor area

Exterior Wall	S.F. Area	1000	2000	3000	4000	5000	10000	15000	20000	25000
	L.F. Perimeter	126	179	219	253	283	400	490	568	632
Decorative Concrete Block	Steel Frame	295.15	248.25	230.20	220.25	213.95	199.30	193.35	190.05	187.80
	Bearing Walls	295.85	248.55	230.25	220.20	213.80	198.90	193.00	189.55	187.25
Face Brick with Concrete Block Back-up	Steel Frame	329.10	273.45	251.35	239.05	231.10	212.45	204.80	200.45	197.40
	Bearing Walls	326.30	270.15	247.85	235.45	227.45	208.60	200.85	196.40	193.35
Metal Sandwich Panel	Steel Frame	299.00	252.25	234.20	224.30	218.00	203.35	197.50	194.20	191.90
Precast Concrete Panel	Bearing Walls	291.30	245.30	227.60	217.90	211.75	197.50	191.75	188.50	186.35
Perimeter Adj., Add or Deduct	Per 100 L.F.	56.60	28.30	18.85	14.20	11.25	5.65	3.80	2.85	2.25
Story Hgt. Adj., Add or Deduct	Per 1 Ft.	3.80	2.70	2.15	1.90	1.65	1.20	1.00	0.85	0.75

For Basement, add $33.60 per square foot of basement area

The above costs were calculated using the basic specifications shown on the facing page. These costs should be adjusted where necessary for design alternatives and owner's requirements. Reported completed project costs, for this type of structure, range from $108.95 to $266.25 per S.F.

Common additives

Description	Unit	$ Cost
Closed Circuit Surveillance, One station		
Camera and monitor	Each	1975
For additional camera stations, add	Each	1050
Emergency Lighting, 25 watt, battery operated		
Lead battery	Each	320
Nickel cadmium	Each	885
Laundry Equipment		
Dryers, coin operated 30 lb.	Each	3800
Double stacked	Each	8275
50 lb.	Each	4100
Dry cleaner 20 lb.	Each	43,300
30 lb.	Each	64,500
Washers, coin operated	Each	1600
Washer/extractor 20 lb.	Each	7125
30 lb.	Each	11,400
50 lb.	Each	13,300
75 lb.	Each	25,600
Smoke Detectors		
Ceiling type	Each	223
Duct type	Each	555

Important: See the Reference Section for Location Factors.

Model costs calculated for a 1 story building with 12' story height and 3,000 square feet of floor area

Laundromat

				Unit	Unit Cost	Cost Per S.F.	% Of Sub-Total
A. SUBSTRUCTURE							
1010	Standard Foundations	Poured concrete; strip and spread footings		S.F. Ground	3.34	3.34	
1020	Special Foundations	N/A		—	—	—	
1030	Slab on Grade	5" reinforced concrete with vapor barrier and granular base		S.F. Slab	5.72	5.72	8.7%
2010	Basement Excavation	Site preparation for slab and trench for foundation wall and footing		S.F. Ground	.57	.57	
2020	Basement Walls	4' Foundation wall		L.F. Wall	73	5.30	
B. SHELL							
	B10 Superstructure						
1010	Floor Construction	N/A		—	—	—	
1020	Roof Construction	Metal deck, open web steel joists, beams, columns		S.F. Roof	10.33	10.33	6.0 %
	B20 Exterior Enclosure						
2010	Exterior Walls	Decorative concrete block	90% of wall	S.F. Wall	15.80	12.46	
2020	Exterior Windows	Store front	10% of wall	Each	42.65	3.73	10.3%
2030	Exterior Doors	Double aluminum and glass		Each	4725	1.58	
	B30 Roofing						
3010	Roof Coverings	Built-up tar and gravel with flashing; perlite/EPS composite insulation		S.F. Roof	9.88	9.88	5.7%
3020	Roof Openings	N/A		—	—	—	
C. INTERIORS							
1010	Partitions	Gypsum board on metal studs	60 S.F. Floor/L.F. Partition	S.F. Partition	25.80	4.30	
1020	Interior Doors	Single leaf wood	750 S.F. Floor/Door	Each	636	.85	
1030	Fittings	N/A		—	—	—	
2010	Stair Construction	N/A		—	—	—	6.5%
3010	Wall Finishes	Paint		S.F. Surface	.84	.28	
3020	Floor Finishes	Vinyl composition tile		S.F. Floor	1.94	1.94	
3030	Ceiling Finishes	Fiberglass board on exposed grid system		S.F. Ceiling	3.82	3.82	
D. SERVICES							
	D10 Conveying						
1010	Elevators & Lifts	N/A		—	—	—	0.0 %
1020	Escalators & Moving Walks	N/A		—	—	—	
	D20 Plumbing						
2010	Plumbing Fixtures	Toilet and service fixtures, supply and drainage	1 Fixture/600 S.F. Floor	Each	6642	11.07	
2020	Domestic Water Distribution	Gas fired hot water heater		S.F. Floor	49.26	49.26	36.2%
2040	Rain Water Drainage	Roof drains		S.F. Roof	2.03	2.03	
	D30 HVAC						
3010	Energy Supply	N/A		—	—	—	
3020	Heat Generating Systems	Included in D3050		—	—	—	
3030	Cooling Generating Systems	N/A		—	—	—	5.8 %
3050	Terminal & Package Units	Rooftop single zone unit systems		S.F. Floor	10.06	10.06	
3090	Other HVAC Sys. & Equipment	N/A		—	—	—	
	D40 Fire Protection						
4010	Sprinklers	Sprinkler, ordinary hazard		S.F. Floor	5.23	5.23	3.0%
4020	Standpipes	N/A		—	—	—	
	D50 Electrical						
5010	Electrical Service/Distribution	200 ampere service, panel board and feeders		S.F. Floor	4.03	4.03	
5020	Lighting & Branch Wiring	High efficiency fluorescent fixtures, receptacles, switches, A.C. and misc. power		S.F. Floor	22.76	22.76	17.6%
5030	Communications & Security	Addressable alarm systems and emergency lighting		S.F. Floor	3.10	3.10	
5090	Other Electrical Systems	Emergency generator, 7.5 kW		S.F. Floor	.45	.45	
E. EQUIPMENT & FURNISHINGS							
1010	Commercial Equipment	N/A		—	—	—	
1020	Institutional Equipment	N/A		—	—	—	0.0 %
1030	Vehicular Equipment	N/A		—	—	—	
1090	Other Equipment	N/A		—	—	—	
F. SPECIAL CONSTRUCTION							
1020	Integrated Construction	N/A		—	—	—	0.0 %
1040	Special Facilities	N/A		—	—	—	
G. BUILDING SITEWORK	**N/A**						

			Sub-Total	172.09	**100%**
CONTRACTOR FEES (General Requirements: 10%, Overhead: 5%, Profit: 10%)			25%	43.05	
ARCHITECT FEES			7%	15.06	

Total Building Cost	**230.20**

Costs per square foot of floor area

Exterior Wall	S.F. Area	7000	10000	13000	16000	19000	22000	25000	28000	31000
	L.F. Perimeter	240	300	336	386	411	435	472	510	524
Face Brick with Concrete Block Back-up	R/Conc. Frame	193.40	183.95	175.75	172.10	167.45	163.90	162.20	160.90	158.50
	Steel Frame	194.35	184.90	176.75	173.10	168.45	164.95	163.20	161.85	159.45
Limestone with Concrete Block	R/Conc. Frame	238.45	221.60	207.30	200.85	192.75	186.70	183.60	181.30	177.15
	Steel Frame	233.80	219.40	206.45	200.85	193.35	187.65	184.90	182.80	178.90
Precast Concrete Panels	R/Conc. Frame	206.60	193.75	183.25	178.45	172.65	168.30	166.05	164.35	161.45
	Steel Frame	207.60	194.75	184.30	179.45	173.65	169.35	167.05	165.35	162.40
Perimeter Adj., Add or Deduct	Per 100 L.F.	23.55	16.50	12.75	10.35	8.70	7.55	6.60	5.85	5.35
Story Hgt. Adj., Add or Deduct	Per 1 Ft.	3.55	3.10	2.65	2.50	2.25	2.15	1.95	1.90	1.75
For Basement, add $48.05 per square foot of basement area										

The above costs were calculated using the basic specifications shown on the facing page. These costs should be adjusted where necessary for design alternatives and owner's requirements. Reported completed project costs, for this type of structure, range from $104.65 to $268.60 per S.F.

Common additives

Description	Unit	$ Cost
Carrels Hardwood	Each	960 - 2300
Closed Circuit Surveillance, One station		
Camera and monitor	Each	1975
For additional camera stations, add	Each	1050
Elevators, Hydraulic passenger, 2 stops		
1500# capacity	Each	66,100
2500# capacity	Each	69,200
3500# capacity	Each	73,200
Emergency Lighting, 25 watt, battery operated		
Lead battery	Each	320
Nickel cadmium	Each	885
Flagpoles, Complete		
Aluminum, 20' high	Each	1775
40' high	Each	3925
70' high	Each	10,800
Fiberglass, 23' high	Each	1325
39'-5" high	Each	3575
59' high	Each	7275

Description	Unit	$ Cost
Library Furnishings		
Bookshelf, 90" high, 10" shelf double face	L.F.	214
single face	L.F.	180
Charging desk, built-in with counter		
Plastic laminated top	L.F.	410
Reading table, laminated		
top 60" x 36"	Each	760

Model costs calculated for a 2 story building with 14' story height and 22,000 square feet of floor area

				Unit	Unit Cost	Cost Per S.F.	% Of Sub-Total
A. SUBSTRUCTURE							
1010	Standard Foundations	Poured concrete; strip and spread footings		S.F. Ground	3.84	1.92	
1020	Special Foundations	N/A		—	—	—	
1030	Slab on Grade	4" reinforced concrete with vapor barrier and granular base		S.F. Slab	5.31	2.66	5.2%
2010	Basement Excavation	Site preparation for slab and trench for foundation wall and footing		S.F. Ground	.32	.16	
2020	Basement Walls	4' foundation wall		L.F. Wall	82	1.61	
B. SHELL							
	B10 Superstructure						
1010	Floor Construction	Concrete waffle slab		S.F. Floor	26.70	13.35	18.8%
1020	Roof Construction	Concrete waffle slab		S.F. Roof	19.06	9.53	
	B20 Exterior Enclosure						
2010	Exterior Walls	Face brick with concrete block backup	90% of wall	S.F. Wall	32.35	16.12	
2020	Exterior Windows	Window wall	10% of wall	Each	53	2.91	16.1%
2030	Exterior Doors	Double aluminum and glass, single leaf hollow metal		Each	5700	.52	
	B30 Roofing						
3010	Roof Coverings	Single ply membrane, EPDM, fully adhered; perlite/EPS composite insulation		S.F. Roof	5.38	2.69	2.2%
3020	Roof Openings	Roof hatches		S.F. Roof	.08	.04	
C. INTERIORS							
1010	Partitions	Gypsum board on metal studs	30 S.F. Floor/L.F. Partition	S.F. Partition	11.90	4.76	
1020	Interior Doors	Single leaf wood	300 S.F. Floor/Door	Each	636	2.12	
1030	Fittings	N/A		—	—	—	
2010	Stair Construction	Concrete filled metal pan		Flight	9400	.85	16.1%
3010	Wall Finishes	Paint		S.F. Surface	.84	.67	
3020	Floor Finishes	50% carpet, 50% vinyl tile		S.F. Floor	4.29	4.29	
3030	Ceiling Finishes	Mineral fiber on concealed zee bars		S.F. Ceiling	6.89	6.89	
D. SERVICES							
	D10 Conveying						
1010	Elevators & Lifts	One hydraulic passenger elevator		Each	86,900	3.95	3.3%
1020	Escalators & Moving Walks	N/A		—	—	—	
	D20 Plumbing						
2010	Plumbing Fixtures	Toilet and service fixtures, supply and drainage	1 Fixture/1835 S.F. Floor	Each	7579	4.13	
2020	Domestic Water Distribution	Gas fired water heater		S.F. Floor	1.35	1.35	5.0%
2040	Rain Water Drainage	Roof drains		S.F. Roof	1.18	.59	
	D30 HVAC						
3010	Energy Supply	N/A		—	—	—	
3020	Heat Generating Systems	Included in D3050		—	—	—	
3030	Cooling Generating Systems	N/A		—	—	—	17.8%
3050	Terminal & Package Units	Multizone unit, gas heating, electric cooling		S.F. Floor	21.60	21.60	
3090	Other HVAC Sys. & Equipment	N/A		—	—	—	
	D40 Fire Protection						
4010	Sprinklers	Wet pipe sprinkler system		S.F. Floor	3.11	3.11	3.3%
4020	Standpipes	Standpipe		S.F. Floor	.94	.94	
	D50 Electrical						
5010	Electrical Service/Distribution	400 ampere service, panel board and feeders		S.F. Floor	1.16	1.16	
5020	Lighting & Branch Wiring	High efficiency fluorescent fixtures, receptacles, switches, A.C. and misc. power		S.F. Floor	11.17	11.17	12.1%
5030	Communications & Security	Addressable alarm systems, internet wiring, and emergency lighting		S.F. Floor	2.09	2.09	
5090	Other Electrical Systems	Emergency generator, 7.5 kW, Uninterruptible power supply		S.F. Floor	.26	.26	
E. EQUIPMENT & FURNISHINGS							
1010	Commercial Equipment	N/A		—	—	—	
1020	Institutional Equipment	N/A		—	—	—	
1030	Vehicular Equipment	N/A		—	—	—	0.0%
1090	Other Equipment	N/A		—	—	—	
F. SPECIAL CONSTRUCTION							
1020	Integrated Construction	N/A		—	—	—	
1040	Special Facilities	N/A		—	—	—	0.0%
G. BUILDING SITEWORK	**N/A**						

			Sub-Total	121.44	100%
CONTRACTOR FEES (General Requirements: 10%, Overhead: 5%, Profit: 10%)			25%	30.32	
ARCHITECT FEES			8%	12.14	

Total Building Cost	**163.90**

Costs per square foot of floor area

Exterior Wall	S.F. Area	4000	5500	7000	8500	10000	11500	13000	14500	16000
	L.F. Perimeter	280	320	380	440	453	503	510	522	560
Face Brick with Concrete Block Back-up	Steel Joists	220.70	211.40	208.10	205.95	201.20	199.95	196.65	194.25	193.50
	Wood Truss	227.45	218.20	214.90	212.75	208.00	206.75	203.45	201.05	200.25
Stucco on Concrete Block	Steel Joists	208.95	201.60	199.05	197.30	193.60	192.60	190.05	188.30	187.65
	Wood Truss	215.75	208.40	205.80	204.10	200.40	199.35	196.85	195.00	194.40
Brick Veneer	Wood Truss	220.00	211.55	208.60	206.60	202.25	201.15	198.20	196.00	195.30
Wood Siding	Wood Frame	212.20	205.45	203.00	201.40	198.10	197.15	194.85	193.20	192.60
Perimeter Adj., Add or Deduct	Per 100 L.F.	17.25	12.60	9.90	8.20	6.95	6.00	5.35	4.85	4.30
Story Hgt. Adj., Add or Deduct	Per 1 Ft.	3.50	2.95	2.80	2.65	2.35	2.20	2.00	1.85	1.80

For Basement, add $31.30 per square foot of basement area

The above costs were calculated using the basic specifications shown on the facing page. These costs should be adjusted where necessary for design alternatives and owner's requirements. Reported completed project costs, for this type of structure, range from $88.20 to $226.85 per S.F.

Common additives

Description	Unit	$ Cost	Description	Unit	$ Cost
Cabinets, Hospital, base			Directory Boards, Plastic, glass covered		
Laminated plastic	L.F.	410	30" x 20"	Each	630
Stainless steel	L.F.	660	36" x 48"	Each	1500
Counter top, laminated plastic	L.F.	79.50	Aluminum, 24" x 18"	Each	630
Stainless steel	L.F.	194	36" x 24"	Each	735
For drop-in sink, add	Each	1100	48" x 32"	Each	1050
Nurses station, door type			48" x 60"	Each	2200
Laminated plastic	L.F.	460	Heat Therapy Unit		
Enameled steel	L.F.	445	Humidified, 26" x 78" x 28"	Each	3925
Stainless steel	L.F.	770	Smoke Detectors		
Wall cabinets, laminated plastic	L.F.	298	Ceiling type	Each	223
Enameled steel	L.F.	350	Duct type	Each	555
Stainless steel	L.F.	615	Tables, Examining, vinyl top		
			with base cabinets	Each	1475 - 6675
			Utensil Washer, Sanitizer	Each	12,600
			X-Ray, Mobile	Each	18,300 - 84,500

Important: See the Reference Section for Location Factors.

Model costs calculated for a 1 story building with 10' story height and 7,000 square feet of floor area

				Unit	Unit Cost	Cost Per S.F.	% Of Sub-Total
A.	**SUBSTRUCTURE**						
1010	Standard Foundations	Poured concrete; strip and spread footings		S.F. Ground	2.13	2.13	
1020	Special Foundations	N/A		—	—	—	
1030	Slab on Grade	4" reinforced concrete with vapor barrier and granular base		S.F. Slab	5.31	5.31	7.7%
2010	Basement Excavation	Site preparation for slab and trench for foundation wall and footing		S.F. Ground	.32	.32	
2020	Basement Walls	4' foundation wall		L.F. Wall	82	4.43	
B.	**SHELL**						
	B10 Superstructure						
1010	Floor Construction	N/A		—	—	—	4.3 %
1020	Roof Construction	Plywood on wood trusses		S.F. Roof	6.85	6.85	
	B20 Exterior Enclosure						
2010	Exterior Walls	Face brick with concrete block backup	70% of wall	S.F. Wall	32.34	12.29	
2020	Exterior Windows	Wood double hung	30% of wall	Each	637	6.10	13.2%
2030	Exterior Doors	Aluminum and glass doors and entrance with transoms		Each	1460	2.50	
	B30 Roofing						
3010	Roof Coverings	Asphalt shingles with flashing (Pitched); rigid fiber glass insulation, gutters		S.F. Roof	4.68	4.68	3.0%
3020	Roof Openings	N/A		—	—	—	
C.	**INTERIORS**						
1010	Partitions	Gypsum bd. & sound deadening bd. on wood studs w/insul.	6 S.F. Floor/L.F. Partition	S.F. Partition	9.14	12.19	
1020	Interior Doors	Single leaf wood	60 S.F. Floor/Door	Each	636	10.60	
1030	Fittings	N/A		—	—	—	
2010	Stair Construction	N/A		—	—	—	24.1%
3010	Wall Finishes	50% paint, 50% vinyl wall covering		S.F. Surface	1.41	3.77	
3020	Floor Finishes	50% carpet, 50% vinyl composition tile		S.F. Floor	5.47	5.47	
3030	Ceiling Finishes	Mineral fiber tile on concealed zee bars		S.F. Ceiling	5.99	5.99	
D.	**SERVICES**						
	D10 Conveying						
1010	Elevators & Lifts	N/A		—	—	—	0.0 %
1020	Escalators & Moving Walks	N/A		—	—	—	
	D20 Plumbing						
2010	Plumbing Fixtures	Toilet, exam room and service fixtures, supply and drainage	1 Fixture/195 S.F. Floor	Each	4280	21.95	
2020	Domestic Water Distribution	Gas fired water heater		S.F. Floor	3.47	3.47	16.8%
2040	Rain Water Drainage	Roof drains		S.F. Roof	1.03	1.03	
	D30 HVAC						
3010	Energy Supply	N/A		—	—	—	
3020	Heat Generating Systems	Included in D3050		—	—	—	
3030	Cooling Generating Systems	N/A		—	—	—	9.8 %
3050	Terminal & Package Units	Multizone unit, gas heating, electric cooling		S.F. Floor	15.40	15.40	
3090	Other HVAC Sys. & Equipment	N/A		—	—	—	
	D40 Fire Protection						
4010	Sprinklers	Wet pipe sprinkler system		S.F. Floor	4.76	4.76	3.8%
4020	Standpipes	Standpipe		S.F. Floor	1.18	1.18	
	D50 Electrical						
5010	Electrical Service/Distribution	200 ampere service, panel board and feeders		S.F. Floor	1.61	1.61	
5020	Lighting & Branch Wiring	High efficiency fluorescent fixtures, receptacles, switches, A.C. and misc. power		S.F. Floor	7.51	7.51	11.3%
5030	Communications & Security	Alarm systems, internet and phone wiring, intercom system, and emergency lighting		S.F. Floor	7.87	7.87	
5090	Other Electrical Systems	Emergency generator, 7.5 kW		S.F. Floor	.82	.82	
E.	**EQUIPMENT & FURNISHINGS**						
1010	Commercial Equipment	N/A		—	—	—	
1020	Institutional Equipment	Exam room casework and countertops		S.F. Floor	9.49	9.49	6.0 %
1030	Vehicular Equipment	N/A		—	—	—	
1090	Other Equipment	N/A		—	—	—	
F.	**SPECIAL CONSTRUCTION**						
1020	Integrated Construction	N/A		—	—	—	0.0 %
1040	Special Facilities	N/A		—	—	—	
G.	**BUILDING SITEWORK**	**N/A**					

					Sub-Total	157.72	100%
	CONTRACTOR FEES (General Requirements: 10%, Overhead: 5%, Profit: 10%)				25%	39.44	
	ARCHITECT FEES				9%	17.74	

			Total Building Cost	**214.90**

Costs per square foot of floor area

Exterior Wall	S.F. Area	4000	5500	7000	8500	10000	11500	13000	14500	16000
	L.F. Perimeter	180	210	240	270	286	311	336	361	386
Face Brick with Concrete Block Back-up	Steel Joists	263.70	251.35	244.35	239.80	234.90	232.20	230.10	228.50	227.20
	Wood Joists	268.65	256.35	249.30	244.75	239.85	237.20	235.05	233.50	232.15
Stucco on Concrete Block	Steel Joists	251.35	240.85	234.80	231.00	226.95	224.65	222.90	221.55	220.45
	Wood Joists	256.65	246.15	240.15	236.30	232.25	229.95	228.25	226.85	225.75
Brick Veneer	Wood Frame	261.70	250.40	244.00	239.85	235.45	233.00	231.05	229.65	228.45
Wood Siding	Wood Frame	250.20	240.70	235.25	231.75	228.15	226.10	224.50	223.30	222.30
Perimeter Adj., Add or Deduct	Per 100 L.F.	30.65	22.30	17.50	14.45	12.20	10.70	9.50	8.50	7.65
Story Hgt. Adj., Add or Deduct	Per 1 Ft.	4.45	3.90	3.40	3.20	2.85	2.75	2.65	2.50	2.40

For Basement, add $34.75 per square foot of basement area

The above costs were calculated using the basic specifications shown on the facing page. These costs should be adjusted where necessary for design alternatives and owner's requirements. Reported completed project costs, for this type of structure, range from $90.55 to $309.25 per S.F.

Common additives

Description	Unit	$ Cost
Cabinets, Hospital, base		
Laminated plastic	L.F.	410
Stainless steel	L.F.	660
Counter top, laminated plastic	L.F.	79.50
Stainless steel	L.F.	194
For drop-in sink, add	Each	1100
Nurses station, door type		
Laminated plastic	L.F.	460
Enameled steel	L.F.	445
Stainless steel	L.F.	770
Wall cabinets, laminated plastic	L.F.	298
Enameled steel	L.F.	350
Stainless steel	L.F.	615
Elevators, Hydraulic passenger, 2 stops		
1500# capacity	Each	66,100
2500# capacity	Each	69,200
3500# capacity	Each	73,200

Description	Unit	$ Cost
Directory Boards, Plastic, glass covered		
30" x 20"	Each	630
36" x 48"	Each	1500
Aluminum, 24" x 18"	Each	630
36" x 24"	Each	735
48" x 32"	Each	1050
48" x 60"	Each	2200
Emergency Lighting, 25 watt, battery operated		
Lead battery	Each	320
Nickel cadmium	Each	885
Heat Therapy Unit		
Humidified, 26" x 78" x 28"	Each	3925
Smoke Detectors		
Ceiling type	Each	223
Duct type	Each	555
Tables, Examining, vinyl top		
with base cabinets	Each	1475 - 6675
Utensil Washer, Sanitizer	Each	12,600
X-Ray, Mobile	Each	18,300 - 84,500

Important: See the Reference Section for Location Factors.

Model costs calculated for a 2 story building with 10' story height and 7,000 square feet of floor area

Medical Office, 2 Story

				Unit	Unit Cost	Cost Per S.F.	% Of Sub-Total
A. SUBSTRUCTURE							
1010	Standard Foundations	Poured concrete; strip and spread footings		S.F. Ground	3.40	1.70	
1020	Special Foundations	N/A		—	—	—	
1030	Slab on Grade	4" reinforced concrete with vapor barrier and granular base		S.F. Slab	5.31	2.66	4.2%
2010	Basement Excavation	Site preparation for slab and trench for foundation wall and footing		S.F. Ground	.18	.09	
2020	Basement Walls	4' foundation wall		L.F. Wall	82	2.80	
B. SHELL							
	B10 Superstructure						
1010	Floor Construction	Open web steel joists, slab form, concrete, columns		S.F. Floor	13.62	6.81	5.7%
1020	Roof Construction	Metal deck, open web steel joists, beams, columns		S.F. Roof	6.18	3.09	
	B20 Exterior Enclosure						
2010	Exterior Walls	Stucco on concrete block		S.F. Wall	18.81	9.03	
2020	Exterior Windows	Outward projecting metal	30% of wall	Each	525	7.20	10.4%
2030	Exterior Doors	Aluminum and glass doors with transoms		Each	5700	1.63	
	B30 Roofing						
3010	Roof Coverings	Built-up tar and gravel with flashing; perlite/EPS composite insulation		S.F. Roof	7.48	3.74	2.2%
3020	Roof Openings	Roof hatches		S.F. Roof	.26	.13	
C. INTERIORS							
1010	Partitions	Gypsum bd. & acous. insul. on metal studs	6 S.F. Floor/L.F. Partition	S.F. Partition	7.64	10.19	
1020	Interior Doors	Single leaf wood	60 S.F. Floor/Door	Each	636	10.60	
1030	Fittings	N/A		—	—	—	
2010	Stair Construction	Concrete filled metal pan		Flight	14,450	4.13	23.3%
3010	Wall Finishes	45% paint, 50% vinyl wall coating, 5% ceramic tile		S.F. Surface	1.41	3.77	
3020	Floor Finishes	50% carpet, 50% vinyl composition tile		S.F. Floor	5.47	5.47	
3030	Ceiling Finishes	Mineral fiber tile on concealed zee bars		S.F. Ceiling	5.99	5.99	
D. SERVICES							
	D10 Conveying						
1010	Elevators & Lifts	One hydraulic hospital elevator		Each	102,900	14.70	8.5%
1020	Escalators & Moving Walks	N/A		—	—	—	
	D20 Plumbing						
2010	Plumbing Fixtures	Toilet, exam room and service fixtures, supply and drainage	1 Fixture/160 S.F. Floor	Each	3995	24.97	
2020	Domestic Water Distribution	Gas fired water heater		S.F. Floor	3.47	3.47	17.1%
2040	Rain Water Drainage	Roof drains		S.F. Roof	2.20	1.10	
	D30 HVAC						
3010	Energy Supply	N/A		—	—	—	
3020	Heat Generating Systems	Included in D3050		—	—	—	
3030	Cooling Generating Systems	N/A		—	—	—	8.9 %
3050	Terminal & Package Units	Multizone unit, gas heating, electric cooling		S.F. Floor	15.40	15.40	
3090	Other HVAC Sys. & Equipment	N/A		—	—	—	
	D40 Fire Protection						
4010	Sprinklers	Wet pipe sprinkler system		S.F. Floor	3.79	3.79	3.2%
4020	Standpipes	Standpipe		S.F. Floor	1.77	1.77	
	D50 Electrical						
5010	Electrical Service/Distribution	400 ampere service, panel board and feeders		S.F. Floor	2.44	2.44	
5020	Lighting & Branch Wiring	High efficiency fluorescent fixtures, receptacles, switches, A.C. and misc. power		S.F. Floor	7.51	7.51	10.8%
5030	Communications & Security	Alarm system, internet and phone wiring, intercom system, and emergency lighting		S.F. Floor	7.87	7.87	
5090	Other Electrical Systems	Emergency generator, 7.5 kW		S.F. Floor	.82	.82	
E. EQUIPMENT & FURNISHINGS							
1010	Commercial Equipment	N/A		—	—	—	
1020	Institutional Equipment	Exam room casework and contertops		S.F. Floor	9.49	9.49	5.5 %
1030	Vehicular Equipment	N/A		—	—	—	
1090	Other Equipment	N/A		—	—	—	
F. SPECIAL CONSTRUCTION							
1020	Integrated Construction	N/A		—	—	—	0.0 %
1040	Special Facilities	N/A		—	—	—	
G. BUILDING SITEWORK	**N/A**						

			Sub-Total	172.36	100%
CONTRACTOR FEES (General Requirements: 10%, Overhead: 5%, Profit: 10%)			25%	43.05	
ARCHITECT FEES			9%	19.39	

Total Building Cost | **234.80**

Costs per square foot of floor area

Exterior Wall	S.F. Area	2000	3000	4000	6000	8000	10000	12000	14000	16000
	L.F. Perimeter	240	260	280	380	480	560	580	660	740
Brick Veneer	Wood Frame	203.45	177.95	165.20	158.40	154.95	151.70	146.60	145.50	144.65
Aluminum Siding	Wood Frame	185.75	165.20	154.90	149.05	146.10	143.45	139.45	138.55	137.85
Wood Siding	Wood Frame	185.75	165.15	154.85	149.05	146.05	143.45	139.50	138.55	137.80
Wood Shingles	Wood Frame	188.70	167.25	156.60	150.55	147.50	144.75	140.60	139.65	138.95
Precast Concrete Block	Wood Truss	184.65	164.35	154.25	148.45	145.55	142.95	139.05	138.10	137.40
Brick on Concrete Block	Wood Truss	212.85	184.75	170.70	163.35	159.65	156.10	150.35	149.20	148.25
Perimeter Adj., Add or Deduct	Per 100 L.F.	29.75	19.80	14.85	9.90	7.40	5.95	5.00	4.25	3.70
Story Hgt. Adj., Add or Deduct	Per 1 Ft.	4.90	3.55	2.90	2.55	2.45	2.30	1.95	1.90	1.90

For Basement, add $23.90 per square foot of basement area

The above costs were calculated using the basic specifications shown on the facing page. These costs should be adjusted where necessary for design alternatives and owner's requirements. Reported completed project costs, for this type of structure, range from $73.05 to $345.90 per S.F.

Common additives

Description	Unit	$ Cost
Closed Circuit Surveillance, One station		
Camera and monitor	Each	1975
For additional camera stations, add	Each	1050
Emergency Lighting, 25 watt, battery operated		
Lead battery	Each	320
Nickel cadmium	Each	885
Laundry Equipment		
Dryer, gas, 16 lb. capacity	Each	965
30 lb. capacity	Each	3800
Washer, 4 cycle	Each	1175
Commercial	Each	1600
Sauna, Prefabricated, complete		
6' x 4'	Each	6800
6' x 6'	Each	7950
6' x 9'	Each	9725
8' x 8'	Each	11,500
8' x 10'	Each	12,800
10' x 12'	Each	15,400
Smoke Detectors		
Ceiling type	Each	223
Duct type	Each	555

Description	Unit	$ Cost
Swimming Pools, Complete, gunite	S.F.	90.50 - 113
TV Antenna, Master system, 12 outlet	Outlet	280
30 outlet	Outlet	218
100 outlet	Outlet	206

Important: See the Reference Section for Location Factors.

Model costs calculated for a 1 story building with 9' story height and 8,000 square feet of floor area

Motel, 1 Story

				Unit	Unit Cost	Cost Per S.F.	% Of Sub-Total

A. SUBSTRUCTURE

				Unit	Unit Cost	Cost Per S.F.	% Of Sub-Total
1010	Standard Foundations	Poured concrete; strip and spread footings		S.F. Ground	3.22	3.22	
1020	Special Foundations	N/A		—	—	—	
1030	Slab on Grade	4" reinforced concrete with vapor barrier and granular base		S.F. Slab	5.31	5.31	13.1%
2010	Basement Excavation	Site preparation for slab and trench for foundation wall and footing		S.F. Ground	.32	.32	
2020	Basement Walls	4' foundation wall		L.F. Wall	77	6.33	

B. SHELL

B10 Superstructure

				Unit	Unit Cost	Cost Per S.F.	% Of Sub-Total
1010	Floor Construction	N/A		—	—	—	5.9 %
1020	Roof Construction	Plywood on wood trusses		S.F. Roof	6.85	6.85	

B20 Exterior Enclosure

				Unit	Unit Cost	Cost Per S.F.	% Of Sub-Total
2010	Exterior Walls	Face brick on wood studs with sheathing, insulation and paper	80% of wall	S.F. Wall	24.79	10.71	
2020	Exterior Windows	Wood double hung	20% of wall	Each	510	3.93	16.1%
2030	Exterior Doors	Wood solid core		Each	1460	4.01	

B30 Roofing

				Unit	Unit Cost	Cost Per S.F.	% Of Sub-Total
3010	Roof Coverings	Asphalt shingles with flashing (pitched); rigid fiberglass insulation		S.F. Roof	4.48	4.48	3.9%
3020	Roof Openings	N/A		—	—	—	

C. INTERIORS

				Unit	Unit Cost	Cost Per S.F.	% Of Sub-Total
1010	Partitions	Gypsum bd. and sound deadening bd. on wood studs	9 S.F. Floor/L.F. Partition	S.F. Partition	9.78	8.69	
1020	Interior Doors	Single leaf hollow core wood	300 S.F. Floor/Door	Each	557	1.85	
1030	Fittings	N/A		—	—	—	
2010	Stair Construction	N/A		—	—	—	21.7%
3010	Wall Finishes	90% paint, 10% ceramic tile		S.F. Surface	1.47	2.62	
3020	Floor Finishes	85% carpet, 15% ceramic tile		S.F. Floor	7.57	7.57	
3030	Ceiling Finishes	Painted gypsum board on furring		S.F. Ceiling	4.39	4.39	

D. SERVICES

D10 Conveying

				Unit	Unit Cost	Cost Per S.F.	% Of Sub-Total
1010	Elevators & Lifts	N/A		—	—	—	0.0 %
1020	Escalators & Moving Walks	N/A		—	—	—	

D20 Plumbing

				Unit	Unit Cost	Cost Per S.F.	% Of Sub-Total
2010	Plumbing Fixtures	Toilet and service fixtures, supply and drainage	1 Fixture/90 S.F. Floor	Each	1951	21.68	
2020	Domestic Water Distribution	Gas fired water heater		S.F. Floor	1.85	1.85	21.6%
2040	Rain Water Drainage	Roof Drains		S.F. Roof	1.51	1.51	

D30 HVAC

				Unit	Unit Cost	Cost Per S.F.	% Of Sub-Total
3010	Energy Supply	N/A		—	—	—	
3020	Heat Generating Systems	Included in D3050		—	—	—	
3030	Cooling Generating Systems	N/A		—	—	—	2.4 %
3050	Terminal & Package Units	Through the wall electric heating and cooling units		S.F. Floor	2.82	2.82	
3090	Other HVAC Sys. & Equipment	N/A		—	—	—	

D40 Fire Protection

				Unit	Unit Cost	Cost Per S.F.	% Of Sub-Total
4010	Sprinklers	Wet pipe sprinkler system		S.F. Floor	4.76	4.76	5.0%
4020	Standpipes	Standpipe, wet, Class III		S.F. Floor	1.04	1.04	

D50 Electrical

				Unit	Unit Cost	Cost Per S.F.	% Of Sub-Total
5010	Electrical Service/Distribution	200 ampere service, panel board and feeders		S.F. Floor	1.33	1.33	
5020	Lighting & Branch Wiring	Fluorescent fixtures, receptacles, switches and misc. power		S.F. Floor	6.92	6.92	9.4%
5030	Communications & Security	Addressable alarm systems		S.F. Floor	2.68	2.68	
5090	Other Electrical Systems	N/A		—	—	—	

E. EQUIPMENT & FURNISHINGS

				Unit	Unit Cost	Cost Per S.F.	% Of Sub-Total
1010	Commercial Equipment	Laundry equipment		S.F. Floor	.97	.97	
1020	Institutional Equipment	N/A		—	—	—	
1030	Vehicular Equipment	N/A		—	—	—	0.8%
1090	Other Equipment	N/A		—	—	—	

F. SPECIAL CONSTRUCTION

				Unit	Unit Cost	Cost Per S.F.	% Of Sub-Total
1020	Integrated Construction	N/A		—	—	—	0.0 %
1040	Special Facilities	N/A		—	—	—	

G. BUILDING SITEWORK   N/A

	Sub-Total	115.84	**100%**
CONTRACTOR FEES (General Requirements: 10%, Overhead: 5%, Profit: 10%)	25%	28.97	
ARCHITECT FEES	7%	10.14	
	Total Building Cost	**154.95**	

Costs per square foot of floor area

Exterior Wall	S.F. Area	25000	37000	49000	61000	73000	81000	88000	96000	104000
	L.F. Perimeter	433	593	606	720	835	911	978	1054	1074
Decorative Concrete Block	Wood Joists	164.50	161.45	156.20	155.00	154.30	153.90	153.60	153.30	152.50
	Precast Conc.	177.35	173.10	167.35	165.85	164.85	164.40	164.05	163.60	162.75
Stucco on Concrete Block	Wood Joists	166.60	161.95	155.85	154.20	153.10	152.65	152.25	151.80	150.85
	Precast Conc.	178.50	173.80	167.75	166.10	165.00	164.50	164.10	163.70	162.75
Wood Siding	Wood Frame	160.40	157.55	153.05	151.95	151.25	150.95	150.70	150.40	149.75
Brick Veneer	Wood Frame	169.65	164.85	158.05	156.35	155.15	154.65	154.20	153.80	152.70
Perimeter Adj., Add or Deduct	Per 100 L.F.	4.90	3.30	2.50	2.00	1.65	1.50	1.40	1.30	1.15
Story Hgt. Adj., Add or Deduct	Per 1 Ft.	1.75	1.55	1.20	1.20	1.10	1.15	1.15	1.15	1.05

For Basement, add $31.35 per square foot of basement area

The above costs were calculated using the basic specifications shown on the facing page. These costs should be adjusted where necessary for design alternatives and owner's requirements. Reported completed project costs, for this type of structure, range from $67.30 to $345.90 per S.F.

Common additives

Description	Unit	$ Cost	Description	Unit	$ Cost
Closed Circuit Surveillance, One station			Sauna, Prefabricated, complete		
Camera and monitor	Each	1975	6' x 4'	Each	6800
For additional camera station, add	Each	1050	6' x 6'	Each	7950
Elevators, Hydraulic passenger, 2 stops			6' x 9'	Each	9725
1500# capacity	Each	66,100	8' x 8'	Each	11,500
2500# capacity	Each	69,200	8' x 10'	Each	12,800
3500# capacity	Each	73,200	10' x 12'	Each	15,400
Additional stop, add	Each	8575	Smoke Detectors		
Emergency Lighting, 25 watt, battery operated			Ceiling type	Each	223
Lead battery	Each	320	Duct type	Each	555
Nickel cadmium	Each	885	Swimming Pools, Complete, gunite	S.F.	90.50 - 113
Laundry Equipment			TV Antenna, Master system, 12 outlet	Outlet	280
Dryer, gas, 16 lb. capacity	Each	965	30 outlet	Outlet	218
30 lb. capacity	Each	3800	100 outlet	Outlet	206
Washer, 4 cycle	Each	1175			
Commercial	Each	1600			

Important: See the Reference Section for Location Factors.

Model costs calculated for a 3 story building with 9' story height and 49,000 square feet of floor area

				Unit	Unit Cost	Cost Per S.F.	% Of Sub-Total
A. SUBSTRUCTURE							
1010	Standard Foundations	Poured concrete; strip and spread footings		S.F. Ground	1.47	.49	
1020	Special Foundations	N/A		—	—	—	
1030	Slab on Grade	4" reinforced concrete with vapor barrier and granular base		S.F. Slab	5.31	1.77	3.4%
2010	Basement Excavation	Site preparation for slab and trench for foundation wall and footing		S.F. Ground	.18	.06	
2020	Basement Walls	4' foundation wall		L.F. Wall	82	2.02	
B. SHELL							
B10 Superstructure							
1010	Floor Construction	Precast concrete plank		S.F. Floor	10.37	6.91	8.1%
1020	Roof Construction	Precast concrete plank		S.F. Roof	9.84	3.28	
B20 Exterior Enclosure							
2010	Exterior Walls	Decorative concrete block	85% of wall	S.F. Wall	17.90	5.08	
2020	Exterior Windows	Aluminum sliding	15% of wall	Each	585	1.95	10.7%
2030	Exterior Doors	Aluminum and glass doors and entrance with transom		Each	1966	6.49	
B30 Roofing							
3010	Roof Coverings	Built-up tar and gravel with flashing; perlite/EPS composite insulation		S.F. Roof	6.72	2.24	1.8%
3020	Roof Openings	Roof hatches		S.F. Roof	.12	.04	
C. INTERIORS							
1010	Partitions	Concrete block	7 S.F. Floor/L.F. Partition	S.F. Partition	19.28	22.03	
1020	Interior Doors	Wood hollow core	70 S.F. Floor/Door	Each	557	7.96	
1030	Fittings	N/A		—	—	—	
2010	Stair Construction	Concrete filled metal pan		Flight	14,450	3.54	38.4%
3010	Wall Finishes	90% paint, 10% ceramic tile		S.F. Surface	1.47	3.37	
3020	Floor Finishes	85% carpet, 5% vinyl composition tile, 10% ceramic tile		S.F. Floor	7.57	7.57	
3030	Ceiling Finishes	Textured finish		S.F. Ceiling	4.07	4.07	
D. SERVICES							
D10 Conveying							
1010	Elevators & Lifts	Two hydraulic passenger elevators		Each	108,535	4.43	3.5%
1020	Escalators & Moving Walks	N/A		—	—	—	
D20 Plumbing							
2010	Plumbing Fixtures	Toilet and service fixtures, supply and drainage	1 Fixture/180 S.F. Floor	Each	4327	24.04	
2020	Domestic Water Distribution	Gas fired water heater		S.F. Floor	1.29	1.29	20.4%
2040	Rain Water Drainage	Roof drains		S.F. Roof	1.35	.45	
D30 HVAC							
3010	Energy Supply	N/A		—	—	—	
3020	Heat Generating Systems	Included in D3050		—	—	—	
3030	Cooling Generating Systems	N/A		—	—	—	2.0%
3050	Terminal & Package Units	Through the wall electric heating and cooling units		S.F. Floor	2.54	2.54	
3090	Other HVAC Sys. & Equipment	N/A		—	—	—	
D40 Fire Protection							
4010	Sprinklers	Sprinklers, wet, light hazard		S.F. Floor	2.95	2.95	2.5%
4020	Standpipes	Standpipe, wet, Class III		S.F. Floor	.23	.23	
D50 Electrical							
5010	Electrical Service/Distribution	800 ampere service, panel board and feeders		S.F. Floor	1.62	1.62	
5020	Lighting & Branch Wiring	Fluorescent fixtures, receptacles, switches and misc. power		S.F. Floor	7.59	7.59	8.8%
5030	Communications & Security	Addressable alarm systems and emergency lighting		S.F. Floor	1.85	1.85	
5090	Other Electrical Systems	Emergency generator, 7.5 kW		S.F. Floor	.11	.11	
E. EQUIPMENT & FURNISHINGS							
1010	Commercial Equipment	Commercial laundry equipment		S.F. Floor	.32	.32	
1020	Institutional Equipment	N/A		—	—	—	0.3%
1030	Vehicular Equipment	N/A		—	—	—	
1090	Other Equipment	N/A		—	—	—	
F. SPECIAL CONSTRUCTION							
1020	Integrated Construction	N/A		—	—	—	0.0%
1040	Special Facilities	N/A		—	—	—	
G. BUILDING SITEWORK	**N/A**						
				Sub-Total		126.29	100%
	CONTRACTOR FEES (General Requirements: 10%, Overhead: 5%, Profit: 10%)				25%	31.59	
	ARCHITECT FEES				6%	9.47	
				Total Building Cost		**167.35**	

Costs per square foot of floor area

Exterior Wall	S.F. Area	9000	10000	12000	13000	14000	15000	16000	18000	20000
	L.F. Perimeter	385	410	440	460	480	500	510	547	583
Decorative Concrete Block	Steel Joists	176.90	172.50	164.50	161.75	159.40	157.40	155.00	152.00	149.55
Painted Concrete Block	Steel Joists	168.70	164.70	157.50	155.00	152.90	151.00	148.95	146.15	143.95
Face Brick on Conc. Block	Steel Joists	191.70	186.65	177.15	174.00	171.30	168.85	166.00	162.50	159.60
Precast Concrete Panels	Steel Joists	201.70	196.30	185.80	182.30	179.35	176.70	173.50	169.65	166.40
Tilt-up Panels	Steel Joists	173.95	169.65	161.95	159.30	157.05	155.05	152.75	149.90	147.50
Metal Sandwich Panels	Steel Joists	172.75	168.55	160.95	158.25	156.10	154.15	151.95	149.00	146.70
Perimeter Adj., Add or Deduct	Per 100 L.F.	9.30	8.35	7.00	6.40	6.00	5.50	5.25	4.65	4.15
Story Hgt. Adj., Add or Deduct	Per 1 Ft.	1.30	1.30	1.15	1.10	1.10	1.00	1.00	0.95	0.90
Basement—Not Applicable										

The above costs were calculated using the basic specifications shown on the facing page. These costs should be adjusted where necessary for design alternatives and owner's requirements. Reported completed project costs, for this type of structure, range from $86.10 to $225.15 per S.F.

Common additives

Description	Unit	$ Cost
Emergency Lighting, 25 watt, battery operated		
Lead battery	Each	320
Nickel cadmium	Each	885
Seating		
Auditorium chair, all veneer	Each	300
Veneer back, padded seat	Each	315
Upholstered, spring seat	Each	315
Classroom, movable chair & desk	Set	81 - 171
Lecture hall, pedestal type	Each	258 - 610
Smoke Detectors		
Ceiling type	Each	223
Duct type	Each	555
Sound System		
Amplifier, 250 watts	Each	2025
Speaker, ceiling or wall	Each	208
Trumpet	Each	400

Important: See the Reference Section for Location Factors.

Model costs calculated for a 1 story building with 20′ story height and 12,000 square feet of floor area

Movie Theater

				Unit	Unit Cost	Cost Per S.F.	% Of Sub-Total
A.	**SUBSTRUCTURE**						
1010	Standard Foundations	Poured concrete; strip and spread footings		S.F. Ground	1.43	1.43	
1020	Special Foundations	N/A		—	—	—	
1030	Slab on Grade	4″ reinforced concrete with vapor barrier and granular base		S.F. Slab	5.31	5.31	11.0%
2010	Basement Excavation	Site preparation for slab and trench for foundation wall and footing		S.F. Ground	3.85	3.85	
2020	Basement Walls	4′ foundation wall		L.F. Wall	82	2.99	
B.	**SHELL**						
	B10 Superstructure						
1010	Floor Construction	Open web steel joists, slab form, concrete	mezzanine 2250 S.F.	S.F. Floor	11.60	2.17	10.4%
1020	Roof Construction	Metal deck on open web steel joists		S.F. Roof	10.67	10.67	
	B20 Exterior Enclosure						
2010	Exterior Walls	Decorative concrete block	100% of wall	S.F. Wall	20	14.67	
2020	Exterior Windows	N/A		—	—	—	12.9%
2030	Exterior Doors	Sliding mallfront aluminum and glass and hollow metal		Each	2508	1.25	
	B30 Roofing						
3010	Roof Coverings	Built-up tar and gravel with flashing; perlite/EPS composite insulation		S.F. Roof	6.25	6.25	5.1%
3020	Roof Openings	N/A		—	—	—	
C.	**INTERIORS**						
1010	Partitions	Concrete block	40 S.F. Floor/L.F. Partition	S.F. Partition	9.38	3.75	
1020	Interior Doors	Single leaf hollow metal	705 S.F. Floor/Door	Each	1152	1.63	
1030	Fittings	Toilet partitions		S.F. Floor	.62	.62	
2010	Stair Construction	Concrete filled metal pan		Flight	17,250	2.87	19.3%
3010	Wall Finishes	Paint		S.F. Surface	4.86	3.89	
3020	Floor Finishes	Carpet 50%, ceramic tile 5%	50% of area	S.F. Floor	8.06	4.03	
3030	Ceiling Finishes	Mineral fiber tile on concealed zee runners suspended		S.F. Ceiling	6.89	6.89	
D.	**SERVICES**						
	D10 Conveying						
1010	Elevators & Lifts	N/A		—	—	—	0.0 %
1020	Escalators & Moving Walks	N/A		—	—	—	
	D20 Plumbing						
2010	Plumbing Fixtures	Toilet and service fixtures, supply and drainage	1 Fixture/500 S.F. Floor	Each	4760	9.52	
2020	Domestic Water Distribution	Gas fired water heater		S.F. Floor	.47	.47	9.2%
2040	Rain Water Drainage	Roof drains		S.F. Roof	1.34	1.34	
	D30 HVAC						
3010	Energy Supply	N/A		—	—	—	
3020	Heat Generating Systems	Included in D3050		—	—	—	
3030	Cooling Generating Systems	N/A		—	—	—	8.3 %
3050	Terminal & Package Units	Single zone rooftop unit, gas heating, electric cooling		S.F. Floor	10.18	10.18	
3090	Other HVAC Sys. & Equipment	N/A		—	—	—	
	D40 Fire Protection						
4010	Sprinklers	Wet pipe sprinkler system		S.F. Floor	4.25	4.25	4.1%
4020	Standpipes	Standpipe		S.F. Floor	.84	.84	
	D50 Electrical						
5010	Electrical Service/Distribution	400 ampere service, panel board and feeders		S.F. Floor	1.79	1.79	
5020	Lighting & Branch Wiring	High efficiency fluorescent fixtures, receptacles, switches, A.C. and misc. power		S.F. Floor	6.48	6.48	8.7%
5030	Communications & Security	Addressable alarm systems, sound system and emergency lighting		S.F. Floor	2.29	2.29	
5090	Other Electrical Systems	Emergency generator, 7.5 kW		S.F. Floor	.16	.16	
E.	**EQUIPMENT & FURNISHINGS**						
1010	Commercial Equipment	N/A		—	—	—	
1020	Institutional Equipment	Projection equipment, screen		S.F. Floor	8.98	8.98	10.9 %
1030	Vehicular Equipment	N/A		—	—	—	
2010	Fixed Furnishings	Movie theater seating		S.F. Floor	4.44	4.44	
F.	**SPECIAL CONSTRUCTION**						
1020	Integrated Construction	N/A		—	—	—	0.0 %
1040	Special Facilities	N/A		—	—	—	
G.	**BUILDING SITEWORK**	**N/A**					

				Sub-Total	123.01	100%
CONTRACTOR FEES (General Requirements: 10%, Overhead: 5%, Profit: 10%)			25%	30.73		
ARCHITECT FEES			7%	10.76		

Total Building Cost	**164.50**

Costs per square foot of floor area

Exterior Wall	S.F. Area	10000	15000	20000	25000	30000	35000	40000	45000	50000
	L.F. Perimeter	286	370	453	457	513	568	624	680	735
Precast Concrete Panels	Bearing Walls	229.55	220.60	216.00	208.20	205.80	203.95	202.70	201.65	200.85
	Steel Frame	238.05	229.10	224.55	216.70	214.30	212.50	211.25	210.20	209.40
Face Brick with Concrete Block Back-up	Bearing Walls	220.50	212.80	208.90	202.45	200.45	198.90	197.80	196.95	196.25
	Steel Joists	229.95	222.30	218.35	211.95	209.90	208.35	207.25	206.40	205.70
Stucco on Concrete Block	Bearing Walls	211.45	205.00	201.75	196.65	195.00	193.75	192.90	192.15	191.60
	Steel Joists	220.95	214.55	211.20	206.15	204.50	203.25	202.35	201.70	201.10
Perimeter Adj., Add or Deduct	Per 100 L.F.	15.95	10.65	8.05	6.45	5.30	4.60	4.00	3.60	3.20
Story Hgt. Adj., Add or Deduct	Per 1 Ft.	3.80	3.30	3.05	2.45	2.30	2.20	2.10	2.10	1.95

For Basement, add $32.55 per square foot of basement area

The above costs were calculated using the basic specifications shown on the facing page. These costs should be adjusted where necessary for design alternatives and owner's requirements. Reported completed project costs, for this type of structure, range from $92.40 to $231.70 per S.F.

Common additives

Description	Unit	$ Cost
Beds, Manual	Each	865 - 2750
Elevators, Hydraulic passenger, 2 stops		
1500# capacity	Each	66,100
2500# capacity	Each	69,200
3500# capacity	Each	73,200
Emergency Lighting, 25 watt, battery operated		
Lead battery	Each	320
Nickel cadmium	Each	885
Intercom System, 25 station capacity		
Master station	Each	3175
Intercom outlets	Each	184
Handset	Each	505
Kitchen Equipment		
Broiler	Each	4000
Coffee urn, twin 6 gallon	Each	2975
Cooler, 6 ft. long	Each	4100
Dishwasher, 10-12 racks per hr.	Each	4225
Food warmer	Each	725
Freezer, 44 C.F., reach-in	Each	5125

Description	Unit	$ Cost
Kitchen Equipment, cont.		
Ice cube maker, 50 lb. per day	Each	1950
Range with 1 oven	Each	3000
Laundry Equipment		
Dryer, gas, 16 lb. capacity	Each	965
30 lb. capacity	Each	3800
Washer, 4 cycle	Each	1175
Commercial	Each	1600
Nurses Call System		
Single bedside call station	Each	330
Pillow speaker	Each	273
Refrigerator, Prefabricated, walk-in		
7'-6" high, 6' x 6'	S.F.	195
10' x 10'	S.F.	154
12' x 14'	S.F.	136
12' x 20'	S.F.	119
TV Antenna, Master system, 12 outlet	Outlet	280
30 outlet	Outlet	218
100 outlet	Outlet	206
Whirlpool Bath, Mobile, 18" x 24" x 60"	Each	5325
X-Ray, Mobile	Each	18,300 - 84,500

Important: See the Reference Section for Location Factors.

Model costs calculated for a 2 story building with 10' story height and 25,000 square feet of floor area

				Unit	Unit Cost	Cost Per S.F.	% Of Sub-Total
A. SUBSTRUCTURE							
1010	Standard Foundations	Poured concrete; strip and spread footings		S.F. Ground	1.44	.72	
1020	Special Foundations	N/A		—	—	—	
1030	Slab on Grade	4" reinforced concrete with vapor barrier and granular base		S.F. Slab	5.31	2.66	3.5%
2010	Basement Excavation	Site preparation for slab and trench for foundation wall and footing		S.F. Ground	.32	.16	
2020	Basement Walls	4' foundation wall		L.F. Wall	73	1.73	
B. SHELL							
	B10 Superstructure						
1010	Floor Construction	Pre-cast double tees with concrete topping		S.F. Floor	12.76	6.38	7.8%
1020	Roof Construction	Pre-cast double tees		S.F. Roof	10.78	5.39	
	B20 Exterior Enclosure						
2010	Exterior Walls	Precast concrete panels		S.F. Wall	45.69	14.20	
2020	Exterior Windows	Wood double hung	15% of wall	Each	585	2.13	11.2%
2030	Exterior Doors	Double aluminum & glass doors, single leaf hollow metal		Each	2308	.46	
	B30 Roofing						
3010	Roof Coverings	Built-up tar and gravel with flashing; perlite/EPS composite insulation		S.F. Roof	6.72	3.36	2.3%
3020	Roof Openings	Roof hatches		S.F. Roof	.08	.04	
C. INTERIORS							
1010	Partitions	Gypsum board on metal studs	8 S.F. Floor/L.F. Partition	S.F. Partition	7.47	7.47	
1020	Interior Doors	Single leaf wood	80 S.F. Floor/Door	Each	636	7.95	
1030	Fittings	N/A		—	—	—	
2010	Stair Construction	Concrete stair		Flight	6625	1.59	19.0%
3010	Wall Finishes	50% vinyl wall coverings, 45% paint, 5% ceramic tile		S.F. Surface	1.74	3.47	
3020	Floor Finishes	95% vinyl tile, 5% ceramic tile		S.F. Floor	3.87	3.87	
3030	Ceiling Finishes	Painted gypsum board		S.F. Ceiling	4.12	4.12	
D. SERVICES							
	D10 Conveying						
1010	Elevators & Lifts	One hydraulic hospital elevator		Each	103,000	4.12	2.7%
1020	Escalators & Moving Walks	N/A		—	—	—	
	D20 Plumbing						
2010	Plumbing Fixtures	Kitchen, toilet and service fixtures, supply and drainage	1 Fixture/230 S.F. Floor	Each	10,148	44.12	
2020	Domestic Water Distribution	Oil fired water heater		S.F. Floor	1.37	1.37	30.7%
2040	Rain Water Drainage	Roof drains		S.F. Roof	1.14	.57	
	D30 HVAC						
3010	Energy Supply	Oil fired hot water, wall fin radiation		S.F. Floor	8.60	8.60	
3020	Heat Generating Systems	N/A		—	—	—	
3030	Cooling Generating Systems	N/A		—	—	—	11.4%
3050	Terminal & Package Units	Split systems with air cooled condensing units		S.F. Floor	8.53	8.53	
3090	Other HVAC Sys. & Equipment	N/A		—	—	—	
	D40 Fire Protection						
4010	Sprinklers	Sprinkler, light hazard		S.F. Floor	3.11	3.11	2.4%
4020	Standpipes	Standpipe		S.F. Floor	.43	.43	
	D50 Electrical						
5010	Electrical Service/Distribution	800 ampere service, panel board and feeders		S.F. Floor	1.64	1.64	
5020	Lighting & Branch Wiring	High efficiency fluorescent fixtures, receptacles, switches, A.C. and misc. power		S.F. Floor	9.99	9.99	9.0%
5030	Communications & Security	Addressable alarm systems and emergency lighting		S.F. Floor	1.39	1.39	
5090	Other Electrical Systems	Emergency generator, 15 kW		S.F. Floor	.48	.48	
E. EQUIPMENT & FURNISHINGS							
1010	Commercial Equipment	N/A		—	—	—	
1020	Institutional Equipment	N/A		—	—	—	
1030	Vehicular Equipment	N/A		—	—	—	0.0%
1090	Other Equipment	N/A		—	—	—	
F. SPECIAL CONSTRUCTION							
1020	Integrated Construction	N/A		—	—	—	
1040	Special Facilities	N/A		—	—	—	0.0%
G. BUILDING SITEWORK	**N/A**						
				Sub-Total		150.05	**100%**

CONTRACTOR FEES (General Requirements: 10%, Overhead: 5%, Profit: 10%)		25%	37.52
ARCHITECT FEES		11%	20.63
Total Building Cost			**208.20**

Costs per square foot of floor area

Exterior Wall	S.F. Area	2000	3000	5000	7000	9000	12000	15000	20000	25000
	L.F. Perimeter	220	260	320	360	420	480	520	640	700
Wood Siding	Wood Truss	207.45	187.90	170.40	161.50	157.70	153.10	149.75	147.60	145.20
Brick Veneer	Wood Truss	255.30	229.90	206.95	195.20	190.15	184.10	179.55	176.80	173.55
Brick on Block	Wood Truss	195.70	168.70	144.20	131.50	126.15	119.55	114.65	111.70	108.10
	Steel Roof Deck	252.45	224.10	198.25	184.95	179.30	172.35	167.20	164.15	160.30
EIFS on Metal Studs	Steel Roof Deck	233.30	210.10	189.15	178.50	173.90	168.35	164.30	161.75	158.75
Tiltup Concrete Panel	Steel Roof Deck	234.70	210.70	189.10	178.15	173.35	167.65	163.50	160.90	157.90
Perimeter Adj., Add or Deduct	Per 100 L.F.	23.85	15.90	9.60	6.85	5.30	4.00	3.15	2.40	1.90
Story Hgt. Adj., Add or Deduct	Per 1 Ft.	2.90	2.25	1.70	1.35	1.15	1.05	0.85	0.85	0.70

For Basement, add $33.00 per square foot of basement area

The above costs were calculated using the basic specifications shown on the facing page. These costs should be adjusted where necessary for design alternatives and owner's requirements. Reported completed project costs, for this type of structure, range from $70.55 to $272.80 per S.F.

Common additives

Description	Unit	$ Cost
Closed circuit surveillance, one station		
Camera and monitor	Each	1975
For additional camera stations, add	Each	1050
Directory boards, plastic, glass covered		
30" x 20"	Each	630
36" x 48"	Each	1500
Aluminum, 24" x 18"	Each	630
36" x 24"	Each	735
48" x 32"	Each	1050
48" x 60"	Each	2200
Electronic, wall mounted	S.F.	2525
Free standing	S.F.	3100
Pedestal access floor system w/ plastic laminate cover		
Computer room, less than 6000 SF	S.F.	12
Greater than 6000 SF	S.F.	11.25
Office, greater than 6000 S.F.	S.F.	8.05

Description	Unit	$ Cost
Security access systems		
Metal detectors, wand type	Each	98
Walk-through portal type, single-zone	Each	4350
Multi-zone		5450
X-ray equipment	Each	
Desk top, for mail, small packages	Each	3875
Conveyer type, including monitor, minimum	Each	17,700
Maximum	Each	31,400
Explosive detection equipment		
Hand held, battery operated	Each	28,100
Walk-through portal type	Each	48,400
Uninterruptible power supply, 15 kVA/12.75 kW	kW	1795

Important: See the Reference Section for Location Factors.

Model costs calculated for a 1 story building with 12' story height and 7,000 square feet of floor area

Office, 1 Story

			Unit	Unit Cost	Cost Per S.F.	% Of Sub-Total
A. SUBSTRUCTURE						
1010	Standard Foundations	Poured concrete; strip and spread footings	S.F. Ground	2.80	2.80	
1020	Special Foundations	N/A	—	—	—	
1030	Slab on Grade	4" reinforced concrete with vapor barrier and granular base	S.F. Slab	5.31	5.31	9.6%
2010	Basement Excavation	Site preparation for slab and trench for foundation wall and footing	S.F. Ground	.32	.32	
2020	Basement Walls	4' foundation wall	L.F. Wall	154	4.40	
B. SHELL						
	B10 Superstructure					
1010	Floor Construction	N/A	—	—	—	7.7 %
1020	Roof Construction	Steel joists, girders & deck on columns	S.F. Roof	10.30	10.30	
	B20 Exterior Enclosure					
2010	Exterior Walls	E.I.F.S. on metal studs	S.F. Wall	17.26	8.52	
2020	Exterior Windows	Aluminum outward projecting 20% of wall	Each	736	3.95	11.6%
2030	Exterior Doors	Aluminum and glass, hollow metal	Each	3473	2.97	
	B30 Roofing					
3010	Roof Coverings	Single ply membrane, loose laid and ballasted	S.F. Roof	9.26	9.26	7.1%
3020	Roof Openings	Roof hatch	S.F. Roof	.18	.18	
C. INTERIORS						
1010	Partitions	Gypsum board on metal studs 20 S.F. Floor/L.F. Partition	S.F. Partition	8.90	4.45	
1020	Interior Doors	Single leaf hollow metal 200 S.F. Floor/Door	Each	1152	5.76	
1030	Fittings	Toilet partitions	S.F. Floor	.49	.49	
2010	Stair Construction	N/A	—	—	—	19.1%
3010	Wall Finishes	60% vinyl wall covering, 40% paint	S.F. Surface	1.52	1.52	
3020	Floor Finishes	60% carpet, 30% vinyl composition tile, 10% ceramic tile	S.F. Floor	6.34	6.34	
3030	Ceiling Finishes	Mineral fiber tile on concealed zee bars	S.F. Ceiling	6.89	6.89	
D. SERVICES						
	D10 Conveying					
1010	Elevators & Lifts	N/A	—	—	—	0.0 %
1020	Escalators & Moving Walks	N/A	—	—	—	
	D20 Plumbing					
2010	Plumbing Fixtures	Toilet and service fixtures, supply and drainage 1 Fixture/1320 S.F. Floor	Each	8765	6.64	
2020	Domestic Water Distribution	Gas fired water heater	S.F. Floor	1.37	1.37	6.6%
2040	Rain Water Drainage	Roof drains	S.F. Roof	.83	.83	
	D30 HVAC					
3010	Energy Supply	N/A	—	—	—	
3020	Heat Generating Systems	Included in D3050	—	—	—	
3030	Cooling Generating Systems	N/A	—	—	—	16.3 %
3050	Terminal & Package Units	Multizone unit gas heating, electric cooling	S.F. Floor	21.70	21.70	
3090	Other HVAC Sys. & Equipment	N/A	—	—	—	
	D40 Fire Protection					
4010	Sprinklers	Sprinkler system, light hazard	S.F. Floor	3.56	3.56	3.7%
4020	Standpipes	Standpipes and hose systems	S.F. Floor	1.42	1.42	
	D50 Electrical					
5010	Electrical Service/Distribution	400 ampere service, panel board and feeders	S.F. Floor	4.87	4.87	
5020	Lighting & Branch Wiring	High efficiency fluorescent fixtures, receptacles, switches, A.C. and misc. power	S.F. Floor	12.22	12.22	18.3%
5030	Communications & Security	Addressable alarm systems, internet and phone wiring, and emergency lighting	S.F. Floor	7.21	7.21	
5090	Other Electrical Systems	Emergency generator, 7.5 kW	S.F. Floor	.19	.19	
E. EQUIPMENT & FURNISHINGS						
1010	Commercial Equipment	N/A	—	—	—	
1020	Institutional Equipment	N/A	—	—	—	
1030	Vehicular Equipment	N/A	—	—	—	0.0 %
1090	Other Equipment	N/A	—	—	—	
F. SPECIAL CONSTRUCTION						
1020	Integrated Construction	N/A	—	—	—	0.0 %
1040	Special Facilities	N/A	—	—	—	
G. BUILDING SITEWORK	**N/A**					

		Sub-Total	133.47	100%
CONTRACTOR FEES (General Requirements: 10%, Overhead: 5%, Profit: 10%)			25%	33.35
ARCHITECT FEES			7%	11.68

Total Building Cost	**178.50**

Costs per square foot of floor area

Exterior Wall	S.F. Area	5000	8000	12000	16000	20000	35000	50000	65000	80000
	L.F. Perimeter	220	260	310	330	360	440	490	548	580
Face Brick with Concrete Block Back-up	Wood Joists	246.20	215.75	198.30	185.85	179.35	166.45	160.05	156.90	154.30
	Steel Joists	249.90	219.40	201.95	189.45	183.00	170.10	163.75	160.60	157.95
Glass and Metal Curtain Wall	Steel Frame	295.45	254.60	231.10	213.95	205.15	187.25	178.45	174.05	170.35
	R/Conc. Frame	291.15	250.80	227.55	210.65	201.85	184.15	175.40	171.00	167.30
Wood Siding	Wood Frame	194.45	173.45	161.50	153.40	149.10	140.65	136.60	134.50	132.90
Brick Veneer	Wood Frame	217.10	190.25	174.80	164.00	158.35	147.10	141.65	138.85	136.60
Perimeter Adj., Add or Deduct	Per 100 L.F.	39.40	24.65	16.35	12.25	9.85	5.55	3.90	3.05	2.45
Story Hgt. Adj., Add or Deduct	Per 1 Ft.	6.40	4.75	3.75	3.00	2.65	1.85	1.45	1.25	1.05
For Basement, add $36.90 per square foot of basement area										

The above costs were calculated using the basic specifications shown on the facing page. These costs should be adjusted where necessary for design alternatives and owner's requirements. Reported completed project costs, for this type of structure, range from $73.85 to $286.05 per S.F.

Common additives

Description	Unit	$ Cost
Closed circuit surveillance, one station		
Camera and monitor	Each	1975
For additional camera stations, add	Each	1050
Directory boards, plastic, glass covered		
30" x 20"	Each	630
36" x 48"	Each	1500
Aluminum, 24" x 18"	Each	630
36" x 24"	Each	735
48" x 32"	Each	1050
48" x 60"	Each	2200
Electronic, wall mounted	S.F.	2525
Free standing	S.F.	3100
Escalators, 10' rise, 32" wide, glass balustrade	Each	140,500
Metal balustrade	Each	147,500
48" wide, glass balustrade	Each	147,500
Metal balustrade	Each	155,500
Pedestal access floor system w/ plastic laminate cover		
Computer room, less than 6000 SF	S.F.	12
Greater than 6000 SF	S.F.	11.25
Office, greater than 6000 S.F.	S.F.	8.05

Description	Unit	$ Cost
Security access systems		
Metal detectors, wand type	Each	98
Walk-through portal type, single-zone	Each	4350
Multi-zone		5450
X-ray equipment	Each	
Desk top, for mail, small packages	Each	3875
Conveyer type, including monitor, minimum	Each	17,700
Maximum	Each	31,400
Explosive detection equipment		
Hand held, battery operated	Each	28,100
Walk-through portal type	Each	48,400
Uninterruptible power supply, 15 kVA/12.75 kW	kW	1795

Important: See the Reference Section for Location Factors.

Model costs calculated for a 3 story building with 12' story height and 20,000 square feet of floor area

Office, 2-4 Story

				Unit	Unit Cost	Cost Per S.F.	% Of Sub-Total
A. SUBSTRUCTURE							
1010	Standard Foundations	Poured concrete; strip and spread footings		S.F. Ground	7.47	2.49	
1020	Special Foundations	N/A		—	—	—	
1030	Slab on Grade	4" reinforced concrete with vapor barrier and granular base		S.F. Slab	5.31	1.77	4.4%
2010	Basement Excavation	Site preparation for slab and trench for foundation wall and footing		S.F. Ground	.18	.06	
2020	Basement Walls	4' foundation wall		L.F. Wall	77	1.73	
B. SHELL							
	B10 Superstructure						
1010	Floor Construction	Open web steel joists, slab form, concrete, columns		S.F. Floor	19.14	12.76	11.1%
1020	Roof Construction	Metal deck, open web steel joists, columns		S.F. Roof	7.35	2.45	
	B20 Exterior Enclosure						
2010	Exterior Walls	Face brick with concrete block backup	80% of wall	S.F. Wall	32.89	17.05	
2020	Exterior Windows	Aluminum outward projecting	20% of wall	Each	736	4.15	16.3%
2030	Exterior Doors	Aluminum and glass, hollow metal		Each	3473	1.04	
	B30 Roofing						
3010	Roof Coverings	Built-up tar and gravel with flashing; perlite/EPS composite		S.F. Roof	7.17	2.39	1.7%
3020	Roof Openings	N/A		—	—	—	
C. INTERIORS							
1010	Partitions	Gypsum board on metal studs	20 S.F. Floor/L.F. Partition	S.F. Partition	10.05	4.02	
1020	Interior Doors	Single leaf hollow metal	200 S.F. Floor/Door	Each	1152	5.76	
1030	Fittings	Toilet partitions		S.F. Floor	1.02	1.02	
2010	Stair Construction	Concrete filled metal pan		Flight	14,450	5.06	22.2%
3010	Wall Finishes	60% vinyl wall covering, 40% paint		S.F. Surface	1.54	1.23	
3020	Floor Finishes	60% carpet, 30% vinyl composition tile, 10% ceramic tile		S.F. Floor	6.34	6.34	
3030	Ceiling Finishes	Mineral fiber tile on concealed zee bars		S.F. Ceiling	6.89	6.89	
D. SERVICES							
	D10 Conveying						
1010	Elevators & Lifts	Two hydraulic passenger elevators		Each	118,700	11.87	8.7%
1020	Escalators & Moving Walks	N/A		—	—	—	
	D20 Plumbing						
2010	Plumbing Fixtures	Toilet and service fixtures, supply and drainage	1 Fixture/1320 S.F. Floor	Each	5148	3.90	
2020	Domestic Water Distribution	Gas fired water heater		S.F. Floor	.48	.48	3.7%
2040	Rain Water Drainage	Roof drains		S.F. Roof	2.04	.68	
	D30 HVAC						
3010	Energy Supply	N/A		—	—	—	
3020	Heat Generating Systems	Included in D3050		—	—	—	
3030	Cooling Generating Systems	N/A		—	—	—	12.8 %
3050	Terminal & Package Units	Multizone unit gas heating, electric cooling		S.F. Floor	17.45	17.45	
3090	Other HVAC Sys. & Equipment	N/A		—	—	—	
	D40 Fire Protection						
4010	Sprinklers	Wet pipe sprinkler system		S.F. Floor	3.67	3.67	3.3%
4020	Standpipes	Standpipes and hose systems		S.F. Floor	.91	.91	
	D50 Electrical						
5010	Electrical Service/Distribution	1000 ampere service, panel board and feeders		S.F. Floor	3.66	3.66	
5020	Lighting & Branch Wiring	High efficiency fluorescent fixtures, receptacles, switches, A.C. and misc. power		S.F. Floor	11.73	11.73	15.8%
5030	Communications & Security	Addressable alarm systems, internet and phone wiring, and emergency lighting		S.F. Floor	6.04	6.04	
5090	Other Electrical Systems	Emergency generator, 7.5 kW, uninterruptible power supply		S.F. Floor	.24	.24	
E. EQUIPMENT & FURNISHINGS							
1010	Commercial Equipment	N/A		—	—	—	
1020	Institutional Equipment	N/A		—	—	—	0.0 %
1030	Vehicular Equipment	N/A		—	—	—	
1090	Other Equipment	N/A		—	—	—	
F. SPECIAL CONSTRUCTION							
1020	Integrated Construction	N/A		—	—	—	0.0 %
1040	Special Facilities	N/A		—	—	—	
G. BUILDING SITEWORK	**N/A**						

		Sub-Total	136.84	100%
CONTRACTOR FEES (General Requirements: 10%, Overhead: 5%, Profit: 10%)		25%	34.19	
ARCHITECT FEES		7%	11.97	
	Total Building Cost		**183**	

Costs per square foot of floor area

Exterior Wall	S.F. Area	20000	40000	60000	80000	100000	150000	200000	250000	300000
	L.F. Perimeter	260	360	400	420	460	520	600	640	700
Precast Concrete Panel	Steel Frame	232.45	201.55	184.85	174.90	170.20	162.15	158.85	155.85	154.25
	R/Conc. Frame	230.40	199.25	182.50	172.50	167.80	159.75	156.45	153.35	151.85
Face Brick with Concrete Block Back-up	Steel Frame	217.60	190.30	176.25	167.85	163.90	157.15	154.35	151.85	150.55
	R/Conc. Frame	212.80	187.10	173.50	165.40	161.60	155.05	152.35	149.90	148.65
Limestone Panel Concrete Block Back-up	Steel Frame	261.70	221.75	199.80	186.65	180.50	169.95	165.50	161.55	159.50
	R/Conc. Frame	259.25	219.25	197.35	184.15	178.05	167.45	163.10	159.10	157.00
Perimeter Adj., Add or Deduct	Per 100 L.F.	32.05	15.95	10.65	8.00	6.45	4.35	3.25	2.55	2.15
Story Hgt. Adj., Add or Deduct	Per 1 Ft.	6.70	4.60	3.40	2.65	2.40	1.80	1.55	1.30	1.20
For Basement, add $39.80 per square foot of basement area										

The above costs were calculated using the basic specifications shown on the facing page. These costs should be adjusted where necessary for design alternatives and owner's requirements. Reported completed project costs, for this type of structure, range from $83.10 to $244.35 per S.F.

Common additives

Description	Unit	$ Cost
Closed circuit surveillance, one station		
Camera and monitor	Each	1975
For additional camera stations, add	Each	1050
Directory boards, plastic, glass covered		
30" x 20"	Each	630
36" x 48"	Each	1500
Aluminum, 24" x 18"	Each	630
36" x 24"	Each	735
48" x 32"	Each	1050
48" x 60"	Each	2200
Electronic, wall mounted	S.F.	2525
Free standing	S.F.	3100
Escalators, 10' rise, 32" wide, glass balustrade	Each	140,500
Metal balustrade	Each	147,500
48" wide, glass balustrade	Each	147,500
Metal balustrade	Each	155,500
Pedestal access floor system w/ plastic laminate cover		
Computer room, less than 6000 SF	S.F.	12
Greater than 6000 SF	S.F.	11.25
Office, greater than 6000 S.F.	S.F.	8.05

Description	Unit	$ Cost
Security access systems		
Metal detectors, wand type	Each	98
Walk-through portal type, single-zone	Each	4350
Multi-zone	Each	5450
X-ray equipment		
Desk top, for mail, small packages	Each	3875
Conveyer type, including monitor, minimum	Each	17,700
Maximum	Each	31,400
Explosive detection equipment		
Hand held, battery operated	Each	28,100
Walk-through portal type	Each	48,400
Uninterruptible power supply, 15 kVA/12.75 kW	kW	1795

Important: See the Reference Section for Location Factors.

Model costs calculated for a 8 story building with 12' story height and 80,000 square feet of floor area

				Unit	Unit Cost	Cost Per S.F.	% Of Sub-Total
A. SUBSTRUCTURE							
1010	Standard Foundations	Poured concrete; strip and spread footings		S.F. Ground	12.16	1.52	
1020	Special Foundations	N/A		—	—	—	
1030	Slab on Grade	4" reinforced concrete with vapor barrier and granular base		S.F. Slab	5.31	.67	2.1%
2010	Basement Excavation	Site preparation for slab and trench for foundation wall and footing		S.F. Ground	.32	.04	
2020	Basement Walls	4' foundation wall		L.F. Wall	82	.55	
B. SHELL							
	B10 Superstructure						
1010	Floor Construction	Concrete slab with metal deck and beams		S.F. Floor	24.57	21.50	17.0%
1020	Roof Construction	Metal deck, open web steel joists, interior columns		S.F. Roof	7.12	.89	
	B20 Exterior Enclosure						
2010	Exterior Walls	Precast concrete panels	80% of wall	S.F. Wall	46.21	18.63	
2020	Exterior Windows	Vertical pivoted steel	20% of wall	Each	585	3.94	17.3%
2030	Exterior Doors	Double aluminum and glass doors and entrance with transoms		Each	4168	.27	
	B30 Roofing						
3010	Roof Coverings	Built-up tar and gravel with flashing; perlite/EPS composite insulation		S.F. Roof	6.24	.78	0.6%
3020	Roof Openings	N/A		—	—	—	
C. INTERIORS							
1010	Partitions	Gypsum board on metal studs	30 S.F. Floor/L.F. Partition	S.F. Partition	9.90	3.30	
1020	Interior Doors	Single leaf hollow metal	400 S.F. Floor/Door	Each	1152	2.89	
1030	Fittings	Toilet Partitions		S.F. Floor	.69	.69	
2010	Stair Construction	Concrete filled metal pan		Flight	14,450	3.07	18.3%
3010	Wall Finishes	60% vinyl wall covering, 40% paint		S.F. Surface	1.55	1.03	
3020	Floor Finishes	60% carpet, 30% vinyl composition tile, 10% ceramic tile		S.F. Floor	6.34	6.34	
3030	Ceiling Finishes	Mineral fiber tile on concealed zee bars		S.F. Ceiling	6.89	6.89	
D. SERVICES							
	D10 Conveying						
1010	Elevators & Lifts	Four geared passenger elevators		Each	307,600	15.38	11.7%
1020	Escalators & Moving Walks	N/A		—	—	—	
	D20 Plumbing						
2010	Plumbing Fixtures	Toilet and service fixtures, supply and drainage	1 Fixture/1370 S.F. Floor	Each	3781	2.76	
2020	Domestic Water Distribution	Gas fired water heater		S.F. Floor	.59	.59	2.8%
2040	Rain Water Drainage	Roof drains		S.F. Roof	2.40	.30	
	D30 HVAC						
3010	Energy Supply	N/A		—	—	—	
3020	Heat Generating Systems	Included in D3050		—	—	—	
3030	Cooling Generating Systems	N/A		—	—	—	13.2%
3050	Terminal & Package Units	Multizone unit gas heating, electric cooling		S.F. Floor	17.45	17.45	
3090	Other HVAC Sys. & Equipment	N/A		—	—	—	
	D40 Fire Protection						
4010	Sprinklers	Wet pipe sprinkler system		S.F. Floor	2.87	2.87	3.0%
4020	Standpipes	Standpipes and hose systems		S.F. Floor	1.05	1.05	
	D50 Electrical						
5010	Electrical Service/Distribution	1600 ampere service, panel board and feeders		S.F. Floor	1.40	1.40	
5020	Lighting & Branch Wiring	High efficiency fluorescent fixtures, receptacles, switches, A.C. and misc. power		S.F. Floor	11.64	11.64	14.1%
5030	Communications & Security	Addressable alarm systems, internet and phone wiring, emergency lighting		S.F. Floor	4.53	4.53	
5090	Other Electrical Systems	Emergency generator, 100 kW, uninterruptible power supply		S.F. Floor	1.02	1.02	
E. EQUIPMENT & FURNISHINGS							
1010	Commercial Equipment	N/A		—	—	—	
1020	Institutional Equipment	N/A		—	—	—	0.0%
1030	Vehicular Equipment	N/A		—	—	—	
1090	Other Equipment	N/A		—	—	—	
F. SPECIAL CONSTRUCTION							
1020	Integrated Construction	N/A		—	—	—	0.0%
1040	Special Facilities	N/A		—	—	—	
G. BUILDING SITEWORK	**N/A**						

	Sub-Total	131.99	100%
CONTRACTOR FEES (General Requirements: 10%, Overhead: 5%, Profit: 10%)	25%	33.01	
ARCHITECT FEES	6%	9.90	

Total Building Cost | **174.90**

Costs per square foot of floor area

Exterior Wall	S.F. Area	120000	145000	170000	200000	230000	260000	400000	600000	800000
	L.F. Perimeter	420	450	470	490	510	530	600	730	820
Double Glazed Heat Absorbing Tinted Plate Glass Panels	Steel Frame	205.70	197.25	190.30	183.85	179.10	175.45	164.70	158.85	155.10
	R/Conc. Frame	195.85	187.55	180.70	174.40	169.75	166.15	155.60	149.85	146.20
Face Brick with Concrete Block Back-up	Steel Frame	177.35	172.05	167.85	163.95	161.10	158.95	152.55	148.95	146.75
	R/Conc. Frame	198.45	193.35	189.25	185.50	182.75	180.60	174.45	170.95	168.80
Precast Concrete Panel With Exposed Aggregate	Steel Frame	183.80	177.80	173.00	168.50	165.20	162.70	155.35	151.20	148.65
	R/Conc. Frame	173.95	168.10	163.40	159.10	155.85	153.40	146.25	142.20	139.70
Perimeter Adj., Add or Deduct	Per 100 L.F.	14.35	11.75	10.05	8.55	7.45	6.60	4.25	2.80	2.15
Story Hgt. Adj., Add or Deduct	Per 1 Ft.	5.80	5.10	4.55	4.05	3.70	3.40	2.50	2.00	1.70

For Basement, add $39.80 per square foot of basement area

The above costs were calculated using the basic specifications shown on the facing page. These costs should be adjusted where necessary for design alternatives and owner's requirements. Reported completed project costs, for this type of structure, range from $104.25 to $254.35 per S.F.

Common additives

Description	Unit	$ Cost
Closed circuit surveillance, one station-		
Camera and monitor	Each	1975
For additional camera stations, add	Each	1050
Directory boards, plastic, glass covered		
30" x 20"	Each	630
36" x 48"	Each	1500
Aluminum, 24" x 18"	Each	630
36" x 24"	Each	735
48" x 32"	Each	1050
48" x 60"	Each	2200
Electronic, wall mounted	S.F.	2525
Free standing	S.F.	3100
Escalators, 10' rise, 32" wide, glass balustrade	Each	140,500
Metal balustrade	Each	147,500
48" wide, glass balustrade	Each	147,500
Metal balustrade	Each	155,500
Pedestal access floor system w/ plastic laminate cover		
Computer room, less than 6000 SF	S.F.	12
Greater than 6000 SF	S.F.	11.25
Office, greater than 6000 S.F.	S.F.	8.05

Description	Unit	$ Cost
Security access systems		
Metal detectors, wand type	Each	98
Walk-through portal type, single-zone	Each	4350
Multi-zone		5450
X-ray equipment	Each	
Desk top, for mail, small packages	Each	3875
Conveyer type, including monitor, minimum	Each	17,700
Maximum	Each	31,400
Explosive detection equipment		
Hand held, battery operated	Each	28,100
Walk-through portal type	Each	48,400
Uninterruptible power supply, 15 kVA/12.75 kW	kW	1795

Model costs calculated for a 16 story building with 10' story height and 260,000 square feet of floor area

Office, 11-20 Story

				Unit	Unit Cost	Cost Per S.F.	% Of Sub-Total
A. SUBSTRUCTURE							
1010	Standard Foundations	CIP concrete pile caps		S.F. Ground	9.92	.62	
1020	Special Foundations	Steel H-piles, concrete grade beams		S.F. Ground	61	3.81	
1030	Slab on Grade	4" reinforced concrete with vapor barrier and granular base		S.F. Slab	5.31	.33	3.9%
2010	Basement Excavation	Site preparation for slab, piles and grade beams		S.F. Ground	.32	.02	
2020	Basement Walls	4' foundation wall		L.F. Wall	82	.40	
B. SHELL							
B10 Superstructure							
1010	Floor Construction	Concrete slab, metal deck, beams		S.F. Floor	28.26	26.49	20.4%
1020	Roof Construction	Metal deck, open web steel joists, beams, columns		S.F. Roof	8.64	.54	
B20 Exterior Enclosure							
2010	Exterior Walls	N/A		—	—	—	
2020	Exterior Windows	Double glazed heat absorbing, tinted plate glass wall panels	100% of wall	Each	75	24.29	18.8 %
2030	Exterior Doors	Double aluminum & glass doors		Each	6311	.67	
B30 Roofing							
3010	Roof Coverings	Single ply membrane, fully adhered; perlite/EPS composite insulation		S.F. Roof	5.76	.36	0.3%
3020	Roof Openings	N/A		—	—	—	
C. INTERIORS							
1010	Partitions	Gypsum board on metal studs	30 S.F. Floor/L.F. Partition	S.F. Partition	11.10	2.96	
1020	Interior Doors	Single leaf hollow metal	400 S.F. Floor/Door	Each	1152	2.89	
1030	Fittings	Toilet partitions		S.F. Floor	.39	.39	
2010	Stair Construction	Concrete filled metal pan		Flight	17,250	2.33	16.2%
3010	Wall Finishes	60% vinyl wall covering, 40% paint		S.F. Surface	1.52	.81	
3020	Floor Finishes	60% carpet tile, 30% vinyl composition tile, 10% ceramic tile		S.F. Floor	5.23	5.23	
3030	Ceiling Finishes	Mineral fiber tile on concealed zee bars		S.F. Ceiling	6.89	6.89	
D. SERVICES							
D10 Conveying							
1010	Elevators & Lifts	Four geared passenger elevators		Each	499,200	7.68	5.8%
1020	Escalators & Moving Walks	N/A		—	—	—	
D20 Plumbing							
2010	Plumbing Fixtures	Toilet and service fixtures, supply and drainage	1 Fixture/1345 S.F. Floor	Each	5622	4.18	
2020	Domestic Water Distribution	Oil fired water heater		S.F. Floor	.35	.35	3.6%
2040	Rain Water Drainage	Roof drains		S.F. Roof	2.88	.18	
D30 HVAC							
3010	Energy Supply	N/A		—	—	—	
3020	Heat Generating Systems	Boiler, heat exchanger and fans		Each	486,175	2.57	
3030	Cooling Generating Systems	Chilled water, fan coil units		S.F. Floor	16.78	16.78	14.6 %
3050	Terminal & Package Units	N/A		—	—	—	
3090	Other HVAC Sys. & Equipment	N/A		—	—	—	
D40 Fire Protection							
4010	Sprinklers	Sprinkler system, light hazard		S.F. Floor	2.78	2.78	2.5%
4020	Standpipes	Standpipes and hose systems		S.F. Floor	.54	.54	
D50 Electrical							
5010	Electrical Service/Distribution	2400 ampere service, panel board and feeders		S.F. Floor	.89	.89	
5020	Lighting & Branch Wiring	High efficiency fluorescent fixtures, receptacles, switches, A.C. and misc. power		S.F. Floor	11.51	11.51	13.8%
5030	Communications & Security	Addressable alarm systems, internet and phone wiring, emergency lighting		S.F. Floor	5.40	5.40	
5090	Other Electrical Systems	Emergency generator, 200 kW, uninterruptible power supply		S.F. Floor	.54	.54	
E. EQUIPMENT & FURNISHINGS							
1010	Commercial Equipment	N/A		—	—	—	
1020	Institutional Equipment	N/A		—	—	—	
1030	Vehicular Equipment	N/A		—	—	—	0.0 %
1090	Other Equipment	N/A		—	—	—	
F. SPECIAL CONSTRUCTION							
1020	Integrated Construction	N/A		—	—	—	
1040	Special Facilities	N/A		—	—	—	0.0 %
G. BUILDING SITEWORK	**N/A**						

		Sub-Total	132.43	100%
CONTRACTOR FEES (General Requirements: 10%, Overhead: 5%, Profit: 10%)		25%	33.09	
ARCHITECT FEES		6%	9.93	

Total Building Cost	**175.45**

Costs per square foot of floor area

Exterior Wall	S.F. Area	5000	7500	10000	12500	15000	17500	20000	22500	25000
	L.F. Perimeter	284	350	410	450	490	530	570	600	632
Brick Veneer	Wood Truss	437.60	424.45	417.35	411.45	407.55	404.75	402.65	400.65	399.00
Brick Veneer	Steel Frame	443.00	430.40	423.60	417.95	414.25	411.55	409.50	407.60	406.05
Decorative Concrete Block	Steel Frame	444.80	431.90	424.90	419.15	415.30	412.55	410.45	408.45	406.90
Decorative Concrete Block	Bearing Wall	433.90	425.70	421.35	417.90	415.60	413.95	412.70	411.60	410.70
Tiltup Concrete Panel	Steel Frame	437.50	425.95	419.65	414.55	411.15	408.75	406.90	405.10	403.75
EIFS on Concrete Block	Steel Frame	440.75	427.00	419.60	413.90	410.05	407.35	405.20	403.35	401.85
Perimeter Adj., Add or Deduct	Per 100 L.F.	19.70	13.20	9.85	7.95	6.60	5.65	4.95	4.30	3.95
Story Hgt. Adj., Add or Deduct	Per 1 Ft.	3.00	2.45	2.15	1.80	1.75	1.60	1.50	1.35	1.30

For Basement, add $31.30 per square foot of basement area

The above costs were calculated using the basic specifications shown on the facing page. These costs should be adjusted where necessary for design alternatives and owner's requirements. Reported completed project costs, for this type of structure, range from $182.55 to $946.55 per S.F.

Common additives

Description	Unit	$ Cost
Cabinets, base, door units, metal	L.F.	315
Drawer units	L.F.	625
Tall storage cabinets, open, 7' high	L.F.	590
With glazed doors	L.F.	860
Wall cabinets, metal, 12-1/2" deep, open	L.F.	238
With doors	L.F.	430
Counter top, laminated plastic, no backsplash	L.F.	79.50
Stainless steel counter top	L.F.	194
For drop-in stainless 43" x 21" sink, add	Ea.	1100
Nurse Call Station		
Single bedside call station	Ea.	330
Ceiling speaker station	Ea.	154
Emergency call station	Ea.	159
Pillow speaker	Ea.	273
Standard call button	Ea.	175
Master control station for 20 stations	Total	6300

Description	Unit	$ Cost
Directory Boards, Plastic, glass covered		
Plastic, glass covered, 30" x 20"	Ea.	630
36" x 48"	Ea.	1500
Building directory, alum., black felt panels, 1 door, 24" x 18"	Ea.	630
36" x 24"	Ea.	735
48" x 32"	Ea.	1050
48" x 60"	Ea.	2200
Tables, Examining, vinyl top		
with base cabinets	Ea.	1475
Utensil washer-sanitizer	Ea.	12,600
X-ray, mobile, minimum	Ea.	18,300

Important: See the Reference Section for Location Factors.

Model costs calculated for a 1 story building with 15'-4" story height and 12,500 square feet of floor area

Outpatient Surgery Center

				Unit	Unit Cost	Cost Per S.F.	% Of Sub-Total
A.	**SUBSTRUCTURE**						
1010	Standard Foundations	Poured concrete; strip and spread footings		S.F. Ground	1.98	1.98	
1020	Special Foundations	N/A		—	—	—	
1030	Slab on Grade	4" reinforced concrete with vapor barrier and granular base		S.F. Slab	6.52	6.52	3.9%
2010	Basement Excavation	Site preparation for slab and trench for foundation wall and footing		S.F. Ground	.32	.32	
2020	Basement Walls	4' Foundation wall		L.F. Wall	82	2.93	
B.	**SHELL**						
	B10 Superstructure						
1010	Floor Construction	N/A		—	—	—	2.6 %
1020	Roof Construction	Steel Joists and girders on columns		S.F. Roof	7.76	7.76	
	B20 Exterior Enclosure						
2010	Exterior Walls	Brick veneer	85% of wall	S.F. Wall	18.87	8.85	
2020	Exterior Windows	Aluminum frame, fixed	15% of wall	Each	825	4.55	6.1%
2030	Exterior Doors	Aluminum and glass entry; steel flush doors		Each	6588	5.28	
	B30 Roofing						
3010	Roof Coverings	Single-ply membrane, loose laid and ballasted; polyisocyanurate insulation		S.F. Roof	6.40	6.40	2.1%
3020	Roof Openings	Roof hatches		S.F. Roof	.10	.10	
C.	**INTERIORS**						
1010	Partitions	Gypsum board on metal studs	7 S.F. Floor/L.F. Partition	S.F. Partition	7.79	11.13	
1020	Interior Doors	Single and double leaf fire doors	200 S.F. Floor/Door	Each	1377	6.89	
1030	Fittings	Stainless steel toilet partitions, steel lockers		S.F. Floor	1.66	1.66	
2010	Stair Construction	N/A		—	—	—	13.1%
3010	Wall Finishes	80% Paint, 10% vinyl wall covering, 10% ceramic tile		S.F. Surface	2	5.71	
3020	Floor Finishes	10% Carpet, 80% vinyl sheet, 10% ceramic tile		S.F. Floor	10.33	10.33	
3030	Ceiling Finishes	Mineral fiber tile and plastic coated tile on suspension system		S.F. Ceiling	4.04	4.04	
D.	**SERVICES**						
	D10 Conveying						
1010	Elevators & Lifts	N/A		—	—	—	0.0 %
1020	Escalators & Moving Walks	N/A		—	—	—	
	D20 Plumbing						
2010	Plumbing Fixtures	Medical, patient & specialty fixtures, supply and drainage	1 fixture/350 S.F. Floor	Each	3553	10.15	
2020	Domestic Water Distribution	Electric water heater		S.F. Floor	1.64	1.64	4.6%
2040	Rain Water Drainage	Roof drains		S.F. Roof	2.30	2.30	
	D30 HVAC						
3010	Energy Supply	Hot water reheat for surgery		S.F. Floor	11.65	11.65	
3020	Heat Generating Systems	Boiler		Each	60,325	6.69	
3030	Cooling Generating Systems	N/A		—	—	—	37.1%
3050	Terminal & Package Units	N/A		—	—	—	
3090	Other HVAC Sys. & Equipment	Rooftop AC, CAV, roof vents, heat exchanger, surgical air curtains		S.F. Floor	95	94.69	
	D40 Fire Protection						
4010	Sprinklers	Wet pipe sprinkler system		S.F. Floor	3.56	3.56	1.7%
4020	Standpipes	Standpipe		S.F. Floor	1.58	1.58	
	D50 Electrical						
5010	Electrical Service/Distribution	1200 ampere service, panel board and feeders		S.F. Floor	6.80	6.80	
5020	Lighting & Branch Wiring	T-8 fluorescent light fixtures, receptacles, switches, A.C. and misc. power		S.F. Floor	16.64	16.64	13.0%
5030	Communications & Security	Addressable alarm system, internet wiring, communications system, emergency lighting		S.F. Slab	9.99	9.99	
5090	Other Electrical Systems	Emergency generator, 300 kW with fuel tank		S.F. Floor	6.02	6.02	
E.	**EQUIPMENT & FURNISHINGS**						
1010	Commercial Equipment	N/A		—	—	—	
1020	Institutional Equipment	Medical gas system, cabinetry, scrub sink, sterilizer		S.F. Floor	47.10	47.10	15.8 %
1030	Vehicular Equipment	N/A		—	—	—	
1090	Other Equipment	Ice maker, washing machine		S.F. Floor	1	1	
F.	**SPECIAL CONSTRUCTION & DEMOLITION**						
1020	Integrated Construction	N/A		—	—	—	0.0 %
1040	Special Facilities	N/A		—	—	—	
G.	**BUILDING SITEWORK**	**N/A**					

						Sub-Total	304.26	100%
	CONTRACTOR FEES (General Requirements: 10%, Overhead: 5%, Profit: 10%)					25%	76.06	
	ARCHITECT FEES					9%	34.23	

Total Building Cost 414.55

183

Costs per square foot of floor area

Exterior Wall	S.F. Area	7000	9000	11000	13000	15000	17000	19000	21000	23000
	L.F. Perimeter	240	280	303	325	354	372	397	422	447
Limestone with Concrete Block Back-up	Bearing Walls	282.90	264.55	248.65	237.60	230.65	223.65	219.10	215.40	212.30
	R/Conc. Frame	295.85	278.10	263.15	252.60	246.00	239.40	235.10	231.55	228.65
Face Brick with Concrete Block Back-up	Bearing Walls	242.95	228.15	216.45	208.25	202.95	197.95	194.50	191.70	189.45
	R/Conc. Frame	264.35	249.55	237.80	229.60	224.35	219.30	215.90	213.10	210.80
Decorative Concrete Block	Bearing Walls	231.40	217.70	207.15	199.85	194.95	190.60	187.50	184.95	182.90
	R/Conc. Frame	253.85	240.20	229.60	222.35	217.45	213.05	209.95	207.40	205.35
Perimeter Adj., Add or Deduct	Per 100 L.F.	37.65	29.30	24.05	20.25	17.55	15.55	13.85	12.50	11.55
Story Hgt. Adj., Add or Deduct	Per 1 Ft.	6.75	6.10	5.45	4.85	4.65	4.35	4.10	3.90	3.85

For Basement, add $31.30 per square foot of basement area

The above costs were calculated using the basic specifications shown on the facing page. These costs should be adjusted where necessary for design alternatives and owner's requirements. Reported completed project costs, for this type of structure, range from $119.75 to $312.40 per S.F.

Common additives

Description	Unit	$ Cost	Description	Unit	$ Cost
Cells Prefabricated, 5'-6' wide,			Lockers, Steel, Single tier, 60" to 72"	Opening	218 - 365
7'-8' high, 7'-8' deep	Each	12,700	2 tier, 60" or 72" total	Opening	113 - 156
Elevators, Hydraulic passenger, 2 stops			5 tier, box lockers	Opening	71.50 - 85
1500# capacity	Each	66,100	Locker bench, lam. maple top only	L.F.	26.50
2500# capacity	Each	69,200	Pedestals, steel pipe	Each	74
3500# capacity	Each	73,200	Safe, Office type, 1 hour rating		
Emergency Lighting, 25 watt, battery operated			30" x 18" x 18"	Each	2500
Lead battery	Each	320	60" x 36" x 18", double door	Each	8075
Nickel cadmium	Each	885	Shooting Range, Incl. bullet traps,		
Flagpoles, Complete			target provisions, and contols,		
Aluminum, 20' high	Each	1775	not incl. structural shell	Each	50,500
40' high	Each	3925	Smoke Detectors		
70' high	Each	10,800	Ceiling type	Each	223
Fiberglass, 23' high	Each	1325	Duct type	Each	555
39'-5" high	Each	3575	Sound System		
59' high	Each	7275	Amplifier, 250 watts	Each	2025
			Speaker, ceiling or wall	Each	208
			Trumpet	Each	400

Important: See the Reference Section for Location Factors.

Model costs calculated for a 2 story building with 12' story height and 11,000 square feet of floor area

Police Station

				Unit	Unit Cost	Cost Per S.F.	% Of Sub-Total
A.	**SUBSTRUCTURE**						
1010	Standard Foundations	Poured concrete; strip and spread footings		S.F. Ground	2.86	1.43	
1020	Special Foundations	N/A		—	—	—	
1030	Slab on Grade	4" reinforced concrete with vapor barrier and granular base		S.F. Slab	5.31	2.66	4.0%
2010	Basement Excavation	Site preparation for slab and trench for foundation wall and footing		S.F. Ground	.32	.16	
2020	Basement Walls	4' foundation wall		L.F. Wall	82	2.98	
B.	**SHELL**						
	B10 Superstructure						
1010	Floor Construction	Open web steel joists, slab form, concrete		S.F. Floor	12.26	6.13	4.7%
1020	Roof Construction	Metal deck on open web steel joists		S.F. Roof	4.88	2.44	
	B20 Exterior Enclosure						
2010	Exterior Walls	Limestone with concrete block backup	80% of wall	S.F. Wall	68	35.96	
2020	Exterior Windows	Metal horizontal sliding	20% of wall	Each	1144	10.08	26.3%
2030	Exterior Doors	Hollow metal		Each	2688	1.96	
	B30 Roofing						
3010	Roof Coverings	Built-up tar and gravel with flashing; perlite/EPS composite insulation		S.F. Roof	7.22	3.61	2.0%
3020	Roof Openings	N/A		—	—	—	
C.	**INTERIORS**						
1010	Partitions	Concrete block	20 S.F. Floor/L.F. Partition	S.F. Partition	9.38	4.69	
1020	Interior Doors	Single leaf kalamein fire door	200 S.F. Floor/Door	Each	1152	5.76	
1030	Fittings	Toilet partitions		S.F. Floor	.93	.93	
2010	Stair Construction	Concrete filled metal pan		Flight	17,250	3.13	16.3%
3010	Wall Finishes	90% paint, 10% ceramic tile		S.F. Surface	3.79	3.79	
3020	Floor Finishes	70% vinyl composition tile, 20% carpet tile, 10% ceramic tile		S.F. Floor	4.59	4.59	
3030	Ceiling Finishes	Mineral fiber tile on concealed zee bars		S.F. Ceiling	6.89	6.89	
D.	**SERVICES**						
	D10 Conveying						
1010	Elevators & Lifts	One hydraulic passenger elevator		Each	83,380	7.58	4.2%
1020	Escalators & Moving Walks	N/A		—	—	—	
	D20 Plumbing						
2010	Plumbing Fixtures	Toilet and service fixtures, supply and drainage	1 Fixture/580 S.F. Floor	Each	4884	8.42	
2020	Domestic Water Distribution	Oil fired water heater		S.F. Floor	3.76	3.76	7.7%
2040	Rain Water Drainage	Roof drains		S.F. Roof	3.64	1.82	
	D30 HVAC						
3010	Energy Supply	N/A		—	—	—	
3020	Heat Generating Systems	N/A		—	—	—	
3030	Cooling Generating Systems	N/A		—	—	—	11.9%
3050	Terminal & Package Units	Multizone HVAC air cooled system		S.F. Floor	21.70	21.70	
3090	Other HVAC Sys. & Equipment	N/A		—	—	—	
	D40 Fire Protection						
4010	Sprinklers	Wet pipe sprinkler system		S.F. Floor	3.79	3.79	2.6%
4020	Standpipes	Standpipe		S.F. Floor	.98	.98	
	D50 Electrical						
5010	Electrical Service/Distribution	400 ampere service, panel board and feeders		S.F. Floor	2.01	2.01	
5020	Lighting & Branch Wiring	T-8 fluorescent fixtures, receptacles, switches, A.C. and misc. power		S.F. Floor	11.96	11.96	11.7%
5030	Communications & Security	Addressable alarm systems, internet wiring, intercom and emergency lighting		S.F. Floor	7.19	7.19	
5090	Other Electrical Systems	Emergency generator, 15 kW		S.F. Floor	.21	.21	
E.	**EQUIPMENT & FURNISHINGS**						
1010	Commercial Equipment	N/A		—	—	—	
1020	Institutional Equipment	Lockers, detention rooms, cells, gasoline dispensers		S.F. Floor	13.45	13.45	8.7%
1030	Vehicular Equipment	Gasoline dispenser system		S.F. Floor	2.45	2.45	
1090	Other Equipment	N/A		—	—	—	
F.	**SPECIAL CONSTRUCTION**						
1020	Integrated Construction	N/A		—	—	—	0.0%
1040	Special Facilities	N/A		—	—	—	
G.	**BUILDING SITEWORK**	**N/A**					

			Sub-Total	182.51	100%
CONTRACTOR FEES (General Requirements: 10%, Overhead: 5%, Profit: 10%)			25%	45.61	
ARCHITECT FEES			9%	20.53	
			Total Building Cost	**248.65**	

Costs per square foot of floor area

Exterior Wall	S.F. Area	600	750	925	1150	1450	1800	2100	2600	3200
	L.F. Perimeter	100	112	128	150	164	182	200	216	240
Steel Siding on Wood Studs	Wood Truss	74.15	68.75	65.30	62.70	57.75	54.25	52.50	49.05	46.80
Aluminum Siding	Wood Truss	73.30	68.60	65.45	63.20	58.75	55.70	54.20	51.15	49.15
Wood Board Siding	Wood Truss	76.15	71.10	67.90	65.40	60.70	57.45	55.85	52.65	50.45
Plywood Siding	Wood Truss	74.10	69.25	66.20	63.80	59.35	56.20	54.65	51.60	49.50
Perimeter Adj., Add or Deduct	Per 100 L.F.	44.20	35.40	28.70	23.10	18.25	14.75	12.60	10.25	8.25
Story Hgt. Adj., Add or Deduct	Per 1 Ft.	3.15	2.85	2.65	2.50	2.10	1.90	1.80	1.60	1.40
Basement—Not Applicable										

The above costs were calculated using the basic specifications shown on the facing page. These costs should be adjusted where necessary for design alternatives and owner's requirements. Reported completed project costs, for this type of structure, range from $38.30 to $152.80 per S.F.

Common additives

Description	Unit	$ Cost
Slab on Grade		
4" thick, non-industrial, non-reinforced	S.F.	4.78
Reinforced	S.F.	5.31
Light industrial, non-reinforced	S.F.	5.99
Reinforced	S.F.	6.52
Industrial, non-reinforced	S.F.	10.22
Reinforced	S.F.	10.78
6" thick, non-industrial, non-reinforced	S.F.	5.57
Reinforced	S.F.	6.29
Light industrial, non-reinforced	S.F.	6.80
Reinforced	S.F.	7.82
Heavy industrial, non-reinforced	S.F.	13.11
Reinforced	S.F.	13.84
Insulation		
Fiberboard, low density, 1" thick, R2.78	S.F.	1.30
Foil on reinforced scrim, single bubble air space, R8.8	C.S.F.	66
Vinyl faced fiberglass, 1-1/2" thick, R5	S.F.	0.80
Vinyl/scrim/foil (VSF), 1-1/2" thick, R5	S.F.	0.96

Description	Unit	$ Cost
Roof ventilation, ridge vent, aluminum	L.F.	7.80
Mushroom vent, aluminum	Each	137
Gutter, aluminum, 5" K type, enameled	L.F.	8.20
Steel, half round or box, 5", enameled	L.F.	7.70
Wood, clear treated cedar, fir or hemlock, 4" x 5"	L.F.	27
Downspout, aluminum, 3" x 4", enameled	L.F.	7.95
Steel, round, 4" diameter	L.F.	7.50

Model costs calculated for a 1 story building with 14' story height and 1,800 square feet of floor area

Post Frame Barn

			Unit	Unit Cost	Cost Per S.F.	% Of Sub-Total
A.	**SUBSTRUCTURE**					
1010	Standard Foundations	Included in B2010 Exterior Walls	—	—	—	
1020	Special Foundations	N/A	—	—	—	
1030	Slab on Grade	N/A	—	—	—	0.0%
2010	Basement Excavation	N/A	—	—	—	
2020	Basement Walls	N/A	—	—	—	
B.	**SHELL**					
	B10 Superstructure					
1010	Floor Construction	N/A	—	—	—	15.8 %
1020	Roof Construction	Wood truss, 4/12 pitch	S.F. Roof	6.33	6.33	
	B20 Exterior Enclosure					
2010	Exterior Walls	2 x 6 Wood framing, 6 x 6 wood posts in concrete; steel siding panels	S.F. Wall	11.68	15.71	
2020	Exterior Windows	Steel windows, fixed	Each	530	4.17	59.7%
2030	Exterior Doors	Steel overhead, hollow metal doors	Each	1850	4.11	
	B30 Roofing					
3010	Roof Coverings	Metal panel roof	S.F. Roof	4.20	4.20	10.5%
3020	Roof Openings	N/A	—	—	—	
C.	**INTERIORS**					
1010	Partitions	N/A	—	—	—	
1020	Interior Doors	N/A	—	—	—	
1030	Fittings	N/A	—	—	—	
2010	Stair Construction	N/A	—	—	—	0.0 %
3010	Wall Finishes	N/A	—	—	—	
3020	Floor Finishes	N/A	—	—	—	
3030	Ceiling Finishes	N/A	—	—	—	
D.	**SERVICES**					
	D10 Conveying					
1010	Elevators & Lifts	N/A	—	—	—	0.0 %
1020	Escalators & Moving Walks	N/A	—	—	—	
	D20 Plumbing					
2010	Plumbing Fixtures	N/A	—	—	—	
2020	Domestic Water Distribution	N/A	—	—	—	0.0 %
2040	Rain Water Drainage	N/A	—	—	—	
	D30 HVAC					
3010	Energy Supply	N/A	—	—	—	
3020	Heat Generating Systems	N/A	—	—	—	
3030	Cooling Generating Systems	N/A	—	—	—	0.0 %
3050	Terminal & Package Units	N/A	—	—	—	
3090	Other HVAC Sys. & Equipment	N/A	—	—	—	
	D40 Fire Protection					
4010	Sprinklers	N/A	—	—	—	0.0 %
4020	Standpipes	N/A	—	—	—	
	D50 Electrical					
5010	Electrical Service/Distribution	60 Ampere service, panel board & feeders	S.F. Floor	1.89	1.89	
5020	Lighting & Branch Wiring	High bay fixtures, receptacles & switches	S.F. Floor	3.76	3.76	14.1%
5030	Communications & Security	N/A	—	—	—	
5090	Other Electrical Systems	N/A	—	—	—	
E.	**EQUIPMENT & FURNISHINGS**					
1010	Commercial Equipment	N/A	—	—	—	
1020	Institutional Equipment	N/A	—	—	—	
1030	Vehicular Equipment	N/A	—	—	—	0.0 %
1090	Other Equipment	N/A	—	—	—	
F.	**SPECIAL CONSTRUCTION & DEMOLITION**					
1020	Integrated Construction	N/A	—	—	—	0.0 %
1040	Special Facilities	N/A	—	—	—	
G.	**BUILDING SITEWORK**	**N/A**				
			Sub-Total		40.17	**100%**
	CONTRACTOR FEES (General Requirements: 10%, Overhead: 5%, Profit: 10%)			25%	10.06	
	ARCHITECT FEES			8%	4.02	
			Total Building Cost		**54.25**	

Costs per square foot of floor area

Exterior Wall	S.F. Area	5000	7000	9000	11000	13000	15000	17000	19000	21000
	L.F. Perimeter	300	380	420	468	486	513	540	580	620
Face Brick with Concrete Block Back-up	Steel Frame	172.75	163.10	153.60	148.20	142.40	138.65	135.80	134.15	132.90
	Bearing Walls	170.10	160.40	150.90	145.55	139.75	136.05	133.15	131.50	130.25
Limestone with Concrete Block Back-up	Steel Frame	204.85	192.20	178.55	171.00	162.45	157.00	152.85	150.50	148.70
	Bearing Walls	201.95	189.30	175.65	168.15	159.55	154.10	149.90	147.60	145.80
Decorative Concrete Block	Steel Frame	160.90	152.40	144.40	139.85	135.05	131.95	129.55	128.10	127.05
	Bearing Walls	158.30	149.70	141.75	137.20	132.40	129.30	126.90	125.45	124.40
Perimeter Adj., Add or Deduct	Per 100 L.F.	18.55	13.25	10.35	8.50	7.20	6.20	5.50	4.90	4.40
Story Hgt. Adj., Add or Deduct	Per 1 Ft.	2.85	2.55	2.25	2.10	1.80	1.70	1.55	1.45	1.35

For Basement, add $30.50 per square foot of basement area

The above costs were calculated using the basic specifications shown on the facing page. These costs should be adjusted where necessary for design alternatives and owner's requirements. Reported completed project costs, for this type of structure, range from $99.35 to $257.90 per S.F.

Common additives

Description	Unit	$ Cost
Closed Circuit Surveillance, One station		
Camera and monitor	Each	1975
For additional camera stations, add	Each	1050
Emergency Lighting, 25 watt, battery operated		
Lead battery	Each	320
Nickel cadmium	Each	885
Flagpoles, Complete		
Aluminum, 20' high	Each	1775
40' high	Each	3925
70' high	Each	10,800
Fiberglass, 23' high	Each	1325
39'-5" high	Each	3575
59' high	Each	7275

Description	Unit	$ Cost
Mail Boxes, Horizontal, key lock, 15" x 6" x 5"	Each	55
Double 15" x 12" x 5"	Each	95.50
Quadruple 15" x 12" x 10"	Each	137
Vertical, 6" x 5" x 15", aluminum	Each	49.50
Bronze	Each	60.50
Steel, enameled	Each	49.50
Scales, Dial type, 5 ton cap.		
8' x 6' platform	Each	11,700
9' x 7' platform	Each	14,700
Smoke Detectors		
Ceiling type	Each	223
Duct type	Each	555

Important: See the Reference Section for Location Factors.

Model costs calculated for a 1 story building with 14' story height and 13,000 square feet of floor area

				Unit	Unit Cost	Cost Per S.F.	% Of Sub-Total
A. SUBSTRUCTURE							
1010	Standard Foundations	Poured concrete; strip and spread footings		S.F. Ground	2.02	2.02	
1020	Special Foundations	N/A		—	—	—	
1030	Slab on Grade	4" reinforced concrete with vapor barrier and granular base		S.F. Slab	5.31	5.31	11.1%
2010	Basement Excavation	Site preparation for slab and trench for foundation wall and footing		S.F. Ground	.32	.32	
2020	Basement Walls	4' foundation wall		L.F. Wall	82	3.96	
B. SHELL							
B10 Superstructure							
1010	Floor Construction	Steel column fireproofing		L.F. Column	35.05	.11	9.0%
1020	Roof Construction	Metal deck, open web steel joists, columns		S.F. Roof	9.34	9.34	
B20 Exterior Enclosure							
2010	Exterior Walls	Face brick with concrete block backup	80% of wall	S.F. Wall	32.89	13.77	
2020	Exterior Windows	Double strength window glass	20% of wall	Each	736	3.35	17.6%
2030	Exterior Doors	Double aluminum & glass, single aluminum, hollow metal, steel overhead		Each	2672	1.24	
B30 Roofing							
3010	Roof Coverings	Built-up tar and gravel with flashing; perlite/EPS composite insulation		S.F. Roof	6.48	6.48	6.2%
3020	Roof Openings	N/A		—	—	—	
C. INTERIORS							
1010	Partitions	Concrete block	15 S.F. Floor/L.F. Partition	S.F. Partition	9.38	7.50	
1020	Interior Doors	Single leaf hollow metal	150 S.F. Floor/Door	Each	1152	7.68	
1030	Fittings	Toilet partitions, cabinets, shelving, lockers		S.F. Floor	1.44	1.44	
2010	Stair Construction	N/A		—	—	—	23.7%
3010	Wall Finishes	Paint		S.F. Surface	2.34	3.74	
3020	Floor Finishes	50% vinyl tile, 50% paint		S.F. Floor	2.67	2.67	
3030	Ceiling Finishes	Mineral fiber tile on concealed zee bars	25% of area	S.F. Ceiling	6.89	1.73	
D. SERVICES							
D10 Conveying							
1010	Elevators & Lifts	N/A		—	—	—	0.0%
1020	Escalators & Moving Walks	N/A		—	—	—	
D20 Plumbing							
2010	Plumbing Fixtures	Toilet and service fixtures, supply and drainage	1 Fixture/1180 S.F. Floor	Each	2502	2.12	
2020	Domestic Water Distribution	Gas fired water heater		S.F. Floor	.43	.43	3.7%
2040	Rain Water Drainage	Roof drains		S.F. Roof	1.35	1.35	
D30 HVAC							
3010	Energy Supply	N/A		—	—	—	
3020	Heat Generating Systems	Included in D3050		—	—	—	
3030	Cooling Generating Systems	N/A		—	—	—	8.1%
3050	Terminal & Package Units	Single zone, gas heating, electric cooling		S.F. Floor	8.51	8.51	
3090	Other HVAC Sys. & Equipment	N/A		—	—	—	
D40 Fire Protection							
4010	Sprinklers	Wet pipe sprinkler system		S.F. Floor	4.55	4.55	5.2%
4020	Standpipes	Standpipe		S.F. Floor	.89	.89	
D50 Electrical							
5010	Electrical Service/Distribution	600 ampere service, panel board and feeders		S.F. Floor	2.48	2.48	
5020	Lighting & Branch Wiring	T-8 fluorescent fixtures, receptacles, switches, A.C. and misc. power		S.F. Floor	8.85	8.85	15.3%
5030	Communications & Security	Addressable alarm systems, internet wiring and emergency lighting		S.F. Floor	4.55	4.55	
5090	Other Electrical Systems	Emergency generator, 15 kW		S.F. Floor	.12	.12	
E. EQUIPMENT & FURNISHINGS							
1010	Commercial Equipment	N/A		—	—	—	
1020	Institutional Equipment	N/A		—	—	—	0.0%
1030	Vehicular Equipment	N/A		—	—	—	
1090	Other Equipment	N/A		—	—	—	
F. SPECIAL CONSTRUCTION							
1020	Integrated Construction	N/A		—	—	—	0.0%
1040	Special Facilities	N/A		—	—	—	
G. BUILDING SITEWORK	**N/A**						

	Sub-Total	104.51	**100%**
CONTRACTOR FEES (General Requirements: 10%, Overhead: 5%, Profit: 10%)	25%	26.13	
ARCHITECT FEES	9%	11.76	
	Total Building Cost	142.40	

Costs per square foot of floor area

Exterior Wall	S.F. Area	5000	10000	15000	21000	25000	30000	40000	50000	60000
	L.F. Perimeter	287	400	500	600	660	700	834	900	1000
Face Brick with Concrete Block Back-up	Steel Frame	247.40	213.15	200.40	191.60	187.65	182.50	178.10	173.30	171.00
	Bearing Walls	233.35	204.95	194.15	186.50	183.05	178.25	174.30	169.85	167.65
Concrete Block	Steel Frame	213.00	189.15	180.35	174.45	171.85	168.50	165.55	162.50	161.00
Brick Veneer	Steel Frame	236.45	205.55	194.05	186.20	182.65	178.05	174.10	169.90	167.80
Galvanized Steel Siding	Steel Frame	201.00	180.50	173.00	168.00	165.75	163.05	160.60	158.05	156.75
Metal Sandwich Panel	Steel Frame	254.85	218.30	204.65	195.30	191.05	185.55	180.75	175.65	173.15
Perimeter Adj., Add or Deduct	Per 100 L.F.	30.80	15.40	10.20	7.30	6.20	5.15	3.80	3.05	2.55
Story Hgt. Adj., Add or Deduct	Per 1 Ft.	6.25	4.35	3.55	3.15	2.95	2.55	2.25	1.95	1.80

For Basement, add $29.35 per square foot of basement area

The above costs were calculated using the basic specifications shown on the facing page. These costs should be adjusted where necessary for design alternatives and owner's requirements. Reported completed project costs, for this type of structure, range from $94.15 to $293.50 per S.F.

Common additives

Description	Unit	$ Cost	Description	Unit	$ Cost
Bar, Front Bar	L.F.	415	Lockers, Steel, single tier, 60" or 72"	Opening	218 - 365
Back Bar	L.F.	330	2 tier, 60" or 72" total	Opening	113 - 156
Booth, Upholstered, custom straight	L.F.	241 - 440	5 tier, box lockers	Opening	71.50 - 85
"L" or "U" shaped	L.F.	249 - 425	Locker bench, lam. maple top only	L.F.	26.50
Bleachers, Telescoping, manual			Pedestals, steel pipe	Each	74
To 15 tier	Seat	135 - 187	Sauna, Prefabricated, complete		
21-30 tier	Seat	295 - 385	6' x 4'	Each	6800
Courts			6' x 9'	Each	9725
Ceiling	Court	9775	8' x 8'	Each	11,500
Floor	Court	16,400	8' x 10'	Each	12,800
Walls	Court	28,100	10' x 12'	Each	15,400
Emergency Lighting, 25 watt, battery operated			Sound System		
Lead battery	Each	320	Amplifier, 250 watts	Each	2025
Nickel cadmium	Each	885	Speaker, ceiling or wall	Each	208
Kitchen Equipment			Trumpet	Each	400
Broiler	Each	4000	Steam Bath, Complete, to 140 C.F.	Each	2175
Cooler, 6 ft. long, reach-in	Each	4100	To 300 C.F.	Each	2325
Dishwasher, 10-12 racks per hr.	Each	4225	To 800 C.F.	Each	8850
Food warmer, counter 1.2 KW	Each	725	To 2500 C.F.	Each	10,900
Freezer, reach-in, 44 C.F.	Each	5125			
Ice cube maker, 50 lb. per day	Each	1950			

Important: See the Reference Section for Location Factors.

Model costs calculated for a 2 story building with 12' story height and 30,000 square feet of floor area

					Unit	Unit Cost	Cost Per S.F.	% Of Sub-Total
A. SUBSTRUCTURE								
1010	Standard Foundations	Poured concrete; strip and spread footings			S.F. Ground	3.50	1.75	
1020	Special Foundations	N/A			—	—	—	
1030	Slab on Grade	5" reinforced concrete with vapor barrier and granular base			S.F. Slab	6.93	4.50	6.2%
2010	Basement Excavation	Site preparation for slab and trench for foundation wall and footing			S.F. Ground	.32	.21	
2020	Basement Walls	4' foundation wall			L.F. Wall	82	1.90	
B. SHELL								
B10 Superstructure								
1010	Floor Construction	Open web steel joists, slab form, concrete, columns	50% of area		S.F. Floor	18.76	9.38	10.7%
1020	Roof Construction	Metal deck on open web steel joists, columns			S.F. Roof	10.08	5.04	
B20 Exterior Enclosure								
2010	Exterior Walls	Face brick with concrete block backup	95% of wall		S.F. Wall	32.35	17.21	
2020	Exterior Windows	Storefront	5% of wall		S.F. Window	101	2.82	15.1%
2030	Exterior Doors	Aluminum and glass and hollow metal			Each	3090	.42	
B30 Roofing								
3010	Roof Coverings	Built-up tar and gravel with flashing; perlite/EPS composite insulation			S.F. Roof	8.10	4.05	3.0%
3020	Roof Openings	Roof hatches			S.F. Roof	.12	.06	
C. INTERIORS								
1010	Partitions	Concrete block, gypsum board on metal studs	25 S.F. Floor/L.F. Partition		S.F. Partition	14.48	5.79	
1020	Interior Doors	Single leaf hollow metal	810 S.F. Floor/Door		Each	1152	1.42	
1030	Fittings	Toilet partitions			S.F. Floor	.39	.39	
2010	Stair Construction	Concrete filled metal pan			Flight	14,450	1.45	13.0%
3010	Wall Finishes	Paint			S.F. Surface	1.44	1.15	
3020	Floor Finishes	80% carpet tile, 20% ceramic tile	50% of floor area		S.F. Floor	6.34	3.17	
3030	Ceiling Finishes	Mineral fiber tile on concealed zee bars	60% of area		S.F. Ceiling	6.89	4.14	
D. SERVICES								
D10 Conveying								
1010	Elevators & Lifts	N/A			—	—	—	0.0 %
1020	Escalators & Moving Walks	N/A			—	—	—	
D20 Plumbing								
2010	Plumbing Fixtures	Kitchen, bathroom and service fixtures, supply and drainage	1 Fixture/1000 S.F. Floor		Each	4080	4.08	
2020	Domestic Water Distribution	Gas fired water heater			S.F. Floor	3.28	3.28	5.7%
2040	Rain Water Drainage	Roof drains			S.F. Roof	.76	.38	
D30 HVAC								
3010	Energy Supply	N/A			—	—	—	
3020	Heat Generating Systems	Included in D3050			—	—	—	
3030	Cooling Generating Systems	N/A			—	—	—	21.7 %
3050	Terminal & Package Units	Multizone unit, gas heating, electric cooling			S.F. Floor	29.40	29.40	
3090	Other HVAC Sys. & Equipment	N/A			—	—	—	
D40 Fire Protection								
4010	Sprinklers	Sprinklers, light hazard			S.F. Floor	3.33	3.33	2.7%
4020	Standpipes	Standpipe			S.F. Floor	.35	.35	
D50 Electrical								
5010	Electrical Service/Distribution	400 ampere service, panel board and feeders			S.F. Floor	.90	.90	
5020	Lighting & Branch Wiring	Fluorescent and high intensity discharge fixtures, receptacles, switches, A.C. and misc. power			S.F. Floor	8.08	8.08	7.5%
5030	Communications & Security	Addressable alarm systems and emergency lighting			S.F. Floor	1.08	1.08	
5090	Other Electrical Systems	Emergency generator, 15 kW			S.F. Floor	.05	.05	
E. EQUIPMENT & FURNISHINGS								
1010	Commercial Equipment	N/A			—	—	—	
1020	Institutional Equipment	N/A			—	—	—	14.4 %
1030	Vehicular Equipment	N/A			—	—	—	
1090	Other Equipment	Courts, sauna baths			S.F. Floor	19.40	19.40	
F. SPECIAL CONSTRUCTION								
1020	Integrated Construction	N/A			—	—	—	0.0 %
1040	Special Facilities	N/A			—	—	—	
G. BUILDING SITEWORK	**N/A**							

	Sub-Total	135.18	**100%**
CONTRACTOR FEES (General Requirements: 10%, Overhead: 5%, Profit: 10%)		25%	33.80
ARCHITECT FEES		8%	13.52
Total Building Cost			**182.50**

Costs per square foot of floor area

Exterior Wall	S.F. Area	5000	6000	7000	8000	9000	10000	11000	12000	13000
	L.F. Perimeter	286	320	353	386	397	425	454	460	486
Face Brick with Concrete Block Back-up	Steel Joists	191.50	186.95	183.55	181.05	177.00	175.25	173.85	171.05	170.05
	Wood Joists	192.85	188.05	184.50	181.90	177.65	175.80	174.35	171.35	170.30
Stucco on Concrete Block	Steel Joists	193.30	189.15	186.05	183.80	180.20	178.60	177.35	174.85	173.95
	Wood Joists	181.70	177.70	174.75	172.55	169.10	167.55	166.30	163.95	163.05
Limestone with Concrete Block Back-up	Steel Joists	231.45	224.65	219.60	215.85	209.40	206.75	204.60	200.15	198.60
	Wood Joists	220.70	214.05	209.10	205.40	199.15	196.55	194.45	190.10	188.55
Perimeter Adj., Add or Deduct	Per 100 L.F.	17.05	14.25	12.20	10.65	9.50	8.55	7.70	7.10	6.55
Story Hgt. Adj., Add or Deduct	Per 1 Ft.	3.00	2.80	2.60	2.50	2.35	2.25	2.15	2.00	1.90

For Basement, add $30.85 per square foot of basement area

The above costs were calculated using the basic specifications shown on the facing page. These costs should be adjusted where necessary for design alternatives and owner's requirements. Reported completed project costs, for this type of structure, range from $82.20 to $254.50 per S.F.

Common additives

Description	Unit	$ Cost	Description	Unit	$ Cost
Carrels Hardwood	Each	960 - 2300	Lockers, Steel, single tier, 60" to 72"	Opening	218 - 365
Emergency Lighting, 25 watt, battery operated			2 tier, 60" to 72" total	Opening	113 - 156
Lead battery	Each	320	5 tier, box lockers	Opening	71.50 - 85
Nickel cadmium	Each	885	Locker bench, lam. maple top only	L.F.	26.50
Flagpoles, Complete			Pedestals, steel pipe	Each	74
Aluminum, 20' high	Each	1775	Seating		
40' high	Each	3925	Auditorium chair, all veneer	Each	300
70' high	Each	10,800	Veneer back, padded seat	Each	315
Fiberglass, 23' high	Each	1325	Upholstered, spring seat	Each	315
39'-5" high	Each	3575	Classroom, movable chair & desk	Set	81 - 171
59' high	Each	7275	Lecture hall, pedestal type	Each	258 - 610
Gym Floor, Incl. sleepers and finish, maple	S.F.	14.30	Smoke Detectors		
Intercom System, 25 Station capacity			Ceiling type	Each	223
Master station	Each	3175	Duct type	Each	555
Intercom outlets	Each	184	Sound System		
Handset	Each	505	Amplifier, 250 watts	Each	2025
			Speaker, ceiling or wall	Each	208
			Trumpet	Each	400
			Swimming Pools, Complete, gunite	S.F.	90.50 - 113

Model costs calculated for a 1 story building with 12' story height and 10,000 square feet of floor area

				Unit	Unit Cost	Cost Per S.F.	% Of Sub-Total
A. SUBSTRUCTURE							
1010	Standard Foundations	Poured concrete; strip and spread footings		S.F. Ground	2.43	2.43	
1020	Special Foundations	N/A		—	—	—	
1030	Slab on Grade	4" reinforced concrete with vapor barrier and granular base		S.F. Slab	5.31	5.31	9.0%
2010	Basement Excavation	Site preparation for slab and trench for foundation wall and footing		S.F. Ground	.32	.32	
2020	Basement Walls	4' foundation wall		L.F. Wall	82	3.47	
B. SHELL							
	B10 Superstructure						
1010	Floor Construction	N/A		—	—	—	7.3 %
1020	Roof Construction	Metal deck, open web steel joists, beams, interior columns		S.F. Roof	9.35	9.35	
	B20 Exterior Enclosure						
2010	Exterior Walls	Face brick with concrete block backup	85% of wall	S.F. Wall	32.90	14.26	
2020	Exterior Windows	Window wall	15% of wall	Each	47.80	3.66	15.9%
2030	Exterior Doors	Double aluminum and glass		Each	6375	2.56	
	B30 Roofing						
3010	Roof Coverings	Built-up tar and gravel with flashing; perlite/EPS composite insulation		S.F. Roof	6.48	6.48	5.0%
3020	Roof Openings	N/A		—	—	—	
C. INTERIORS							
1010	Partitions	Concrete block	8 S.F. Floor/S.F. Partition	S.F. Partition	9.37	11.71	
1020	Interior Doors	Single leaf hollow metal	700 S.F. Floor/Door	Each	1152	1.65	
1030	Fittings	Toilet partitions		S.F. Floor	1.17	1.17	
2010	Stair Construction	N/A		—	—	—	25.4%
3010	Wall Finishes	Paint		S.F. Surface	2.40	6	
3020	Floor Finishes	50% vinyl tile, 50% carpet		S.F. Floor	5.22	5.22	
3030	Ceiling Finishes	Mineral fiber tile on concealed zee bars		S.F. Ceiling	6.89	6.89	
D. SERVICES							
	D10 Conveying						
1010	Elevators & Lifts	N/A		—	—	—	0.0 %
1020	Escalators & Moving Walks	N/A		—	—	—	
	D20 Plumbing						
2010	Plumbing Fixtures	Toilet and service fixtures, supply and drainage	1 Fixture/455 S.F. Floor	Each	3858	8.48	
2020	Domestic Water Distribution	Gas fired water heater		S.F. Floor	1.64	1.64	8.7%
2040	Rain Water Drainage	Roof drains		S.F. Roof	1.08	1.08	
	D30 HVAC						
3010	Energy Supply	N/A		—	—	—	
3020	Heat Generating Systems	N/A		—	—	—	
3030	Cooling Generating Systems	N/A		—	—	—	19.6 %
3050	Terminal & Package Units	Multizone HVAC air cooled system		S.F. Floor	25.25	25.25	
3090	Other HVAC Sys. & Equipment	N/A		—	—	—	
	D40 Fire Protection						
4010	Sprinklers	Sprinkler, light hazard		S.F. Floor	3.56	3.56	3.2%
4020	Standpipes	Standpipe		S.F. Floor	.56	.56	
	D50 Electrical						
5010	Electrical Service/Distribution	200 ampere service, panel board and feeders		S.F. Floor	1.11	1.11	
5020	Lighting & Branch Wiring	T-8 fluorescent fixtures, receptacles, switches, A.C. and misc. power		S.F. Floor	2.87	2.87	5.9%
5030	Communications & Security	Addressable alarm systems, partial internet wiring and emergency lighting		S.F. Floor	3.51	3.51	
5090	Other Electrical Systems	Emergency generator, 15 kW		S.F. Floor	.08	.08	
E. EQUIPMENT & FURNISHINGS							
1010	Commercial Equipment	N/A		—	—	—	
1020	Institutional Equipment	N/A		—	—	—	0.0 %
1030	Vehicular Equipment	N/A		—	—	—	
1090	Other Equipment	N/A		—	—	—	
F. SPECIAL CONSTRUCTION							
1020	Integrated Construction	N/A		—	—	—	0.0 %
1040	Special Facilities	N/A		—	—	—	
G. BUILDING SITEWORK	**N/A**						

			Sub-Total	128.62	100%
CONTRACTOR FEES (General Requirements: 10%, Overhead: 5%, Profit: 10%)		25%	32.16		
ARCHITECT FEES		9%	14.47		

Total Building Cost	**175.25**

Costs per square foot of floor area

Exterior Wall	S.F. Area	2000	2800	3500	4200	5000	5800	6500	7200	8000
	L.F. Perimeter	180	212	240	268	300	314	336	344	368
Wood Siding	Wood Frame	246.65	233.85	227.55	223.25	219.85	215.65	213.65	210.95	209.50
Brick Veneer	Wood Frame	259.45	244.65	237.30	232.35	228.40	223.35	221.00	217.75	216.05
Face Brick with Concrete Block Back-up	Wood Joists	267.65	251.50	243.55	238.15	233.85	228.30	225.70	222.05	220.20
	Steel Joists	263.30	245.45	236.65	230.65	225.90	219.60	216.75	212.65	210.60
Stucco on Concrete Block	Wood Joists	253.50	239.65	232.80	228.15	224.45	219.80	217.60	214.55	213.00
	Steel Joists	240.45	226.60	219.75	215.10	211.40	206.75	204.55	201.50	199.95
Perimeter Adj., Add or Deduct	Per 100 L.F.	28.75	20.60	16.40	13.70	11.60	9.95	8.90	8.00	7.20
Story Hgt. Adj., Add or Deduct	Per 1 Ft.	2.95	2.55	2.25	2.15	2.00	1.80	1.70	1.55	1.50

For Basement, add $35.70 per square foot of basement area

The above costs were calculated using the basic specifications shown on the facing page. These costs should be adjusted where necessary for design alternatives and owner's requirements. Reported completed project costs, for this type of structure, range from $127.40 to $296.95 per S.F.

Common additives

Description	Unit	$ Cost	Description	Unit	$ Cost
Bar, Front Bar	L.F.	415	Fireplace, Brick, not incl. chimney or foundation		
Back bar	L.F.	330	30" x 29" opening	Each	3125
Booth, Upholstered, custom straight	L.F.	241 - 440	Chimney, standard brick		
"L" or "U" shaped	L.F.	249 - 425	Single flue, 16" x 20"	V.L.F.	106
Cupola, Stock unit, redwood			20" x 20"	V.L.F.	128
30" square, 37" high, aluminum roof	Each	770	2 Flue, 20" x 24"	V.L.F.	153
Copper roof	Each	430	20" x 32"	V.L.F.	198
Fiberglass, 5'-0" base, 63" high	Each	4000 - 4700	Kitchen Equipment		
6'-0" base, 63" high	Each	5200 - 7500	Broiler	Each	4000
Decorative Wood Beams, Non load bearing			Coffee urn, twin 6 gallon	Each	2975
Rough sawn, 4" x 6"	L.F.	8.60	Cooler, 6 ft. long	Each	4100
4" x 8"	L.F.	9.75	Dishwasher, 10-12 racks per hr.	Each	4225
4" x 10"	L.F.	11.55	Food warmer, counter, 1.2 KW	Each	725
4" x 12"	L.F.	13.15	Freezer, 44 C.F., reach-in	Each	5125
8" x 8"	L.F.	13.95	Ice cube maker, 50 lb. per day	Each	1950
Emergency Lighting, 25 watt, battery operated			Range with 1 oven	Each	3000
Lead battery	Each	320	Refrigerators, Prefabricated, walk-in		
Nickel cadmium	Each	885	7'-6" high, 6' x 6'	S.F.	195
			10' x 10'	S.F.	154
			12' x 14'	S.F.	136
			12' x 20'	S.F.	119

Important: See the Reference Section for Location Factors.

Model costs calculated for a 1 story building with 12' story height and 5,000 square feet of floor area

Restaurant

				Unit	Unit Cost	Cost Per S.F.	% Of Sub-Total
A. SUBSTRUCTURE							
1010	Standard Foundations	Poured concrete; strip and spread footings		S.F. Ground	2.64	2.64	
1020	Special Foundations	N/A		—	—	—	
1030	Slab on Grade	4" reinforced concrete with vapor barrier and granular base		S.F. Slab	5.31	5.31	8.2%
2010	Basement Excavation	Site preparation for slab and trench for foundation wall and footing		S.F. Ground	.57	.57	
2020	Basement Walls	4' foundation wall		L.F. Wall	82	4.89	
B. SHELL							
	B10 Superstructure						
1010	Floor Construction	Wood columns		S.F. Floor	.33	.83	5.2%
1020	Roof Construction	Plywood on wood truss (pitched)		S.F. Roof	6.84	7.66	
	B20 Exterior Enclosure						
2010	Exterior Walls	Cedar siding on wood studs with insulation	70% of wall	S.F. Wall	12.16	6.13	
2020	Exterior Windows	Storefront windows	30% of wall	Each	43.65	9.42	12.7%
2030	Exterior Doors	Aluminum and glass doors and entrance with transom		Each	5294	5.30	
	B30 Roofing						
3010	Roof Coverings	Cedar shingles with flashing (pitched); rigid fiberglass insulation		S.F. Roof	20.03	8.60	5.3%
3020	Roof Openings	Skylights		S.F. Roof	.09	.09	
C. INTERIORS							
1010	Partitions	Gypsum board on wood studs	25 S.F. Floor/L.F. Partition	S.F. Partition	10.38	4.15	
1020	Interior Doors	Hollow core wood	250 S.F. Floor/Door	Each	557	2.23	
1030	Fittings	Toilet partitions		S.F. Floor	.69	.69	
2010	Stair Construction	N/A		—	—	—	15.1%
3010	Wall Finishes	75% paint, 25% ceramic tile		S.F. Surface	2.43	1.94	
3020	Floor Finishes	65% carpet, 35% quarry tile		S.F. Floor	8.88	8.88	
3030	Ceiling Finishes	Mineral fiber tile on concealed zee bars		S.F. Ceiling	6.89	6.89	
D. SERVICES							
	D10 Conveying						
1010	Elevators & Lifts	N/A		—	—	—	0.0 %
1020	Escalators & Moving Walks	N/A		—	—	—	
	D20 Plumbing						
2010	Plumbing Fixtures	Kitchen, bathroom and service fixtures, supply and drainage	1 Fixture/355 S.F. Floor	Each	4104	11.56	
2020	Domestic Water Distribution	Gas fired water heater		S.F. Floor	8.71	8.71	13.4%
2040	Rain Water Drainage	Roof drains		S.F. Roof	1.83	1.83	
	D30 HVAC						
3010	Energy Supply	N/A		—	—	—	
3020	Heat Generating Systems	Included in D3050		—	—	—	
3030	Cooling Generating Systems	N/A		—	—	—	22.8 %
3050	Terminal & Package Units	Multizone unit, gas heating, electric cooling; kitchen ventilation		S.F. Floor	37.52	37.52	
3090	Other HVAC Sys. & Equipment	N/A		—	—	—	
	D40 Fire Protection						
4010	Sprinklers	Sprinklers, light hazard and ordinary hazard kitchen		S.F. Floor	8.61	8.61	6.4%
4020	Standpipes	Standpipe		S.F. Floor	1.98	1.98	
	D50 Electrical						
5010	Electrical Service/Distribution	400 ampere service, panel board and feeders		S.F. Floor	4.61	4.61	
5020	Lighting & Branch Wiring	T-8 fluorescent fixtures, receptacles, switches, A.C. and misc. power		S.F. Floor	9.49	9.49	10.9%
5030	Communications & Security	Addressable alarm systems and emergency lighting		S.F. Floor	3.55	3.55	
5090	Other Electrical Systems	Emergency generator, 15 kW		S.F. Floor	.33	.33	
E. EQUIPMENT & FURNISHINGS							
1010	Commercial Equipment	N/A		—	—	—	
1020	Institutional Equipment	N/A		—	—	—	0.0 %
1030	Vehicular Equipment	N/A		—	—	—	
1090	Other Equipment	N/A		—	—	—	
F. SPECIAL CONSTRUCTION							
1020	Integrated Construction	N/A		—	—	—	0.0 %
1040	Special Facilities	N/A		—	—	—	
G. BUILDING SITEWORK	**N/A**						

		Sub-Total	164.41	100%
CONTRACTOR FEES (General Requirements: 10%, Overhead: 5%, Profit: 10%)		25%	41.05	
ARCHITECT FEES		7%	14.39	

Total Building Cost	**219.85**

Costs per square foot of floor area

Exterior Wall	S.F. Area	2000	2800	3500	4000	5000	5800	6500	7200	8000
	L.F. Perimeter	180	212	240	260	300	314	336	344	368
Face Brick with Concrete Block Back-up	Bearing Walls	242.00	231.35	226.00	223.35	219.60	215.25	213.40	210.50	209.15
	Steel Frame	245.45	234.80	229.45	226.80	223.00	218.65	216.80	213.90	212.60
Concrete Block With Stucco	Bearing Walls	229.35	220.55	216.20	214.00	210.90	207.35	205.80	203.40	202.30
	Steel Frame	233.70	225.10	220.80	218.70	215.70	212.15	210.65	208.30	207.25
Wood Siding	Wood Frame	222.55	214.75	210.90	208.95	206.25	203.00	201.70	199.55	198.55
Brick Veneer	Steel Frame	239.30	229.80	225.05	222.70	219.40	215.50	213.85	211.25	210.05
Perimeter Adj., Add or Deduct	Per 100 L.F.	37.45	26.70	21.35	18.65	14.95	12.85	11.50	10.40	9.30
Story Hgt. Adj., Add or Deduct	Per 1 Ft.	4.95	4.10	3.70	3.55	3.30	2.90	2.80	2.60	2.50
Basement—Not Applicable										

The above costs were calculated using the basic specifications shown on the facing page. These costs should be adjusted where necessary for design alternatives and owner's requirements. Reported completed project costs, for this type of structure, range from $127.15 to $247.90 per S.F.

Common additives

Description	Unit	$ Cost	Description	Unit	$ Cost
Bar, Front Bar	L.F.	415	Refrigerators, Prefabricated, walk-in		
Back bar	L.F.	330	7'-6" High, 6' x 6'	S.F.	195
Booth, Upholstered, custom straight	L.F.	241 - 440	10' x 10'	S.F.	154
"L" or "U" shaped	L.F.	249 - 425	12' x 14'	S.F.	136
Drive-up Window	Each	8950 - 12,900	12' x 20'	S.F.	119
Emergency Lighting, 25 watt, battery operated			Serving		
Lead battery	Each	320	Counter top (Stainless steel)	L.F.	194
Nickel cadmium	Each	885	Base cabinets	L.F.	410 - 660
Kitchen Equipment			Sound System		
Broiler	Each	4000	Amplifier, 250 watts	Each	2025
Coffee urn, twin 6 gallon	Each	2975	Speaker, ceiling or wall	Each	208
Cooler, 6 ft. long	Each	4100	Trumpet	Each	400
Dishwasher, 10-12 racks per hr.	Each	4225	Storage		
Food warmer, counter, 1.2 KW	Each	725	Shelving	S.F.	8.85
Freezer, 44 C.F., reach-in	Each	5125	Washing		
Ice cube maker, 50 lb. per day	Each	1950	Stainless steel counter	L.F.	194
Range with 1 oven	Each	3000			

Important: See the Reference Section for Location Factors.

Model costs calculated for a 1 story building with 10' story height and 4,000 square feet of floor area

Restaurant, Fast Food

				Unit	Unit Cost	Cost Per S.F.	% Of Sub-Total
A. SUBSTRUCTURE							
1010	Standard Foundations	Poured concrete; strip and spread footings		S.F. Ground	2.55	2.55	
1020	Special Foundations	N/A		—	—	—	
1030	Slab on Grade	4" reinforced concrete with vapor barrier and granular base		S.F. Slab	5.31	5.31	8.3%
2010	Basement Excavation	Site preparation for slab and trench for foundation wall and footing		S.F. Ground	.57	.57	
2020	Basement Walls	4' foundation wall		L.F. Wall	82	5.30	
B. SHELL							
	B10 Superstructure						
1010	Floor Construction	N/A		—	—	—	4.7 %
1020	Roof Construction	Metal deck on open web steel joists		S.F. Roof	7.80	7.80	
	B20 Exterior Enclosure						
2010	Exterior Walls	Face brick with concrete block backup	70% of wall	S.F. Wall	32.90	14.97	
2020	Exterior Windows	Window wall	30% of wall	Each	49.60	9.67	19.7%
2030	Exterior Doors	Aluminum and glass		Each	3948	7.90	
	B30 Roofing						
3010	Roof Coverings	Built-up tar and gravel with flashing; perlite/EPS composite insulation		S.F. Roof	6.91	6.91	4.5%
3020	Roof Openings	Roof hatches		S.F. Roof	.52	.52	
C. INTERIORS							
1010	Partitions	Gypsum board on metal studs	25 S.F. Floor/L.F. Partition	S.F. Partition	6.25	2.25	
1020	Interior Doors	Hollow core wood	1000 S.F. Floor/Door	Each	557	.56	
1030	Fittings	N/A		—	—	—	
2010	Stair Construction	N/A		—	—	—	16.8%
3010	Wall Finishes	Paint		S.F. Surface	2.92	2.10	
3020	Floor Finishes	Quarry tile		S.F. Floor	15.94	15.94	
3030	Ceiling Finishes	Mineral fiber tile on concealed zee bars		S.F. Ceiling	6.89	6.89	
D. SERVICES							
	D10 Conveying						
1010	Elevators & Lifts	N/A		—	—	—	0.0 %
1020	Escalators & Moving Walks	N/A		—	—	—	
	D20 Plumbing						
2010	Plumbing Fixtures	Kitchen, bathroom and service fixtures, supply and drainage	1 Fixture/400 S.F. Floor	Each	4256	10.64	
2020	Domestic Water Distribution	Gas fired water heater		S.F. Floor	6.26	6.26	11.4%
2040	Rain Water Drainage	Roof drains		S.F. Roof	2.01	2.01	
	D30 HVAC						
3010	Energy Supply	N/A		—	—	—	
3020	Heat Generating Systems	Included in D3050		—	—	—	
3030	Cooling Generating Systems	N/A		—	—	—	11.8 %
3050	Terminal & Package Units	Multizone unit, gas heating, electric cooling; kitchen ventilation		S.F. Floor	19.58	19.58	
3090	Other HVAC Sys. & Equipment	N/A		—	—	—	
	D40 Fire Protection						
4010	Sprinklers	Sprinklers, light hazard		S.F. Floor	8.61	8.61	6.5%
4020	Standpipes	Standpipe		S.F. Floor	2.07	2.07	
	D50 Electrical						
5010	Electrical Service/Distribution	400 ampere service, panel board and feeders		S.F. Floor	4.80	4.80	
5020	Lighting & Branch Wiring	T-8 fluorescent fixtures, receptacles, switches, A.C. and misc. power		S.F. Floor	10.28	10.28	12.0%
5030	Communications & Security	Addressable alarm systems and emergency lighting		S.F. Floor	4.42	4.42	
5090	Other Electrical Systems	Emergency generator, 7.5 kW		S.F. Floor	.38	.38	
E. EQUIPMENT & FURNISHINGS							
1010	Commercial Equipment	N/A		—	—	—	
1020	Institutional Equipment	N/A		—	—	—	4.3 %
1030	Vehicular Equipment	N/A		—	—	—	
1090	Other Equipment	Walk-in refrigerator		S.F. Floor	7.16	7.16	
F. SPECIAL CONSTRUCTION							
1020	Integrated Construction	N/A		—	—	—	0.0 %
1040	Special Facilities	N/A		—	—	—	
G. BUILDING SITEWORK	**N/A**						

			Sub-Total	165.45	100%
CONTRACTOR FEES (General Requirements: 10%, Overhead: 5%, Profit: 10%)		25%	41.36		
ARCHITECT FEES		8%	16.54		

Total Building Cost   223.35

197

Costs per square foot of floor area

Exterior Wall	S.F. Area	10000	15000	20000	25000	30000	35000	40000	45000	50000
	L.F. Perimeter	450	500	600	700	740	822	890	920	966
Face Brick with Concrete Block Back-up	Steel Frame	200.00	182.75	177.75	174.70	169.85	168.05	166.25	163.65	162.00
	Lam. Wood Truss	198.70	182.20	177.40	174.50	169.85	168.20	166.45	164.00	162.35
Concrete Block	Steel Frame	197.55	187.60	184.70	182.90	180.10	179.10	178.05	176.60	175.60
	Lam. Wood Truss	176.30	166.35	163.40	161.65	158.80	157.85	156.80	155.30	154.35
Galvanized Steel Siding	Steel Frame	186.05	176.30	173.50	171.70	168.95	167.95	166.95	165.50	164.55
Metal Sandwich Panel	Steel Joists	196.25	183.85	180.25	178.05	174.55	173.25	172.00	170.15	168.90
Perimeter Adj., Add or Deduct	Per 100 L.F.	14.30	9.55	7.15	5.75	4.75	4.10	3.55	3.15	2.85
Story Hgt. Adj., Add or Deduct	Per 1 Ft.	2.20	1.65	1.50	1.35	1.20	1.15	1.15	1.00	0.95
Basement—Not Applicable										

The above costs were calculated using the basic specifications shown on the facing page. These costs should be adjusted where necessary for design alternatives and owner's requirements. Reported completed project costs, for this type of structure, range from $75.20 to $234.05 per S.F.

Common additives

Description	Unit	$ Cost
Bar, Front Bar	L.F.	415
Back bar	L.F.	330
Booth, Upholstered, custom straight	L.F.	241 - 440
"L" or "U" shaped	L.F.	249 - 425
Bleachers, Telescoping, manual		
To 15 tier	Seat	135 - 187
16-20 tier	Seat	277 - 340
21-30 tier	Seat	295 - 385
For power operation, add	Seat	54.50 - 84.50
Emergency Lighting, 25 watt, battery operated		
Lead battery	Each	320
Nickel cadmium	Each	885
Lockers, Steel, single tier, 60" or 72"	Opening	218 - 365
2 tier, 60" or 72" total	Opening	113 - 156
5 tier, box lockers	Opening	71.50 - 85
Locker bench, lam. maple top only	L.F.	26.50
Pedestals, steel pipe	Each	74

Description	Unit	$ Cost
Rink		
Dasher boards & top guard	Each	186,500
Mats, rubber	S.F.	22
Score Board	Each	13,100 - 17,900

Important: See the Reference Section for Location Factors.

Rink, Hockey/Indoor Soccer

Model costs calculated for a 1 story building with 24' story height and 30,000 square feet of floor area

				Unit	Unit Cost	Cost Per S.F.	% Of Sub-Total
A. SUBSTRUCTURE							
1010	Standard Foundations	Poured concrete; strip and spread footings		S.F. Ground	1.78	1.78	
1020	Special Foundations	N/A		—	—	—	
1030	Slab on Grade	6" reinforced concrete with vapor barrier and granular base		S.F. Slab	6.29	6.29	8.1%
2010	Basement Excavation	Site preparation for slab and trench for foundation wall and footing		S.F. Ground	.18	.18	
2020	Basement Walls	4' foundation wall		L.F. Wall	77	2.61	
B. SHELL							
	B10 Superstructure						
1010	Floor Construction	Wide flange beams and columns		S.F. Floor	28.63	20.04	27.4%
1020	Roof Construction	Metal deck on steel joist		S.F. Roof	16.81	16.81	
	B20 Exterior Enclosure						
2010	Exterior Walls	Concrete block	95% of wall	S.F. Wall	14.54	8.18	
2020	Exterior Windows	Store front	5% of wall	Each	47.80	1.41	7.8%
2030	Exterior Doors	Aluminum and glass, hollow metal, overhead		Each	3226	.86	
	B30 Roofing						
3010	Roof Coverings	Elastomeric neoprene membrane with flashing; perlite/EPS composite insulation		S.F. Roof	4.91	4.91	3.8%
3020	Roof Openings	Roof hatches		S.F. Roof	.24	.24	
C. INTERIORS							
1010	Partitions	Concrete block	140 S.F. Floor/L.F. Partition	S.F. Partition	9.33	.80	
1020	Interior Doors	Hollow metal	2500 S.F. Floor/Door	Each	1152	.46	
1030	Fittings	N/A		—	—	—	
2010	Stair Construction	N/A		—	—	—	6.4%
3010	Wall Finishes	Paint		S.F. Surface	12.60	2.16	
3020	Floor Finishes	80% rubber mat, 20% paint	50% of floor area	S.F. Floor	8.94	4.47	
3030	Ceiling Finishes	Mineral fiber tile on concealed zee bar	10% of area	S.F. Ceiling	6.89	.69	
D. SERVICES							
	D10 Conveying						
1010	Elevators & Lifts	N/A		—	—	—	0.0 %
1020	Escalators & Moving Walks	N/A		—	—	—	
	D20 Plumbing						
2010	Plumbing Fixtures	Toilet and service fixtures, supply and drainage	1 Fixture/1070 S.F. Floor	Each	6399	5.98	
2020	Domestic Water Distribution	Oil fired water heater		S.F. Floor	3.28	3.28	6.9%
2040	Rain Water Drainage	N/A		—	—	—	
	D30 HVAC						
3010	Energy Supply	Oil fired hot water, unit heaters	10% of area	S.F. Floor	.89	.89	
3020	Heat Generating Systems	N/A		—	—	—	
3030	Cooling Generating Systems	N/A		—	—	—	10.4%
3050	Terminal & Package Units	Single zone, electric cooling	90% of area	S.F. Floor	13.10	13.10	
3090	Other HVAC Sys. & Equipment	N/A		—	—	—	
	D40 Fire Protection						
4010	Sprinklers	N/A		—	—	—	0.5 %
4020	Standpipes	Standpipe		S.F. Floor	.64	.64	
	D50 Electrical						
5010	Electrical Service/Distribution	600 ampere service, panel board and feeders		S.F. Floor	1.52	1.52	
5020	Lighting & Branch Wiring	High intensity discharge and fluorescent fixtures, receptacles, switches, A.C. and misc. power		S.F. Floor	7.81	7.81	8.6%
5030	Communications & Security	Addressable alarm systems, emergency lighting and public address		S.F. Floor	2.05	2.05	
5090	Other Electrical Systems	Emergency generator		S.F. Floor	.19	.19	
E. EQUIPMENT & FURNISHINGS							
1010	Commercial Equipment	N/A		—	—	—	
1020	Institutional Equipment	N/A		—	—	—	0.0 %
1030	Vehicular Equipment	N/A		—	—	—	
1090	Other Equipment	N/A		—	—	—	
F. SPECIAL CONSTRUCTION							
1020	Integrated Construction	N/A		—	—	—	20.3 %
1040	Special Facilities	Dasher boards and rink (including ice making system)		S.F. Floor	27.30	27.30	
G. BUILDING SITEWORK	**N/A**						

		Sub-Total	134.65	**100%**
CONTRACTOR FEES (General Requirements: 10%, Overhead: 5%, Profit: 10%)		25%	33.67	
ARCHITECT FEES		7%	11.78	
		Total Building Cost	**180.10**	

Costs per square foot of floor area

Exterior Wall	S.F. Area	25000	30000	35000	40000	45000	50000	55000	60000	65000
	L.F. Perimeter	900	1050	1200	1350	1510	1650	1800	1970	2100
Face Brick with Concrete Block Back-up	Steel Frame	183.20	181.65	180.45	179.65	179.20	178.40	178.00	178.05	177.35
	Bearing Walls	175.75	174.20	173.00	172.20	171.75	170.95	170.55	170.60	169.90
Stucco on Concrete Block	Steel Frame	176.15	174.75	173.75	173.00	172.65	171.95	171.60	171.55	171.05
	Bearing Walls	168.75	167.30	166.30	165.55	165.20	164.50	164.15	164.15	163.60
Decorative Concrete Block	Steel Frame	175.35	173.90	172.85	172.15	171.70	171.05	170.70	170.75	170.10
	Bearing Walls	170.80	169.40	168.35	167.60	167.20	166.55	166.20	166.15	165.60
Perimeter Adj., Add or Deduct	Per 100 L.F.	4.60	3.75	3.25	2.80	2.55	2.35	2.10	1.90	1.70
Story Hgt. Adj., Add or Deduct	Per 1 Ft.	1.70	1.60	1.65	1.55	1.55	1.55	1.55	1.55	1.55

For Basement, add $26.45 per square foot of basement area

The above costs were calculated using the basic specifications shown on the facing page. These costs should be adjusted where necessary for design alternatives and owner's requirements. Reported completed project costs, for this type of structure, range from $87.85 to $223.50 per S.F.

Common additives

Description	Unit	$ Cost
Bleachers, Telescoping, manual		
To 15 tier	Seat	135 - 187
16-20 tier	Seat	277 - 340
21-30 tier	Seat	295 - 385
For power operation, add	Seat	54.50 - 84.50
Carrels Hardwood	Each	960 - 2300
Clock System		
20 room	Each	19,500
50 room	Each	45,700
Emergency Lighting, 25 watt, battery operated		
Lead battery	Each	320
Nickel cadmium	Each	885
Flagpoles, Complete		
Aluminum, 20' high	Each	1775
40' high	Each	3925
Fiberglass, 23' high	Each	1325
39'-5" high	Each	3575
Kitchen Equipment		
Broiler	Each	4000
Cooler, 6 ft. long, reach-in	Each	4100

Description	Unit	$ Cost
Kitchen Equipment, cont.		
Dishwasher, 10-12 racks per hr.	Each	4225
Food warmer, counter, 1.2 KW	Each	725
Freezer, 44 C.F., reach-in	Each	5125
Ice cube maker, 50 lb. per day	Each	1950
Range with 1 oven	Each	3000
Lockers, Steel, single tier, 60" to 72"	Opening	218 - 365
2 tier, 60" to 72" total	Opening	113 - 156
5 tier, box lockers	Opening	71.50 - 85
Locker bench, lam. maple top only	L.F.	26.50
Pedestals, steel pipe	Each	74
Seating		
Auditorium chair, all veneer	Each	300
Veneer back, padded seat	Each	315
Upholstered, spring seat	Each	315
Classroom, movable chair & desk	Set	81 - 171
Lecture hall, pedestal type	Each	258 - 610
Sound System		
Amplifier, 250 watts	Each	2025
Speaker, ceiling or wall	Each	208
Trumpet	Each	400

Important: See the Reference Section for Location Factors.

Model costs calculated for a 1 story building with 15' story height and 45,000 square feet of floor area

School, Elementary

					Unit	Unit Cost	Cost Per S.F.	% Of Sub-Total
A.	**SUBSTRUCTURE**							
1010	Standard Foundations	Poured concrete; strip and spread footings			S.F. Ground	4.99	4.99	
1020	Special Foundations	N/A			—	—	—	
1030	Slab on Grade	4" reinforced concrete with vapor barrier and granular base			S.F. Slab	5.31	5.31	11.8%
2010	Basement Excavation	Site preparation for slab and trench for foundation wall and footing			S.F. Ground	.18	.18	
2020	Basement Walls	4' foundation wall			L.F. Wall	82	4.65	
B.	**SHELL**							
	B10 Superstructure							
1010	Floor Construction	N/A			—	—	—	
1020	Roof Construction	Metal deck on open web steel joists			S.F. Roof	4.45	4.45	3.5%
	B20 Exterior Enclosure							
2010	Exterior Walls	Face brick with concrete block backup		70% of wall	S.F. Wall	32.89	11.59	
2020	Exterior Windows	Steel outward projecting		25% of wall	Each	736	4.83	13.3%
2030	Exterior Doors	Metal and glass		5% of wall	Each	3785	.67	
	B30 Roofing							
3010	Roof Coverings	Single-ply membrane with flashing; polyisocyanurate insulation			S.F. Roof	7.14	7.14	5.6%
3020	Roof Openings	N/A			—	—	—	
C.	**INTERIORS**							
1010	Partitions	Concrete block	20 S.F. Floor/L.F. Partition		S.F. Partition	9.96	4.98	
1020	Interior Doors	Single leaf kalamein fire doors	700 S.F. Floor/Door		Each	1152	1.65	
1030	Fittings	Toilet partitions			S.F. Floor	1.82	1.82	
2010	Stair Construction	N/A			—	—	—	20.8%
3010	Wall Finishes	75% paint, 15% glazed coating, 10% ceramic tile			S.F. Surface	4.70	4.70	
3020	Floor Finishes	65% vinyl composition tile, 25% carpet, 10% terrazzo			S.F. Floor	6.71	6.71	
3030	Ceiling Finishes	Mineral fiber tile on concealed zee bars			S.F. Ceiling	6.89	6.89	
D.	**SERVICES**							
	D10 Conveying							
1010	Elevators & Lifts	N/A			—	—	—	0.0%
1020	Escalators & Moving Walks	N/A			—	—	—	
	D20 Plumbing							
2010	Plumbing Fixtures	Kitchen, bathroom and service fixtures, supply and drainage	1 Fixture/625 S.F. Floor		Each	7938	12.70	
2020	Domestic Water Distribution	Gas fired water heater			S.F. Floor	.66	.66	11.4%
2040	Rain Water Drainage	Roof drains			S.F. Roof	1.25	1.25	
	D30 HVAC							
3010	Energy Supply	Oil fired hot water, wall fin radiation			S.F. Floor	10.34	10.34	
3020	Heat Generating Systems	N/A			—	—	—	
3030	Cooling Generating Systems	N/A			—	—	—	19.0%
3050	Terminal & Package Units	Split systems with air cooled condensing units			S.F. Floor	14.05	14.05	
3090	Other HVAC Sys. & Equipment	N/A			—	—	—	
	D40 Fire Protection							
4010	Sprinklers	Sprinklers, light hazard			S.F. Floor	2.85	2.85	2.5%
4020	Standpipes	Standpipe			S.F. Floor	.39	.39	
	D50 Electrical							
5010	Electrical Service/Distribution	800 ampere service, panel board and feeders			S.F. Floor	1.10	1.10	
5020	Lighting & Branch Wiring	High efficiency fluorescent fixtures, receptacles, switches, A.C. and misc. power			S.F. Floor	10.54	10.54	12.0%
5030	Communications & Security	Addressable alarm systems, internet wiring, communications systems and emergency lighting			S.F. Floor	3.72	3.72	
5090	Other Electrical Systems	Emergency generator, 15 kW			S.F. Floor	.07	.07	
E.	**EQUIPMENT & FURNISHINGS**							
1010	Commercial Equipment	N/A			—	—	—	
1020	Institutional Equipment	Chalkboards			S.F. Floor	.18	.18	0.1%
1030	Vehicular Equipment	N/A			—	—	—	
1090	Other Equipment	N/A			—	—	—	
F.	**SPECIAL CONSTRUCTION**							
1020	Integrated Construction	N/A			—	—	—	0.0%
1040	Special Facilities	N/A			—	—	—	
G.	**BUILDING SITEWORK**	**N/A**						

	Sub-Total	128.41	**100%**
CONTRACTOR FEES (General Requirements: 10%, Overhead: 5%, Profit: 10%)	25%	32.10	
ARCHITECT FEES	7%	11.24	
Total Building Cost		**171.75**	

Costs per square foot of floor area

Exterior Wall	S.F. Area	50000	70000	90000	110000	130000	150000	170000	190000	210000
	L.F. Perimeter	850	1140	1420	1700	1980	2280	2560	2840	3120
Face Brick with Concrete Block Back-up	Steel Frame	174.90	172.20	170.55	169.40	168.70	168.45	168.00	167.65	167.35
	R/Conc. Frame	180.05	176.30	174.00	172.50	171.45	171.05	170.45	169.90	169.55
Decorative Concrete Block	Steel Frame	170.85	167.35	165.30	163.90	162.95	162.55	162.00	161.50	161.15
	R/Conc. Frame	171.30	167.75	165.70	164.30	163.35	162.95	162.40	161.90	161.60
Limestone with Concrete Block Back-up	Steel Frame	195.40	190.85	188.05	186.20	184.95	184.50	183.75	183.10	182.65
	R/Conc. Frame	202.30	197.80	195.00	193.10	191.85	191.40	190.65	190.00	189.50
Perimeter Adj., Add or Deduct	Per 100 L.F.	4.20	3.00	2.30	1.95	1.60	1.40	1.20	1.00	0.95
Story Hgt. Adj., Add or Deduct	Per 1 Ft.	2.10	2.05	1.95	2.00	1.90	1.90	1.85	1.80	1.85

For Basement, add $34.55 per square foot of basement area

The above costs were calculated using the basic specifications shown on the facing page. These costs should be adjusted where necessary for design alternatives and owner's requirements. Reported completed project costs, for this type of structure, range from $102.10 to $240.50 per S.F.

Common additives

Description	Unit	$ Cost	Description	Unit	$ Cost
Bleachers, Telescoping, manual			Kitchen Equipment		
To 15 tier	Seat	135 - 187	Broiler	Each	4000
16-20 tier	Seat	277 - 340	Cooler, 6 ft. long, reach-in	Each	4100
21-30 tier	Seat	295 - 385	Dishwasher, 10-12 racks per hr.	Each	4225
For power operation, add	Seat	54.50 - 84.50	Food warmer, counter, 1.2 KW	Each	725
Carrels Hardwood	Each	960 - 2300	Freezer, 44 C.F., reach-in	Each	5125
Clock System			Lockers, Steel, single tier, 60" or 72"	Opening	218 - 365
20 room	Each	19,500	2 tier, 60" or 72" total	Opening	113 - 156
50 room	Each	45,700	5 tier, box lockers	Opening	71.50 - 85
Elevators, Hydraulic passenger, 2 stops			Locker bench, lam. maple top only	L.F.	26.50
1500# capacity	Each	66,100	Pedestals, steel pipe	Each	74
2500# capacity	Each	69,200	Seating		
Emergency Lighting, 25 watt, battery operated			Auditorium chair, all veneer	Each	300
Lead battery	Each	320	Veneer back, padded seat	Each	315
Nickel cadmium	Each	885	Upholstered, spring seat	Each	315
Flagpoles, Complete			Classroom, movable chair & desk	Set	81 - 171
Aluminum, 20' high	Each	1775	Lecture hall, pedestal type	Each	258 - 610
40' high	Each	3925	Sound System		
Fiberglass, 23' high	Each	1325	Amplifier, 250 watts	Each	2025
39'-5" high	Each	3575	Speaker, ceiling or wall	Each	208
			Trumpet	Each	400

Important: See the Reference Section for Location Factors.

School, High, 2-3 Story

Model costs calculated for a 2 story building with 15' story height and 130,000 square feet of floor area

					Unit	Unit Cost	Cost Per S.F.	% Of Sub-Total
A. SUBSTRUCTURE								
1010	Standard Foundations	Poured concrete; strip and spread footings			S.F. Ground	2.70	1.35	
1020	Special Foundations	N/A			—	—	—	
1030	Slab on Grade	4" reinforced concrete with vapor barrier and granular base			S.F. Slab	5.31	2.66	4.2%
2010	Basement Excavation	Site preparation for slab and trench for foundation wall and footing			S.F. Ground	.18	.09	
2020	Basement Walls	4' foundation wall			L.F. Wall	82	1.24	
B. SHELL								
B10 Superstructure								
1010	Floor Construction	Concrete slab without drop panel, concrete columns			S.F. Floor	21.94	10.97	14.5%
1020	Roof Construction	Concrete slab without drop panel			S.F. Roof	15.16	7.58	
B20 Exterior Enclosure								
2010	Exterior Walls	Face brick with concrete block backup	75% of wall		S.F. Wall	32.89	11.27	
2020	Exterior Windows	Window wall	25% of wall		Each	73	8.34	15.7%
2030	Exterior Doors	Metal and glass			Each	2238	.50	
B30 Roofing								
3010	Roof Coverings	Single-ply membrane and standing seam metal; polyisocyanurate insulation			S.F. Roof	11.08	5.54	4.4%
3020	Roof Openings	Roof hatches			S.F. Roof	.10	.05	
C. INTERIORS								
1010	Partitions	Concrete block	25 S.F. Floor/L.F. Partition		S.F. Partition	12.60	6.05	
1020	Interior Doors	Single leaf kalamein fire doors	700 S.F. Floor/Door		Each	1152	1.65	
1030	Fittings	Toilet partitions, chalkboards			S.F. Floor	1.28	1.28	
2010	Stair Construction	Concrete filled metal pan			Flight	14,450	.66	20.6%
3010	Wall Finishes	75% paint, 15% glazed coating, 10% ceramic tile			S.F. Surface	3.52	3.38	
3020	Floor Finishes	70% vinyl composition tile, 20% carpet, 10% terrazzo			S.F. Floor	6.52	6.52	
3030	Ceiling Finishes	Mineral fiber tile on concealed zee bars			S.F. Ceiling	6.89	6.89	
D. SERVICES								
D10 Conveying								
1010	Elevators & Lifts	One hydraulic passenger elevator			Each	84,500	.65	0.5%
1020	Escalators & Moving Walks	N/A			—	—	—	
D20 Plumbing								
2010	Plumbing Fixtures	Kitchen, bathroom and service fixtures, supply and drainage	1 Fixture/860 S.F. Floor		Each	4618	5.37	
2020	Domestic Water Distribution	Gas fired water heater			S.F. Floor	1.11	1.11	5.6%
2040	Rain Water Drainage	Roof drains			S.F. Roof	1.42	.71	
D30 HVAC								
3010	Energy Supply	Oil fired hot water, wall fin radiation			S.F. Floor	5.10	5.10	
3020	Heat Generating Systems	N/A			—	—	—	
3030	Cooling Generating Systems	Chilled water, cooling tower systems			S.F. Floor	18.23	18.23	18.2%
3050	Terminal & Package Units	N/A			—	—	—	
3090	Other HVAC Sys. & Equipment	N/A			—	—	—	
D40 Fire Protection								
4010	Sprinklers	Sprinklers, light hazard			S.F. Floor	2.48	2.48	2.2%
4020	Standpipes	Standpipe, wet, Class III			S.F. Floor	.33	.33	
D50 Electrical								
5010	Electrical Service/Distribution	2000 ampere service, panel board and feeders			S.F. Floor	1.07	1.07	
5020	Lighting & Branch Wiring	High efficiency fluorescent fixtures, receptacles, switches, A.C. and misc. power			S.F. Floor	9.79	9.79	11.9%
5030	Communications & Security	Addressable alarm systems, internet wiring, communications systems and emergency lighting			S.F. Floor	4	4	
5090	Other Electrical Systems	Emergency generator, 250 kW			S.F. Floor	.44	.44	
E. EQUIPMENT & FURNISHINGS								
1010	Commercial Equipment	N/A			—	—	—	
1020	Institutional Equipment	Laboratory casework and counters			S.F. Floor	1.96	1.96	2.3%
1030	Vehicular Equipment	N/A			—	—	—	
1090	Other Equipment	Built-in athletic equipment, bleachers and scoreboard			S.F. Floor	.93	.93	
F. SPECIAL CONSTRUCTION								
1020	Integrated Construction	N/A			—	—	—	0.0%
1040	Special Facilities	N/A			—	—	—	
G. BUILDING SITEWORK	**N/A**							

	Sub-Total	128.19	100%
CONTRACTOR FEES (General Requirements: 10%, Overhead: 5%, Profit: 10%)	25%	32.04	
ARCHITECT FEES	7%	11.22	
Total Building Cost		**171.45**	

203

Costs per square foot of floor area

Exterior Wall	S.F. Area	50000	65000	80000	95000	110000	125000	140000	155000	170000
	L.F. Perimeter	850	1060	1280	1490	1700	1920	2140	2340	2560
Face Brick with Concrete Block Back-up	Steel Frame	179.30	177.10	175.85	174.90	174.15	173.80	173.50	173.00	172.80
	Bearing Walls	171.65	169.45	168.20	167.25	166.50	166.10	165.85	165.35	165.10
Concrete Block Stucco Face	Steel Frame	171.10	169.15	168.10	167.30	166.65	166.25	166.00	165.60	165.45
	Bearing Walls	164.30	162.40	161.30	160.55	159.85	159.50	159.25	158.85	158.70
Decorative Concrete Block	Steel Frame	172.80	170.85	169.70	168.90	168.25	167.90	167.65	167.25	167.05
	Bearing Walls	164.60	162.60	161.50	160.70	160.00	159.65	159.40	159.00	158.75
Perimeter Adj., Add or Deduct	Per 100 L.F.	3.80	2.85	2.35	1.95	1.70	1.50	1.30	1.25	1.10
Story Hgt. Adj., Add or Deduct	Per 1 Ft.	1.90	1.75	1.75	1.70	1.75	1.65	1.65	1.65	1.65

For Basement, add $36.00 per square foot of basement area

The above costs were calculated using the basic specifications shown on the facing page. These costs should be adjusted where necessary for design alternatives and owner's requirements. Reported completed project costs, for this type of structure, range from $96.40 to $226.55 per S.F.

Common additives

Description	Unit	$ Cost
Bleachers, Telescoping, manual		
To 15 tier	Seat	135 - 187
16-20 tier	Seat	277 - 340
21-30 tier	Seat	295 - 385
For power operation, add	Seat	54.50 - 84.50
Carrels Hardwood	Each	960 - 2300
Clock System		
20 room	Each	19,500
50 room	Each	45,700
Elevators, Hydraulic passenger, 2 stops		
1500# capacity	Each	66,100
2500# capacity	Each	69,200
Emergency Lighting, 25 watt, battery operated		
Lead battery	Each	320
Nickel cadmium	Each	885
Flagpoles, Complete		
Aluminum, 20' high	Each	1775
40' high	Each	3925
Fiberglass, 23' high	Each	1325
39'-5" high	Each	3575

Description	Unit	$ Cost
Kitchen Equipment		
Broiler	Each	4000
Cooler, 6 ft. long, reach-in	Each	4100
Dishwasher, 10-12 racks per hr.	Each	4225
Food warmer, counter, 1.2 KW	Each	725
Freezer, 44 C.F., reach-in	Each	5125
Lockers, Steel, single tier, 60" to 72"	Opening	218 - 365
2 tier, 60" to 72" total	Opening	113 - 156
5 tier, box lockers	Opening	71.50 - 85
Locker bench, lam. maple top only	L.F.	26.50
Pedestals, steel pipe	Each	74
Seating		
Auditorium chair, all veneer	Each	300
Veneer back, padded seat	Each	315
Upholstered, spring seat	Each	315
Classroom, movable chair & desk	Set	81 - 171
Lecture hall, pedestal type	Each	258 - 610
Sound System		
Amplifier, 250 watts	Each	2025
Speaker, ceiling or wall	Each	208
Trumpet	Each	400

Important: See the Reference Section for Location Factors.

Model costs calculated for a 2 story building with 15' story height and 110,000 square feet of floor area

				Unit	Unit Cost	Cost Per S.F.	% Of Sub-Total
A. SUBSTRUCTURE							
1010	Standard Foundations	Poured concrete; strip and spread footings		S.F. Ground	2.42	1.21	
1020	Special Foundations	N/A		—	—	—	
1030	Slab on Grade	4" reinforced concrete with vapor barrier and granular base		S.F. Slab	5.31	2.66	4.0%
2010	Basement Excavation	Site preparation for slab and trench for foundation wall and footing		S.F. Ground	.18	.09	
2020	Basement Walls	4' foundation wall		L.F. Wall	82	1.26	
B. SHELL							
B10 Superstructure							
1010	Floor Construction	Open web steel joists, slab form, concrete, columns		S.F. Floor	28.60	14.30	15.6%
1020	Roof Construction	Metal deck, open web steel joists, columns		S.F. Roof	11.90	5.95	
B20 Exterior Enclosure							
2010	Exterior Walls	Face brick with concrete block backup	75% of wall	S.F. Wall	32.90	11.44	
2020	Exterior Windows	Window wall	25% of wall	Each	55	6.37	14.2%
2030	Exterior Doors	Double aluminum & glass		Each	2362	.64	
B30 Roofing							
3010	Roof Coverings	Single-ply membrane and standing seam metal; polyisocyanurate insulation		S.F. Roof	11.24	5.62	4.3%
3020	Roof Openings	Roof hatches		S.F. Roof	.04	.02	
C. INTERIORS							
1010	Partitions	Concrete block	20 S.F. Floor/L.F. Partition	S.F. Partition	9.37	5.62	
1020	Interior Doors	Single leaf kalamein fire doors	750 S.F. Floor/Door	Each	1152	1.54	
1030	Fittings	Toilet partitions, chalkboards		S.F. Floor	1.38	1.38	
2010	Stair Construction	Concrete filled metal pan		Flight	14,450	.79	23.5%
3010	Wall Finishes	50% paint, 40% glazed coatings, 10% ceramic tile		S.F. Surface	4.23	5.08	
3020	Floor Finishes	50% vinyl composition tile, 30% carpet, 20% terrrazzo		S.F. Floor	9.26	9.26	
3030	Ceiling Finishes	Mineral fiberboard on concealed zee bars		S.F. Ceiling	6.89	6.89	
D. SERVICES							
D10 Conveying							
1010	Elevators & Lifts	One hydraulic passenger elevator		Each	83,600	.76	0.6%
1020	Escalators & Moving Walks	N/A		—	—	—	
D20 Plumbing							
2010	Plumbing Fixtures	Kitchen, toilet and service fixtures, supply and drainage	1 Fixture/1170 S.F. Floor	Each	6728	5.75	
2020	Domestic Water Distribution	Gas fired water heater		S.F. Floor	.67	.67	5.5%
2040	Rain Water Drainage	Roof drains		S.F. Roof	1.46	.73	
D30 HVAC							
3010	Energy Supply	N/A		—	—	—	
3020	Heat Generating Systems	Included in D3050		—	—	—	
3030	Cooling Generating Systems	N/A		—	—	—	15.7 %
3050	Terminal & Package Units	Multizone unit, gas heating, electric cooling		S.F. Floor	20.45	20.45	
3090	Other HVAC Sys. & Equipment	N/A		—	—	—	
D40 Fire Protection							
4010	Sprinklers	Sprinklers, light hazard	10% of area	S.F. Floor	2.48	2.48	2.2%
4020	Standpipes	Standpipe, wet, Class III		S.F. Floor	.39	.39	
D50 Electrical							
5010	Electrical Service/Distribution	1600 ampere service, panel board and feeders		S.F. Floor	1.03	1.03	
5020	Lighting & Branch Wiring	High efficiency fluorescent fixtures, receptacles, switches, A.C. and misc. power		S.F. Floor	9.79	9.79	11.9%
5030	Communications & Security	Addressable alarm systems, internet wiring, communications systems and emergency lighting		S.F. Floor	4.30	4.30	
5090	Other Electrical Systems	Emergency generator, 100 kW		S.F. Floor	.33	.33	
E. EQUIPMENT & FURNISHINGS							
1010	Commercial Equipment	N/A		—	—	—	
1020	Institutional Equipment	Laboratory casework and counters		S.F. Floor	2.30	2.30	2.6 %
1030	Vehicular Equipment	N/A		—	—	—	
1090	Other Equipment	Bleachers, basketball backstops		S.F. Floor	1.12	1.12	
F. SPECIAL CONSTRUCTION							
1020	Integrated Construction	N/A		—	—	—	0.0 %
1040	Special Facilities	N/A		—	—	—	
G. BUILDING SITEWORK	**N/A**						

			Sub-Total	130.22	100%
CONTRACTOR FEES (General Requirements: 10%, Overhead: 5%, Profit: 10%)			25%	32.54	
ARCHITECT FEES			7%	11.39	
		Total Building Cost		174.15	

Costs per square foot of floor area

Exterior Wall	S.F. Area	20000	30000	40000	50000	60000	70000	80000	90000	100000
	L.F. Perimeter	440	590	740	900	1050	1200	1360	1510	1660
Face Brick with Concrete Block Back-up	Steel Frame	186.20	180.00	176.95	175.45	174.15	173.15	172.75	172.10	171.65
	Bearing Walls	180.10	173.95	170.90	169.35	168.10	167.20	166.70	166.15	165.70
Decorative Concrete Block	Steel Frame	172.30	167.60	165.20	164.00	163.00	162.30	161.95	161.50	161.15
	Bearing Walls	166.60	161.85	159.50	158.25	157.25	156.55	156.20	155.75	155.35
Steel Siding on Steel Studs	Steel Frame	166.50	162.40	160.30	159.30	158.35	157.75	157.45	157.00	156.75
Metal Sandwich Panel	Steel Frame	189.60	183.05	179.75	178.20	176.75	175.75	175.30	174.65	174.15
Perimeter Adj., Add or Deduct	Per 100 L.F.	9.50	6.35	4.70	3.80	3.10	2.75	2.35	2.15	1.90
Story Hgt. Adj., Add or Deduct	Per 1 Ft.	2.30	2.05	1.90	1.90	1.80	1.80	1.80	1.80	1.80

For Basement, add $34.90 per square foot of basement area

The above costs were calculated using the basic specifications shown on the facing page. These costs should be adjusted where necessary for design alternatives and owner's requirements. Reported completed project costs, for this type of structure, range from $86.55 to $247.25 per S.F.

Common additives

Description	Unit	$ Cost	Description	Unit	$ Cost
Carrels Hardwood	Each	960 - 2300	Flagpoles, Complete		
Clock System			Aluminum, 20' high	Each	1775
20 room	Each	19,500	40' high	Each	3925
50 room	Each	45,700	Fiberglass, 23' high	Each	1325
Directory Boards, Plastic, glass covered			39'-5" high	Each	3575
30" x 20"	Each	630	Seating		
36" x 48"	Each	1500	Auditorium chair, all veneer	Each	300
Aluminum, 24" x 18"	Each	630	Veneer back, padded seat	Each	315
36" x 24"	Each	735	Upholstered, spring seat	Each	315
48" x 32"	Each	1050	Classroom, movable chair & desk	Set	81 - 171
48" x 60"	Each	2200	Lecture hall, pedestal type	Each	258 - 610
Elevators, Hydraulic passenger, 2 stops			Shops & Workroom:		
1500# capacity	Each	66,100	Benches, metal	Each	820
2500# capacity	Each	69,200	Parts bins 6'-3" high, 3' wide, 12" deep, 72 bins	Each	690
3500# capacity	Each	73,200	Shelving, metal 1' x 3'	S.F.	12.30
Emergency Lighting, 25 watt, battery operated			Wide span 6' wide x 24" deep	S.F.	8.85
Lead battery	Each	320	Sound System		
Nickel cadmium	Each	885	Amplifier, 250 watts	Each	2025
			Speaker, ceiling or wall	Each	208
			Trumpet	Each	400

Important: See the Reference Section for Location Factors.

Model costs calculated for a 2 story building with 16' story height and 40,000 square feet of floor area

School, Vocational

				Unit	Unit Cost	Cost Per S.F.	% Of Sub-Total
A. SUBSTRUCTURE							
1010	Standard Foundations	Poured concrete; strip and spread footings		S.F. Ground	2.78	1.39	
1020	Special Foundations	N/A		—	—	—	
1030	Slab on Grade	5" reinforced concrete with vapor barrier and granular base		S.F. Slab	13.05	6.53	7.5%
2010	Basement Excavation	Site preparation for slab and trench for foundation wall and footing		S.F. Ground	.18	.09	
2020	Basement Walls	4' foundation wall		L.F. Wall	82	1.51	
B. SHELL							
	B10 Superstructure						
1010	Floor Construction	Open web steel joists, slab form, concrete, beams, columns		S.F. Floor	18.80	9.40	9.9%
1020	Roof Construction	Metal deck, open web steel joists, beams, columns		S.F. Roof	6.52	3.26	
	B20 Exterior Enclosure						
2010	Exterior Walls	Face brick with concrete block backup	85% of wall	S.F. Wall	32.89	16.55	
2020	Exterior Windows	Tubular aluminum framing with insulated glass	15% of wall	Each	55	4.88	17.2%
2030	Exterior Doors	Metal and glass doors		Each	2861	.58	
	B30 Roofing						
3010	Roof Coverings	Single-ply membrane with polyisocyanurate insulation		S.F. Roof	6.48	3.24	2.7%
3020	Roof Openings	Roof hatches		S.F. Roof	.34	.17	
C. INTERIORS							
1010	Partitions	Concrete block	20 S.F. Floor/L.F. Partition	S.F. Partition	9.37	5.62	
1020	Interior Doors	Single leaf kalamein fire doors	600 S.F. Floor/Door	Each	1152	1.92	
1030	Fittings	Toilet partitions, chalkboards		S.F. Floor	1.51	1.51	
2010	Stair Construction	Concrete filled metal pan		Flight	14,450	1.45	20.9%
3010	Wall Finishes	50% paint, 40% glazed coating, 10% ceramic tile		S.F. Surface	4.66	5.59	
3020	Floor Finishes	70% vinyl composition tile, 20% carpet, 10% terrazzo		S.F. Floor	6.52	6.52	
3030	Ceiling Finishes	Mineral fiber tile on concealed zee bars	60% of area	S.F. Ceiling	6.89	4.14	
D. SERVICES							
	D10 Conveying						
1010	Elevators & Lifts	One hydraulic passenger elevator		Each	83,200	2.08	1.6%
1020	Escalators & Moving Walks	N/A		—	—	—	
	D20 Plumbing						
2010	Plumbing Fixtures	Toilet and service fixtures, supply and drainage	1 Fixture/700 S.F. Floor	Each	3374	4.82	
2020	Domestic Water Distribution	Gas fired water heater		S.F. Floor	1.09	1.09	5.3%
2040	Rain Water Drainage	Roof drains		S.F. Roof	1.84	.92	
	D30 HVAC						
3010	Energy Supply	Oil fired hot water, wall fin radiation		S.F. Floor	9.76	9.76	
3020	Heat Generating Systems	N/A		—	—	—	
3030	Cooling Generating Systems	Chilled water, cooling tower systems		S.F. Floor	15.45	15.45	19.7%
3050	Terminal & Package Units	N/A		—	—	—	
3090	Other HVAC Sys. & Equipment	N/A		—	—	—	
	D40 Fire Protection						
4010	Sprinklers	Sprinklers, light hazard		S.F. Floor	3.11	3.11	3.2%
4020	Standpipes	Standpipe, wet, Class III		S.F. Floor	.93	.93	
	D50 Electrical						
5010	Electrical Service/Distribution	800 ampere service, panel board and feeders		S.F. Floor	1.25	1.25	
5020	Lighting & Branch Wiring	High efficiency fluorescent fixtures, receptacles, switches, A.C. and misc. power		S.F. Floor	10.59	10.59	11.8%
5030	Communications & Security	Addressable alarm systems, internet wiring, communications systems and emergency lighting		S.F. Floor	3.15	3.15	
5090	Other Electrical Systems	Emergency generator, 11.5 kW		S.F. Floor	.11	.11	
E. EQUIPMENT & FURNISHINGS							
1010	Commercial Equipment	N/A		—	—	—	
1020	Institutional Equipment	Stainless steel countertops		S.F. Floor	.15	.15	0.1%
1030	Vehicular Equipment	N/A		—	—	—	
1090	Other Equipment	N/A		—	—	—	
F. SPECIAL CONSTRUCTION							
1020	Integrated Construction	N/A		—	—	—	0.0%
1040	Special Facilities	N/A		—	—	—	
G. BUILDING SITEWORK	**N/A**						

			Sub-Total	127.76	100%
CONTRACTOR FEES (General Requirements: 10%, Overhead: 5%, Profit: 10%)			25%	31.96	
ARCHITECT FEES			7%	11.18	

Total Building Cost	**170.90**

207

Costs per square foot of floor area

Exterior Wall	S.F. Area	1000	2000	3000	4000	6000	8000	10000	12000	15000
	L.F. Perimeter	126	179	219	253	310	358	400	438	490
Wood Siding	Wood Frame	155.95	132.40	122.95	117.60	111.65	108.20	105.90	104.20	102.50
Face Brick Veneer	Wood Frame	183.60	151.45	138.10	130.40	121.65	116.55	113.15	110.70	108.00
Stucco on Concrete Block	Steel Frame	178.75	149.55	137.55	130.65	122.90	118.30	115.35	113.15	110.80
	Bearing Walls	174.45	145.30	133.25	126.40	118.60	114.10	111.10	108.90	106.55
Metal Sandwich Panel	Steel Frame	192.90	159.80	146.05	138.15	129.10	123.80	120.35	117.75	114.95
Precast Concrete	Steel Frame	228.75	184.85	166.10	155.35	142.85	135.55	130.55	126.95	123.05
Perimeter Adj., Add or Deduct	Per 100 L.F.	38.15	19.15	12.75	9.60	6.30	4.80	3.80	3.20	2.50
Story Hgt. Adj., Add or Deduct	Per 1 Ft.	2.65	1.95	1.60	1.35	1.05	0.90	0.85	0.80	0.65
For Basement, add $26.35 per square foot of basement area										

The above costs were calculated using the basic specifications shown on the facing page. These costs should be adjusted where necessary for design alternatives and owner's requirements. Reported completed project costs, for this type of structure, range from $71.65 to $248.45 per S.F.

Common additives

Description	Unit	$ Cost	Description	Unit	$ Cost
Check Out Counter			Refrigerated Food Cases, cont.		
Single belt	Each	3550	Frozen food, chest type, 12' long	Each	9300
Double belt	Each	5075	Glass door reach-in, 5 door	Each	15,700
Emergency Lighting, 25 watt, battery operated			Island case 12' long, single deck	Each	8300
Lead battery	Each	320	Multi deck	Each	9675
Nickel cadmium	Each	885	Meat cases, 12' long, single deck	Each	8300
Refrigerators, Prefabricated, walk-in			Multi deck	Each	11,700
7'-6" high, 6' x 6'	S.F.	195	Produce, 12' long single deck	Each	7825
10' x 10'	S.F.	154	Multi deck	Each	9875
12' x 14'	S.F.	136	Safe, Office type, 1 hour rating		
12' x 20'	S.F.	119	30" x 18" x 18"	Each	2500
Refrigerated Food Cases			60" x 36" x 18", double door	Each	8075
Dairy, multi deck, 12' long	Each	12,700	Smoke Detectors		
Delicatessen case, single deck, 12' long	Each	8750	Ceiling type	Each	223
Multi deck, 18 S.F. shelf display	Each	8200	Duct type	Each	555
Freezer, self-contained chest type, 30 C.F.	Each	9600	Sound System		
Glass door upright, 78 C.F.	Each	11,500	Amplifier, 250 watts	Each	2025
			Speaker, ceiling or wall	Each	208
			Trumpet	Each	400

Important: See the Reference Section for Location Factors.

Model costs calculated for a 1 story building with 12' story height and 4,000 square feet of floor area

Store, Convenience

				Unit	Unit Cost	Cost Per S.F.	% Of Sub-Total
A. SUBSTRUCTURE							
1010	Standard Foundations	Poured concrete; strip and spread footings		S.F. Ground	1.66	1.66	
1020	Special Foundations	N/A		—	—	—	
1030	Slab on Grade	4" reinforced concrete with vapor barrier and granular base		S.F. Slab	5.31	5.31	13.8%
2010	Basement Excavation	Site preparation for slab and trench for foundation wall and footing		S.F. Ground	.57	.57	
2020	Basement Walls	4' foundation wall		L.F. Wall	73	4.59	
B. SHELL							
B10 Superstructure							
1010	Floor Construction	N/A		—	—	—	
1020	Roof Construction	Wood truss with plywood sheathing		S.F. Roof	6.85	6.85	7.8 %
B20 Exterior Enclosure							
2010	Exterior Walls	Wood siding on wood studs, insulated	80% of wall	S.F. Wall	9.98	6.06	
2020	Exterior Windows	Storefront	20% of wall	Each	44.60	4.54	14.6%
2030	Exterior Doors	Double aluminum and glass, solid core wood		Each	2982	2.25	
B30 Roofing							
3010	Roof Coverings	Asphalt shingles; rigid fiberglass insulation		S.F. Roof	5.44	5.44	6.2%
3020	Roof Openings	N/A		—	—	—	
C. INTERIORS							
1010	Partitions	Gypsum board on wood studs	60 S.F. Floor/L.F. Partition	S.F. Partition	13.32	2.22	
1020	Interior Doors	Single leaf wood, hollow metal	1300 S.F. Floor/Door	Each	1258	.96	
1030	Fittings	N/A		—	—	—	
2010	Stair Construction	N/A		—	—	—	14.8%
3010	Wall Finishes	Paint		S.F. Surface	1.17	.39	
3020	Floor Finishes	Vinyl composition tile		S.F. Floor	3.48	3.48	
3030	Ceiling Finishes	Mineral fiber tile on wood furring		S.F. Ceiling	5.99	5.99	
D. SERVICES							
D10 Conveying							
1010	Elevators & Lifts	N/A		—	—	—	0.0 %
1020	Escalators & Moving Walks	N/A		—	—	—	
D20 Plumbing							
2010	Plumbing Fixtures	Toilet and service fixtures, supply and drainage	1 Fixture/1000 S.F. Floor	Each	4400	4.40	
2020	Domestic Water Distribution	Gas fired water heater		S.F. Floor	1.40	1.40	6.6%
2040	Rain Water Drainage	N/A		—	—	—	
D30 HVAC							
3010	Energy Supply	N/A		—	—	—	
3020	Heat Generating Systems	Included in D3050		—	—	—	
3030	Cooling Generating Systems	N/A		—	—	—	9.4 %
3050	Terminal & Package Units	Single zone rooftop unit, gas heating, electric cooling		S.F. Floor	8.28	8.28	
3090	Other HVAC Sys. & Equipment	N/A		—	—	—	
D40 Fire Protection							
4010	Sprinklers	Sprinkler, ordinary hazard		S.F. Floor	4.76	4.76	7.8%
4020	Standpipes	Standpipe		S.F. floor	2.07	2.07	
D50 Electrical							
5010	Electrical Service/Distribution	200 ampere service, panel board and feeders		S.F. Floor	3.03	3.03	
5020	Lighting & Branch Wiring	High efficiency fluorescent fixtures, receptacles, switches, A.C. and misc. power		S.F. Floor	10.57	10.57	19.0%
5030	Communications & Security	Addressable alarm systems and emergency lighting		S.F. Floor	2.77	2.77	
5090	Other Electrical Systems	Emergency generator, 7.5 kW		S.F. Floor	.34	.34	
E. EQUIPMENT & FURNISHINGS							
1010	Commercial Equipment	N/A		—	—	—	
1020	Institutional Equipment	N/A		—	—	—	0.0 %
1030	Vehicular Equipment	N/A		—	—	—	
1090	Other Equipment	N/A		—	—	—	
F. SPECIAL CONSTRUCTION							
1020	Integrated Construction	N/A		—	—	—	0.0 %
1040	Special Facilities	N/A		—	—	—	
G. BUILDING SITEWORK	**N/A**						

			Sub-Total	87.93	100%
CONTRACTOR FEES (General Requirements: 10%, Overhead: 5%, Profit: 10%)			25%	21.98	
ARCHITECT FEES			7%	7.69	
		Total Building Cost		**117.60**	

Costs per square foot of floor area

Exterior Wall	S.F. Area	50000	65000	80000	95000	110000	125000	140000	155000	170000
	L.F. Perimeter	920	1065	1167	1303	1333	1433	1533	1633	1733
Face Brick with Concrete Block Back-up	R/Conc. Frame	125.75	123.30	121.30	120.15	118.50	117.75	117.15	116.60	116.25
	Steel Frame	110.75	108.30	106.25	105.15	103.55	102.80	102.15	101.65	101.30
Decorative Concrete Block	R/Conc. Frame	120.30	118.40	116.95	116.05	114.90	114.35	113.90	113.55	113.25
	Steel Joists	106.40	104.35	102.80	101.90	100.65	100.05	99.55	99.10	98.85
Precast Concrete Panels	R/Conc. Frame	124.40	122.10	120.30	119.20	117.75	117.05	116.50	116.10	115.75
	Steel Joists	108.80	106.55	104.70	103.70	102.25	101.55	101.00	100.50	100.20
Perimeter Adj., Add or Deduct	Per 100 L.F.	1.90	1.45	1.15	1.00	0.85	0.80	0.65	0.65	0.60
Story Hgt. Adj., Add or Deduct	Per 1 Ft.	1.00	0.85	0.75	0.75	0.60	0.60	0.55	0.60	0.55

For Basement, add $ 25.90 per square foot of basement area

The above costs were calculated using the basic specifications shown on the facing page. These costs should be adjusted where necessary for design alternatives and owner's requirements. Reported completed project costs, for this type of structure, range from $ 61.85 to $ 153.85 per S.F.

Common additives

Description	Unit	$ Cost
Closed Circuit Surveillance, One station		
Camera and monitor	Each	1975
For additional camera stations, add	Each	1050
Directory Boards, Plastic, glass covered		
30" x 20"	Each	630
36" x 48"	Each	1500
Aluminum, 24" x 18"	Each	630
36" x 24"	Each	735
48" x 32"	Each	1050
48" x 60"	Each	2200
Emergency Lighting, 25 watt, battery operated		
Lead battery	Each	320
Nickel cadmium	Each	885
Safe, Office type, 1 hour rating		
30" x 18" x 18"	Each	2500
60" x 36" x 18", double door	Each	8075
Sound System		
Amplifier, 250 watts	Each	2025
Speaker, ceiling or wall	Each	208
Trumpet	Each	400

Model costs calculated for a 1 story building with 14' story height and 110,000 square feet of floor area

Store, Department, 1 Story

				Unit	Unit Cost	Cost Per S.F.	% Of Sub-Total
A. SUBSTRUCTURE							
1010	Standard Foundations	Poured concrete; strip and spread footings		S.F. Ground	.93	.93	
1020	Special Foundations	N/A		—	—	—	
1030	Slab on Grade	4" reinforced concrete with vapor barrier and granular base		S.F. Slab	5.31	5.31	8.4%
2010	Basement Excavation	Site preparation for slab and trench for foundation wall and footing		S.F. Ground	.31	.31	
2020	Basement Walls	4' foundation wall		L.F. Wall	82	.99	
B. SHELL							
	B10 Superstructure						
1010	Floor Construction	Cast-in-place concrete columns		L.F. Column	73	.92	25.1%
1020	Roof Construction	Precast concrete beam and plank, concrete columns		S.F. Roof	21.56	21.56	
	B20 Exterior Enclosure						
2010	Exterior Walls	Face brick with concrete block backup	90% of wall	S.F. Wall	32.35	4.94	
2020	Exterior Windows	Storefront	10% of wall	Each	66	1.12	7.2%
2030	Exterior Doors	Sliding electric operated entrance, hollow metal		Each	7613	.42	
	B30 Roofing						
3010	Roof Coverings	Built-up tar and gravel with flashing; perlite/EPS composite insulation		S.F. Roof	5.34	5.34	6.0%
3020	Roof Openings	Roof hatches		S.F. Roof	.05	.05	
C. INTERIORS							
1010	Partitions	Gypsum board on metal studs	60 S.F. Floor/L.F. Partition	S.F. Partition	10.50	1.75	
1020	Interior Doors	Single leaf hollow metal	600 S.F. Floor/Door	Each	1152	1.92	
1030	Fittings	N/A		—	—	—	
2010	Stair Construction	N/A		—	—	—	26.0%
3010	Wall Finishes	Paint		S.F. Surface	.84	.28	
3020	Floor Finishes	50% ceramic tile, 50% carpet tile		S.F. Floor	14.89	14.89	
3030	Ceiling Finishes	Mineral fiber board on exposed grid system, suspended		S.F. Ceiling	4.37	4.37	
D. SERVICES							
	D10 Conveying						
1010	Elevators & Lifts	N/A		—	—	—	0.0 %
1020	Escalators & Moving Walks	N/A		—	—	—	
	D20 Plumbing						
2010	Plumbing Fixtures	Toilet and service fixtures, supply and drainage	1 Fixture/4075 S.F. Floor	Each	6724	1.65	
2020	Domestic Water Distribution	Gas fired water heater		S.F. Floor	.40	.40	3.2%
2040	Rain Water Drainage	Roof drains		S.F. Roof	.81	.81	
	D30 HVAC						
3010	Energy Supply	N/A		—	—	—	
3020	Heat Generating Systems	Included in D3050		—	—	—	
3030	Cooling Generating Systems	N/A		—	—	—	8.8 %
3050	Terminal & Package Units	Single zone unit gas heating, electric cooling		S.F. Floor	7.83	7.83	
3090	Other HVAC Sys. & Equipment	N/A		—	—	—	
	D40 Fire Protection						
4010	Sprinklers	Sprinklers, light hazard		S.F. Floor	2.85	2.85	3.5%
4020	Standpipes	Standpipe		S.F. Floor	.25	.25	
	D50 Electrical						
5010	Electrical Service/Distribution	1200 ampere service, panel board and feeders		S.F. Floor	.78	.78	
5020	Lighting & Branch Wiring	High efficiency fluorescent fixtures, receptacles, switches, A.C. and misc. power		S.F. Floor	8.50	8.50	11.8%
5030	Communications & Security	Addressable alarm systems, internet wiring and emergency lighting		S.F. Floor	1.23	1.23	
5090	Other Electrical Systems	Emergency generator, 7.5 kW		S.F. Floor	.04	.04	
E. EQUIPMENT & FURNISHINGS							
1010	Commercial Equipment	N/A		—	—	—	
1020	Institutional Equipment	N/A		—	—	—	0.0 %
1030	Vehicular Equipment	N/A		—	—	—	
1090	Other Equipment	N/A		—	—	—	
F. SPECIAL CONSTRUCTION							
1020	Integrated Construction	N/A		—	—	—	0.0 %
1040	Special Facilities	N/A		—	—	—	
G. BUILDING SITEWORK	**N/A**						

		Sub-Total	89.44	100%
CONTRACTOR FEES (General Requirements: 10%, Overhead: 5%, Profit: 10%)		25%	22.35	
ARCHITECT FEES		6%	6.71	

Total Building Cost 118.50

Costs per square foot of floor area

Exterior Wall	S.F. Area	50000	65000	80000	95000	110000	125000	140000	155000	170000
	L.F. Perimeter	533	593	670	715	778	840	871	923	976
Face Brick with Concrete Block Back-up	Steel Frame	156.75	150.80	147.70	144.60	142.80	141.45	139.80	138.80	138.00
	R/Conc. Frame	155.50	149.55	146.40	143.35	141.55	140.20	138.55	137.55	136.75
Face Brick on Steel Studs	Steel Frame	151.95	146.70	143.90	141.25	139.60	138.40	137.00	136.10	135.40
	R/Conc. Frame	153.25	147.95	145.20	142.50	140.95	139.70	138.25	137.40	136.70
Precast Concrete Panels Exposed Aggregate	Steel Frame	161.95	155.25	151.80	148.30	146.30	144.75	142.90	141.80	140.90
	R/Conc. Frame	162.70	156.00	152.55	149.05	147.05	145.50	143.60	142.45	141.55
Perimeter Adj., Add or Deduct	Per 100 L.F.	5.15	3.95	3.15	2.70	2.30	2.05	1.85	1.65	1.50
Story Hgt. Adj., Add or Deduct	Per 1 Ft.	1.60	1.35	1.20	1.15	1.05	1.00	0.95	0.90	0.90

For Basement, add $43.95 per square foot of basement area

The above costs were calculated using the basic specifications shown on the facing page. These costs should be adjusted where necessary for design alternatives and owner's requirements. Reported completed project costs, for this type of structure, range from $63.90 to $171.00 per S.F.

Common additives

Description	Unit	$ Cost		Description	Unit	$ Cost
Closed Circuit Surveillance, One station				Escalators, Metal		
Camera and monitor	Each	1975		32" wide, 10' story height	Each	147,500
For additional camera stations, add	Each	1050		20' story height	Each	180,500
Directory Boards, Plastic, glass covered				48" wide, 10' story height	Each	155,500
30" x 20"	Each	630		20' story height	Each	189,500
36" x 48"	Each	1500		Glass		
Aluminum, 24" x 18"	Each	630		32" wide, 10' story height	Each	140,500
36" x 24"	Each	735		20' story height	Each	172,000
48" x 32"	Each	1050		48" wide, 10' story height	Each	147,500
48" x 60"	Each	2200		20' story height	Each	180,500
Elevators, Hydraulic passenger, 2 stops				Safe, Office type, 1 hour rating		
1500# capacity	Each	66,100		30" x 18" x 18"	Each	2500
2500# capacity	Each	69,200		60" x 36" x 18", double door	Each	8075
3500# capacity	Each	73,200		Sound System		
Additional stop, add	Each	8575		Amplifier, 250 watts	Each	2025
Emergency Lighting, 25 watt, battery operated				Speaker, ceiling or wall	Each	208
Lead battery	Each	320		Trumpet	Each	400
Nickel cadmium	Each	885				

Important: See the Reference Section for Location Factors.

Model costs calculated for a 3 story building with 16' story height and 95,000 square feet of floor area

Store, Department, 3 Story

				Unit	Unit Cost	Cost Per S.F.	% Of Sub-Total
A. SUBSTRUCTURE							
1010	Standard Foundations	Poured concrete; strip and spread footings		S.F. Ground	3.66	1.22	
1020	Special Foundations	N/A		—	—	—	
1030	Slab on Grade	4" reinforced concrete with vapor barrier and granular base		S.F. Slab	5.31	1.77	3.4%
2010	Basement Excavation	Site preparation for slab and trench for foundation wall and footing		S.F. Ground	.18	.06	
2020	Basement Walls	4' foundation wall		L.F. Wall	77	.65	
B. SHELL							
	B10 Superstructure						
1010	Floor Construction	Concrete slab with metal deck and beams, steel columns		S.F. Floor	29.88	19.92	21.4%
1020	Roof Construction	Metal deck, open web steel joists, beams, columns		S.F. Roof	10.47	3.49	
	B20 Exterior Enclosure						
2010	Exterior Walls	Face brick with concrete block backup	90% of wall	S.F. Wall	32.36	10.52	
2020	Exterior Windows	Storefront	10% of wall	Each	47.40	1.71	12.8%
2030	Exterior Doors	Revolving and sliding panel, mall-front		Each	11,897	1.76	
	B30 Roofing						
3010	Roof Coverings	Built-up tar and gravel with flashing; perlite/EPS composite insulation		S.F. Roof	5.82	1.94	1.8%
3020	Roof Openings	Roof hatches		S.F. Roof	.21	.07	
C. INTERIORS							
1010	Partitions	Gypsum board on metal studs	60 S.F. Floor/L.F. Partition	S.F. Partition	6.30	1.05	
1020	Interior Doors	Single leaf hollow metal	600 S.F. Floor/Door	Each	1152	1.92	
1030	Fittings	N/A		—	—	—	
2010	Stair Construction	Concrete filled metal pan		Flight	20,150	2.12	26.4%
3010	Wall Finishes	70% paint, 20% vinyl wall covering, 10% ceramic tile		S.F. Surface	4.95	1.65	
3020	Floor Finishes	50% carpet tile, 40% marble tile, 10% terrazzo		S.F. Floor	15.14	15.14	
3030	Ceiling Finishes	Mineral fiber tile on concealed zee bars		S.F. Ceiling	6.89	6.89	
D. SERVICES							
	D10 Conveying						
1010	Elevators & Lifts	One hydraulic passenger, one hydraulic freight		Each	312,550	3.29	8.9%
1020	Escalators & Moving Walks	Four escalators		Each	153,425	6.46	
	D20 Plumbing						
2010	Plumbing Fixtures	Toilet and service fixtures, supply and drainage	1 Fixture/2570 S.F. Floor	Each	4626	1.80	
2020	Domestic Water Distribution	Gas fired water heater		S.F. Floor	.46	.46	2.6%
2040	Rain Water Drainage	Roof drains		S.F. Roof	1.59	.53	
	D30 HVAC						
3010	Energy Supply	N/A		—	—	—	
3020	Heat Generating Systems	Included in D3050		—	—	—	
3030	Cooling Generating Systems	N/A		—	—	—	7.2 %
3050	Terminal & Package Units	Multizone rooftop unit, gas heating, electric cooling		S.F. Floor	7.83	7.83	
3090	Other HVAC Sys. & Equipment	N/A		—	—	—	
	D40 Fire Protection						
4010	Sprinklers	Sprinklers, light hazard		S.F. Floor	2.37	2.37	3.7%
4020	Standpipes	Standpipe		S.F. Floor	1.62	1.62	
	D50 Electrical						
5010	Electrical Service/Distribution	1200 ampere service, panel board and feeders		S.F. Floor	1.25	1.25	
5020	Lighting & Branch Wiring	High efficiency fluorescent fixtures, receptacles, switches, A.C. and misc. power		S.F. Floor	8.91	8.91	11.8%
5030	Communications & Security	Addressable alarm systems, internet wiring and emergency lighting		S.F. Floor	2.47	2.47	
5090	Other Electrical Systems	Emergency generator, 50 kW		S.F. Floor	.27	.27	
E. EQUIPMENT & FURNISHINGS							
1010	Commercial Equipment	N/A		—	—	—	
1020	Institutional Equipment	N/A		—	—	—	0.0 %
1030	Vehicular Equipment	N/A		—	—	—	
1090	Other Equipment	N/A		—	—	—	
F. SPECIAL CONSTRUCTION							
1020	Integrated Construction	N/A		—	—	—	0.0 %
1040	Special Facilities	N/A		—	—	—	
G. BUILDING SITEWORK	**N/A**						

		Sub-Total	109.14	**100%**
CONTRACTOR FEES (General Requirements: 10%, Overhead: 5%, Profit: 10%)		25%	27.27	
ARCHITECT FEES		6%	8.19	
		Total Building Cost	**144.60**	

Costs per square foot of floor area

Exterior Wall	S.F. Area	4000	6000	8000	10000	12000	15000	18000	20000	22000
	L.F. Perimeter	260	340	360	410	440	490	540	565	594
Split Face Concrete Block	Steel Joists	151.25	137.95	126.35	121.35	116.95	112.80	109.95	108.25	107.00
Stucco on Concrete Block	Steel Joists	148.55	135.60	124.50	119.70	115.40	111.40	108.70	107.10	105.90
EIFS on Metal Studs	Steel Joists	150.90	137.60	126.10	121.15	116.70	112.55	109.80	108.05	106.80
Face Brick on Concrete Block	Steel Joists	167.25	151.90	137.45	131.45	125.95	120.80	117.35	115.20	113.65
Painted Reinforced Concrete	Steel Joists	159.15	144.85	131.85	126.35	121.40	116.75	113.65	111.70	110.30
Tilt-up Concrete Panels	Steel Joists	145.95	133.35	122.75	118.05	113.95	110.10	107.50	105.95	104.80
Perimeter Adj., Add or Deduct	Per 100 L.F.	16.55	11.00	8.30	6.65	5.55	4.40	3.65	3.30	3.00
Story Hgt. Adj., Add or Deduct	Per 1 Ft.	2.05	1.80	1.45	1.35	1.20	1.00	0.95	0.90	0.85

For Basement, add $36.45 per square foot of basement area

The above costs were calculated using the basic specifications shown on the facing page. These costs should be adjusted where necessary for design alternatives and owner's requirements. Reported completed project costs, for this type of structure, range from $62.35 to $216.85 per S.F.

Common additives

Description	Unit	$ Cost
Emergency Lighting, 25 watt, battery operated		
Lead battery	Each	320
Nickel cadmium	Each	885
Safe, Office type, 1 hour rating		
30" x 18" x 18"	Each	2500
60" x 36" x 18", double door	Each	8075
Smoke Detectors		
Ceiling type	Each	223
Duct type	Each	555
Sound System		
Amplifier, 250 watts	Each	2025
Speaker, ceiling or wall	Each	208
Trumpet	Each	400

Important: See the Reference Section for Location Factors.

Model costs calculated for a 1 story building with 14' story height and 8,000 square feet of floor area

				Unit	Unit Cost	Cost Per S.F.	% Of Sub-Total
A.	**SUBSTRUCTURE**						
1010	Standard Foundations	Poured concrete; strip and spread footings		S.F. Ground	1.90	1.90	
1020	Special Foundations	N/A		—	—	—	
1030	Slab on Grade	4" reinforced concrete with vapor barrier and granular base		S.F. Slab	5.31	5.31	12.0%
2010	Basement Excavation	Site preparation for slab and trench for foundation wall and footing		S.F. Ground	.32	.32	
2020	Basement Walls	4' foundation wall		L.F. Wall	82	3.67	
B.	**SHELL**						
	B10 Superstructure						
1010	Floor Construction	N/A		—	—	—	8.0 %
1020	Roof Construction	Metal deck, open web steel joists, beams, interior columns		S.F. Roof	7.47	7.47	
	B20 Exterior Enclosure						
2010	Exterior Walls	Decorative concrete block	90% of wall	S.F. Wall	17.90	10.15	
2020	Exterior Windows	Storefront windows	10% of wall	Each	47.40	2.99	14.6%
2030	Exterior Doors	Sliding entrance door and hollow metal service doors		Each	2260	.56	
	B30 Roofing						
3010	Roof Coverings	Built-up tar and gravel with flashing; perlite/EPS composite insulation		S.F. Roof	6.57	6.57	7.1%
3020	Roof Openings	Roof hatches		S.F. Roof	.12	.12	
C.	**INTERIORS**						
1010	Partitions	Gypsum board on metal studs	60 S.F. Floor/L.F. Partition	S.F. Partition	6.30	1.05	
1020	Interior Doors	Single leaf hollow metal	600 S.F. Floor/Door	Each	1152	1.92	
1030	Fittings	N/A		—	—	—	
2010	Stair Construction	N/A		—	—	—	16.5%
3010	Wall Finishes	Paint		S.F. Surface	6.45	2.15	
3020	Floor Finishes	Vinyl tile		S.F. Floor	3.48	3.48	
3030	Ceiling Finishes	Mineral fiber tile on concealed zee bars		S.F. Ceiling	6.89	6.89	
D.	**SERVICES**						
	D10 Conveying						
1010	Elevators & Lifts	N/A		—	—	—	0.0 %
1020	Escalators & Moving Walks	N/A		—	—	—	
	D20 Plumbing						
2010	Plumbing Fixtures	Toilet and service fixtures, supply and drainage	1 Fixture/890 S.F. Floor	Each	3160	3.55	
2020	Domestic Water Distribution	Gas fired water heater		S.F. Floor	5.42	5.42	11.3%
2040	Rain Water Drainage	Roof drains		S.F. Roof	1.64	1.64	
	D30 HVAC						
3010	Energy Supply	N/A		—	—	—	
3020	Heat Generating Systems	Included in D3050		—	—	—	
3030	Cooling Generating Systems	N/A		—	—	—	8.4 %
3050	Terminal & Package Units	Single zone unit, gas heating, electric cooling		S.F. Floor	7.83	7.83	
3090	Other HVAC Sys. & Equipment	N/A		—	—	—	
	D40 Fire Protection						
4010	Sprinklers	Wet pipe sprinkler system		S.F. Floor	4.55	4.55	6.0%
4020	Standpipes	Standpipe, wet, Class III		S.F. Floor	1.04	1.04	
	D50 Electrical						
5010	Electrical Service/Distribution	400 ampere service, panel board and feeders		S.F. Floor	2.76	2.76	
5020	Lighting & Branch Wiring	High efficiency fluorescent fixtures, receptacles, switches, A.C. and misc. power		S.F. Floor	10.40	10.40	16.0%
5030	Communications & Security	Addressable alarm systems and emergency lighting		S.F. Floor	1.66	1.66	
5090	Other Electrical Systems	Emergency generator, 15 kW		S.F. Floor	.20	.20	
E.	**EQUIPMENT & FURNISHINGS**						
1010	Commercial Equipment	N/A		—	—	—	
1020	Institutional Equipment	N/A		—	—	—	0.0 %
1030	Vehicular Equipment	N/A		—	—	—	
1090	Other Equipment	N/A		—	—	—	
F.	**SPECIAL CONSTRUCTION**						
1020	Integrated Construction	N/A		—	—	—	0.0 %
1040	Special Facilities	N/A		—	—	—	
G.	**BUILDING SITEWORK**	**N/A**					

		Sub-Total	93.60	**100%**
	CONTRACTOR FEES (General Requirements: 10%, Overhead: 5%, Profit: 10%)	25%	23.39	
	ARCHITECT FEES	8%	9.36	

Total Building Cost 126.35

Costs per square foot of floor area

Exterior Wall		S.F. Area	12000	16000	20000	26000	32000	38000	44000	52000	60000
		L.F. Perimeter	450	510	570	650	716	780	840	920	1020
Face Brick with Concrete Block Back-up	Steel Frame		142.35	132.15	126.15	120.05	115.70	112.70	110.35	108.10	106.85
	Bearing Walls		142.15	132.00	125.95	119.90	115.50	112.45	110.15	107.90	106.70
Stucco on Concrete Block	Steel Frame		131.65	123.10	118.00	112.90	109.30	106.80	104.95	103.05	102.00
	Bearing Walls		132.20	123.65	118.55	113.50	109.85	107.35	105.45	103.60	102.55
Precast Concrete Panels	Steel Frame		150.35	138.95	132.20	125.40	120.45	117.00	114.45	111.85	110.45
Metal Sandwich Panels	Steel Frame		142.60	132.40	126.35	120.20	115.80	112.80	110.50	108.20	106.95
Perimeter Adj., Add or Deduct	Per 100 L.F.		10.20	7.70	6.05	4.70	3.85	3.15	2.75	2.35	2.05
Story Hgt. Adj., Add or Deduct	Per 1 Ft.		2.10	1.85	1.60	1.40	1.20	1.15	1.05	0.95	0.95

For Basement, add $26.50 per square foot of basement area

The above costs were calculated using the basic specifications shown on the facing page. These costs should be adjusted where necessary for design alternatives and owner's requirements. Reported completed project costs, for this type of structure, range from $72.85 to $208.60 per S.F.

Common additives

Description	Unit	$ Cost	Description	Unit	$ Cost
Check Out Counter			Refrigerated Food Cases, cont.		
Single belt	Each	3550	Frozen food, chest type, 12' long	Each	9300
Double belt	Each	5075	Glass door reach in, 5 door	Each	15,700
Scanner, registers, guns & memory 2 lanes	Each	18,100	Island case 12' long, single deck	Each	8300
10 lanes	Each	171,500	Multi deck	Each	9675
Power take away	Each	5950	Meat case 12' long, single deck	Each	8300
Emergency Lighting, 25 watt, battery operated			Multi deck	Each	11,700
Lead battery	Each	320	Produce, 12' long single deck	Each	7825
Nickel cadmium	Each	885	Multi deck	Each	9875
Refrigerators, Prefabricated, walk-in			Safe, Office type, 1 hour rating		
7'-6" High, 6' x 6'	S.F.	195	30" x 18" x 18"	Each	2500
10' x 10'	S.F.	154	60" x 36" x 18", double door	Each	8075
12' x 14'	S.F.	136	Smoke Detectors		
12' x 20'	S.F.	119	Ceiling type	Each	223
Refrigerated Food Cases			Duct type	Each	555
Dairy, multi deck, 12' long	Each	12,700	Sound System		
Delicatessen case, single deck, 12' long	Each	8750	Amplifier, 250 watts	Each	2025
Multi deck, 18 S.F. shelf display	Each	8200	Speaker, ceiling or wall	Each	208
Freezer, self-contained chest type, 30 C.F.	Each	9600	Trumpet	Each	400
Glass door upright, 78 C.F.	Each	11,500			

Important: See the Reference Section for Location Factors.

Model costs calculated for a 1 story building with 14' story height and 8,000 square feet of floor area

Store, Retail

				Unit	Unit Cost	Cost Per S.F.	% Of Sub-Total
A.	**SUBSTRUCTURE**						
1010	Standard Foundations	Poured concrete; strip and spread footings		S.F. Ground	1.90	1.90	
1020	Special Foundations	N/A		—	—	—	
1030	Slab on Grade	4" reinforced concrete with vapor barrier and granular base		S.F. Slab	5.31	5.31	12.0%
2010	Basement Excavation	Site preparation for slab and trench for foundation wall and footing		S.F. Ground	.32	.32	
2020	Basement Walls	4' foundation wall		L.F. Wall	82	3.67	
B.	**SHELL**						
	B10 Superstructure						
1010	Floor Construction	N/A		—	—	—	
1020	Roof Construction	Metal deck, open web steel joists, beams, interior columns		S.F. Roof	7.47	7.47	8.0 %
	B20 Exterior Enclosure						
2010	Exterior Walls	Decorative concrete block	90% of wall	S.F. Wall	17.90	10.15	
2020	Exterior Windows	Storefront windows	10% of wall	Each	47.40	2.99	14.6%
2030	Exterior Doors	Sliding entrance door and hollow metal service doors		Each	2260	.56	
	B30 Roofing						
3010	Roof Coverings	Built-up tar and gravel with flashing; perlite/EPS composite insulation		S.F. Roof	6.57	6.57	7.1%
3020	Roof Openings	Roof hatches		S.F. Roof	.12	.12	
C.	**INTERIORS**						
1010	Partitions	Gypsum board on metal studs	60 S.F. Floor/L.F. Partition	S.F. Partition	6.30	1.05	
1020	Interior Doors	Single leaf hollow metal	600 S.F. Floor/Door	Each	1152	1.92	
1030	Fittings	N/A		—	—	—	
2010	Stair Construction	N/A		—	—	—	16.5%
3010	Wall Finishes	Paint		S.F. Surface	6.45	2.15	
3020	Floor Finishes	Vinyl tile		S.F. Floor	3.48	3.48	
3030	Ceiling Finishes	Mineral fiber tile on concealed zee bars		S.F. Ceiling	6.89	6.89	
D.	**SERVICES**						
	D10 Conveying						
1010	Elevators & Lifts	N/A		—	—	—	0.0 %
1020	Escalators & Moving Walks	N/A		—	—	—	
	D20 Plumbing						
2010	Plumbing Fixtures	Toilet and service fixtures, supply and drainage	1 Fixture/890 S.F. Floor	Each	3160	3.55	
2020	Domestic Water Distribution	Gas fired water heater		S.F. Floor	5.42	5.42	11.3%
2040	Rain Water Drainage	Roof drains		S.F. Roof	1.64	1.64	
	D30 HVAC						
3010	Energy Supply	N/A		—	—	—	
3020	Heat Generating Systems	Included in D3050		—	—	—	
3030	Cooling Generating Systems	N/A		—	—	—	8.4 %
3050	Terminal & Package Units	Single zone unit, gas heating, electric cooling		S.F. Floor	7.83	7.83	
3090	Other HVAC Sys. & Equipment	N/A		—	—	—	
	D40 Fire Protection						
4010	Sprinklers	Wet pipe sprinkler system		S.F. Floor	4.55	4.55	6.0%
4020	Standpipes	Standpipe, wet, Class III		S.F. Floor	1.04	1.04	
	D50 Electrical						
5010	Electrical Service/Distribution	400 ampere service, panel board and feeders		S.F. Floor	2.76	2.76	
5020	Lighting & Branch Wiring	High efficiency fluorescent fixtures, receptacles, switches, A.C. and misc. power		S.F. Floor	10.40	10.40	16.0%
5030	Communications & Security	Addressable alarm systems and emergency lighting		S.F. Floor	1.66	1.66	
5090	Other Electrical Systems	Emergency generator, 15 kW		S.F. Floor	.20	.20	
E.	**EQUIPMENT & FURNISHINGS**						
1010	Commercial Equipment	N/A		—	—	—	
1020	Institutional Equipment	N/A		—	—	—	
1030	Vehicular Equipment	N/A		—	—	—	0.0 %
1090	Other Equipment	N/A		—	—	—	
F.	**SPECIAL CONSTRUCTION**						
1020	Integrated Construction	N/A		—	—	—	0.0 %
1040	Special Facilities	N/A		—	—	—	
G.	**BUILDING SITEWORK**	**N/A**					

		Sub-Total	93.60	100%
CONTRACTOR FEES (General Requirements: 10%, Overhead: 5%, Profit: 10%)		25%	23.39	
ARCHITECT FEES		8%	9.36	
	Total Building Cost		**126.35**	

Costs per square foot of floor area

Exterior Wall	S.F. Area	12000	16000	20000	26000	32000	38000	44000	52000	60000
	L.F. Perimeter	450	510	570	650	716	780	840	920	1020
Face Brick with Concrete Block Back-up	Steel Frame	142.35	132.15	126.15	120.05	115.70	112.70	110.35	108.10	106.85
	Bearing Walls	142.15	132.00	125.95	119.90	115.50	112.45	110.15	107.90	106.70
Stucco on Concrete Block	Steel Frame	131.65	123.10	118.00	112.90	109.30	106.80	104.95	103.05	102.00
	Bearing Walls	132.20	123.65	118.55	113.50	109.85	107.35	105.45	103.60	102.55
Precast Concrete Panels	Steel Frame	150.35	138.95	132.20	125.40	120.45	117.00	114.45	111.85	110.45
Metal Sandwich Panels	Steel Frame	142.60	132.40	126.35	120.20	115.80	112.80	110.50	108.20	106.95
Perimeter Adj., Add or Deduct	Per 100 L.F.	10.20	7.70	6.05	4.70	3.85	3.15	2.75	2.35	2.05
Story Hgt. Adj., Add or Deduct	Per 1 Ft.	2.10	1.85	1.60	1.40	1.20	1.15	1.05	0.95	0.95

For Basement, add $26.50 per square foot of basement area

The above costs were calculated using the basic specifications shown on the facing page. These costs should be adjusted where necessary for design alternatives and owner's requirements. Reported completed project costs, for this type of structure, range from $72.85 to $208.60 per S.F.

Common additives

Description	Unit	$ Cost
Check Out Counter		
Single belt	Each	3550
Double belt	Each	5075
Scanner, registers, guns & memory 2 lanes	Each	18,100
10 lanes	Each	171,500
Power take away	Each	5950
Emergency Lighting, 25 watt, battery operated		
Lead battery	Each	320
Nickel cadmium	Each	885
Refrigerators, Prefabricated, walk-in		
7'-6" High, 6' x 6'	S.F.	195
10' x 10'	S.F.	154
12' x 14'	S.F.	136
12' x 20'	S.F.	119
Refrigerated Food Cases		
Dairy, multi deck, 12' long	Each	12,700
Delicatessen case, single deck, 12' long	Each	8750
Multi deck, 18 S.F. shelf display	Each	8200
Freezer, self-contained chest type, 30 C.F.	Each	9600
Glass door upright, 78 C.F.	Each	11,500

Description	Unit	$ Cost
Refrigerated Food Cases, cont.		
Frozen food, chest type, 12' long	Each	9300
Glass door reach in, 5 door	Each	15,700
Island case 12' long, single deck	Each	8300
Multi deck	Each	9675
Meat case 12' long, single deck	Each	8300
Multi deck	Each	11,700
Produce, 12' long single deck	Each	7825
Multi deck	Each	9875
Safe, Office type, 1 hour rating		
30" x 18" x 18"	Each	2500
60" x 36" x 18", double door	Each	8075
Smoke Detectors		
Ceiling type	Each	223
Duct type	Each	555
Sound System		
Amplifier, 250 watts	Each	2025
Speaker, ceiling or wall	Each	208
Trumpet	Each	400

Important: See the Reference Section for Location Factors.

Model costs calculated for a 1 story building with 18' story height and 44,000 square feet of floor area

				Unit	Unit Cost	Cost Per S.F.	% Of Sub-Total
A. SUBSTRUCTURE							
1010	Standard Foundations	Poured concrete; strip and spread footings		S.F. Ground	1.12	1.12	
1020	Special Foundations	N/A		—	—	—	
1030	Slab on Grade	4" reinforced concrete with vapor barrier and granular base		S.F. Slab	5.31	5.31	9.9%
2010	Basement Excavation	Site preparation for slab and trench for foundation wall and footing		S.F. Ground	.18	.18	
2020	Basement Walls	4' foundation wall		L.F. Wall	82	1.56	
B. SHELL							
B10 Superstructure							
1010	Floor Construction	N/A		—	—	—	
1020	Roof Construction	Metal deck, open web steel joists, beams, interior columns		S.F. Roof	8.11	8.11	9.8 %
B20 Exterior Enclosure							
2010	Exterior Walls	Face brick with concrete block backup	85% of wall	S.F. Wall	32.90	9.61	
2020	Exterior Windows	Storefront windows	15% of wall	Each	75	3.86	18.0%
2030	Exterior Doors	Sliding entrance doors with electrical operator, hollow metal		Each	5273	1.32	
B30 Roofing							
3010	Roof Coverings	Built-up tar and gravel with flashing; perlite/EPS composite insulation		S.F. Roof	5.60	5.60	7.0%
3020	Roof Openings	Roof hatches		S.F. Roof	.13	.13	
C. INTERIORS							
1010	Partitions	50% concrete block, 50% gypsum board on metal studs	50 S.F. Floor/L.F. Partition	S.F. Partition	7.79	1.87	
1020	Interior Doors	Single leaf hollow metal	2000 S.F. Floor/Door	Each	1152	.58	
1030	Fittings	N/A		—	—	—	
2010	Stair Construction	N/A		—	—	—	18.7%
3010	Wall Finishes	Paint		S.F. Surface	5.31	2.55	
3020	Floor Finishes	Vinyl composition tile		S.F. Floor	3.48	3.48	
3030	Ceiling Finishes	Mineral fiber tile on concealed zee bars		S.F. Ceiling	6.89	6.89	
D. SERVICES							
D10 Conveying							
1010	Elevators & Lifts	N/A		—	—	—	0.0 %
1020	Escalators & Moving Walks	N/A		—	—	—	
D20 Plumbing							
2010	Plumbing Fixtures	Toilet and service fixtures, supply and drainage	1 Fixture/1820 S.F. Floor	Each	2184	1.20	
2020	Domestic Water Distribution	Gas fired water heater		S.F. Floor	.42	.42	3.2%
2040	Rain Water Drainage	Roof drains		S.F. Roof	.98	.98	
D30 HVAC							
3010	Energy Supply	N/A		—	—	—	
3020	Heat Generating Systems	Included in D3050		—	—	—	
3030	Cooling Generating Systems	N/A		—	—	—	6.2%
3050	Terminal & Package Units	Single zone rooftop unit, gas heating, electric cooling		S.F. Floor	5.12	5.12	
3090	Other HVAC Sys. & Equipment	N/A		—	—	—	
D40 Fire Protection							
4010	Sprinklers	Sprinklers, light hazard		S.F. Floor	3.56	3.56	5.0%
4020	Standpipes	Standpipe		S.F. Floor	.52	.52	
D50 Electrical							
5010	Electrical Service/Distribution	1600 ampere service, panel board and feeders		S.F. Floor	2.55	2.55	
5020	Lighting & Branch Wiring	High efficiency fluorescent fixtures, receptacles, switches, A.C. and misc. power		S.F. Floor	13.60	13.60	22.3%
5030	Communications & Security	Addressable alarm systems, partial internet wiring and emergency lighting		S.F. Floor	2.21	2.21	
5090	Other Electrical Systems	Emergency generator, 15 kW		S.F. Floor	.04	.04	
E. EQUIPMENT & FURNISHINGS							
1010	Commercial Equipment	N/A		—	—	—	
1020	Institutional Equipment	N/A		—	—	—	0.0 %
1030	Vehicular Equipment	N/A		—	—	—	
1090	Other Equipment	N/A		—	—	—	
F. SPECIAL CONSTRUCTION							
1020	Integrated Construction	N/A		—	—	—	0.0 %
1040	Special Facilities	N/A		—	—	—	
G. BUILDING SITEWORK	**N/A**						

		Sub-Total	82.37	100%
CONTRACTOR FEES (General Requirements: 10%, Overhead: 5%, Profit: 10%)		25%	20.57	
ARCHITECT FEES		7%	7.21	
	Total Building Cost		110.15	

217

Costs per square foot of floor area

Exterior Wall	S.F. Area	10000	16000	20000	22000	24000	26000	28000	30000	32000
	L.F. Perimeter	420	510	600	640	660	684	706	740	737
Face Brick with Concrete Block Back-up	Wood Truss	276.80	257.40	253.60	251.85	248.85	246.65	244.65	243.55	240.60
	Precast Conc.	312.65	289.10	284.45	282.30	278.70	276.00	273.50	272.20	268.55
Metal Sandwich Panel	Wood Truss	280.20	261.35	257.00	255.10	252.50	250.40	248.70	247.60	245.15
Precast Concrete Panel	Precast Conc.	313.20	286.35	280.45	277.85	274.00	271.00	268.40	266.85	263.15
Painted Concrete Block	Wood Frame	274.25	260.20	257.35	256.00	253.95	252.35	250.95	250.10	248.05
	Precast Conc.	296.35	273.70	268.60	266.40	263.15	260.65	258.50	257.20	254.15
Perimeter Adj., Add or Deduct	Per 100 L.F.	17.35	10.85	8.65	7.80	7.20	6.70	6.15	5.80	5.45
Story Hgt. Adj., Add or Deduct	Per 1 Ft.	2.15	1.65	1.55	1.50	1.45	1.40	1.25	1.25	1.15

For Basement, add $39.30 per square foot of basement area

The above costs were calculated using the basic specifications shown on the facing page. These costs should be adjusted where necessary for design alternatives and owner's requirements. Reported completed project costs, for this type of structure, range from $115.05 to $338.25 per S.F.

Common additives

Description	Unit	$ Cost	Description	Unit	$ Cost
Bleachers, Telescoping, manual			Sauna, Prefabricated, complete		
To 15 tier	Seat	135 - 187	6' x 4'	Each	6800
16-20 tier	Seat	277 - 340	6' x 6'	Each	7950
21-30 tier	Seat	295 - 385	6' x 9'	Each	9725
For power operation, add	Seat	54.50 - 84.50	8' x 8'	Each	11,500
Emergency Lighting, 25 watt, battery operated			8' x 10'	Each	12,800
Lead battery	Each	320	10' x 12'	Each	15,400
Nickel cadmium	Each	885	Sound System		
Lockers, Steel, single tier, 60" or 72"	Opening	218 - 365	Amplifier, 250 watts	Each	2025
2 tier, 60" or 72" total	Opening	113 - 156	Speaker, ceiling or wall	Each	208
5 tier, box lockers	Opening	71.50 - 85	Trumpet	Each	400
Locker bench, lam. maple top only	L.F.	26.50	Steam Bath, Complete, to 140 C.F.	Each	2175
Pedestal, steel pipe	Each	74	To 300 C.F.	Each	2325
Pool Equipment			To 800 C.F.	Each	8850
Diving stand, 3 meter	Each	18,700	To 2500 C.F.	Each	10,900
1 meter	Each	10,100			
Diving board, 16' aluminum	Each	4775			
Fiberglass	Each	3950			
Lifeguard chair, fixed	Each	3875			
Portable	Each	3000			
Lights, underwater, 12 volt, 300 watt	Each	1000			

Important: See the Reference Section for Location Factors.

Model costs calculated for a 1 story building with 24' story height and 20,000 square feet of floor area

Swimming Pool, Enclosed

				Unit	Unit Cost	Cost Per S.F.	% Of Sub-Total
A. SUBSTRUCTURE							
1010	Standard Foundations	Poured concrete; strip and spread footings		S.F. Ground	1.62	1.62	
1020	Special Foundations	N/A		—	—	—	
1030	Slab on Grade	4" reinforced concrete with vapor barrier and granular base		S.F. Slab	5.31	5.31	14.7%
2010	Basement Excavation	Site preparation for slab and trench for foundation wall and footing		S.F. Ground	10.85	10.85	
2020	Basement Walls	4' foundation wall		L.F. Wall	82	9.79	
B. SHELL							
B10 Superstructure							
1010	Floor Construction	N/A		—	—	—	9.9 %
1020	Roof Construction	Wood deck on laminated wood truss		S.F. Roof	18.69	18.69	
B20 Exterior Enclosure							
2010	Exterior Walls	Face brick with concrete block backup	80% of wall	S.F. Wall	32.34	18.63	
2020	Exterior Windows	Outward projecting steel	20% of wall	Each	47.40	6.83	13.9%
2030	Exterior Doors	Double aluminum and glass, hollow metal		Each	2636	.65	
B30 Roofing							
3010	Roof Coverings	Asphalt shingles with flashing; perlite/EPS composite insulation		S.F. Roof	2.44	2.44	1.3%
3020	Roof Openings	N/A		—	—	—	
C. INTERIORS							
1010	Partitions	Concrete block	100 S.F. Floor/L.F. Partition	S.F. Partition	9.40	.94	
1020	Interior Doors	Single leaf hollow metal	1000 S.F. Floor/Door	Each	1152	1.15	
1030	Fittings	Toilet partitions		S.F. Floor	.17	.17	
2010	Stair Construction	N/A		—	—	—	14.9%
3010	Wall Finishes	Acrylic glazed coating		S.F. Surface	11.70	2.34	
3020	Floor Finishes	70% terrazzo, 30% ceramic tile		S.F. Floor	22.44	22.44	
3030	Ceiling Finishes	Mineral fiber tile on concealed zee bars	20% of area	S.F. Ceiling	4.37	.88	
D. SERVICES							
D10 Conveying							
1010	Elevators & Lifts	N/A		—	—	—	0.0 %
1020	Escalators & Moving Walks	N/A		—	—	—	
D20 Plumbing							
2010	Plumbing Fixtures	Toilet and service fixtures, supply and drainage	1 Fixture/210 S.F. Floor	Each	1245	5.93	
2020	Domestic Water Distribution	Gas fired water heater		S.F. Floor	4.35	4.35	5.5%
2040	Rain Water Drainage	N/A		—	—	—	
D30 HVAC							
3010	Energy Supply	Terminal unit heaters	10% of area	S.F. Floor	.89	.89	
3020	Heat Generating Systems	N/A		—	—	—	
3030	Cooling Generating Systems	N/A		—	—	—	7.4%
3050	Terminal & Package Units	Single zone unit gas heating, electric cooling		S.F. Floor	13.10	13.10	
3090	Other HVAC Sys. & Equipment	N/A		—	—	—	
D40 Fire Protection							
4010	Sprinklers	Sprinklers, light hazard		S.F. Floor	1.78	1.78	1.2%
4020	Standpipes	Standpipe		S.F. Floor	.53	.53	
D50 Electrical							
5010	Electrical Service/Distribution	400 ampere service, panel board and feeders		S.F. Floor	1.15	1.15	
5020	Lighting & Branch Wiring	High efficiency fluorescent fixtures, receptacles, switches, A.C. and misc. power		S.F. Floor	20.70	20.70	12.2%
5030	Communications & Security	Addressable alarm systems and emergency lighting		S.F. Floor	1.04	1.04	
5090	Other Electrical Systems	Emergency generator, 15 kW		S.F. Floor	.08	.08	
E. EQUIPMENT & FURNISHINGS							
1010	Commercial Equipment	N/A		—	—	—	
1020	Institutional Equipment	N/A		—	—	—	
1030	Vehicular Equipment	N/A		—	—	—	18.9 %
1090	Other Equipment	Swimming pool		S.F. Floor	35.57	35.57	
F. SPECIAL CONSTRUCTION							
1020	Integrated Construction	N/A		—	—	—	0.0 %
1040	Special Facilities	N/A		—	—	—	
G. BUILDING SITEWORK	N/A						

		Sub-Total	187.85	**100%**
CONTRACTOR FEES (General Requirements: 10%, Overhead: 5%, Profit: 10%)		25%	46.97	
ARCHITECT FEES		8%	18.78	

Total Building Cost	**253.60**

Costs per square foot of floor area

Exterior Wall	S.F. Area	2000	3000	4000	5000	6000	7000	8000	9000	10000
	L.F. Perimeter	180	220	260	286	320	353	368	397	425
Face Brick with Concrete Block Back-up	Steel Frame	223.50	198.25	185.75	175.35	169.75	165.60	160.30	157.75	155.55
	Bearing Walls	213.65	191.25	180.15	170.65	165.60	161.85	156.85	154.55	152.55
Limestone with Concrete Block Back-up	Steel Frame	260.45	230.25	215.25	202.10	195.30	190.20	183.10	179.90	177.20
	Bearing Walls	260.90	227.85	211.40	197.40	189.95	184.50	177.10	173.65	170.75
Decorative Concrete Block	Steel Frame	208.05	185.70	174.60	165.50	160.60	156.95	152.40	150.15	148.25
	Bearing Walls	203.35	181.00	169.85	160.80	155.90	152.25	147.70	145.45	143.55
Perimeter Adj., Add or Deduct	Per 100 L.F.	49.45	33.00	24.65	19.80	16.45	14.15	12.40	10.95	9.85
Story Hgt. Adj., Add or Deduct	Per 1 Ft.	5.80	4.75	4.15	3.70	3.45	3.25	2.90	2.80	2.75

For Basement, add $38.10 per square foot of basement area

The above costs were calculated using the basic specifications shown on the facing page. These costs should be adjusted where necessary for design alternatives and owner's requirements. Reported completed project costs, for this type of structure, range from $101.70 to $366.95 per S.F.

Common additives

Description	Unit	$ Cost
Emergency Lighting, 25 watt, battery operated		
Lead battery	Each	320
Nickel cadmium	Each	885
Smoke Detectors		
Ceiling type	Each	223
Duct type	Each	555
Emergency Generators, complete system, gas		
15 kw	Each	16,200
85 kw	Each	33,900
170 kw	Each	84,500
Diesel, 50 kw	Each	25,500
150 kw	Each	44,000
350 kw	Each	69,000

Important: See the Reference Section for Location Factors.

Model costs calculated for a 1 story building with 12' story height and 5,000 square feet of floor area

				Unit	Unit Cost	Cost Per S.F.	% Of Sub-Total
A. SUBSTRUCTURE							
1010	Standard Foundations	Poured concrete; strip and spread footings		S.F. Ground	2.78	2.78	
1020	Special Foundations	N/A		—	—	—	
1030	Slab on Grade	4" reinforced concrete with vapor barrier and granular base		S.F. Slab	5.31	5.31	10.5%
2010	Basement Excavation	Site preparation for slab and trench for foundation wall and footing		S.F. Ground	.57	.57	
2020	Basement Walls	4' foundation wall		L.F. Wall	82	4.67	
B. SHELL							
B10 Superstructure							
1010	Floor Construction	N/A		—	—	—	8.2 %
1020	Roof Construction	Metal deck, open web steel joists, beams, columns		S.F. Roof	10.33	10.33	
B20 Exterior Enclosure							
2010	Exterior Walls	Face brick with concrete block backup	80% of wall	S.F. Wall	32.91	18.07	
2020	Exterior Windows	Outward projecting steel	20% of wall	Each	1725	11.84	24.9%
2030	Exterior Doors	Single aluminum glass with transom		Each	3898	1.56	
B30 Roofing							
3010	Roof Coverings	Built-up tar and gravel with flashing; perlite/EPS composite insulation		S.F. Roof	7.03	7.03	5.6%
3020	Roof Openings						
C. INTERIORS							
1010	Partitions	Double layer gypsum board on metal studs	15 S.F. Floor/L.F. Partition	S.F. Partition	6.26	4.17	
1020	Interior Doors	Single leaf hollow metal	150 S.F. Floor/Door	Each	1152	7.68	
1030	Fittings	Toilet partitions		S.F. Floor	1.17	1.17	
2010	Stair Construction	N/A		—	—	—	21.8%
3010	Wall Finishes	Paint		S.F. Surface	2.20	2.93	
3020	Floor Finishes	90% carpet, 10% terrazzo		S.F. Floor	7.02	7.02	
3030	Ceiling Finishes	Fiberglass board on exposed grid system, suspended		S.F. Ceiling	4.57	4.57	
D. SERVICES							
D10 Conveying							
1010	Elevators & Lifts	N/A		—	—	—	0.0 %
1020	Escalators & Moving Walks	N/A		—	—	—	
D20 Plumbing							
2010	Plumbing Fixtures	Kitchen, toilet and service fixtures, supply and drainage	1 Fixture/715 S.F. Floor	Each	3947	5.52	
2020	Domestic Water Distribution	Gas fired water heater		S.F. Floor	2.47	2.47	7.2%
2040	Rain Water Drainage	Roof drains		S.F. Roof	1.13	1.13	
D30 HVAC							
3010	Energy Supply	N/A		—	—	—	
3020	Heat Generating Systems	Included in D3050		—	—	—	
3030	Cooling Generating Systems	N/A		—	—	—	7.3 %
3050	Terminal & Package Units	Single zone unit, gas heating, electric cooling		S.F. Floor	9.25	9.25	
3090	Other HVAC Sys. & Equipment	N/A		—	—	—	
D40 Fire Protection							
4010	Sprinklers	Wet pipe sprinkler system		S.F. Floor	5.23	5.23	5.7%
4020	Standpipes	Standpipe		S.F. Floor	1.98	1.98	
D50 Electrical							
5010	Electrical Service/Distribution	200 ampere service, panel board and feeders		S.F. Floor	1.92	1.92	
5020	Lighting & Branch Wiring	High efficiency fluorescent fixtures, receptacles, switches, A.C. and misc. power		S.F. Floor	6.11	6.11	8.8%
5030	Communications & Security	Addressable alarm systems and emergency lighting		S.F. Floor	2.92	2.92	
5090	Other Electrical Systems	Emergency generator, 15 kW		S.F. Floor	.16	.16	
E. EQUIPMENT & FURNISHINGS							
1010	Commercial Equipment	N/A		—	—	—	
1020	Institutional Equipment	N/A		—	—	—	0.0 %
1030	Vehicular Equipment	N/A		—	—	—	
1090	Other Equipment	N/A		—	—	—	
F. SPECIAL CONSTRUCTION							
1020	Integrated Construction	N/A		—	—	—	0.0 %
1040	Special Facilities	N/A		—	—	—	
G. BUILDING SITEWORK	**N/A**						

	Sub-Total	126.39	**100%**
CONTRACTOR FEES (General Requirements: 10%, Overhead: 5%, Profit: 10%)	25%	31.58	
ARCHITECT FEES	11%	17.38	
Total Building Cost		**175.35**	

Costs per square foot of floor area

Exterior Wall	S.F. Area	5000	6500	8000	9500	11000	14000	17500	21000	24000
	L.F. Perimeter	300	360	386	396	435	510	550	620	680
Face Brick with Concrete Block Back-up	Steel Joists	162.25	156.10	148.85	142.35	139.95	136.40	131.55	129.60	128.35
	Wood Joists	162.20	155.90	148.45	141.80	139.35	135.70	130.75	128.70	127.45
Stone with Concrete Block Back-up	Steel Joists	169.90	163.15	154.90	147.65	145.00	141.00	135.60	133.30	131.95
	Wood Joists	169.80	162.90	154.50	147.10	144.40	140.35	134.75	132.45	131.00
Brick Veneer	Wood Frame	152.90	147.20	140.60	134.95	132.70	129.45	125.15	123.35	122.20
E.I.F.S.	Wood Frame	140.70	135.65	130.25	125.50	123.60	120.85	117.30	115.75	114.85
Perimeter Adj., Add or Deduct	Per 100 L.F.	16.15	12.40	10.05	8.55	7.35	5.80	4.65	3.80	3.30
Story Hgt. Adj., Add or Deduct	Per 1 Ft.	2.95	2.70	2.30	2.05	1.95	1.75	1.60	1.40	1.35

For Basement, add $31.35 per square foot of basement area

The above costs were calculated using the basic specifications shown on the facing page. These costs should be adjusted where necessary for design alternatives and owner's requirements. Reported completed project costs, for this type of structure, range from $96.15 to $252.85 per S.F.

Common additives

Description	Unit	$ Cost		Description	Unit	$ Cost
Directory Boards, Plastic, glass covered				Smoke Detectors		
30" x 20"	Each	630		Ceiling type	Each	223
36" x 48"	Each	1500		Duct type	Each	555
Aluminum, 24" x 18"	Each	630		Vault Front, Door & frame		
36" x 24"	Each	735		1 Hour test, 32" x 78"	Opening	8200
48" x 32"	Each	1050		2 Hour test, 32" door	Opening	10,000
48" x 60"	Each	2200		40" door	Opening	11,600
Emergency Lighting, 25 watt, battery operated				4 Hour test, 32" door	Opening	10,600
Lead battery	Each	320		40" door	Opening	12,500
Nickel cadmium	Each	885		Time lock movement; two movement	Each	2800
Flagpoles, Complete						
Aluminum, 20' high	Each	1775				
40' high	Each	3925				
70' high	Each	10,800				
Fiberglass, 23' high	Each	1325				
39'-5" high	Each	3575				
59' high	Each	7275				
Safe, Office type, 1 hour rating						
30" x 18" x 18"	Each	2500				
60" x 36" x 18", double door	Each	8075				

Important: See the Reference Section for Location Factors.

Model costs calculated for a 1 story building with 12' story height and 11,000 square feet of floor area

				Unit	Unit Cost	Cost Per S.F.	% Of Sub-Total
A. SUBSTRUCTURE							
1010	Standard Foundations	Poured concrete; strip and spread footings		S.F. Ground	1.70	1.70	
1020	Special Foundations	N/A		—	—	—	
1030	Slab on Grade	4" reinforced concrete with vapor barrier and granular base		S.F. Slab	5.31	5.31	10.3%
2010	Basement Excavation	Site preparation for slab and trench for foundation wall and footing		S.F. Ground	.32	.32	
2020	Basement Walls	4' foundation wall		L.F. Wall	82	3.23	
B. SHELL							
B10 Superstructure							
1010	Floor Construction	N/A		—	—	—	
1020	Roof Construction	Metal deck, open web steel joists, beams, interior columns		S.F. Roof	7.80	7.80	7.6 %
B20 Exterior Enclosure							
2010	Exterior Walls	Face brick with concrete block backup	70% of wall	S.F. Wall	32.87	10.92	
2020	Exterior Windows	Metal outward projecting	30% of wall	Each	736	4.56	16.1%
2030	Exterior Doors	Metal and glass with transom		Each	2828	1.03	
B30 Roofing							
3010	Roof Coverings	Built-up tar and gravel with flashing; perlite/EPS composite insulation		S.F. Roof	6.56	6.56	6.4%
3020	Roof Openings	Roof hatches		S.F. Roof			
C. INTERIORS							
1010	Partitions	Gypsum board on metal studs	20 S.F. Floor/L.F. Partition	S.F. Partition	9.30	4.65	
1020	Interior Doors	Wood solid core	200 S.F. Floor/Door	Each	636	3.19	
1030	Fittings	Toilet partitions		S.F. Floor	.46	.46	
2010	Stair Construction	N/A		—	—	—	24.2%
3010	Wall Finishes	90% paint, 10% ceramic tile		S.F. Surface	1.48	1.48	
3020	Floor Finishes	70% carpet tile, 15% terrazzo, 15% vinyl composition tile		S.F. Floor	8.16	8.16	
3030	Ceiling Finishes	Mineral fiber tile on concealed zee bars		S.F. Ceiling	6.89	6.89	
D. SERVICES							
D10 Conveying							
1010	Elevators & Lifts	N/A		—	—	—	0.0 %
1020	Escalators & Moving Walks	N/A		—	—	—	
D20 Plumbing							
2010	Plumbing Fixtures	Kitchen, toilet and service fixtures, supply and drainage	1 Fixture/500 S.F. Floor	Each	2475	4.95	
2020	Domestic Water Distribution	Gas fired water heater		S.F. Floor	1.53	1.53	7.8%
2040	Rain Water Drainage	Roof drains		S.F. Roof	1.54	1.54	
D30 HVAC							
3010	Energy Supply	N/A		—	—	—	
3020	Heat Generating Systems	Included in D3050		—	—	—	
3030	Cooling Generating Systems	N/A		—	—	—	8.3 %
3050	Terminal & Package Units	Multizone unit, gas heating, electric cooling		S.F. Floor	8.51	8.51	
3090	Other HVAC Sys. & Equipment	N/A		—	—	—	
D40 Fire Protection							
4010	Sprinklers	Wet pipe sprinkler system		S.F. Floor	3.56	3.56	4.2%
4020	Standpipes	Standpipe, wet, Class III		S.F. Floor	.75	.75	
D50 Electrical							
5010	Electrical Service/Distribution	400 ampere service, panel board and feeders		S.F. Floor	2.01	2.01	
5020	Lighting & Branch Wiring	High efficiency fluorescent fixtures, receptacles, switches, A.C. and misc. power		S.F. Floor	10.22	10.22	15.2%
5030	Communications & Security	Addressable alarm systems, internet wiring, and emergency lighting		S.F. Floor	3.26	3.26	
5090	Other Electrical Systems	Emergency generator, 15 kW		S.F. Floor	.15	.15	
E. EQUIPMENT & FURNISHINGS							
1010	Commercial Equipment	N/A		—	—	—	
1020	Institutional Equipment	N/A		—	—	—	0.0 %
1030	Vehicular Equipment	N/A		—	—	—	
1090	Other Equipment	N/A		—	—	—	
F. SPECIAL CONSTRUCTION							
1020	Integrated Construction	N/A		—	—	—	0.0 %
1040	Special Facilities	N/A		—	—	—	
G. BUILDING SITEWORK	**N/A**						

		Sub-Total	102.74	100%
CONTRACTOR FEES (General Requirements: 10%, Overhead: 5%, Profit: 10%)		25%	25.65	
ARCHITECT FEES		9%	11.56	
	Total Building Cost		**139.95**	

Costs per square foot of floor area

Exterior Wall	S.F. Area	8000	10000	12000	15000	18000	24000	28000	35000	40000
	L.F. Perimeter	206	233	260	300	320	360	393	451	493
Face Brick with Concrete Block Back-up	Steel Frame	215.95	204.40	196.70	188.90	181.60	172.40	168.85	164.70	162.60
	R/Conc. Frame	222.85	211.30	203.60	195.80	188.50	179.30	175.80	171.65	169.55
Stone with Concrete Block Back-up	Steel Frame	212.95	202.30	195.20	188.00	180.95	172.15	168.75	164.80	162.85
	R/Conc. Frame	232.65	220.20	211.85	203.45	195.30	185.05	181.10	176.55	174.20
Limestone with Concrete Block Back-up	Steel Frame	236.50	222.10	212.50	202.75	192.80	180.25	175.60	170.10	167.35
	R/Conc. Frame	243.45	229.00	219.40	209.65	199.70	187.20	182.50	177.00	174.25
Perimeter Adj., Add or Deduct	Per 100 L.F.	24.65	19.75	16.45	13.20	11.00	8.15	7.05	5.65	4.95
Story Hgt. Adj., Add or Deduct	Per 1 Ft.	3.70	3.35	3.15	2.95	2.60	2.15	2.05	1.95	1.80

For Basement, add $30.55 per square foot of basement area

The above costs were calculated using the basic specifications shown on the facing page. These costs should be adjusted where necessary for design alternatives and owner's requirements. Reported completed project costs, for this type of structure, range from $86.15 to $252.85 per S.F.

Common additives

Description	Unit	$ Cost
Directory Boards, Plastic, glass covered		
30" x 20"	Each	630
36" x 48"	Each	1500
Aluminum, 24" x 18"	Each	630
36" x 24"	Each	735
48" x 32"	Each	1050
48" x 60"	Each	2200
Elevators, Hydraulic passenger, 2 stops		
1500# capacity	Each	66,100
2500# capacity	Each	69,200
3500# capacity	Each	73,200
Additional stop, add	Each	8575
Emergency Lighting, 25 watt, battery operated		
Lead battery	Each	320
Nickel cadmium	Each	885

Description	Unit	$ Cost
Flagpoles, Complete		
Aluminum, 20' high	Each	1775
40' high	Each	3925
70' high	Each	10,800
Fiberglass, 23' high	Each	1325
39'-5" high	Each	3575
59' high	Each	7275
Safe, Office type, 1 hour rating		
30" x 18" x 18"	Each	2500
60" x 36" x 18", double door	Each	8075
Smoke Detectors		
Ceiling type	Each	223
Duct type	Each	555
Vault Front, Door & frame		
1 Hour test, 32" x 78"	Opening	8200
2 Hour test, 32" door	Opening	10,000
40" door	Opening	11,600
4 Hour test, 32" door	Opening	10,600
40" door	Opening	12,500
Time lock movement; two movement	Each	2800

Important: See the Reference Section for Location Factors.

Model costs calculated for a 3 story building with 12' story height and 18,000 square feet of floor area

Town Hall, 2-3 Story

				Unit	Unit Cost	Cost Per S.F.	% Of Sub-Total
A. SUBSTRUCTURE							
1010	Standard Foundations	Poured concrete; strip and spread footings		S.F. Ground	4.08	1.36	
1020	Special Foundations	N/A		—	—	—	
1030	Slab on Grade	4" reinforced concrete with vapor barrier and granular base		S.F. Slab	5.31	1.77	3.6%
2010	Basement Excavation	Site preparation for slab and trench for foundation wall and footing		S.F. Ground	.18	.06	
2020	Basement Walls	4' foundation wall		L.F. Wall	77	1.62	
B. SHELL							
	B10 Superstructure						
1010	Floor Construction	Open web steel joists, slab form, concrete, wide flange steel columns		S.F. Floor	26.27	17.51	15.3%
1020	Roof Construction	Metal deck, open web steel joists, beams, interior columns		S.F. Roof	8.52	2.84	
	B20 Exterior Enclosure						
2010	Exterior Walls	Stone with concrete block backup	70% of wall	S.F. Wall	44.02	19.72	
2020	Exterior Windows	Metal outward projecting	10% of wall	Each	1140	2.63	17.4%
2030	Exterior Doors	Metal and glass with transoms		Each	2636	.73	
	B30 Roofing						
3010	Roof Coverings	Built-up tar and gravel with flashing; perlite/EPS composite insulation		S.F. Roof	6.54	2.18	1.6%
3020	Roof Openings	N/A		—	—	—	
C. INTERIORS							
1010	Partitions	Gypsum board on metal studs	20 S.F. Floor/L.F. Partition	S.F. Partition	10.34	5.17	
1020	Interior Doors	Wood solid core	200 S.F. Floor/Door	Each	636	3.19	
1030	Fittings	Toilet partitions		S.F. Floor	.28	.28	
2010	Stair Construction	Concrete filled metal pan		Flight	17,250	5.75	23.3%
3010	Wall Finishes	90% paint, 10% ceramic tile		S.F. Surface	1.48	1.48	
3020	Floor Finishes	70% carpet tile, 15% terrazzo, 15% vinyl composition tile		S.F. Floor	8.16	8.16	
3030	Ceiling Finishes	Mineral fiber tile on concealed zee bars		S.F. Ceiling	6.89	6.89	
D. SERVICES							
	D10 Conveying						
1010	Elevators & Lifts	Two hydraulic elevators		Each	118,710	13.19	9.9%
1020	Escalators & Moving Walks	N/A		—	—	—	
	D20 Plumbing						
2010	Plumbing Fixtures	Toilet and service fixtures, supply and drainage	1 Fixture/1385 S.F. Floor	Each	6634	4.79	
2020	Domestic Water Distribution	Gas fired water heater		S.F. Floor	.67	.67	4.6%
2040	Rain Water Drainage	Roof drains		S.F. Roof	1.77	.59	
	D30 HVAC						
3010	Energy Supply	N/A		—	—	—	
3020	Heat Generating Systems	Included in D3050		—	—	—	
3030	Cooling Generating Systems	N/A		—	—	—	6.4%
3050	Terminal & Package Units	Multizone unit, gas heating, electric cooling		S.F. Floor	8.51	8.51	
3090	Other HVAC Sys. & Equipment	N/A		—	—	—	
	D40 Fire Protection						
4010	Sprinklers	Sprinklers, light hazard		S.F. Floor	3.28	3.28	4.8%
4020	Standpipes	Standpipe, wet, Class III		S.F. Floor	3.07	3.07	
	D50 Electrical						
5010	Electrical Service/Distribution	400 ampere service, panel board and feeders		S.F. Floor	1.71	1.71	
5020	Lighting & Branch Wiring	High efficiency fluorescent fixtures, receptacles, switches, A.C. and misc. power		S.F. Floor	12.12	12.12	13.1%
5030	Communications & Security	Addressable alarm systems, internet wiring, and emergency lighting		S.F. Floor	3.39	3.39	
5090	Other Electrical Systems	Emergency generator, 15 kW		S.F. Floor	.17	.17	
E. EQUIPMENT & FURNISHINGS							
1010	Commercial Equipment	N/A		—	—	—	
1020	Institutional Equipment	N/A		—	—	—	0.0%
1030	Vehicular Equipment	N/A		—	—	—	
1090	Other Equipment	N/A		—	—	—	
F. SPECIAL CONSTRUCTION							
1020	Integrated Construction	N/A		—	—	—	0.0%
1040	Special Facilities	N/A		—	—	—	
G. BUILDING SITEWORK	**N/A**						

			Sub-Total	132.83	100%
CONTRACTOR FEES (General Requirements: 10%, Overhead: 5%, Profit: 10%)			25%	33.18	
ARCHITECT FEES			9%	14.94	

Total Building Cost	**180.95**

225

Costs per square foot of floor area

Exterior Wall	S.F. Area	3500	5000	7500	9000	11000	12500	15000	20000	25000
	L.F. Perimeter	240	290	350	390	430	460	510	580	650
E.I.F.S.	Wood Truss	198.65	188.90	179.75	176.90	173.75	172.05	169.95	166.60	164.55
	Steel Joists	185.50	175.35	165.80	162.80	159.50	157.75	155.50	152.00	149.85
Wood Siding	Wood Truss	180.00	170.45	161.55	158.75	155.65	154.00	151.90	148.70	146.70
Brick Veneer	Wood Truss	191.10	179.85	169.05	165.70	161.95	159.90	157.40	153.35	150.90
Brick on Block	Wood Truss	192.30	179.90	167.95	164.20	160.00	157.75	154.90	150.35	147.55
Tilt Up Concrete	Steel Joists	178.25	169.00	160.50	157.85	154.90	153.35	151.35	148.35	146.45
Perimeter Adj., Add or Deduct	Per 100 L.F.	14.30	10.00	6.70	5.60	4.55	4.00	3.35	2.45	2.05
Story Hgt. Adj., Add or Deduct	Per 1 Ft.	1.60	1.35	1.10	1.05	0.90	0.80	0.75	0.70	0.60

For Basement, add $33.00 per square foot of basement area

The above costs were calculated using the basic specifications shown on the facing page. These costs should be adjusted where necessary for design alternatives and owner's requirements. Reported completed project costs, for this type of structure, range from $70.55 to $272.80 per S.F.

Common additives

Description	Unit	$ Cost
Closed circuit surveillance, one station		
Camera and monitor	Each	1975
For additional camera stations, add	Each	1050
Directory boards, plastic, glass covered		
30" x 20"	Each	630
36" x 48"	Each	1500
Aluminum, 24" x 18"	Each	630
36" x 24"	Each	735
48" x 32"	Each	1050
48" x 60"	Each	2200
Electronic, wall mounted	S.F.	2525
Free standing	S.F.	3100
Kennel fencing		
Kennel fencing, 1-1/2" mesh, 6' long, 3'-6" wide, 6'-2" high	Each	775
12' long	Each	1000
Top covers, 1-1/2" mesh, 6' long	Each	210
12' long	Each	285

Description	Unit	$ Cost
Kennel doors		
2 way, swinging type, 13" x 19" opening	Opng.	202
17" x 29" opening	Opng.	224
9" x 9" opening, electronic with accessories	Opng.	261

Model costs calculated for a 1 story building with 12' story height and 7,500 square feet of floor area

Veterinary Hospital

				Unit	Unit Cost	Cost Per S.F.	% Of Sub-Total
A. SUBSTRUCTURE							
1010	Standard Foundations	Poured concrete; strip and spread footings		S.F. Ground	4.45	4.45	
1020	Special Foundations	N/A		—	—	—	
1030	Slab on Grade	4" and 5" reinforced concrete with vapor barrier and granular base		S.F. Slab	11.03	5.33	11.9%
2010	Basement Excavation	Site preparation for slab and trench for foundation wall and footing		S.F. Ground	.57	.57	
2020	Basement Walls	4' foundation wall		L.F. Wall	82	3.81	
B. SHELL							
B10 Superstructure							
1010	Floor Construction	6 x 6 wood columns		S.F. Floor	.24	.24	8.0%
1020	Roof Construction	Wood roof truss with plywood sheathing		S.F. Roof	9.27	9.27	
B20 Exterior Enclosure							
2010	Exterior Walls	Cedar bevel siding on wood studs, insulated	85% of wall	S.F. Wall	13.21	6.29	
2020	Exterior Windows	Wood double hung and awning	15% of wall	Each	1158	3.92	10.4%
2030	Exterior Doors	Aluminum and glass		Each	2673	2.14	
B30 Roofing							
3010	Roof Coverings	Asphalt shingles with flashing (pitched); al. gutters and downspouts		S.F. Roof	4.96	4.96	4.2%
3020	Roof Openings	N/A		—	—	—	
C. INTERIORS							
1010	Partitions	Gypsum board on wood studs	8 S.F. Floor/L.F. Partition	S.F. Partition	5.07	6.34	
1020	Interior Doors	Solid core wood	180 S.F. Floor/Door	Each	715	3.97	
1030	Fittings	Lockers		Each	.42	.42	
2010	Stair Construction	N/A		—	—	—	19.3%
3010	Wall Finishes	Paint on drywall		S.F. Surface	1	2.51	
3020	Floor Finishes	90% vinyl composition tile, 5% ceramic tile, 5% sealed concrete		S.F. Floor	3.95	3.95	
3030	Ceiling Finishes	90% acoustic tile, 10% gypsum board		S.F. Ceiling	5.74	5.74	
D. SERVICES							
D10 Conveying							
1010	Elevators & Lifts	N/A		—	—	—	0.0%
1020	Escalators & Moving Walks	N/A		—	—	—	
D20 Plumbing							
2010	Plumbing Fixtures	Toilet and service fixtures, supply and drainage	1 Fixture/1075 S.F. Floor	Each	1926	3.44	
2020	Domestic Water Distribution	Electric water heater		S.F. Floor	1.15	1.15	3.9%
2040	Rain Water Drainage	N/A		—	—	—	
D30 HVAC							
3010	Energy Supply	N/A		—	—	—	
3020	Heat Generating Systems	N/A		—	—	—	
3030	Cooling Generating Systems	N/A		—	—	—	5.9%
3050	Terminal & Package Units	Split system with air cooled condensing units		S.F. Floor	6.96	6.96	
3090	Other HVAC Sys. & Equipment	N/A		—	—	—	
D40 Fire Protection							
4010	Sprinklers	Wet pipe sprinkler system		S.F. Floor	3.56	3.56	3.0%
4020	Standpipes	N/A		—	—	—	
D50 Electrical							
5010	Electrical Service/Distribution	800 ampere service, panel board and feeders		S.F. Floor	6.84	6.84	
5020	Lighting & Branch Wiring	High efficiency fluorescent fixtures, receptacles, switches, A.C. and misc. power		S.F. Floor	11.96	11.96	19.9%
5030	Communications & Security	Addressable alarm systems, internet wiring, and emergency lighting		S.F. Floor	4.78	4.78	
5090	Other Electrical Systems	Emergency generator, 100 kW		S.F. Floor	.05	.05	
E. EQUIPMENT & FURNISHINGS							
1010	Commercial Equipment	N/A		—	—	—	
1020	Institutional Equipment	Eye wash station		S.F. Floor	14.02	14.02	13.4%
1030	Vehicular Equipment	N/A		—	—	—	
1090	Other Equipment	Countertop, plastic laminate		S.F. Floor	1.90	1.90	
F. SPECIAL CONSTRUCTION & DEMOLITION							
1020	Integrated Construction	N/A		—	—	—	0.0%
1040	Special Facilities	N/A		—	—	—	
G. BUILDING SITEWORK	**N/A**						

		Sub-Total	118.57	100%
CONTRACTOR FEES (General Requirements: 10%, Overhead: 5%, Profit: 10%)		25%	29.64	
ARCHITECT FEES		9%	13.34	
		Total Building Cost	**161.55**	

227

Costs per square foot of floor area

Exterior Wall	S.F. Area	10000	15000	20000	25000	30000	35000	40000	50000	60000
	L.F. Perimeter	410	500	600	640	700	766	833	966	1000
Tiltup Concrete Panels	Steel Frame	118.55	108.45	103.75	99.10	96.55	94.85	93.60	91.80	89.40
Brick with Block Back-up	Bearing Walls	140.30	125.25	118.35	110.90	106.90	104.20	102.30	99.55	95.50
Concrete Block	Steel Frame	122.90	114.75	111.10	107.10	105.00	103.55	102.50	100.95	98.80
	Bearing Walls	126.25	117.95	114.25	110.25	108.00	106.55	105.55	104.00	101.80
Galvanized Steel Siding	Steel Frame	130.70	122.30	118.45	114.25	112.05	110.55	109.45	107.85	105.55
Metal Sandwich Panels	Steel Frame	131.85	122.00	117.65	112.65	110.05	108.30	107.00	105.20	102.45
Perimeter Adj., Add or Deduct	Per 100 L.F.	7.45	4.95	3.75	2.95	2.50	2.10	1.85	1.45	1.20
Story Hgt. Adj., Add or Deduct	Per 1 Ft.	0.85	0.65	0.60	0.60	0.50	0.45	0.45	0.35	0.30

For Basement, add $29.35 per square foot of basement area

The above costs were calculated using the basic specifications shown on the facing page. These costs should be adjusted where necessary for design alternatives and owner's requirements. Reported completed project costs, for this type of structure, range from $38.25 to $152.80 per S.F.

Common additives

Description	Unit	$ Cost
Dock Leveler, 10 ton cap.		
6' x 8'	Each	6975
7' x 8'	Each	8000
Emergency Lighting, 25 watt, battery operated		
Lead battery	Each	320
Nickel cadmium	Each	885
Fence, Chain link, 6' high		
9 ga. wire	L.F.	28
6 ga. wire	L.F.	30
Gate	Each	375
Flagpoles, Complete		
Aluminum, 20' high	Each	1775
40' high	Each	3925
70' high	Each	10,800
Fiberglass, 23' high	Each	1325
39'-5" high	Each	3575
59' high	Each	7275
Paving, Bituminous		
Wearing course plus base course	S.Y.	7.50
Sidewalks, Concrete 4" thick	S.F.	4.39

Description	Unit	$ Cost
Sound System		
Amplifier, 250 watts	Each	2025
Speaker, ceiling or wall	Each	208
Trumpet	Each	400
Yard Lighting, 20' aluminum pole with 400 watt high pressure sodium fixture.	Each	3150

Important: See the Reference Section for Location Factors.

Model costs calculated for a 1 story building with 24' story height and 30,000 square feet of floor area

					Unit	Unit Cost	Cost Per S.F.	% Of Sub-Total
A. SUBSTRUCTURE								
1010	Standard Foundations	Poured concrete; strip and spread footings			S.F. Ground	1.44	1.44	
1020	Special Foundations	N/A			—	—	—	
1030	Slab on Grade	5" reinforced concrete with vapor barrier and granular base			S.F. Slab	13.05	13.05	21.2%
2010	Basement Excavation	Site preparation for slab and trench for foundation wall and footing			S.F. Ground	.18	.18	
2020	Basement Walls	4' foundation wall			L.F. Wall	82	2.47	
B. SHELL								
B10 Superstructure								
1010	Floor Construction	Mezzanine: open web steel joists, slab form, concrete beams, columns		10% of area	S.F. Floor	21.70	2.17	11.8%
1020	Roof Construction	Metal deck, open web steel joists, beams, columns			S.F. Roof	7.37	7.37	
B20 Exterior Enclosure								
2010	Exterior Walls	Concrete block		95% of wall	S.F. Wall	12.88	6.85	
2020	Exterior Windows	N/A			—	—	—	9.9%
2030	Exterior Doors	Steel overhead, hollow metal		5% of wall	Each	3121	1.15	
B30 Roofing								
3010	Roof Coverings	Built-up tar and gravel with flashing; perlite/EPS composite insulation			S.F. Roof	5.76	5.76	7.5%
3020	Roof Openings	Roof hatches and skylight			S.F. Roof	.33	.33	
C. INTERIORS								
1010	Partitions	Concrete block (office and washrooms)		100 S.F. Floor/L.F. Partition	S.F. Partition	9.38	.75	
1020	Interior Doors	Single leaf hollow metal		5000 S.F. Floor/Door	Each	1152	.23	
1030	Fittings	N/A			—	—	—	
2010	Stair Construction	Steel gate with rails			Flight	14,300	.96	8.6%
3010	Wall Finishes	Paint			S.F. Surface	14.31	2.29	
3020	Floor Finishes	90% hardener, 10% vinyl composition tile			S.F. Floor	2.04	2.04	
3030	Ceiling Finishes	Suspended mineral tile on zee channels in office area		10% of area	S.F. Ceiling	6.89	.69	
D. SERVICES								
D10 Conveying								
1010	Elevators & Lifts	N/A			—	—	—	0.0 %
1020	Escalators & Moving Walks	N/A			—	—	—	
D20 Plumbing								
2010	Plumbing Fixtures	Toilet and service fixtures, supply and drainage		1 Fixture/2500 S.F. Floor	Each	3725	1.49	
2020	Domestic Water Distribution	Gas fired water heater			S.F. Floor	.41	.41	4.5%
2040	Rain Water Drainage	Roof drains			S.F. Roof	1.72	1.72	
D30 HVAC								
3010	Energy Supply	N/A			—	—	—	
3020	Heat Generating Systems	Ventilation with heat			Each	145,800	5.25	
3030	Cooling Generating Systems	N/A			—	—	—	7.7 %
3050	Terminal & Package Units	Single zone unit gas, heating, electric cooling		10% of area	S.F. Floor	.96	.96	
3090	Other HVAC Sys. & Equipment	N/A			—	—	—	
D40 Fire Protection								
4010	Sprinklers	Sprinklers, ordinary hazard			S.F. Floor	3.96	3.96	7.6%
4020	Standpipes	Standpipe			S.F. Floor	2.18	2.18	
D50 Electrical								
5010	Electrical Service/Distribution	200 ampere service, panel board and feeders			S.F. Floor	.54	.54	
5020	Lighting & Branch Wiring	High efficiency fluorescent fixtures, receptacles, switches, A.C. and misc. power			S.F. Floor	5.96	5.96	11.4%
5030	Communications & Security	Addressable alarm systems			S.F. Floor	2.69	2.69	
5090	Other Electrical Systems	N/A			—	—	—	
E. EQUIPMENT & FURNISHINGS								
1010	Commercial Equipment	N/A			—	—	—	
1020	Institutional Equipment	N/A			—	—	—	3.3 %
1030	Vehicular Equipment	Dock boards, dock levelers			S.F. Floor	2.66	2.66	
1090	Other Equipment	N/A			—	—	—	
F. SPECIAL CONSTRUCTION								
1020	Integrated Construction	N/A			—	—	—	6.5 %
1040	Special Facilities	N/A			—	—	—	
G. BUILDING SITEWORK	**N/A**							

		Sub-Total	80.77	100%
CONTRACTOR FEES (General Requirements: 10%, Overhead: 5%, Profit: 10%)		25%	20.16	
ARCHITECT FEES		7%	7.07	
	Total Building Cost		108	

Costs per square foot of floor area

Exterior Wall	S.F. Area	2000	3000	5000	8000	12000	20000	30000	50000	100000
	L.F. Perimeter	180	220	300	420	580	900	1300	2100	4100
Concrete Block	Steel Frame	119.10	108.80	100.60	95.90	93.35	91.35	90.30	89.45	88.80
	R/Conc. Frame	123.70	116.95	111.55	108.40	106.75	105.40	104.75	104.20	103.75
Metal Sandwich Panel	Steel Frame	112.55	105.00	98.95	95.45	93.60	92.10	91.35	90.75	90.20
Tilt-up Concrete Panel	Steel and Concrete	93.60	87.00	81.75	78.75	77.05	75.75	75.10	74.55	74.10
Precast Concrete Panel	Steel Frame	122.80	112.95	105.15	100.70	98.20	96.25	95.30	94.50	93.90
	R/Conc. Frame	143.25	134.00	126.65	122.40	120.10	118.25	117.35	116.55	116.00
Perimeter Adj., Add or Deduct	Per 100 L.F.	14.65	9.80	5.85	3.70	2.45	1.45	0.85	0.55	0.30
Story Hgt. Adj., Add or Deduct	Per 1 Ft.	0.70	0.55	0.45	0.45	0.40	0.35	0.30	0.35	0.35
Basement—Not Applicable										

The above costs were calculated using the basic specifications shown on the facing page. These costs should be adjusted where necessary for design alternatives and owner's requirements. Reported completed project costs, for this type of structure, range from $36.65 to $210.25 per S.F.

Common additives

Description	Unit	$ Cost
Dock Leveler, 10 ton cap.		
6' x 8'	Each	6975
7' x 8'	Each	8000
Emergency Lighting, 25 watt, battery operated		
Lead battery	Each	320
Nickel cadmium	Each	885
Fence, Chain link, 6' high		
9 ga. wire	L.F.	28
6 ga. wire	L.F.	30
Gate	Each	375
Flagpoles, Complete		
Aluminum, 20' high	Each	1775
40' high	Each	3925
70' high	Each	10,800
Fiberglass, 23' high	Each	1325
39'-5" high	Each	3575
59' high	Each	7275
Paving, Bituminous		
Wearing course plus base course	S.Y.	7.50
Sidewalks, Concrete 4" thick	S.F.	4.39

Description	Unit	$ Cost
Sound System		
Amplifier, 250 watts	Each	2025
Speaker, ceiling or wall	Each	208
Trumpet	Each	400
Yard Lighting, 20' aluminum pole with 400 watt high pressure sodium fixture	Each	3150

Model costs calculated for a 1 story building with 12' story height and 20,000 square feet of floor area

Warehouse Self Storage

					Unit	Unit Cost	Cost Per S.F.	% Of Sub-Total
A. SUBSTRUCTURE								
1010	Standard Foundations	Poured concrete; strip and spread footings			S.F. Ground	1.95	1.95	
1020	Special Foundations	N/A			—	—	—	
1030	Slab on Grade	4" reinforced concrete with vapor barrier and granular base			S.F. Slab	6.52	6.52	17.7%
2010	Basement Excavation	Site preparation for slab and trench for foundation wall and footing			S.F. Ground	.32	.32	
2020	Basement Walls	4' foundation wall			L.F. Wall	73	3.27	
B. SHELL								
	B10 Superstructure							
1010	Floor Construction	N/A			—	—	—	9.7 %
1020	Roof Construction	Metal deck, open web steel joists, beams, columns			S.F. Roof	6.65	6.65	
	B20 Exterior Enclosure							
2010	Exterior Walls	Concrete block	53% of wall		S.F. Wall	42	12.02	
2020	Exterior Windows	Aluminum projecting	1% of wall		Each	825	.08	26.4%
2030	Exterior Doors	Steel overhead, hollow metal	46% of wall		Each	1460	5.92	
	B30 Roofing							
3010	Roof Coverings	Metal panel roof; perlite/EPS composite insulation			S.F. Roof	20.87	20.87	30.6%
3020	Roof Openings	N/A			—	—	—	
C. INTERIORS								
1010	Partitions	metal panels on metal studs	11S.F. Floor/L.F. Partition		S.F. Partition	1.13	1.23	
1020	Interior Doors	Single leaf hollow metal	20,000 S.F. Floor/Door		Each	600	.06	
1030	Fittings	N/A			—	—	—	
2010	Stair Construction	N/A			—	—	—	1.9%
3010	Wall Finishes	N/A			—	—	—	
3020	Floor Finishes	N/A			—	—	—	
3030	Ceiling Finishes	N/A			—	—	—	
D. SERVICES								
	D10 Conveying							
1010	Elevators & Lifts	N/A			—	—	—	0.0 %
1020	Escalators & Moving Walks	N/A			—	—	—	
	D20 Plumbing							
2010	Plumbing Fixtures	Toilet and service fixtures, supply and drainage	1 Fixture/10,000 S.F. Floor		Each	2800	.28	
2020	Domestic Water Distribution	Gas fired water heater			S.F. Floor	.28	.28	0.8%
2040	Rain Water Drainage	N/A			—	—	—	
	D30 HVAC							
3010	Energy Supply	N/A			—	—	—	
3020	Heat Generating Systems	N/A			—	—	—	
3030	Cooling Generating Systems	N/A			—	—	—	2.1 %
3050	Terminal & Package Units	Single zone rooftop unit			S.F. Floor	1.42	1.42	
3090	Other HVAC Sys. & Equipment	N/A			—	—	—	
	D40 Fire Protection							
4010	Sprinklers	N/A			—	—	—	0.0 %
4020	Standpipes	N/A			—	—	—	
	D50 Electrical							
5010	Electrical Service/Distribution	60 ampere service, panel board and feeders			S.F. Floor	.41	.41	
5020	Lighting & Branch Wiring	High bay fixtures, receptacles, switches and misc. power			S.F. Floor	5.67	5.67	10.8%
5030	Communications & Security	Addressable alarm systems			S.F. Floor	1.32	1.32	
5090	Other Electrical Systems	N/A			—	—	—	
E. EQUIPMENT & FURNISHINGS								
1010	Commercial Equipment	N/A			—	—	—	
1020	Institutional Equipment	N/A			—	—	—	0.0 %
1030	Vehicular Equipment	N/A			—	—	—	
1090	Other Equipment	N/A			—	—	—	
F. SPECIAL CONSTRUCTION								
1020	Integrated Construction	N/A			—	—	—	0.0 %
1040	Special Facilities	N/A			—	—	—	
G. BUILDING SITEWORK	**N/A**							

		Sub-Total	68.27	100%
CONTRACTOR FEES (General Requirements: 10%, Overhead: 5%, Profit: 10%)		25%	17.11	
ARCHITECT FEES		7%	5.97	
	Total Building Cost		**91.35**	

Deterioration occurs within the structure itself and is determined by the observation of both materials and equipment.

Curable deterioration can be remedied either by maintenance, repair or replacement, within prudent economic limits.

Incurable deterioration that has progressed to the point of actually affecting the structural integrity of the structure, making repair or replacement not economically feasible.

Actual Versus Observed Age

The observed age of a structure refers to the age that the structure appears to be. Periodic maintenance, remodeling, and renovation all tend to reduce the amount of deterioration that has taken place, thereby decreasing the observed age. Actual age, on the other hand, relates solely to the year that the structure was built.

The Depreciation Table shown here relates to the observed age.

Obsolescence arises from conditions either occurring within the structure (functional) or caused by factors outside the limits of the structure (economic).

Functional obsolescence is any inadequacy caused by outmoded design, dated construction materials, or oversized or undersized areas, all of which cause excessive operation costs.

Incurable is so costly as not to economically justify the capital expenditure required to correct the deficiency.

Economic obsolescence is caused by factors outside the limits of the structure. The prime causes of economic obsolescence are:

- zoning and environmental laws
- government legislation
- negative neighborhood influences
- business climate
- proximity to transportation facilities

Depreciation Table
Commercial/Industrial/Institutional

Building Material			
Observed Age (Years)	Frame	Masonry On Wood	Masonry On Masonry Or Steel
1	1%	0%	0%
2	2	1	0
3	3	2	1
4	4	3	2
5	6	5	3
10	20	15	8
15	25	20	15
20	30	25	20
25	35	30	25
30	40	35	30
35	45	40	35
40	50	45	40
45	55	50	45
50	60	55	50
55	65	60	55
60	70	65	60

Green Commercial/Industrial/Institutional Section

Table of Contents

Table No.	Page
Green Models	
Building Types	
G.050 Bank	234
G.120 College, Classroom, 2-3 Story	236
G.130 College, Dorm., 2-3 Story	238
G.140 College, Dorm., 4-8 Story	240
G.150 College, Laboratory	242
G.220 Fire Station, 1 Story	244
G.230 Fire Station, 2 Story	246
G.250 Funeral Home	248

Table No.	Page
G.390 Library	250
G.400 Medical Office, 1 Story	252
G.410 Medical Office, 2 Story	254
G.420 Motel, 1 Story	256
G.430 Motel, 2-3 Story	258
G.455 Office, 1 Story	260
G.460 Office, 2-4 Story	262
G.470 Office, 5-10 Story	264
G.480 Office, 11-20 Story	266
G.490 Police Station	268

Table No.	Page
G.530 Restaurant	270
G.560 School, Elementary	272
G.570 School, High, 2-3 Story	274
G.580 School, Jr. High, 2-3 Story	276
G.590 School, Vocational	278
G.640 Supermarket	280
G.690 Warehouse	282

Costs per square foot of floor area

Exterior Wall	S.F. Area	2000	2700	3400	4100	4800	5500	6200	6900	7600
	L.F. Perimeter	180	208	236	256	280	303	317	337	357
Face Brick with Concrete Block Back-up	Steel Frame	298.15	278.10	266.30	256.30	250.20	245.40	240.15	236.90	234.30
	R/Conc. Frame	313.20	293.10	281.30	271.30	265.15	260.40	255.20	251.95	249.35
Precast Concrete Panel	Steel Frame	297.75	277.65	265.80	255.85	249.70	244.95	239.70	236.45	233.80
	R/Conc. Frame	316.30	295.10	282.60	272.15	265.70	260.70	255.30	251.85	249.10
Limestone with Concrete Block Back-up	Steel Frame	333.65	308.50	293.60	280.90	273.15	267.10	260.30	256.15	252.80
	R/Conc. Frame	349.40	324.25	309.40	296.65	288.95	282.90	276.05	271.95	268.55
Perimeter Adj., Add or Deduct	Per 100 L.F.	54.45	40.25	31.95	26.55	22.65	19.80	17.55	15.80	14.25
Story Hgt. Adj., Add or Deduct	Per 1 Ft.	5.30	4.55	4.05	3.65	3.40	3.20	3.05	2.85	2.70
For Basement, add $36.90 per square foot of basement area										

The above costs were calculated using the basic specifications shown on the facing page. These costs should be adjusted where necessary for design alternatives and owner's requirements. Reported completed project costs, for this type of structure, range from $153.35 to $377.50 per S.F.

Common additives

Description	Unit	$ Cost
Bulletproof Teller Window, 44" x 60"	Each	5100
60" x 48"	Each	6975
Closed Circuit Surveillance, one station, camera & monitor	Each	1975
For additional camera stations, add	Each	1050
Counters, complete, dr & frame, 3' x 6'-8", bullet resist stl with vision panel	Each	7350 - 9500
Drive-up Window, drawer & micr., not incl. glass	Each	8950 - 12,900
Night Depository	Each	9650 - 14,600
Package Receiver, painted	Each	1950
Stainless steel	Each	3000
Partitions, bullet resistant to 8' high	L.F.	330 - 530
Pneumatic Tube Systems, 2 station	Each	33,300
With TV viewer	Each	61,000
Service Windows, pass thru, steel, 24" x 36"	Each	3800
48" x 48"	Each	4125
Twenty-four Hour Teller, automatic deposit cash & memo	Each	53,500
Vault Front, door & frame, 2 hour test, 32" door	Opening	10,000
4 hour test, 40" door	Opening	12,500
Time lock, two movement, add	Each	2800

Description	Unit	$ Cost
Commissioning Fees, sustainable commercial construction	S.F.	0.24 - 3.04
Energy Modelling Fees, banks to 10,000 SF	Each	11,000
Green Bldg Cert Fees for comm construction project reg	Project	900
Photovoltaic Pwr Sys, grid connected, 20 kW (~2400 SF), roof	Each	272,300
Green Roofs, 6" soil depth, w/ treated wd edging & sedum mats	S.F.	11.05
10" Soil depth, with treated wood edging & sedum mats	S.F.	12.68
Greywater Recovery Systems, prepackaged comm, 1530 gal	Each	42,415
Rainwater Harvest Sys, prepckged comm, 10,000 gal, sys contrller	Each	31,375
20,000 gal. w/ system controller	Each	50,500
30,000 gal. w/ system controller	Each	80,225
Solar Domestic HW, closed loop, add-on sys, ext heat exchanger	Each	10,950
Draindown, hot water system, 120 gal tank	Each	14,550

Important: See the Reference Section for Location Factors.

Model costs calculated for a 1 story building with 14' story height and 4,100 square feet of floor area

G Bank

					Unit	Unit Cost	Cost Per S.F.	% Of Sub-Total
A.	**SUBSTRUCTURE**							
1010	Standard Foundations	Poured concrete; strip and spread footings			S.F. Ground	4.21	4.21	
1020	Special Foundations	N/A			—	—	—	
1030	Slab on Grade	4" reinforced concrete with recycled vapor barrier and granular base			S.F. Slab	5.33	5.33	8.4%
2010	Basement Excavation	Site preparation for slab and trench for foundation wall and footing			S.F. Ground	.32	.32	
2020	Basement Walls	4' Foundation wall			L.F. Wall	89	6.63	
B.	**SHELL**							
	B10 Superstructure							
1010	Floor Construction	Cast-in-place columns			L.F. Column	5.95	5.95	11.1%
1020	Roof Construction	Cast-in-place concrete flat plate			S.F. Roof	15.75	15.75	
	B20 Exterior Enclosure							
2010	Exterior Walls	Face brick with concrete block backup	80% of wall		S.F. Wall	38.15	26.68	
2020	Exterior Windows	Horizontal aluminum sliding	20% of wall		Each	585	6.81	18.0%
2030	Exterior Doors	Double aluminum and glass and hollow metal, low VOC paint			Each	3298	1.61	
	B30 Roofing							
3010	Roof Coverings	Single-ply TPO membrane, 60 mils, heat welded seams w/4" thk. R20 insul.			S.F. Roof	6.92	6.92	3.5%
3020	Roof Openings	N/A			—	—	—	
C.	**INTERIORS**							
1010	Partitions	Gypsum board on metal studs w/sound attenuation	20 SF of Flr./LF Part.		S.F. Partition	11.90	5.95	
1020	Interior Doors	Single leaf hollow metal , low VOC paint	200 S.F. Floor/Door		Each	1152	5.76	
1030	Fittings	N/A			—	—	—	
2010	Stair Construction	N/A			—	—	—	13.1%
3010	Wall Finishes	50% vinyl wall covering, 50% paint, low VOC			S.F. Surface	1.49	1.49	
3020	Floor Finishes	50% carpet tile, 40% vinyl composition tile, recycled, 10% quarry tile			S.F. Floor	5.57	5.57	
3030	Ceiling Finishes	Mineral fiber tile on concealed zee bars			S.F. Ceiling	6.89	6.89	
D.	**SERVICES**							
	D10 Conveying							
1010	Elevators & Lifts	N/A			—	—	—	0.0 %
1020	Escalators & Moving Walks	N/A			—	—	—	
	D20 Plumbing							
2010	Plumbing Fixtures	Toilet low flow, auto sensor and service fixt., supply and drainage	1 Fixt./580 SF Flr.		Each	5823	10.04	
2020	Domestic Water Distribution	Tankless, on demand water heaters, natural gas/propane			S.F. Floor	1.11	1.11	6.5%
2040	Rain Water Drainage	Roof drains			S.F. Roof	1.54	1.54	
	D30 HVAC							
3010	Energy Supply	N/A			—	—	—	
3020	Heat Generating Systems	Included in D3050			—	—	—	
3040	Distribution Systems	Enthalpy heat recovery packages			Each	14,775	3.61	6.5 %
3050	Terminal & Package Units	Single zone rooftop air conditioner			S.F. Floor	9.06	9.06	
3090	Other HVAC Sys. & Equipment	N/A			—	—	—	
	D40 Fire Protection							
4010	Sprinklers	Wet pipe sprinkler system			S.F. Floor	4.76	4.76	3.9%
4020	Standpipes	Standpipe			S.F. Floor	2.83	2.83	
	D50 Electrical							
5010	Electrical Service/Distribution	200 ampere service, panel board and feeders			S.F. Floor	1.46	1.46	
5020	Lighting & Branch Wiring	LED fixtures, daylt. dimming & ltg. on/off control, receptacles, switches, A.C.			S.F. Floor	13.34	13.34	16.1%
5030	Communications & Security	Alarm systems, internet / phone wiring, and security television			S.F. Floor	10.81	10.81	
5090	Other Electrical Systems	Emergency generator, 15 kW, UPS, energy monitoring systems			S.F. Floor	5.87	5.87	
E.	**EQUIPMENT & FURNISHINGS**							
1010	Commercial Equipment	Automatic teller, drive up window, night depository			S.F. Floor	7.93	7.93	
1020	Institutional Equipment	Closed circuit TV monitoring system			S.F. Floor	2.85	2.85	6.2%
1090	Other Equipment	Waste handling recycling tilt truck			Each	1.34	1.34	
2020	Moveable Furnishings	No smoking signage			Each	.02	.02	
F.	**SPECIAL CONSTRUCTION**							
1020	Integrated Construction	N/A			—	—	—	6.7 %
1040	Special Facilities	Security vault door			S.F. Floor	13.09	13.09	
G.	**BUILDING SITEWORK**	**N/A**						

		Unit	Cost Per S.F.	% Of Sub-Total
	Sub-Total		195.53	100%
CONTRACTOR FEES (General Requirements: 10%, Overhead: 5%, Profit: 10%)		25%	48.88	
ARCHITECT FEES		11%	26.89	
	Total Building Cost		**271.30**	

235

Costs per square foot of floor area

Exterior Wall	S.F. Area	15000	20000	28000	38000	50000	65000	85000	100000	150000
	L.F. Perimeter	350	400	480	550	630	660	750	825	1035
Face Brick with Concrete Block Back-up	Steel Frame	236.75	226.60	217.90	210.90	206.05	200.65	197.40	196.05	192.85
	Bearing Walls	241.80	229.50	218.85	210.10	204.00	197.05	192.95	191.15	187.15
Decorative Concrete Block	Steel Frame	228.05	219.15	211.45	205.45	201.30	196.90	194.10	192.95	190.30
	Bearing Walls	232.60	221.50	211.95	204.15	198.80	192.75	189.15	187.65	184.05
Stucco on Concrete Block	Steel Frame	241.15	230.40	221.15	213.60	208.40	202.55	199.10	197.60	194.15
	Bearing Walls	246.20	233.25	222.10	212.80	206.40	198.95	194.60	192.70	188.45
Perimeter Adj., Add or Deduct	Per 100 L.F.	11.00	8.25	5.85	4.25	3.25	2.50	2.00	1.60	1.15
Story Hgt. Adj., Add or Deduct	Per 1 Ft.	2.80	2.35	1.95	1.65	1.45	1.20	1.10	1.00	0.85

For Basement, add $39.60 per square foot of basement area

The above costs were calculated using the basic specifications shown on the facing page. These costs should be adjusted where necessary for design alternatives and owner's requirements. Reported completed project costs, for this type of structure, range from $137.35 to $322.85 per S.F.

Common additives

Description	Unit	$ Cost
Clock System, 20 room	Each	19,500
50 room	Each	45,700
Elevators, hydraulic passenger, 2 stops, 2000# capacity	Each	67,600
3500# capacity	Each	73,200
Additional stop, add	Each	8575
Seating, auditorium chair, all veneer	Each	300
Veneer back, padded seat	Each	315
Upholstered, spring seat	Each	315
Classroom, movable chair & desk	Set	81 - 171
Lecture hall, pedestal type	Each	258 - 610
Sound System, amplifier, 250 watts	Each	2025
Speaker, ceiling or wall	Each	208
Trumpet	Each	400
TV Antenna, Master system, 30 outlet	Outlet	218
100 outlet	Outlet	206

Description	Unit	$ Cost
Commissioning Fees, sustainable institutional construction	S.F.	0.58 - 2.47
Energy Modelling Fees, academic buildings to 10,000 SF	Each	9000
Greater than 10,000 SF add	S.F.	0.20
Green Bldg Cert Fees for school construction project reg	Project	900
Photovoltaic Pwr Sys, grid connected, 20 kW (~2400 SF), roof	Each	272,300
Green Roofs, 6" soil depth, w/ treated wd edging & sedum mats	S.F.	11.05
10" Soil depth, with treated wood edging & sedum mats	S.F.	12.68
Greywater Recovery Systems, prepackaged comm, 3060 gal.	Each	57,740
4590 gal.	Each	72,025
Rainwater Harvest Sys, prepckged comm, 10,000 gal, sys contrller	Each	31,375
20,000 gal. w/ system controller	Each	50,500
30,000 gal. w/ system controller	Each	80,225
Solar Domestic HW, closed loop, add-on sys, ext heat exchanger	Each	10,950
Drainback, hot water system, 120 gal tank	Each	14,125
Draindown, hot water system, 120 gal tank	Each	14,550

Important: See the Reference Section for Location Factors.

Model costs calculated for a 2 story building with 12' story height and 50,000 square feet of floor area

G College, Classroom, 2-3 Story

				Unit	Unit Cost	Cost Per S.F.	% Of Sub-Total
A. SUBSTRUCTURE							
1010	Standard Foundations	Poured concrete; strip and spread footings		S.F. Ground	1.32	.66	
1020	Special Foundations	N/A		—	—	—	
1030	Slab on Grade	4" reinforced concrete with vapor barrier and granular base		S.F. Slab	5.33	2.67	3.5%
2010	Basement Excavation	Site preparation for slab and trench for foundation wall and footing		S.F. Ground	.31	.16	
2020	Basement Walls	4' Foundation wall		L.F. Wall	169	1.72	
B. SHELL							
	B10 Superstructure						
1010	Floor Construction	Open web steel joists, slab form, concrete		S.F. Floor	17.06	8.53	9.1%
1020	Roof Construction	Metal deck on open web steel joists, columns		S.F. Roof	9.90	4.95	
	B20 Exterior Enclosure						
2010	Exterior Walls	Decorative concrete block	65% of wall	S.F. Wall	20.10	3.95	
2020	Exterior Windows	Window wall	35% of wall	Each	50	5.03	6.5%
2030	Exterior Doors	Double glass and aluminum with transom		Each	5700	.69	
	B30 Roofing						
3010	Roof Coverings	Built-up tar and gravel with flashing; perlite/EPS composite insulation		S.F. Roof	5.38	2.69	1.8%
3020	Roof Openings	N/A		—	—	—	
C. INTERIORS							
1010	Partitions	Concrete block	20 SF Flr.LF Part.	S.F. Partition	21.96	10.98	
1020	Interior Doors	Single leaf hollow metal	200 S.F. Floor/Door	Each	1152	5.76	
1030	Fittings	Chalkboards, counters, cabinets		S.F. Floor	6.02	6.02	
2010	Stair Construction	Concrete filled metal pan		Flight	17,250	3.45	27.8%
3010	Wall Finishes	95% paint, 5% ceramic tile		S.F. Surface	4.33	4.33	
3020	Floor Finishes	70% vinyl composition tile, 25% carpet, 5% ceramic tile		S.F. Floor	3.85	3.85	
3030	Ceiling Finishes	Mineral fiber tile on concealed zee bars		S.F. Ceiling	6.89	6.89	
D. SERVICES							
	D10 Conveying						
1010	Elevators & Lifts	Two hydraulic passenger elevators		Each	83,500	3.34	2.2%
1020	Escalators & Moving Walks	N/A		—	—	—	
	D20 Plumbing						
2010	Plumbing Fixtures	Toilet, low flow, auto sensor & service fixt., supply & drain.	1 Fixt./455 SF Flr.	Each	9177	20.17	
2020	Domestic Water Distribution	Oil fired hot water heater		S.F. Floor	.98	.98	14.7%
2040	Rain Water Drainage	Roof drains		S.F. Roof	1.34	.67	
	D30 HVAC						
3010	Energy Supply	N/A		—	—	—	
3020	Heat Generating Systems	Included in D3050		—	—	—	
3040	Distribution Systems	Enthalpy heat recovery packages		Each	36,875	2.21	14.5 %
3050	Terminal & Package Units	Multizone unit, gas heating, electric cooling, SEER 14		S.F. Floor	19.30	19.30	
3090	Other HVAC Sys. & Equipment	N/A		—	—	—	
	D40 Fire Protection						
4010	Sprinklers	Sprinklers, light hazard		S.F. Floor	3.11	3.11	2.3%
4020	Standpipes	Standpipe, dry, Class III		S.F. Floor	.34	.34	
	D50 Electrical						
5010	Electrical Service/Distribution	2000 ampere service, panel board and feeders		S.F. Floor	3.07	3.07	
5020	Lighting & Branch Wiring	LED fixtures, receptacles, switches, A.C. & misc. power		S.F. Floor	14.30	14.30	17.6%
5030	Communications & Security	Addressable alarm sys., internet wiring, comm. sys. & emerg. ltg.		S.F. Floor	7.07	7.07	
5090	Other Electrical Systems	Emergency generator, 100 kW		S.F. Floor	1.65	1.65	
E. EQUIPMENT & FURNISHINGS							
1010	Commercial Equipment	N/A		—	—	—	
1020	Institutional Equipment	N/A		—	—	—	
1090	Other Equipment	Waste handling recycling tilt truck		Each	.11	.11	0.1 %
2020	Moveable Furnishings	No smoking signage		Each			
F. SPECIAL CONSTRUCTION							
1020	Integrated Construction	N/A		—	—	—	
1040	Special Facilities	N/A		—	—	—	0.0 %
G. BUILDING SITEWORK	**N/A**						

		Sub-Total	148.65	100%
CONTRACTOR FEES (General Requirements: 10%, Overhead: 5%, Profit: 10%)		25%	37.14	
ARCHITECT FEES		7%	13.01	
	Total Building Cost		**198.80**	

Costs per square foot of floor area

Exterior Wall	S.F. Area	10000	15000	25000	40000	55000	70000	80000	90000	100000
	L.F. Perimeter	260	320	400	476	575	628	684	721	772
Face Brick with Concrete Block Back-up	R/Conc. Frame	244.05	229.25	214.00	203.05	199.00	195.25	194.05	192.70	191.95
	Steel Frame	268.40	253.55	238.30	227.30	223.25	219.55	218.35	217.00	216.25
Decorative Concrete Block	R/Conc. Frame	237.45	225.90	214.35	206.25	203.15	200.45	199.60	198.55	198.00
	Steel Frame	250.30	238.75	227.15	219.05	216.00	213.30	212.45	211.40	210.85
Precast Concrete Panels	R/Conc. Frame	256.30	241.30	225.90	214.85	210.75	206.95	205.80	204.40	203.60
	Steel Frame	269.10	254.15	238.70	227.65	223.55	219.75	218.65	217.20	216.45
Perimeter Adj., Add or Deduct	Per 100 L.F.	21.45	14.30	8.55	5.35	3.90	3.05	2.70	2.35	2.10
Story Hgt. Adj., Add or Deduct	Per 1 Ft.	4.15	3.45	2.55	1.90	1.65	1.40	1.40	1.30	1.25

For Basement, add $38.55 per square foot of basement area

The above costs were calculated using the basic specifications shown on the facing page. These costs should be adjusted where necessary for design alternatives and owner's requirements. Reported completed project costs, for this type of structure, range from $88.70 to $261.50 per S.F.

Common additives

Description	Unit	$ Cost
Closed Circuit Surveillance, one station, camera & monitor	Each	1975
For additional camera stations, add	Each	1050
Elevators, hydraulic passenger, 2 stops, 3500# capacity	Each	73,200
Additional stop, add	Each	8575
Furniture	Student	2800 - 5350
Intercom System, 25 station capacity		
Master station	Ea.	3175
Intercom outlets	Each	184
Kitchen Equipment		
Broiler	Each	4000
Coffee urn, twin 6 gallon	Each	2975
Cooler, 6 ft. long	Each	4100
Dishwasher, 10-12 racks per hr.	Each	4225
Food warmer	Each	725
Freezer, 44 C.F., reach-in	Each	5125
Ice cube maker, 50 lb. per day	Each	1950
Range with 1 oven	Each	3000
Laundry Equipment, dryer, 30 lb. capacity	Each	3800
Washer, commercial	Each	1600
TV Antenna, Master system, 30 outlet	Outlet	218
100 outlet	Outlet	206

Description	Unit	$ Cost
Commissioning Fees, sustainable institutional construction	S.F.	0.58 - 2.47
Energy Modelling Fees, academic buildings to 10,000 SF	Each	9000
Greater than 10,000 SF add	S.F.	0.20
Green Bldg Cert Fees for school construction project reg	Project	900
Photovoltaic Pwr Sys, grid connected, 20 kW (~2400 SF), roof	Each	272,300
Green Roofs, 6" soil depth, w/ treated wd edging & sedum mats	S.F.	11.05
10" Soil depth, with treated wood edging & sedum mats	S.F.	12.68
Greywater Recovery Systems, prepackaged comm, 3060 gal.	Each	57,740
4590 gal.	Each	72,025
Rainwater Harvest Sys, prepckged comm, 30,000 gal, sys contrller	Each	80,225
Solar Domestic HW, closed loop, add-on sys, ext heat exchanger	Each	10,950
Drainback, hot water system, 120 gal tank	Each	14,125
Draindown, hot water system, 120 gal tank	Each	14,550

Important: See the Reference Section for Location Factors.

Model costs calculated for a 3 story building with 12' story height and 25,000 square feet of floor area

G College, Dormitory, 2-3 Story

				Unit	Unit Cost	Cost Per S.F.	% Of Sub-Total
A. SUBSTRUCTURE							
1010	Standard Foundations	Poured concrete; strip and spread footings		S.F. Ground	6.18	2.06	
1020	Special Foundations	N/A		—	—	—	
1030	Slab on Grade	4" reinforced concrete with recycled vapor barrier and granular base		S.F. Slab	5.33	1.77	3.3%
2010	Basement Excavation	Site preparation for slab and trench for foundation wall and footing		S.F. Ground	.18	.06	
2020	Basement Walls	4' Foundation wall		L.F. Wall	89	1.42	
B. SHELL							
B10 Superstructure							
1010	Floor Construction	Concrete flat plate		S.F. Floor	25.08	16.72	13.3%
1020	Roof Construction	Concrete flat plate		S.F. Roof	13.56	4.52	
B20 Exterior Enclosure							
2010	Exterior Walls	Face brick with concrete block backup	80% of wall	S.F. Wall	38.15	17.58	
2020	Exterior Windows	Aluminum horizontal sliding	20% of wall	Each	736	3.68	14.2%
2030	Exterior Doors	Double glass & aluminum doors		Each	5925	1.42	
B30 Roofing							
3010	Roof Coverings	Single-ply TPO membrane, heat welded w/ R-20 insul.		S.F. Roof	6.30	2.10	1.3%
3020	Roof Openings	N/A		—	—	—	
C. INTERIORS							
1010	Partitions	Gypsum board on metal studs, CMU w/ foamed-in insul.	9 SF Flr./LF Part.	S.F. Partition	7.58	8.42	
1020	Interior Doors	Single leaf wood, low VOC paint	90 S.F. Floor/Door	Each	636	7.06	
1030	Fittings	Closet shelving, mirrors, bathroom accessories		S.F. Floor	1.95	1.95	
2010	Stair Construction	Cast in place concrete		Flight	5250	2.73	19.2%
3010	Wall Finishes	95% paint, low VOC paint, 5% ceramic tile		S.F. Surface	2.06	4.57	
3020	Floor Finishes	80% carpet tile, 10% vinyl comp. tile, recycled content, 10% ceramic tile		S.F. Floor	4.85	4.85	
3030	Ceiling Finishes	90% paint, low VOC, 10% suspended fiberglass board		S.F. Ceiling	1.08	1.07	
D. SERVICES							
D10 Conveying							
1010	Elevators & Lifts	One hydraulic passenger elevator		Each	115,000	4.60	2.9%
1020	Escalators & Moving Walks	N/A		—	—	—	
D20 Plumbing							
2010	Plumbing Fixtures	Toilet, low flow, auto sensor, & service fixt., supply & drain.	1 Fixt./455 SF Flr.	Each	11,821	25.98	
2020	Domestic Water Distribution	Electric, point-of-use water heater		S.F. Floor	1.51	1.51	17.5%
2040	Rain Water Drainage	Roof drains		S.F. Roof	1.32	.44	
D30 HVAC							
3010	Energy Supply	N/A		—	—	—	
3020	Heat Generating Systems	Included in D3050		—	—	—	
3040	Distribution Systems	Enthalpy heat recovery packages		Each	30,350	2.43	9.5 %
3050	Terminal & Package Units	Rooftop multizone unit system, SEER 14		S.F. Floor	12.77	12.77	
3090	Other HVAC Sys. & Equipment	N/A		—	—	—	
D40 Fire Protection							
4010	Sprinklers	Wet pipe sprinkler system		S.F. Floor	2.95	2.95	2.4%
4020	Standpipes	Standpipe, dry, Class III		S.F. Floor	.85	.85	
D50 Electrical							
5010	Electrical Service/Distribution	800 ampere service, panel board and feeders		S.F. Floor	1.61	1.61	
5020	Lighting & Branch Wiring	LED fixtures, daylt. dim., ltg. on/off, recept., switches, and A.C. power		S.F. Floor	12.72	12.72	14.4%
5030	Communications & Security	Alarm sys., internet & phone wiring, comm. sys. and emergency ltg.		S.F. Floor	7.32	7.32	
5090	Other Electrical Systems	Emergency generator, 7.5 kW, energy monitoring systems		S.F. Floor	1.34	1.34	
E. EQUIPMENT & FURNISHINGS							
1010	Commercial Equipment	N/A		—	—	—	
1020	Institutional Equipment	N/A		—	—	—	2.2 %
1090	Other Equipment	Waste handling recycling tilt truck		Each	.22	.22	
2020	Moveable Furnishings	Dormitory furniture, no smoking signage		S.F. Floor	3.27	3.27	
F. SPECIAL CONSTRUCTION							
1020	Integrated Construction	N/A		—	—	—	0.0 %
1040	Special Facilities	N/A		—	—	—	
G. BUILDING SITEWORK	**N/A**						

	Sub-Total	159.99	**100%**
CONTRACTOR FEES (General Requirements: 10%, Overhead: 5%, Profit: 10%)	25%	40.01	
ARCHITECT FEES	7%	14	
	Total Building Cost	214	

Costs per square foot of floor area

Exterior Wall	S.F. Area	20000	35000	45000	65000	85000	110000	135000	160000	200000
	L.F. Perimeter	260	340	400	440	500	540	560	590	640
Face Brick with Concrete Block Back-up	R/Conc. Frame	254.10	235.55	230.65	220.25	215.75	211.10	207.50	205.35	203.00
	Steel Frame	268.15	249.50	244.65	234.25	229.75	225.10	221.50	219.35	217.00
Decorative Concrete Block	R/Conc. Frame	237.80	223.25	219.45	211.75	208.35	204.95	202.30	200.75	199.00
	Steel Frame	243.50	229.05	225.25	217.50	214.15	210.70	208.10	206.45	204.80
Precast Concrete Panels With Exposed Aggregate	R/Conc. Frame	254.50	235.75	230.90	220.50	215.90	211.25	207.65	205.45	203.10
	Steel Frame	268.35	249.65	244.80	234.35	229.85	225.20	221.60	219.40	217.05
Perimeter Adj., Add or Deduct	Per 100 L.F.	20.90	11.90	9.25	6.45	4.95	3.80	3.10	2.60	2.15
Story Hgt. Adj., Add or Deduct	Per 1 Ft.	4.20	3.10	2.90	2.20	1.90	1.65	1.40	1.20	1.10
For Basement, add $38.55 per square foot of basement area										

The above costs were calculated using the basic specifications shown on the facing page. These costs should be adjusted where necessary for design alternatives and owner's requirements. Reported completed project costs, for this type of structure, range from $126.10 to $304.15 per S.F.

Common additives

Description	Unit	$ Cost
Closed Circuit Surveillance, one station, camera & monitor	Each	1975
For additional camera stations, add	Each	1050
Elevators, electric passenger, 5 stops, 3500# capacity	Each	171,700
Additional stop, add	Each	12,700
Furniture	Student	2800 - 5350
Intercom System, 25 station capacity		
Master station	Each	3175
Intercom outlets	Each	184
Kitchen Equipment		
Broiler	Each	4000
Coffee urn, twin, 6 gallon	Each	2975
Cooler, 6 ft. long	Each	4100
Dishwasher, 10-12 racks per hr.	Each	4225
Food warmer	Each	725
Freezer, 44 C.F., reach-in	Each	5125
Ice cube maker, 50 lb. per day	Each	1950
Range with 1 oven	Each	3000
Laundry Equipment, dryer, 30 lb. capacity	Each	3800
Washer, commercial	Each	1600
TV Antenna, Master system, 30 outlet	Outlet	218
100 outlet	Outlet	206

Description	Unit	$ Cost
Commissioning Fees, sustainable institutional construction	S.F.	0.58 - 2.47
Energy Modelling Fees, academic buildings to 10,000 SF	Each	9000
Greater than 10,000 SF add	S.F.	0.20
Green Bldg Cert Fees for school construction project reg	Project	900
Photovoltaic Pwr Sys, grid connected, 20 kW (~2400 SF), roof	Each	272,300
Green Roofs, 6" soil depth, w/ treated wd edging & sedum mats	S.F.	11.05
10" Soil depth, with treated wood edging & sedum mats	S.F.	12.68
Greywater Recovery Systems, prepackaged comm, 3060 gal.	Each	57,740
4590 gal.	Each	72,025
Rainwater Harvest Sys, prepckged comm, 30,000 gal, sys contrller	Each	80,225
Solar Domestic HW, closed loop, add-on sys, ext heat exchanger	Each	10,950
Drainback, hot water system, 120 gal tank	Each	14,125
Draindown, hot water system, 120 gal tank	Each	14,550

Important: See the Reference Section for Location Factors.

Model costs calculated for a 6 story building with 12' story height and 85,000 square feet of floor area

G College, Dormitory, 4-8 Story

					Unit	Unit Cost	Cost Per S.F.	% Of Sub-Total
A. SUBSTRUCTURE								
1010	Standard Foundations	Poured concrete; strip and spread footings			S.F. Ground	9.06	1.51	
1020	Special Foundations	N/A			—	—	—	
1030	Slab on Grade	4" reinforced concrete with recycled vapor barrier and granular base			S.F. Slab	5.33	.89	2.0%
2010	Basement Excavation	Site preparation for slab and trench for foundation wall and footing			S.F. Ground	.31	.05	
2020	Basement Walls	4' foundation wall			L.F. Wall	169	.72	
B. SHELL								
	B10 Superstructure							
1010	Floor Construction	Concrete slab with metal deck and beams			S.F. Floor	29.39	24.49	17.6%
1020	Roof Construction	Concrete slab with metal deck and beams			S.F. Roof	21.96	3.66	
	B20 Exterior Enclosure							
2010	Exterior Walls	Decorative concrete block	80% of wall		S.F. Wall	21.81	7.39	
2020	Exterior Windows	Aluminum horizontal sliding	20% of wall		Each	525	2.96	6.7%
2030	Exterior Doors	Double glass & aluminum doors			Each	3619	.34	
	B30 Roofing							
3010	Roof Coverings	Single-ply TPO membrane, 60 mils, heat welded seams w/R-20 insul.			S.F. Roof	5.82	.97	0.6%
3020	Roof Openings	N/A			—	—	—	
C. INTERIORS								
1010	Partitions	Concrete block w/foamed-in insulation	9 SF Floor/LF Part.		S.F. Partition	12.02	13.36	
1020	Interior Doors	Single leaf wood, low VOC paint	90 S.F. Floor/Door		Each	636	7.06	
1030	Fittings	Closet shelving, mirrors, bathroom accessories			S.F. Floor	1.60	1.60	
2010	Stair Construction	Concrete filled metal pan			Flight	17,250	3.65	23.6%
3010	Wall Finishes	95% paint, low VOC, 5% ceramic tile			S.F. Surface	2.80	6.22	
3020	Floor Finishes	80% carpet tile, 10% vinyl comp. tile, recycled, 10% ceramic tile			S.F. Floor	4.85	4.85	
3030	Ceiling Finishes	Mineral fiber tile on concealed zee bars, paint			S.F. Ceiling	1.08	1.07	
D. SERVICES								
	D10 Conveying							
1010	Elevators & Lifts	Four geared passenger elevators			Each	247,563	11.65	7.3%
1020	Escalators & Moving Walks	N/A			—	—	—	
	D20 Plumbing							
2010	Plumbing Fixtures	Toilet, low flow, auto sensor, & service fixt., supply & drain.	1 Fixt./390 SF Flr.		Each	10,093	25.88	
2020	Domestic Water Distribution	Electric water heater, point-of-use, energy saver			S.F. Floor	.85	.85	16.9%
2040	Rain Water Drainage	Roof drains			S.F. Roof	2.10	.35	
	D30 HVAC							
3010	Energy Supply	N/A			—	—	—	
3020	Heat Generating Systems	N/A			—	—	—	
3040	Distribution Systems	Enthalpy heat recovery packages			Each	30,350	2.15	9.3 %
3050	Terminal & Package Units	Multizone rooftop air conditioner, SEER 14			S.F. Floor	12.77	12.77	
3090	Other HVAC Sys. & Equipment	N/A			—	—	—	
	D40 Fire Protection							
4010	Sprinklers	Sprinklers, light hazard			S.F. Floor	2.88	2.88	2.2%
4020	Standpipes	Standpipe, dry, Class III			S.F. Floor	.64	.64	
	D50 Electrical							
5010	Electrical Service/Distribution	1200 ampere service, panel board and feeders			S.F. Floor	.84	.84	
5020	Lighting & Branch Wiring	LED fixtures, daylt. dim., ltg. on/off, recept. switches, and A.C. power			S.F. Floor	11.35	11.35	
5030	Communications & Security	Alarm systems, internet & phone wiring, comm. systems and emerg. ltg.			S.F. Floor	6.30	6.30	12.1%
5090	Other Electrical Systems	Emergency generator, 30 kW, energy monitoring systems			S.F. Floor	.91	.91	
E. EQUIPMENT & FURNISHINGS								
1010	Commercial Equipment	N/A			—	—	—	
1020	Institutional Equipment	N/A			—	—	—	
1090	Other Equipment	Waste handling recycling tilt truck			Each	.07	.07	1.7 %
2020	Moveable Furnishings	Built-in dormitory furnishings, no smoking signage			S.F. Floor	2.66	2.66	
F. SPECIAL CONSTRUCTION								
1020	Integrated Construction	N/A			—	—	—	
1040	Special Facilities	N/A			—	—	—	0.0%
G. BUILDING SITEWORK		**N/A**						

				Sub-Total	160.09	**100%**
CONTRACTOR FEES (General Requirements: 10%, Overhead: 5%, Profit: 10%)				25%	40.05	
ARCHITECT FEES				7%	14.01	
				Total Building Cost	**214.15**	

Costs per square foot of floor area

Exterior Wall	S.F. Area	12000	20000	28000	37000	45000	57000	68000	80000	92000
	L.F. Perimeter	470	600	698	793	900	1060	1127	1200	1320
Face Brick with Concrete Brick Back-up	Steel Frame	359.70	296.60	267.80	249.75	240.50	231.50	224.25	218.70	215.25
	Bearing Walls	338.70	275.55	246.75	228.70	219.50	210.45	203.25	197.65	194.30
Decorative Concrete Block	Steel Frame	351.75	290.50	262.70	245.40	236.45	227.65	220.90	215.65	212.35
	Bearing Walls	346.60	285.35	257.65	240.30	231.35	222.60	215.75	210.50	207.25
Stucco on Concrete Block	Steel Frame	364.10	300.00	270.60	252.20	242.75	233.60	226.15	220.40	216.95
	Bearing Walls	359.00	294.85	265.50	247.05	237.65	228.45	221.05	215.30	211.80
Perimeter Adj., Add or Deduct	Per 100 L.F.	12.15	7.25	5.20	3.90	3.25	2.50	2.15	1.80	1.65
Story Hgt. Adj., Add or Deduct	Per 1 Ft.	2.30	1.75	1.50	1.25	1.15	1.10	1.00	0.90	0.90

For Basement, add $24.95 per square foot of basement area

The above costs were calculated using the basic specifications shown on the facing page. These costs should be adjusted where necessary for design alternatives and owner's requirements. Reported completed project costs, for this type of structure, range from $181.65 to $339.20 per S.F.

Common additives

Description	Unit	$ Cost
Cabinets, Base, door units, metal	L.F.	315
Drawer units	L.F.	625
Tall storage cabinets, open	L.F.	590
With doors	L.F.	860
Wall, metal 12-1/2" deep, open	L.F.	238
With doors	L.F.	430
Countertops, not incl. base cabinets, acid proof	S.F.	58 - 70.50
Stainless steel	S.F.	156
Fume Hood, Not incl. ductwork	L.F.	750 - 1575
Ductwork	Hood	5750 - 9500
Glassware Washer, Distilled water rinse	Each	7625 - 15,700
Seating, auditorium chair, veneer back, padded seat	Each	315
Upholstered, spring seat	Each	315
Classroom, movable chair & desk	Set	81 - 171
Lecture hall, pedestal type	Each	258 - 610
Safety Equipment, Eye wash; hand held	Each	445
Deluge shower	Each	840
Tables, acid resist. top, drawers	L.F.	216
Titration Unit, Four 2000 ml reservoirs	Each	6050

Description	Unit	$ Cost
Commissioning Fees, sustainable institutional construction	S.F.	0.58 - 2.47
Energy Modelling Fees, academic buildings to 10,000 SF	Each	9000
Greater than 10,000 SF add	S.F.	0.20
Green Bldg Cert Fees for school construction project reg	Project	900
Photovoltaic Pwr Sys, grid connected, 20 kW (~2400 SF), roof	Each	272,300
Green Roofs, 6" soil depth, w/ treated wd edging & sedum mats	S.F.	11.05
10" Soil depth, with treated wood edging & sedum mats	S.F.	12.68
Greywater Recovery Systems, prepackaged comm, 3060 gal.	Each	57,740
4590 gal.	Each	72,025
Rainwater Harvest Sys, prepckged comm, 30,000 gal, sys contrller	Each	80,225
Solar Domestic HW, closed loop, add-on sys, ext heat exchanger	Each	10,950
Drainback, hot water system, 120 gal tank	Each	14,125
Draindown, hot water system, 120 gal tank	Each	14,550

Important: See the Reference Section for Location Factors.

Model costs calculated for a 1 story building with 12′ story height and 45,000 square feet of floor area

G College, Laboratory

				Unit	Unit Cost	Cost Per S.F.	% Of Sub-Total
A.	**SUBSTRUCTURE**						
1010	Standard Foundations	Poured concrete; strip and spread footings		S.F. Ground	3.13	3.13	
1020	Special Foundations	N/A		—	—	—	
1030	Slab on Grade	4″ reinforced concrete with recycled vapor barrier and granular base		S.F. Slab	5.33	5.33	9.7%
2010	Basement Excavation	Site preparation for slab and trench for foundation wall and footing		S.F. Ground	.18	.18	
2020	Basement Walls	4′ foundation wall		L.F. Wall	169	6.91	
B.	**SHELL**						
	B10 Superstructure						
1010	Floor Construction	Metal deck on open web steel joists	(5680 S.F.)	S.F. Floor	2.22	2.22	4.5%
1020	Roof Construction	Metal deck on open web steel joists		S.F. Roof	5.03	5.03	
	B20 Exterior Enclosure						
2010	Exterior Walls	Face brick with concrete block backup	75% of wall	S.F. Wall	38.17	6.87	
2020	Exterior Windows	Window wall	25% of wall	Each	50	2.85	7.5%
2030	Exterior Doors	Glass and metal doors and entrances with transom		Each	4904	2.19	
	B30 Roofing						
3010	Roof Coverings	Single-ply TPO membrane, 60 mils, heat welded w/R-20 insul.		S.F. Roof	5.11	5.11	3.4%
3020	Roof Openings	Skylight		S.F. Roof	.35	.35	
C.	**INTERIORS**						
1010	Partitions	Concrete block, foamed-in insulation	10 SF Flr./LF Part.	S.F. Partition	13.78	13.78	
1020	Interior Doors	Single leaf-kalamein fire doors, low VOC paint	820 S.F. Floor/Door	Each	1265	1.54	
1030	Fittings	Lockers		S.F. Floor	.05	.05	
2010	Stair Construction	N/A		—	—	—	21.2%
3010	Wall Finishes	60% paint, low VOC, 40% epoxy coating		S.F. Surface	2.73	5.46	
3020	Floor Finishes	60% epoxy, 20% carpet, 20% vinyl composition tile, recycled content		S.F. Floor	6.04	6.04	
3030	Ceiling Finishes	Mineral fiber tile on concealed zee runners		S.F. Ceiling	6.89	6.89	
D.	**SERVICES**						
	D10 Conveying						
1010	Elevators & Lifts	N/A		—	—	—	0.0 %
1020	Escalators & Moving Walks	N/A		—	—	—	
	D20 Plumbing						
2010	Plumbing Fixtures	Toilet, low flow, auto sensor & service fixt., supply & drain.	1 Fixt./260 SF Flr.	Each	9188	35.34	
2020	Domestic Water Distribution	Electric, point-of-use water heater		S.F. Floor	1.92	1.92	23.8%
2040	Rain Water Drainage	Roof drains		S.F. Roof	.72	.72	
	D30 HVAC						
3010	Energy Supply	N/A		—	—	—	
3020	Heat Generating Systems	Included in D3050		—	—	—	
3040	Distribution Systems	Enthalpy heat recovery packages		Each	30,350	4.04	14.6 %
3050	Terminal & Package Units	Multizone rooftop air conditioner, SEER 14		S.F. Floor	19.30	19.30	
3090	Other HVAC Sys. & Equipment	N/A		—	—	—	
	D40 Fire Protection						
4010	Sprinklers	Sprinklers, light hazard		S.F. Floor	2.85	2.85	2.0%
4020	Standpipes	Standpipe, wet, Class III		S.F. Floor	.31	.31	
	D50 Electrical						
5010	Electrical Service/Distribution	1000 ampere service, panel board and feeders		S.F. Floor	1.37	1.37	
5020	Lighting & Branch Wiring	LED fixtures, daylt. dim., ltg. on/off, recept., switches, & A.C. power		S.F. Floor	13.78	13.78	12.3%
5030	Communications & Security	Addressable alarm systems, internet wiring, & emergency lighting		S.F. Floor	3.50	3.50	
5090	Other Electrical Systems	Emergency generator, 11.5 kW, UPS, and energy monitoring systems		S.F. Floor	1.02	1.02	
E.	**EQUIPMENT & FURNISHINGS**						
1010	Commercial Equipment	N/A		—	—	—	
1020	Institutional Equipment	Cabinets, fume hoods, lockers, glassware washer		S.F. Floor	1.39	1.39	1.0 %
1090	Other Equipment	Waste handling recycling tilt truck		Each	.12	.12	
2020	Moveable Furnishings	No smoking signage		Each	.02	.02	
F.	**SPECIAL CONSTRUCTION**						
1020	Integrated Construction	N/A		—	—	—	0.0 %
1040	Special Facilities	N/A		—	—	—	
G.	**BUILDING SITEWORK**	**N/A**					

				Sub-Total	159.61	**100%**
CONTRACTOR FEES (General Requirements: 10%, Overhead: 5%, Profit: 10%)				25%	39.94	
ARCHITECT FEES				10%	19.95	

		Total Building Cost	**219.50**

Costs per square foot of floor area

Exterior Wall	S.F. Area	4000	4500	5000	5500	6000	6500	7000	7500	8000
	L.F. Perimeter	260	280	300	310	320	336	353	370	386
Face Brick Concrete Block Back-up	Steel Joists	210.90	206.60	203.20	198.55	194.85	192.50	190.60	189.00	187.45
	Bearing Walls	211.05	206.70	203.30	198.65	195.00	192.60	190.70	189.10	187.65
Decorative Concrete Block	Steel Joists	202.05	198.40	195.55	191.85	188.90	186.95	185.35	184.10	182.85
	Bearing Walls	194.55	190.95	188.05	184.40	181.45	179.45	177.95	176.60	175.40
Limestone with Concrete Block Back-up	Steel Joists	242.00	236.65	232.50	226.50	221.75	218.80	216.40	214.40	212.50
	Bearing Walls	234.55	229.20	225.00	219.05	214.25	211.30	208.95	207.00	205.10
Perimeter Adj., Add or Deduct	Per 100 L.F.	23.40	20.75	18.60	17.00	15.60	14.35	13.40	12.45	11.70
Story Hgt. Adj., Add or Deduct	Per 1 Ft.	3.15	2.95	2.85	2.75	2.55	2.45	2.40	2.35	2.35
For Basement, add $42.25 per square foot of basement area										

The above costs were calculated using the basic specifications shown on the facing page. These costs should be adjusted where necessary for design alternatives and owner's requirements. Reported completed project costs, for this type of structure, range from $83.20 to $246.15 per S.F.

Common additives

Description	Unit	$ Cost
Appliances, cooking range, 30" free standing		
1 oven	Each	570 - 2425
2 oven	Each	1425 - 2875
Microwave oven	Each	291 - 825
Compactor, residential, 4-1 compaction	Each	820 - 1300
Dishwasher, built-in, 2 cycles	Each	595 - 1125
4 cycles	Each	745 - 1875
Garbage disposer, sink type	Each	228 - 370
Hood for range, 2 speed, vented, 30" wide	Each	320 - 1250
Refrigerator, no frost 10-12 C.F.	Each	550 - 635
14-16 C.F.	Each	650 - 855
18-20 C.F.	Each	800 - 1775
Lockers, Steel, single tier, 60" or 72"	Opening	218 - 365
Locker bench, lam. maple top only	L.F.	26.50
Pedestals, steel pipe	Each	74
Sound System, amplifier, 250 watts	Each	2025
Speaker, ceiling or wall	Each	208
Trumpet	Each	400

Description	Unit	$ Cost
Commissioning Fees, sustainable commercial construction	S.F.	0.24 - 3.04
Energy Modelling Fees, Fire Stations to 10,000 SF	Each	11,000
Green Bldg Cert Fees for comm construction project reg	Project	900
Photovoltaic Pwr Sys, grid connected, 20 kW (~2400 SF), roof	Each	272,300
Green Roofs, 6" soil depth, w/ treated wd edging & sedum mats	S.F.	11.05
10" Soil depth, with treated wood edging & sedum mats	S.F.	12.68
Greywater Recovery Systems, prepackaged comm, 3060 gal.	Each	57,740
4590 gal.	Each	72,025
Rainwater Harvest Sys, prepckged comm, 10,000 gal, sys contrller	Each	31,375
20,000 gal. w/ system controller	Each	50,500
30,000 gal. w/ system controller	Each	80,225
Solar Domestic HW, closed loop, add-on sys, ext heat exchanger	Each	10,950
Drainback, hot water system, 120 gal tank	Each	14,125

Important: See the Reference Section for Location Factors.

Model costs calculated for a 1 story building with 14′ story height and 6,000 square feet of floor area

G Fire Station, 1 Story

				Unit	Unit Cost	Cost Per S.F.	% Of Sub-Total
A. SUBSTRUCTURE							
1010	Standard Foundations	Poured concrete; strip and spread footings		S.F. Ground	3.34	3.34	
1020	Special Foundations	N/A		—	—	—	
1030	Slab on Grade	6″ reinforced concrete with recycled vapor barrier and granular base		S.F. Slab	6.95	6.95	10.8%
2010	Basement Excavation	Site preparation for slab and trench for foundation wall and footing		S.F. Ground	.57	.57	
2020	Basement Walls	4′ foundation wall		L.F. Wall	89	4.72	
B. SHELL							
B10 Superstructure							
1010	Floor Construction	N/A		—	—	—	7.1 %
1020	Roof Construction	Metal deck, open web steel joists, beams on columns		S.F. Roof	10.30	10.30	
B20 Exterior Enclosure							
2010	Exterior Walls	Face brick with concrete block backup	75% of wall	S.F. Wall	38.14	21.36	
2020	Exterior Windows	Aluminum insulated glass	10% of wall	Each	861	2.01	19.3%
2030	Exterior Doors	Single aluminum and glass, overhead, hollow metal, low VOC paint	15% of wall	S.F. Door	2618	4.48	
B30 Roofing							
3010	Roof Coverings	Single-ply TPO membrane, 60 mil, with flashing, R-20 insulation and roof edges		S.F. Roof	6.54	6.54	4.6%
3020	Roof Openings	Skylights, roof hatches		S.F. Roof	.16	.16	
C. INTERIORS							
1010	Partitions	Concrete block w/foamed-in insulation	17 S.F. Floor/LF Part.	S.F. Partition	10.97	6.45	
1020	Interior Doors	Single leaf hollow metal, low VOC paint	500 S.F. Floor/Door	Each	1152	2.30	
1030	Fittings	Toilet partitions		S.F. Floor	.48	.48	
2010	Stair Construction	N/A		—	—	—	12.6%
3010	Wall Finishes	Paint, low VOC		S.F. Surface	2.44	2.87	
3020	Floor Finishes	50% vinyl tile with recycled content, 50% paint, low VOC		S.F. Floor	2.61	2.61	
3030	Ceiling Finishes	Mineral board acoustic ceiling tiles, concealed grid, suspended	50% of area	S.F. Ceiling	3.45	3.45	
D. SERVICES							
D10 Conveying							
1010	Elevators & Lifts	N/A		—	—	—	0.0 %
1020	Escalators & Moving Walks	N/A		—	—	—	
D20 Plumbing							
2010	Plumbing Fixtures	Kitchen, toilet, low flow, auto sensor & service fixt., supply & drain.	1 Fixt./375 SF Flr.	Each	4421	11.79	
2020	Domestic Water Distribution	Water heater, tankless, on-demand, natural gas/propane		S.F. Floor	2.58	2.58	10.9%
2040	Rain Water Drainage	Roof drains		S.F. Roof	1.30	1.30	
D30 HVAC							
3010	Energy Supply	N/A		—	—	—	
3020	Heat Generating Systems	Included in D3050		—	—	—	
3040	Distribution Systems	Enthalpy heat recovery packages		Each	17,475	2.92	17.0 %
3050	Terminal & Package Units	Multizone rooftop air conditioner, SEER 14		S.F. Floor	21.68	21.68	
3090	Other HVAC Sys. & Equipment	N/A		—	—	—	
D40 Fire Protection							
4010	Sprinklers	Wet pipe sprinkler system		S.F. Floor	4.76	4.76	4.3%
4020	Standpipes	Standpipe, wet, Class III		S.F. Floor	1.38	1.38	
D50 Electrical							
5010	Electrical Service/Distribution	200 ampere service, panel board and feeders		S.F. Floor	1.33	1.33	
5020	Lighting & Branch Wiring	LED fixt., daylt. dimming & ltg. on/off control, receptacles, switches, A.C. & misc. pwr.		S.F. Floor	9.98	9.98	12.7%
5030	Communications & Security	Addressable alarm systems		S.F. Floor	1.95	1.95	
5090	Other Electrical Systems	Energy monitoring systems			5.12	5.12	
E. EQUIPMENT & FURNISHINGS							
1010	Commercial Equipment	N/A		—	—	—	
1020	Institutional Equipment	N/A		—	—	—	0.7 %
1090	Other Equipment	Waste handling recycling tilt truck		Each	.92	.92	
2020	Moveable Furnishings	No smoking signage		Each	.04	.04	
F. SPECIAL CONSTRUCTION							
1020	Integrated Construction	N/A		—	—	—	0.0 %
1040	Special Facilities	N/A		—	—	—	
G. BUILDING SITEWORK	**N/A**						

	Sub-Total	144.34	**100%**
CONTRACTOR FEES (General Requirements: 10%, Overhead: 5%, Profit: 10%)	25%	36.08	
ARCHITECT FEES	8%	14.43	
	Total Building Cost	**194.85**	

Costs per square foot of floor area

Exterior Wall	S.F. Area	6000	7000	8000	9000	10000	11000	12000	13000	14000
	L.F. Perimeter	220	240	260	280	286	303	320	336	353
Face Brick with Concrete Block Back-up	Steel Joists	224.90	218.35	213.30	209.50	204.15	201.35	199.10	197.05	195.35
	Precast Conc.	233.40	226.85	221.85	218.10	212.85	210.00	207.85	205.75	204.05
Decorative Concrete Block	Steel Joists	193.70	188.10	183.80	180.55	176.20	173.80	171.95	170.15	168.75
	Precast Conc.	218.65	213.00	208.85	205.55	201.30	198.95	197.05	195.35	193.95
Limestone with Concrete Block Back-up	Steel Joists	251.30	243.00	236.70	231.85	224.70	221.20	218.30	215.60	213.50
	Precast Conc.	259.55	251.30	245.10	240.30	233.20	229.60	226.80	224.15	222.00
Perimeter Adj., Add or Deduct	Per 100 L.F.	27.20	23.20	20.45	18.10	16.30	14.80	13.60	12.50	11.65
Story Hgt. Adj., Add or Deduct	Per 1 Ft.	3.60	3.35	3.20	3.05	2.85	2.70	2.60	2.50	2.45

For Basement, add $41.05 per square foot of basement area

The above costs were calculated using the basic specifications shown on the facing page. These costs should be adjusted where necessary for design alternatives and owner's requirements. Reported completed project costs, for this type of structure, range from $82.95 to $246.15 per S.F.

Common additives

Description	Unit	$ Cost
Appliances		
Cooking range, 30" free standing		
1 oven	Each	570 - 2425
2 oven	Each	1425 - 2875
Microwave oven	Each	291 - 825
Compactor, residential, 4-1 compaction	Each	820 - 1300
Dishwasher, built-in, 2 cycles	Each	595 - 1125
4 cycles	Each	745 - 1875
Garbage diposer, sink type	Each	228 - 370
Hood for range, 2 speed, vented, 30" wide	Each	320 - 1250
Refrigerator, no frost 10-12 C.F.	Each	550 - 635
14-16 C.F.	Each	650 - 855
18-20 C.F.	Each	800 - 1775
Elevators, hydraulic passenger, 2 stops, 2500# capacity	Each	69,200
3500# capacity	Each	73,200
Lockers, Steel, single tier, 60" or 72"	Opening	218 - 365
Locker bench, lam. maple top only	L.F.	26.50
Pedestals, steel pipe	Each	74
Sound System, amplifier, 250 watts	Each	2025
Speaker, ceiling or wall	Each	208
Trumpet	Each	400

Description	Unit	$ Cost
Commissioning Fees, sustainable commercial construction	S.F.	0.24 - 3.04
Energy Modelling Fees, Fire Stations to 10,000 SF	Each	11,000
Greater than 10,000 SF add	S.F.	0.04
Green Bldg Cert Fees for comm construction project reg	Project	900
Photovoltaic Pwr Sys, grid connected, 20 kW (~2400 SF), roof	Each	272,300
Green Roofs, 6" soil depth, w/ treated wd edging & sedum mats	S.F.	11.05
10" Soil depth, with treated wood edging & sedum mats	S.F.	12.68
Greywater Recovery Systems, prepackaged comm, 3060 gal.	Each	57,740
4590 gal.	Each	72,025
Rainwater Harvest Sys, prepckged comm, 10,000 gal, sys contrller	Each	31,375
20,000 gal. w/ system controller	Each	50,500
30,000 gal. w/ system controller	Each	80,225
Solar Domestic HW, closed loop, add-on sys, ext heat exchanger	Each	10,950
Drainback, hot water system, 120 gal tank	Each	14,125

Important: See the Reference Section for Location Factors.

Model costs calculated for a 2 story building with 14' story height and 10,000 square feet of floor area

				Unit	Unit Cost	Cost Per S.F.	% Of Sub-Total
A. SUBSTRUCTURE							
1010	Standard Foundations	Poured concrete; strip and spread footings		S.F. Ground	3.14	1.57	
1020	Special Foundations	N/A		—	—	—	
1030	Slab on Grade	6" reinforced concrete with recycled vapor barrier and granular base		S.F. Slab	6.95	3.48	6.2%
2010	Basement Excavation	Site preparation for slab and trench for foundation wall and footing		S.F. Ground	.57	.29	
2020	Basement Walls	4' foundation wall with insulation		L.F. Wall	97	2.77	
B. SHELL							
	B10 Superstructure						
1010	Floor Construction	Open web steel joists, slab form, concrete		S.F. Floor	14.58	7.29	7.5%
1020	Roof Construction	Metal deck on open web steel joists		S.F. Roof	5.04	2.52	
	B20 Exterior Enclosure						
2010	Exterior Walls	Decorative concrete block, insul.	75% of wall	S.F. Wall	23.96	14.39	
2020	Exterior Windows	Aluminum insulated glass	10% of wall	Each	736	2.56	15.8%
2030	Exterior Doors	Single aluminum and glass, steel overhead, hollow metal, low VOC paint	15% of wall	S.F. Door	1930	3.69	
	B30 Roofing						
3010	Roof Coverings	Single-ply TPO, 60 mils, heat welded seams w/ R-20 insul.		S.F. Roof	6.74	3.37	2.6%
3020	Roof Openings	N/A		—	—	—	
C. INTERIORS							
1010	Partitions	Concrete block, foamed-in insul.	10 SF Floor/LF Part.	S.F. Partition	10.97	6.45	
1020	Interior Doors	Single leaf hollow metal, low VOC paint	500 S.F. Floor/Door	Each	1265	2.53	
1030	Fittings	Toilet partitions		S.F. Floor	.43	.43	
2010	Stair Construction	Concrete filled metal pan		Flight	20,150	4.03	17.6%
3010	Wall Finishes	Paint, low VOC		S.F. Surface	3.93	4.62	
3020	Floor Finishes	50% vinyl tile, (recycled content) 50% paint (low VOC)		S.F. Floor	2.61	2.61	
3030	Ceiling Finishes	Fiberglass board on exposed grid, suspended	50% of area	S.F. Ceiling	2.29	2.29	
D. SERVICES							
	D10 Conveying						
1010	Elevators & Lifts	One hydraulic passenger elevator		Each	83,400	8.34	6.4%
1020	Escalators & Moving Walks	N/A		—	—	—	
	D20 Plumbing						
2010	Plumbing Fixtures	Kitchen, toilet low flow, auto sensor & service fixt., supply & drain.	1 Fixt./400 SF Flr.	Each	4484	11.21	
2020	Domestic Water Distribution	Gas fired tankless water heater		S.F. Floor	.91	.91	9.9%
2040	Rain Water Drainage	Roof drains		S.F. Roof	1.66	.83	
	D30 HVAC						
3010	Energy Supply	N/A		—	—	—	
3020	Heat Generating Systems	Included in D3050		—	—	—	
3040	Distribution Systems	Enthalpy heat recovery packages		Each	14,775	2.96	18.9 %
3050	Terminal & Package Units	Multizone rooftop air conditioner, SEER 14		S.F. Floor	21.68	21.68	
3090	Other HVAC Sys. & Equipment	N/A		—	—	—	
	D40 Fire Protection						
4010	Sprinklers	Wet pipe sprinkler system		S.F. Floor	3.79	3.79	4.0%
4020	Standpipes	Standpipe, wet, Class III		S.F. Floor	1.42	1.42	
	D50 Electrical						
5010	Electrical Service/Distribution	400 ampere service, panel board and feeders		S.F. Floor	1.11	1.11	
5020	Lighting & Branch Wiring	LED fixt., daylt. dimming & ltg. on/off control., receptacles, switches, A.C. and misc. pwr.		S.F. Floor	8.77	8.77	10.8%
5030	Communications & Security	Addressable alarm systems and emergency lighting		S.F. Floor	1.51	1.51	
5090	Other Electrical Systems	Emergency generator, 15 kW, and energy monitoring systems		S.F. Floor	2.77	2.77	
E. EQUIPMENT & FURNISHINGS							
1010	Commercial Equipment	N/A		—	—	—	
1020	Institutional Equipment	N/A		—	—	—	0.3 %
1090	Other Equipment	Waste handling recycling tilt truck		Each	.31	.31	
2020	Moveable Furnishings	No smoking signage		Each	.02	.02	
F. SPECIAL CONSTRUCTION							
1020	Integrated Construction	N/A		—	—	—	0.0 %
1040	Special Facilities	N/A		—	—	—	
G. BUILDING SITEWORK	**N/A**						
			Sub-Total			130.52	**100%**
	CONTRACTOR FEES (General Requirements: 10%, Overhead: 5%, Profit: 10%)			25%		32.63	
	ARCHITECT FEES			8%		13.05	
			Total Building Cost			**176.20**	

247

Costs per square foot of floor area

Exterior Wall	S.F. Area	4000	6000	8000	10000	12000	14000	16000	18000	20000
	L.F. Perimeter	260	320	384	424	460	484	510	540	576
Vertical Redwood Siding	Wood Frame	165.05	153.50	147.95	143.40	140.20	137.45	135.45	134.10	133.05
Brick Veneer	Wood Frame	180.65	167.05	160.55	154.95	151.05	147.60	145.20	143.45	142.25
Aluminum Siding	Wood Frame	166.40	155.30	150.00	145.65	142.60	140.00	138.15	136.90	135.90
Brick on Block	Wood Truss	193.35	177.75	170.40	163.95	159.30	155.25	152.35	150.35	148.90
Limestone on Block	Wood Truss	223.45	202.40	192.50	183.40	176.90	171.10	166.90	164.00	162.00
Stucco on Block	Wood Truss	199.85	182.40	174.15	166.75	161.50	156.80	153.50	151.20	149.55
Perimeter Adj., Add or Deduct	Per 100 L.F.	12.85	8.55	6.40	5.15	4.25	3.65	3.15	2.80	2.60
Story Hgt. Adj., Add or Deduct	Per 1 Ft.	1.55	1.30	1.15	1.00	0.90	0.80	0.75	0.70	0.65
For Basement, add $34.80 per square foot of basement area										

The above costs were calculated using the basic specifications shown on the facing page. These costs should be adjusted where necessary for design alternatives and owner's requirements. Reported completed project costs, for this type of structure, range from $118.15 to $363.20 per S.F.

Common additives

Description	Unit	$ Cost	Description	Unit	$ Cost
Autopsy Table, standard	Each	11,300	Commissioning Fees, sustainable commercial construction	S.F.	0.24 - 3.04
Deluxe	Each	17,600	Energy Modelling Fees, commercial buildings to 10,000 SF	Each	11,000
Directory Boards, plastic, glass covered, 30" x 20"	Each	630	Greater than 10,000 SF add	S.F.	0.04
36" x 48"	Each	1500	Green Bldg Cert Fees for comm construction project reg	Project	900
Aluminum, 24" x 18"	Each	630	Photovoltaic Pwr Sys, grid connected, 20 kW (~2400 SF), roof	Each	272,300
36" x 24"	Each	735	Green Roofs, 6" soil depth, w/ treated wd edging & sedum mats	S.F.	11.05
48" x 32"	Each	1050	10" Soil depth, with treated wood edging & sedum mats	S.F.	12.68
Mortuary Refrigerator, end operated			Greywater Recovery Systems, prepackaged comm, 3060 gal.	Each	57,740
Two capacity	Each	13,400	4590 gal.	Each	72,025
Six capacity	Each	24,100	Rainwater Harvest Sys, prepckged comm, 10,000 gal, sys contrller	Each	31,375
Planters, precast concrete, 48" diam., 24" high	Each	740	20,000 gal. w/ system controller	Each	50,500
7" diam., 36" high	Each	1800	30,000 gal. w/ system controller	Each	80,225
Fiberglass, 36" diam., 24" high	Each	840	Solar Domestic HW, closed loop, add-on sys, ext heat exchanger	Each	10,950
60" diam., 24" high	Each	1300	Drainback, hot water system, 120 gal tank	Each	14,125
			Draindown, hot water system, 120 gal tank	Each	14,550

Important: See the Reference Section for Location Factors.

Model costs calculated for a 1 story building with 12′ story height and 10,000 square feet of floor area

G Funeral Home

				Unit	Unit Cost	Cost Per S.F.	% Of Sub-Total
A. SUBSTRUCTURE							
1010	Standard Foundations	Poured concrete; strip and spread footings		S.F. Ground	1.82	1.82	
1020	Special Foundations	N/A		—	—	—	
1030	Slab on Grade	4″ reinforced concrete with recycled plastic vapor barrier and granular base		S.F. Slab	5.33	5.33	10.6%
2010	Basement Excavation	Site preparation for slab and trench for foundation wall and footing		S.F. Ground	.32	.32	
2020	Basement Walls	4′ foundation wall		L.F. Wall	80	3.73	
B. SHELL							
B10 Superstructure							
1010	Floor Construction	N/A		—	—	—	4.7 %
1020	Roof Construction	Plywood on wood truss		S.F. Roof	4.93	4.93	
B20 Exterior Enclosure							
2010	Exterior Walls	1″ x 4″ vertical T & G redwood siding on 2x6 wood studs with insul.	90% of wall	S.F. Wall	12.80	5.86	
2020	Exterior Windows	Double hung wood	10% of wall	Each	510	2.16	8.8%
2030	Exterior Doors	Wood swinging double doors, single leaf hollow metal, low VOC paint		Each	1978	1.19	
B30 Roofing							
3010	Roof Coverings	Single ply membrane, TPO, 45 mil, fully adhered; polyisocyanurate sheets		S.F. Roof	6.20	6.20	5.9%
3020	Roof Openings	N/A		—	—	—	
C. INTERIORS							
1010	Partitions	Gypsum board on wood studs with sound deadening board	15 SF Flr./LF Part.	S.F. Partition	9.71	5.18	
1020	Interior Doors	Single leaf wood, low VOC paint	150 S.F. Floor/Door	Each	636	4.24	
1030	Fittings	N/A		—	—	—	
2010	Stair Construction	N/A		—	—	—	23.0%
3010	Wall Finishes	50% wallpaper, 25% wood paneling, 25% paint (low VOC)		S.F. Surface	3.37	3.59	
3020	Floor Finishes	70% carpet tile, 30% ceramic tile		S.F. Floor	6.59	6.59	
3030	Ceiling Finishes	Fiberglass board on exposed grid, suspended		S.F. Ceiling	4.57	4.57	
D. SERVICES							
D10 Conveying							
1010	Elevators & Lifts	N/A		—	—	—	0.0 %
1020	Escalators & Moving Walks	N/A		—	—	—	
D20 Plumbing							
2010	Plumbing Fixtures	Toilets, low flow, auto sensor, urinals & service fixt., supply & drain.	1 Fixt./770 SF Flr.	Each	3742	4.86	
2020	Domestic Water Distribution	Electric water heater, point-of-use		S.F. Floor	.55	.55	6.1%
2040	Rain Water Drainage	Roof drain		S.F. Roof	1	1	
D30 HVAC							
3010	Energy Supply	N/A		—	—	—	
3020	Heat Generating Systems	Included in D3050		—	—	—	
3040	Distribution Systems	Enthalpy heat recovery packages		Each	36,875	3.69	21.3 %
3050	Terminal & Package Units	Multizone rooftop air conditioner, SEER 14		S.F. Floor	18.76	18.76	
3090	Other HVAC Sys. & Equipment	N/A		—	—	—	
D40 Fire Protection							
4010	Sprinklers	Wet pipe sprinkler system		S.F. Floor	3.56	3.56	4.2%
4020	Standpipes	Standpipe, wet, Class III		S.F. Floor	.83	.83	
D50 Electrical							
5010	Electrical Service/Distribution	400 ampere service, panel board and feeders		S.F. Floor	1.50	1.50	
5020	Lighting & Branch Wiring	LED light fixtures, daylt. dimming control & ltg. on/off sys., recept., switches, & A.C. power		S.F. Floor	10.14	10.14	14.9%
5030	Communications & Security	Addressable alarm systems		S.F. Floor	1.51	1.51	
5090	Other Electrical Systems	Emergency generator, 15 kW and energy monitoring systems		S.F. Floor	2.53	2.53	
E. EQUIPMENT & FURNISHINGS							
1010	Commercial Equipment	N/A		—	—	—	
1020	Institutional Equipment	N/A		—	—	—	
1090	Other Equipment	Waste handling recycling tilt truck		Each	.55	.55	0.6 %
2020	Moveable Furnishings	No smoking signage		Each	.04	.04	
F. SPECIAL CONSTRUCTION							
1020	Integrated Construction	N/A		—	—	—	0.0 %
1040	Special Facilities	N/A		—	—	—	
G. BUILDING SITEWORK	**N/A**						

			Sub-Total	105.23	**100%**
CONTRACTOR FEES (General Requirements: 10%, Overhead: 5%, Profit: 10%)		25%	26.33		
ARCHITECT FEES		9%	11.84		

Total Building Cost	**143.40**

Costs per square foot of floor area

Exterior Wall	S.F. Area	7000	10000	13000	16000	19000	22000	25000	28000	31000
	L.F. Perimeter	240	300	336	386	411	435	472	510	524
Face Brick with Concrete Block Back-up	R/Conc. Frame	207.50	196.55	187.20	183.00	177.75	173.80	171.80	170.25	167.65
	Steel Frame	209.65	198.70	189.35	185.15	179.90	176.00	174.00	172.40	169.75
Limestone with Concrete Block	R/Conc. Frame	247.65	231.25	217.00	210.70	202.55	196.45	193.40	191.05	186.90
	Steel Frame	246.90	231.30	217.45	211.35	203.45	197.50	194.50	192.20	188.15
Precast Concrete Panels	R/Conc. Frame	213.50	201.40	191.25	186.65	181.00	176.80	174.60	172.85	170.05
	Steel Frame	214.50	202.35	192.25	187.65	182.00	177.75	175.60	173.85	171.00
Perimeter Adj., Add or Deduct	Per 100 L.F.	25.70	17.95	13.85	11.20	9.40	8.20	7.20	6.40	5.75
Story Hgt. Adj., Add or Deduct	Per 1 Ft.	3.90	3.35	2.90	2.70	2.45	2.30	2.15	2.05	1.90

For Basement, add $51.90 per square foot of basement area

The above costs were calculated using the basic specifications shown on the facing page. These costs should be adjusted where necessary for design alternatives and owner's requirements. Reported completed project costs, for this type of structure, range from $113.05 to $290.05 per S.F.

Common additives

Description	Unit	$ Cost
Carrels Hardwood	Each	960 - 2300
Closed Circuit Surveillance, one station, camera and monitor	Each	1975
For additional camera stations, add	Each	1050
Elevators, hydraulic passenger, 2 stops, 1500# capacity	Each	66,100
2500# capacity	Each	69,200
3500# capacity	Each	73,200
Library Furnishings, bookshelf, 90" high, 10" shelf double face	L.F.	214
Single face	L.F.	180
Charging desk, built-in with counter		
Plastic laminated top	L.F.	410
Reading table, laminated		
Top 60" x 36"	Each	760

Description	Unit	$ Cost
Commissioning Fees, sustainable institutional construction	S.F.	0.58 - 2.47
Energy Modelling Fees, commercial buildings to 10,000 SF	Each	11,000
Greater than 10,000 SF add	S.F.	0.04
Green Bldg Cert Fees for comm construction project reg	Project	900
Photovoltaic Pwr Sys, grid connected, 20 kW (~2400 SF), roof	Each	272,300
Green Roofs, 6" soil depth, w/ treated wd edging & sedum mats	S.F.	11.05
10" Soil depth, with treated wood edging & sedum mats	S.F.	12.68
Greywater Recovery Systems, prepackaged comm, 3060 gal.	Each	57,740
4590 gal.	Each	72,025
Rainwater Harvest Sys, prepckged comm, 10,000 gal, sys contrller	Each	31,375
20,000 gal. w/ system controller	Each	50,500
30,000 gal. w/ system controller	Each	80,225
Solar Domestic HW, closed loop, add-on sys, ext heat exchanger	Each	10,950
Drainback, hot water system, 120 gal tank	Each	14,125
Draindown, hot water system, 120 gal tank	Each	14,550

Important: See the Reference Section for Location Factors.

Model costs calculated for a 2 story building with 14' story height and 22,000 square feet of floor area

G Library

				Unit	Unit Cost	Cost Per S.F.	% Of Sub-Total
A. SUBSTRUCTURE							
1010	Standard Foundations	Poured concrete; strip and spread footings		S.F. Ground	3.84	1.92	
1020	Special Foundations	N/A		—	—	—	
1030	Slab on Grade	4" reinforced concrete with recycled vapor barrier and granular base		S.F. Slab	5.33	2.67	5.0%
2010	Basement Excavation	Site preparation for slab and trench for foundation wall and footing		S.F. Ground	.32	.16	
2020	Basement Walls	4' foundation wall		L.F. Wall	89	1.75	
B. SHELL							
B10 Superstructure							
1010	Floor Construction	Concrete waffle slab		S.F. Floor	26.70	13.35	17.8%
1020	Roof Construction	Concrete waffle slab		S.F. Roof	19.06	9.53	
B20 Exterior Enclosure							
2010	Exterior Walls	Face brick with concrete block backup	90% of wall	S.F. Wall	36.21	18.04	
2020	Exterior Windows	Window wall	10% of wall	Each	53	2.91	16.7%
2030	Exterior Doors	Double aluminum and glass, single leaf hollow metal, low VOC paint		Each	5700	.52	
B30 Roofing							
3010	Roof Coverings	Single-ply TPO membrane, 60 mil, heat welded w/ R-20 insulation		S.F. Roof	5.76	2.88	2.3%
3020	Roof Openings	Roof hatches		S.F. Roof	.08	.04	
C. INTERIORS							
1010	Partitions	Gypsum board on metal studs w/ sound attenuation insul.	30 SF Flr./LF Part.	S.F. Partition	13.25	5.30	
1020	Interior Doors	Single leaf wood, low VOC paint	300 S.F. Floor/Door	Each	636	2.12	
1030	Fittings	N/A		—	—	—	
2010	Stair Construction	Concrete filled metal pan		Flight	9400	.85	16.2%
3010	Wall Finishes	Paint, low VOC		S.F. Surface	2.01	1.61	
3020	Floor Finishes	50% carpet tile, 50% vinyl composition tile, recycled content		S.F. Floor	4.14	4.14	
3030	Ceiling Finishes	Mineral fiber on concealed zee bars		S.F. Ceiling	6.89	6.89	
D. SERVICES							
D10 Conveying							
1010	Elevators & Lifts	One hydraulic passenger elevator		Each	86,900	3.95	3.1%
1020	Escalators & Moving Walks	N/A		—	—	—	
D20 Plumbing							
2010	Plumbing Fixtures	Toilet, low flow, auto sensor & service fixt., supply & drain.	1 Fixt./1835 SF.Flr.	Each	8331	4.54	
2020	Domestic Water Distribution	Tankless, on demand water heater, gas/propane		S.F. Floor	.70	.70	4.5%
2040	Rain Water Drainage	Roof drains		S.F. Roof	1.18	.59	
D30 HVAC							
3010	Energy Supply	N/A		—	—	—	
3020	Heat Generating Systems	Included in D3050		—	—	—	
3040	Distribution Systems	Enthalpy heat recovery packages		Each	30,350	2.76	17.6 %
3050	Terminal & Package Units	Multizone rooftop air conditioner, SEER 14		S.F. Floor	19.85	19.85	
3090	Other HVAC Sys. & Equipment	N/A		—	—	—	
D40 Fire Protection							
4010	Sprinklers	Wet pipe sprinkler system		S.F. Floor	3.11	3.11	3.1%
4020	Standpipes	Standpipe		S.F. Floor	.94	.94	
D50 Electrical							
5010	Electrical Service/Distribution	400 ampere service, panel board and feeders		S.F. Floor	.53	.53	
5020	Lighting & Branch Wiring	LED fixtures, daylt. dim., ltg. on/off, recept., switches, and A.C. power		S.F. Floor	13.11	13.11	13.5%
5030	Communications & Security	Addressable alarm systems, internet wiring, and emergency lighting		S.F. Floor	2.09	2.09	
5090	Other Electrical Systems	Emergency generator, 7.5 kW, UPS, energy monitoring systems		S.F. Floor	1.64	1.64	
E. EQUIPMENT & FURNISHINGS							
1010	Commercial Equipment	N/A		—	—	—	
1020	Institutional Equipment	N/A		—	—	—	
1090	Other Equipment	Waste handling recycling tilt truck		Each	.25	.25	0.2 %
2020	Moveable Furnishings	No smoking signage		Each			
F. SPECIAL CONSTRUCTION							
1020	Integrated Construction	N/A		—	—	—	0.0 %
1040	Special Facilities	N/A		—	—	—	
G. BUILDING SITEWORK	**N/A**						

				Sub-Total	128.74	100%
CONTRACTOR FEES (General Requirements: 10%, Overhead: 5%, Profit: 10%)			25%	32.19		
ARCHITECT FEES			8%	12.87		

Total Building Cost **173.80**

251

Costs per square foot of floor area

Exterior Wall	S.F. Area	4000	5500	7000	8500	10000	11500	13000	14500	16000
	L.F. Perimeter	280	320	380	440	453	503	510	522	560
Face Brick with Concrete Block Back-up	Steel Joists	248.75	237.15	232.70	229.75	224.25	222.50	218.80	216.05	215.00
	Wood Truss	250.70	239.10	234.65	231.70	226.15	224.50	220.75	218.05	217.00
Stucco on Concrete Block	Steel Joists	256.10	243.25	238.35	235.20	228.95	227.15	222.90	219.85	218.70
	Wood Truss	262.85	250.05	245.20	241.95	235.75	233.95	229.65	226.60	225.45
Brick Veneer	Wood Truss	245.55	235.25	231.20	228.55	223.70	222.20	218.90	216.55	215.60
Wood Siding	Wood Frame	238.00	229.35	225.85	223.60	219.70	218.40	215.75	213.85	213.05
Perimeter Adj., Add or Deduct	Per 100 L.F.	18.45	13.50	10.55	8.75	7.35	6.45	5.65	5.10	4.70
Story Hgt. Adj., Add or Deduct	Per 1 Ft.	3.80	3.15	2.90	2.80	2.45	2.40	2.10	2.00	1.90

For Basement, add $ 33.80 per square foot of basement area

The above costs were calculated using the basic specifications shown on the facing page. These costs should be adjusted where necessary for design alternatives and owner's requirements. Reported completed project costs, for this type of structure, range from $ 95.25 to $ 245.00 per S.F.

Common additives

Description	Unit	$ Cost
Cabinets, hospital, base, laminated plastic	L.F.	410
Counter top, laminated plastic	L.F.	79.50
Nurses station, door type , laminated plastic	L.F.	460
Wall cabinets, laminated plastic	L.F.	298
Directory Boards, plastic, glass covered, 30" x 20"	Each	630
36" x 48"	Each	1500
Aluminum, 36" x 24"	Each	735
48" x 32"	Each	1050
Heat Therapy Unit, humidified, 26" x 78" x 28"	Each	3925
Tables, examining, vinyl top, with base cabinets	Each	1475 - 6675
Utensil Washer, Sanitizer	Each	12,600
X-Ray, Mobile	Each	18,300 - 84,500

Description	Unit	$ Cost
Commissioning Fees, sustainable commercial construction	S.F.	0.24 - 3.04
Energy Modelling Fees, commercial buildings to 10,000 SF	Each	11,000
Greater than 10,000 SF add	S.F.	0.04
Green Bldg Cert Fees for comm construction project reg	Project	900
Photovoltaic Pwr Sys, grid connected, 20 kW (~2400 SF), roof	Each	272,300
Green Roofs, 6" soil depth, w/ treated wd edging & sedum mats	S.F.	11.05
10" Soil depth, with treated wood edging & sedum mats	S.F.	12.68
Greywater Recovery Systems, prepackaged comm, 3060 gal.	Each	57,740
4590 gal.	Each	72,025
Rainwater Harvest Sys, prepckged comm, 10,000 gal, sys contrller	Each	31,375
20,000 gal. w/ system controller	Each	50,500
30,000 gal. w/ system controller	Each	80,225
Solar Domestic HW, closed loop, add-on sys, ext heat exchanger	Each	10,950
Drainback, hot water system, 120 gal tank	Each	14,125
Draindown, hot water system, 120 gal tank	Each	14,550

Important: See the Reference Section for Location Factors.

Model costs calculated for a 1 story building with 10′ story height and 7,000 square feet of floor area

				Unit	Unit Cost	Cost Per S.F.	% Of Sub-Total
A. SUBSTRUCTURE							
1010	Standard Foundations	Poured concrete; strip and spread footings		S.F. Ground	2.13	2.13	
1020	Special Foundations	N/A					
1030	Slab on Grade	4″ reinforced concrete with recycled vapor barrier and granular base		S.F. Slab	5.33	5.33	7.3%
2010	Basement Excavation	Site preparation for slab and trench for foundation wall and footing		S.F. Ground	.32	.32	
2020	Basement Walls	4′ foundation wall		L.F. Wall	89	4.80	
B. SHELL							
B10 Superstructure							
1010	Floor Construction	N/A		—	—	—	4.0 %
1020	Roof Construction	Plywood on wood trusses		S.F. Roof	6.85	6.85	
B20 Exterior Enclosure							
2010	Exterior Walls	Face brick with concrete block backup	70% of wall	S.F. Wall	36.21	13.76	
2020	Exterior Windows	Wood double hung	30% of wall	Each	637	6.10	13.0%
2030	Exterior Doors	Aluminum and glass doors and entrance with transoms		Each	1460	2.50	
B30 Roofing							
3010	Roof Coverings	Asphalt shingles with flashing (Pitched); rigid fiber glass insulation, gutters		S.F. Roof	8.33	8.33	4.8%
3020	Roof Openings	N/A		—	—	—	
C. INTERIORS							
1010	Partitions	Gypsum bd. & sound deadening bd. on wood studs w/insul.	6 SF Flr./LF Part.	S.F. Partition	9.36	12.48	
1020	Interior Doors	Single leaf wood, low VOC paint	60 S.F. Floor/Door	Each	636	10.60	
1030	Fittings	N/A		—	—	—	
2010	Stair Construction	N/A		—	—	—	21.2%
3010	Wall Finishes	50% paint, low VOC, 50% vinyl wall covering		S.F. Surface	1.41	3.77	
3020	Floor Finishes	50% carpet tile, 50% vinyl composition tile, recycled content		S.F. Floor	3.73	3.73	
3030	Ceiling Finishes	Mineral fiber tile on concealed zee bars		S.F. Ceiling	5.99	5.99	
D. SERVICES							
D10 Conveying							
1010	Elevators & Lifts	N/A		—	—	—	0.0%
1020	Escalators & Moving Walks	N/A		—	—	—	
D20 Plumbing							
2010	Plumbing Fixtures	Toilet, low flow, auto sensor, exam room & service fixt., supply & drain.	1 Fixt./195 SF Flr.	Each	4994	25.61	
2020	Domestic Water Distribution	Gas fired tankless water heater		S.F. Floor	3.14	3.14	17.3%
2040	Rain Water Drainage	Roof drains		S.F. Roof	1.03	1.03	
D30 HVAC							
3010	Energy Supply	N/A		—	—	—	
3020	Heat Generating Systems	Included in D3050		—	—	—	
3040	Distribution Systems	Enthalpy heat recovery packages		Each	17,475	2.50	9.5 %
3050	Terminal & Package Units	Multizone rooftop air conditioner, SEER 14		S.F. Floor	13.89	13.89	
3090	Other HVAC Sys. & Equipment	N/A		—	—	—	
D40 Fire Protection							
4010	Sprinklers	Wet pipe sprinkler system		S.F. Floor	4.76	4.76	3.4%
4020	Standpipes	Standpipe		S.F. Floor	1.18	1.18	
D50 Electrical							
5010	Electrical Service/Distribution	200 ampere service, panel board and feeders		S.F. Floor	1.26	1.26	
5020	Lighting & Branch Wiring	LED fixtures, daylt. dim., ltg. on/off, recept., switches, and A.C. power		S.F. Floor	10.01	10.01	13.4%
5030	Communications & Security	Alarm systems, internet & phone wiring, intercom system, & emerg. ltg.		S.F. Floor	7.87	7.87	
5090	Other Electrical Systems	Emergency generator, 7.5 kW, and energy monitoring systems		S.F. Floor	3.90	3.90	
E. EQUIPMENT & FURNISHINGS							
1010	Commercial Equipment	N/A		—	—	—	
1020	Institutional Equipment	Exam room casework and countertops		S.F. Floor	9.49	9.49	6.0 %
1090	Other Equipment	Waste handling recycling tilt truck		Each	.79	.79	
2020	Moveable Furnishings	No smoking signage		Each	.10	.10	
F. SPECIAL CONSTRUCTION							
1020	Integrated Construction	N/A		—	—	—	0.0 %
1040	Special Facilities	N/A		—	—	—	
G. BUILDING SITEWORK	**N/A**						
				Sub-Total		172.22	**100%**
	CONTRACTOR FEES (General Requirements: 10%, Overhead: 5%, Profit: 10%)				25%	43.05	
	ARCHITECT FEES				9%	19.38	
				Total Building Cost		**234.65**	

Costs per square foot of floor area

Exterior Wall	S.F. Area	4000	5500	7000	8500	10000	11500	13000	14500	16000
	L.F. Perimeter	180	210	240	270	286	311	336	361	386
Face Brick with Concrete Block Back-up	Steel Joists	285.20	272.80	265.75	261.20	256.20	253.40	251.40	249.70	248.35
	Wood Joists	290.15	277.80	270.75	266.15	261.15	258.40	256.35	254.65	253.35
Stucco on Concrete Block	Steel Joists	268.25	258.40	252.80	249.10	245.30	243.10	241.50	240.20	239.15
	Wood Joists	278.30	267.75	261.75	257.85	253.65	251.30	249.60	248.10	247.00
Brick Veneer	Wood Frame	278.80	268.20	262.15	258.15	253.95	251.60	249.80	248.40	247.25
Wood Siding	Wood Frame	267.20	258.30	253.25	250.00	246.55	244.60	243.15	242.00	241.10
Perimeter Adj., Add or Deduct	Per 100 L.F.	33.45	24.35	19.15	15.75	13.35	11.70	10.30	9.25	8.35
Story Hgt. Adj., Add or Deduct	Per 1 Ft.	4.90	4.25	3.80	3.50	3.10	3.00	2.85	2.75	2.70
For Basement, add $37.50 per square foot of basement area										

The above costs were calculated using the basic specifications shown on the facing page. These costs should be adjusted where necessary for design alternatives and owner's requirements. Reported completed project costs, for this type of structure, range from $97.75 to $334.00 per S.F.

Common additives

Description	Unit	$ Cost	Description	Unit	$ Cost
Cabinets, hospital, base, laminated plastic	L.F.	410	Commissioning Fees, sustainable commercial construction	S.F.	0.24 - 3.04
Counter top, laminated plastic	L.F.	79.50	Energy Modelling Fees, commercial buildings to 10,000 SF	Each	11,000
Nurses station, door type , laminated plastic	L.F.	460	Greater than 10,000 SF add	S.F.	0.04
Wall cabinets, laminated plastic	L.F.	298	Green Bldg Cert Fees for comm construction project reg	Project	900
Elevators, hydraulic passenger, 2 stops, 2500# capacity	Each	69,200	Photovoltaic Pwr Sys, grid connected, 20 kW (~2400 SF), roof	Each	272,300
3500# capacity	Each	73,200	Green Roofs, 6" soil depth, w/ treated wd edging & sedum mats	S.F.	11.05
Directory Boards, plastic, glass covered, 30" x 20"	Each	630	10" Soil depth, with treated wood edging & sedum mats	S.F.	12.68
36" x 48"	Each	1500	Greywater Recovery Systems, prepackaged comm, 3060 gal.	Each	57,740
Aluminum, 36" x 24"	Each	735	4590 gal.	Each	72,025
48" x 32"	Each	1050	Rainwater Harvest Sys, prepckged comm, 10,000 gal, sys contrller	Each	31,375
Heat Therapy Unit, humidified, 26" x 78" x 28"	Each	3925	20,000 gal. w/ system controller	Each	50,500
Tables, examining, vinyl top, with base cabinets	Each	1475 - 6675	30,000 gal. w/ system controller	Each	80,225
Utensil Washer, Sanitizer	Each	12,600	Solar Domestic HW, closed loop, add-on sys, ext heat exchanger	Each	10,950
X-Ray, Mobile	Each	18,300 - 84,500	Drainback, hot water system, 120 gal tank	Each	14,125
			Draindown, hot water system, 120 gal tank	Each	14,550

Important: See the Reference Section for Location Factors.

Model costs calculated for a 2 story building with 10' story height and 7,000 square feet of floor area

G Medical Office, 2 Story

				Unit	Unit Cost	Cost Per S.F.	% Of Sub-Total
A. SUBSTRUCTURE							
1010	Standard Foundations	Poured concrete; strip and spread footings		S.F. Ground	3.40	1.70	
1020	Special Foundations	N/A		—	—	—	
1030	Slab on Grade	4" reinforced concrete with vapor barrier and granular base		S.F. Slab	5.33	2.67	4.0%
2010	Basement Excavation	Site preparation for slab and trench for foundation wall and footing		S.F. Ground	.18	.09	
2020	Basement Walls	4' foundation wall		L.F. Wall	89	3.03	
B. SHELL							
	B10 Superstructure						
1010	Floor Construction	Open web steel joists, slab form, concrete, columns		S.F. Floor	13.62	6.81	5.3%
1020	Roof Construction	Metal deck, open web steel joists, beams, columns		S.F. Roof	6.18	3.09	
	B20 Exterior Enclosure						
2010	Exterior Walls	Stucco on concrete block		S.F. Wall	18.81	9.03	
2020	Exterior Windows	Outward projecting metal	30% of wall	Each	525	7.20	9.6%
2030	Exterior Doors	Aluminum and glass doors with transoms		Each	5700	1.63	
	B30 Roofing						
3010	Roof Coverings	Built-up tar and gravel with flashing; perlite/EPS composite insulation		S.F. Roof	6.88	3.44	1.9%
3020	Roof Openings	Roof hatches		S.F. Roof	.26	.13	
C. INTERIORS							
1010	Partitions	Gypsum bd. & acous. insul. on metal studs	6 SF Floor/LF Part.	S.F. Partition	7.69	10.25	
1020	Interior Doors	Single leaf wood	60 S.F. Floor/Door	Each	636	10.60	
1030	Fittings	N/A		—	—	—	
2010	Stair Construction	Concrete filled metal pan		Flight	14,450	4.13	20.7%
3010	Wall Finishes	45% paint, 50% vinyl wall coating, 5% ceramic tile		S.F. Surface	1.41	3.77	
3020	Floor Finishes	50% carpet, 50% vinyl composition tile		S.F. Floor	3.73	3.73	
3030	Ceiling Finishes	Mineral fiber tile on concealed zee bars		S.F. Ceiling	5.99	5.99	
D. SERVICES							
	D10 Conveying						
1010	Elevators & Lifts	One hydraulic hospital elevator		Each	102,900	14.70	7.9%
1020	Escalators & Moving Walks	N/A		—	—	—	
	D20 Plumbing						
2010	Plumbing Fixtures	Toilet, exam room & service fixt., supply & drain.	1 Fixt./160 SF Flr.	Each	4731	29.57	
2020	Domestic Water Distribution	Gas fired water heater		S.F. Floor	3.14	3.14	18.2%
2040	Rain Water Drainage	Roof drains		S.F. Roof	2.20	1.10	
	D30 HVAC						
3010	Energy Supply	N/A		—	—	—	
3020	Heat Generating Systems	Included in D3050		—	—	—	
3040	Distribution Systems	Enthalpy heat recovery packages		Each	17,475	2.50	8.8 %
3050	Terminal & Package Units	Multizone rooftop air conditioner, SEER 14		S.F. Floor	13.89	13.89	
3090	Other HVAC Sys. & Equipment	N/A		—	—	—	
	D40 Fire Protection						
4010	Sprinklers	Wet pipe sprinkler system		S.F. Floor	3.79	3.79	3.0%
4020	Standpipes	Standpipe		S.F. Floor	1.77	1.77	
	D50 Electrical						
5010	Electrical Service/Distribution	400 ampere service, panel board and feeders		S.F. Floor	1.61	1.61	
5020	Lighting & Branch Wiring	LED fixtures, receptacles, switches, A.C. and misc. power		S.F. Floor	14.34	14.34	15.0%
5030	Communications & Security	Alarm system, internet & phone wiring, intercom system, & emergency ltg.		S.F. Floor	7.87	7.87	
5090	Other Electrical Systems	Emergency generator, 7.5 kW		S.F. Floor	4.02	4.02	
E. EQUIPMENT & FURNISHINGS							
1010	Commercial Equipment	N/A		—	—	—	
1020	Institutional Equipment	Exam room casework and contertops		S.F. Floor	9.49	9.49	5.4 %
1090	Other Equipment	Waste handling recycling tilt truck		Each	.44	.44	
2020	Moveable Furnishings	No smoking signage		Each	.02	.02	
F. SPECIAL CONSTRUCTION							
1020	Integrated Construction	N/A		—	—	—	0.0 %
1040	Special Facilities	N/A		—	—	—	
G. BUILDING SITEWORK	**N/A**						

			Sub-Total	185.54	100%
CONTRACTOR FEES (General Requirements: 10%, Overhead: 5%, Profit: 10%)			25%	46.39	
ARCHITECT FEES			9%	20.87	

Total Building Cost 252.80

Costs per square foot of floor area

Exterior Wall	S.F. Area	2000	3000	4000	6000	8000	10000	12000	14000	16000
	L.F. Perimeter	240	260	280	380	480	560	580	660	740
Brick Veneer	Wood Frame	227.25	198.85	184.65	176.70	172.65	169.05	163.50	162.20	161.20
Aluminum Siding	Wood Frame	209.70	186.15	174.35	167.35	163.80	160.70	156.30	155.20	154.35
Wood Siding	Wood Frame	209.70	186.10	174.35	167.35	163.80	160.75	156.30	155.20	154.30
Wood Shingles	Wood Frame	212.75	188.30	176.00	168.90	165.25	162.05	157.45	156.30	155.45
Precast Concrete Block	Wood Truss	212.55	188.20	176.00	168.85	165.20	162.10	157.50	156.30	155.40
Brick on Concrete Block	Wood Truss	242.25	209.60	193.30	184.55	180.10	175.95	169.40	167.95	166.90
Perimeter Adj., Add or Deduct	Per 100 L.F.	30.90	20.60	15.40	10.35	7.75	6.10	5.20	4.45	3.90
Story Hgt. Adj., Add or Deduct	Per 1 Ft.	4.85	3.55	2.80	2.60	2.45	2.30	2.00	1.90	1.95
For Basement, add $25.80 per square foot of basement area										

The above costs were calculated using the basic specifications shown on the facing page. These costs should be adjusted where necessary for design alternatives and owner's requirements. Reported completed project costs, for this type of structure, range from $78.90 to $373.60 per S.F.

Common additives

Description	Unit	$ Cost
Closed Circuit Surveillance, one station, camera & monitor	Each	1975
For additional camera stations, add	Each	1050
Laundry Equipment, dryer, gas, 30 lb. capacity	Each	3800
Washer, commercial	Each	1600
Sauna, prefabricated, complete, 6' x 9'	Each	9725
8' x 8'	Each	11,500
Swimming Pools, Complete, gunite	S.F.	90.50 - 113
TV Antenna, Master system, 12 outlet	Outlet	280
30 outlet	Outlet	218
100 outlet	Outlet	206

Description	Unit	$ Cost
Commissioning Fees, sustainable commercial construction	S.F.	0.24 - 3.04
Energy Modelling Fees, commercial buildings to 10,000 SF	Each	11,000
Greater than 10,000 SF add	S.F.	0.04
Green Bldg Cert Fees for comm construction project reg	Project	900
Photovoltaic Pwr Sys, grid connected, 20 kW (~2400 SF), roof	Each	272,300
Green Roofs, 6" soil depth, w/ treated wd edging & sedum mats	S.F.	11.05
10" Soil depth, with treated wood edging & sedum mats	S.F.	12.68
Greywater Recovery Systems, prepackaged comm, 3060 gal.	Each	57,740
4590 gal.	Each	72,025
Rainwater Harvest Sys, prepckged comm, 10,000 gal, sys contrller	Each	31,375
20,000 gal. w/ system controller	Each	50,500
30,000 gal. w/ system controller	Each	80,225
Solar Domestic HW, closed loop, add-on sys, ext heat exchanger	Each	10,950
Drainback, hot water system, 120 gal tank	Each	14,125
Draindown, hot water system, 120 gal tank	Each	14,550

Important: See the Reference Section for Location Factors.

Model costs calculated for a 1 story building with 9' story height and 8,000 square feet of floor area

				Unit	Unit Cost	Cost Per S.F.	% Of Sub-Total
A. SUBSTRUCTURE							
1010	Standard Foundations	Poured concrete; strip and spread footings		S.F. Ground	3.22	3.22	
1020	Special Foundations	N/A		—			
1030	Slab on Grade	4" reinforced concrete with recycled vapor barrier and granular base		S.F. Slab	5.33	5.33	12.5%
2010	Basement Excavation	Site preparation for slab and trench for foundation wall and footing		S.F. Ground	.32	.32	
2020	Basement Walls	4' foundation wall		L.F. Wall	89	7.28	
B. SHELL							
	B10 Superstructure						
1010	Floor Construction	N/A		—	—	—	
1020	Roof Construction	Plywood on wood trusses		S.F. Roof	6.85	6.85	5.3 %
	B20 Exterior Enclosure						
2010	Exterior Walls	Face brick on wood studs with sheathing, insulation and paper	80% of wall	S.F. Wall	24.95	10.78	
2020	Exterior Windows	Wood double hung	20% of wall	Each	510	3.93	14.5%
2030	Exterior Doors	Wood solid core		Each	1460	4.01	
	B30 Roofing						
3010	Roof Coverings	Asphalt strip shingles, 210-235 lbs/Sq., R-10 insul. & weather barrier-recycled		S.F. Roof	8.13	8.13	6.3 %
3020	Roof Openings	N/A		—	—	—	
C. INTERIORS							
1010	Partitions	Gypsum bd. and sound deadening bd. on wood studs	9 SF Flr./LF Part.	S.F. Partition	10.01	8.90	
1020	Interior Doors	Single leaf hollow core wood, low VOC paint	300 S.F. Floor/Door	Each	557	1.85	
1030	Fittings	N/A		—	—	—	
2010	Stair Construction	N/A		—	—	—	18.1%
3010	Wall Finishes	90% paint, low VOC, 10% ceramic tile		S.F. Surface	1.59	2.82	
3020	Floor Finishes	85% carpet tile, 15% ceramic tile		S.F. Floor	5.31	5.31	
3030	Ceiling Finishes	Painted gypsum board on furring, low VOC paint		S.F. Ceiling	4.45	4.45	
D. SERVICES							
	D10 Conveying						
1010	Elevators & Lifts	N/A		—	—	—	
1020	Escalators & Moving Walks	N/A		—	—	—	0.0 %
	D20 Plumbing						
2010	Plumbing Fixtures	Toilet, low flow, auto sensor, & service fixt., supply & drainage	1 Fixt./90 SF Flr.	Each	2378	26.42	
2020	Domestic Water Distribution	Gas fired tankless water heater		S.F. Floor	.41	.41	22.0%
2040	Rain Water Drainage	Roof Drains		S.F. Roof	1.51	1.51	
	D30 HVAC						
3010	Energy Supply	N/A		—	—	—	
3020	Heat Generating Systems	Included in D3050		—	—	—	
3030	Cooling Generating Systems	N/A		—	—	—	2.2 %
3050	Terminal & Package Units	Through the wall electric heating and cooling units		S.F. Floor	2.82	2.82	
3090	Other HVAC Sys. & Equipment	N/A		—	—	—	
	D40 Fire Protection						
4010	Sprinklers	Wet pipe sprinkler system		S.F. Floor	4.76	4.76	4.5%
4020	Standpipes	Standpipe, wet, Class III		S.F. Floor	1.04	1.04	
	D50 Electrical						
5010	Electrical Service/Distribution	200 ampere service, panel board and feeders		S.F. Floor	1.25	1.25	
5020	Lighting & Branch Wiring	LED fixt., daylit. dim., ltg. on/off control, recept., switches and misc. pwr.		S.F. Floor	10.34	10.34	13.3%
5030	Communications & Security	Addressable alarm systems		S.F. Floor	2.68	2.68	
5090	Other Electrical Systems	Emergency generator, 7.5 kW, and energy monitoring systems			2.87	2.87	
E. EQUIPMENT & FURNISHINGS							
1010	Commercial Equipment	Laundry equipment		S.F. Floor	.97	.97	
1020	Institutional Equipment	N/A		—	—	—	
1090	Other Equipment	Waste handling recycling tilt truck		Each	.69	.69	1.4%
2020	Moveable Furnishings	No smoking signage		Each	.16	.16	
F. SPECIAL CONSTRUCTION							
1020	Integrated Construction	N/A		—	—	—	
1040	Special Facilities	N/A		—	—	—	0.0 %
G. BUILDING SITEWORK	**N/A**						

	Sub-Total	129.10	100%
CONTRACTOR FEES (General Requirements:10%, Overhead: 5%, Profit:10%)	25%	32.25	
ARCHITECT FEES	7%	11.30	
Total Building Cost		**172.65**	

Costs per square foot of floor area

Exterior Wall	S.F. Area	25000	37000	49000	61000	73000	81000	88000	96000	104000
	L.F. Perimeter	433	593	606	720	835	911	978	1054	1074
Decorative Concrete Block	Wood Joists	178.55	174.65	168.65	167.20	166.25	165.80	165.45	165.05	164.10
	Precast Conc.	190.50	186.40	180.20	178.75	177.70	177.20	176.85	176.40	175.50
Stucco on Concrete Block	Wood Joists	180.20	175.60	168.85	167.20	166.05	165.55	165.10	164.70	163.65
	Precast Conc.	192.55	187.95	181.20	179.60	178.50	177.95	177.55	177.10	176.10
Wood Siding	Wood Frame	172.60	169.10	164.15	162.90	162.10	161.70	161.40	161.05	160.25
Brick Veneer	Wood Frame	180.45	175.80	169.05	167.40	166.30	165.75	165.35	164.90	163.85
Perimeter Adj., Add or Deduct	Per 100 L.F.	5.45	3.70	2.75	2.25	1.90	1.65	1.55	1.45	1.25
Story Hgt. Adj., Add or Deduct	Per 1 Ft.	1.95	1.85	1.35	1.30	1.30	1.25	1.25	1.25	1.15

For Basement, add $33.85 per square foot of basement area

The above costs were calculated using the basic specifications shown on the facing page. These costs should be adjusted where necessary for design alternatives and owner's requirements. Reported completed project costs, for this type of structure, range from $72.65 to $373.60 per S.F.

Common additives

Description	Unit	$ Cost
Closed Circuit Surveillance, one station, camera & monitor	Each	1975
For additional camera station, add	Each	1050
Elevators, hydraulic passenger, 2 stops, 2500# capacity	Each	69,200
3500# capacity	Each	73,200
Additional stop, add	Each	8575
Laundry Equipment, dryer, gas, 30 lb. capacity	Each	3800
Washer, commercial	Each	1600
Sauna, prefabricated, complete, 6' x 9'	Each	9725
8' x 8'	Each	11,500
Swimming Pools, Complete, gunite	S.F.	90.50 - 113
TV Antenna, Master system, 12 outlet	Outlet	280
30 outlet	Outlet	218
100 outlet	Outlet	206

Description	Unit	$ Cost
Commissioning Fees, sustainable commercial construction	S.F.	0.24 - 3.04
Energy Modelling Fees, commercial buildings to 10,000 SF	Each	11,000
Greater than 10,000 SF add	S.F.	0.04
Green Bldg Cert Fees for comm construction project reg	Project	900
Photovoltaic Pwr Sys, grid connected, 20 kW (~2400 SF), roof	Each	272,300
Green Roofs, 6" soil depth, w/ treated wd edging & sedum mats	S.F.	11.05
10" Soil depth, with treated wood edging & sedum mats	S.F.	12.68
Greywater Recovery Systems, prepackaged comm, 3060 gal.	Each	57,740
4590 gal.	Each	72,025
Rainwater Harvest Sys, prepckged comm, 10,000 gal, sys contrller	Each	31,375
20,000 gal. w/ system controller	Each	50,500
30,000 gal. w/ system controller	Each	80,225
Solar Domestic HW, closed loop, add-on sys, ext heat exchanger	Each	10,950
Drainback, hot water system, 120 gal tank	Each	14,125
Draindown, hot water system, 120 gal tank	Each	14,550

Important: See the Reference Section for Location Factors.

Model costs calculated for a 3 story building with 9' story height and 49,000 square feet of floor area

G Motel, 2-3 Story

				Unit	Unit Cost	Cost Per S.F.	% Of Sub-Total
A. SUBSTRUCTURE							
1010	Standard Foundations	Poured concrete; strip and spread footings		S.F. Ground	1.47	.49	
1020	Special Foundations	N/A		—	—	—	
1030	Slab on Grade	4" reinforced concrete with recycled vapor barrier and granular base		S.F. Slab	5.33	1.77	3.3%
2010	Basement Excavation	Site preparation for slab and trench for foundation wall and footing		S.F. Ground	.18	.06	
2020	Basement Walls	4' foundation wall		L.F. Wall	89	2.19	
B. SHELL							
B10 Superstructure							
1010	Floor Construction	Precast concrete plank		S.F. Floor	10.37	6.91	7.5%
1020	Roof Construction	Precast concrete plank		S.F. Roof	9.84	3.28	
B20 Exterior Enclosure							
2010	Exterior Walls	Decorative concrete block	85% of wall	S.F. Wall	21.81	6.19	
2020	Exterior Windows	Aluminum sliding	15% of wall	Each	585	1.95	10.8%
2030	Exterior Doors	Aluminum and glass doors and entrance with transom		Each	1966	6.49	
B30 Roofing							
3010	Roof Coverings	Single-ply TPO membrane, 60 mils w/ R-20 insul.		S.F. Roof	6.12	2.04	1.5%
3020	Roof Openings	Roof hatches		S.F. Roof	.12	.04	
C. INTERIORS							
1010	Partitions	Concrete block w/ foamed-in insul.	7 SF Flr./LF Part.	S.F. Partition	21.19	24.22	
1020	Interior Doors	Wood hollow core, low VOC paint	70 S.F. Floor/Door	Each	557	7.96	
1030	Fittings	N/A	—	—	—	—	
2010	Stair Construction	Concrete filled metal pan		Flight	14,450	3.54	35.8%
3010	Wall Finishes	90% paint, low VOC, 10% ceramic tile		S.F. Surface	1.59	3.64	
3020	Floor Finishes	85% carpet tile, 5% vinyl composition tile, recycled content, 10% ceramic tile		S.F. Floor	5.31	5.31	
3030	Ceiling Finishes	Textured finish		S.F. Ceiling	4.07	4.07	
D. SERVICES							
D10 Conveying							
1010	Elevators & Lifts	Two hydraulic passenger elevators		Each	108,535	4.43	3.3%
1020	Escalators & Moving Walks	N/A		—	—	—	
D20 Plumbing							
2010	Plumbing Fixtures	Toilet, low flow, auto sensor & service fixtures, supply & drain.	1 Fixt./180 SF Flr.	Each	5263	29.24	
2020	Domestic Water Distribution	Gas fired, tankless water heater		S.F. Floor	.32	.32	22.1%
2040	Rain Water Drainage	Roof drains		S.F. Roof	1.35	.45	
D30 HVAC							
3010	Energy Supply	N/A		—	—	—	
3020	Heat Generating Systems	Included in D3050		—	—	—	
3030	Cooling Generating Systems	N/A		—	—	—	1.9 %
3050	Terminal & Package Units	Through the wall electric heating and cooling units		S.F. Floor	2.54	2.54	
3090	Other HVAC Sys. & Equipment	N/A		—	—	—	
D40 Fire Protection							
4010	Sprinklers	Sprinklers, wet, light hazard		S.F. Floor	2.95	2.95	2.3%
4020	Standpipes	Standpipe, wet, Class III		S.F. Floor	.23	.23	
D50 Electrical							
5010	Electrical Service/Distribution	800 ampere service, panel board and feeders		S.F. Floor	1.27	1.27	
5020	Lighting & Branch Wiring	LED fixtures, daylt. dim., ltg. on/off, recept., switches and misc. power		S.F. Floor	11.01	11.01	11.2%
5030	Communications & Security	Addressable alarm systems and emergency lighting		S.F. Floor	1.85	1.85	
5090	Other Electrical Systems	Emergency generator, 7.5 kW, energy monitoring systems		S.F. Floor	1.15	1.15	
E. EQUIPMENT & FURNISHINGS							
1010	Commercial Equipment	Commercial laundry equipment		S.F. Floor	.32	.32	
1020	Institutional Equipment	N/A		—	—	—	
1090	Other Equipment	Waste handling recycling tilt truck		Each	.06	.06	0.3%
2020	Moveable Furnishings	No smoking signage		Each	.02	.02	
F. SPECIAL CONSTRUCTION							
1020	Integrated Construction	N/A		—	—	—	0.0 %
1040	Special Facilities	N/A		—	—	—	
G. BUILDING SITEWORK	**N/A**						

	Sub-Total	135.99	**100%**
CONTRACTOR FEES (General Requirements: 10%, Overhead: 5%, Profit: 10%)	25%	34.01	
ARCHITECT FEES	6%	10.20	
	Total Building Cost	180.20	

Costs per square foot of floor area

Exterior Wall	S.F. Area	2000	3000	5000	7000	9000	12000	15000	20000	25000
	L.F. Perimeter	220	260	320	360	420	480	520	640	700
Wood Siding	Wood Truss	215.75	195.55	177.50	168.35	164.35	159.65	156.20	154.00	151.50
Brick Veneer	Wood Truss	263.80	237.90	214.55	202.60	197.45	191.30	186.65	183.85	180.55
Brick on Block	Wood Truss	212.65	183.80	157.65	144.10	138.35	131.35	126.00	122.90	119.10
	Steel Roof Deck	266.65	236.45	208.95	194.80	188.70	181.40	175.85	172.50	168.45
EIFS on Metal Studs	Steel Roof Deck	241.95	218.05	196.60	185.65	180.90	175.20	171.05	168.45	165.40
Tiltup Concrete Panel	Steel Roof Deck	250.25	224.30	200.90	188.95	183.75	177.55	173.00	170.20	166.85
Perimeter Adj., Add or Deduct	Per 100 L.F.	24.35	16.25	9.80	7.00	5.45	4.10	3.25	2.45	2.00
Story Hgt. Adj., Add or Deduct	Per 1 Ft.	2.90	2.20	1.65	1.35	1.20	1.05	0.90	0.80	0.70
For Basement, add $35.65 per square foot of basement area										

The above costs were calculated using the basic specifications shown on the facing page. These costs should be adjusted where necessary for design alternatives and owner's requirements. Reported completed project costs, for this type of structure, range from $76.20 to $294.60 per S.F.

Common additives

Description	Unit	$ Cost
Closed Circuit Surveillance, one station, camera & monitor	Each	1975
For additional camera stations, add	Each	1050
Directory boards, plastic, glass covered, 30" x 20"	Each	630
36" x 48"	Each	1500
Aluminum, 36" x 24"	Each	735
48" x 32"	Each	1050
Electronic, wall mounted	S.F.	2525
Pedestal access flr sys w/ PLAM cover, comp rm,		
Less than 6000 SF	S.F.	12
Greater than 6000 SF	S.F.	11.25
Office, greater than 6000 S.F.	S.F.	8.05
Uninterruptible power supply, 15 kVA/12.75 kW	kW	1795

Description	Unit	$ Cost
Commissioning Fees, sustainable commercial construction	S.F.	0.24 - 3.04
Energy Modelling Fees, commercial buildings to 10,000 SF	Each	11,000
Greater than 10,000 SF add	S.F.	0.04
Green Bldg Cert Fees for comm construction project reg	Project	900
Photovoltaic Pwr Sys, grid connected, 20 kW (~2400 SF), roof	Each	272,300
Green Roofs, 6" soil depth, w/ treated wd edging & sedum mats	S.F.	11.05
10" Soil depth, with treated wood edging & sedum mats	S.F.	12.68
Greywater Recovery Systems, prepackaged comm, 3060 gal.	Each	57,740
4590 gal.	Each	72,025
Rainwater Harvest Sys, prepckged comm, 10,000 gal, sys contrller	Each	31,375
20,000 gal. w/ system controller	Each	50,500
30,000 gal. w/ system controller	Each	80,225
Solar Domestic HW, closed loop, add-on sys, ext heat exchanger	Each	10,950
Drainback, hot water system, 120 gal tank	Each	14,125
Draindown, hot water system, 120 gal tank	Each	14,550

Important: See the Reference Section for Location Factors.

Model costs calculated for a 1 story building with 12' story height and 7,000 square feet of floor area

				Unit	Unit Cost	Cost Per S.F.	% Of Sub-Total
A. SUBSTRUCTURE							
1010	Standard Foundations	Poured concrete; strip and spread footings		S.F. Ground	2.80	2.80	
1020	Special Foundations	N/A		—	—	—	
1030	Slab on Grade	4" reinforced concrete with recycled vapor barrier and granular base		S.F. Slab	5.33	5.33	9.5%
2010	Basement Excavation	Site preparation for slab and trench for foundation wall and footing		S.F. Ground	.32	.32	
2020	Basement Walls	4' foundation wall		L.F. Wall	169	4.78	
B. SHELL							
B10 Superstructure							
1010	Floor Construction	N/A		—	—	—	7.4 %
1020	Roof Construction	Steel joists, girders & deck on columns		S.F. Roof	10.30	10.30	
B20 Exterior Enclosure							
2010	Exterior Walls	E.I.F.S. on metal studs		S.F. Wall	17.26	8.52	
2020	Exterior Windows	Aluminum outward projecting	20% of wall	Each	736	3.95	11.1%
2030	Exterior Doors	Aluminum and glass, hollow metal		Each	3473	2.97	
B30 Roofing							
3010	Roof Coverings	Single-ply TPO membrane, 45 mils, heat welded seams w/R-20 insul.		S.F. Roof	9.56	9.56	7.0%
3020	Roof Openings	Roof hatch		S.F. Roof	.18	.18	
C. INTERIORS							
1010	Partitions	Gyp. bd. on mtl. studs w/sound attenuation	20 SF Flr/LF Part.	S.F. Partition	10.04	5.02	
1020	Interior Doors	Single leaf hollow metal, low VOC paint	200 S.F. Floor/Door	Each	1152	5.76	
1030	Fittings	Toilet partitions		S.F. Floor	.83	.83	
2010	Stair Construction	N/A		—	—	—	17.8%
3010	Wall Finishes	60% vinyl wall covering, 40% paint, low VOC		S.F. Surface	1.58	1.58	
3020	Floor Finishes	60% carpet tile, 30% vinyl composition tile, recycled content, 10% ceramic tile		S.F. Floor	4.64	4.64	
3030	Ceiling Finishes	Mineral fiber tile on concealed zee bars		S.F. Ceiling	6.89	6.89	
D. SERVICES							
D10 Conveying							
1010	Elevators & Lifts	N/A		—	—	—	0.0 %
1020	Escalators & Moving Walks	N/A		—	—	—	
D20 Plumbing							
2010	Plumbing Fixtures	Toilet, low flow, auto sensor, & service fixt., supply & drain.	1 Fixt./1320 SF Flr.	Each	9728	7.37	
2020	Domestic Water Distribution	Tankless, on-demand water heater, gas/propane		S.F. Floor	1.10	1.10	6.7%
2040	Rain Water Drainage	Roof drains		S.F. Roof	.83	.83	
D30 HVAC							
3010	Energy Supply	N/A		—	—	—	
3020	Heat Generating Systems	Included in D3050		—	—	—	
3040	Distribution Systems	Enthalpy heat recovery packages		Each	17,475	2.50	16.0 %
3050	Terminal & Package Units	Multizone rooftop air conditioner, SEER 14		S.F. Floor	19.70	19.70	
3090	Other HVAC Sys. & Equipment	N/A		—	—	—	
D40 Fire Protection							
4010	Sprinklers	Sprinkler system, light hazard		S.F. Floor	3.56	3.56	3.6%
4020	Standpipes	Standpipes and hose systems		S.F. Floor	1.42	1.42	
D50 Electrical							
5010	Electrical Service/Distribution	400 ampere service, panel board and feeders		S.F. Floor	2.04	2.04	
5020	Lighting & Branch Wiring	LED fixtures, daylt. dim., ltg. on/off, recept., switches, and A.C. power		S.F. Floor	15.56	15.56	20.2%
5030	Communications & Security	Addressable alarm systems, internet and phone wiring, and emergency lighting		S.F. Floor	7.21	7.21	
5090	Other Electrical Systems	Emergency generator, 7.5 kW, energy monitoring systems		S.F. Floor	3.27	3.27	
E. EQUIPMENT & FURNISHINGS							
1010	Commercial Equipment	N/A		—	—	—	
1020	Institutional Equipment	N/A		—	—	—	0.6 %
1090	Other Equipment	Waste handling recycling tilt truck		Each	.79	.79	
2020	Moveable Furnishings	No smoking signage		Each	.04	.04	
F. SPECIAL CONSTRUCTION							
1020	Integrated Construction	N/A		—	—	—	0.0 %
1040	Special Facilities	N/A		—	—	—	
G. BUILDING SITEWORK	**N/A**						

	Sub-Total	138.82	**100%**
CONTRACTOR FEES (General Requirements: 10%, Overhead: 5%, Profit: 10%)	25%	34.68	
ARCHITECT FEES	7%	12.15	
	Total Building Cost	185.65	

Costs per square foot of floor area

Exterior Wall	S.F. Area	5000	8000	12000	16000	20000	35000	50000	65000	80000
	L.F. Perimeter	220	260	310	330	360	440	490	548	580
Face Brick with Concrete Block Back-up	Wood Joists	268.45	233.80	214.00	199.95	192.65	178.10	170.95	167.35	164.40
	Steel Joists	269.40	234.75	214.95	200.90	193.60	179.05	171.90	168.30	165.35
Glass and Metal Curtain Wall	Steel Frame	318.30	273.10	247.15	228.40	218.70	199.15	189.45	184.60	180.55
	R/Conc. Frame	313.95	269.35	243.65	225.05	215.40	196.00	186.35	181.55	177.60
Wood Siding	Wood Frame	207.80	185.00	172.00	163.30	158.75	149.75	145.45	143.30	141.55
Brick Veneer	Wood Frame	230.65	201.90	185.45	174.05	168.10	156.30	150.60	147.65	145.35
Perimeter Adj., Add or Deduct	Per 100 L.F.	43.70	27.40	18.15	13.65	10.90	6.25	4.35	3.40	2.75
Story Hgt. Adj., Add or Deduct	Per 1 Ft.	7.20	5.35	4.20	3.40	2.95	2.00	1.60	1.35	1.20

For Basement, add $39.85 per square foot of basement area

The above costs were calculated using the basic specifications shown on the facing page. These costs should be adjusted where necessary for design alternatives and owner's requirements. Reported completed project costs, for this type of structure, range from $79.75 to $308.95 per S.F.

Common additives

Description	Unit	$ Cost
Closed Circuit Surveillance, one station, camera and monitor	Each	1975
For additional camera stations, add	Each	1050
Directory Boards, plastic, glass covered, 30" x 20"	Each	630
36" x 48"	Each	1500
Aluminum, 36" x 24"	Each	735
48" x 32"	Each	1050
Electronic, wall mounted	S.F.	2525
Escalators, 10' rise, 32" wide, glass balustrade	Each	140,500
48" wide, glass balustrade	Each	147,500
Pedestal access flr sys w/ PLAM cover, comp rm,		
Less than 6000 SF	S.F.	12
Greater than 6000 SF	S.F.	11.25
Office, greater than 6000 S.F.	S.F.	8.05
Uninterruptible power supply, 15 kVA/12.75 kW	kW	1795

Description	Unit	$ Cost
Commissioning Fees, sustainable commercial construction	S.F.	0.24 - 3.04
Energy Modelling Fees, commercial buildings to 10,000 SF	Each	11,000
Greater than 10,000 SF add	S.F.	0.04
Green Bldg Cert Fees for comm construction project reg	Project	900
Photovoltaic Pwr Sys, grid connected, 20 kW (~2400 SF), roof	Each	272,300
Green Roofs, 6" soil depth, w/ treated wd edging & sedum mats	S.F.	11.05
10" Soil depth, with treated wood edging & sedum mats	S.F.	12.68
Greywater Recovery Systems, prepackaged comm, 3060 gal.	Each	57,740
4590 gal.	Each	72,025
Rainwater Harvest Sys, prepckged comm, 10,000 gal, sys contrller	Each	31,375
20,000 gal. w/ system controller	Each	50,500
30,000 gal. w/ system controller	Each	80,225
Solar Domestic HW, closed loop, add-on sys, ext heat exchanger	Each	10,950
Drainback, hot water system, 120 gal tank	Each	14,125
Draindown, hot water system, 120 gal tank	Each	14,550

Important: See the Reference Section for Location Factors.

Model costs calculated for a 3 story building with 12' story height and 20,000 square feet of floor area

G Office, 2-4 Story

				Unit	Unit Cost	Cost Per S.F.	% Of Sub-Total
A. SUBSTRUCTURE							
1010	Standard Foundations	Poured concrete; strip and spread footings		S.F. Ground	7.47	2.49	
1020	Special Foundations	N/A		—	—	—	
1030	Slab on Grade	4" reinforced concrete with recycled vapor barrier and granular base		S.F. Slab	5.33	1.77	4.3%
2010	Basement Excavation	Site preparation for slab and trench for foundation wall and footing		S.F. Ground	.18	.06	
2020	Basement Walls	4' foundation wall		L.F. Wall	169	1.88	
B. SHELL							
B10 Superstructure							
1010	Floor Construction	Open web steel joists, slab form, concrete, columns		S.F. Floor	19.14	12.76	10.5%
1020	Roof Construction	Metal deck, open web steel joists, columns		S.F. Roof	7.35	2.45	
B20 Exterior Enclosure							
2010	Exterior Walls	Face brick with concrete block backup	80% of wall	S.F. Wall	38.16	19.78	
2020	Exterior Windows	Aluminum outward projecting	20% of wall	Each	736	4.15	17.2%
2030	Exterior Doors	Aluminum and glass, hollow metal		Each	3473	1.04	
B30 Roofing							
3010	Roof Coverings	Single-ply, TPO membrane, 60 mils, heat welded seams w/ R-20 insul.		S.F. Roof	6.99	2.33	1.6%
3020	Roof Openings	N/A		—	—	—	
C. INTERIORS							
1010	Partitions	Gypsum board on metal studs	20 SF Flr/LF Part.	S.F. Partition	10.23	4.09	
1020	Interior Doors	Single leaf hollow metal, low VOC paint	200 S.F. Floor/Door	Each	1152	5.76	
1030	Fittings	Toilet partitions		S.F. Floor	1.75	1.75	
2010	Stair Construction	Concrete filled metal pan		Flight	14,450	5.06	20.4%
3010	Wall Finishes	60% vinyl wall covering, 40% paint, low VOC		S.F. Surface	1.59	1.27	
3020	Floor Finishes	60% carpet tile, 30% vinyl composition tile, recycled content, 10% ceramic tile		S.F. Floor	4.64	4.64	
3030	Ceiling Finishes	Mineral fiber tile on concealed zee bars		S.F. Ceiling	6.89	6.89	
D. SERVICES							
D10 Conveying							
1010	Elevators & Lifts	Two hydraulic passenger elevators		Each	118,700	11.87	8.2%
1020	Escalators & Moving Walks	N/A		—	—	—	
D20 Plumbing							
2010	Plumbing Fixtures	Toilet, low flow, auto sensor, & service fixt., supply & drain.	1 Fixt./1320 SF Flr.	Each	5821	4.41	
2020	Domestic Water Distribution	Gas fired, tankless water heater		S.F. Floor	.23	.23	3.7%
2040	Rain Water Drainage	Roof drains		S.F. Roof	2.04	.68	
D30 HVAC							
3010	Energy Supply	N/A		—	—	—	
3020	Heat Generating Systems	Included in D3050		—	—	—	
3040	Distribution Systems	Enthalpy heat recovery packages		Each	17,475	2.62	12.8 %
3050	Terminal & Package Units	Multizone rooftop air conditioner. SEER 14		S.F. Floor	15.90	15.90	
3090	Other HVAC Sys. & Equipment	N/A		—	—	—	
D40 Fire Protection							
4010	Sprinklers	Wet pipe sprinkler system		S.F. Floor	3.67	3.67	3.2%
4020	Standpipes	Standpipes and hose systems		S.F. Floor	.91	.91	
D50 Electrical							
5010	Electrical Service/Distribution	1000 ampere service, panel board and feeders		S.F. Floor	2.91	2.91	
5020	Lighting & Branch Wiring	LED fixtures, daylt. dim., ltg. on/off, recept., switches, and A.C. power		S.F. Floor	15.25	15.25	18.0%
5030	Communications & Security	Addressable alarm systems, internet and phone wiring, & emergency ltg.		S.F. Floor	6.04	6.04	
5090	Other Electrical Systems	Emergency generator, 7.5 kW, UPS, energy monitoring systems		S.F. Floor	1.80	1.80	
E. EQUIPMENT & FURNISHINGS							
1010	Commercial Equipment	N/A		—	—	—	
1020	Institutional Equipment	N/A		—	—	—	
1090	Other Equipment	Waste handling recycling tilt truck		Each	.28	.28	0.2 %
2020	Moveable Furnishings	No smoking signage		Each	.02	.02	
F. SPECIAL CONSTRUCTION							
1020	Integrated Construction	N/A		—	—	—	
1040	Special Facilities	N/A		—	—	—	0.0 %
G. BUILDING SITEWORK	**N/A**						

	Sub-Total	144.76	100%
CONTRACTOR FEES (General Requirements: 10%, Overhead: 5%, Profit: 10%)	25%	36.17	
ARCHITECT FEES	7%	12.67	

Total Building Cost	**193.60**

263

Costs per square foot of floor area

Exterior Wall	S.F. Area	20000	40000	60000	80000	100000	150000	200000	250000	300000
	L.F. Perimeter	260	360	400	420	460	520	600	640	700
Precast Concrete Panel	Steel Frame	241.70	208.70	191.10	180.65	175.65	167.20	163.75	160.50	158.90
	R/Conc. Frame	240.15	207.05	189.35	178.90	173.95	165.45	161.95	158.70	157.10
Face Brick with Concrete Block Back-up	Steel Frame	229.25	200.25	185.00	175.95	171.65	164.40	161.35	158.55	157.20
	R/Conc. Frame	226.85	197.80	182.55	173.55	169.25	161.90	158.85	156.05	154.75
Limestone Panel Concrete Block Back-up	Steel Frame	271.45	229.45	206.65	193.00	186.60	175.60	171.05	166.80	164.75
	R/Conc. Frame	268.95	226.95	204.15	190.50	184.10	173.10	168.60	164.40	162.25
Perimeter Adj., Add or Deduct	Per 100 L.F.	33.15	16.60	11.00	8.25	6.70	4.45	3.30	2.70	2.25
Story Hgt. Adj., Add or Deduct	Per 1 Ft.	6.95	4.75	3.50	2.75	2.50	1.85	1.60	1.40	1.25

For Basement, add $43.00 per square foot of basement area

The above costs were calculated using the basic specifications shown on the facing page. These costs should be adjusted where necessary for design alternatives and owner's requirements. Reported completed project costs, for this type of structure, range from $89.75 to $263.90 per S.F.

Common additives

Description	Unit	$ Cost
Closed Circuit Surveillance, one station, camera and monitor	Each	1975
For additional camera stations, add	Each	1050
Directory Boards, plastic, glass covered, 30" x 20"	Each	630
36" x 48"	Each	1500
Aluminum, 36" x 24"	Each	735
48" x 32"	Each	1050
Electronic, wall mounted	S.F.	2525
Escalators, 10' rise, 32" wide, glass balustrade	Each	140,500
48" wide, glass balustrade	Each	147,500
Pedestal access flr sys w/ PLAM cover, comp rm,		
Less than 6000 SF	S.F.	12
Greater than 6000 SF	S.F.	11.25
Office, greater than 6000 S.F.	S.F.	8.05
Uninterruptible power supply, 15 kVA/12.75 kW	kW	1795

Description	Unit	$ Cost
Commissioning Fees, sustainable commercial construction	S.F.	0.24 - 3.04
Energy Modelling Fees, commercial buildings to 10,000 SF	Each	11,000
Greater than 10,000 SF add	S.F.	0.04
Green Bldg Cert Fees for comm construction project reg	Project	900
Photovoltaic Pwr Sys, grid connected, 20 kW (~2400 SF), roof	Each	272,300
Green Roofs, 6" soil depth, w/ treated wd edging & sedum mats	S.F.	11.05
10" Soil depth, with treated wood edging & sedum mats	S.F.	12.68
Greywater Recovery Systems, prepackaged comm, 3060 gal.	Each	57,740
4590 gal.	Each	72,025
Rainwater Harvest Sys, prepckged comm, 10,000 gal, sys contrller	Each	31,375
20,000 gal. w/ system controller	Each	50,500
30,000 gal. w/ system controller	Each	80,225
Solar Domestic HW, closed loop, add-on sys, ext heat exchanger	Each	10,950
Drainback, hot water system, 120 gal tank	Each	14,125
Draindown, hot water system, 120 gal tank	Each	14,550

Model costs calculated for a 8 story building with 12' story height and 80,000 square feet of floor area

G Office, 5-10 Story

				Unit	Unit Cost	Cost Per S.F.	% Of Sub-Total
A. SUBSTRUCTURE							
1010	Standard Foundations	Poured concrete; strip and spread footings		S.F. Ground	12.16	1.52	
1020	Special Foundations	N/A		—	—	—	
1030	Slab on Grade	4" reinforced concrete with recycled vapor barrier and granular base		S.F. Slab	5.33	.67	2.1%
2010	Basement Excavation	Site preparation for slab and trench for foundation wall and footing		S.F. Ground	.32	.04	
2020	Basement Walls	4' foundation wall		L.F. Wall	89	.60	
B. SHELL							
B10 Superstructure							
1010	Floor Construction	Concrete slab with metal deck and beams		S.F. Floor	24.57	21.50	16.4%
1020	Roof Construction	Metal deck, open web steel joists, interior columns		S.F. Roof	7.12	.89	
B20 Exterior Enclosure							
2010	Exterior Walls	Precast concrete panels	80% of wall	S.F. Wall	48.24	19.45	
2020	Exterior Windows	Vertical pivoted steel	20% of wall	Each	585	3.94	17.4%
2030	Exterior Doors	Double aluminum and glass doors and entrance with transoms		Each	4168	.27	
B30 Roofing							
3010	Roof Coverings	Single-ply TPO membrane, 60 mils, welded seams w/R-20 insul.		S.F. Roof	5.68	.71	0.5%
3020	Roof Openings	N/A		—	—	—	
C. INTERIORS							
1010	Partitions	Gypsum board on metal studs w/ sound attenuation	30 SF Flr./LF Part.	S.F. Partition	11.10	3.70	
1020	Interior Doors	Single leaf hollow metal, low VOC paint	400 S.F. Floor/Door	Each	1152	2.89	
1030	Fittings	Toilet Partitions		S.F. Floor	1.17	1.17	
2010	Stair Construction	Concrete filled metal pan		Flight	14,450	3.07	17.2%
3010	Wall Finishes	60% vinyl wall covering, 40% paint, low VOC paint		S.F. Surface	1.59	1.06	
3020	Floor Finishes	60% carpet tile, 30% vinyl composition tile, recycled content, 10% ceramic tile		S.F. Floor	4.64	4.64	
3030	Ceiling Finishes	Mineral fiber tile on concealed zee bars		S.F. Ceiling	6.89	6.89	
D. SERVICES							
D10 Conveying							
1010	Elevators & Lifts	Four geared passenger elevators		Each	307,600	15.38	11.3%
1020	Escalators & Moving Walks	N/A		—	—	—	
D20 Plumbing							
2010	Plumbing Fixtures	Toilet, low flow, auto sensor, & service fixt., supply & drain.	1 Fixt./1370 SF Flr.	Each	4261	3.11	
2020	Domestic Water Distribution	Gas fired tankless water heater		S.F. Floor	.45	.45	2.8%
2040	Rain Water Drainage	Roof drains		S.F. Roof	2.40	.30	
D30 HVAC							
3010	Energy Supply	N/A		—	—	—	
3020	Heat Generating Systems	Included in D3050		—	—	—	
3040	Distribution Systems	Enthalpy heat recovery packages		Each	36,875	1.84	13.0 %
3050	Terminal & Package Units	Multizone rooftop air conditioner, SEER 14		S.F. Floor	15.90	15.90	
3090	Other HVAC Sys. & Equipment	N/A		—	—	—	
D40 Fire Protection							
4010	Sprinklers	Wet pipe sprinkler system		S.F. Floor	2.87	2.87	2.9%
4020	Standpipes	Standpipes and hose systems		S.F. Floor	1.05	1.05	
D50 Electrical							
5010	Electrical Service/Distribution	1600 ampere service, panel board and feeders		S.F. Floor	1.08	1.08	
5020	Lighting & Branch Wiring	LED fixtures, daylt. dim., ltg. on/off, recept., switches, and A.C. power		S.F. Floor	14.98	14.98	16.4%
5030	Communications & Security	Addressable alarm systems, internet and phone wiring, emergency lighting		S.F. Floor	4.53	4.53	
5090	Other Electrical Systems	Emergency generator, 100 kW, UPS, energy monitoring systems		S.F. Floor	1.80	1.80	
E. EQUIPMENT & FURNISHINGS							
1010	Commercial Equipment	N/A		—	—	—	
1020	Institutional Equipment	N/A		—	—	—	
1090	Other Equipment	Waste handling recycling tilt truck		Each	.04	.04	0.0 %
2020	Moveable Furnishings	No smoking signage		Each			
F. SPECIAL CONSTRUCTION							
1020	Integrated Construction	N/A		—	—	—	0.0 %
1040	Special Facilities	N/A		—	—	—	
G. BUILDING SITEWORK	**N/A**						

	Sub-Total	136.34	**100%**
CONTRACTOR FEES (General Requirements: 10%, Overhead: 5%, Profit: 10%)	25%	34.08	
ARCHITECT FEES	6%	10.23	
Total Building Cost		**180.65**	

Costs per square foot of floor area

Exterior Wall	S.F. Area	120000	145000	170000	200000	230000	260000	400000	600000	800000
	L.F. Perimeter	420	450	470	490	510	530	600	730	820
Double Glazed Heat Absorbing Tinted Plate Glass Panels	Steel Frame	215.40	206.20	198.65	191.65	186.45	182.50	170.70	164.30	160.20
	R/Conc. Frame	205.50	196.45	189.00	182.10	177.00	173.10	161.50	155.25	151.20
Face Brick with Concrete Block Back-up	Steel Frame	184.60	178.80	174.25	170.05	166.85	164.45	157.45	153.50	151.10
	R/Conc. Frame	208.45	202.90	198.45	194.30	191.30	188.90	182.05	178.25	175.90
Precast Concrete Panel With Exposed Aggregate	Steel Frame	188.80	182.55	177.55	172.95	169.50	166.85	159.20	154.95	152.35
	R/Conc. Frame	178.95	172.85	168.00	163.50	160.15	157.55	150.10	145.95	143.35
Perimeter Adj., Add or Deduct	Per 100 L.F.	15.70	12.95	11.05	9.35	8.15	7.15	4.65	3.10	2.40
Story Hgt. Adj., Add or Deduct	Per 1 Ft.	6.40	5.65	5.00	4.45	4.00	3.65	2.70	2.20	1.85
For Basement, add $43.00 per square foot of basement area										

The above costs were calculated using the basic specifications shown on the facing page. These costs should be adjusted where necessary for design alternatives and owner's requirements. Reported completed project costs, for this type of structure, range from $112.55 to $274.65 per S.F.

Common additives

Description	Unit	$ Cost
Closed Circuit Surveillance, one station, camera and monitor	Each	1975
For additional camera stations, add	Each	1050
Directory Boards, plastic, glass covered, 30" x 20"	Each	630
36" x 48"	Each	1500
Aluminum, 36" x 24"	Each	735
48" x 32"	Each	1050
Electronic, wall mounted	S.F.	2525
Escalators, 10' rise, 32" wide, glass balustrade	Each	140,500
48" wide, glass balustrade	Each	147,500
Pedestal access flr sys w/ PLAM cover, comp rm,		
Less than 6000 SF	S.F.	12
Greater than 6000 SF	S.F.	11.25
Office, greater than 6000 S.F.	S.F.	8.05
Uninterruptible power supply, 15 kVA/12.75 kW	kW	1795

Description	Unit	$ Cost
Commissioning Fees, sustainable commercial construction	S.F.	0.24 - 3.04
Energy Modelling Fees, commercial buildings to 10,000 SF	Each	11,000
Greater than 10,000 SF add	S.F.	0.04
Green Bldg Cert Fees for comm construction project reg	Project	900
Photovoltaic Pwr Sys, grid connected, 20 kW (~2400 SF), roof	Each	272,300
Green Roofs, 6" soil depth, w/ treated wd edging & sedum mats	S.F.	11.05
10" Soil depth, with treated wood edging & sedum mats	S.F.	12.68
Greywater Recovery Systems, prepackaged comm, 3060 gal.	Each	57,740
4590 gal.	Each	72,025
Rainwater Harvest Sys, prepckged comm, 10,000 gal, sys contrller	Each	31,375
20,000 gal. w/ system controller	Each	50,500
30,000 gal. w/ system controller	Each	80,225
Solar Domestic HW, closed loop, add-on sys, ext heat exchanger	Each	10,950
Drainback, hot water system, 120 gal tank	Each	14,125
Draindown, hot water system, 120 gal tank	Each	14,550

Important: See the Reference Section for Location Factors.

Model costs calculated for a 16 story building with 10' story height and 260,000 square feet of floor area

				Unit	Unit Cost	Cost Per S.F.	% Of Sub-Total
A. SUBSTRUCTURE							
1010	Standard Foundations	CIP concrete pile caps		S.F. Ground	9.92	.62	
1020	Special Foundations	Steel H-piles, concrete grade beams		S.F. Ground	61	3.81	
1030	Slab on Grade	4" reinforced concrete with recycled vapor barrier and granular base		S.F. Slab	5.33	.33	3.8%
2010	Basement Excavation	Site preparation for slab, piles and grade beams		S.F. Ground	.32	.02	
2020	Basement Walls	4' foundation wall		L.F. Wall	89	.43	
B. SHELL							
B10 Superstructure							
1010	Floor Construction	Concrete slab, metal deck, beams		S.F. Floor	28.26	26.49	19.6%
1020	Roof Construction	Metal deck, open web steel joists, beams, columns		S.F. Roof	8.64	.54	
B20 Exterior Enclosure							
2010	Exterior Walls	N/A		—			
2020	Exterior Windows	Double glazed heat absorbing, tinted plate glass wall panels	100% of wall	Each	82	26.75	19.9%
2030	Exterior Doors	Double aluminum & glass doors		Each	6311	.67	
B30 Roofing							
3010	Roof Coverings	Single ply membrane, fully adhered; perlite/EPS R-20 insulation		S.F. Roof	6.40	.40	0.3%
3020	Roof Openings	N/A					
C. INTERIORS							
1010	Partitions	Gypsum board on metal studs, sound attenuation	30 SF Flr./LF Part.	S.F. Partition	12.49	3.33	
1020	Interior Doors	Single leaf hollow metal, low VOC paint	400 S.F. Floor/Door	Each	1152	2.89	
1030	Fittings	Toilet partitions		S.F. Floor	.67	.67	
2010	Stair Construction	Concrete filled metal pan		Flight	17,250	2.33	16.0%
3010	Wall Finishes	60% vinyl wall covering, 40% paint, low VOC		S.F. Surface	1.58	.84	
3020	Floor Finishes	60% carpet tile, 30% vinyl composition tile, recycled content, 10% ceramic tile		S.F. Floor	5.14	5.14	
3030	Ceiling Finishes	Mineral fiber tile on concealed zee bars		S.F. Ceiling	6.89	6.89	
D. SERVICES							
D10 Conveying							
1010	Elevators & Lifts	Four geared passenger elevators		Each	499,200	7.68	5.6%
1020	Escalators & Moving Walks	N/A		—	—	—	
D20 Plumbing							
2010	Plumbing Fixtures	Toilet, low flow, auto sensor, & service fixt., supply & drain.	1 Fixt./1345 SF Flr.	Each	6469	4.81	
2020	Domestic Water Distribution	Gas fired, tankless water heater		S.F. Floor	.18	.18	3.8%
2040	Rain Water Drainage	Roof drains		S.F. Roof	2.88	.18	
D30 HVAC							
3010	Energy Supply	N/A		—	—	—	
3020	Heat Generating Systems	N/A		—	—	—	
3040	Distribution Systems	Enthalpy heat recovery packages		Each	36,875	1.56	12.7%
3050	Terminal & Package Units	Multizone rooftop air conditioner		S.F. Floor	15.90	15.90	
3090	Other HVAC Sys. & Equipment	N/A		—	—	—	
D40 Fire Protection							
4010	Sprinklers	Sprinkler system, light hazard		S.F. Floor	2.78	2.78	2.4%
4020	Standpipes	Standpipes and hose systems		S.F. Floor	.54	.54	
D50 Electrical							
5010	Electrical Service/Distribution	2400 ampere service, panel board and feeders		S.F. Floor	.71	.71	
5020	Lighting & Branch Wiring	LED fixtures, daylt. dim., ltg. on/off, recept., switches, and A.C. power		S.F. Floor	14.85	14.85	15.9%
5030	Communications & Security	Addressable alarm systems, internet & phone wiring, emergency ltg.		S.F. Floor	5.40	5.40	
5090	Other Electrical Systems	Emergency generator, 200 kW, UPS, energy monitoring systems		S.F. Floor	.96	.96	
E. EQUIPMENT & FURNISHINGS							
1010	Commercial Equipment	N/A		—	—	—	
1020	Institutional Equipment	N/A		—	—	—	
1090	Other Equipment	Waste handling recycling tilt truck		Each	.01	.01	0.0%
2020	Moveable Furnishings	No smoking signage		Each			
F. SPECIAL CONSTRUCTION							
1020	Integrated Construction	N/A		—	—	—	
1040	Special Facilities	N/A		—	—	—	0.0%
G. BUILDING SITEWORK	**N/A**						

		Sub-Total	137.71	100%
CONTRACTOR FEES (General Requirements: 10%, Overhead: 5%, Profit: 10%)		25%	34.46	
ARCHITECT FEES		6%	10.33	

Total Building Cost	**182.50**

Costs per square foot of floor area

Exterior Wall	S.F. Area	7000	9000	11000	13000	15000	17000	19000	21000	23000
	L.F. Perimeter	240	280	303	325	354	372	397	422	447
Limestone with Concrete Block Back-up	Bearing Walls	296.95	279.85	264.90	254.35	247.80	241.10	236.85	233.30	230.40
	R/Conc. Frame	296.55	280.10	266.00	256.00	249.80	243.55	239.50	236.15	233.45
Face Brick with Concrete Block Back-up	Bearing Walls	246.60	232.85	221.65	213.80	208.75	203.95	200.75	198.05	195.85
	R/Conc. Frame	268.00	254.20	243.00	235.20	230.15	225.30	222.05	219.40	217.25
Decorative Concrete Block	Bearing Walls	233.85	221.25	211.40	204.50	200.00	195.80	192.95	190.55	188.65
	R/Conc. Frame	256.35	243.75	233.90	227.00	222.50	218.30	215.45	213.00	211.10
Perimeter Adj., Add or Deduct	Per 100 L.F.	37.80	29.40	24.00	20.30	17.65	15.55	13.85	12.60	11.55
Story Hgt. Adj., Add or Deduct	Per 1 Ft.	6.75	6.15	5.40	4.90	4.65	4.35	4.10	3.95	3.80

For Basement, add $33.80 per square foot of basement area

The above costs were calculated using the basic specifications shown on the facing page. These costs should be adjusted where necessary for design alternatives and owner's requirements. Reported completed project costs, for this type of structure, range from $129.35 to $337.40 per S.F.

Common additives

Description	Unit	$ Cost
Cells Prefabricated, 5'-6" x 7'-8", 7'-8' high	Each	12,700
Elevators, hydraulic passenger, 2 stops, 2500# capacity	Each	69,200
3500# capacity	Each	73,200
Lockers, Steel, Single tier, 60" to 72"	Opening	218 - 365
Locker bench, lam. maple top only	L.F.	26.50
Pedestals, steel pipe	Each	74
Safe, Office type, 1 hr rating, 60"x36"x18", double door	Each	8075
Shooting Range, incl. bullet traps,		
Target provisions & controls, excl. struct shell	Each	50,500
Sound System, amplifier, 250 watts	Each	2025
Speaker, ceiling or wall	Each	208
Trumpet	Each	400

Description	Unit	$ Cost
Commissioning Fees, sustainable commercial construction	S.F.	0.24 - 3.04
Energy Modelling Fees, commercial buildings to 10,000 SF	Each	11,000
Greater than 10,000 SF add	S.F.	0.04
Green Bldg Cert Fees for comm construction project reg	Project	900
Photovoltaic Pwr Sys, grid connected, 20 kW (~2400 SF), roof	Each	272,300
Green Roofs, 6" soil depth, w/ treated wd edging & sedum mats	S.F.	11.05
10" Soil depth, with treated wood edging & sedum mats	S.F.	12.68
Greywater Recovery Systems, prepackaged comm, 3060 gal.	Each	57,740
4590 gal.	Each	72,025
Rainwater Harvest Sys, prepckged comm, 10,000 gal, sys contrller	Each	31,375
20,000 gal. w/ system controller	Each	50,500
30,000 gal. w/ system controller	Each	80,225
Solar Domestic HW, closed loop, add-on sys, ext heat exchanger	Each	10,950
Drainback, hot water system, 120 gal tank	Each	14,125
Draindown, hot water system, 120 gal tank	Each	14,550

Important: See the Reference Section for Location Factors.

Model costs calculated for a 2 story building with 12' story height and 11,000 square feet of floor area

G Police Station

				Unit	Unit Cost	Cost Per S.F.	% Of Sub-Total
A. SUBSTRUCTURE							
1010	Standard Foundations	Poured concrete; strip and spread footings		S.F. Ground	2.86	1.43	
1020	Special Foundations	N/A		—	—	—	
1030	Slab on Grade	4" reinforced concrete with recycled vapor barrier and granular base		S.F. Slab	5.33	2.67	3.9%
2010	Basement Excavation	Site preparation for slab and trench for foundation wall and footing		S.F. Ground	.32	.16	
2020	Basement Walls	4' foundation wall		L.F. Wall	89	3.25	
B. SHELL							
B10 Superstructure							
1010	Floor Construction	Open web steel joists, slab form, concrete		S.F. Floor	12.26	6.13	4.4%
1020	Roof Construction	Metal deck on open web steel joists		S.F. Roof	4.88	2.44	
B20 Exterior Enclosure							
2010	Exterior Walls	Limestone with concrete block backup	80% of wall	S.F. Wall	70	37.02	
2020	Exterior Windows	Metal horizontal sliding	20% of wall	Each	1144	10.08	25.2%
2030	Exterior Doors	Hollow metal		Each	2688	1.96	
B30 Roofing							
3010	Roof Coverings	Single-ply TPO membrane, 60 mils, heat welded w/R-20 insul.		S.F. Roof	6.62	3.31	1.7%
3020	Roof Openings	N/A		—	—	—	
C. INTERIORS							
1010	Partitions	Concrete block w/foamed-in insul.	20 SF Flr./LF Part.	S.F. Partition	10.98	5.49	
1020	Interior Doors	Single leaf kalamein fire door, low VOC paint	200 S.F. Floor/Door	Each	1152	5.76	
1030	Fittings	Toilet partitions		S.F. Floor	.93	.93	
2010	Stair Construction	Concrete filled metal pan		Flight	17,250	3.13	15.1%
3010	Wall Finishes	90% paint, low VOC, 10% ceramic tile		S.F. Surface	2.71	2.71	
3020	Floor Finishes	70% vinyl composition tile, recycled content, 20% carpet tile, 10% ceramic tile		S.F. Floor	4.39	4.39	
3030	Ceiling Finishes	Mineral fiber tile on concealed zee bars		S.F. Ceiling	6.89	6.89	
D. SERVICES							
D10 Conveying							
1010	Elevators & Lifts	One hydraulic passenger elevator		Each	83,380	7.58	3.9%
1020	Escalators & Moving Walks	N/A		—	—	—	
D20 Plumbing							
2010	Plumbing Fixtures	Toilet, low flow, auto sensor, & service fixt., supply & drainage	1 Fixt./580 SF Flr.	Each	5481	9.45	
2020	Domestic Water Distribution	Electric water heater, point-of-use, energy saver		S.F. Floor	1.47	1.47	6.6%
2040	Rain Water Drainage	Roof drains		S.F. Roof	3.64	1.82	
D30 HVAC							
3010	Energy Supply	N/A		—	—	—	
3020	Heat Generating Systems	N/A		—	—	—	
3040	Distribution Systems	Enthalpy heat recovery packages		Each	30,350	2.76	11.6%
3050	Terminal & Package Units	Multizone rooftop air conditioner, SEER 14		S.F. Floor	19.70	19.70	
3090	Other HVAC Sys. & Equipment	N/A		—	—	—	
D40 Fire Protection							
4010	Sprinklers	Wet pipe sprinkler system		S.F. Floor	3.79	3.79	2.5%
4020	Standpipes	Standpipe		S.F. Floor	.98	.98	
D50 Electrical							
5010	Electrical Service/Distribution	400 ampere service, panel board and feeders		S.F. Floor	1	1	
5020	Lighting & Branch Wiring	LED fixtures, daylt. dim., ltg. on/off cntrl., recept., switches, & A.C. pwr.		S.F. Floor	22.23	22.23	16.8%
5030	Communications & Security	Addressable alarm systems, internet wiring, intercom &emergency ltg.		S.F. Floor	7.19	7.19	
5090	Other Electrical Systems	Emergency generator, 15 kW, energy monitoring systems		S.F. Floor	2.24	2.24	
E. EQUIPMENT & FURNISHINGS							
1020	Institutional Equipment	Lockers, detention rooms, cells, gasoline dispensers		S.F. Floor	13.45	13.45	
1030	Vehicular Equipment	Gasoline dispenser system		S.F. Floor	2.45	2.45	8.5%
1090	Other Equipment	Waste handling recycling tilt truck		Each	.50	.50	
2020	Moveable Furnishings	No smoking signage		Each	.04	.04	
F. SPECIAL CONSTRUCTION							
1020	Integrated Construction	N/A		—	—	—	0.0%
1040	Special Facilities	N/A		—	—	—	
G. BUILDING SITEWORK	**N/A**						

	Sub-Total	194.40	**100%**
CONTRACTOR FEES (General Requirements: 10%, Overhead: 5%, Profit: 10%)	25%	48.63	
ARCHITECT FEES	9%	21.87	
	Total Building Cost	**264.90**	

269

Costs per square foot of floor area

Exterior Wall	S.F. Area	2000	2800	3500	4200	5000	5800	6500	7200	8000
	L.F. Perimeter	180	212	240	268	300	314	336	344	368
Wood Siding	Wood Frame	277.05	261.70	254.00	248.90	244.85	239.85	237.55	234.40	232.70
Brick Veneer	Wood Frame	284.95	267.55	258.90	253.10	248.50	242.75	240.10	236.45	234.45
Face Brick with Concrete Block Back-up	Wood Joists	298.30	278.75	269.05	262.55	257.45	250.80	247.75	243.50	241.25
	Steel Joists	297.15	275.45	264.65	257.45	251.70	244.20	240.75	235.85	233.40
Stucco on Concrete Block	Wood Joists	284.40	267.05	258.45	252.75	248.15	242.45	239.80	236.10	234.20
	Steel Joists	271.50	254.25	245.65	239.90	235.35	229.65	226.95	223.30	221.35
Perimeter Adj., Add or Deduct	Per 100 L.F.	31.35	22.35	17.90	14.95	12.55	10.85	9.65	8.75	7.80
Story Hgt. Adj., Add or Deduct	Per 1 Ft.	3.30	2.75	2.50	2.35	2.20	2.00	1.85	1.75	1.65

For Basement, add $38.55 per square foot of basement area

The above costs were calculated using the basic specifications shown on the facing page. These costs should be adjusted where necessary for design alternatives and owner's requirements. Reported completed project costs, for this type of structure, range from $137.60 to $320.70 per S.F.

Common additives

Description	Unit	$ Cost	Description	Unit	$ Cost
Bar, Front Bar	L.F.	415	Commissioning Fees, sustainable commercial construction	S.F.	0.24 - 3.04
Back bar	L.F.	330	Energy Modelling Fees, commercial buildings to 10,000 SF	Each	11,000
Booth, Upholstered, custom straight	L.F.	241 - 440	Greater than 10,000 SF add	S.F.	0.04
"L" or "U" shaped	L.F.	249 - 425	Green Bldg Cert Fees for comm construction project reg	Project	900
Fireplace, brick, excl. chimney or foundation, 30"x29" opening	Each	3125	Photovoltaic Pwr Sys, grid connected, 20 kW (~2400 SF), roof	Each	272,300
Chimney, standard brick, single flue, 16" x 20"	V.L.F.	106	Green Roofs, 6" soil depth, w/ treated wd edging & sedum mats	S.F.	11.05
2 Flue, 20" x 24"	V.L.F.	153	10" Soil depth, with treated wood edging & sedum mats	S.F.	12.68
Kitchen Equipment			Greywater Recovery Systems, prepackaged comm, 3060 gal.	Each	57,740
Broiler	Each	4000	4590 gal.	Each	72,025
Coffee urn, twin 6 gallon	Each	2975	Rainwater Harvest Sys, prepckged comm, 10,000 gal, sys contrller	Each	31,375
Cooler, 6 ft. long	Each	4100	20,000 gal. w/ system controller	Each	50,500
Dishwasher, 10-12 racks per hr.	Each	4225	30,000 gal. w/ system controller	Each	80,225
Food warmer, counter, 1.2 KW	Each	725	Solar Domestic HW, closed loop, add-on sys, ext heat exchanger	Each	10,950
Freezer, 44 C.F., reach-in	Each	5125	Drainback, hot water system, 120 gal tank	Each	14,125
Ice cube maker, 50 lb. per day	Each	1950	Draindown, hot water system, 120 gal tank	Each	14,550
Range with 1 oven	Each	3000			
Refrigerators, prefabricated, walk-in, 7'-6" high, 6' x 6'	S.F.	195			
10' x 10'	S.F.	154			
12' x 14'	S.F.	136			
12' x 20'	S.F.	119			

Important: See the Reference Section for Location Factors.

Model costs calculated for a 1 story building with 12' story height and 5,000 square feet of floor area

				Unit	Unit Cost	Cost Per S.F.	% Of Sub-Total
A. SUBSTRUCTURE							
1010	Standard Foundations	Poured concrete; strip and spread footings		S.F. Ground	2.64	2.64	
1020	Special Foundations	N/A		—	—	—	
1030	Slab on Grade	4" reinforced concrete with recycled vapor barrier and granular base		S.F. Slab	5.33	5.33	7.6%
2010	Basement Excavation	Site preparation for slab and trench for foundation wall and footing		S.F. Ground	.57	.57	
2020	Basement Walls	4' foundation wall		L.F. Wall	89	5.31	
B. SHELL							
B10 Superstructure							
1010	Floor Construction	Wood columns		S.F. Floor	.83	.83	4.6%
1020	Roof Construction	Plywood on wood truss (pitched)		S.F. Roof	7.66	7.66	
B20 Exterior Enclosure							
2010	Exterior Walls	Cedar siding on wood studs with insulation	70% of wall	S.F. Wall	12.76	6.43	
2020	Exterior Windows	Storefront windows	30% of wall	Each	53	10.93	12.4%
2030	Exterior Doors	Aluminum and glass doors and entrance with transom		Each	5294	5.30	
B30 Roofing							
3010	Roof Coverings	Cedar shingles with flashing (pitched); rigid fiberglass insulation		S.F. Roof	12.06	12.06	6.6%
3020	Roof Openings	Skylights		S.F. Roof	.09	.09	
C. INTERIORS							
1010	Partitions	Gypsum board on wood studs	25 SF Floor/LF Part.	S.F. Partition	11.73	4.69	
1020	Interior Doors	Hollow core wood, low VOC paint	250 S.F. Floor/Door	Each	557	2.23	
1030	Fittings	Toilet partitions		S.F. Floor	1.17	1.17	
2010	Stair Construction	N/A		—	—	—	14.1%
3010	Wall Finishes	75% paint, low VOC, 25% ceramic tile		S.F. Surface	2.51	2.01	
3020	Floor Finishes	65% carpet, 35% quarry tile		S.F. Floor	8.88	8.88	
3030	Ceiling Finishes	Mineral fiber tile on concealed zee bars		S.F. Ceiling	6.89	6.89	
D. SERVICES							
D10 Conveying							
1010	Elevators & Lifts	N/A		—	—	—	0.0 %
1020	Escalators & Moving Walks	N/A		—	—	—	
D20 Plumbing							
2010	Plumbing Fixtures	Kitchen, toilet, low flow, auto sensor, & service fixt., supply & drain.	1 Fixt./335 SF Flr.	Each	4043	11.39	
2020	Domestic Water Distribution	Tankless, on-demand water heater gas/propane		S.F. Floor	3.24	3.24	9.0%
2040	Rain Water Drainage	Roof drains		S.F. Roof	1.83	1.83	
D30 HVAC							
3010	Energy Supply	N/A		—	—	—	
3020	Heat Generating Systems	Included in D3050		—	—	—	
3040	Distribution Systems	Enthalpy heat recovery packages and kitchen exhaust/make-up air system		Each	43,100	8.62	26.1 %
3050	Terminal & Package Units	Multizone rooftop air conditioner, SEER 14		S.F. Floor	39.20	39.20	
3090	Other HVAC Sys. & Equipment	N/A		—	—	—	
D40 Fire Protection							
4010	Sprinklers	Sprinklers, light hazard and ordinary hazard kitchen		S.F. Floor	8.61	8.61	5.8%
4020	Standpipes	Standpipe		S.F. Floor	1.98	1.98	
D50 Electrical							
5010	Electrical Service/Distribution	400 ampere service, panel board and feeders		S.F. Floor	2.31	2.31	
5020	Lighting & Branch Wiring	LED fixtures, daylt. dim., ltg. on/off, receptacles, switches, and A.C. power		S.F. Floor	13.49	13.49	13.1%
5030	Communications & Security	Addressable alarm systems and emergency lighting		S.F. Floor	3.55	3.55	
5090	Other Electrical Systems	Emergency generator, 15 kW and energy monitoring systems		S.F. Floor	4.65	4.65	
E. EQUIPMENT & FURNISHINGS							
1010	Commercial Equipment	N/A		—	—	—	
1020	Institutional Equipment	N/A		—	—	—	0.6 %
1090	Other Equipment	Waste handling recycling tilt truck		Each	1.10	1.10	
2020	Moveable Furnishings	No smoking signage		Each	.06	.06	
F. SPECIAL CONSTRUCTION							
1020	Integrated Construction	N/A		—	—	—	0.0 %
1040	Special Facilities	N/A		—	—	—	
G. BUILDING SITEWORK	**N/A**						

			Sub-Total	183.05	**100%**
CONTRACTOR FEES (General Requirements: 10%, Overhead: 5%, Profit: 10%)		25%	45.78	
ARCHITECT FEES		7%	16.02	

Total Building Cost	**244.85**

Costs per square foot of floor area

Exterior Wall	S.F. Area	25000	30000	35000	40000	45000	50000	55000	60000	65000
	L.F. Perimeter	900	1050	1200	1350	1510	1650	1800	1970	2100
Face Brick with Concrete Block Back-up	Steel Frame	196.45	194.10	192.45	191.25	190.50	189.55	188.90	188.85	188.00
	Bearing Walls	188.40	186.40	184.95	183.85	183.25	182.35	181.80	181.75	181.00
Stucco on Concrete Block	Steel Frame	189.50	187.40	185.85	184.75	184.05	183.15	182.55	182.50	181.75
	Bearing Walls	183.10	180.95	179.45	178.30	177.65	176.75	176.20	176.05	175.30
Decorative Concrete Block	Steel Frame	187.90	185.80	184.30	183.15	182.45	181.55	181.00	180.90	180.20
	Bearing Walls	184.40	182.25	180.80	179.65	178.95	178.05	177.55	177.40	176.65
Perimeter Adj., Add or Deduct	Per 100 L.F.	4.90	4.10	3.55	3.10	2.80	2.50	2.25	2.05	1.85
Story Hgt. Adj., Add or Deduct	Per 1 Ft.	1.85	1.85	1.80	1.75	1.80	1.70	1.70	1.70	1.65

For Basement, add $28.55 per square foot of basement area

The above costs were calculated using the basic specifications shown on the facing page. These costs should be adjusted where necessary for design alternatives and owner's requirements. Reported completed project costs, for this type of structure, range from $94.90 to $241.35 per S.F.

Common additives

Description	Unit	$ Cost
Bleachers, Telescoping, manual, 16-20 tier	Seat	277 - 340
21-30 tier	Seat	295 - 385
For power operation, add	Seat	54.50 - 84.50
Carrels Hardwood	Each	960 - 2300
Clock System, 20 room	Each	19,500
50 room	Each	45,700
Kitchen Equipment		
Broiler	Each	4000
Cooler, 6 ft. long, reach-in	Each	4100
Dishwasher, 10-12 racks per hr.	Each	4225
Food warmer, counter, 1.2 KW	Each	725
Freezer, 44 C.F., reach-in	Each	5125
Ice cube maker, 50 lb. per day	Each	1950
Range with 1 oven	Each	3000
Lockers, Steel, single tier, 60" to 72"	Opening	218 - 365
2 tier, 60" to 72" total	Opening	113 - 156
Locker bench, lam. maple top only	L.F.	26.50
Pedestals, steel pipe	Each	74
Seating, auditorium chair, veneer back, padded seat	Each	315
Classroom, movable chair & desk	Set	81 - 171
Lecture hall, pedestal type	Each	258 - 610

Description	Unit	$ Cost
Sound System, amplifier, 250 watts	Each	2025
Speaker, ceiling or wall	Each	208
Commissioning Fees, sustainable institutional construction	S.F.	0.58 - 2.47
Energy Modelling Fees, academic buildings to 10,000 SF	Each	9000
Greater than 10,000 SF add	S.F.	0.20
Green Bldg Cert Fees for school construction project reg	Project	900
Photovoltaic Pwr Sys, grid connected, 20 kW (~2400 SF), roof	Each	272,300
Green Roofs, 6" soil depth, w/ treated wd edging & sedum mats	S.F.	11.05
10" Soil depth, with treated wood edging & sedum mats	S.F.	12.68
Greywater Recovery Systems, prepackaged comm, 3060 gal.	Each	57,740
4590 gal.	Each	72,025
Rainwater Harvest Sys, prepckged comm, 10,000 gal, sys contrller	Each	31,375
20,000 gal. w/ system controller	Each	50,500
30,000 gal. w/ system controller	Each	80,225
Solar Domestic HW, closed loop, add-on sys, ext heat exchanger	Each	10,950
Drainback, hot water system, 120 gal tank	Each	14,125
Draindown, hot water system, 120 gal tank	Each	14,550

Important: See the Reference Section for Location Factors.

Model costs calculated for a 1 story building with 15' story height and 45,000 square feet of floor area

G School, Elementary

					Unit	Unit Cost	Cost Per S.F.	% Of Sub-Total
A. SUBSTRUCTURE								
1010	Standard Foundations	Poured concrete; strip and spread footings			S.F. Ground	4.99	4.99	
1020	Special Foundations	N/A			—			
1030	Slab on Grade	4" reinforced concrete with recycled vapor barrier and granular base			S.F. Slab	5.33	5.33	11.3%
2010	Basement Excavation	Site preparation for slab and trench for foundation wall and footing			S.F. Ground	.18	.18	
2020	Basement Walls	4' foundation wall			L.F. Wall	89	5.05	
B. SHELL								
B10 Superstructure								
1010	Floor Construction	N/A			—	—	—	
1020	Roof Construction	Metal deck on open web steel joists			S.F. Roof	4.45	4.45	3.2 %
B20 Exterior Enclosure								
2010	Exterior Walls	Face brick with concrete block backup	70% of wall		S.F. Wall	38.15	13.44	
2020	Exterior Windows	Steel outward projecting	25% of wall		Each	736	4.83	13.8%
2030	Exterior Doors	Metal and glass	5% of wall		Each	3785	.67	
B30 Roofing								
3010	Roof Coverings	Single-ply TPO membrane, 60 mils, w/ flashing; polyiso. insulation			S.F. Roof	10.07	10.07	7.3%
3020	Roof Openings	N/A			—			
C. INTERIORS								
1010	Partitions	Concrete block w/ foamed-in insul.	20 SF Flr./LF Part.		S.F. Partition	11.50	5.75	
1020	Interior Doors	Single leaf kalamein fire doors, low VOC paint	700 S.F. Floor/Door		Each	1152	1.65	
1030	Fittings	Toilet partitions			S.F. Floor	1.82	1.82	
2010	Stair Construction	N/A			—	—	—	19.6%
3010	Wall Finishes	75% paint, low VOC, 15% glazed coating, 10% ceramic tile			S.F. Surface	4.89	4.89	
3020	Floor Finishes	65% vinyl composition tile, recycled content, 25% carpet tile, 10% terrazzo			S.F. Floor	5.85	5.85	
3030	Ceiling Finishes	Mineral fiber tile on concealed zee bars			S.F. Ceiling	6.89	6.89	
D. SERVICES								
D10 Conveying								
1010	Elevators & Lifts	N/A			—	—	—	
1020	Escalators & Moving Walks	N/A			—	—	—	0.0 %
D20 Plumbing								
2010	Plumbing Fixtures	Kitchen, toilet, low flow, auto sensor, & service fixt., supply & drain.	1 Fixt./625 SF Flr.		Each	9294	14.87	
2020	Domestic Water Distribution	Gas fired, tankless water heater			S.F. Floor	.17	.17	11.9%
2040	Rain Water Drainage	Roof drains			S.F. Roof	1.25	1.25	
D30 HVAC								
3010	Energy Supply	N/A			—	—	—	
3020	Heat Generating Systems	N/A			—	—	—	
3040	Distribution Systems	Enthalpy heat recovery packages			Each	36,875	2.46	15.9 %
3050	Terminal & Package Units	Multizone rooftop air conditioner			S.F. Floor	19.30	19.30	
3090	Other HVAC Sys. & Equipment	N/A			—	—	—	
D40 Fire Protection								
4010	Sprinklers	Sprinklers, light hazard			S.F. Floor	2.85	2.85	2.4%
4020	Standpipes	Standpipe			S.F. Floor	.39	.39	
D50 Electrical								
5010	Electrical Service/Distribution	800 ampere service, panel board and feeders			S.F. Floor	.86	.86	
5020	Lighting & Branch Wiring	LED fixtures, daylt. dim., ltg. on/off, recept., switches, and A.C. power			S.F. Floor	13.88	13.88	14.3%
5030	Communications & Security	Addressable alarm systems, internet wiring, comm. systems & emerg. ltg.			S.F. Floor	3.72	3.72	
5090	Other Electrical Systems	Emergency generator, 15 kW, energy monitoring systems			S.F. Floor	1.14	1.14	
E. EQUIPMENT & FURNISHINGS								
1010	Commercial Equipment	N/A			—	—	—	
1020	Institutional Equipment	Chalkboards			S.F. Floor	.18	.18	0.2 %
1090	Other Equipment	Waste handling recycling tilt truck			Each	.07	.07	
2020	Moveable Furnishings	No smoking signage			Each	.01	.01	
F. SPECIAL CONSTRUCTION								
1020	Integrated Construction	N/A			—	—	—	0.0 %
1040	Special Facilities	N/A			—	—	—	
G. BUILDING SITEWORK	**N/A**							

	Sub-Total	137.01	**100%**
CONTRACTOR FEES (General Requirements: 10%, Overhead: 5%, Profit: 10%)	25%	34.25	
ARCHITECT FEES	7%	11.99	
	Total Building Cost	**183.25**	

273

Costs per square foot of floor area

Exterior Wall	S.F. Area	50000	70000	90000	110000	130000	150000	170000	190000	210000
	L.F. Perimeter	850	1140	1420	1700	1980	2280	2560	2840	3120
Face Brick with Concrete Block Back-up	Steel Frame	183.50	180.50	178.65	177.45	176.60	176.35	175.85	175.40	175.05
	R/Conc. Frame	187.15	184.15	182.30	181.10	180.25	179.90	179.50	179.00	178.70
Decorative Concrete Block	Steel Frame	176.40	173.75	172.10	171.00	170.25	170.00	169.55	169.15	168.90
	R/Conc. Frame	176.80	174.15	172.50	171.40	170.65	170.40	169.95	169.55	169.30
Limestone with Concrete Block Back-up	Steel Frame	200.00	196.30	193.95	192.40	191.35	191.05	190.45	189.95	189.50
	R/Conc. Frame	206.85	203.20	200.90	199.30	198.25	197.95	197.35	196.80	196.40
Perimeter Adj., Add or Deduct	Per 100 L.F.	4.50	3.25	2.50	2.10	1.75	1.45	1.25	1.20	1.15
Story Hgt. Adj., Add or Deduct	Per 1 Ft.	2.30	2.20	2.15	2.10	2.05	2.00	2.05	2.00	2.05

For Basement, add $37.35 per square foot of basement area

The above costs were calculated using the basic specifications shown on the facing page. These costs should be adjusted where necessary for design alternatives and owner's requirements. Reported completed project costs, for this type of structure, range from $110.30 to $259.75 per S.F.

Common additives

Description	Unit	$ Cost
Bleachers, Telescoping, manual, 16-20 tier	Seat	277 - 340
21-30 tier	Seat	295 - 385
For power operation, add	Seat	54.50 - 84.50
Carrels Hardwood	Each	960 - 2300
Clock System, 20 room	Each	19,500
50 room	Each	45,700
Elevators, hydraulic passenger, 2 stops, 2500# capacity	Each	69,200
3500# capacity	Each	73,200
Kitchen Equipment		
Broiler	Each	4000
Cooler, 6 ft. long, reach-in	Each	4100
Dishwasher, 10-12 racks per hr.	Each	4225
Food warmer, counter, 1.2 KW	Each	725
Freezer, 44 C.F., reach-in	Each	5125
Lockers, Steel, single tier, 60" or 72"	Opening	218 - 365
2 tier, 60" or 72" total	Opening	113 - 156
Locker bench, lam. maple top only	L.F.	26.50
Pedestals, steel pipe	Each	74
Seat, auditorium chair, veneer back, padded seat	Each	315
Classroom, movable chair & desk	Set	81 - 171
Lecture hall, pedestal type	Each	258 - 610

Description	Unit	$ Cost
Sound System, amplifier, 250 watts	Each	2025
Speaker, ceiling or wall	Each	208
Commissioning Fees, sustainable institutional construction	S.F.	0.58 - 2.47
Energy Modelling Fees, academic buildings to 10,000 SF	Each	9000
Greater than 10,000 SF add	S.F.	0.20
Green Bldg Cert Fees for school construction project reg	Project	900
Photovoltaic Pwr Sys, grid connected, 20 kW (~2400 SF), roof	Each	272,300
Green Roofs, 6" soil depth, w/ treated wd edging & sedum mats	S.F.	11.05
10" Soil depth, with treated wood edging & sedum mats	S.F.	12.68
Greywater Recovery Systems, prepackaged comm, 3060 gal.	Each	57,740
4590 gal.	Each	72,025
Rainwater Harvest Sys, prepckged comm, 10,000 gal, sys contrller	Each	31,375
20,000 gal. w/ system controller	Each	50,500
30,000 gal. w/ system controller	Each	80,225
Solar Domestic HW, closed loop, add-on sys, ext heat exchanger	Each	10,950
Drainback, hot water system, 120 gal tank	Each	14,125
Draindown, hot water system, 120 gal tank	Each	14,550

Model costs calculated for a 2 story building with 15' story height and 130,000 square feet of floor area

G School, High, 2-3 Story

				Unit	Unit Cost	Cost Per S.F.	% Of Sub-Total
A. SUBSTRUCTURE							
1010	Standard Foundations	Poured concrete; strip and spread footings		S.F. Ground	2.70	1.35	
1020	Special Foundations	N/A		—	—	—	
1030	Slab on Grade	4" reinforced concrete with recycled vapor barrier and granular base		S.F. Slab	5.33	2.67	4.1%
2010	Basement Excavation	Site preparation for slab and trench for foundation wall and footing		S.F. Ground	.18	.09	
2020	Basement Walls	4' foundation wall		L.F. Wall	89	1.35	
B. SHELL							
	B10 Superstructure						
1010	Floor Construction	Concrete slab without drop panel, concrete columns		S.F. Floor	21.94	10.97	13.8%
1020	Roof Construction	Concrete slab without drop panel		S.F. Roof	15.16	7.58	
	B20 Exterior Enclosure						
2010	Exterior Walls	Face brick with concrete block backup	75% of wall	S.F. Wall	38.17	13.08	
2020	Exterior Windows	Window wall	25% of wall	Each	73	8.34	16.3%
2030	Exterior Doors	Metal and glass		Each	2238	.50	
	B30 Roofing						
3010	Roof Coverings	Single-ply TPO membrane and standing seam metal; polyiso. insulation		S.F. Roof	13.44	6.72	5.0%
3020	Roof Openings	Roof hatches		S.F. Roof	.10	.05	
C. INTERIORS							
1010	Partitions	Concrete block w/foamed-in insul.	25 SF Flr./LF Part.	S.F. Partition	14.27	6.85	
1020	Interior Doors	Single leaf kalamein fire doors, low VOC paint	700 S.F. Floor/Door	Each	1152	1.65	
1030	Fittings	Toilet partitions, chalkboards		S.F. Floor	1.28	1.28	
2010	Stair Construction	Concrete filled metal pan		Flight	14,450	.66	19.6%
3010	Wall Finishes	75% paint, low VOC. 15% glazed coating, 10% ceramic tile		S.F. Surface	3.45	3.31	
3020	Floor Finishes	70% vinyl comp. tile, recycled content, 20% carpet tile, 10% terrazzo		S.F. Floor	5.80	5.80	
3030	Ceiling Finishes	Mineral fiber tile on concealed zee bars		S.F. Ceiling	6.89	6.89	
D. SERVICES							
	D10 Conveying						
1010	Elevators & Lifts	One hydraulic passenger elevator		Each	84,500	.65	0.5%
1020	Escalators & Moving Walks	N/A		—	—	—	
	D20 Plumbing						
2010	Plumbing Fixtures	Kitchen, toilet, low flow, auto sensor & service fixt., supply & drain.	1 Fixt./860 SF Flr.	Each	5022	5.84	
2020	Domestic Water Distribution	Gas fired, tankless water heater		S.F. Floor	.34	.34	5.1%
2040	Rain Water Drainage	Roof drains		S.F. Roof	1.42	.71	
	D30 HVAC						
3010	Energy Supply	N/A		—	—	—	
3020	Heat Generating Systems	N/A		—	—	—	
3040	Distribution Systems	Enthalpy heat recovery packages		Each	36,875	2.26	16.0%
3050	Terminal & Package Units	Multizone rooftop air conditioner, SEER 14		S.F. Floor	19.30	19.30	
3090	Other HVAC Sys. & Equipment	N/A		—	—	—	
	D40 Fire Protection						
4010	Sprinklers	Sprinklers, light hazard		S.F. Floor	2.48	2.48	2.1%
4020	Standpipes	Standpipe, wet, Class III		S.F. Floor	.33	.33	
	D50 Electrical						
5010	Electrical Service/Distribution	2000 ampere service, panel board and feeders		S.F. Floor	.87	.87	
5020	Lighting & Branch Wiring	LED fixtures, daylt. dim., ltg. on/off, recept., switches, and A.C. power		S.F. Floor	15.07	15.07	15.4%
5030	Communications & Security	Addressable alarm systems, internet wiring, comm. systems and emerg. ltg.		S.F. Floor	4	4	
5090	Other Electrical Systems	Emergency generator, 250 kW, and energy monitoring systems		S.F. Floor	.83	.83	
E. EQUIPMENT & FURNISHINGS							
1010	Commercial Equipment	N/A		—	—	—	
1020	Institutional Equipment	Laboratory casework and counters		S.F. Floor	1.96	1.96	2.2%
1090	Other Equipment	Waste handlg. recyc. tilt truck, built-in athletic equip., bleachers & backstp.		Each	.96	.96	
2020	Moveable Furnishings	No smoking signage		Each	.02	.02	
F. SPECIAL CONSTRUCTION							
1020	Integrated Construction	N/A		—	—	—	0.0%
1040	Special Facilities	N/A		—	—	—	
G. BUILDING SITEWORK	**N/A**						

		Sub-Total	134.76	100%
CONTRACTOR FEES (General Requirements: 10%, Overhead: 5%, Profit: 10%)		25%	33.70	
ARCHITECT FEES		7%	11.79	
	Total Building Cost		**180.25**	

Costs per square foot of floor area

Exterior Wall	S.F. Area	50000	65000	80000	95000	110000	125000	140000	155000	170000
	L.F. Perimeter	850	1060	1280	1490	1700	1920	2140	2340	2560
Face Brick with Concrete Block Back-up	Steel Frame	191.10	188.90	187.75	186.75	186.00	185.60	185.35	184.80	184.65
	Bearing Walls	182.60	180.35	179.20	178.20	177.45	177.05	176.80	176.30	176.10
Concrete Block Stucco Face	Steel Frame	195.95	193.40	192.15	191.00	190.20	189.75	189.45	188.90	188.70
	Bearing Walls	189.15	186.65	185.40	184.25	183.45	183.00	182.70	182.10	181.90
Decorative Concrete Block	Steel Frame	183.10	181.10	180.10	179.25	178.65	178.20	177.95	177.60	177.40
	Bearing Walls	174.90	172.90	171.90	171.00	170.35	170.00	169.75	169.35	169.15
Perimeter Adj., Add or Deduct	Per 100 L.F.	4.20	3.20	2.55	2.15	1.95	1.65	1.45	1.35	1.20
Story Hgt. Adj., Add or Deduct	Per 1 Ft.	2.15	2.00	1.95	1.90	1.90	1.90	1.85	1.90	1.80

For Basement, add $ 38.85 per square foot of basement area

The above costs were calculated using the basic specifications shown on the facing page. These costs should be adjusted where necessary for design alternatives and owner's requirements. Reported completed project costs, for this type of structure, range from $ 104.10 to $ 244.65 per S.F.

Common additives

Description	Unit	$ Cost
Bleachers, Telescoping, manual, 16-20 tier	Seat	277 - 340
21-30 tier	Seat	295 - 385
For power operation, add	Seat	54.50 - 84.50
Carrels Hardwood	Each	960 - 2300
Clock System, 20 room	Each	19,500
50 room	Each	45,700
Elevators, hydraulic passenger, 2 stops, 2500# capacity	Each	69,200
3500# capacity	Each	73,200
Kitchen Equipment		
Broiler	Each	4000
Cooler, 6 ft. long, reach-in	Each	4100
Dishwasher, 10-12 racks per hr.	Each	4225
Food warmer, counter, 1.2 KW	Each	725
Freezer, 44 C.F., reach-in	Each	5125
Lockers, Steel, single tier, 60" to 72"	Opening	218 - 365
2 tier, 60" to 72" total	Opening	113 - 156
Locker bench, lam. maple top only	L.F.	26.50
Pedestals, steel pipe	Each	74

Description	Unit	$ Cost
Seating, auditorium chair, veneer back, padded seat	Each	315
Upholstered, spring seat	Each	315
Classroom, movable chair & desk	Set	81 - 171
Lecture hall, pedestal type	Each	258 - 610
Sound System, amplifier, 250 watts	Each	2025
Speaker, ceiling or wall	Each	208
Commissioning Fees, sustainable institutional construction	S.F.	0.58 - 2.47
Energy Modelling Fees, academic buildings to 10,000 SF	Each	9000
Greater than 10,000 SF add	S.F.	0.20
Green Bldg Cert Fees for school construction project reg	Project	900
Photovoltaic Pwr Sys, grid connected, 20 kW (~2400 SF), roof	Each	272,300
Green Roofs, 6" soil depth, w/ treated wd edging & sedum mats	S.F.	11.05
10" Soil depth, with treated wood edging & sedum mats	S.F.	12.68
Greywater Recovery Systems, prepackaged comm, 3060 gal.	Each	57,740
4590 gal.	Each	72,025
Rainwater Harvest Sys, prepckged comm, 10,000 gal, sys contrller	Each	31,375
20,000 gal. w/ system controller	Each	50,500
30,000 gal. w/ system controller	Each	80,225
Solar Domestic HW, closed loop, add-on sys, ext heat exchanger	Each	10,950
Drainback, hot water system, 120 gal tank	Each	14,125
Draindown, hot water system, 120 gal tank	Each	14,550

Important: See the Reference Section for Location Factors.

Model costs calculated for a 2 story building with 15′ story height and 110,000 square feet of floor area

G School, Jr High, 2-3 Story

				Unit	Unit Cost	Cost Per S.F.	% Of Sub-Total
A. SUBSTRUCTURE							
1010	Standard Foundations	Poured concrete; strip and spread footings		S.F. Ground	2.42	1.21	
1020	Special Foundations	N/A		—	—	—	
1030	Slab on Grade	4″ reinforced concrete with recycled vapor barrier and granular base		S.F. Slab	5.33	2.67	3.8%
2010	Basement Excavation	Site preparation for slab and trench for foundation wall and footing		S.F. Ground	.18	.09	
2020	Basement Walls	4′ foundation wall		L.F. Wall	89	1.37	
B. SHELL							
B10 Superstructure							
1010	Floor Construction	Open web steel joists, slab form, concrete, columns		S.F. Floor	28.60	14.30	14.6%
1020	Roof Construction	Metal deck, open web steel joists, columns		S.F. Roof	11.90	5.95	
B20 Exterior Enclosure							
2010	Exterior Walls	Face brick with concrete block backup	75% of wall	S.F. Wall	38.16	13.27	
2020	Exterior Windows	Window wall	25% of wall	Each	61	6.79	14.9%
2030	Exterior Doors	Double aluminum & glass		Each	2362	.64	
B30 Roofing							
3010	Roof Coverings	Single-ply TPO membrane & standing seam metal; polyiso. insulation		S.F. Roof	13.60	6.80	4.9%
3020	Roof Openings	Roof hatches		S.F. Roof	.04	.02	
C. INTERIORS							
1010	Partitions	Concrete block w/foamed-in insul.	20 SF Flr./LF Part.	S.F. Partition	12.02	7.21	
1020	Interior Doors	Single leaf kalamein fire doors, low VOC paint	750 S.F. Floor/Door	Each	1152	1.54	
1030	Fittings	Toilet partitions, chalkboards		S.F. Floor	1.38	1.38	
2010	Stair Construction	Concrete filled metal pan		Flight	14,450	.79	22.1%
3010	Wall Finishes	50% paint, low VOC, 40% glazed coatings, 10% ceramic tile		S.F. Surface	3.81	4.57	
3020	Floor Finishes	50% vinyl comp. tile, recycled content, 30% carpet tile, 20% terrrazzo		S.F. Floor	8.32	8.32	
3030	Ceiling Finishes	Mineral fiberboard on concealed zee bars		S.F. Ceiling	6.89	6.89	
D. SERVICES							
D10 Conveying							
1010	Elevators & Lifts	One hydraulic passenger elevator		Each	83,600	.76	0.5%
1020	Escalators & Moving Walks	N/A		—	—	—	
D20 Plumbing							
2010	Plumbing Fixtures	Kitchen, toilet, low flow, auto sensor, & service fixt., supply & drain.	1 Fixt./1170 SF Flr.	Each	7301	6.24	
2020	Domestic Water Distribution	Gas fired, tankless water heater		S.F. Floor	.40	.40	5.3%
2040	Rain Water Drainage	Roof drains		S.F. Roof	1.46	.73	
D30 HVAC							
3010	Energy Supply	N/A		—	—	—	
3020	Heat Generating Systems	Included in D3050		—	—	—	
3040	Distribution Systems	Enthalpy heat recovery packages		Each	36,875	2.35	15.6 %
3050	Terminal & Package Units	Multizone rooftop air conditioner, SEER 14		S.F. Floor	19.30	19.30	
3090	Other HVAC Sys. & Equipment	N/A		—	—	—	
D40 Fire Protection							
4010	Sprinklers	Sprinklers, light hazard	10% of area	S.F. Floor	2.48	2.48	2.1%
4020	Standpipes	Standpipe, wet, Class III		S.F. Floor	.39	.39	
D50 Electrical							
5010	Electrical Service/Distribution	1600 ampere service, panel board and feeders		S.F. Floor	.78	.78	
5020	Lighting & Branch Wiring	LED fixtures, daylt. dim., ltg. on/off, recept., switches, and A.C. power		S.F. Floor	13.26	13.26	13.8%
5030	Communications & Security	Addressable alarm systems, internet wiring, comm. systems and emerg. ltg.		S.F. Floor	4.30	4.30	
5090	Other Electrical Systems	Emergency generator, 100 kW, and energy monitoring systems		S.F. Floor	.80	.80	
E. EQUIPMENT & FURNISHINGS							
1010	Commercial Equipment	N/A		—	—	—	
1020	Institutional Equipment	Laboratory casework and counters		S.F. Floor	2.30	2.30	2.5 %
1090	Other Equipment	Waste handlg. recyc. tilt truck, built-in athletic equip., bleachers & backstps.		Each	1.15	1.15	
2020	Moveable Furnishings	No smoking signage		Each	.02	.02	
F. SPECIAL CONSTRUCTION							
1020	Integrated Construction	N/A		—	—	—	0.0%
1040	Special Facilities	N/A		—	—	—	
G. BUILDING SITEWORK	**N/A**						

Sub-Total		139.07	**100%**
CONTRACTOR FEES (General Requirements: 10%, Overhead: 5%, Profit: 10%)		25%	34.76
ARCHITECT FEES		7%	12.17
Total Building Cost		186	

Costs per square foot of floor area

Exterior Wall	S.F. Area	20000	30000	40000	50000	60000	70000	80000	90000	100000
	L.F. Perimeter	440	590	740	900	1050	1200	1360	1510	1660
Face Brick with Concrete Block Back-up	Steel Frame	194.80	187.95	184.50	182.90	181.45	180.35	179.85	179.25	178.75
	Bearing Walls	191.05	184.20	180.75	179.15	177.75	176.70	176.15	175.55	175.05
Decorative Concrete Block	Steel Frame	179.85	174.55	171.90	170.60	169.55	168.65	168.30	167.80	167.40
	Bearing Walls	172.55	167.25	164.60	163.30	162.20	161.35	161.00	160.50	160.10
Steel Siding on Steel Studs	Steel Frame	170.25	165.95	163.80	162.75	161.85	161.20	160.85	160.45	160.15
Metal Sandwich Panel	Steel Frame	196.80	189.65	186.10	184.45	182.95	181.80	181.30	180.65	180.10
Perimeter Adj., Add or Deduct	Per 100 L.F.	10.65	7.10	5.30	4.25	3.55	3.10	2.70	2.40	2.15
Story Hgt. Adj., Add or Deduct	Per 1 Ft.	2.65	2.30	2.20	2.15	2.10	2.10	2.05	2.00	2.00

For Basement, add $37.70 per square foot of basement area

The above costs were calculated using the basic specifications shown on the facing page. These costs should be adjusted where necessary for design alternatives and owner's requirements. Reported completed project costs, for this type of structure, range from $93.45 to $267.00 per S.F.

Common additives

Description	Unit	$ Cost
Carrels Hardwood	Each	960 - 2300
Clock System, 20 room	Each	19,500
50 room	Each	45,700
Directory Boards, plastic, glass covered, 36" x 48"	Each	1500
Aluminum, 36" x 24"	Each	735
48" x 60"	Each	2200
Elevators, hydraulic passenger, 2 stops, 2500# capacity	Each	69,200
3500# capacity	Each	73,200
Seating, auditorium chair, veneer back, padded seat	Each	315
Classroom, movable chair & desk	Set	81 - 171
Lecture hall, pedestal type	Each	258 - 610
Shops & Workroom, benches, metal	Each	820
Parts bins 6'-3" high, 3' wide, 12" deep, 72 bins	Each	690
Shelving, metal 1' x 3'	S.F.	12.30
Wide span 6' wide x 24" deep	S.F.	8.85

Description	Unit	$ Cost
Sound System, amplifier, 250 watts	Each	2025
Speaker, ceiling or wall	Each	208
Commissioning Fees, sustainable institutional construction	S.F.	0.58 - 2.47
Energy Modelling Fees, academic buildings to 10,000 SF	Each	9000
Greater than 10,000 SF add	S.F.	0.20
Green Bldg Cert Fees for school construction project reg	Project	900
Photovoltaic Pwr Sys, grid connected, 20 kW (~2400 SF), roof	Each	272,300
Green Roofs, 6" soil depth, w/ treated wd edging & sedum mats	S.F.	11.05
10" Soil depth, with treated wood edging & sedum mats	S.F.	12.68
Greywater Recovery Systems, prepackaged comm, 3060 gal.	Each	57,740
4590 gal.	Each	72,025
Rainwater Harvest Sys, prepckged comm, 10,000 gal, sys contrller	Each	31,375
20,000 gal. w/ system controller	Each	50,500
30,000 gal. w/ system controller	Each	80,225
Solar Domestic HW, closed loop, add-on sys, ext heat exchanger	Each	10,950
Drainback, hot water system, 120 gal tank	Each	14,125
Draindown, hot water system, 120 gal tank	Each	14,550

Important: See the Reference Section for Location Factors.

Model costs calculated for a 2 story building with 16' story height and 40,000 square feet of floor area

				Unit	Unit Cost	Cost Per S.F.	% Of Sub-Total
A. SUBSTRUCTURE							
1010	Standard Foundations	Poured concrete; strip and spread footings		S.F. Ground	2.78	1.39	
1020	Special Foundations	N/A		—	—	—	
1030	Slab on Grade	5" reinforced concrete with recycled vapor barrier and granular base		S.F. Slab	13.06	6.53	7.1%
2010	Basement Excavation	Site preparation for slab and trench for foundation wall and footing		S.F. Ground	.18	.09	
2020	Basement Walls	4' foundation wall		L.F. Wall	89	1.63	
B. SHELL							
B10 Superstructure							
1010	Floor Construction	Open web steel joists, slab form, concrete, beams, columns		S.F. Floor	18.80	9.40	9.4%
1020	Roof Construction	Metal deck, open web steel joists, beams, columns		S.F. Roof	6.52	3.26	
B20 Exterior Enclosure							
2010	Exterior Walls	Face brick with concrete block backup	85% of wall	S.F. Wall	38.16	19.20	
2020	Exterior Windows	Tubular aluminum framing with insulated glass	15% of wall	Each	61	5.20	18.5%
2030	Exterior Doors	Metal and glass doors, low VOC paint		Each	2861	.58	
B30 Roofing							
3010	Roof Coverings	Single-ply TPO membrane, 60 mils, heat welded seams w/polyiso. insul.		S.F. Roof	8.78	4.39	3.4%
3020	Roof Openings	Roof hatches		S.F. Roof	.34	.17	
C. INTERIORS							
1010	Partitions	Concrete block w/foamed-in insul.	20 SF Flr./LF Part.	S.F. Partition	10.97	6.58	
1020	Interior Doors	Single leaf kalamein fire doors, low VOC paint	600 S.F. Floor/Door	Each	1152	1.92	
1030	Fittings	Toilet partitions, chalkboards		S.F. Floor	1.51	1.51	
2010	Stair Construction	Concrete filled metal pan		Flight	14,450	1.45	19.9%
3010	Wall Finishes	50% paint, low VOC, 40% glazed coating, 10% ceramic tile		S.F. Surface	4.62	5.54	
3020	Floor Finishes	70% vinyl comp. tile, recycled content, 20% carpet tile, 10% terrazzo		S.F. Floor	5.80	5.80	
3030	Ceiling Finishes	Mineral fiber tile on concealed zee bars	60% of area	S.F. Ceiling	4.13	4.14	
D. SERVICES							
D10 Conveying							
1010	Elevators & Lifts	One hydraulic passenger elevator		Each	83,200	2.08	1.5%
1020	Escalators & Moving Walks	N/A		—	—	—	
D20 Plumbing							
2010	Plumbing Fixtures	Toilet, low flow, auto sensor, & service fixt., supply & drain.	1 Fixt./700 SF.Flr.	Each	3738	5.34	
2020	Domestic Water Distribution	Gas fired, tankless water heater		S.F. Floor	.35	.35	4.9%
2040	Rain Water Drainage	Roof drains		S.F. Roof	1.84	.92	
D30 HVAC							
3010	Energy Supply	N/A		—	—	—	
3020	Heat Generating Systems	N/A		—	—	—	
3040	Distribution Systems	Enthalpy heat recovery packages		Each	30,350	5.31	18.2 %
3050	Terminal & Package Units	Multizone rooftop air conditioner, SEER 14		S.F. Floor	19.30	19.30	
3090	Other HVAC Sys. & Equipment	N/A		—	—	—	
D40 Fire Protection							
4010	Sprinklers	Sprinklers, light hazard		S.F. Floor	3.11	3.11	3.0%
4020	Standpipes	Standpipe, wet, Class III		S.F. Floor	.93	.93	
D50 Electrical							
5010	Electrical Service/Distribution	800 ampere service, panel board and feeders		S.F. Floor	.98	.98	
5020	Lighting & Branch Wiring	LED fixtures, daylt. dim., ltg. on/off, recept., switches, and A.C. power		S.F. Floor	13.26	13.26	13.9%
5030	Communications & Security	Addressable alarm systems, internet wiring, comm. systems & emerg. ltg.		S.F. Floor	3.15	3.15	
5090	Other Electrical Systems	Emergency generator, 11.5 kW, and energy monitoring systems		S.F. Floor	1.33	1.33	
E. EQUIPMENT & FURNISHINGS							
1010	Commercial Equipment	N/A		—	—	—	
1020	Institutional Equipment	Stainless steel countertops		S.F. Floor	.15	.15	0.2 %
1090	Other Equipment	Waste handling recycling tilt truck		Each	.14	.14	
2020	Moveable Furnishings	No smoking signage		Each	.02	.02	
F. SPECIAL CONSTRUCTION							
1020	Integrated Construction	N/A		—	—	—	0.0%
1040	Special Facilities	N/A		—	—	—	
G. BUILDING SITEWORK	**N/A**						

		Sub-Total	135.15	**100%**
CONTRACTOR FEES (General Requirements: 10%, Overhead: 5%, Profit: 10%)		25%	33.77	
ARCHITECT FEES		7%	11.83	

	Total Building Cost	**180.75**

Costs per square foot of floor area

Exterior Wall	S.F. Area	12000	16000	20000	26000	32000	38000	44000	52000	60000
	L.F. Perimeter	450	510	570	650	716	780	840	920	1020
Face Brick with Concrete Block Back-up	Steel Frame	174.75	163.50	156.85	150.15	145.40	142.05	139.55	137.05	135.75
	Bearing Walls	161.35	150.10	143.40	136.75	131.95	128.65	126.15	123.65	122.35
Stucco on Concrete Block	Steel Frame	164.25	154.55	148.90	143.15	139.15	136.35	134.25	132.15	131.00
	Bearing Walls	164.75	155.05	149.35	143.65	139.60	136.85	134.75	132.70	131.50
Precast Concrete Panels	Steel Frame	179.45	167.50	160.40	153.30	148.20	144.65	142.00	139.35	137.90
Metal Sandwich Panels	Steel Frame	174.10	162.95	156.35	149.75	145.00	141.70	139.25	136.80	135.50
Perimeter Adj., Add or Deduct	Per 100 L.F.	10.75	8.10	6.45	5.00	4.05	3.45	2.95	2.50	2.15
Story Hgt. Adj., Add or Deduct	Per 1 Ft.	2.25	1.90	1.70	1.55	1.30	1.20	1.15	1.10	1.00

For Basement, add $28.65 per square foot of basement area

The above costs were calculated using the basic specifications shown on the facing page. These costs should be adjusted where necessary for design alternatives and owner's requirements. Reported completed project costs, for this type of structure, range from $78.65 to $225.30 per S.F.

Common additives

Description	Unit	$ Cost	Description	Unit	$ Cost
Check Out Counter, single belt	Each	3550	Sound System, amplifier, 250 watts	Each	2025
Scanner, registers, guns & memory 10 lanes	Each	171,500	Speaker, ceiling or wall	Each	208
Power take away	Each	5950	Commissioning Fees, sustainable commercial construction	S.F.	0.24 - 3.04
Refrigerators, prefabricated, walk-in, 7'-6" High, 10' x 10'	S.F.	154	Energy Modelling Fees, commercial buildings to 10,000 SF	Each	11,000
12' x 14'	S.F.	136	Greater than 10,000 SF add	S.F.	0.04
12' x 20'	S.F.	119	Green Bldg Cert Fees for comm construction project reg	Project	900
Refrigerated Food Cases, dairy, multi deck, 12' long	Each	12,700	Photovoltaic Pwr Sys, grid connected, 20 kW (~2400 SF), roof	Each	272,300
Delicatessen case, multi deck, 18 S.F. shelf display	Each	8200	Green Roofs, 6" soil depth, w/ treated wd edging & sedum mats	S.F.	11.05
Freezer, glass door upright, 78 C.F.	Each	11,500	10" Soil depth, with treated wood edging & sedum mats	S.F.	12.68
Frozen food, chest type, 12' long	Each	9300	Greywater Recovery Systems, prepackaged comm, 3060 gal.	Each	57,740
Glass door reach in, 5 door	Each	15,700	4590 gal.	Each	72,025
Island case 12' long, multi deck	Each	9675	Rainwater Harvest Sys, prepckged comm, 10,000 gal, sys contrller	Each	31,375
Meat case, 12' long, multi deck	Each	11,700	20,000 gal. w/ system controller	Each	50,500
Produce, 12' long multi deck	Each	9875	30,000 gal. w/ system controller	Each	80,225
Safe, Office type, 1 hr rating, 60"x36"x18", double door	Each	8075	Solar Domestic HW, closed loop, add-on sys, ext heat exchanger	Each	10,950
			Drainback, hot water system, 120 gal tank	Each	14,125
			Draindown, hot water system, 120 gal tank	Each	14,550

Important: See the Reference Section for Location Factors.

Model costs calculated for a 1 story building with 18' story height and 44,000 square feet of floor area

			Unit	Unit Cost	Cost Per S.F.	% Of Sub-Total
A. SUBSTRUCTURE						
1010	Standard Foundations	Poured concrete; strip and spread footings	S.F. Ground	1.12	1.12	
1020	Special Foundations	N/A	—	—	—	
1030	Slab on Grade	4" reinforced concrete with recycled vapor barrier and granular base	S.F. Slab	5.33	5.33	8.8%
2010	Basement Excavation	Site preparation for slab and trench for foundation wall and footing	S.F. Ground	.18	.18	
2020	Basement Walls	4' foundation wall	L.F. Wall	89	1.69	
B. SHELL						
B10 Superstructure						
1010	Floor Construction	N/A	—	—	—	8.6 %
1020	Roof Construction	Metal deck, open web steel joists, beams, interior columns	S.F. Roof	8.11	8.11	
B20 Exterior Enclosure						
2010	Exterior Walls	Face brick with concrete block backup 85% of wall	S.F. Wall	38.14	11.14	
2020	Exterior Windows	Storefront windows 15% of wall	Each	62	3.19	16.6%
2030	Exterior Doors	Sliding entrance doors with electrical operator, hollow metal	Each	5273	1.32	
B30 Roofing						
3010	Roof Coverings	Single-ply TPO membrane, 60 mils, heat welded seams w/R-20 insul.	S.F. Roof	4.99	4.99	5.4%
3020	Roof Openings	Roof hatches	S.F. Roof	.13	.13	
C. INTERIORS						
1010	Partitions	50% CMU w/ foamed-in insul., 50% gyp. bd. on mtl. studs 50 SF Flr./LF Part.	S.F. Partition	9.21	2.21	
1020	Interior Doors	Single leaf hollow metal, low VOC paint 2000 S.F. Floor/Door	Each	1152	.58	
1030	Fittings	N/A	—	—	—	
2010	Stair Construction	N/A	—	—	—	16.5%
3010	Wall Finishes	Paint, low VOC	S.F. Surface	5.58	2.68	
3020	Floor Finishes	Vinyl composition tile, recycled content	S.F. Floor	3.19	3.19	
3030	Ceiling Finishes	Mineral fiber tile on concealed zee bars	S.F. Ceiling	6.89	6.89	
D. SERVICES						
D10 Conveying						
1010	Elevators & Lifts	N/A	—	—	—	0.0 %
1020	Escalators & Moving Walks	N/A	—	—	—	
D20 Plumbing						
2010	Plumbing Fixtures	Toilet, low flow, auto sensor, & service fixt., supply & drain. 1 Fixt./1820 SF Flr.	Each	2493	1.37	
2020	Domestic Water Distribution	Point of use water heater, electric, energy saver	S.F. Floor	.25	.25	2.8%
2040	Rain Water Drainage	Roof drains	S.F. Roof	.98	.98	
D30 HVAC						
3010	Energy Supply	N/A	—	—	—	
3020	Heat Generating Systems	Included in D3050	—	—	—	
3040	Distribution Systems	Enthalpy heat recovery packages	Each	30,350	2.76	7.0 %
3050	Terminal & Package Units	Single zone rooftop air conditioner	S.F. Floor	3.86	3.86	
3090	Other HVAC Sys. & Equipment	N/A	—	—	—	
D40 Fire Protection						
4010	Sprinklers	Sprinklers, light hazard	S.F. Floor	3.56	3.56	4.3%
4020	Standpipes	Standpipe	S.F. Floor	.52	.52	
D50 Electrical						
5010	Electrical Service/Distribution	1600 ampere service, panel board and feeders	S.F. Floor	1.93	1.93	
5020	Lighting & Branch Wiring	LED fixtures, daylt. dim., ltg. on/off, receptacles, switches, and A.C.power	S.F. Floor	22.82	22.82	29.8%
5030	Communications & Security	Addressable alarm systems, partial internet wiring and emergency lighting	S.F. Floor	2.21	2.21	
5090	Other Electrical Systems	Emergency generator, 15 kW and energy monitoring systems	S.F. Floor	1.16	1.16	
E. EQUIPMENT & FURNISHINGS						
1010	Commercial Equipment	N/A	—	—	—	
1020	Institutional Equipment	N/A	—	—	—	0.1 %
1090	Other Equipment	Waste handling recycling tilt truck	Each	.12	.12	
2020	Moveable Furnishings	No smoking signage	Each	.02	.02	
F. SPECIAL CONSTRUCTION						
1020	Integrated Construction	N/A	—	—	—	0.0 %
1040	Special Facilities	N/A	—	—	—	
G. BUILDING SITEWORK	**N/A**					

		Sub-Total	94.31	100%
CONTRACTOR FEES (General Requirements: 10%, Overhead: 5%, Profit: 10%)		25%	23.59	
ARCHITECT FEES		7%	8.25	

Total Building Cost	**126.15**

Costs per square foot of floor area

Exterior Wall	S.F. Area	10000	15000	20000	25000	30000	35000	40000	50000	60000
	L.F. Perimeter	410	500	600	640	700	766	833	966	1000
Tiltup Concrete Panels	Steel Frame	150.05	137.80	132.15	126.60	123.55	121.50	119.95	117.85	114.95
Brick with Block Back-up	Bearing Walls	173.75	156.20	148.30	139.80	135.20	132.15	129.85	126.70	122.05
Concrete Block	Steel Frame	155.75	145.15	140.30	135.30	132.60	130.80	129.45	127.50	124.85
	Bearing Walls	141.25	130.40	125.50	120.40	117.60	115.70	114.30	112.45	109.65
Galvanized Steel Siding	Steel Frame	162.85	151.90	146.90	141.65	138.85	136.90	135.50	133.55	130.75
Metal Sandwich Panels	Steel Frame	161.15	149.50	144.25	138.70	135.70	133.60	132.10	130.05	127.00
Perimeter Adj., Add or Deduct	Per 100 L.F.	8.55	5.70	4.20	3.45	2.90	2.40	2.10	1.70	1.45
Story Hgt. Adj., Add or Deduct	Per 1 Ft.	1.05	0.85	0.70	0.70	0.60	0.50	0.55	0.45	0.45

For Basement, add $31.70 per square foot of basement area

The above costs were calculated using the basic specifications shown on the facing page. These costs should be adjusted where necessary for design alternatives and owner's requirements. Reported completed project costs, for this type of structure, range from $41.35 to $165.05 per S.F.

Common additives

Description	Unit	$ Cost
Dock Leveler, 10 ton cap., 6' x 8'	Each	6975
7' x 8'	Each	8000
Fence, Chain link, 6' high, 9 ga. wire	L.F.	28
6 ga. wire	L.F.	30
Gate	Each	375
Paving, Bituminous, wearing course plus base course	S.Y.	7.50
Sidewalks, Concrete 4" thick	S.F.	4.39
Sound System, amplifier, 250 watts	Each	2025
Speaker, ceiling or wall	Each	208
Yard Lighting, 20' aluminum pole, 400W, HP sodium fixture	Each	3150

Description	Unit	$ Cost
Commissioning Fees, sustainable industrial construction	S.F.	0.20 - 1.06
Energy Modelling Fees, commercial buildings to 10,000 SF	Each	11,000
Greater than 10,000 SF add	S.F.	0.04
Green Bldg Cert Fees for comm construction project reg	Project	900
Photovoltaic Pwr Sys, grid connected, 20 kW (~2400 SF), roof	Each	272,300
Green Roofs, 6" soil depth, w/ treated wd edging & sedum mats	S.F.	11.05
10" Soil depth, with treated wood edging & sedum mats	S.F.	12.68
Greywater Recovery Systems, prepackaged comm, 3060 gal.	Each	57,740
4590 gal.	Each	72,025
Rainwater Harvest Sys, prepckged comm, 10,000 gal, sys contrller	Each	31,375
20,000 gal. w/ system controller	Each	50,500
30,000 gal. w/ system controller	Each	80,225
Solar Domestic HW, closed loop, add-on sys, ext heat exchanger	Each	10,950
Drainback, hot water system, 120 gal tank	Each	14,125
Draindown, hot water system, 120 gal tank	Each	14,550

Model costs calculated for a 1 story building with 24' story height and 30,000 square feet of floor area

G Warehouse

				Unit	Unit Cost	Cost Per S.F.	% Of Sub-Total
A. SUBSTRUCTURE							
1010	Standard Foundations	Poured concrete; strip and spread footings		S.F. Ground	1.44	1.44	
1020	Special Foundations	N/A		—	—	—	
1030	Slab on Grade	5" reinforced concrete with recycled vapor barrier and granular base		S.F. Slab	13.06	13.06	19.7%
2010	Basement Excavation	Site preparation for slab and trench for foundation wall and footing		S.F. Ground	.18	.18	
2020	Basement Walls	4' foundation wall		L.F. Wall	89	2.68	
B. SHELL							
B10 Superstructure							
1010	Floor Construction	Mezzanine: open web steel joists, slab form, concrete beams, columns	10% of area	S.F. Floor	2.17	2.17	10.9%
1020	Roof Construction	Metal deck, open web steel joists, beams, columns		S.F. Roof	7.37	7.37	
B20 Exterior Enclosure							
2010	Exterior Walls	Concrete block	95% of wall	S.F. Wall	16.79	8.93	
2020	Exterior Windows	N/A		—	—	—	11.5%
2030	Exterior Doors	Steel overhead, hollow metal	5% of wall	Each	3121	1.15	
B30 Roofing							
3010	Roof Coverings	Single-ply TPO membrane, 60 mils, heat welded w/R-20 insul.		S.F. Roof	5.15	5.15	6.2%
3020	Roof Openings	Roof hatches and skylight		S.F. Roof	.33	.33	
C. INTERIORS							
1010	Partitions	Concrete block w/foamed-in insul. (office and washrooms)	100 SF Flr./LF Part.	S.F. Partition	10.88	.87	
1020	Interior Doors	Single leaf hollow metal, low VOC paint	5000 S.F. Floor/Door	Each	1152	.23	
1030	Fittings	N/A		—	—	—	
2010	Stair Construction	Steel gate with rails		Flight	14,300	.96	8.0%
3010	Wall Finishes	Paint, low VOC		S.F. Surface	14.44	2.31	
3020	Floor Finishes	90% hardener, 10% vinyl composition tile, recycled content		S.F. Floor	2.01	2.01	
3030	Ceiling Finishes	Suspended mineral tile on zee channels in office area	10% of area	S.F. Ceiling	.69	.69	
D. SERVICES							
D10 Conveying							
1010	Elevators & Lifts	N/A		—	—	—	0.0 %
1020	Escalators & Moving Walks	N/A		—	—	—	
D20 Plumbing							
2010	Plumbing Fixtures	Toilet, low flow, auto sensor & service fixt., supply & drainage	1 Fixt./2500 SF Flr.	Each	4400	1.76	
2020	Domestic Water Distribution	Tankless, on-demand water heater, gas/propane		S.F. Floor	.52	.52	4.6%
2040	Rain Water Drainage	Roof drains		S.F. Roof	1.72	1.72	
D30 HVAC							
3010	Energy Supply	N/A		—	—	—	
3020	Heat Generating Systems	Ventilation with heat		Each	145,800	5.25	
3030	Cooling Generating Systems	N/A		—	—	—	6.8 %
3050	Terminal & Package Units	Single zone rooftop air conditioner, SEER 14		S.F. Floor	.75	.75	
3090	Other HVAC Sys. & Equipment	N/A		—	—	—	
D40 Fire Protection							
4010	Sprinklers	Sprinklers, ordinary hazard		S.F. Floor	3.96	3.96	7.0%
4020	Standpipes	Standpipe		S.F. Floor	2.18	2.18	
D50 Electrical							
5010	Electrical Service/Distribution	200 ampere service, panel board and feeders		S.F. Floor	.30	.30	
5020	Lighting & Branch Wiring	LED fixtures, daylt. dim., ltg. on/off, receptacles, switches, and A.C. power		S.F. Floor	9.74	9.74	16.1%
5030	Communications & Security	Addressable alarm systems		S.F. Floor	2.69	2.69	
5090	Other Electrical Systems	Energy monitoring systems		S.F. Floor	1.43	1.43	
E. EQUIPMENT & FURNISHINGS							
1010	Commercial Equipment	N/A		—	—	—	
1030	Vehicular Equipment	Dock boards, dock levelers		S.F. Floor	2.66	2.66	3.3 %
1090	Other Equipment	Waste handling recycling tilt truck		Each	.18	.18	
2020	Moveable Furnishings	No smoking signage		Each	.02	.02	
F. SPECIAL CONSTRUCTION							
1020	Integrated Construction	Shipping & receiving air curtain		S.F. Floor	5.22	5.22	5.9%
1040	Special Facilities	N/A		—	—	—	
G. BUILDING SITEWORK	**N/A**						
				Sub-Total		87.91	**100%**
	CONTRACTOR FEES (General Requirements: 10%, Overhead: 5%, Profit: 10%)				25%	22	
	ARCHITECT FEES				7%	7.69	
				Total Building Cost		**117.60**	

283

Assemblies Section

Table of Contents

Table No.	Page

A SUBSTRUCTURE

A1010   Standard Foundations
A1010 110 Strip Footings 304
A1010 210 Spread Footings 305
A1010 320 Foundation Dampproofing 305

A1030   Slab on Grade
A1030 120 Plain & Reinforced 307

A2010   Basement Excavation
A2010 110 Building Excavation & Backfill 308

A2020   Basement Walls
A2020 110 Walls, Cast in Place 309

B SHELL

B1010   Floor Construction
B1010 203 C.I.P. Column, Square Tied 312
B1010 204 C.I.P. Column, Square Tied-Minimum Reinforcing 313
B1010 206 Tied, Concentric Loaded Precast Concrete Columns 314
B1010 207 Tied, Eccentric Loaded Precast Concrete Columns 314
B1010 208 Steel Columns 315
B1010 210 Wood Columns 318
B1010 214 "T" Shaped Precast Beams 319
B1010 215 "L" Shaped Precast Beams 319
B1010 217 Cast in Place Slabs, One Way 320
B1010 219 Cast in Place Beam & Slab, One Way 320
B1010 220 Cast in Place Beam & Slab, Two Way 321
B1010 222 Cast in Place Flat Slab with Drop Panels 321
B1010 223 Cast in Place Flat Plate 322
B1010 226 Cast in Place Multispan Joist Slab 322
B1010 227 Cast in Place Waffle Slab 323
B1010 229 Precast Plank with No Topping 324
B1010 230 Precast Plank with 2" Concrete Topping 324
B1010 234 Precast Double "T" Beams with No Topping 325
B1010 235 Precast Double "T" Beams With 2" Topping 325
B1010 236 Precast Beam & Plank with No Topping 326
B1010 238 Precast Beam & Plank with 2" Topping 326
B1010 239 Precast Double "T" & 2" Topping on Precast Beams 327
B1010 241 W Shape Beams & Girders 328
B1010 244 Light Gauge Steel Floor Systems 329
B1010 246 Deck & Joists on Bearing Walls 330
B1010 248 Steel Joists on Beam & Wall 331
B1010 250 Steel Joists, Beams & Slab on Columns 333
B1010 252 Composite Beam & Cast in Place Slab 335
B1010 254 W Shape, Composite Deck, & Slab 336
B1010 256 Composite Beams, Deck & Slab 337
B1010 258 Metal Deck/Concrete Fill 338
B1010 261 Wood Joist 338
B1010 264 Wood Beam & Joist 338
B1010 720 Steel Column Fireproofing 339

B1020   Roof Construction
B1020 102 Wood/Flat or Pitched 340
B1020 108 Steel Joists, Beams & Deck on Columns & Walls 341
B1020 112 Steel Joists, Beams, & Deck on Columns 342
B1020 116 Steel Joists & Deck on Bearing Walls 343
B1020 120 Steel Joists, Joist Girders & Deck on Columns & Walls 344
B1020 124 Steel Joists & Joist Girders on Columns 345

B2010   Exterior Walls
B2010 101 Cast In Place Concrete 346
B2010 102 Flat Precast Concrete 346
B2010 103 Fluted Window or Mullion Precast Concrete 347
B2010 104 Ribbed Precast Concrete 348
B2010 105 Precast Concrete Specialties 349
B2010 106 Tilt-Up Concrete Panel 350
B2010 109 Concrete Block Wall - Regular Weight 351
B2010 110 Concrete Block Wall - Lightweight 351
B2010 111 Reinforced Concrete Block Wall - Regular Weight 352
B2010 112 Reinforced Concrete Block Wall - Lightweight 352
B2010 113 Split Ribbed Block Wall - Regular Weight 354
B2010 115 Reinforced Split Ribbed Block Wall - Regular Weight 354
B2010 117 Split Face Block Wall - Regular Weight 356
B2010 119 Reinforced Split Face Block Wall - Regular Weight 357
B2010 125 Solid Brick Walls - Single Wythe 358
B2010 126 Solid Brick Walls - Double Wythe 359
B2010 127 Reinforced Brick Walls 359
B2010 128 Stone Veneer 361
B2010 129 Brick Veneer/Wood Stud Backup 363
B2010 130 Brick Veneer/Metal Stud Backup 363
B2010 132 Brick Face Composite Wall - Double Wythe 365
B2010 133 Brick Face Composite Wall - Triple Wythe 367
B2010 134 Brick Face Cavity Wall 368
B2010 135 Brick Face Cavity Wall - Insulated Backup 370
B2010 140 Glass Block 372
B2010 146 Metal Siding Panel 373
B2010 148 Panel, Shingle & Lap Siding 374
B2010 151 Stucco Wall 376
B2010 152 E.I.F.S. 376
B2010 154 Metal Siding Support 378
B2010 160 Pole Barn Exterior Wall 379

B2020   Exterior Windows
B2020 102 Wood Windows 380
B2020 104 Steel Windows 381
B2020 106 Aluminum Windows 381
B2020 210 Tubular Aluminum Framing 382
B2020 220 Curtain Wall Panels 383

B2030   Exterior Doors
B2030 110 Glazed Doors, Steel or Aluminum 384
B2030 210 Wood Doors 386
B2030 220 Steel Doors 386

Table of Contents

Table No.	Page
B2030 230 Aluminum Doors	387

B3010   Roof Coverings
B3010 105 Built-Up	388
B3010 120 Single Ply Membrane	389
B3010 130 Preformed Metal Roofing	389
B3010 135 Formed Metal	389
B3010 140 Shingle & Tile	390
B3010 320 Roof Deck Rigid Insulation	391
B3010 420 Roof Edges	391
B3010 430 Flashing	392
B3010 610 Gutters	393
B3010 620 Downspouts	393
B3010 630 Gravel Stop	393

B3020   Roof Openings
B3020 110 Skylights	394
B3020 210 Hatches	394

C INTERIORS

C1010   Partitions
C1010 102 Concrete Block Partitions - Regular Weight	396
C1010 104 Concrete Block Partitions - Lightweight	397
C1010 120 Tile Partitions	398
C1010 124 Drywall Partitions/Wood Stud Framing	399
C1010 126 Drywall Partitions/Metal Stud Framing	400
C1010 128 Drywall Components	401
C1010 140 Plaster Partitions/Metal Stud Framing	402
C1010 142 Plaster Partitions/Wood Stud Framing	403
C1010 144 Plaster Partition Components	404
C1010 205 Partitions	405

C1020   Interior Doors
C1020 102 Special Doors	406

C1030   Fittings
C1030 110 Toilet Partitions	407
C1030 310 Storage Specialties, EACH	408
C1030 510 Identifying/Visual Aid Specialties, EACH	408
C1030 520 Identifying/Visual Aid Specialties, S.F.	408
C1030 710 Bath and Toilet Accessories, EACH	408
C1030 730 Bath and Toilet Accessories, L.F.	408
C1030 830 Fabricated Cabinets & Counters, L.F.	408
C1030 910 Other Fittings, EACH	409

C2010   Stair Construction
C2010 110 Stairs	410

C3010   Wall Finishes
C3010 230 Paint & Covering	411
C3010 235 Paint Trim	412

C3020   Floor Finishes
C3020 410 Tile & Covering	413

C3030   Ceiling Finishes
C3030 105 Plaster Ceilings	415
C3030 110 Drywall Ceilings	415
C3030 140 Plaster Ceiling Components	416
C3030 210 Acoustical Ceilings	416
C3030 240 Acoustical Ceiling Components	417

D SERVICES

D1010   Elevators and Lifts
D1010 110 Hydraulic	420
D1010 140 Traction Geared Elevators	420
D1010 150 Traction Gearless Elevators	421

D2010   Plumbing Fixtures
D2010 110 Water Closet Systems	424
D2010 120 Water Closets, Group	424
D2010 210 Urinal Systems	424
D2010 310 Lavatory Systems	425
D2010 410 Kitchen Sink Systems	425
D2010 420 Laundry Sink Systems	426
D2010 430 Laboratory Sink Systems	426
D2010 440 Service Sink Systems	427
D2010 510 Bathtub Systems	428
D2010 610 Group Wash Fountain Systems	428
D2010 710 Shower Systems	429
D2010 810 Drinking Fountain Systems	429
D2010 820 Water Cooler Systems	430
D2010 920 Two Fixture Bathroom, Two Wall Plumbing	431
D2010 922 Two Fixture Bathroom, One Wall Plumbing	431
D2010 924 Three Fixture Bathroom, One Wall Plumbing	431
D2010 926 Three Fixture Bathroom, Two Wall Plumbing	431
D2010 928 Four Fixture Bathroom, Two Wall Plumbing	432
D2010 932 Five Fixture Bathroom, Two Wall Plumbing	432

D2020   Domestic Water Distribution
D2020 220 Gas Fired Water Heaters - Residential Systems	433
D2020 230 Oil Fired Water Heaters - Residential Systems	433
D2020 240 Electric Water Heaters - Commercial Systems	434
D2020 250 Gas Fired Water Heaters - Commercial Systems	434
D2020 260 Oil Fired Water Heaters - Commercial Systems	435

D2040   Rain Water Drainage
D2040 210 Roof Drain Systems	436

D2090   Other Plumbing Systems
D2090 810 Piping - Installed - Unit Costs	437

D3010   Energy Supply
D3010 510 Apartment Building Heating - Fin Tube Radiation	440
D3010 520 Commercial Building Heating - Fin Tube Radiation	440
D3010 530 Commercial Bldg. Heating - Terminal Unit Heaters	440

D3020   Heat Generating Systems
D3020 102 Small Heating Systems, Hydronic, Electric Boilers	441
D3020 104 Large Heating Systems, Hydronic, Electric Boilers	441
D3020 106 Boilers, Hot Water & Steam	442
D3020 108 Heating Systems, Unit Heaters	443

Table of Contents

Table No.	Page
D3020 110 Heating System, Fin Tube Radiation	444

D3030   Cooling Generating Systems
D3030 110 Chilled Water, Air Cooled Condenser Systems	445
D3030 115 Chilled Water, Cooling Tower Systems	447

D3050   Terminal & Package Units
D3050 150 Rooftop Single Zone Unit Systems	449
D3050 155 Rooftop Multizone Unit Systems	451
D3050 160 Self-contained, Water Cooled Unit Systems	453
D3050 165 Self-contained, Air Cooled Unit Systems	455
D3050 170 Split Systems With Air Cooled Condensing Units	457

D3090   Other HVAC Systems/Equip
D3090 320 Garage Exhaust Systems	459

D4010   Sprinklers
D4010 310 Dry Pipe Sprinkler Systems	462
D4010 350 Preaction Sprinkler Systems	464
D4010 370 Deluge Sprinkler Systems	466
D4010 390 Firecycle Sprinkler Systems	468
D4010 410 Wet Pipe Sprinkler Systems	470

D4020   Standpipes
D4020 310 Wet Standpipe Risers, Class I	472
Wet Standpipe Risers, Class II	472
Wet Standpipe Risers, Class III	472
D4020 330 Dry Standpipe Risers, Class I	473
Dry Standpipe Risers, Class II	473
Dry Standpipe Risers, Class III	473
D4020 410 Fire Hose Equipment	474

D4090   Other Fire Protection Systems
D4090 910 Fire Suppression Unit Components	475
D4090 920 FM200 Systems	475

D5010   Electrical Service/Distribution
D5010 120 Overhead Electric Service, 3 Phase - 4 Wire	476
D5010 130 Underground Electric Service	477
D5010 230 Feeder Installation	478
D5010 240 Switchgear	479
D5010 250 Panelboard	480

D5020   Lighting and Branch Wiring
D5020 110 Receptacle (by Wattage)	481
D5020 115 Receptacles, Floor	481
D5020 130 Wall Switch by Sq. Ft.	482
D5020 135 Miscellaneous Power	482
D5020 140 Central A. C. Power (by Wattage)	482
D5020 145 Motor Installation	483
D5020 155 Motor Feeder	484
D5020 210 Fluorescent Fixtures (by Wattage)	485
D5020 216 Incandescent Fixture (by Wattage)	485
D5020 226 H.I.D. Fixture, High Bay, 16' (by Wattage)	486
D5020 234 H.I.D. Fixture, High Bay, 30' (by Wattage)	486
D5020 238 H.I.D. Fixture, Low Bay, 8'-10' (by Wattage)	486
D5020 242 H.I.D. Fixture, Low Bay, 16' (by Wattage)	487

Table No.	Page

D5030   Communications and Security
D5030 910 Communication & Alarm Systems	488

D5090   Other Electrical Systems
D5090 210 Generators (by kW)	489

E EQUIPMENT & FURNISHINGS

E1010   Commercial Equipment
E1010 110 Security/Vault, EACH	492
E1010 510 Mercantile Equipment, EACH	492
E1010 610 Laundry/Dry Cleaning, EACH	492

E1020   Institutional Equipment
E1020 110 Ecclesiastical Equipment, EACH	493
E1020 130 Ecclesiastical Equipment, L.F.	493
E1020 210 Library Equipment, EACH	493
E1020 230 Library Equipment, L.F.	493
E1020 310 Theater and Stage Equipment, EACH	493
E1020 320 Theater and Stage Equipment, S.F.	493
E1020 330 Theater and Stage Equipment, L.F.	493
E1020 610 Detention Equipment, EACH	493
E1020 710 Laboratory Equipment, EACH	494
E1020 720 Laboratory Equipment, S.F.	494
E1020 730 Laboratory Equipment, L.F.	494
E1020 810 Medical Equipment, EACH	494

E1030   Vehicular Equipment
E1030 110 Vehicular Service Equipment, EACH	495
E1030 210 Parking Control Equipment, EACH	495
E1030 310 Loading Dock Equipment, EACH	495

E1090   Other Equipment
E1090 210 Solid Waste Handling Equipment, EACH	496
E1090 350 Food Service Equipment, EACH	496
E1090 360 Food Service Equipment, S.F.	496
E1090 410 Residential Equipment, EACH	496
E1090 610 School Equipment, EACH	496
E1090 620 School Equipment, S.F.	497
E1090 810 Athletic, Recreational, and Therapeutic Equipment, EACH	497
E1090 820 Athletic, Recreational, and Therapeutic Equipment, S.F.	497

E2010   Fixed Furnishings
E2010 310 Window Treatment, EACH	498
E2010 320 Window Treatment, S.F.	498
E2010 420 Fixed Floor Grilles and Mats, S.F.	498
E2010 510 Fixed Multiple Seating, EACH	498

E2020   Moveable Furnishings
E2020 210 Furnishings/EACH	499
E2020 220 Furniture and Accessories, L.F.	499

F SPECIAL CONSTRUCTION

F1010   Special Structures
F1010 120 Air-Supported Structures, S.F.	502
F1010 210 Pre-Engineered Structures, EACH	502

Table of Contents

Table No.		Page
F1010 320	Other Special Structures, S.F.	502
F1010 330	Special Structures, EACH	502
F1010 340	Special Structures, S.F.	502

F1020   Integrated Construction

F1020 110	Integrated Construction, EACH	503
F1020 120	Integrated Construction, S.F.	503
F1020 250	Special Purpose Room, EACH	503
F1020 260	Special Purpose Room, S.F.	503
F1020 330	Special Construction, L.F.	503

F1030   Special Construction Systems

F1030 120	Sound, Vibration, and Seismic Construction, S.F.	504
F1030 210	Radiation Protection, EACH	504
F1030 220	Radiation Protection, S.F.	504
F1030 910	Other Special Construction Systems, EACH	504

F1040   Special Facilities

F1040 210	Ice Rinks, EACH	505
F1040 510	Liquid & Gas Storage Tanks, EACH	505
F1040 910	Special Construction, EACH	506

Table No.		Page
G BUILDING SITEWORK		

G1030   Site Earthwork

G1030 805	Trenching Common Earth	508
G1030 806	Trenching Loam & Sandy Clay	508
G1030 807	Trenching Sand & Gravel	508
G1030 815	Pipe Bedding	510

G2010   Roadways

G2010 232	Bituminous Roadways Crushed Stone	511

G2020   Parking Lots

G2020 210	Parking Lots Gravel Base	513

G2040   Site Development

G2040 810	Flagpoles	514
G2040 950	Other Site Development, EACH	514

G3030   Storm Sewer

G3030 210	Manholes & Catch Basins	515

G4020   Site Lighting

G4020 210	Light Pole (Installed)	516

Introduction to the Assemblies Section

This section of the manual contains the technical description and installed cost of all components used in the commercial/industrial/institutional section. In most cases, there is an illustration of the component to aid in identification.

All Costs Include:

Materials purchased in lot sizes typical of normal construction projects with discounts appropriate to established contractors.

Installation work performed by union labor working under standard conditions at a normal pace.

Installing Contractor's Overhead & Profit

Standard installing contractor's overhead & profit are included in the assemblies costs.

These assemblies costs contain no provisions for General Contractor's overhead and profit or Architect's fees, nor do they include premiums for labor or materials, or savings which may be realized under certain economic situations.

The assemblies tables are arranged by physical size (dimensions) of the component wherever possible.

How RSMeans Assemblies Data Works

Assemblies estimating provides a fast and reasonably accurate way to develop construction costs. An assembly is the grouping of individual work items, with appropriate quantities, to provide a cost for a major construction component in a convenient unit of measure.

An assemblies estimate is often used during early stages of design development to compare the cost impact of various design alternatives on total building cost.

Assemblies estimates are also used as an efficient tool to verify construction estimates.

Assemblies estimates do not require a completed design or detailed drawings. Instead, they are based on the general size of the structure and other known parameters of the project. The degree of accuracy of an assemblies estimate is generally within +/- 15%.

NARRATIVE FORMAT

C20 Stairs

C2010 Stair Construction

General Design: See reference section for code requirements. Maximum height between landings is 12'; usual stair angle is 20° to 50° with 30° to 35° best. Usual relation of riser to treads is:
  Riser + tread = 17.5.
  2x (Riser) + tread = 25.
  Riser x tread = 70 or 75.
Maximum riser height is 7" for commercial, 8-1/4" for residential.
Usual riser height is 6-1/2" to 7-1/4".

Minimum tread width is 11" for commercial and 9" for residential.
For additional information please see reference section.

Cost Per Flight: Table below lists the cost per flight for 4'-0" wide stairs. Side walls are not included. Railings are included.

RSMeans assemblies are identified by a **unique 12-character identifier**. The assemblies are numbered using UNIFORMAT II, ASTM Standard E1557. The first 6 characters represent this system to Level 4. The last 6 characters represent further breakdown by RSMeans in order to arrange items in understandable groups of similar tasks. Line numbers are consistent across all RSMeans publications, so a line number in any RSMeans assemblies data set will always refer to the same work.

System Components	QUANTITY	UNIT	COST PER FLIGHT		
			MAT.	INST.	TOTAL
SYSTEM C2010 110 0560					
STAIRS, C.I.P. CONCRETE WITH LANDING, 12 RISERS					
Concrete in place, free standing stairs not incl. safety treads	48.000	L.F.	285.60	1,941.12	2,226.72
Concrete in place, free standing stair landing	32.000	S.F.	154.56	538.56	693.12
Cast alum nosing insert, abr surface, pre-drilled, 3" wide x 4' long	12.000	Ea.	882	201.60	1,083.60
Industrial railing, welded, 2 rail 3'-6" high 1-1/2" pipe	18.000	L.F.	540	217.08	757.08
Wall railing with returns, steel pipe	17.000	L.F.	289.85	205.02	494.87
TOTAL			2,152.01	3,103.38	5,255.39

Information is available in the Reference Section to assist the estimator with estimating procedures, alternate pricing methods, and additional technical information.

The **Reference Box** indicates the exact location of this information in the Reference Section at the back of the book. The "R" stands for "reference," and the remaining characters are the RSMeans line numbers.

C2010 110	Stairs		COST PER FLIGHT		
			MAT	INST	TOTAL
0470	Stairs, C.I.P. concrete, w/o landing, 12 risers, w/o nosing	RC2010 -100	1,125	2,375	3,500
0480	With nosing		2,000	2,575	4,575
0550	W/landing, 12 risers, w/o nosing		1,275	2,900	4,175
0560	With nosing		2,150	3,100	5,250
0570	16 risers, w/o nosing		1,550	3,625	5,175
0580	With nosing		2,725	3,900	6,625
0590	20 risers, w/o nosing		1,825	4,400	6,225
0600	With nosing		3,300	4,725	8,025
0610	24 risers, w/o nosing		2,125	5,125	7,250
0620	With nosing		3,875	5,525	9,400
0630	Steel, grate type w/nosing & rails, 12 risers, w/o landing		5,700	1,250	6,950
0640	With landing		7,975	1,675	9,650
0660	16 risers, with landing		9,875	2,100	11,975
0680	20 risers, with landing		11,800	2,500	14,300
0700	24 risers, with landing		13,700	2,925	16,625
0710	Concrete fill metal pan & picket rail, 12 risers, w/o landing		7,375	1,250	8,625
0720	With landing		9,725	1,850	11,575
0740	16 risers, with landing		12,200	2,250	14,450
0760	20 risers, with landing		14,600	2,650	17,250
0780	24 risers, with landing		17,100	3,050	20,150
0790	Cast iron tread & pipe rail, 12 risers, w/o landing		7,375	1,250	8,625
0800	With landing		9,725	1,850	11,575
0820	16 risers, with landing		12,200	2,250	14,450
0840	20 risers, with landing		14,600	2,650	17,250

RSMeans assemblies descriptions appear in two formats: narrative and table. **Narrative descriptions** are shown in a hierarchical structure to make them readable. In order to read a complete description, read up through the indents to the top of the section. Include everything that is above and to the left that is not contradicted by information below.

For supplemental customizable square foot estimating forms, visit: **http://www.reedconstructiondata.com/rsmeans/assemblies**

Most assemblies consist of three major elements: a graphic, the system components, and the cost data itself. The **Graphic** is a visual representation showing the typical appearance of the assembly in question, frequently accompanied by additional explanatory technical information describing the class of items. The **System Components** is a listing of the individual tasks that make up the assembly, including the quantity and unit of measure for each item, along with the cost of material and installation. The **Assemblies Data** below lists prices for other similar systems with dimensional and/or size variations.

All RSMeans assemblies costs represent the cost for the installing contractor. An allowance for profit has been added to all material, labor, and equipment rental costs. A markup for labor burdens, including workers' compensation, fixed overhead, and business overhead, is included with installation costs.

The data published in RSMeans print books represents a "national average" cost. This data should be modified to the project location using the **City Cost Indexes** or **Location Factors** tables found in the Reference Section in the back of the book.

TABLE FORMAT

A20 Basement Construction

A2020 Basement Walls

The Foundation Bearing Wall System includes: forms up to 16' high (four uses); 3,000 p.s.i. concrete placed and vibrated; and form removal with breaking form ties and patching walls. The wall systems list walls from 6" to 16" thick and are designed with minimum reinforcement.

Excavation and backfill are not included.

Please see the reference section for further design and cost information.

All RSMeans assemblies data includes a typical **Unit of Measure** used for estimating that item. For instance, for continuous footings or foundation walls the unit is linear feet (L.F.). For spread footings the unit is each (Ea.). The estimator needs to take special care that the unit in the data matches the unit in the takeoff. Abbreviations and unit conversions can be found in the Reference Section.

System Components			COST PER L.F.		
	QUANTITY	UNIT	MAT.	INST.	TOTAL
SYSTEM A2020 110 1500 **FOUNDATION WALL, CAST IN PLACE, DIRECT CHUTE, 4' HIGH, 6" THICK**					
Formwork	8.000	SFCA	6	44	50
Reinforcing	3.300	Lb.	1.82	1.40	3.22
Unloading & sorting reinforcing	3.300	Lb.		.08	.08
Concrete, 3,000 psi	.074	C.Y.	8.07		8.07
Place concrete, direct chute	.074	C.Y.		2.35	2.35
Finish walls, break ties and patch voids, one side	4.000	S.F.	.16	3.84	4
TOTAL			16.05	51.67	67.72

System components are listed separately to detail what is included in the development of the total system price.

A2020 110			Walls, Cast in Place					
	WALL HEIGHT (FT.)	PLACING METHOD	CONCRETE (C.Y. per L.F.)	REINFORCING (LBS. per L.F.)	WALL THICKNESS (IN.)	COST PER L.F.		
						MAT.	INST.	TOTAL
1500	4'	direct chute	.074	3.3	6	16.05	51.50	67.55
1520			.099	4.8	8	19.60	53	72.60
1540			.123	6.0	10	23	54	77
1560	RA2020 -210		.148	7.2	12	26.50	55	81.50
1580			.173	8.1	14	29.50	56	85.50
1600			.197	9.44	16	33	57.50	90.50
1700	4'	pumped	.074	3.3	6	16.05	52.50	68.55
1720			.099	4.8	8	19.60	55	74.60
1740			.123	6.0	10	23	56	79
1760			.148	7.2	12	26.50	57	83.50
1780			.173	8.1	14	29.50	58.50	88
1800			.197	9.44	16	33	60	93
3000	6'	direct chute	.111	4.95	6	24	77.50	101.50
3020			.149	7.20	8	29.50	79.50	109
3040			.184	9.00	10	34.50	81	115.50
3060			.222	10.8	12	39.50	83	122.50
3080			.260	12.15	14	44.50	84	128.50
3100			.300	14.39	16	50	86.50	136.50

Table descriptions work in a similar fashion, except that if there is a blank in the column at a particular line number, read up to the description above in the same column.

How RSMeans Assemblies Data Works (Continued)

Sample Estimate

This sample demonstrates the elements of an estimate, including a tally of the RSMeans data lines. Published assemblies costs include all markups for labor burden and profit for the installing contractor. This estimate adds a summary of the markups applied by a general contractor on the installing contractors' work. These figures represent the total cost to the owner. The RSMeans location factor is added at the bottom of the estimate to adjust the cost of the work to a specific location

Work performed: The body of the estimate shows the RSMeans data selected, including line numbers, a brief description of each item, its takeoff quantity and unit, and the total installed cost, including the installing contractor's overhead and profit.

Location Factor: RSMeans published data is based on national average costs. If necessary, adjust the total cost of the project using a location factor from the "Location Factor" table or the "City Cost Indexes" table, found in the Reference Section. Use location factors if the work is general, covering the work of multiple trades. If the work is by a single trade (e.g. masonry) use the more specific data found in the City Cost Indexes.

To adjust costs by location factors, multiply the base cost by the factor and divide by 100.

Contingency: A factor for contingency may be added to any estimate to represent the cost of unknowns that may occur between the time that the estimate is performed and the time the project is constructed. The amount of the allowance will depend on the stage of design at which the estimate is done, and the contractor's assessment of the risk invloved.

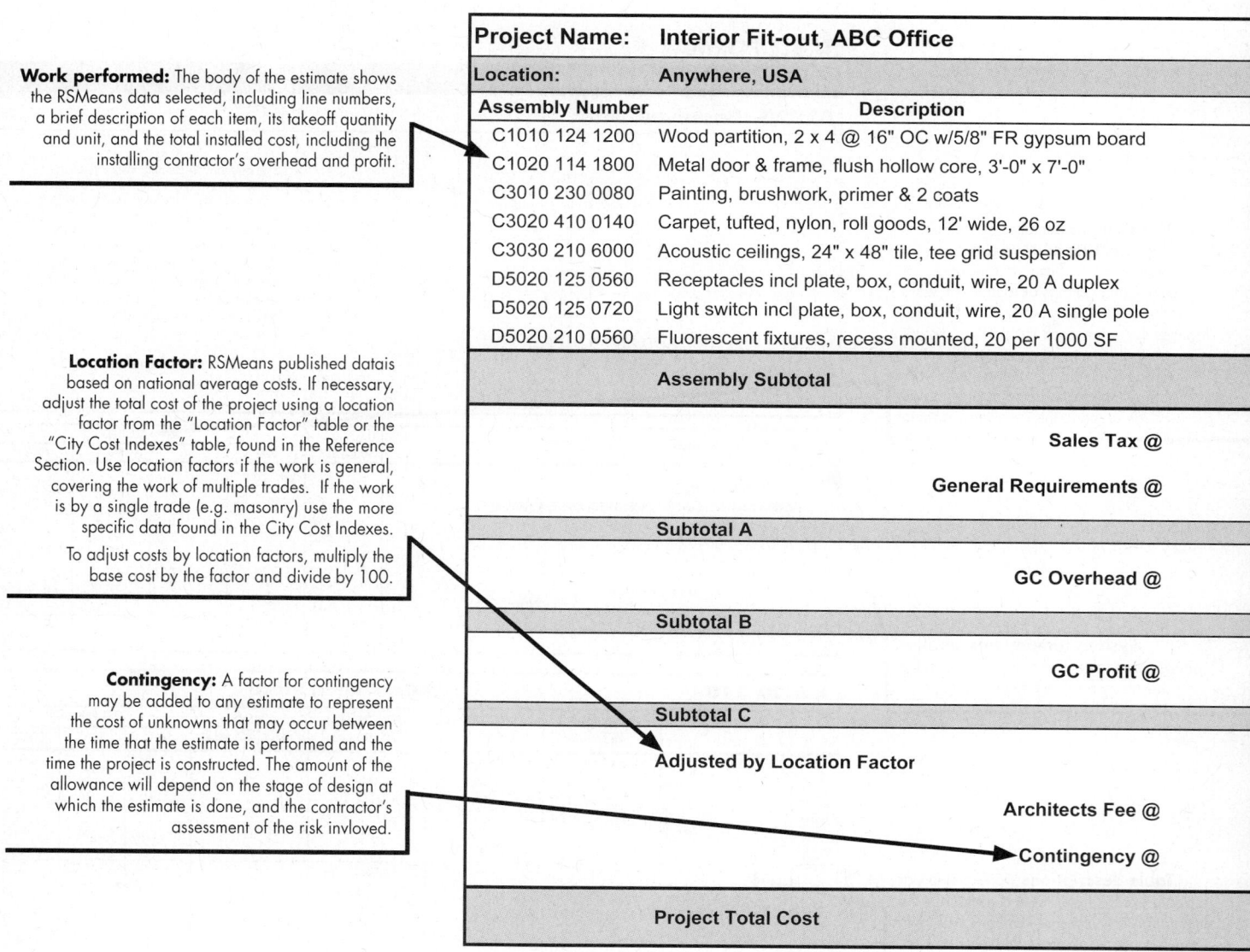

Project Name:	Interior Fit-out, ABC Office
Location:	**Anywhere, USA**
Assembly Number	**Description**
C1010 124 1200	Wood partition, 2 x 4 @ 16" OC w/5/8" FR gypsum board
C1020 114 1800	Metal door & frame, flush hollow core, 3'-0" x 7'-0"
C3010 230 0080	Painting, brushwork, primer & 2 coats
C3020 410 0140	Carpet, tufted, nylon, roll goods, 12' wide, 26 oz
C3030 210 6000	Acoustic ceilings, 24" x 48" tile, tee grid suspension
D5020 125 0560	Receptacles incl plate, box, conduit, wire, 20 A duplex
D5020 125 0720	Light switch incl plate, box, conduit, wire, 20 A single pole
D5020 210 0560	Fluorescent fixtures, recess mounted, 20 per 1000 SF
Assembly Subtotal	
	Sales Tax @
	General Requirements @
Subtotal A	
	GC Overhead @
Subtotal B	
	GC Profit @
Subtotal C	
Adjusted by Location Factor	
	Architects Fee @
	Contingency @
Project Total Cost	

This estimate is based on an interactive spreadsheet.
A copy of this spreadsheet is located on the RSMeans website at
http://www.reedconstructiondata.com/rsmeans/extras/546011.
You are free to download it and adjust it to your methodology.

292

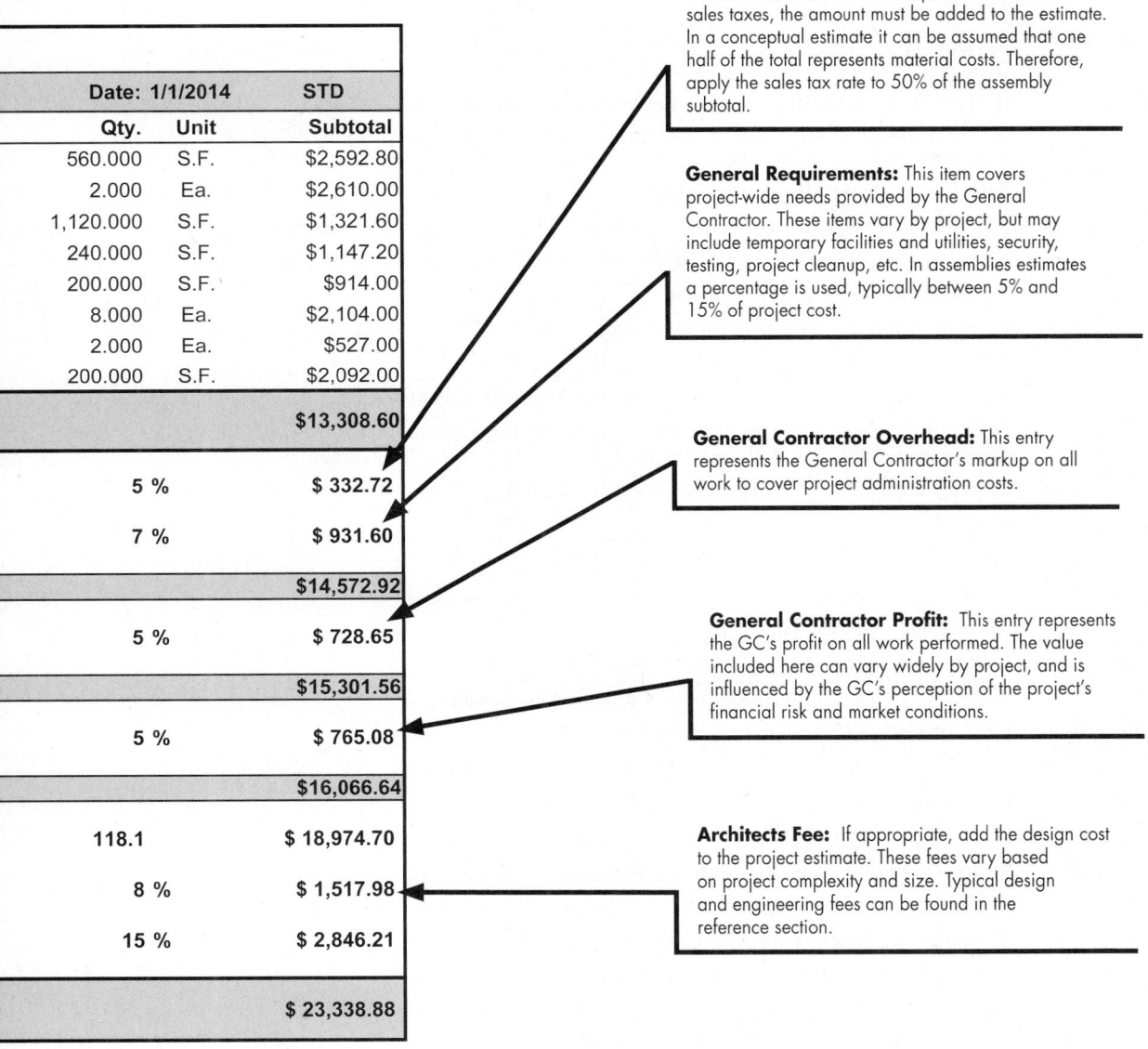

Date: 1/1/2014		STD
Qty.	Unit	Subtotal
560.000	S.F.	$2,592.80
2.000	Ea.	$2,610.00
1,120.000	S.F.	$1,321.60
240.000	S.F.	$1,147.20
200.000	S.F.	$914.00
8.000	Ea.	$2,104.00
2.000	Ea.	$527.00
200.000	S.F.	$2,092.00
		$13,308.60
5 %		$ 332.72
7 %		$ 931.60
		$14,572.92
5 %		$ 728.65
		$15,301.56
5 %		$ 765.08
		$16,066.64
118.1		$ 18,974.70
8 %		$ 1,517.98
15 %		$ 2,846.21
		$ 23,338.88

Sales Tax: If the work is subject to state or local sales taxes, the amount must be added to the estimate. In a conceptual estimate it can be assumed that one half of the total represents material costs. Therefore, apply the sales tax rate to 50% of the assembly subtotal.

General Requirements: This item covers project-wide needs provided by the General Contractor. These items vary by project, but may include temporary facilities and utilities, security, testing, project cleanup, etc. In assemblies estimates a percentage is used, typically between 5% and 15% of project cost.

General Contractor Overhead: This entry represents the General Contractor's markup on all work to cover project administration costs.

General Contractor Profit: This entry represents the GC's profit on all work performed. The value included here can vary widely by project, and is influenced by the GC's perception of the project's financial risk and market conditions.

Architects Fee: If appropriate, add the design cost to the project estimate. These fees vary based on project complexity and size. Typical design and engineering fees can be found in the reference section.

Example

Assemblies costs can be used to calculate the cost for each component of a building and, accumulated with appropriate markups, produce a cost for the complete structure. Components from a model building with similar characteristics in conjunction with Assemblies components may be used to calculate costs for a complete structure.

Example:

Outline Specifications

General	Building size—60' x 100', 8 suspended floors, 12' floor to floor, 4' high parapet above roof, full basement 11'-8" floor to floor, bay size 25' x30', ceiling heights -9' in office area and 8' in core area.
A Substructure	Concrete, spread and strip footings, concrete walls waterproofed, 4" slab on grade.
B Shell	
B10 Superstructure	Columns, wide flange; 3 hr. fire rated; Floors, composite steel frame & deck with concrete slab; Roof, steel beams, open web joists and deck.
B20 Exterior Enclosure	Walls; North, East & West, brick & lightweight concrete block with 2" cavity insulation, 25% window; South, 8" lightweight concrete block insulated, 10% window. Doors, aluminum & glass. Windows, aluminum, 3'-0" x5'-4", insulating glass.
B30 Roofing	Tar & gravel, 2" rigid insulation, R 12.5.
C Interiors	Core—6" lightweight concrete block, full height with plaster on exposed faces to ceiling height.
	Corridors—1st & 2nd floor; 3-5/8" steel studs with F.R. gypsum board, full height.
	Exterior Wall—plaster, ceiling height.
	Fittings—Toilet accessories, directory boards.
	Doors—hollow metal.
	Wall Finishes—lobby, mahogany paneling on furring, remainder plaster & gypsum board, paint.
	Floor Finishes—1st floor lobby, corridors & toilet rooms, terrazzo; remainder concrete, tenant developed. 2nd thru 8th, toilet rooms, ceramic tile; office & corridor, carpet.
	Ceiling Finishes—24" x48" fiberglass board on Tee grid.
D Services	
D10 Conveying	2-2500 lb. capacity, 200 F.P.M. geared elevators, 9 stops.
D20 Plumbing	Fixtures, see sketch.
	Roof Drains—2-4" C.I. pipe.
D30 HVAC	Heating—fin tube radiation, forced hot water.
	Air Conditioning—chilled water with water cooled condenser.
D40 Fire Protection	Fire Protection—4" standpipe, 9 hose cabinets.
D50 Electrical	Lighting, 1st thru 8th, 15 fluorescent fixtures/1000 S.F., 3 Watts/S.F.
	Basement, 10 fluorescent fixtures/1000 S.F., 2 Watts/S.F.
	Receptacles, 1st thru 8th, 16.5/1000 S.F., 2 Watts/S.F.
	Basement, 10 receptacles/1000 S.F., 1.2 Watts/S.F.
	Air Conditioning, 4 Watts/S.F.
	Miscellaneous Connections, 1.2 Watts/S.F.
	Elevator Power, 2-10 H.P., 230 volt motors.
	Wall Switches, 2/1000 S.F.
	Service, panel board & feeder, 2000 Amp.
	Fire Detection System, pull stations, signals, smoke and heat detectors.
	Emergency Lighting Generator, 30 KW.
E Equipment & Furnishings	NA.
F Special Construction	NA.
G Building Sitework	NA.

Front Elevation

Basement Plan

Ground Floor Plan

Typical Floor plan

Example

If spread footing & column sizes are unknown, develop approximate loads as follows. Enter tables with these loads to determine costs.

Approximate loads/S.F. for roof & floors.

Roof. Assume 40 psf superimposed load.

Steel joists, beams & deck.

Table B1020 112—Line 3900

Superimposed Load Ranges

Apartments & Residential Structures	65	to	75 psf
Assembly Areas & Retail Stores	110	to	125 psf
Commercial & Manufacturing	150	to	250 psf
Offices	75	to	100 psf

B1020 112		Steel Joists, Beams, & Deck on Columns							
	BAY SIZE (FT.)	SUPERIMPOSED LOAD (P.S.F.)	DEPTH (IN.)	TOTAL LOAD (P.S.F.)	COLUMN ADD	COST PER S.F.			
						MAT.	INST.	TOTAL	
3500	25x30	20	22	40		5.50	1.61	7.11	
3600					columns	1.21	.28	1.49	
3900		40	25	60		6.60	1.91	8.51	
4000					columns	1.45	.34	1.79	

B1010 256		Composite Beams, Deck & Slab						
	BAY SIZE (FT.)	SUPERIMPOSED LOAD (P.S.F.)	SLAB THICKNESS (IN.)	TOTAL DEPTH (FT.-IN.)	TOTAL LOAD (P.S.F.)	COST PER S.F.		
						MAT.	INST.	TOTAL
3400	25x30	40	5-1/2	1 - 11-1/2	83	12.20	5.85	18.05
3600		75	5-1/2	1 - 11-1/2	119	13.20	5.85	19.05
3900		125	5-1/2	1 - 11-1/2	170	15.40	6.65	22.05
4000		200	6-1/4	2 - 6-1/4	252	19.05	7.55	26.60

Floors—Total load, 119 psf.
Interior foundation load.
Roof

[(25' x 30' x 60 psf) + 8 floors x (25' x 30' x 119 psf)] x 1/1000 lb./Kip =	759 Kips
Approximate Footing Loads, Interior footing =	759 Kips
Exterior footing (1/2 bay) 759 k x .6=	455 Kips
Corner footing (1/4 bay) 759 k x .45=	342 Kips
[Factors to convert Interior load to Exterior & Corner loads]	
Approximate average Column load 759 k/2 =	379 Kips

PRELIMINARY ESTIMATE

PROJECT **Office Building**	TOTAL SITE AREA
BUILDING TYPE	OWNER
LOCATION	ARCHITECT
DATE OF CONSTRUCTION	ESTIMATED CONSTRUCTION PERIOD

BRIEF DESCRIPTION **Building size: 60' x 100' - 8 structural floors - 12' floor to floor**

4' high parapet above roof, full basement 11' - 8" floor to floor, bay size

25' x 30', ceiling heights - 9' in office area + 8' in core area

TYPE OF PLAN		TYPE OF CONSTRUCTION
QUALITY		BUILDING CAPACITY

Floor			**Wall Area**				
Below Grade Levels			Foundation Walls	L.F.		Ht.	S.F.
Area		S.F.	Frost Walls	L.F.		Ht.	S.F.
Area		S.F.	Exterior Closure		Total		S.F.
Total Area		S.F.	Comment				
Ground Floor			Fenestration		%		S.F.
Area		S.F.			%		S.F.
Area		S.F.	Exterior Wall		%		S.F.
Total Area		S.F.			%		S.F.
Supported Levels			**Site Work**				
Area			Parking		S.F. (For		Cars)
Area		S.F.	Access Roads		L.F. (X		Ft. Wide)
Area		S.F.	Sidewalk		L.F. (X		Ft. Wide)
Area		S.F.	Landscaping		S.F. (		% Unbuilt Site)
Area		S.F.	**Building Codes**				
Total Area		S.F.	City		Country		
Miscellaneous			National		Other		
Area		S.F.	**Loading**				
Area		S.F.	Roof	psf	Ground Floor		psf
Area		S.F.	Supported Floors	psf	Corridor		psf
Area		S.F.	Balcony	psf	Partition, allow		psf
Total Area		S.F.	Miscellaneous				psf
Net Finished Area		S.F.	Live Load Reduction				
Net Floor Area		S.F.	Wind				
Gross Floor Area	**54,000**	S.F.	Earthquake		Zone		
Roof			Comment				
Total Area		S.F.	Soil Type				
Comments			Bearing Capacity				K.S.F.
			Frost Depth				Ft.
Volume			**Frame**				
Depth of Floor System			Type		Bay Spacing		
Minimum		In.	Foundation				
Maximum		In.	Special				
Foundation Wall Height		Ft.	Substructure				
Floor to Floor Height		Ft.	Comment				
Floor to Ceiling Height		Ft.	Superstructure, Vertical				
Subgrade Volume		C.F.	Fireproofing		☐ Columns		Hrs.
Above Grade Volume		C.F.	☐ Girders	Hrs.	☐ Beams		Hrs.
Total Building Volume	**648,000**	C.F.	☐ Floor	Hrs.	☐ None		

NUMBER		QTY.	UNIT	TOTAL COST UNIT	TOTAL	COST PER S.F.
A	**SUBSTRUCTURE**					
A1010 210 7900	Corner Footings 8'-6" SQ. x 27"	4	Ea.	1,890.00	7,560	
8010	Exterior 9' -6" SQ. x 30"	8		2,525.00	20,200	
8300	Interior 12' SQ.	3		4,650.00	13,950	
A1010 110 2700	Strip 2' Wide x 1' Thick					
	320 L.F. [(4 x 8.5) + 8 x 9.5)] =	320	L.F.	39.15	12,528	
A2020 110 7260	Foundation Wall 12' High, 1' Thick	320		252.00	80,640	
A1010 320 2800	Foundation Waterproofing	320		23.35	7,472	
A1030 120 2240	4", non-industrial, reinf. slab on grade	6000	S.F.	5.31	31,860	
A2010 110 3440	Building Excavation + Backfill	6000	S.F.	7.13	42,780	
3500	(Interpolated ; 12' Between					
4620	8' and 16' ; 6,000 Between					
4680	4,000 and 10,000 S.F.					
	Total				216,990	4.02
B	**SHELL**					
B10	**Superstructure**					
B1010 208 5800	Columns: Load 379K Use 400K					
	Exterior 12 x 96' + Interior 3 x 108'	1476	V.L.F.	150.75	222,507	
B1010 720 3650	Column Fireproofing - Interior 4 sides					
3700	Exterior 1/2 (Interpolated for 12")	900	V.L.F	35.38	31,842	
B1010 256 3600	Floors: Composite steel + lt. wt. conc.	48000	S.F.	19.05	914,400	
B1020 112 3900	Roof: Open web joists, beams + decks	6000	S.F.	8.51	51,060	
	Total				1,219,809	22.59
B20	**Exterior Enclosure**					
B2010 134 1200	4" Brick + 6" Block - Insulated					
	75% NE + W Walls 220' x 100' x .75	16500	S.F.	30.35	500,775	
B2010 110 3410	8" Block - Insulated 90%					
	100' x 100' x .9	9000	S.F.	11.95	107,550	
B2030 110 6950	Double Aluminum + Glass Door	1	Pr.	5,700.00	5,700	
6300	Single	2	Ea.	2,900.00	5,800	
B2020 106 8800	Aluminum windows - Insul. glass					
	(5,500 S.F. + 1,000 S.F.)/(3 x 5.33)	406	Ea.	909.00	369,054	
B2010 105 8480	Precast concrete coping	320	L.F.	41.30	13,216	
	Total				1,002,095	18.56
B30	**Roofing**					
B3010 320 4020	Insulation: Perlite/Polyisocyanurate	6000	S.F.	1.81	10,860	
B3010 105 1400	Roof: 4 Ply T & G composite	6000		2.95	17,700	
B3010 430 0300	Flashing: Aluminum - fabric backed	640		3.31	2,118	
B3020 210 0500	Roof hatch	1	Ea.	1,249.00	1,249	
	Total				31,927	0.59

ASSEMBLY NUMBER		QTY.	UNIT	TOTAL COST		COST PER S.F.
				UNIT	TOTAL	
C	**INTERIORS**					
C1010 104 5500	Core partitions: 6" Lt. Wt. concrete					
	block 288 L.F. x 11.5' x 8 Floors	26,449	S.F.	9.37	247,827	
C1010 144 0920	Plaster: [(196 L.F. x 8') + (144 L.F. x 9')] 8					
	+ Ext. Wall [(320 x 9 x 8 Floors) - 6500]	39,452	S.F.	3.13	123,485	
C1010 126 5400	Corridor partitions 1st + 2nd floors					
	steel studs + F.R. gypsum board	2,530	S.F.	4.18	10,575	
C1020 102 2600	Interior doors	66	Ea.	1,152.00	76,032	
	Wall finishes - Lobby: Mahogany w/furring					
C1010 128 0652	Furring: 150 L.F. x 9' + Ht.	1,350	S.F.	1.60	2,160	
C1030 710 0120	Towel Dispenser	16	Ea.	84.50	1,352	
C1030 710 0140	Grab Bar	32	Ea.	55.50	1,776	
C1030 710 0160	Mirror	31	Ea.	233.50	7,239	
C1030 710 0180	Toilet Tissue Dispenser	31	Ea.	38.45	1,192	
C1030 510 0140	Directory Board	8	Ea.	335.00	2,680	
C2010 110 0780	Stairs: Steel w/conc. fill	18	Flt.	20,150.00	362,700	
C3010 230 1662	Mahogany paneling	1,350	S.F.	6.02	8,127	
C3010 230 0080	Paint, primer + 2 coats finish, on plaster or gyp. board					
	39,452 + [(220' x 9' x 2) - 1350] + 72	42,134	S.F.	1.18	49,718	
	Floor Finishes					
C3020 410 1100	1st floor lobby + terrazzo	2,175	S.F.	19.86	43,196	
	Remainder: Concrete - Tenant finished					
C3020 410 0060	2nd - 8th: Carpet - 4725 S.F. x 7	33,075	S.F.	4.24	140,238	
C3020 410 1720	Ceramic Tile - 300 S.F. x 7	2,100	S.F.	11.30	23,730	
C3030 240 2780	Suspended Ceiling Tiles- 5200 S.F. x 8	41,600	S.F.	1.89	78,624	
C3030 240 3260	Suspended Ceiling Grid- 5200 S.F. x 8	41,600	S.F.	1.48	61,568	
C1030 110 0700	Toilet partitions	31	Ea.	702.00	21,762	
0760	Handicapped addition	16	Ea.	345.00	5,520	
	Total				1,269,500	23.51
D	**SERVICES**					
D10	**Conveying**					
	2 Elevators - 2500# 200'/min. Geared					
D1010 140 1600	5 Floors $171,200					
1800	15 Floors $428,500					
	Diff. $257,300/10 = 25,730/Flr.					
	$171,200 + (4 x25,730) = $274,120/Ea.	2	Ea.	274,120.00	548,240	
	Total				548,240	10.15
D20	**Plumbing**					
D2010 310 1600	Plumbing - Lavatories	31	Ea.	1,390.00	43,090	
D2010 440 4340	-Service Sink	8	Ea.	4,200.00	33,600	
D2010 210 2000	-Urinals	8	Ea.	1,445.00	11,560	

ASSEMBLY NUMBER		QTY.	UNIT	TOTAL COST UNIT	TOTAL	COST PER S.F.
D2010 110 2080	-Water Closets	31	Ea.	2,760.00	85,560	
	Water Control, Waste Vent Piping	45%			78,215	
D2040 210 4200	- Roof Drains, 4" C.I.	2	Ea.	1,830.00	3,660	
4240	- Pipe, 9 Flr. x 12' x 12' Ea.	216	L.F.	41.55	8,975	
	Total				264,659	4.90
D30	HVAC					
D3010 520 2000	10,000 S.F. @ $10.34/S.F. Interpolate					
2040	100,000 S.F. @ $4.43/S.F.	48,000	S.F.	7.85	376,800	
	Cooling - Chilled Water, Air Cool, Cond.					
D3030 115 4000	40,000 S.F. @14.30/S.F. Interpolate	48,000	S.F.	14.87	713,760	
4040	60,000 S.F. @15.25/S.F.					
	Total				1,090,560	20.20
D40	Fire Protection					
D4020 310 0560	Wet Stand Pipe: 4" x 10' 1st floor	12/10	Ea.	8,175.00	9,810	
0580	Additional Floors: (12'/10 x 8)	9.6	Ea.	2,150.00	20,640	
D4020 410 8400	Cabinet Assembly	9	Ea.	1,185.00	10,665	
	Total				41,115	0.76
D50	Electrical					
D5020 210 0280	Office Lighting, 15/1000 S.F. - 3 Watts/S.F.	48,000	S.F.	7.74	371,520	
0240	Basement Lighting, 10/1000 S.F. - 2 Watts/S.F.	6,000	S.F.	5.15	30,900	
D5020 110 0640	Office Receptacles 16.5/1000 S.F. - 2 Watts/S.F.	48,000	S.F.	4.53	217,440	
0560	Basement Receptacles 10/1000 S.F. - 1.2 Watts/S.F.	6,000	S.F.	3.48	20,880	
D5020 140 0280	Central A.C. - 4 Watts/S.F.	48,000	S.F.	0.43	20,640	
D5020 135 0320	Misc. Connections - 1.2 Watts/S.F.	48,000	S.F.	0.32	15,360	
D5020 145 0680	Elevator Motor Power - 10 H.P.	2	Ea.	2,950.00	5,900	
D5020 130 0280	Wall Switches - 2/1000 S.F.	54,000	S.F.	0.46	24,840	
D5010 120 0560	2000 Amp Service	1	Ea.	33,400.00	33,400	
D5010 240 0400	Switchgear	1	Ea.	37,400.00	37,400	
D5010 230 0560	Feeder	50	L.F.	527.00	26,350	
D5030 910 0400	Fire Detection System - 50 Detectors	1	Ea.	33,700.00	33,700	
D5090 210 0320	Emergency Generator - 30 kW	30	kW	546.00	16,380	
	Total				854,710	15.83
E	EQUIPMENT & FURNISHINGS					
G	BUILDING SITEWORK					
	Miscellaneous					

Preliminary Estimate Cost Summary

PROJECT: Office Building	TOTAL AREA	54,000 S.F.	SHEET NO.	
LOCATION	TOTAL VOLUME	648,000 C.F.	ESTIMATE NO.	
ARCHITECT	COST PER S.F.		DATE	
OWNER	COST PER C.F.		NO OF STORIES	
QUANTITIES BY	EXTENSIONS BY		CHECKED BY	

DIV	DESCRIPTION	SUBTOTAL COST	COST/S.F.	PERCENTAGE
A	SUBSTRUCTURE	216,990	$ 4.02	
B10	SHELL: SUPERSTRUCTURE	1,219,809	$ 22.59	
B20	SHELL: EXTERIOR ENCLOSURE	1,002,095	$ 18.56	
B30	SHELL: ROOFING	31,927	$ 0.59	
C	INTERIORS	1,269,500	$ 23.51	
D10	SERVICES: CONVEYING	548,240	$ 10.15	
D20	SERVICES: PLUMBING	264,659	$ 4.90	
D30	SERVICES: HVAC	1,090,560	$ 20.20	
D40	SERVICES: FIRE PROTECTION	41,115	$ 0.76	
D50	SERVICES: ELECTRICAL	854,710	$ 15.83	
E	EQUIPMENT & FURNISHINGS			
F	SPECIAL CONSTRUCTION & DEMO.			
G	BUILDING SITEWORK			

BUILDING SUBTOTAL	$ 6,539,606		$ 6,539,606	
Sales Tax % x Subtotal /2	N/A		$ -	
General Conditions 10 % x Subtotal			$ 653,961	
		Subtotal "A"	$ 7,193,567	
Overhead 5 % x Subtotal "A"			$ 359,678	
		Subtotal "B"	$ 7,553,245	
Profit 10% x Subtotal "B"			$ 755,324	
		Subtotal "C"	$ 8,308,569	
Location Factor % x Subtotal "C"	N/A	Localized Cost		
Architects Fee 6.5% x Localized Cost =			$ 540,057	
Contingency x Localized Cost =	N/A		$ -	
		Project Total Cost	$ 8,848,627	
Square Foot Cost $8,845,298/ 54,000 S.F. =		S.F. Cost	$ 163.86	
Cubic Foot Cost $8,845,298/ 648,000 C.F. =		C.F. Cost	$ 13.66	

A1010 Standard Foundations

The Strip Footing System includes: excavation; hand trim; all forms needed for footing placement; forms for 2″ x 6″ keyway (four uses); dowels; and 3,000 p.s.i. concrete.

The footing size required varies for different soils. Soil bearing capacities are listed for 3 KSF and 6 KSF. Depths of the system range from 8″ and deeper. Widths range from 16″ and wider. Smaller strip footings may not require reinforcement.

Please see the reference section for further design and cost information.

A1010 110	Strip Footings	COST PER L.F.		
		MAT.	INST.	TOTAL
2100	Strip footing, load 2.6 KLF, soil capacity 3 KSF, 16″ wide x 8″ deep, plain	8.30	13.95	22.25
2300	Load 3.9 KLF, soil capacity, 3 KSF, 24″ wide x 8″ deep, plain	10.15	15.35	25.50
2500	Load 5.1 KLF, soil capacity 3 KSF, 24″ wide x 12″ deep, reinf.	16.15	23	39.15
2700	Load 11.1 KLF, soil capacity 6 KSF, 24″ wide x 12″ deep, reinf.	16.15	23	39.15
2900	Load 6.8 KLF, soil capacity 3 KSF, 32″ wide x 12″ deep, reinf.	19.55	25	44.55
3100	Load 14.8 KLF, soil capacity 6 KSF, 32″ wide x 12″ deep, reinf.	19.55	25	44.55
3300	Load 9.3 KLF, soil capacity 3 KSF, 40″ wide x 12″ deep, reinf.	23	27	50
3500	Load 18.4 KLF, soil capacity 6 KSF, 40″ wide x 12″ deep, reinf.	23	27.50	50.50
4500	Load 10 KLF, soil capacity 3 KSF, 48″ wide x 16″ deep, reinf.	32	34.50	66.50
4700	Load 22 KLF, soil capacity 6 KSF, 48″ wide, 16″ deep, reinf.	33	35.50	68.50
5700	Load 15 KLF, soil capacity 3 KSF, 72″ wide x 20″ deep, reinf.	55.50	49	104.50
5900	Load 33 KLF, soil capacity 6 KSF, 72″ wide x 20″ deep, reinf.	58.50	52.50	111

A1010 Standard Foundations

Dampproofing

Spread Footing

Strip Footing

A1010 210	Spread Footings	COST EACH		
		MAT.	INST.	TOTAL
7090	Spread footings, 3000 psi concrete, chute delivered			
7100	Load 25K, soil capacity 3 KSF, 3'-0" sq. x 12" deep	56.50	122	178.50
7150	Load 50K, soil capacity 3 KSF, 4'-6" sq. x 12" deep	122	209	331
7200	Load 50K, soil capacity 6 KSF, 3'-0" sq. x 12" deep	56.50	122	178.50
7250	Load 75K, soil capacity 3 KSF, 5'-6" sq. x 13" deep	194	294	488
7300	Load 75K, soil capacity 6 KSF, 4'-0" sq. x 12" deep	98.50	179	277.50
7350	Load 100K, soil capacity 3 KSF, 6'-0" sq. x 14" deep	245	355	600
7410	Load 100K, soil capacity 6 KSF, 4'-6" sq. x 15" deep	150	246	396
7450	Load 125K, soil capacity 3 KSF, 7'-0" sq. x 17" deep	390	505	895
7500	Load 125K, soil capacity 6 KSF, 5'-0" sq. x 16" deep	193	295	488
7550	Load 150K, soil capacity 3 KSF 7'-6" sq. x 18" deep	470	590	1,060
7610	Load 150K, soil capacity 6 KSF, 5'-6" sq. x 18" deep	257	370	627
7650	Load 200K, soil capacity 3 KSF, 8'-6" sq. x 20" deep	670	775	1,445
7700	Load 200K, soil capacity 6 KSF, 6'-0" sq. x 20" deep	340	455	795
7750	Load 300K, soil capacity 3 KSF, 10'-6" sq. x 25" deep	1,225	1,275	2,500
7810	Load 300K, soil capacity 6 KSF, 7'-6" sq. x 25" deep	640	765	1,405
7850	Load 400K, soil capacity 3 KSF, 12'-6" sq. x 28" deep	1,975	1,900	3,875
7900	Load 400K, soil capacity 6 KSF, 8'-6" sq. x 27" deep	895	995	1,890
8010	Load 500K, soil capacity 6 KSF, 9'-6" sq. x 30" deep	1,225	1,300	2,525
8100	Load 600K, soil capacity 6 KSF, 10'-6" sq. x 33" deep	1,675	1,675	3,350
8200	Load 700K, soil capacity 6 KSF, 11'-6" sq. x 36" deep	2,125	2,025	4,150
8300	Load 800K, soil capacity 6 KSF, 12'-0" sq. x 37" deep	2,400	2,250	4,650
8400	Load 900K, soil capacity 6 KSF, 13'-0" sq. x 39" deep	2,950	2,675	5,625
8500	Load 1000K, soil capacity 6 KSF, 13'-6" sq. x 41" deep	3,350	2,975	6,325

A1010 320	Foundation Dampproofing	COST PER L.F.		
		MAT.	INST.	TOTAL
1000	Foundation dampproofing, bituminous, 1 coat, 4' high	1	4.55	5.55
1400	8' high	2	9.10	11.10
1800	12' high	3	14.10	17.10
2000	2 coats, 4' high	2	5.65	7.65
2400	8' high	4	11.25	15.25
2800	12' high	6	17.35	23.35
3000	Asphalt with fibers, 1/16" thick, 4' high	1.48	5.65	7.13
3400	8' high	2.96	11.25	14.21
3800	12' high	4.44	17.35	21.79
4000	1/8" thick, 4' high	2.60	6.65	9.25
4400	8' high	5.20	13.35	18.55
4800	12' high	7.80	20.50	28.30
5000	Asphalt coated board and mastic, 1/4" thick, 4' high	4.40	6.10	10.50
5400	8' high	8.80	12.20	21

A1010 Standard Foundations

A1010 320	Foundation Dampproofing	COST PER L.F.		
		MAT.	INST.	TOTAL
5800	12' high	13.20	18.80	32
6000	1/2" thick, 4' high	6.60	8.50	15.10
6400	8' high	13.20	17	30.20
6800	12' high	19.80	26	45.80
7000	Cementitious coating, on walls, 1/8" thick coating, 4' high	2.64	8.80	11.44
7400	8' high	5.30	17.60	22.90
7800	12' high	7.90	26.50	34.40
8000	Cementitious/metallic slurry, 4 coat, 1/2"thick, 2' high	.67	8.70	9.37
8400	4' high	1.34	17.40	18.74
8800	6' high	2.01	26	28.01

A1030 Slab on Grade

Fibre Expansion Joint

Wire Mesh Reinforcing

Concrete Slab

Vapor Barrier

Compacted Gravel

Reinforced Slab on Grade

A Slab on Grade system includes fine grading; 6" of compacted gravel; vapor barrier; 3500 p.s.i. concrete; bituminous fiber expansion joint; all necessary edge forms 4 uses; steel trowel finish; and sprayed on membrane curing compound. Wire mesh reinforcing used in all reinforced slabs.

Non-industrial slabs are for foot traffic only with negligible abrasion. Light industrial slabs are for pneumatic wheels and light abrasion. Industrial slabs are for solid rubber wheels and moderate abrasion. Heavy industrial slabs are for steel wheels and severe abrasion.

A1030 120	Plain & Reinforced	MAT.	INST.	TOTAL
2220	Slab on grade, 4" thick, non industrial, non reinforced	2.06	2.72	4.78
2240	Reinforced	2.22	3.09	5.31
2260	Light industrial, non reinforced	2.66	3.33	5.99
2280	Reinforced	2.82	3.70	6.52
2300	Industrial, non reinforced	3.27	6.95	10.22
2320	Reinforced	3.43	7.35	10.78
3340	5" thick, non industrial, non reinforced	2.40	2.79	5.19
3360	Reinforced	2.56	3.16	5.72
3380	Light industrial, non reinforced	3	3.40	6.40
3400	Reinforced	3.16	3.77	6.93
3420	Heavy industrial, non reinforced	4.25	8.30	12.55
3440	Reinforced	4.35	8.70	13.05
4460	6" thick, non industrial, non reinforced	2.84	2.73	5.57
4480	Reinforced	3.07	3.22	6.29
4500	Light industrial, non reinforced	3.46	3.34	6.80
4520	Reinforced	3.82	4	7.82
4540	Heavy industrial, non reinforced	4.71	8.40	13.11
4560	Reinforced	4.94	8.90	13.84
5580	7" thick, non industrial, non reinforced	3.19	2.82	6.01
5600	Reinforced	3.48	3.35	6.83
5620	Light industrial, non reinforced	3.82	3.43	7.25
5640	Reinforced	4.11	3.96	8.07
5660	Heavy industrial, non reinforced	5.05	8.30	13.35
5680	Reinforced	5.30	8.75	14.05
6700	8" thick, non industrial, non reinforced	3.53	2.88	6.41
6720	Reinforced	3.78	3.32	7.10
6740	Light industrial, non reinforced	4.16	3.49	7.65
6760	Reinforced	4.41	3.93	8.34
6780	Heavy industrial, non reinforced	5.45	8.40	13.85
6800	Reinforced	5.80	8.85	14.65

Cost Per S.F.

A2010 Basement Excavation

Sand & Gravel 1:1

Clay 1/2:1

Line of Excavation

In general, the following items are accounted for in the table below.

Costs:
1) Excavation for building or other structure to depth and extent indicated.
2) Backfill compacted in place
3) Haul of excavated waste
4) Replacement of unsuitable backfill material with bank run gravel.

A2010 110	Building Excavation & Backfill	COST PER S.F.		
		MAT.	INST.	TOTAL
2220	Excav & fill, 1000 S.F., 4' sand, gravel, or common earth, on site storage		1.04	1.04
2240	Off site storage		1.57	1.57
2260	Clay excavation, bank run gravel borrow for backfill	2.40	2.42	4.82
2280	8' deep, sand, gravel, or common earth, on site storage		6.30	6.30
2300	Off site storage		13.90	13.90
2320	Clay excavation, bank run gravel borrow for backfill	9.75	11.30	21.05
2340	16' deep, sand, gravel, or common earth, on site storage		17.20	17.20
2350	Off site storage		34	34
2360	Clay excavation, bank run gravel borrow for backfill	27	29	56
3380	4000 S.F., 4' deep, sand, gravel, or common earth, on site storage		.57	.57
3400	Off site storage		1.11	1.11
3420	Clay excavation, bank run gravel borrow for backfill	1.22	1.22	2.44
3440	8' deep, sand, gravel, or common earth, on site storage		4.44	4.44
3460	Off site storage		7.80	7.80
3480	Clay excavation, bank run gravel borrow for backfill	4.44	6.80	11.24
3500	16' deep, sand, gravel, or common earth, on site storage		10.65	10.65
3520	Off site storage		21.50	21.50
3540	Clay, excavation, bank run gravel borrow for backfill	11.90	16.15	28.05
4560	10,000 S.F., 4' deep, sand gravel, or common earth, on site storage		.32	.32
4580	Off site storage		.65	.65
4600	Clay excavation, bank run gravel borrow for backfill	.74	.74	1.48
4620	8' deep, sand, gravel, or common earth, on site storage		3.85	3.85
4640	Off site storage		5.85	5.85
4660	Clay excavation, bank run gravel borrow for backfill	2.69	5.30	7.99
4680	16' deep, sand, gravel, or common earth, on site storage		8.75	8.75
4700	Off site storage		14.90	14.90
4720	Clay excavation, bank run gravel borrow for backfill	7.15	12.10	19.25
5740	30,000 S.F., 4' deep, sand, gravel, or common earth, on site storage		.18	.18
5760	Off site storage		.38	.38
5780	Clay excavation, bank run gravel borrow for backfill	.43	.43	.86
5860	16' deep, sand, gravel, or common earth, on site storage		7.50	7.50
5880	Off site storage		10.85	10.85
5900	Clay excavation, bank run gravel borrow for backfill	3.96	9.35	13.31
6910	100,000 S.F., 4' deep, sand, gravel, or common earth, on site storage		.11	.11
6940	8' deep, sand, gravel, or common earth, on site storage		3.24	3.24
6970	16' deep, sand, gravel, or common earth, on site storage		6.80	6.80
6980	Off site storage		8.55	8.55
6990	Clay excavation, bank run gravel borrow for backfill	2.14	7.80	9.94

A2020 Basement Walls

The Foundation Bearing Wall System includes: forms up to 16' high (four uses); 3,000 p.s.i. concrete placed and vibrated; and form removal with breaking form ties and patching walls. The wall systems list walls from 6" to 16" thick and are designed with minimum reinforcement.

Excavation and backfill are not included.

Please see the reference section for further design and cost information.

A2020 110		Walls, Cast in Place						
	WALL HEIGHT (FT.)	PLACING METHOD	CONCRETE (C.Y. per L.F.)	REINFORCING (LBS. per L.F.)	WALL THICKNESS (IN.)	COST PER L.F.		
						MAT.	INST.	TOTAL
1500	4'	direct chute	.074	3.3	6	16.05	51.50	67.55
1520			.099	4.8	8	19.60	53	72.60
1540			.123	6.0	10	23	54	77
1560			.148	7.2	12	26.50	55	81.50
1580			.173	8.1	14	29.50	56	85.50
1600			.197	9.44	16	33	57.50	90.50
3000	6'	direct chute	.111	4.95	6	24	77.50	101.50
3020			.149	7.20	8	29.50	79.50	109
3040			.184	9.00	10	34.50	81	115.50
3060			.222	10.8	12	39.50	83	122.50
5000	8'	direct chute	.148	6.6	6	32	103	135
5020			.199	9.6	8	39.50	106	145.50
5040			.250	12	10	46	108	154
5061			.296	14.39	12	52.50	110	162.50
6020	10'	direct chute	.248	12	8	49	133	182
6040			.307	14.99	10	57	135	192
6061			.370	17.99	12	65.50	138	203.50
7220	12'	pumped	.298	14.39	8	59	164	223
7240			.369	17.99	10	68.50	167	235.50
7260			.444	21.59	12	79	173	252
9220	16'	pumped	.397	19.19	8	78.50	218	296.50
9240			.492	23.99	10	91.50	223	314.50
9260			.593	28.79	12	105	230	335

B1010 Floor Construction

General: It is desirable for purposes of consistency and simplicity to maintain constant column sizes throughout building height. To do this, concrete strength may be varied (higher strength concrete at lower stories and lower strength concrete at upper stories), as well as varying the amount of reinforcing.

The table provides probably minimum column sizes with related costs and weight per lineal foot of story height.

B1010 203		C.I.P. Column, Square Tied						
	LOAD (KIPS)	STORY HEIGHT (FT.)	COLUMN SIZE (IN.)	COLUMN WEIGHT (P.L.F.)	CONCRETE STRENGTH (PSI)	COST PER V.L.F.		
						MAT.	INST.	TOTAL
0640	100	10	10	96	4000	10.70	48	58.70
0680		12	10	97	4000	10.90	48.50	59.40
0700		14	12	142	4000	14.30	58.50	72.80
0840	200	10	12	140	4000	15.70	60.50	76.20
0860		12	12	142	4000	16	61	77
0900		14	14	196	4000	18.65	67.50	86.15
0920	300	10	14	192	4000	19.75	69.50	89.25
0960		12	14	194	4000	20	70	90
0980		14	16	253	4000	23.50	77.50	101
1020	400	10	16	248	4000	25	79.50	104.50
1060		12	16	251	4000	25.50	80.50	106
1080		14	16	253	4000	25.50	81	106.50
1200	500	10	18	315	4000	29	89	118
1250		12	20	394	4000	35	101	136
1300		14	20	397	4000	36	102	138
1350	600	10	20	388	4000	36.50	103	139.50
1400		12	20	394	4000	37.50	105	142.50
1600		14	20	397	4000	38	106	144
3400	900	10	24	560	4000	49.50	128	177.50
3800		12	24	567	4000	50.50	130	180.50
4000		14	24	571	4000	52	132	184
7300	300	10	14	192	6000	19.90	69	88.90
7500		12	14	194	6000	20.50	69.50	90
7600		14	14	196	6000	20.50	70	90.50
8000	500	10	16	248	6000	25.50	79.50	105
8050		12	16	251	6000	26	80.50	106.50
8100		14	16	253	6000	26.50	81	107.50
8200	600	10	18	315	6000	29.50	89.50	119
8300		12	18	319	6000	30	90.50	120.50
8400		14	18	321	6000	30.50	91.50	122
8800	800	10	20	388	6000	36	101	137
8900		12	20	394	6000	37	102	139
9000		14	20	397	6000	37.50	103	140.50

B10 Superstructure

B1010 Floor Construction

B1010 203 — C.I.P. Column, Square Tied

	LOAD (KIPS)	STORY HEIGHT (FT.)	COLUMN SIZE (IN.)	COLUMN WEIGHT (P.L.F.)	CONCRETE STRENGTH (PSI)	COST PER V.L.F.		
						MAT.	INST.	TOTAL
9100	900	10	20	388	6000	39	106	145
9300		12	20	394	6000	40	107	147
9600		14	20	397	6000	41	108	149

B1010 204 — C.I.P. Column, Square Tied-Minimum Reinforcing

	LOAD (KIPS)	STORY HEIGHT (FT.)	COLUMN SIZE (IN.)	COLUMN WEIGHT (P.L.F.)	CONCRETE STRENGTH (PSI)	COST PER V.L.F.		
						MAT.	INST.	TOTAL
9913	150	10-14	12	135	4000	12.90	56.50	69.40
9918	300	10-14	16	240	4000	21	73.50	94.50
9924	500	10-14	20	375	4000	31	95.50	126.50
9930	700	10-14	24	540	4000	43	118	161
9936	1000	10-14	28	740	4000	56.50	144	200.50
9942	1400	10-14	32	965	4000	69.50	162	231.50
9948	1800	10-14	36	1220	4000	86.50	189	275.50

B1010 Floor Construction

Concentric Load

Eccentric Load

General: Data presented here is for plant produced members transported 50 miles to 100 miles to the site and erected.

Design and pricing assumptions:
Normal wt. concrete, f'c = 5 KSI

Main reinforcement, fy = 60 KSI
Ties, fy = 40 KSI

Minimum design eccentricity, 0.1t.

Concrete encased structural steel haunches are assumed where practical; otherwise galvanized rebar haunches are assumed.

Base plates are integral with columns.

Foundation anchor bolts, nuts and washers are included in price.

B1010 206		Tied, Concentric Loaded Precast Concrete Columns						
	LOAD (KIPS)	STORY HEIGHT (FT.)	COLUMN SIZE (IN.)	COLUMN WEIGHT (P.L.F.)	LOAD LEVELS	COST PER V.L.F.		
						MAT.	INST.	TOTAL
0560	100	10	12x12	164	2	160	14.05	174.05
0570		12	12x12	162	2	155	11.70	166.70
0580		14	12x12	161	2	155	11.50	166.50
0590	150	10	12x12	166	3	154	11.40	165.40
0600		12	12x12	169	3	154	10.20	164.20
0610		14	12x12	162	3	154	10.10	164.10
0620	200	10	12x12	168	4	154	12.15	166.15
0630		12	12x12	170	4	154	11	165
0640		14	12x12	220	4	154	10.90	164.90

B1010 207		Tied, Eccentric Loaded Precast Concrete Columns						
	LOAD (KIPS)	STORY HEIGHT (FT.)	COLUMN SIZE (IN.)	COLUMN WEIGHT (P.L.F.)	LOAD LEVELS	COST PER V.L.F.		
						MAT.	INST.	TOTAL
1130	100	10	12x12	161	2	152	14.05	166.05
1140		12	12x12	159	2	151	11.70	162.70
1150		14	12x12	159	2	151	11.50	162.50
1390	600	10	18x18	385	4	223	12.15	235.15
1400		12	18x18	380	4	224	11	235
1410		14	18x18	375	4	222	10.90	232.90
1480	800	10	20x20	490	4	203	12.15	215.15
1490		12	20x20	480	4	203	11	214
1500		14	20x20	475	4	202	10.90	212.90

B10 Superstructure

B1010 Floor Construction

 (A) Wide Flange

 (B) Pipe

 (C) Pipe, Concrete Filled

 (G) Rectangular Tube, Concrete Filled

B1010 208						Steel Columns		
	LOAD (KIPS)	UNSUPPORTED HEIGHT (FT.)	WEIGHT (P.L.F.)	SIZE (IN.)	TYPE	COST PER V.L.F.		
						MAT.	INST.	TOTAL
1000	25	10	13	4	A	23	10.75	33.75
1020			7.58	3	B	13.40	10.75	24.15
1040			15	3-1/2	C	16.30	10.75	27.05
1120			20	4x3	G	18.85	10.75	29.60
1200		16	16	5	A	26	8.05	34.05
1220			10.79	4	B	17.65	8.05	25.70
1240			36	5-1/2	C	24.50	8.05	32.55
1320			64	8x6	G	38	8.05	46.05
1600	50	10	16	5	A	28.50	10.75	39.25
1620			14.62	5	B	26	10.75	36.75
1640			24	4-1/2	C	19.45	10.75	30.20
1720			28	6x3	G	25	10.75	35.75
1800		16	24	8	A	39	8.05	47.05
1840			36	5-1/2	C	24.50	8.05	32.55
1920			64	8x6	G	38	8.05	46.05
2000		20	28	8	A	43.50	8.05	51.55
2040			49	6-5/8	C	30.50	8.05	38.55
2120			64	8x6	G	36	8.05	44.05
2200	75	10	20	6	A	35.50	10.75	46.25
2240			36	4-1/2	C	49	10.75	59.75
2320			35	6x4	G	28	10.75	38.75
2400		16	31	8	A	50.50	8.05	58.55
2440			49	6-5/8	C	32	8.05	40.05
2520			64	8x6	G	38	8.05	46.05
2600		20	31	8	A	48	8.05	56.05
2640			81	8-5/8	C	45.50	8.05	53.55
2720			64	8x6	G	36	8.05	44.05
2800	100	10	24	8	A	42.50	10.75	53.25
2840			35	4-1/2	C	49	10.75	59.75
2920			46	8x4	G	34.50	10.75	45.25

B1010 208			Steel Columns					
	LOAD (KIPS)	UNSUPPORTED HEIGHT (FT.)	WEIGHT (P.L.F.)	SIZE (IN.)	TYPE	COST PER V.L.F.		
						MAT.	INST.	TOTAL
3000	100	16	31	8	A	50.50	8.05	58.55
3040			56	6-5/8	C	47.50	8.05	55.55
3120			64	8x6	G	38	8.05	46.05
3200		20	40	8	A	62	8.05	70.05
3240			81	8-5/8	C	45.50	8.05	53.55
3320			70	8x6	G	51.50	8.05	59.55
3400	125	10	31	8	A	55	10.75	65.75
3440			81	8	C	52	10.75	62.75
3520			64	8x6	G	41	10.75	51.75
3600		16	40	8	A	65.50	8.05	73.55
3640			81	8	C	48	8.05	56.05
3720			64	8x6	G	38	8.05	46.05
3800		20	48	8	A	74.50	8.05	82.55
3840			81	8	C	45.50	8.05	53.55
3920			60	8x6	G	51.50	8.05	59.55
4000	150	10	35	8	A	62	10.75	72.75
4040			81	8-5/8	C	52	10.75	62.75
4120			64	8x6	G	41	10.75	51.75
4200		16	45	10	A	73.50	8.05	81.55
4240			81	8-5/8	C	48	8.05	56.05
4320			70	8x6	G	54.50	8.05	62.55
4400		20	49	10	A	76	8.05	84.05
4440			123	10-3/4	C	65	8.05	73.05
4520			86	10x6	G	51	8.05	59.05
4600	200	10	45	10	A	79.50	10.75	90.25
4640			81	8-5/8	C	52	10.75	62.75
4720			70	8x6	G	58.50	10.75	69.25
4800		16	49	10	A	80	8.05	88.05
4840			123	10-3/4	C	68.50	8.05	76.55
4920			85	10x6	G	63	8.05	71.05
5200	300	10	61	14	A	108	10.75	118.75
5240			169	12-3/4	C	91	10.75	101.75
5320			86	10x6	G	87.50	10.75	98.25
5400		16	72	12	A	118	8.05	126.05
5440			169	12-3/4	C	84.50	8.05	92.55
5600		20	79	12	A	122	8.05	130.05
5640			169	12-3/4	C	80	8.05	88.05
5800	400	10	79	12	A	140	10.75	150.75
5840			178	12-3/4	C	119	10.75	129.75
6000		16	87	12	A	142	8.05	150.05
6040			178	12-3/4	C	110	8.05	118.05
6400	500	10	99	14	A	175	10.75	185.75
6600		16	109	14	A	178	8.05	186.05
6800		20	120	12	A	186	8.05	194.05
7000	600	10	120	12	A	212	10.75	222.75
7200		16	132	14	A	216	8.05	224.05
7400		20	132	14	A	204	8.05	212.05
7600	700	10	136	12	A	240	10.75	250.75
7800		16	145	14	A	237	8.05	245.05
8000		20	145	14	A	224	8.05	232.05
8200	800	10	145	14	A	256	10.75	266.75
8300		16	159	14	A	260	8.05	268.05
8400		20	176	14	A	272	8.05	280.05

B10 Superstructure

B1010 Floor Construction

B1010 208	Steel Columns

	LOAD (KIPS)	UNSUPPORTED HEIGHT (FT.)	WEIGHT (P.L.F.)	SIZE (IN.)	TYPE	COST PER V.L.F.		
						MAT.	INST.	TOTAL
8800	900	10	159	14	A	281	10.75	291.75
8900		16	176	14	A	288	8.05	296.05
9000		20	193	14	A	299	8.05	307.05
9100	1000	10	176	14	A	310	10.75	320.75
9200		16	193	14	A	315	8.05	323.05
9300		20	211	14	A	325	8.05	333.05

B1010 Floor Construction

Description: Table below lists costs per S.F. of bay size for wood columns of various sizes and unsupported heights and the maximum allowable total load per S.F. per bay size.

B1010 210	Wood Columns							
	NOMINAL COLUMN SIZE (IN.)	BAY SIZE (FT.)	UNSUPPORTED HEIGHT (FT.)	MATERIAL (BF per M.S.F.)	TOTAL LOAD (P.S.F.)	COST PER S.F.		
						MAT.	INST.	TOTAL
1000	4 x 4	10 x 8	8	133	100	.19	.25	.44
1050			10	167	60	.23	.31	.54
1200		10 x 10	8	106	80	.15	.20	.35
1250			10	133	50	.19	.25	.44
1400		10 x 15	8	71	50	.10	.13	.23
1450			10	88	30	.12	.17	.29
1600		15 x 15	8	47	30	.07	.09	.16
1650			10	59	15	.08	.11	.19
2000	6 x 6	10 x 15	8	160	230	.25	.28	.53
2050			10	200	210	.31	.35	.66
2200		15 x 15	8	107	150	.17	.19	.36
2250			10	133	140	.21	.23	.44
2400		15 x 20	8	80	110	.12	.14	.26
2450			10	100	100	.16	.18	.34
2600		20 x 20	8	60	80	.09	.11	.20
2650			10	75	70	.12	.13	.25
2800		20 x 25	8	48	60	.07	.08	.15
2850			10	60	50	.09	.11	.20
3400	8 x 8	20 x 20	8	107	160	.16	.17	.33
3450			10	133	160	.20	.22	.42
3600		20 x 25	8	85	130	.12	.16	.28
3650			10	107	130	.15	.20	.35
3800		25 x 25	8	68	100	.11	.10	.21
3850			10	85	100	.14	.13	.27
4200	10 x 10	20 x 25	8	133	210	.21	.20	.41
4250			10	167	210	.27	.25	.52
4400		25 x 25	8	107	160	.17	.16	.33
4450			10	133	160	.21	.20	.41
4700	12 x 12	20 x 25	8	192	310	.32	.27	.59
4750			10	240	310	.40	.34	.74
4900		25 x 25	8	154	240	.26	.22	.48
4950			10	192	240	.32	.27	.59

B10 Superstructure

B1010 Floor Construction

"T" Shaped
Precast Beams

"L" Shaped
Precast Beams

B1010 214			"T" Shaped Precast Beams					
	SPAN (FT.)	SUPERIMPOSED LOAD (K.L.F.)	SIZE W X D (IN.)	BEAM WEIGHT (P.L.F.)	TOTAL LOAD (K.L.F.)	COST PER L.F.		
						MAT.	INST.	TOTAL
2300	15	2.8	12x16	260	3.06	171	20.50	191.50
2500		8.37	12x28	515	8.89	202	22	224
8900	45	3.34	12x60	1165	4.51	325	13.05	338.05
9900		6.5	24x60	1915	8.42	350	18.30	368.30

B1010 215			"L" Shaped Precast Beams					
	SPAN (FT.)	SUPERIMPOSED LOAD (K.L.F.)	SIZE W X D (IN.)	BEAM WEIGHT (P.L.F.)	TOTAL LOAD (K.L.F.)	COST PER L.F.		
						MAT.	INST.	TOTAL
2250	15	2.58	12x16	230	2.81	160	20.50	180.50
2400		5.92	12x24	370	6.29	176	20.50	196.50
4000	25	2.64	12x28	435	3.08	176	13.20	189.20
4450		6.44	18x36	790	7.23	219	15.70	234.70
5300	30	2.80	12x36	565	3.37	197	11.95	208.95
6400		8.66	24x44	1245	9.90	262	17.15	279.15

B1010 Floor Construction

Cast in Place Floor Slab, One Way
General: Solid concrete slabs of uniform depth reinforced for flexure in one direction and for temperature and shrinkage in the other direction.

Cast in Place Beam & Slab, One Way
General: Solid concrete one way slab cast monolithically with reinforced concrete beams and girders.

B1010 217		Cast in Place Slabs, One Way						
	SLAB DESIGN & SPAN (FT.)	SUPERIMPOSED LOAD (P.S.F.)	THICKNESS (IN.)	TOTAL LOAD (P.S.F.)		COST PER S.F.		
						MAT.	INST.	TOTAL
2500	Single 8	40	4	90		4.02	8.20	12.22
2600		75	4	125		4.05	8.95	13
2700		125	4-1/2	181		4.22	9	13.22
2800		200	5	262		4.69	9.30	13.99
3000	Single 10	40	4	90		4.20	8.85	13.05
3100		75	4	125		4.20	8.85	13.05
3200		125	5	188		4.66	9.05	13.71
3300		200	7-1/2	293		6.15	10.15	16.30
3500	Single 15	40	5-1/2	90		5	8.95	13.95
3600		75	6-1/2	156		5.60	9.40	15
3700		125	7-1/2	219		6.05	9.65	15.70
3800		200	8-1/2	306		6.55	9.90	16.45
4000	Single 20	40	7-1/2	115		6.05	9.45	15.50
4100		75	9	200		6.60	9.40	16
4200		125	10	250		7.25	9.80	17.05
4300		200	10	324		7.80	10.25	18.05

B1010 219		Cast in Place Beam & Slab, One Way						
	BAY SIZE (FT.)	SUPERIMPOSED LOAD (P.S.F.)	MINIMUM COL. SIZE (IN.)	SLAB THICKNESS (IN.)	TOTAL LOAD (P.S.F.)	COST PER S.F.		
						MAT.	INST.	TOTAL
5000	20x25	40	12	5-1/2	121	5.10	11.25	16.35
5200		125	16	5-1/2	215	6	12.90	18.90
5500	25x25	40	12	6	129	5.35	11	16.35
5700		125	18	6	227	6.85	13.60	20.45
7500	30x35	40	16	8	158	6.70	12.45	19.15
7600		75	18	8	196	7.20	12.85	20.05
7700		125	22	8	254	8.05	14.30	22.35
7800		200	26	8	332	8.80	14.80	23.60
8000	35x35	40	16	9	169	7.55	12.90	20.45
8200		75	20	9	213	8.15	14.05	22.20
8400		125	24	9	272	9	14.55	23.55
8600		200	26	9	355	9.95	15.60	25.55

B1010 Floor Construction

General: Solid concrete two way slab cast monolithically with reinforced concrete support beams and girders.

General: Flat Slab: Solid uniform depth concrete two way slabs with drop panels at columns and no column capitals.

B1010 220	Cast in Place Beam & Slab, Two Way							
	BAY SIZE (FT.)	SUPERIMPOSED LOAD (P.S.F.)	MINIMUM COL. SIZE (IN.)	SLAB THICKNESS (IN.)	TOTAL LOAD (P.S.F.)	COST PER S.F.		
						MAT.	INST.	TOTAL
4000	20 x 25	40	12	7	141	5.90	11.35	17.25
4300		75	14	7	181	6.80	12.40	19.20
4500		125	16	7	236	6.90	12.75	19.65
5100	25 x 25	40	12	7-1/2	149	6.15	11.50	17.65
5200		75	16	7-1/2	185	6.75	12.30	19.05
5300		125	18	7-1/2	250	7.30	13.35	20.65
7600	30 x 35	40	16	10	188	8.20	12.95	21.15
7700		75	18	10	225	8.75	13.45	22.20
8000		125	22	10	282	9.75	14.50	24.25
8500	35 x 35	40	16	10-1/2	193	8.85	13.25	22.10
8600		75	20	10-1/2	233	9.30	13.75	23.05
9000		125	24	10-1/2	287	10.40	14.75	25.15

B1010 222	Cast in Place Flat Slab with Drop Panels							
	BAY SIZE (FT.)	SUPERIMPOSED LOAD (P.S.F.)	MINIMUM COL. SIZE (IN.)	SLAB & DROP (IN.)	TOTAL LOAD (P.S.F.)	COST PER S.F.		
						MAT.	INST.	TOTAL
1960	20 x 20	40	12	7 - 3	132	5.20	9.10	14.30
1980		75	16	7 - 4	168	5.55	9.30	14.85
2000		125	18	7 - 6	221	6.20	9.65	15.85
3200	25 x 25	40	12	8-1/2 - 5-1/2	154	6.15	9.50	15.65
4000		125	20	8-1/2 - 8-1/2	243	7.05	10.15	17.20
4400		200	24	9 - 8-1/2	329	7.40	10.45	17.85
5000	25 x 30	40	14	9-1/2 - 7	168	6.75	9.90	16.65
5200		75	18	9-1/2 - 7	203	7.20	10.25	17.45
5600		125	22	9-1/2 - 8	256	7.55	10.50	18.05
6400	30 x 30	40	14	10-1/2 - 7-1/2	182	7.30	10.15	17.45
6600		75	18	10-1/2 - 7-1/2	217	7.80	10.50	18.30
6800		125	22	10-1/2 - 9	269	8.20	10.75	18.95
7400	30 x 35	40	16	11-1/2 - 9	196	7.95	10.50	18.45
7900		75	20	11-1/2 - 9	231	8.55	10.95	19.50
8000		125	24	11-1/2 - 11	284	8.90	11.20	20.10
9000	35 x 35	40	16	12 - 9	202	8.20	10.60	18.80
9400		75	20	12 - 11	240	8.85	11.10	19.95
9600		125	24	12 - 11	290	9.15	11.30	20.45

B1010 Floor Construction

General: Flat Plates: Solid uniform depth concrete two way slab without drops or interior beams. Primary design limit is shear at columns.

Multispan Joist Slab

General: Combination of thin concrete slab and monolithic ribs at uniform spacing to reduce dead weight and increase rigidity.

B1010 223		Cast in Place Flat Plate						
	BAY SIZE (FT.)	SUPERIMPOSED LOAD (P.S.F.)	MINIMUM COL. SIZE (IN.)	SLAB THICKNESS (IN.)	TOTAL LOAD (P.S.F.)	COST PER S.F.		
						MAT.	INST.	TOTAL
3000	15 x 20	40	14	7	127	4.91	8.70	13.61
3400		75	16	7-1/2	169	5.25	8.90	14.15
3600		125	22	8-1/2	231	5.80	9.15	14.95
3800		175	24	8-1/2	281	5.85	9.15	15
4200	20 x 20	40	16	7	127	4.93	8.65	13.58
4400		75	20	7-1/2	175	5.30	8.90	14.20
4600		125	24	8-1/2	231	5.80	9.10	14.90
5000		175	24	8-1/2	281	5.85	9.15	15
5600	20 x 25	40	18	8-1/2	146	5.75	9.10	14.85
6000		75	20	9	188	5.95	9.20	15.15
6400		125	26	9-1/2	244	6.45	9.45	15.90
6600		175	30	10	300	6.75	9.65	16.40
7000	25 x 25	40	20	9	152	5.95	9.20	15.15
7400		75	24	9-1/2	194	6.35	9.40	15.75
7600		125	30	10	250	6.75	9.65	16.40

B1010 226		Cast in Place Multispan Joist Slab						
	BAY SIZE (FT.)	SUPERIMPOSED LOAD (P.S.F.)	MINIMUM COL. SIZE (IN.)	RIB DEPTH (IN.)	TOTAL LOAD (P.S.F.)	COST PER S.F.		
						MAT.	INST.	TOTAL
2000	15 x 15	40	12	8	115	6.25	10.70	16.95
2100		75	12	8	150	6.25	10.75	17
2200		125	12	8	200	6.40	10.85	17.25
2300		200	14	8	275	6.60	11.25	17.85
2600	15 x 20	40	12	8	115	6.35	10.70	17.05
2800		75	12	8	150	6.50	11.30	17.80
3000		125	14	8	200	6.70	11.45	18.15
3300		200	16	8	275	7.05	11.65	18.70
3600	20 x 20	40	12	10	120	6.50	10.55	17.05
3900		75	14	10	155	6.80	11.15	17.95
4000		125	16	10	205	6.85	11.40	18.25
4100		200	18	10	280	7.15	11.85	19
6200	30 x 30	40	14	14	131	7.20	11.05	18.25
6400		75	18	14	166	7.45	11.40	18.85
6600		125	20	14	216	7.90	11.95	19.85
6700		200	24	16	297	8.45	12.45	20.90

B1010 Floor Construction

Waffle Slab

B1010 227	Cast in Place Waffle Slab

	BAY SIZE (FT.)	SUPERIMPOSED LOAD (P.S.F.)	MINIMUM COL. SIZE (IN.)	RIB DEPTH (IN.)	TOTAL LOAD (P.S.F.)	COST PER S.F.		
						MAT.	INST.	TOTAL
3900	20 x 20	40	12	8	144	7.90	10.60	18.50
4000		75	12	8	179	8.05	10.75	18.80
4100		125	16	8	229	8.25	10.85	19.10
4200		200	18	8	304	8.70	11.25	19.95
4400	20 x 25	40	12	8	146	8.10	10.65	18.75
4500		75	14	8	181	8.30	10.80	19.10
4600		125	16	8	231	8.45	10.95	19.40
4700		200	18	8	306	8.90	11.30	20.20
4900	25 x 25	40	12	10	150	8.30	10.75	19.05
5000		75	16	10	185	8.60	11	19.60
5300		125	18	10	235	8.85	11.20	20.05
5500		200	20	10	310	9.10	11.40	20.50
5700	25 x 30	40	14	10	154	8.50	10.85	19.35
5800		75	16	10	189	8.75	11.05	19.80
5900		125	18	10	239	9	11.25	20.25
6000		200	20	12	329	9.90	11.75	21.65
6400	30 x 30	40	14	12	169	9.05	11.10	20.15
6500		75	18	12	204	9.25	11.25	20.50
6600		125	20	12	254	9.45	11.40	20.85
6700		200	24	12	329	10.30	12	22.30
6900	30 x 35	40	16	12	169	9.25	11.20	20.45
7000		75	18	12	204	9.25	11.20	20.45
7100		125	22	12	254	9.75	11.55	21.30
7200		200	26	14	334	10.85	12.30	23.15
7400	35 x 35	40	16	14	174	9.80	11.50	21.30
7500		75	20	14	209	10	11.70	21.70
7600		125	24	14	259	10.25	11.85	22.10
7700		200	26	16	346	11.05	12.50	23.55
8000	35 x 40	40	18	14	176	10.05	11.70	21.75
8300		75	22	14	211	10.40	12	22.40
8500		125	26	16	271	10.95	12.25	23.20
8750		200	30	20	372	12	12.90	24.90
9200	40 x 40	40	18	14	176	10.40	12	22.40
9400		75	24	14	211	10.85	12.30	23.15
9500		125	26	16	271	11.10	12.40	23.50
9700	40 x 45	40	20	16	186	10.80	12.15	22.95
9800		75	24	16	221	11.25	12.50	23.75
9900		125	28	16	271	11.45	12.65	24.10

B1010 Floor Construction

Precast Plank with No Topping

Precast Plank with 2″ Concrete Topping

B1010 229	Precast Plank with No Topping							
	SPAN (FT.)	SUPERIMPOSED LOAD (P.S.F.)	TOTAL DEPTH (IN.)	DEAD LOAD (P.S.F.)	TOTAL LOAD (P.S.F.)	COST PER S.F.		
						MAT.	INST.	TOTAL
0720	10	40	4	50	90	6.45	3.43	9.88
0750		75	6	50	125	6.90	2.94	9.84
0770		100	6	50	150	6.90	2.94	9.84
0800	15	40	6	50	90	6.90	2.94	9.84
0820		75	6	50	125	6.90	2.94	9.84
0850		100	6	50	150	6.90	2.94	9.84
0950	25	40	6	50	90	6.90	2.94	9.84
0970		75	8	55	130	7.80	2.57	10.37
1000		100	8	55	155	7.80	2.57	10.37
1200	30	40	8	55	95	7.80	2.57	10.37
1300		75	8	55	130	7.80	2.57	10.37
1400		100	10	70	170	8	2.29	10.29
1500	40	40	10	70	110	8	2.29	10.29
1600		75	12	70	145	8.65	2.06	10.71
1700	45	40	12	70	110	8.65	2.06	10.71

B1010 230	Precast Plank with 2″ Concrete Topping							
	SPAN (FT.)	SUPERIMPOSED LOAD (P.S.F.)	TOTAL DEPTH (IN.)	DEAD LOAD (P.S.F.)	TOTAL LOAD (P.S.F.)	COST PER S.F.		
						MAT.	INST.	TOTAL
2000	10	40	6	75	115	7.45	5.80	13.25
2100		75	8	75	150	7.90	5.30	13.20
2200		100	8	75	175	7.90	5.30	13.20
2500	15	40	8	75	115	7.90	5.30	13.20
2600		75	8	75	150	7.90	5.30	13.20
2700		100	8	75	175	7.90	5.30	13.20
3100	25	40	8	75	115	7.90	5.30	13.20
3200		75	8	75	150	7.90	5.30	13.20
3300		100	10	80	180	8.80	4.92	13.72
3400	30	40	10	80	120	8.80	4.92	13.72
3500		75	10	80	155	8.80	4.92	13.72
3600		100	10	80	180	8.80	4.92	13.72
4000	40	40	12	95	135	9	4.64	13.64
4500		75	14	95	170	9.65	4.41	14.06
5000	45	40	14	95	135	9.65	4.41	14.06

B1010 Floor Construction

Precast Double "T" Beams with No Topping

Precast Double "T" Beams with 2″ Topping

Most widely used for moderate span floors and moderate and long span roofs. At shorter spans, they tend to be competitive with hollow core slabs. They are also used as wall panels.

B1010 234	Precast Double "T" Beams with No Topping							
	SPAN (FT.)	SUPERIMPOSED LOAD (P.S.F.)	DBL. "T" SIZE D (IN.) W (FT.)	CONCRETE "T" TYPE	TOTAL LOAD (P.S.F.)	COST PER S.F.		
						MAT.	INST.	TOTAL
4300	50	30	20x8	Lt. Wt.	66	9.30	1.57	10.87
4400		40	20x8	Lt. Wt.	76	9.35	1.42	10.77
4500		50	20x8	Lt. Wt.	86	9.45	1.71	11.16
4600		75	20x8	Lt. Wt.	111	9.50	1.95	11.45
5600	70	30	32x10	Lt. Wt.	78	9.30	1.08	10.38
5750		40	32x10	Lt. Wt.	88	9.40	1.31	10.71
5900		50	32x10	Lt. Wt.	98	9.45	1.50	10.95
6000		75	32x10	Lt. Wt.	123	9.55	1.82	11.37
6100		100	32x10	Lt. Wt.	148	9.80	2.47	12.27
6200	80	30	32x10	Lt. Wt.	78	9.45	1.50	10.95
6300		40	32x10	Lt. Wt.	88	9.55	1.82	11.37
6400		50	32x10	Lt. Wt.	98	9.65	2.14	11.79

B1010 235	Precast Double "T" Beams With 2″ Topping							
	SPAN (FT.)	SUPERIMPOSED LOAD (P.S.F.)	DBL. "T" SIZE D (IN.) W (FT.)	CONCRETE "T" TYPE	TOTAL LOAD (P.S.F.)	COST PER S.F.		
						MAT.	INST.	TOTAL
7100	40	30	18x8	Reg. Wt.	120	8.20	3.19	11.39
7200		40	20x8	Reg. Wt.	130	9.60	3.05	12.65
7300		50	20x8	Reg. Wt.	140	9.65	3.33	12.98
7400		75	20x8	Reg. Wt.	165	9.70	3.46	13.16
7500		100	20x8	Reg. Wt.	190	9.85	3.87	13.72
7550	50	30	24x8	Reg. Wt.	120	9.60	3.20	12.80
7600		40	24x8	Reg. Wt.	130	9.65	3.31	12.96
7750		50	24x8	Reg. Wt.	140	9.65	3.33	12.98
7800		75	24x8	Reg. Wt.	165	9.80	3.73	13.53
7900		100	32x10	Reg. Wt.	189	9.70	3.05	12.75

B1010 Floor Construction

Precast Beam and Plank with No Topping

Precast Beam and Plank with 2″ Topping

B1010 236	Precast Beam & Plank with No Topping							
	BAY SIZE (FT.)	SUPERIMPOSED LOAD (P.S.F.)	PLANK THICKNESS (IN.)	TOTAL DEPTH (IN.)	TOTAL LOAD (P.S.F.)	COST PER S.F.		
						MAT.	INST.	TOTAL
6200	25x25	40	8	28	118	20.50	3.43	23.93
6400		75	8	36	158	20	3.43	23.43
6500		100	8	36	183	20	3.43	23.43
7000	25x30	40	8	36	110	18.45	3.31	21.76
7200		75	10	36	159	19.10	3.04	22.14
7400		100	12	36	188	19.40	2.78	22.18
7600	30x30	40	8	36	121	18.90	3.20	22.10
8000		75	10	44	140	18.80	3.22	22.02
8250		100	12	52	206	21	2.72	23.72
8500	30x35	40	12	44	135	18.30	2.63	20.93
8750		75	12	52	176	19.20	2.62	21.82
9000	35x35	40	12	52	141	19.20	2.57	21.77
9250		75	12	60	181	19.80	2.57	22.37
9500	35x40	40	12	52	137	19.20	2.57	21.77

B1010 238	Precast Beam & Plank with 2″ Topping							
	BAY SIZE (FT.)	SUPERIMPOSED LOAD (P.S.F.)	PLANK THICKNESS (IN.)	TOTAL DEPTH (IN.)	TOTAL LOAD (P.S.F.)	COST PER S.F.		
						MAT.	INST.	TOTAL
4300	20x20	40	6	22	135	21.50	6.10	27.60
4400		75	6	24	173	22.50	6.15	28.65
4500		100	6	28	200	22.50	6.15	28.65
4600	20x25	40	6	26	134	20.50	5.95	26.45
5000		75	8	30	177	21	5.50	26.50
5200		100	8	30	202	21	5.50	26.50
5400	25x25	40	6	38	143	20.50	5.70	26.20
5600		75	8	38	183	16.40	5.40	21.80
6000		100	8	46	216	16.80	4.96	21.76
6200	25x30	40	8	38	144	19.25	5.15	24.40
6400		75	10	46	200	19.75	4.86	24.61
6600		100	10	46	225	20	4.87	24.87
7000	30x30	40	8	46	150	20	5.05	25.05
7200		75	10	54	181	21	5.05	26.05
7600		100	10	54	231	21	5.05	26.05
7800	30x35	40	10	54	166	19.60	4.68	24.28
8000		75	12	54	200	20	4.43	24.43

B1010 Floor Construction

With Topping

General: Beams and double tees priced here are for plant produced prestressed members transported to the site and erected.

The 2″ structural topping is applied after the beams and double tees are in place and is reinforced with W.W.F.

B1010 239		Precast Double "T" & 2″ Topping on Precast Beams							
	BAY SIZE (FT.)	SUPERIMPOSED LOAD (P.S.F.)	DEPTH (IN.)		TOTAL LOAD (P.S.F.)	COST PER S.F.			
						MAT.	INST.	TOTAL	
3000	25x30	40	38		130	20.50	4.31	24.81	
3100		75	38		168	20.50	4.31	24.81	
3300		100	46		196	20.50	4.28	24.78	
3600	30x30	40	46		150	21	4.17	25.17	
3750		75	46		174	21	4.17	25.17	
4000		100	54		203	21.50	4.16	25.66	
4100	30x40	40	46		136	18.35	3.76	22.11	
4300		75	54		173	18.90	3.74	22.64	
4400		100	62		204	19.50	3.74	23.24	
4600	30x50	40	54		138	17.10	3.49	20.59	
4800		75	54		181	16.95	3.52	20.47	
5000		100	54		219	17	3.22	20.22	
5200	30x60	40	62		151	16.70	3.15	19.85	
5400		75	62		192	16.35	3.20	19.55	
5600		100	62		215	16.45	3.20	19.65	
5800	35x40	40	54		139	19.15	3.71	22.86	
6000		75	62		179	19.25	3.55	22.80	
6250		100	62		212	19.35	3.68	23.03	
6500	35x50	40	62		142	17.70	3.45	21.15	
6750		75	62		186	17.70	3.57	21.27	
7300		100	62		231	17.85	3.27	21.12	
7600	35x60	40	54		154	17.15	3.02	20.17	
7750		75	54		179	17.30	3.03	20.33	
8000		100	62		224	17.70	3.09	20.79	
8250	40x40	40	62		145	21	3.71	24.71	
8400		75	62		187	20	3.72	23.72	
8750		100	62		223	20.50	3.81	24.31	
9000	40x50	40	62		151	18.45	3.48	21.93	
9300		75	62		193	17.95	2.59	20.54	
9800	40x60	40	62		164	20.50	2.48	22.98	

B1010 Floor Construction

General: The following table is based upon structural wide flange (WF) beam and girder framing. Non-composite action is assumed between WF framing and decking. Deck costs not included.

The deck spans the short direction. The steel beams and girders are fireproofed with sprayed fiber fireproofing.

No columns included in price.

B1010 241	W Shape Beams & Girders							
	BAY SIZE (FT.) BEAM X GIRD	SUPERIMPOSED LOAD (P.S.F.)	STEEL FRAMING DEPTH (IN.)	FIREPROOFING (S.F. PER S.F.)	TOTAL LOAD (P.S.F.)	COST PER S.F.		
						MAT.	INST.	TOTAL
1350	15x20	40	12	.535	50	5.10	1.93	7.03
1400		40	16	.65	90	6.65	2.49	9.14
1450		75	18	.694	125	8.75	3.12	11.87
1500		125	24	.796	175	12.10	4.42	16.52
2000	20x20	40	12	.55	50	5.70	2.12	7.82
2050		40	14	.579	90	7.80	2.75	10.55
2100		75	16	.672	125	9.35	3.28	12.63
2150		125	16	.714	175	11.15	4.05	15.20
2900	20x25	40	16	.53	50	6.25	2.27	8.52
2950		40	18	.621	96	9.90	3.40	13.30
3000		75	18	.651	131	11.40	3.87	15.27
3050		125	24	.77	200	15.05	5.30	20.35
5200	25x25	40	18	.486	50	6.85	2.41	9.26
5300		40	18	.592	96	10.15	3.45	13.60
5400		75	21	.668	131	12.30	4.14	16.44
5450		125	24	.738	191	16.20	5.65	21.85
6300	25x30	40	21	.568	50	7.80	2.74	10.54
6350		40	21	.694	90	10.55	3.64	14.19
6400		75	24	.776	125	13.55	4.59	18.14
6450		125	30	.904	175	16.30	5.80	22.10
7700	30x30	40	21	.52	50	8.35	2.87	11.22
7750		40	24	.629	103	12.90	4.27	17.17
7800		75	30	.715	138	15.30	5.05	20.35
7850		125	36	.822	206	20	6.90	26.90
8250	30x35	40	21	.508	50	9.55	3.20	12.75
8300		40	24	.651	109	14.10	4.64	18.74
8350		75	33	.732	150	17.10	5.60	22.70
8400		125	36	.802	225	21.50	7.25	28.75
9550	35x35	40	27	.560	50	9.85	3.35	13.20
9600		40	36	.706	109	18	5.80	23.80
9650		75	36	.750	150	18.60	6.05	24.65
9820		125	36	.797	225	25	8.40	33.40

Description: Table below lists costs for light gage CEE or PUNCHED DOUBLE joists to suit the span and loading with the minimum thickness subfloor required by the joist spacing.

B1010 244		Light Gauge Steel Floor Systems						
	SPAN (FT.)	SUPERIMPOSED LOAD (P.S.F.)	FRAMING DEPTH (IN.)	FRAMING SPAC. (IN.)	TOTAL LOAD (P.S.F.)	COST PER S.F.		
						MAT.	INST.	TOTAL
1500	15	40	8	16	54	2.73	2.22	4.95
1550			8	24	54	2.86	2.28	5.14
1600		65	10	16	80	3.52	2.70	6.22
1650			10	24	80	3.49	2.65	6.14
1700		75	10	16	90	3.52	2.70	6.22
1750			10	24	90	3.49	2.65	6.14
1800		100	10	16	116	4.57	3.43	8
1850			10	24	116	3.49	2.65	6.14
1900		125	10	16	141	4.57	3.43	8
1950			10	24	141	3.49	2.65	6.14
2500	20	40	8	16	55	3.13	2.51	5.64
2550			8	24	55	2.86	2.28	5.14
2600		65	8	16	80	3.62	2.87	6.49
2650			10	24	80	3.50	2.67	6.17
2700		75	10	16	90	3.33	2.57	5.90
2750			12	24	90	3.92	2.33	6.25
2800		100	10	16	115	3.33	2.57	5.90
2850			10	24	116	4.48	3	7.48
2900		125	12	16	142	5.20	2.93	8.13
2950			12	24	141	4.86	3.18	8.04
3500	25	40	10	16	55	3.52	2.70	6.22
3550			10	24	55	3.49	2.65	6.14
3600		65	10	16	81	4.57	3.43	8
3650			12	24	81	4.34	2.52	6.86
3700		75	12	16	92	5.20	2.92	8.12
3750			12	24	91	4.86	3.18	8.04
3800		100	12	16	117	5.85	3.23	9.08
3850		125	12	16	143	6.65	4.25	10.90
4500	30	40	12	16	57	5.20	2.92	8.12
4550			12	24	56	4.32	2.51	6.83
4600		65	12	16	82	5.85	3.22	9.07
4650		75	12	16	92	5.85	3.22	9.07

B10 Superstructure

B1010 Floor Construction

Description: The table below lists costs per S.F. for a floor system on bearing walls using open web steel joists, galvanized steel slab form and 2-1/2″ concrete slab reinforced with welded wire fabric. Costs of the bearing walls are not included.

B1010 246		Deck & Joists on Bearing Walls						
	SPAN (FT.)	SUPERIMPOSED LOAD (P.S.F.)	JOIST SPACING FT. - IN.	DEPTH (IN.)	TOTAL LOAD (P.S.F.)	COST PER S.F.		
						MAT.	INST.	TOTAL
1050	20	40	2-0	14-1/2	83	5.85	3.89	9.74
1070		65	2-0	16-1/2	109	6.35	4.12	10.47
1100		75	2-0	16-1/2	119	6.35	4.12	10.47
1120		100	2-0	18-1/2	145	6.40	4.13	10.53
1150		125	1-9	18-1/2	170	7	4.38	11.38
1170	25	40	2-0	18-1/2	84	6.40	4.13	10.53
1200		65	2-0	20-1/2	109	6.60	4.22	10.82
1220		75	2-0	20-1/2	119	7.05	4.40	11.45
1250		100	2-0	22-1/2	145	7.15	4.45	11.60
1270		125	1-9	22-1/2	170	8.15	4.85	13
1300	30	40	2-0	22-1/2	84	7.15	4.01	11.16
1320		65	2-0	24-1/2	110	7.75	4.18	11.93
1350		75	2-0	26-1/2	121	8	4.26	12.26
1370		100	2-0	26-1/2	146	8.55	4.41	12.96
1400		125	2-0	24-1/2	172	10.05	4.85	14.90
1420	35	40	2-0	26-1/2	85	9.50	4.68	14.18
1450		65	2-0	28-1/2	111	9.80	4.78	14.58
1470		75	2-0	28-1/2	121	9.80	4.78	14.58
1500		100	1-11	28-1/2	147	10.65	5.05	15.70
1520		125	1-8	28-1/2	172	11.70	5.35	17.05
1550	5/8″ gyp. fireproof.							
1560	On metal furring, add					.80	2.93	3.73

B1010   Floor Construction

The table below lists costs for a floor system on exterior bearing walls and interior columns and beams using open web steel joists, galvanized steel slab form, 2-1/2″ concrete slab reinforced with welded wire fabric.

Columns are sized to accommodate one floor plus roof loading but costs for columns are from suspended floor to slab on grade only. Costs of the bearing walls are not included.

Steel Joists and Concrete Slab on Walls and Beams

B1010 248						Steel Joists on Beam & Wall		
	BAY SIZE (FT.)	SUPERIMPOSED LOAD (P.S.F.)	DEPTH (IN.)	TOTAL LOAD (P.S.F.)	COLUMN ADD	COST PER S.F.		
						MAT.	INST.	TOTAL
1720	25x25	40	23	84		8.05	4.44	12.49
1730					columns	.42	.13	.55
1750	25x25	65	29	110		8.45	4.59	13.04
1760					columns	.42	.13	.55
1770	25x25	75	26	120		9.40	4.93	14.33
1780					columns	.48	.14	.62
1800	25x25	100	29	145		10.60	5.40	16
1810					columns	.48	.14	.62
1820	25x25	125	29	170		11.15	5.55	16.70
1830					columns	.54	.16	.70
2020	30x30	40	29	84		9.25	4.44	13.69
2030					columns	.37	.11	.48
2050	30x30	65	29	110		10.45	4.80	15.25
2060					columns	.37	.11	.48
2070	30x30	75	32	120		10.75	4.89	15.64
2080					columns	.43	.13	.56
2100	30x30	100	35	145		11.90	5.20	17.10
2110					columns	.50	.15	.65
2120	30x30	125	35	172		13.75	5.80	19.55
2130					columns	.60	.18	.78
2170	30x35	40	29	85		10.40	4.79	15.19
2180					columns	.36	.10	.46
2200	30x35	65	29	111		12.45	5.35	17.80
2210					columns	.41	.13	.54
2220	30x35	75	32	121		12.40	5.35	17.75
2230					columns	.42	.13	.55
2250	30x35	100	35	148		12.65	5.45	18.10
2260					columns	.52	.15	.67
2270	30x35	125	38	173		14.15	5.90	20.05
2280					columns	.53	.15	.68
2320	35x35	40	32	85		10.75	4.89	15.64
2330					columns	.37	.11	.48
2350	35x35	65	35	111		13.10	5.60	18.70
2360					columns	.44	.13	.57
2370	35x35	75	35	121		13.40	5.65	19.05
2380					columns	.44	.13	.57
2400	35x35	100	38	148		13.95	5.85	19.80
2410					columns	.55	.16	.71

B1010 248		Steel Joists on Beam & Wall						
	BAY SIZE (FT.)	SUPERIMPOSED LOAD (P.S.F.)	DEPTH (IN.)	TOTAL LOAD (P.S.F.)	COLUMN ADD	COST PER S.F.		
						MAT.	INST.	TOTAL
2460	5/8 gyp. fireproof.							
2475	On metal furring, add					.80	2.93	3.73

B1010 Floor Construction

The table below lists costs per S.F. for a floor system on steel columns and beams using open web steel joists, galvanized steel slab form, 2-1/2″ concrete slab reinforced with welded wire fabric.

Columns are sized to accommodate one floor plus roof loading but costs for columns are from floor to grade only.

Steel Joists and Concrete Slab on Steel Columns and Beams

B1010 250	Steel Joists, Beams & Slab on Columns							
	BAY SIZE (FT.)	SUPERIMPOSED LOAD (P.S.F.)	DEPTH (IN.)	TOTAL LOAD (P.S.F.)	COLUMN ADD	COST PER S.F.		
						MAT.	INST.	TOTAL
2350	15x20	40	17	83		8.35	4.49	12.84
2400					column	1.38	.41	1.79
2450	15x20	65	19	108		9.30	4.76	14.06
2500					column	1.38	.41	1.79
2550	15x20	75	19	119		9.65	4.91	14.56
2600					column	1.51	.44	1.95
2650	15x20	100	19	144		10.25	5.10	15.35
2700					column	1.51	.44	1.95
2750	15x20	125	19	170		10.80	5.25	16.05
2800					column	2.01	.59	2.60
2850	20x20	40	19	83		9.10	4.70	13.80
2900					column	1.13	.33	1.46
2950	20x20	65	23	109		10.05	5	15.05
3000					column	1.51	.44	1.95
3100	20x20	75	26	119		10.60	5.20	15.80
3200					column	1.51	.44	1.95
3400	20x20	100	23	144		11.05	5.30	16.35
3450					column	1.51	.44	1.95
3500	20x20	125	23	170		12.25	5.75	18
3600					column	1.81	.53	2.34
3700	20x25	40	44	83		9.75	4.93	14.68
3800					column	1.21	.35	1.56
3900	20x25	65	26	110		10.70	5.20	15.90
4000					column	1.21	.35	1.56
4100	20x25	75	26	120		11.15	5.40	16.55
4200					column	1.45	.43	1.88
4300	20x25	100	26	145		11.85	5.65	17.50
4400					column	1.45	.43	1.88
4500	20x25	125	29	170		13.15	6.10	19.25
4600					column	1.69	.49	2.18
4700	25x25	40	23	84		10.60	5.15	15.75
4800					column	1.16	.34	1.50
4900	25x25	65	29	110		11.20	5.35	16.55
5000					column	1.16	.34	1.50
5100	25x25	75	26	120		12.40	5.80	18.20
5200					column	1.35	.39	1.74
5300	25x25	100	29	145		13.75	6.30	20.05
5400					column	1.35	.39	1.74

B1010 Floor Construction

B1010 250	Steel Joists, Beams & Slab on Columns

	BAY SIZE (FT.)	SUPERIMPOSED LOAD (P.S.F.)	DEPTH (IN.)	TOTAL LOAD (P.S.F.)	COLUMN ADD	COST PER S.F.		
						MAT.	INST.	TOTAL
5500	25x25	125	32	170		14.55	6.55	21.10
5600					column	1.50	.44	1.94
5700	25x30	40	29	84		12.10	5.25	17.35
5800					column	1.12	.33	1.45
5900	25x30	65	29	110		12.60	5.40	18
6000					column	1.12	.33	1.45
6050	25x30	75	29	120		12.95	5.55	18.50
6100					column	1.24	.37	1.61
6150	25x30	100	29	145		14.05	5.85	19.90
6200					column	1.24	.37	1.61
6250	25x30	125	32	170		15.85	6.40	22.25
6300					column	1.43	.42	1.85
6350	30x30	40	29	84		12.10	5.25	17.35
6400					column	1.04	.30	1.34
6500	30x30	65	29	110		13.80	5.75	19.55
6600					column	1.04	.30	1.34
6700	30x30	75	32	120		14.05	5.85	19.90
6800					column	1.19	.35	1.54
6900	30x30	100	35	145		15.60	6.30	21.90
7000					column	1.39	.41	1.80
7100	30x30	125	35	172		17.85	6.95	24.80
7200					column	1.55	.46	2.01
7300	30x35	40	29	85		13.65	5.70	19.35
7400					column	.89	.26	1.15
7500	30x35	65	29	111		15.90	6.40	22.30
7600					column	1.15	.34	1.49
7700	30x35	75	32	121		15.90	6.40	22.30
7800					column	1.17	.34	1.51
7900	30x35	100	35	148		16.40	6.50	22.90
8000					column	1.43	.42	1.85
8100	30x35	125	38	173		18.20	7.05	25.25
8200					column	1.46	.43	1.89
8300	35x35	40	32	85		14.05	5.85	19.90
8400					column	1.02	.30	1.32
8500	35x35	65	35	111		16.75	6.65	23.40
8600					column	1.23	.37	1.60
9300	35x35	75	38	121		17.15	6.75	23.90
9400					column	1.23	.37	1.60
9500	35x35	100	38	148		18.50	7.15	25.65
9600					column	1.52	.44	1.96
9750	35x35	125	41	173		19.10	7.35	26.45
9800					column	1.54	.46	2
9810	5/8 gyp. fireproof.							
9815	On metal furring, add					.80	2.93	3.73

B10 Superstructure

B1010 Floor Construction

Composite Beam & Cast in Place Slab

General: Composite construction of wide flange beams and concrete slabs is most efficiently used when loads are heavy and spans are moderately long. It is stiffer with less deflection than non-composite construction of similar depth and spans.

B1010 252	Composite Beam & Cast in Place Slab							
	BAY SIZE (FT.)	SUPERIMPOSED LOAD (P.S.F.)	SLAB THICKNESS (IN.)	TOTAL DEPTH (FT.-IN.)	TOTAL LOAD (P.S.F.)	COST PER S.F.		
						MAT.	INST.	TOTAL
3800	20x25	40	4	1 - 8	94	10.15	10.85	21
3900		75	4	1 - 8	130	11.90	11.55	23.45
4000		125	4	1 - 10	181	13.85	12.35	26.20
4100		200	5	2 - 2	272	18.10	13.95	32.05
4200	25x25	40	4-1/2	1 - 8-1/2	99	10.60	11	21.60
4300		75	4-1/2	1 - 10-1/2	136	12.85	11.90	24.75
4400		125	5-1/2	2 - 0-1/2	200	15.25	12.85	28.10
4500		200	5-1/2	2 - 2-1/2	278	19.05	14.25	33.30
4600	25x30	40	4-1/2	1 - 8-1/2	100	11.90	11.45	23.35
4700		75	4-1/2	1 - 10-1/2	136	14	12.25	26.25
4800		125	5-1/2	2 - 2-1/2	202	17.20	13.45	30.65
4900		200	5-1/2	2 - 5-1/2	279	20.50	14.75	35.25
5000	30x30	40	4	1 - 8	95	11.95	11.50	23.45
5200		75	4	2 - 1	131	13.90	12.10	26
5400		125	4	2 - 4	183	17.25	13.35	30.60
5600		200	5	2 - 10	274	22	15.10	37.10
5800	30x35	40	4	2 - 1	95	12.65	11.70	24.35
6000		75	4	2 - 4	139	15.35	12.60	27.95
6250		125	4	2 - 4	185	20	14.25	34.25
6500		200	5	2 - 11	276	24.50	15.90	40.40
8000	35x35	40	4	2 - 1	96	13.40	11.90	25.30
8250		75	4	2 - 4	133	15.95	12.85	28.80
8500		125	4	2 - 10	185	19.25	14	33.25
8750		200	5	3 - 5	276	25	16.05	41.05
9000	35x40	40	4	2 - 4	97	14.90	12.40	27.30
9250		75	4	2 - 4	134	17.50	13.20	30.70
9500		125	4	2 - 7	186	21.50	14.65	36.15
9750		200	5	3 - 5	278	28	16.80	44.80

B10 Superstructure

B1010 Floor Construction

The table below lists costs per S.F. for floors using steel beams and girders, composite steel deck, concrete slab reinforced with W.W.F. and sprayed fiber fireproofing (non- asbestos) on the steel beams and girders and on the steel deck.

Wide Flange, Composite Deck & Slab

B1010 254				W Shape, Composite Deck, & Slab				
	BAY SIZE (FT.) BEAM X GIRD	SUPERIMPOSED LOAD (P.S.F.)	SLAB THICKNESS (IN.)	TOTAL DEPTH (FT.-IN.)	TOTAL LOAD (P.S.F.)	COST PER S.F.		
						MAT.	INST.	TOTAL
0540	15x20	40	5	1-7	89	11.70	6.60	18.30
0560		75	5	1-9	125	12.90	7	19.90
0580		125	5	1-11	176	15.15	7.65	22.80
0600		200	5	2-2	254	18.65	8.70	27.35
0700	20x20	40	5	1-9	90	12.75	6.90	19.65
0720		75	5	1-9	126	14.45	7.45	21.90
0740		125	5	1-11	177	16.45	8.05	24.50
0760		200	5	2-5	255	19.90	9.05	28.95
0780	20x25	40	5	1-9	90	12.95	6.85	19.80
0800		75	5	1-9	127	16.25	7.85	24.10
0820		125	5	1-11	180	19.45	8.60	28.05
0840		200	5	2-5	256	21.50	9.70	31.20
0940	25x25	40	5	1-11	91	14.75	7.30	22.05
0960		75	5	2-5	178	17.05	8.05	25.10
0980		125	5	2-5	181	21	9	30
1000		200	5-1/2	2-8-1/2	263	24	10.40	34.40
1400	25x30	40	5	2-5	91	14.65	7.55	22.20
1500		75	5	2-5	128	17.90	8.35	26.25
1600		125	5	2-8	180	20.50	9.30	29.80
1700		200	5	2-11	259	25.50	10.75	36.25
2200	30x30	40	5	2-2	92	16.30	8	24.30
2300		75	5	2-5	129	19.15	8.90	28.05
2400		125	5	2-11	182	23	10	33
2500		200	5	3-2	263	31	12.55	43.55
2600	30x35	40	5	2-5	94	17.80	8.50	26.30
2700		75	5	2-11	131	21	9.40	30.40
2800		125	5	3-2	183	24.50	10.45	34.95
2900		200	5-1/2	3-5-1/2	268	30	12.05	42.05
3800	35x35	40	5	2-8	94	18.35	8.45	26.80
3900		75	5	2-11	131	21.50	9.40	30.90
4000		125	5	3-5	184	25.50	10.75	36.25
4100		200	5-1/2	3-5-1/2	270	33	12.70	45.70

B10 Superstructure

B1010 Floor Construction

Composite Beam, Deck & Slab

The table below lists costs per S.F. for floors using composite steel beams with welded shear studs, composite steel deck and light weight concrete slab reinforced with W.W.F.

B1010 256	Composite Beams, Deck & Slab							
	BAY SIZE (FT.)	SUPERIMPOSED LOAD (P.S.F.)	SLAB THICKNESS (IN.)	TOTAL DEPTH (FT.-IN.)	TOTAL LOAD (P.S.F.)	COST PER S.F.		
						MAT.	INST.	TOTAL
2400	20x25	40	5-1/2	1 - 5-1/2	80	12.20	6.20	18.40
2500		75	5-1/2	1 - 9-1/2	115	12.70	6.15	18.85
2750		125	5-1/2	1 - 9-1/2	167	15.60	7.20	22.80
2900		200	6-1/4	1 - 11-1/2	251	17.55	7.80	25.35
3000	25x25	40	5-1/2	1 - 9-1/2	82	11.95	5.85	17.80
3100		75	5-1/2	1 - 11-1/2	118	13.35	5.95	19.30
3200		125	5-1/2	2 - 2-1/2	169	14	6.45	20.45
3300		200	6-1/4	2 - 6-1/4	252	18.95	7.50	26.45
3400	25x30	40	5-1/2	1 - 11-1/2	83	12.20	5.85	18.05
3600		75	5-1/2	1 - 11-1/2	119	13.20	5.85	19.05
3900		125	5-1/2	1 - 11-1/2	170	15.40	6.65	22.05
4000		200	6-1/4	2 - 6-1/4	252	19.05	7.55	26.60
4200	30x30	40	5-1/2	1 - 11-1/2	81	12.35	6	18.35
4400		75	5-1/2	2 - 2-1/2	116	13.30	6.25	19.55
4500		125	5-1/2	2 - 5-1/2	168	16.20	7	23.20
4700		200	6-1/4	2 - 9-1/4	252	19.45	8.15	27.60
4900	30x35	40	5-1/2	2 - 2-1/2	82	12.90	6.20	19.10
5100		75	5-1/2	2 - 5-1/2	117	14.15	6.35	20.50
5300		125	5-1/2	2 - 5-1/2	169	16.70	7.15	23.85
5500		200	6-1/4	2 - 9-1/4	254	19.65	8.15	27.80
5750	35x35	40	5-1/2	2 - 5-1/2	84	13.75	6.25	20
6000		75	5-1/2	2 - 5-1/2	121	15.75	6.60	22.35
7000		125	5-1/2	2 - 8-1/2	170	18.60	7.55	26.15
7200		200	5-1/2	2 - 11-1/2	254	21.50	8.40	29.90
7400	35x40	40	5-1/2	2 - 5-1/2	85	15.25	6.70	21.95
7600		75	5-1/2	2 - 5-1/2	121	16.60	6.85	23.45
8000		125	5-1/2	2 - 5-1/2	171	19.10	7.70	26.80
9000		200	5-1/2	2 - 11-1/2	255	23	8.75	31.75

B10 Superstructure

B1010 Floor Construction

Description: Table B1010 258 lists S.F. costs for steel deck and concrete slabs for various spans.

Description: Table B1010 261 lists the S.F. costs for wood joists and a minimum thickness plywood subfloor.

Description: Table B1010 264 lists the S.F. costs, total load, and member sizes, for various bay sizes and loading conditions.

Metal Deck/Concrete Fill

Wood Joist

Wood Beam and Joist

B1010 258 — Metal Deck/Concrete Fill

	SUPERIMPOSED LOAD (P.S.F.)	DECK SPAN (FT.)	DECK GAGE DEPTH	SLAB THICKNESS (IN.)	TOTAL LOAD (P.S.F.)	COST PER S.F.		
						MAT.	INST.	TOTAL
0900	125	6	22 1-1/2	4	164	2.91	2.52	5.43
0920		7	20 1-1/2	4	164	3.21	2.67	5.88
0950		8	20 1-1/2	4	165	3.21	2.67	5.88
0970		9	18 1-1/2	4	165	3.77	2.67	6.44
1000		10	18 2	4	165	3.66	2.81	6.47
1020		11	18 3	5	169	4.51	3.04	7.55

B1010 261 — Wood Joist

		COST PER S.F.		
		MAT.	INST.	TOTAL
2900	2"x8", 12" O.C.	1.72	1.92	3.64
2950	16" O.C.	1.46	1.64	3.10
3000	24" O.C.	1.55	1.53	3.08
3300	2"x10", 12" O.C.	2.06	2.19	4.25
3350	16" O.C.	1.72	1.84	3.56
3400	24" O.C.	1.70	1.65	3.35
3700	2"x12", 12" O.C.	2.55	2.21	4.76
3750	16" O.C.	2.08	1.85	3.93
3800	24" O.C.	1.96	1.67	3.63
4100	2"x14", 12" O.C.	2.86	2.40	5.26
4150	16" O.C.	2.32	2.01	4.33
4200	24" O.C.	2.12	1.77	3.89
7101	Note: Subfloor cost is included in these prices.			

B1010 264 — Wood Beam & Joist

	BAY SIZE (FT.)	SUPERIMPOSED LOAD (P.S.F.)	GIRDER BEAM (IN.)	JOISTS (IN.)	TOTAL LOAD (P.S.F.)	COST PER S.F.		
						MAT.	INST.	TOTAL
2000	15x15	40	8 x 12 4 x 12	2 x 6 @ 16	53	9.05	4.47	13.52
2050		75	8 x 16 4 x 16	2 x 8 @ 16	90	12.60	4.88	17.48
2100		125	12 x 16 6 x 16	2 x 8 @ 12	144	19.40	6.25	25.65
2150		200	14 x 22 12 x 16	2 x 10 @ 12	227	38.50	9.60	48.10
3000	20x20	40	10 x 14 10 x 12	2 x 8 @ 16	63	10.85	4.50	15.35
3050		75	12 x 16 8 x 16	2 x 10 @ 16	102	16.55	5.05	21.60
3100		125	14 x 22 12 x 16	2 x 10 @ 12	163	32.50	8	40.50

338

B10 Superstructure

B1010 Floor Construction

Steel Column Fireproofing

"T" Shaped
Precast Beams

"L" Shaped
Precast Beams

B1010 720			Steel Column Fireproofing					
	ENCASEMENT SYSTEM	COLUMN SIZE (IN.)	THICKNESS (IN.)	FIRE RATING (HRS.)	WEIGHT (P.L.F.)	COST PER V.L.F.		
						MAT.	INST.	TOTAL
3000	Concrete	8	1	1	110	6.50	36	42.50
3300		14	1	1	258	10.70	52	62.70
3400			2	3	325	12.80	59	71.80
3450	Gypsum board	8	1/2	2	8	3.46	22	25.46
3550	1 layer	14	1/2	2	18	3.72	23.50	27.22
3600	Gypsum board	8	1	3	14	4.71	28	32.71
3650	1/2" fire rated	10	1	3	17	5.05	30	35.05
3700	2 layers	14	1	3	22	5.20	30.50	35.70
3750	Gypsum board	8	1-1/2	3	23	6.20	35.50	41.70
3800	1/2" fire rated	10	1-1/2	3	27	6.95	39	45.95
3850	3 layers	14	1-1/2	3	35	7.65	43	50.65
3900	Sprayed fiber	8	1-1/2	2	6.3	3.93	7.05	10.98
3950	Direct application		2	3	8.3	5.40	9.75	15.15
4050		10	1-1/2	2	7.9	4.75	8.50	13.25
4200	Sprayed fiber	14	1-1/2	2	10.8	5.90	10.55	16.45

B1020 Roof Construction

The table below lists prices per S.F. for roof rafters and sheathing by nominal size and spacing. Sheathing is 5/16" CDX for 12" and 16" spacing and 3/8" CDX for 24" spacing.

Factors for Converting Inclined to Horizontal

Roof Slope	Approx. Angle	Factor	Roof Slope	Approx. Angle	Factor
Flat	0°	1.000	12 in 12	45.0°	1.414
1 in 12	4.8°	1.003	13 in 12	47.3°	1.474
2 in 12	9.5°	1.014	14 in 12	49.4°	1.537
3 in 12	14.0°	1.031	15 in 12	51.3°	1.601
4 in 12	18.4°	1.054	16 in 12	53.1°	1.667
5 in 12	22.6°	1.083	17 in 12	54.8°	1.734
6 in 12	26.6°	1.118	18 in 12	56.3°	1.803
7 in 12	30.3°	1.158	19 in 12	57.7°	1.873
8 in 12	33.7°	1.202	20 in 12	59.0°	1.943
9 in 12	36.9°	1.250	21 in 12	60.3°	2.015
10 in 12	39.8°	1.302	22 in 12	61.4°	2.088
11 in 12	42.5°	1.357	23 in 12	62.4°	2.162

B1020 102	Wood/Flat or Pitched	COST PER S.F.		
		MAT.	INST.	TOTAL
2500	Flat rafter, 2"x4", 12" O.C.	1.10	1.75	2.85
2550	16" O.C.	.98	1.51	2.49
2600	24" O.C.	.81	1.29	2.10
2900	2"x6", 12" O.C.	1.33	1.75	3.08
2950	16" O.C.	1.16	1.50	2.66
3000	24" O.C.	.92	1.28	2.20
3300	2"x8", 12" O.C.	1.68	1.88	3.56
3350	16" O.C.	1.42	1.60	3.02
3400	24" O.C.	1.11	1.35	2.46
3700	2"x10", 12" O.C.	2.02	2.15	4.17
3750	16" O.C.	1.68	1.80	3.48
3800	24" O.C.	1.26	1.47	2.73
4100	2"x12", 12" O.C.	2.51	2.17	4.68
4150	16" O.C.	2.04	1.81	3.85
4200	24" O.C.	1.52	1.49	3.01
4500	2"x14", 12" O.C.	2.83	3.17	6
4550	16" O.C.	2.29	2.57	4.86
4600	24" O.C.	1.68	2	3.68
4900	3"x6", 12" O.C.	2.33	1.85	4.18
4950	16" O.C.	1.91	1.57	3.48
5000	24" O.C.	1.43	1.33	2.76
5300	3"x8", 12" O.C.	3.72	2.06	5.78
5350	16" O.C.	2.95	1.73	4.68
5400	24" O.C.	2.12	1.43	3.55
5700	3"x10", 12" O.C.	4.49	2.35	6.84
5750	16" O.C.	3.54	1.95	5.49
5800	24" O.C.	2.51	1.58	4.09
6100	3"x12", 12" O.C.	5.25	2.83	8.08
6150	16" O.C.	4.11	2.31	6.42
6200	24" O.C.	2.89	1.82	4.71
7001	Wood truss, 4 in 12 slope, 24" O.C., 24' to 29' span	3.72	2.61	6.33
7100	30' to 43' span	4.24	2.61	6.85
7200	44' to 60' span	4.43	2.61	7.04

B10 Superstructure

B1020 Roof Construction

**Steel Joists, Beams and Deck
on Bearing Walls**

The table below lists the cost per S.F. for a roof system with steel columns, beams and deck using open web steel joists and 1-1/2″ galvanized metal deck. Perimeter of system is supported on bearing walls.

Fireproofing is not included. Costs/S.F. are based on a building 4 bays long and 4 bays wide.

Column costs are additive. Costs for the bearing walls are not included.

B1020 108	Steel Joists, Beams & Deck on Columns & Walls							
	BAY SIZE (FT.)	SUPERIMPOSED LOAD (P.S.F.)	DEPTH (IN.)	TOTAL LOAD (P.S.F.)	COLUMN ADD	COST PER S.F.		
						MAT.	INST.	TOTAL
3000	25x25	20	18	40		4.23	1.43	5.66
3100					columns	.39	.09	.48
3200		30	22	50		4.54	1.52	6.06
3300					columns	.52	.12	.64
3400		40	20	60		5.05	1.68	6.73
3500					columns	.52	.12	.64
3600	25x30	20	22	40		4.46	1.38	5.84
3700					columns	.44	.10	.54
3800		30	20	50		5.05	1.54	6.59
3900					columns	.44	.10	.54
4000		40	25	60		5.25	1.58	6.83
4100					columns	.52	.12	.64
4200	30x30	20	25	42		4.92	1.48	6.40
4300					columns	.36	.09	.45
4400		30	22	52		5.40	1.61	7.01
4500					columns	.44	.10	.54
4600		40	28	62		5.60	1.66	7.26
4700					columns	.44	.10	.54
4800	30x35	20	22	42		5.10	1.54	6.64
4900					columns	.37	.09	.46
5000		30	28	52		5.40	1.61	7.01
5100					columns	.37	.09	.46
5200		40	25	62		5.85	1.72	7.57
5300					columns	.44	.10	.54
5400	35x35	20	28	42		5.10	1.55	6.65
5500					columns	.32	.08	.40

B1020 Roof Construction

Steel Joists, Beams and Deck on Columns

Description: The table below lists the cost per S.F. for a roof system with steel columns, beams, and deck, using open web steel joists and 1-1/2″ galvanized metal deck.

Column costs are additive. Fireproofing is not included.

B1020 112	Steel Joists, Beams, & Deck on Columns							
	BAY SIZE (FT.)	SUPERIMPOSED LOAD (P.S.F.)	DEPTH (IN.)	TOTAL LOAD (P.S.F.)	COLUMN ADD	COST PER S.F.		
						MAT.	INST.	TOTAL
1100	15x20	20	16	40		4.18	1.43	5.61
1200					columns	2.26	.53	2.79
1500		40	18	60		4.67	1.58	6.25
1600					columns	2.26	.53	2.79
2300	20x25	20	18	40		4.76	1.59	6.35
2400					columns	1.35	.31	1.66
2700		40	20	60		5.35	1.77	7.12
2800					columns	1.81	.42	2.23
2900	25x25	20	18	40		5.60	1.80	7.40
3000					columns	1.08	.25	1.33
3100		30	22	50		5.80	1.84	7.64
3200					columns	1.45	.34	1.79
3300		40	20	60		6.50	2.04	8.54
3400					columns	1.45	.34	1.79
3500	25x30	20	22	40		5.50	1.61	7.11
3600					columns	1.21	.28	1.49
3900		40	25	60		6.60	1.91	8.51
4000					columns	1.45	.34	1.79
4100	30x30	20	25	42		6.20	1.79	7.99
4200					columns	1	.24	1.24
4300		30	22	52		6.85	1.96	8.81
4400					columns	1.21	.28	1.49
4500		40	28	62		7.20	2.04	9.24
4600					columns	1.21	.28	1.49
5300	35x35	20	28	42		6.75	1.94	8.69
5400					columns	.88	.20	1.08
5500		30	25	52		7.60	2.14	9.74
5600					columns	1.03	.24	1.27
5700		40	28	62		8.20	2.29	10.49
5800					columns	1.14	.26	1.40

B10 Superstructure

B1020 Roof Construction

Description: The table below lists the cost per S.F. for a roof system using open web steel joists and 1-1/2″ galvanized metal deck. The system is assumed supported on bearing walls or other suitable support. Costs for the supports are not included.

B1020 116	Steel Joists & Deck on Bearing Walls							
	BAY SIZE (FT.)	SUPERIMPOSED LOAD (P.S.F.)	DEPTH (IN.)	TOTAL LOAD (P.S.F.)		COST PER S.F.		
						MAT.	INST.	TOTAL
1100	20	20	13-1/2	40		2.65	1.04	3.69
1200		30	15-1/2	50		2.71	1.06	3.77
1300		40	15-1/2	60		2.91	1.14	4.05
1400	25	20	17-1/2	40		2.91	1.15	4.06
1500		30	17-1/2	50		3.14	1.24	4.38
1600		40	19-1/2	60		3.19	1.26	4.45
1700	30	20	19-1/2	40		3.18	1.26	4.44
1800		30	21-1/2	50		3.25	1.28	4.53
1900		40	23-1/2	60		3.50	1.38	4.88
2000	35	20	23-1/2	40		3.46	1.16	4.62
2100		30	25-1/2	50		3.56	1.19	4.75
2200		40	25-1/2	60		3.78	1.25	5.03
2300	40	20	25-1/2	41		3.84	1.27	5.11
2400		30	25-1/2	51		4.08	1.34	5.42
2500		40	25-1/2	61		4.22	1.38	5.60
2600	45	20	27-1/2	41		4.63	1.50	6.13
2700		30	31-1/2	51		4.90	1.58	6.48
2800		40	31-1/2	61		5.20	1.66	6.86
2900	50	20	29-1/2	42		5.20	1.67	6.87
3000		30	31-1/2	52		5.70	1.81	7.51
3100		40	31-1/2	62		6.05	1.92	7.97
3200	60	20	37-1/2	42		6.15	2.20	8.35
3300		30	37-1/2	52		6.85	2.43	9.28
3400		40	37-1/2	62		6.85	2.43	9.28
3500	70	20	41-1/2	42		6.80	2.43	9.23
3600		30	41-1/2	52		7.30	2.59	9.89
3700		40	41-1/2	64		8.85	3.13	11.98
3800	80	20	45-1/2	44		8.60	3.04	11.64
3900		30	45-1/2	54		8.60	3.04	11.64
4000		40	45-1/2	64		9.50	3.36	12.86
4400	100	20	57-1/2	44		8.45	2.89	11.34
4500		30	57-1/2	54		10.10	3.43	13.53
4600		40	57-1/2	65		11.15	3.78	14.93
4700	125	20	69-1/2	44		10.10	3.42	13.52
4800		30	69-1/2	56		11.75	3.97	15.72
4900		40	69-1/2	67		13.40	4.51	17.91

B10 Superstructure

B1020 Roof Construction

Description: The table below lists costs for a roof system supported on exterior bearing walls and interior columns. Costs include bracing, joist girders, open web steel joists and 1-1/2″ galvanized metal deck.

Column costs are additive. Fireproofing is not included.

Costs/S.F. are based on a building 4 bays long and 4 bays wide. Costs for bearing walls are not included.

B1020 120	Steel Joists, Joist Girders & Deck on Columns & Walls							
	BAY SIZE (FT.) GIRD X JOISTS	SUPERIMPOSED LOAD (P.S.F.)	DEPTH (IN.)	TOTAL LOAD (P.S.F.)	COLUMN ADD	COST PER S.F.		
						MAT.	INST.	TOTAL
2350	30x35	20	32-1/2	40		3.90	1.45	5.35
2400					columns	.37	.09	.46
2550		40	36-1/2	60		4.38	1.59	5.97
2600					columns	.43	.10	.53
3000	35x35	20	36-1/2	40		4.26	1.79	6.05
3050					columns	.32	.08	.40
3200		40	36-1/2	60		4.78	1.97	6.75
3250					columns	.41	.10	.51
3300	35x40	20	36-1/2	40		4.32	1.63	5.95
3350					columns	.33	.08	.41
3500		40	36-1/2	60		4.87	1.80	6.67
3550					columns	.36	.09	.45
3900	40x40	20	40-1/2	41		5	1.82	6.82
3950					columns	.32	.08	.40
4100		40	40-1/2	61		5.60	1.99	7.59
4150					columns	.32	.08	.40
5100	45x50	20	52-1/2	41		5.65	2.07	7.72
5150					columns	.23	.05	.28
5300		40	52-1/2	61		6.90	2.45	9.35
5350					columns	.33	.08	.41
5400	50x45	20	56-1/2	41		5.45	2.02	7.47
5450					columns	.23	.05	.28
5600		40	56-1/2	61		7.05	2.51	9.56
5650					columns	.31	.07	.38
5700	50x50	20	56-1/2	42		6.15	2.24	8.39
5750					columns	.23	.05	.28
5900		40	59	64		7.10	2.74	9.84
5950					columns	.32	.08	.40
6300	60x50	20	62-1/2	43		6.20	2.29	8.49
6350					columns	.36	.09	.45
6500		40	71	65		7.25	2.83	10.08
6550					columns	.48	.11	.59

B10 Superstructure

B1020 Roof Construction

Description: The table below lists the cost per S.F. for a roof system supported on columns. Costs include joist girders, open web steel joists and 1-1/2" galvanized metal deck. Column costs are additive.

Fireproofing is not included. Costs/S.F. are based on a building 4 bays long and 4 bays wide.

Costs for wind columns are not included.

B1020 124	Steel Joists & Joist Girders on Columns							
	BAY SIZE (FT.) GIRD X JOISTS	SUPERIMPOSED LOAD (P.S.F.)	DEPTH (IN.)	TOTAL LOAD (P.S.F.)	COLUMN ADD	COST PER S.F.		
						MAT.	INST.	TOTAL
2000	30x30	20	17-1/2	40		3.91	1.73	5.64
2050					columns	1.21	.28	1.49
2100		30	17-1/2	50		4.24	1.86	6.10
2150					columns	1.21	.28	1.49
2200		40	21-1/2	60		4.36	1.91	6.27
2250					columns	1.21	.28	1.49
2300	30x35	20	32-1/2	40		4.19	1.62	5.81
2350					columns	1.03	.24	1.27
2500		40	36-1/2	60		4.72	1.80	6.52
2550					columns	1.21	.28	1.49
3200	35x40	20	36-1/2	40		5.45	2.19	7.64
3250					columns	.90	.21	1.11
3400		40	36-1/2	60		6.15	2.41	8.56
3450					columns	1	.23	1.23
3800	40x40	20	40-1/2	41		5.55	2.19	7.74
3850					columns	.88	.20	1.08
4000		40	40-1/2	61		6.20	2.41	8.61
4050					columns	.88	.20	1.08
4100	40x45	20	40-1/2	41		5.95	2.50	8.45
4150					columns	.78	.18	.96
4200		30	40-1/2	51		6.50	2.65	9.15
4250					columns	.78	.18	.96
4300		40	40-1/2	61		7.20	2.88	10.08
4350					columns	.88	.20	1.08
5000	45x50	20	52-1/2	41		6.30	2.51	8.81
5050					columns	.62	.15	.77
5200		40	52-1/2	61		7.70	2.96	10.66
5250					columns	.80	.19	.99
5300	50x45	20	56-1/2	41		6.10	2.47	8.57
5350					columns	.62	.15	.77
5500		40	56-1/2	61		7.90	3.03	10.93
5550					columns	.80	.19	.99
5600	50x50	20	56-1/2	42		6.85	2.71	9.56
5650					columns	.63	.15	.78
5800		40	59	64		6.15	2.59	8.74
5850					columns	.89	.20	1.09

B2010 Exterior Walls

Cast in Place Concrete Wall

Flat Precast Concrete Wall

Table B2010 101 describes a concrete wall system for exterior closure. There are several types of wall finishes priced from plain finish to a finish with 3/4″ rustication strip.

In Table B2010 103, precast concrete wall panels are either solid or insulated. Prices below are based on delivery within 50 miles of a plant. Small jobs can double the prices below. For large, highly repetitive jobs, deduct up to 15%.

B2010 101	Cast In Place Concrete	COST PER S.F.		
		MAT.	INST.	TOTAL
2100	Conc wall reinforced, 8′ high, 6″ thick, plain finish, 3000 PSI	4.65	16.20	20.85
2700	Aged wood liner, 3000 PSI	5.85	18.40	24.25
3000	Sand blast light 1 side, 3000 PSI	5.20	18.40	23.60
3700	3/4″ bevel rustication strip, 3000 PSI	4.77	17.15	21.92
4000	8″ thick, plain finish, 3000 PSI	5.50	16.60	22.10
4100	4000 PSI	5.60	16.60	22.20
4300	Rub concrete 1 side, 3000 PSI	5.50	19.55	25.05
4550	8″ thick, aged wood liner, 3000 PSI	6.65	18.80	25.45
4750	Sand blast light 1 side, 3000 PSI	6.05	18.85	24.90
5300	3/4″ bevel rustication strip, 3000 PSI	5.60	17.55	23.15
5600	10″ thick, plain finish, 3000 PSI	6.30	17	23.30
5900	Rub concrete 1 side, 3000 PSI	6.30	19.95	26.25
6200	Aged wood liner, 3000 PSI	7.45	19.20	26.65
6500	Sand blast light 1 side, 3000 PSI	6.85	19.25	26.10
7100	3/4″ bevel rustication strip, 3000 PSI	6.40	17.95	24.35
7400	12″ thick, plain finish, 3000 PSI	7.25	17.45	24.70
7700	Rub concrete 1 side, 3000 PSI	7.25	20.50	27.75
8000	Aged wood liner, 3000 PSI	8.40	19.65	28.05
8300	Sand blast light 1 side, 3000 PSI	7.80	19.70	27.50
8900	3/4″ bevel rustication strip, 3000 PSI	7.35	18.40	25.75

B2010 102		Flat Precast Concrete				COST PER S.F.		
	THICKNESS (IN.)	PANEL SIZE (FT.)	FINISHES	RIGID INSULATION (IN)	TYPE	MAT.	INST.	TOTAL
3000	4	5x18	smooth gray	none	low rise	12.40	7.90	20.30
3050		6x18				10.35	6.60	16.95
3100		8x20				20.50	3.18	23.68
3150		12x20				19.40	2.99	22.39
3200	6	5x18	smooth gray	2	low rise	13.40	8.45	21.85
3250		6x18				11.40	7.15	18.55
3300		8x20				22	3.84	25.84
3350		12x20				19.80	3.53	23.33
3400	8	5x18	smooth gray	2	low rise	28.50	4.84	33.34
3450		6x18				27	4.61	31.61
3500		8x20				24.50	4.25	28.75
3550		12x20				22.50	3.90	26.40

B2010 Exterior Walls

B2010 102	Flat Precast Concrete

	THICKNESS (IN.)	PANEL SIZE (FT.)	FINISHES	RIGID INSULATION (IN)	TYPE	COST PER S.F. MAT.	COST PER S.F. INST.	COST PER S.F. TOTAL
3600	4	4x8	white face	none	low rise	47.50	4.54	52.04
3650		8x8				35.50	3.42	38.92
3700		10x10				31.50	2.99	34.49
3750		20x10				28.50	2.71	31.21
3800	5	4x8	white face	none	low rise	48.50	4.64	53.14
3850		8x8				36.50	3.51	40.01
3900		10x10				32.50	3.10	35.60
3950		20x20				29.50	2.85	32.35
4000	6	4x8	white face	none	low rise	50.50	4.81	55.31
4050		8x8				38	3.65	41.65
4100		10x10				33.50	3.22	36.72
4150		20x10				31	2.95	33.95
4200	6	4x8	white face	2	low rise	51.50	5.45	56.95
4250		8x8				39.50	4.29	43.79
4300		10x10				35	3.86	38.86
4350		20x10				31	2.95	33.95
4400	7	4x8	white face	none	low rise	51.50	4.93	56.43
4450		8x8				39.50	3.79	43.29
4500		10x10				35.50	3.39	38.89
4550		20x10				32.50	3.10	35.60
4600	7	4x8	white face	2	low rise	52.50	5.55	58.05
4650		8x8				40.50	4.43	44.93
4700		10x10				36.50	4.03	40.53
4750		20x10				33.50	3.74	37.24
4800	8	4x8	white face	none	low rise	52.50	5.05	57.55
4850		8x8				40.50	3.88	44.38
4900		10x10				36.50	3.48	39.98
4950		20x10				33.50	3.22	36.72
5000	8	4x8	white face	2	low rise	54	5.65	59.65
5050		8x8				42	4.52	46.52
5100		10x10				37.50	4.12	41.62
5150		20x10				35	3.86	38.86

B2010 103	Fluted Window or Mullion Precast Concrete

	THICKNESS (IN.)	PANEL SIZE (FT.)	FINISHES	RIGID INSULATION (IN)	TYPE	COST PER S.F. MAT.	COST PER S.F. INST.	COST PER S.F. TOTAL
5200	4	4x8	smooth gray	none	high rise	28.50	18	46.50
5250		8x8				20.50	12.85	33.35
5300		10x10				39	6.05	45.05
5350		20x10				34.50	5.30	39.80
5400	5	4x8	smooth gray	none	high rise	29	18.30	47.30
5450		8x8				21	13.30	34.30
5500		10x10				41	6.30	47.30
5550		20x10				36	5.60	41.60
5600	6	4x8	smooth gray	none	high rise	29.50	18.80	48.30
5650		8x8				21.50	13.80	35.30
5700		10x10				42	6.50	48.50
5750		20x10				37.50	5.75	43.25
5800	6	4x8	smooth gray	2	high rise	31	19.45	50.45
5850		8x8				23	14.45	37.45
5900		10x10				43	7.15	50.15
5950		20x10				38.50	6.40	44.90

B20 Exterior Enclosure

B2010 Exterior Walls

B2010 103 — Fluted Window or Mullion Precast Concrete

	THICKNESS (IN.)	PANEL SIZE (FT.)	FINISHES	RIGID INSULATION (IN)	TYPE	COST PER S.F.		
						MAT.	INST.	TOTAL
6000	7	4x8	smooth gray	none	high rise	30	19.20	49.20
6050		8x8				22.50	14.15	36.65
6100		10x10				44	6.75	50.75
6150		20x10				38.50	5.95	44.45
6200	7	4x8	smooth gray	2	high rise	31.50	19.85	51.35
6250		8x8				23.50	14.80	38.30
6300		10x10				45	7.40	52.40
6350		20x10				39.50	6.60	46.10
6400	8	4x8	smooth gray	none	high rise	30.50	19.50	50
6450		8x8				23	14.50	37.50
6500		10x10				45	7	52
6550		20x10				40.50	6.25	46.75
6600	8	4x8	smooth gray	2	high rise	32	20	52
6650		8x8				24	15.15	39.15
6700		10x10				46.50	7.60	54.10
6750		20x10				41.50	6.90	48.40

B2010 104 — Ribbed Precast Concrete

	THICKNESS (IN.)	PANEL SIZE (FT.)	FINISHES	RIGID INSULATION (IN.)	TYPE	COST PER S.F.		
						MAT.	INST.	TOTAL
6800	4	4x8	aggregate	none	high rise	33.50	18	51.50
6850		8x8				24.50	13.20	37.70
6900		10x10				41.50	4.75	46.25
6950		20x10				37	4.20	41.20
7000	5	4x8	aggregate	none	high rise	34	18.30	52.30
7050		8x8				25	13.50	38.50
7100		10x10				43	4.94	47.94
7150		20x10				38.50	4.41	42.91
7200	6	4x8	aggregate	none	high rise	34.50	18.70	53.20
7250		8x8				26	13.90	39.90
7300		10x10				44.50	5.10	49.60
7350		20x10				40	4.57	44.57
7400	6	4x8	aggregate	2	high rise	36	19.35	55.35
7450		8x8				27	14.55	41.55
7500		10x10				46	5.75	51.75
7550		20x10				41	5.20	46.20
7600	7	4x8	aggregate	none	high rise	35.50	19.15	54.65
7650		8x8				26.50	14.25	40.75
7700		10x10				46	5.25	51.25
7750		20x10				41	4.70	45.70
7800	7	4x8	aggregate	2	high rise	36.50	19.75	56.25
7850		8x8				27.50	14.90	42.40
7900		10x10				47	5.90	52.90
7950		20x10				42.50	5.35	47.85
8000	8	4x8	aggregate	none	high rise	36	19.45	55.45
8050		8x8				27	14.65	41.65
8100		10x10				47.50	5.45	52.95
8150		20x10				43	4.91	47.91
8200	8	4x8	aggregate	2	high rise	37	20	57
8250		8x8				28.50	15.30	43.80
8300		10x10				49	6.10	55.10
8350		20x10				44	5.55	49.55

B20 Exterior Enclosure

B2010 Exterior Walls

B2010 105						Precast Concrete Specialties		

	TYPE	SIZE				COST PER L.F.		
						MAT.	INST.	TOTAL
8400	Coping, precast	6" wide				18.80	13.45	32.25
8450	Stock units	10" wide				20.50	14.40	34.90
8460		12" wide				22.50	15.50	38
8480		14" wide				24.50	16.80	41.30
8500	Window sills	6" wide				13.10	14.40	27.50
8550	Precast	10" wide				17.10	16.80	33.90
8600		14" wide				17.05	20	37.05
8610								

B2010 Exterior Walls

The advantage of tilt up construction is in the low cost of forms and placing of concrete and reinforcing. Tilt up has been used for several types of buildings, including warehouses, stores, offices, and schools. The panels are cast in forms on the ground, or floor slab. Most jobs use 5-1/2″ thick solid reinforced concrete panels.

Design Assumptions:
Conc. f'c = 3000 psi
Reinf. fy = 60,000

B2010 106	Tilt-Up Concrete Panel	COST PER S.F.		
		MAT.	INST.	TOTAL
3200	Tilt-up conc panels, broom finish, 5-1/2″ thick, 3000 PSI	4.15	6.20	10.35
3250	5000 PSI	4.26	6.10	10.36
3300	6″ thick, 3000 PSI	4.58	6.35	10.93
3350	5000 PSI	4.69	6.25	10.94
3400	7-1/2″ thick, 3000 PSI	5.85	6.55	12.40
3450	5000 PSI	6	6.45	12.45
3500	8″ thick, 3000 PSI	6.25	6.70	12.95
3550	5000 PSI	6.45	6.60	13.05
3700	Steel trowel finish, 5-1/2″ thick, 3000 PSI	4.16	6.25	10.41
3750	5000 PSI	4.26	6.15	10.41
3800	6″ thick, 3000 PSI	4.58	6.40	10.98
3850	5000 PSI	4.69	6.30	10.99
3900	7-1/2″ thick, 3000 PSI	5.85	6.65	12.50
3950	5000 PSI	6	6.50	12.50
4000	8″ thick, 3000 PSI	6.25	6.80	13.05
4050	5000 PSI	6.45	6.65	13.10
4200	Exp. aggregate finish, 5-1/2″ thick, 3000 PSI	4.74	6.35	11.09
4250	5000 PSI	4.84	6.20	11.04
4300	6″ thick, 3000 PSI	5.15	6.45	11.60
4350	5000 PSI	5.25	6.35	11.60
4400	7-1/2″ thick, 3000 PSI	6.40	6.70	13.10
4450	5000 PSI	6.60	6.60	13.20
4500	8″ thick, 3000 PSI	6.85	6.85	13.70
4550	5000 PSI	7.05	6.75	13.80
4600	Exposed aggregate & vert. rustication 5-1/2″ thick, 3000 PSI	7	7.80	14.80
4650	5000 PSI	7.10	7.70	14.80
4700	6″ thick, 3000 PSI	7.40	7.95	15.35
4750	5000 PSI	7.50	7.85	15.35
4800	7-1/2″ thick, 3000 PSI	8.65	8.15	16.80
4850	5000 PSI	8.80	8.05	16.85
4900	8″ thick, 3000 PSI	9.10	8.30	17.40
4950	5000 PSI	9.25	8.20	17.45
5000	Vertical rib & light sandblast, 5-1/2″ thick, 3000 PSI	6.55	10.20	16.75
5100	6″ thick, 3000 PSI	6.95	10.35	17.30
5200	7-1/2″ thick, 3000 PSI	8.20	10.65	18.85
5300	8″ thick, 3000 PSI	8.65	10.80	19.45
6000	Broom finish w/2″ polystyrene insulation, 6″ thick, 3000 PSI	3.95	7.65	11.60
6100	Broom finish 2″ fiberplank insulation, 6″ thick, 3000 PSI	4.54	7.55	12.09
6200	Exposed aggregate w/2″ polystyrene insulation, 6″ thick, 3000 PSI	4.42	7.60	12.02
6300	Exposed aggregate 2″ fiberplank insulation, 6″ thick, 3000 PSI	5	7.55	12.55

B2010 Exterior Walls

Exterior concrete block walls are defined in the following terms; structural reinforcement, weight, percent solid, size, strength and insulation. Within each of these categories, two to four variations are shown. No costs are included for brick shelf or relieving angles.

B2010 109 — Concrete Block Wall - Regular Weight

	TYPE	SIZE (IN.)	STRENGTH (P.S.I.)	CORE FILL		COST PER S.F. MAT.	INST.	TOTAL
1200	Hollow	4x8x16	2,000	none		1.94	6.20	8.14
1250			4,500	none		2.39	6.20	8.59
1400		8x8x16	2,000	perlite		4.38	7.50	11.88
1410				styrofoam		4.34	7.10	11.44
1440				none		2.85	7.10	9.95
1450			4,500	perlite		5.10	7.50	12.60
1460				styrofoam		5.05	7.10	12.15
1490				none		3.58	7.10	10.68
2000	75% solid	4x8x16	2,000	none		2.34	6.25	8.59
2100		6x8x16	2,000	perlite		3.59	6.90	10.49
2500	Solid	4x8x16	2,000	none		2.30	6.40	8.70
2700		8x8x16	2,000	none		4.15	7.40	11.55

B2010 110 — Concrete Block Wall - Lightweight

	TYPE	SIZE (IN.)	WEIGHT (P.C.F.)	CORE FILL		COST PER S.F. MAT.	INST.	TOTAL
3100	Hollow	8x4x16	105	perlite		4.20	7.10	11.30
3110				styrofoam		4.16	6.70	10.86
3200		4x8x16	105	none		2.09	6.05	8.14
3250			85	none		2.62	5.90	8.52
3300		6x8x16	105	perlite		3.96	6.80	10.76
3310				styrofoam		4.24	6.45	10.69
3340				none		2.92	6.45	9.37
3400		8x8x16	105	perlite		5.05	7.35	12.40
3410				styrofoam		5	6.95	11.95
3440				none		3.52	6.95	10.47
3450			85	perlite		5.35	7.15	12.50
4000	75% solid	4x8x16	105	none		3.03	6.10	9.13
4050			85	none		3.24	6	9.24
4100		6x8x16	105	perlite		4.80	6.75	11.55
4500	Solid	4x8x16	105	none		1.96	6.30	8.26
4700		8x8x16	105	none		4.29	7.30	11.59

B20 Exterior Enclosure

B2010 Exterior Walls

B2010 111 — Reinforced Concrete Block Wall - Regular Weight

	TYPE	SIZE (IN.)	STRENGTH (P.S.I.)	VERT. REINF & GROUT SPACING		COST PER S.F. MAT.	INST.	TOTAL
5200	Hollow	4x8x16	2,000	#4 @ 48"		2.09	6.90	8.99
5300		6x8x16	2,000	#4 @ 48"		2.79	7.40	10.19
5330				#5 @ 32"		3	7.65	10.65
5340				#5 @ 16"		3.47	8.60	12.07
5350			4,500	#4 @ 28"		3.21	7.40	10.61
5390				#5 @ 16"		3.89	8.60	12.49
5400		8x8x16	2,000	#4 @ 48"		3.23	7.80	11.03
5430				#5 @ 32"		3.40	8.25	11.65
5440				#5 @ 16"		3.94	9.40	13.34
5450			4,500	#4 @ 48"		3.89	7.95	11.84
5490				#5 @ 16"		4.67	9.40	14.07
5500		12x8x16	2,000	#4 @ 48"		4.69	10.05	14.74
5540				#5 @ 16"		5.75	11.60	17.35
6100	75% solid	6x8x16	2,000	#4 @ 48"		3.21	7.30	10.51
6140				#5 @ 16"		3.66	8.35	12.01
6150			4,500	#4 @ 48"		3.76	7.30	11.06
6190				#5 @ 16"		4.21	8.35	12.56
6200		8x8x16	2,000	#4 @ 48"		3.58	7.90	11.48
6230				#5 @ 32"		3.75	8.15	11.90
6240				#5 @ 16"		4.06	9.10	13.16
6250			4,500	#4 @ 48"		4.54	7.90	12.44
6280				#5 @ 32"		4.71	8.15	12.86
6290				#5 @ 16"		5	9.10	14.10
6500	Solid-double Wythe	2-4x8x16	2,000	#4 @ 48" E.W.		5.45	14.50	19.95
6530				#5 @ 16" E.W.		6.20	15.40	21.60
6550			4,500	#4 @ 48" E.W.		7.45	14.30	21.75
6580				#5 @ 16" E.W.		8.20	15.20	23.40

B2010 112 — Reinforced Concrete Block Wall - Lightweight

	TYPE	SIZE (IN.)	WEIGHT (P.C.F.)	VERT REINF. & GROUT SPACING		COST PER S.F. MAT.	INST.	TOTAL
7100	Hollow	8x4x16	105	#4 @ 48"		2.98	7.55	10.53
7140				#5 @ 16"		3.76	9	12.76
7150			85	#4 @ 48"		4.36	7.35	11.71
7190				#5 @ 16"		5.15	8.80	13.95
7400		8x8x16	105	#4 @ 48"		3.83	7.80	11.63
7440				#5 @ 16"		4.61	9.25	13.86
7450			85	#4 @ 48"		4.13	7.60	11.73
7490				#5 @ 16"		4.91	9.05	13.96
7800		8x8x24	105	#4 @ 48"		2.94	8.40	11.34
7840				#5 @ 16"		3.72	9.85	13.57
7850			85	#4 @ 48"		6.65	7.15	13.80
7890				#5 @ 16"		7.45	8.60	16.05
8100	75% solid	6x8x16	105	#4 @ 48"		4.42	7.15	11.57
8130				#5 @ 32"		4.58	7.40	11.98
8150			85	#4 @ 48"		4.38	7	11.38
8180				#5 @ 32"		4.54	7.25	11.79
8200		8x8x16	105	#4 @ 48"		5.30	7.70	13
8230				#5 @ 32"		5.45	7.95	13.40
8250			85	#4 @ 48"		4.86	7.55	12.41
8280				#5 @ 32"		5.05	7.80	12.85

B20 Exterior Enclosure

B2010 Exterior Walls

B2010 112		Reinforced Concrete Block Wall - Lightweight					

	TYPE	SIZE (IN.)	WEIGHT (P.C.F.)	VERT REINF. & GROUT SPACING		COST PER S.F.		
						MAT.	INST.	TOTAL
8500	Solid-double	2-4x8x16	105	#4 @ 48"		4.78	14.30	19.08
8530	Wythe		105	#5 @ 16"		5.50	15.20	20.70
8600		2-6x8x16	105	#4 @ 48"		7.55	15.35	22.90
8630				#5 @ 16"		8.30	16.25	24.55
8650			85	#4 @ 48"		11.20	14.65	25.85

B2010 Exterior Walls

Exterior split ribbed block walls are defined in the following terms; structural reinforcement, weight, percent solid, size, number of ribs and insulation. Within each of these categories two to four variations are shown. No costs are included for brick shelf or relieving angles. Costs include control joints every 20' and horizontal reinforcing.

B2010 113	Split Ribbed Block Wall - Regular Weight							
	TYPE	SIZE (IN.)	RIBS	CORE FILL		COST PER S.F.		
						MAT.	INST.	TOTAL
1220	Hollow	4x8x16	4	none		4.01	7.65	11.66
1250			8	none		4.36	7.65	12.01
1280			16	none		4.70	7.75	12.45
1430		8x8x16	8	perlite		7.30	9.10	16.40
1440				styrofoam		7.10	8.70	15.80
1450				none		5.80	8.70	14.50
1530		12x8x16	8	perlite		9.25	12.15	21.40
1540				styrofoam		8.60	11.30	19.90
1550				none		6.75	11.30	18.05
2120	75% solid	4x8x16	4	none		5.05	7.75	12.80
2150			8	none		5.50	7.75	13.25
2180			16	none		5.95	7.85	13.80
2520	Solid	4x8x16	4	none		5.75	7.85	13.60
2550			8	none		6.75	7.85	14.60
2580			16	none		6.75	8	14.75

B2010 115	Reinforced Split Ribbed Block Wall - Regular Weight							
	TYPE	SIZE (IN.)	RIBS	VERT. REINF. & GROUT SPACING		COST PER S.F.		
						MAT.	INST.	TOTAL
5200	Hollow	4x8x16	4	#4 @ 48"		4.16	8.35	12.51
5230			8	#4 @ 48"		4.51	8.35	12.86
5260			16	#4 @ 48"		4.85	8.45	13.30
5430		8x8x16	8	#4 @ 48"		6.10	9.55	15.65
5440				#5 @ 32"		6.35	9.85	16.20
5450				#5 @ 16"		6.90	11	17.90
5530		12x8x16	8	#4 @ 48"		7.20	12.15	19.35
5540				#5 @ 32"		7.50	12.50	20
5550				#5 @ 16"		8.25	13.70	21.95
6230	75% solid	6x8x16	8	#4 @ 48"		6.45	8.85	15.30
6240				#5 @ 32"		6.65	9.10	15.75
6250				#5 @ 16"		6.90	9.90	16.80

B2010 Exterior Walls

| B2010 115 | | Reinforced Split Ribbed Block Wall - Regular Weight | | | | | |

	TYPE	SIZE (IN.)	RIBS	VERT. REINF. & GROUT SPACING		COST PER S.F.		
						MAT.	INST.	TOTAL
6330		8x8x16	8	#4 @ 48"		7.45	9.50	16.95
6340				#5 @ 32"		7.60	9.75	17.35
6350				#5 @ 16"		7.90	10.70	18.60

B2010 Exterior Walls

Exterior split face block walls are defined in the following terms; structural reinforcement, weight, percent solid, size, scores and insulation. Within each of these categories two to four variations are shown. No costs are included for brick shelf or relieving angles. Costs include control joints every 20′ and horizontal reinforcing.

B2010 117	Split Face Block Wall - Regular Weight							
	TYPE	SIZE (IN.)	SCORES	CORE FILL		COST PER S.F.		
						MAT.	INST.	TOTAL
1200	Hollow	8x4x16	0	perlite		7	10	17
1210				styrofoam		7	9.60	16.60
1240				none		5.50	9.60	15.10
1250			1	perlite		7.40	10	17.40
1260				styrofoam		7.40	9.60	17
1290				none		5.90	9.60	15.50
1300		12x4x16	0	perlite		9.20	11.45	20.65
1310				styrofoam		8.55	10.60	19.15
1340				none		6.70	10.60	17.30
1350			1	perlite		9.70	11.45	21.15
1360				styrofoam		9.05	10.60	19.65
1390				none		7.20	10.60	17.80
1400		4x8x16	0	none		3.65	7.55	11.20
1450			1	none		3.96	7.65	11.61
1500		6x8x16	0	perlite		5.25	8.70	13.95
1510				styrofoam		5.55	8.35	13.90
1540				none		4.23	8.35	12.58
1550			1	perlite		5.65	8.85	14.50
1560				styrofoam		5.90	8.50	14.40
1590				none		4.59	8.50	13.09
1600		8x8x16	0	perlite		6.40	9.35	15.75
1610				styrofoam		6.35	8.95	15.30
1640				none		4.87	8.95	13.82
1650			1	perlite		6.80	9.50	16.30
1660				styrofoam		6.80	9.10	15.90
1690				none		5.30	9.10	14.40
1700		12x8x16	0	perlite		8.30	12.35	20.65
1710				styrofoam		7.65	11.50	19.15
1740				none		5.80	11.50	17.30
1750			1	perlite		8.80	12.55	21.35
1760				styrofoam		8.15	11.70	19.85
1790				none		6.30	11.70	18

B2010 Exterior Walls

| B2010 117 | | | | Split Face Block Wall - Regular Weight | | | | |

	TYPE	SIZE (IN.)	SCORES	CORE FILL		COST PER S.F.		
						MAT.	INST.	TOTAL
1800	75% solid	8x4x16	0	perlite		7.45	9.95	17.40
1840				none		6.70	9.75	16.45
1850			1	perlite		8	9.95	17.95
1890				none		7.25	9.75	17
2000		4x8x16	0	none		4.58	7.65	12.23
2050			1	none		4.98	7.75	12.73
2400	Solid	8x4x16	0	none		7.50	9.95	17.45
2450			1	none		8.10	9.95	18.05
2900		12x8x16	0	none		8.15	11.90	20.05
2950			1	none		8.85	12.15	21

| B2010 119 | | | | Reinforced Split Face Block Wall - Regular Weight | | | | |

	TYPE	SIZE (IN.)	SCORES	VERT. REINF. & GROUT SPACING		COST PER S.F.		
						MAT.	INST.	TOTAL
5200	Hollow	8x4x16	0	#4 @ 48"		5.80	10.45	16.25
5210				#5 @ 32"		6.05	10.75	16.80
5240				#5 @ 16"		6.60	11.90	18.50
5250			1	#4 @ 48"		6.20	10.45	16.65
5260				#5 @ 32"		6.45	10.75	17.20
5290				#5 @ 16"		7	11.90	18.90
5700		12x8x16	0	#4 @ 48"		6.25	12.35	18.60
5710				#5 @ 32"		6.55	12.70	19.25
5740				#5 @ 16"		7.30	13.90	21.20
5750			1	#4 @ 48"		6.75	12.55	19.30
5760				#5 @ 32"		7.05	12.90	19.95
5790				#5 @ 16"		7.80	14.10	21.90
6000	75% solid	8x4x16	0	#4 @ 48"		6.85	10.45	17.30
6010				#5 @ 32"		7	10.70	17.70
6040				#5 @ 16"		7.30	11.65	18.95
6050			1	#4 @ 48"		7.40	10.45	17.85
6060				#5 @ 32"		7.55	10.70	18.25
6090				#5 @ 16"		7.85	11.65	19.50
6100		12x4x16	0	#4 @ 48"		8.35	11.50	19.85
6110				#5 @ 32"		8.60	11.75	20.35
6140				#5 @ 16"		9	12.55	21.55
6150			1	#4 @ 48"		9	11.50	20.50
6160				#5 @ 32"		9.25	11.75	21
6190				#5 @ 16"		9.70	12.75	22.45
6700	Solid-double Wythe	2-4x8x16	0	#4 @ 48" E.W.		11.25	17.20	28.45
6710				#5 @ 32" E.W.		11.55	17.35	28.90
6740				#5 @ 16" E.W.		12	18.10	30.10
6750			1	#4 @ 48" E.W.		12.15	17.40	29.55
6760				#5 @ 32" E.W.		12.45	17.55	30
6790				#5 @ 16" E.W.		12.90	18.30	31.20
6800		2-6x8x16	0	#4 @ 48" E.W.		12.75	19.05	31.80
6810				#5 @ 32" E.W.		13.05	19.20	32.25
6840				#5 @ 16" E.W.		13.50	19.95	33.45
6850			1	#4 @ 48" E.W.		13.85	19.25	33.10
6860				#5 @ 32" E.W.		14.15	19.40	33.55
6890				#5 @ 16" E.W.		14.60	20	34.60

B2010 Exterior Walls

Exterior solid brick walls are defined in the following terms; structural reinforcement, type of brick, thickness, and bond. Nine different types of face bricks are presented, with single wythes shown in four different bonds. Shelf angles are included in system components. These walls do not include ties and as such are not tied to a backup wall.

B2010 125			Solid Brick Walls - Single Wythe					
	TYPE	THICKNESS (IN.)	BOND			COST PER S.F.		
						MAT.	INST.	TOTAL
1000	Common	4	running			5.60	13.95	19.55
1010			common			6.70	15.95	22.65
1050			Flemish			7.40	19.35	26.75
1100			English			8.30	20.50	28.80
1150	Standard	4	running			5.70	14.45	20.15
1160			common			6.70	16.65	23.35
1200			Flemish			7.40	19.90	27.30
1250			English			8.25	21	29.25
1300	Glazed	4	running			19.70	15	34.70
1310			common			23.50	17.45	40.95
1350			Flemish			26	21	47
1400			English			29.50	22.50	52
1600	Economy	4	running			8.05	11.05	19.10
1610			common			9.50	12.65	22.15
1650			Flemish			10.50	15	25.50
1700			English			20.50	15.95	36.45
1900	Fire	4-1/2	running			12.60	12.65	25.25
1910			common			15	14.45	29.45
1950			Flemish			16.60	17.45	34.05
2000			English			18.70	18.35	37.05
2050	King	3-1/2	running			4.30	11.30	15.60
2060			common			4.99	13.05	18.04
2100			Flemish			6	15.60	21.60
2150			English			6.60	16.30	22.90
2200	Roman	4	running			9.45	13.05	22.50
2210			common			11.20	15	26.20
2250			Flemish			12.40	17.85	30.25
2300			English			13.95	19.35	33.30
2350	Norman	4	running			6.65	10.80	17.45
2360			common			7.80	12.25	20.05
2400			Flemish			17.05	14.70	31.75
2450			English			9.70	15.60	25.30

B20 Exterior Enclosure

B2010 Exterior Walls

B2010 125	Solid Brick Walls - Single Wythe							

	TYPE	THICKNESS (IN.)	BOND			COST PER S.F.		
						MAT.	INST.	TOTAL
2500	Norwegian	4	running			6.45	9.60	16.05
2510			common			7.55	10.90	18.45
2550			Flemish			8.35	13.05	21.40
2600			English			9.35	13.70	23.05

B2010 126	Solid Brick Walls - Double Wythe							

	TYPE	THICKNESS (IN.)	COLLAR JOINT THICKNESS (IN.)			COST PER S.F.		
						MAT.	INST.	TOTAL
4100	Common	8	3/4			10.65	23.50	34.15
4150	Standard	8	1/2			10.65	24	34.65
4200	Glazed	8	1/2			38.50	25	63.50
4250	Engineer	8	1/2			9.90	21.50	31.40
4300	Economy	8	3/4			15.45	18.35	33.80
4350	Double	8	3/4			15.35	14.85	30.20
4400	Fire	8	3/4			24.50	21.50	46
4450	King	7	3/4			7.90	18.75	26.65
4500	Roman	8	1			18.15	22	40.15
4550	Norman	8	3/4			12.60	17.95	30.55
4600	Norwegian	8	3/4			12.15	15.90	28.05
4650	Utility	8	3/4			12.30	13.75	26.05
4700	Triple	8	3/4			8.70	12.35	21.05
4750	SCR	12	3/4			16.25	18.35	34.60
4800	Norwegian	12	3/4			14.50	16.20	30.70
4850	Jumbo	12	3/4			12	14.15	26.15

B2010 127	Reinforced Brick Walls							

	TYPE	THICKNESS (IN.)	WYTHE	REINF. & SPACING		COST PER S.F.		
						MAT.	INST.	TOTAL
7200	Common	4"	1	#4 @ 48"vert		5.80	14.50	20.30
7220				#5 @ 32"vert		5.95	14.65	20.60
7230				#5 @ 16"vert		6.20	15.30	21.50
7700	King	9"	2	#4 @ 48" E.W.		8.30	19.65	27.95
7720				#5 @ 32" E.W.		8.60	19.80	28.40
7730				#5 @ 16" E.W.		9.05	20.50	29.55
7800	Common	10"	2	#4 @ 48" E.W.		11.05	24	35.05
7820				#5 @ 32" E.W.		11.35	24.50	35.85
7830				#5 @ 16" E.W.		11.80	25	36.80
7900	Standard	10"	2	#4 @ 48" E.W.		11.05	25	36.05
7920				#5 @ 32" E.W.		11.35	25	36.35
7930				#5 @ 16" E.W.		11.80	25.50	37.30
8100	Economy	10"	2	#4 @ 48" E.W.		15.85	19.25	35.10
8120				#5 @ 32" E.W.		16.15	19.40	35.55
8130				#5 @ 16" E.W.		16.60	20	36.60
8200	Double	10"	2	#4 @ 48" E.W.		15.75	15.75	31.50
8220				#5 @ 32" E.W.		16.05	15.90	31.95
8230				#5 @ 16" E.W.		16.50	16.50	33
8300	Fire	10"	2	#4 @ 48" E.W.		25	22	47
8320				#5 @ 32" E.W.		25	22.50	47.50
8330				#5 @ 16" E.W.		25.50	23	48.50
8400	Roman	10"	2	#4 @ 48" E.W.		18.55	23	41.55
8420				#5 @ 32" E.W.		18.85	23	41.85
8430				#5 @ 16" E.W.		19.30	23.50	42.80

B20 Exterior Enclosure

B2010 Exterior Walls

B2010 127		Reinforced Brick Walls						

	TYPE	THICKNESS (IN.)	WYTHE	REINF. & SPACING		COST PER S.F.		
						MAT.	INST.	TOTAL
8500	Norman	10″	2	#4 @ 48″ E.W.		13	18.85	31.85
8520				#5 @ 32″ E.W.		13.30	19	32.30
8530				#5 @ 16″ E.W.		13.75	19.60	33.35
8600	Norwegian	10″	2	#4 @ 48″ E.W.		12.55	16.80	29.35
8620				#5 @ 32″ E.W.		12.85	16.95	29.80
8630				#5 @ 16″ E.W.		13.30	17.55	30.85
8800	Triple	10″	2	#4 @ 48″ E.W.		9.10	13.25	22.35
8820				#5 @ 32″ E.W.		9.40	13.40	22.80
8830				#5 @ 16″ E.W.		9.85	14	23.85

B2010 Exterior Walls

Stone Veneer

The table below lists costs per S.F. for stone veneer walls on various backup using different stone.

B2010 128	Stone Veneer	MAT.	INST.	TOTAL
2000	Ashlar veneer, 4", 2" x 4" stud backup, 16" O.C., 8' high, low priced stone	14.80	22	36.80
2100	Metal stud backup, 8' high, 16" O.C.	15.55	22	37.55
2150	24" O.C.	15.20	21.50	36.70
2200	Conc. block backup, 4" thick	16.15	26	42.15
2300	6" thick	16.70	26.50	43.20
2350	8" thick	17	27	44
2400	10" thick	17.55	28.50	46.05
2500	12" thick	18.45	30.50	48.95
3100	High priced stone, wood stud backup, 10' high, 16" O.C.	22	25	47
3200	Metal stud backup, 10' high, 16" O.C.	22.50	25.50	48
3250	24" O.C.	22	25	47
3300	Conc. block backup, 10' high, 4" thick	23	29.50	52.50
3350	6" thick	23.50	29.50	53
3400	8" thick	24	30	54
3450	10" thick	24.50	31.50	56
3500	12" thick	25.50	33.50	59
4000	Indiana limestone 2" thick, sawn finish, wood stud backup, 10' high, 16" O.	40.50	13.45	53.95
4100	Metal stud backup, 10' high, 16" O.C.	41.50	13.75	55.25
4150	24" O.C.	41	13.30	54.30
4200	Conc. block backup, 4" thick	42	17.65	59.65
4250	6" thick	42.50	17.90	60.40
4300	8" thick	43	18.50	61.50
4350	10" thick	43.50	19.85	63.35
4400	12" thick	44	22	66
4450	2" thick, smooth finish, wood stud backup, 8' high, 16" O.C.	40.50	13.45	53.95
4550	Metal stud backup, 8' high, 16" O.C.	41.50	13.55	55.05
4600	24" O.C.	41	13.10	54.10
4650	Conc. block backup, 4" thick	42	17.45	59.45
4700	6" thick	42.50	17.70	60.20
4750	8" thick	43	18.30	61.30
4800	10" thick	43.50	19.85	63.35
4850	12" thick	44	22	66
5350	4" thick, smooth finish, wood stud backup, 8' high, 16" O.C.	47	13.45	60.45
5450	Metal stud backup, 8' high, 16" O.C.	48	13.75	61.75
5500	24" O.C.	47.50	13.30	60.80
5550	Conc. block backup, 4" thick	48.50	17.65	66.15
5600	6" thick	49	17.90	66.90
5650	8" thick	49.50	18.50	68

B20 Exterior Enclosure

B2010 Exterior Walls

B2010 128	Stone Veneer	COST PER S.F.		
		MAT.	INST.	TOTAL
5700	10" thick	50	19.85	69.85
5750	12" thick	50.50	22	72.50
6000	Granite, gray or pink, 2" thick, wood stud backup, 8' high, 16" O.C.	33.50	24.50	58
6100	Metal studs, 8' high, 16" O.C.	34.50	25	59.50
6150	24" O.C.	34	24.50	58.50
6200	Conc. block backup, 4" thick	35	28.50	63.50
6250	6" thick	35.50	29	64.50
6300	8" thick	36	29.50	65.50
6350	10" thick	36.50	31	67.50
6400	12" thick	37	33	70
6900	4" thick, wood stud backup, 8' high, 16" O.C.	44.50	28.50	73
7000	Metal studs, 8' high, 16" O.C.	45.50	29	74.50
7050	24" O.C.	45	28.50	73.50
7100	Conc. block backup, 4" thick	46	32.50	78.50
7150	6" thick	46.50	33	79.50
7200	8" thick	47	33.50	80.50
7250	10" thick	47.50	35	82.50
7300	12" thick	48	37	85

B2010 Exterior Walls

Exterior brick veneer/stud backup walls are defined in the following terms; type of brick and studs, stud spacing and bond. All systems include a brick shelf, ties to the backup and all necessary dampproofing and insulation.

B2010 129	Brick Veneer/Wood Stud Backup						
	FACE BRICK	STUD BACKUP	STUD SPACING (IN.)	BOND	FACE	COST PER S.F.		
						MAT.	INST.	TOTAL
1100	Standard	2x4-wood	16	running		7.35	17.10	24.45
1120				common		8.35	19.30	27.65
1140				Flemish		9.05	22.50	31.55
1160				English		9.90	24	33.90
1400		2x6-wood	16	running		7.55	17.25	24.80
1420				common		8.60	19.45	28.05
1440				Flemish		9.30	22.50	31.80
1460				English		10.15	24	34.15
1700	Glazed	2x4-wood	16	running		21.50	17.65	39.15
1720				common		25	20	45
1740				Flemish		27.50	24	51.50
1760				English		31	25	56
2300	Engineer	2x4-wood	16	running		7	15.30	22.30
2320				common		7.90	17.10	25
2340				Flemish		8.50	20	28.50
2360				English		9.30	21	30.30
2900	Roman	2x4-wood	16	running		11.10	15.70	26.80
2920				common		12.85	17.65	30.50
2940				Flemish		14.05	20.50	34.55
2960				English		15.60	22	37.60
4100	Norwegian	2x4-wood	16	running		8.10	12.25	20.35
4120				common		9.20	13.55	22.75
4140				Flemish		10	15.70	25.70
4160				English		11	16.35	27.35

B2010 130	Brick Veneer/Metal Stud Backup						
	FACE BRICK	STUD BACKUP	STUD SPACING (IN.)	BOND	FACE	COST PER S.F.		
						MAT.	INST.	TOTAL
5100	Standard	25ga.x6"NLB	24	running		6.95	16.75	23.70
5120				common		8	18.95	26.95
5140				Flemish		8.30	21.50	29.80
5160				English		9.55	23.50	33.05
5200		20ga.x3-5/8"NLB	16	running		7.05	17.40	24.45
5220				common		8.10	19.60	27.70
5240				Flemish		8.80	23	31.80
5260				English		9.65	24	33.65

B2010 Exterior Walls

B2010 130	Brick Veneer/Metal Stud Backup

	FACE BRICK	STUD BACKUP	STUD SPACING (IN.)	BOND	FACE	COST PER S.F.		
						MAT.	INST.	TOTAL
5400	Standard	16ga.x3-5/8"LB	16	running		7.80	17.65	25.45
5420				common		8.85	19.85	28.70
5440				Flemish		9.55	23	32.55
5460				English		10.40	24.50	34.90
5500			24	running		7.45	17.20	24.65
5520				common		8.50	19.40	27.90
5540				Flemish		9.20	22.50	31.70
5560				English		10.05	24	34.05
5700	Glazed	25ga.x6"NLB	24	running		21	17.30	38.30
5720				common		24.50	19.75	44.25
5740				Flemish		27	23.50	50.50
5760				English		30.50	25	55.50
5800		20ga.x3-5/8"NLB	24	running		21	17.45	38.45
5820				common		24.50	19.90	44.40
5840				Flemish		27	23.50	50.50
5860				English		30.50	25	55.50
6000		16ga.x3-5/8"LB	16	running		22	18.20	40.20
6020				common		25.50	20.50	46
6040				Flemish		28	24.50	52.50
6060				English		31.50	25.50	57
6300	Engineer	25ga.x6"NLB	24	running		6.60	14.95	21.55
6320				common		7.50	16.75	24.25
6340				Flemish		8.15	19.75	27.90
6360				English		8.95	20.50	29.45
6400		20ga.x3-5/8"NLB	16	running		6.70	15.60	22.30
6420				common		7.60	17.40	25
6440				Flemish		8.25	20.50	28.75
6460				English		9.05	21.50	30.55
6900	Roman	25ga.x6"NLB	24	running		10.75	15.35	26.10
6920				common		12.50	17.20	29.70
6940				Flemish		13.70	20	33.70
6960				English		15.25	21.50	36.75
7000		20ga.x3-5/8"NLB	16	running		10.85	16	26.85
7020				common		12.60	17.95	30.55
7040				Flemish		13.80	21	34.80
7060				English		15.35	22.50	37.85
7500	Norman	25ga.x6"NLB	24	running		7.95	13.10	21.05
7520				common		9.10	14.55	23.65
7540				Flemish		18.35	17	35.35
7560				English		11	17.90	28.90
7600		20ga.x3-5/8"NLB	24	running		7.90	13.25	21.15
7620				common		9.05	14.70	23.75
7640				Flemish		18.30	17.15	35.45
7660				English		10.95	18.05	29
8100	Norwegian	25ga.x6"NLB	24	running		7.75	11.90	19.65
8120				common		8.85	13.20	22.05
8140				Flemish		9.65	15.35	25
8160				English		10.65	16	26.65
8400		16ga.x3-5/8"LB	16	running		8.60	12.80	21.40
8420				common		9.70	14.10	23.80
8440				Flemish		10.50	16.25	26.75
8460				English		11.50	16.90	28.40

B2010 Exterior Walls

Brick Face Composite Wall

B2010 132		Brick Face Composite Wall - Double Wythe						
	FACE BRICK	BACKUP MASONRY	BACKUP THICKNESS (IN.)	BACKUP CORE FILL		COST PER S.F.		
						MAT.	INST.	TOTAL
1000	Standard	common brick	4	none		10.45	26.50	36.95
1040		SCR brick	6	none		13.35	23.50	36.85
1080		conc. block	4	none		8	21.50	29.50
1120			6	perlite		9.60	22	31.60
1160				styrofoam		9.85	21.50	31.35
1200			8	perlite		10.40	22.50	32.90
1240				styrofoam		10.35	22	32.35
1520		glazed block	4	none		17.05	22.50	39.55
1560			6	perlite		18.95	23.50	42.45
1600				styrofoam		19.20	23	42.20
1640			8	perlite		20	24	44
1680				styrofoam		20	23.50	43.50
1720		clay tile	4	none		12.25	20.50	32.75
1760			6	none		14.35	21	35.35
1800			8	none		16.30	21.50	37.80
1840		glazed tile	4	none		19.40	27	46.40
1880								
2000	Glazed	common brick	4	none		24.50	27	51.50
2040		SCR brick	6	none		27.50	24	51.50
2080		conc. block	4	none		22	22	44
2200			8	perlite		24.50	23	47.50
2240				styrofoam		24.50	22.50	47
2280		L.W. block	4	none		22	21.50	43.50
2400			8	perlite		25	23	48
2520		glazed block	4	none		31	23.50	54.50
2560			6	perlite		33	24	57
2600				styrofoam		33	23.50	56.50
2640			8	perlite		34	24.50	58.50
2680				styrofoam		34	24	58

B2010 Exterior Walls

B2010 132	Brick Face Composite Wall - Double Wythe

	FACE BRICK	BACKUP MASONRY	BACKUP THICKNESS (IN.)	BACKUP CORE FILL		COST PER S.F.		
						MAT.	INST.	TOTAL
2720	Glazed	clay tile	4	none		26.50	21	47.50
2760			6	none		28.50	21.50	50
2800			8	none		30.50	22.50	53
2840		glazed tile	4	none		33.50	27.50	61
3000	Engineer	common brick	4	none		10.10	24.50	34.60
3040		SCR brick	6	none		12.95	22	34.95
3080		conc. block	4	none		7.60	19.50	27.10
3200			8	perlite		10	20.50	30.50
3280		L.W. block	4	none		5.95	13.80	19.75
3320			6	perlite		9.60	20	29.60
3520		glazed block	4	none		16.65	21	37.65
3560			6	perlite		18.55	21.50	40.05
3600				styrofoam		18.85	21.50	40.35
3640			8	perlite		19.85	22	41.85
3680				styrofoam		19.80	22	41.80
3720		clay tile	4	none		11.85	18.65	30.50
3800			8	none		15.90	19.95	35.85
3840		glazed tile	4	none		19	25	44
4000	Roman	common brick	4	none		14.25	25	39.25
4040		SCR brick	6	none		17.10	22	39.10
4080		conc. block	4	none		11.75	19.90	31.65
4120			6	perlite		13.35	20.50	33.85
4200			8	perlite		14.15	21	35.15
5000	Norman	common brick	4	none		11.45	23	34.45
5040		SCR brick	6	none		14.30	19.95	34.25
5280		L.W. block	4	none		9.10	17.50	26.60
5320			6	perlite		10.95	18.35	29.30
5720		clay tile	4	none		13.20	16.80	30
5760			6	none		15.30	17.35	32.65
5840		glazed tile	4	none		20.50	23.50	44
6000	Norwegian	common brick	4	none		11.25	21.50	32.75
6040		SCR brick	6	none		14.10	18.75	32.85
6080		conc. block	4	none		8.75	16.45	25.20
6120			6	perlite		10.35	17.25	27.60
6160				styrofoam		10.65	16.90	27.55
6200			8	perlite		11.15	17.75	28.90
6520		glazed block	4	none		17.80	17.90	35.70
6560			6	perlite		19.70	18.60	38.30
7000	Utility	common brick	4	none		11.30	20.50	31.80
7040		SCR brick	6	none		14.15	17.60	31.75
7080		conc. block	4	none		8.80	15.30	24.10
7120			6	perlite		10.40	16.10	26.50
7160				styrofoam		10.70	15.75	26.45
7200			8	perlite		11.20	16.60	27.80
7240				styrofoam		11.15	16.15	27.30
7280		L.W. block	4	none		8.95	15.15	24.10
7320			6	perlite		10.80	15.90	26.70
7520		glazed block	4	none		17.85	16.75	34.60
7560			6	perlite		19.75	17.45	37.20
7720		clay tile	4	none		13.05	14.45	27.50
7760			6	none		15.15	15	30.15
7840		glazed tile	4	none		20	21	41

B20 Exterior Enclosure

B2010 Exterior Walls

B2010 133		Brick Face Composite Wall - Triple Wythe							
	FACE BRICK	MIDDLE WYTHE	INSIDE MASONRY	TOTAL THICKNESS (IN.)		COST PER S.F.			
						MAT.	INST.	TOTAL	
8000	Standard	common brick	standard brick	12		15.30	38	53.30	
8100		4" conc. brick	standard brick	12		14.70	39	53.70	
8120		4" conc. brick	common brick	12		14.60	38.50	53.10	
8200	Glazed	common brick	standard brick	12		29.50	38.50	68	
8300		4" conc. brick	standard brick	12		28.50	39.50	68	
8320		4" conc. brick	glazed brick	12		28.50	39	67.50	

B2010 Exterior Walls

Brick Face Cavity Wall

B2010 134				Brick Face Cavity Wall				
	FACE BRICK	BACKUP MASONRY	TOTAL THICKNESS (IN.)	CAVITY INSULATION		COST PER S.F.		
						MAT.	INST.	TOTAL
1000	Standard	4" common brick	10	polystyrene		10.35	26.50	36.85
1020				none		10.10	26	36.10
1040		6" SCR brick	12	polystyrene		13.25	23.50	36.75
1060				none		13	23	36
1080		4" conc. block	10	polystyrene		7.90	21.50	29.40
1100				none		7.60	20.50	28.10
1120		6" conc. block	12	polystyrene		8.45	22	30.45
1140				none		8.20	21	29.20
1160		4" L.W. block	10	polystyrene		8.05	21	29.05
1180				none		7.75	20.50	28.25
1200		6" L.W. block	12	polystyrene		8.85	21.50	30.35
1220				none		8.60	21	29.60
1240		4" glazed block	10	polystyrene		16.95	23	39.95
1260				none		16.70	22	38.70
1280		6" glazed block	12	polystyrene		16.95	23	39.95
1300				none		16.70	22	38.70
1320		4" clay tile	10	polystyrene		12.15	20.50	32.65
1340				none		11.90	19.80	31.70
1360		4" glazed tile	10	polystyrene		19.30	27	46.30
1380				none		19.05	26.50	45.55
1500	Glazed	4" common brick	10	polystyrene		24.50	27	51.50
1520				none		24	26.50	50.50
1580		4" conc. block	10	polystyrene		22	22	44
1600				none		21.50	21	42.50
1660		4" L.W. block	10	polystyrene		22	22	44
1680				none		22	21	43
1740		4" glazed block	10	polystyrene		31	23.50	54.50
1760				none		30.50	22.50	53
1820		4" clay tile	10	polystyrene		26	21	47
1840				none		26	20.50	46.50
1860		4" glazed tile	10	polystyrene		28.50	21.50	50
1880				none		28	21	49
2000	Engineer	4" common brick	10	polystyrene		10	25	35
2020				none		9.75	24	33.75
2080		4" conc. block	10	polystyrene		7.50	19.55	27.05
2100				none		7.25	18.85	26.10

B2010 Exterior Walls

B2010 134	Brick Face Cavity Wall

	FACE BRICK	BACKUP MASONRY	TOTAL THICKNESS (IN.)	CAVITY INSULATION		COST PER S.F.		
						MAT.	INST.	TOTAL
2160	Engineer	4" L.W. block	10	polystyrene		7.65	19.40	27.05
2180				none		7.40	18.70	26.10
2240		4" glazed block	10	polystyrene		16.55	21	37.55
2260				none		16.30	20.50	36.80
2320		4" clay tile	10	polystyrene		11.75	18.70	30.45
2340				none		11.50	18	29.50
2360		4" glazed tile	10	polystyrene		18.90	25.50	44.40
2380				none		18.65	24.50	43.15
2500	Roman	4" common brick	10	polystyrene		14.15	25	39.15
2520				none		13.90	24.50	38.40
2580		4" conc. block	10	polystyrene		11.65	19.95	31.60
2600				none		11.40	19.25	30.65
2660		4" L.W. block	10	polystyrene		11.80	19.80	31.60
2680				none		11.55	19.10	30.65
2740		4" glazed block	10	polystyrene		20.50	21.50	42
2760				none		20.50	20.50	41
2820		4" clay tile	10	polystyrene		15.90	19.10	35
2840				none		15.65	18.40	34.05
2860		4" glazed tile	10	polystyrene		23	25.50	48.50
2880				none		23	25	48
3000	Norman	4" common brick	10	polystyrene		11.35	23	34.35
3020				none		11.10	22	33.10
3080		4" conc. block	10	polystyrene		8.85	17.70	26.55
3100				none		8.60	17	25.60
3160		4" L.W. block	10	polystyrene		9	17.55	26.55
3180				none		8.75	16.85	25.60
3240		4" glazed block	10	polystyrene		17.90	19.15	37.05
3260				none		17.65	18.45	36.10
3320		4" clay tile	10	polystyrene		13.10	16.85	29.95
3340				none		12.85	16.15	29
3360		4" glazed tile	10	polystyrene		20.50	23.50	44
3380				none		20	22.50	42.50
3500	Norwegian	4" common brick	10	polystyrene		11.15	21.50	32.65
3520				none		10.90	21	31.90
3580		4" conc. block	10	polystyrene		8.65	16.50	25.15
3600				none		8.40	15.80	24.20
3660		4" L.W. block	10	polystyrene		8.80	16.35	25.15
3680				none		8.55	15.65	24.20
3740		4" glazed block	10	polystyrene		17.70	17.95	35.65
3760				none		17.45	17.25	34.70
3820		4" clay tile	10	polystyrene		12.90	15.65	28.55
3840				none		12.65	14.95	27.60
3860		4" glazed tile	10	polystyrene		20	22	42
3880				none		19.80	21.50	41.30
4000	Utility	4" common brick	10	polystyrene		11.20	20.50	31.70
4020				none		10.95	19.85	30.80
4080		4" conc. block	10	polystyrene		8.70	15.35	24.05
4100				none		8.45	14.65	23.10
4160		4" L.W. block	10	polystyrene		8.85	15.20	24.05
4180				none		8.60	14.50	23.10
4240		4" glazed block	10	polystyrene		17.75	16.80	34.55
4260				none		17.50	16.10	33.60

B2010 Exterior Walls

B2010 134 — Brick Face Cavity Wall

	FACE BRICK	BACKUP MASONRY	TOTAL THICKNESS (IN.)	CAVITY INSULATION		COST PER S.F.		
						MAT.	INST.	TOTAL
4320	Utility	4" clay tile	10	polystyrene		12.95	14.50	27.45
4340				none		12.70	13.80	26.50
4360		4" glazed tile	10	polystyrene		20	21	41
4380				none		19.85	20.50	40.35

B2010 135 — Brick Face Cavity Wall - Insulated Backup

	FACE BRICK	BACKUP MASONRY	TOTAL THICKNESS (IN.)	BACKUP CORE FILL		COST PER S.F.		
						MAT.	INST.	TOTAL
5100	Standard	6" conc. block	10	perlite		9.20	21.50	30.70
5120				styrofoam		9.50	21	30.50
5180		6" L.W. block	10	perlite		9.60	21.50	31.10
5200				styrofoam		9.90	21	30.90
5260		6" glazed block	10	perlite		18.55	23	41.55
5280				styrofoam		18.85	22.50	41.35
5340		6" clay tile	10	none		14	20.50	34.50
5360		8" clay tile	12	none		15.95	21	36.95
5600	Glazed	6" conc. block	10	perlite		23	22	45
5620				styrofoam		23.50	21.50	45
5680		6" L.W. block	10	perlite		23.50	22	45.50
5700				styrofoam		24	21.50	45.50
5760		6" glazed block	10	perlite		32.50	23.50	56
5780				styrofoam		33	23	56
5840		6" clay tile	10	none		28	21	49
5860		8" clay tile	8	none		30	21.50	51.50
6100	Engineer	6" conc. block	10	perlite		8.85	19.65	28.50
6120				styrofoam		9.15	19.30	28.45
6180		6" L.W. block	10	perlite		9.25	19.45	28.70
6200				styrofoam		9.50	19.10	28.60
6260		6" glazed block	10	perlite		18.20	21	39.20
6280				styrofoam		18.50	20.50	39
6340		6" clay tile	10	none		13.60	18.55	32.15
6360		8" clay tile	12	none		15.60	19.30	34.90
6600	Roman	6" conc. block	10	perlite		13	20	33
6620				styrofoam		13.25	19.70	32.95
6680		6" L.W. block	10	perlite		13.40	19.85	33.25
6700				styrofoam		13.65	19.50	33.15
6760		6" glazed block	10	perlite		22.50	21.50	44
6780				styrofoam		22.50	21	43.50
6840		6" clay tile	10	none		17.75	18.95	36.70
6860		8" clay tile	12	none		19.75	19.70	39.45
7100	Norman	6" conc. block	10	perlite		10.20	17.80	28
7120				styrofoam		10.45	17.45	27.90
7180		6" L.W. block	10	perlite		10.60	17.60	28.20
7200				styrofoam		10.85	17.25	28.10
7260		6" glazed block	10	perlite		19.55	19.15	38.70
7280				styrofoam		19.80	18.80	38.60
7340		6" clay tile	10	none		14.95	16.70	31.65
7360		8" clay tile	12	none		16.95	17.45	34.40
7600	Norwegian	6" conc. block	10	perlite		10	16.60	26.60
7620				styrofoam		10.25	16.25	26.50
7680		6" L.W. block	10	perlite		10.40	16.40	26.80
7700				styrofoam		10.65	16.05	26.70

B20 Exterior Enclosure

B2010 Exterior Walls

| B2010 135 | Brick Face Cavity Wall - Insulated Backup |

	FACE BRICK	BACKUP MASONRY	TOTAL THICKNESS (IN.)	BACKUP CORE FILL		COST PER S.F.		
						MAT.	INST.	TOTAL
7760	Norwegian	6" glazed block	10	perlite		19.35	17.95	37.30
7780				styrofoam		19.60	17.60	37.20
7840		6" clay tile	10	none		14.75	15.50	30.25
7860		8" clay tile	12	none		16.75	16.25	33
8100	Utility	6" conc. block	10	perlite		10.05	15.45	25.50
8120				styrofoam		10.30	15.10	25.40
8180		6" L.W. block	10	perlite		10.45	15.25	25.70
8200				styrofoam		10.70	14.90	25.60
8220		8" L.W. block	12	perlite		11.55	15.80	27.35
8240				styrofoam		11.50	15.35	26.85
8260		6" glazed block	10	perlite		19.40	16.80	36.20
8280				styrofoam		19.65	16.45	36.10
8300		8" glazed block	12	perlite		20.50	17.40	37.90
8340		6" clay tile	10	none		14.80	14.35	29.15
8360		8" clay tile	12	none		16.80	15.10	31.90

B2010 Exterior Walls

Glass Block

B2010 140	Glass Block	COST PER S.F.		
		MAT.	INST.	TOTAL
2300	Glass block 4" thick, 6"x6" plain, under 1,000 S.F.	32	25	57
2400	1,000 to 5,000 S.F.	31.50	21.50	53
2500	Over 5,000 S.F.	30.50	20.50	51
2600	Solar reflective, under 1,000 S.F.	45	34	79
2700	1,000 to 5,000 S.F.	44.50	29	73.50
2800	Over 5,000 S.F.	43	27.50	70.50
3500	8"x8" plain, under 1,000 S.F.	18.50	18.60	37.10
3600	1,000 to 5,000 S.F.	18.15	16.10	34.25
3700	Over 5,000 S.F.	17.60	14.50	32.10
3800	Solar reflective, under 1,000 S.F.	26	25	51
3900	1,000 to 5,000 S.F.	25.50	21.50	47
4000	Over 5,000 S.F.	24.50	19.30	43.80
5000	12"x12" plain, under 1,000 S.F.	26	17.25	43.25
5100	1,000 to 5,000 S.F.	25.50	14.50	40
5200	Over 5,000 S.F.	25	13.25	38.25
5300	Solar reflective, under 1,000 S.F.	36.50	23	59.50
5400	1,000 to 5,000 S.F.	36	19.30	55.30
5600	Over 5,000 S.F.	35	17.55	52.55
5800	3" thinline, 6"x6" plain, under 1,000 S.F.	23	25	48
5900	Over 5,000 S.F.	22	20.50	42.50
6000	Solar reflective, under 1,000 S.F.	32.50	34	66.50
6100	Over 5,000 S.F.	31	27.50	58.50
6200	8"x8" plain, under 1,000 S.F.	13.20	18.60	31.80
6300	Over 5,000 S.F.	12.60	14.50	27.10
6400	Solar reflective, under 1,000 S.F.	18.40	25	43.40
6500	Over 5,000 S.F.	17.55	19.30	36.85

B2010 Exterior Walls

Metal Siding

The table below lists costs for metal siding of various descriptions, not including the steel frame, or the structural steel, of a building. Costs are per S.F. including all accessories and insulation.

B2010 146	Metal Siding Panel	COST PER S.F.		
		MAT.	INST.	TOTAL
1400	Metal siding aluminum panel, corrugated, .024" thick, natural	2.98	4.10	7.08
1450	Painted	3.16	4.10	7.26
1500	.032" thick, natural	3.33	4.10	7.43
1550	Painted	3.92	4.10	8.02
1600	Ribbed 4" pitch, .032" thick, natural	3.26	4.10	7.36
1650	Painted	3.96	4.10	8.06
1700	.040" thick, natural	3.75	4.10	7.85
1750	Painted	4.29	4.10	8.39
1800	.050" thick, natural	4.22	4.10	8.32
1850	Painted	4.78	4.10	8.88
1900	8" pitch panel, .032" thick, natural	3.11	3.93	7.04
1950	Painted	3.79	3.95	7.74
2000	.040" thick, natural	3.60	3.96	7.56
2050	Painted	4.12	3.99	8.11
2100	.050" thick, natural	4.07	3.97	8.04
2150	Painted	4.65	4.01	8.66
3000	Steel, corrugated or ribbed, 29 Ga., .0135" thick, galvanized	2.17	3.74	5.91
3050	Colored	3.06	3.79	6.85
3100	26 Ga., .0179" thick, galvanized	2.25	3.76	6.01
3150	Colored	3.16	3.81	6.97
3200	24 Ga., .0239" thick, galvanized	2.83	3.78	6.61
3250	Colored	3.56	3.83	7.39
3300	22 Ga., .0299" thick, galvanized	2.86	3.80	6.66
3350	Colored	4.29	3.85	8.14
3400	20 Ga., .0359" thick, galvanized	2.86	3.80	6.66
3450	Colored	4.56	4.07	8.63
4100	Sandwich panels, factory fab., 1" polystyrene, steel core, 26 Ga., galv.	5.75	5.90	11.65
4200	Colored, 1 side	7.05	5.90	12.95
4300	2 sides	9.05	5.90	14.95
4400	2" polystyrene, steel core, 26 Ga., galvanized	6.80	5.90	12.70
4500	Colored, 1 side	8.10	5.90	14
4600	2 sides	10.10	5.90	16
4700	22 Ga., baked enamel exterior	13.40	6.25	19.65
4800	Polyvinyl chloride exterior	14.10	6.25	20.35
5100	Textured aluminum, 4' x 8' x 5/16" plywood backing, single face	4.48	3.57	8.05
5200	Double face	5.80	3.57	9.37

B2010 Exterior Walls

Exterior Wall Siding

The table below lists costs per S.F. for exterior walls with wood siding. A variety of systems are presented using both wood and metal studs at 16″ and 24″ O.C.

B2010 148	Panel, Shingle & Lap Siding	COST PER S.F.		
		MAT.	INST.	TOTAL
1400	Wood siding w/2″ x 4″ studs, 16″ O.C., insul. wall, 5/8″ text 1-11 fir plyw	3.64	5.80	9.44
1450	5/8″ text 1-11 cedar plywood	4.58	5.60	10.18
1500	1″ x 4″ vert T.&G. redwood	4.70	6.70	11.40
1600	1″ x 8″ vert T.&G. redwood	6.40	5.85	12.25
1650	1″ x 5″ rabbetted cedar bev. siding	6.45	6.05	12.50
1700	1″ x 6″ cedar drop siding	6.55	6.05	12.60
1750	1″ x 12″ rough sawn cedar	3.27	5.85	9.12
1800	1″ x 12″ sawn cedar, 1″ x 4″ battens	6.70	5.45	12.15
1850	1″ x 10″ redwood shiplap siding	6.45	5.60	12.05
1900	18″ no. 1 red cedar shingles, 5-1/2″ exposed	4.49	7.65	12.14
1950	6″ exposed	4.30	7.40	11.70
2000	6-1/2″ exposed	4.12	7.15	11.27
2100	7″ exposed	3.93	6.90	10.83
2150	7-1/2″ exposed	3.75	6.65	10.40
3000	8″ wide aluminum siding	4.26	5.20	9.46
3150	8″ plain vinyl siding	2.85	5.30	8.15
3250	8″ insulated vinyl siding	3.18	5.85	9.03
3300				
3400	2″ x 6″ studs, 16″ O.C., insul. wall, w/ 5/8″ text 1-11 fir plywood	4.03	5.95	9.98
3500	5/8″ text 1-11 cedar plywood	4.97	5.95	10.92
3600	1″ x 4″ vert T.&G. redwood	5.10	6.85	11.95
3700	1″ x 8″ vert T.&G. redwood	6.80	6	12.80
3800	1″ x 5″ rabbetted cedar bev siding	6.85	6.20	13.05
3900	1″ x 6″ cedar drop siding	6.95	6.25	13.20
4000	1″ x 12″ rough sawn cedar	3.66	6	9.66
4200	1″ x 12″ sawn cedar, 1″ x 4″ battens	7.10	5.65	12.75
4500	1″ x 10″ redwood shiplap siding	6.85	5.80	12.65
4550	18″ no. 1 red cedar shingles, 5-1/2″ exposed	4.88	7.80	12.68
4600	6″ exposed	4.69	7.55	12.24
4650	6-1/2″ exposed	4.51	7.30	11.81
4700	7″ exposed	4.32	7.05	11.37
4750	7-1/2″ exposed	4.14	6.80	10.94
4800	8″ wide aluminum siding	4.65	5.35	10
4850	8″ plain vinyl siding	3.24	5.45	8.69
4900	8″ insulated vinyl siding	3.57	6	9.57
4910				
5000	2″ x 6″ studs, 24″ O.C., insul. wall, 5/8″ text 1-11, fir plywood	3.87	5.60	9.47
5050	5/8″ text 1-11 cedar plywood	4.81	5.60	10.41
5100	1″ x 4″ vert T.&G. redwood	4.93	6.50	11.43
5150	1″ x 8″ vert T.&G. redwood	6.65	5.65	12.30

B2010 Exterior Walls

B2010 148	Panel, Shingle & Lap Siding	COST PER S.F.		
		MAT.	INST.	TOTAL
5200	1" x 5" rabbetted cedar bev siding	6.70	5.85	12.55
5250	1" x 6" cedar drop siding	6.80	5.90	12.70
5300	1" x 12" rough sawn cedar	3.50	5.65	9.15
5400	1" x 12" sawn cedar, 1" x 4" battens	6.95	5.30	12.25
5450	1" x 10" redwood shiplap siding	6.65	5.45	12.10
5500	18" no. 1 red cedar shingles, 5-1/2" exposed	4.72	7.45	12.17
5550	6" exposed	4.53	7.20	11.73
5650	7" exposed	4.16	6.70	10.86
5700	7-1/2" exposed	3.98	6.45	10.43
5750	8" wide aluminum siding	4.49	5	9.49
5800	8" plain vinyl siding	3.08	5.10	8.18
5850	8" insulated vinyl siding	3.41	5.65	9.06
5900	3-5/8" metal studs, 16 Ga., 16" O.C. insul. wall, 5/8" text 1-11 fir plywoo	4.43	6.10	10.53
5950	5/8" text 1-11 cedar plywood	5.35	6.10	11.45
6000	1" x 4" vert T.&G. redwood	5.50	7	12.50
6050	1" x 8" vert T.&G. redwood	7.20	6.15	13.35
6100	1" x 5" rabbetted cedar bev siding	7.25	6.35	13.60
6150	1" x 6" cedar drop siding	7.35	6.40	13.75
6200	1" x 12" rough sawn cedar	4.06	6.15	10.21
6250	1" x 12" sawn cedar, 1" x 4" battens	7.50	5.75	13.25
6300	1" x 10" redwood shiplap siding	7.25	5.95	13.20
6350	18" no. 1 red cedar shingles, 5-1/2" exposed	5.30	7.95	13.25
6500	6" exposed	5.10	7.70	12.80
6550	6-1/2" exposed	4.91	7.45	12.36
6600	7" exposed	4.72	7.20	11.92
6650	7-1/2" exposed	4.72	7	11.72
6700	8" wide aluminum siding	5.05	5.50	10.55
6750	8" plain vinyl siding	3.64	5.40	9.04
6800	8" insulated vinyl siding	3.97	5.95	9.92
7000	3-5/8" metal studs, 16 Ga. 24" O.C. insul wall, 5/8" text 1-11 fir plywood	4.08	5.40	9.48
7050	5/8" text 1-11 cedar plywood	5	5.40	10.40
7100	1" x 4" vert T.&G. redwood	5.15	6.50	11.65
7150	1" x 8" vert T.&G. redwood	6.85	5.65	12.50
7200	1" x 5" rabbetted cedar bev siding	6.90	5.85	12.75
7250	1" x 6" cedar drop siding	7	5.90	12.90
7300	1" x 12" rough sawn cedar	3.71	5.65	9.36
7350	1" x 12" sawn cedar 1" x 4" battens	7.15	5.30	12.45
7400	1" x 10" redwood shiplap siding	6.90	5.45	12.35
7450	18" no. 1 red cedar shingles, 5-1/2" exposed	5.10	7.70	12.80
7500	6" exposed	4.93	7.45	12.38
7550	6-1/2" exposed	4.74	7.20	11.94
7600	7" exposed	4.56	6.95	11.51
7650	7-1/2" exposed	4.19	6.45	10.64
7700	8" wide aluminum siding	4.70	5	9.70
7750	8" plain vinyl siding	3.29	5.10	8.39
7800	8" insul. vinyl siding	3.62	5.65	9.27

B2010 Exterior Walls

The table below lists costs for some typical stucco walls including all the components as demonstrated in the component block below. Prices are presented for backup walls using wood studs, metal studs and CMU.

Exterior Stucco Wall

B2010 151	Stucco Wall	COST PER S.F.		
		MAT.	INST.	TOTAL
2100	Cement stucco, 7/8" th., plywood sheathing, stud wall, 2" x 4", 16" O.C.	2.85	9.40	12.25
2200	24" O.C.	2.75	9.15	11.90
2300	2" x 6", 16" O.C.	3.24	9.60	12.84
2400	24" O.C.	3.08	9.25	12.33
2500	No sheathing, metal lath on stud wall, 2" x 4", 16" O.C.	1.97	8.20	10.17
2600	24" O.C.	1.87	7.90	9.77
2700	2" x 6", 16" O.C.	2.36	8.35	10.71
2800	24" O.C.	2.20	8	10.20
2900	1/2" gypsum sheathing, 3-5/8" metal studs, 16" O.C.	3.02	8.55	11.57
2950	24" O.C.	2.67	8.05	10.72
3000	Cement stucco, 5/8" th., 2 coats on std. CMU block, 8"x 16", 8" thick	3.27	11.50	14.77
3100	10" thick	4.55	11.80	16.35
3200	12" thick	4.69	13.55	18.24
3300	Std. light Wt. block 8" x 16", 8" thick	3.91	11.30	15.21
3400	10" thick	4.58	11.60	16.18
3500	12" thick	4.80	13.30	18.10
3600	3 coat stucco, self furring metal lath 3.4 Lb/SY, on 8" x 16", 8" thick	3.32	12.15	15.47
3700	10" thick	4.60	12.45	17.05
3800	12" thick	4.74	14.20	18.94
3900	Lt. Wt. block, 8" thick	3.96	11.95	15.91
4000	10" thick	4.63	12.25	16.88
4100	12" thick	4.85	13.95	18.80

B2010 152	E.I.F.S.	COST PER S.F.		
		MAT.	INST.	TOTAL
5100	E.I.F.S., plywood sheathing, stud wall, 2" x 4", 16" O.C., 1" EPS	3.88	9.50	13.38
5110	2" EPS	4.14	9.50	13.64
5120	3" EPS	4.41	9.50	13.91
5130	4" EPS	4.67	9.50	14.17
5140	2" x 6", 16" O.C., 1" EPS	4.27	9.70	13.97
5150	2" EPS	4.53	9.70	14.23
5160	3" EPS	4.80	9.70	14.50
5170	4" EPS	5.05	9.70	14.75
5180	Cement board sheathing, 3-5/8" metal studs, 16" O.C., 1" EPS	4.66	11.75	16.41
5190	2" EPS	4.92	11.75	16.67
5200	3" EPS	5.20	11.75	16.95
5210	4" EPS	6.25	11.75	18
5220	6" metal studs, 16" O.C., 1" EPS	5.20	11.80	17
5230	2" EPS	5.45	11.80	17.25

B20 Exterior Enclosure

B2010 Exterior Walls

B2010 152	E.I.F.S.	COST PER S.F.		
		MAT.	INST.	TOTAL
5240	3″ EPS	5.75	11.80	17.55
5250	4″ EPS	6.80	11.80	18.60
5260	CMU block, 8″ x 8″ x 16″, 1″ EPS	4.90	13.55	18.45
5270	2″ EPS	5.15	13.55	18.70
5280	3″ EPS	5.45	13.55	19
5290	4″ EPS	5.70	13.55	19.25
5300	8″ x 10″ x 16″, 1″ EPS	6.20	13.85	20.05
5310	2″ EPS	6.45	13.85	20.30
5320	3″ EPS	6.70	13.85	20.55
5330	4″ EPS	6.95	13.85	20.80
5340	8″ x 12″ x 16″, 1″ EPS	6.30	15.60	21.90
5350	2″ EPS	6.60	15.60	22.20
5360	3″ EPS	6.85	15.60	22.45
5370	4″ EPS	7.10	15.60	22.70

B2010 Exterior Walls

Description: The table below lists costs, $/S.F., for channel girts with sag rods and connector angles top and bottom for various column spacings, building heights and wind loads. Additive costs are shown for wind columns.

How to Use this Table: Add the cost of girts, sag rods, and angles to the framing costs of steel buildings clad in metal or composition siding. If the column spacing is in excess of the column spacing shown, use intermediate wind columns. Additive costs are shown under "Wind Columns."

B2010 154	Metal Siding Support						
	BLDG. HEIGHT (FT.)	WIND LOAD (P.S.F.)	COL. SPACING (FT.)		INTERMEDIATE COLUMNS	COST PER S.F.		
						MAT.	INST.	TOTAL
3000	18	20	20			2.42	4.04	6.46
3100					wind cols.	1.25	.29	1.54
3200		20	25			2.65	4.09	6.74
3300					wind cols.	1	.23	1.23
3400		20	30			2.92	4.16	7.08
3500					wind cols.	.83	.19	1.02
3600		20	35			3.21	4.23	7.44
3700					wind cols.	.71	.16	.87
3800		30	20			2.68	4.10	6.78
3900					wind cols.	1.25	.29	1.54
4000		30	25			2.92	4.16	7.08
4100					wind cols.	1	.23	1.23
4200		30	30			3.23	4.23	7.46
4300					wind cols.	1.13	.26	1.39
4600	30	20	20			2.35	2.84	5.19
4700					wind cols.	1.77	.41	2.18
4800		20	25			2.64	2.91	5.55
4900					wind cols.	1.41	.33	1.74
5000		20	30			2.97	2.99	5.96
5100					wind cols.	1.39	.33	1.72
5200	30	20	35			3.32	3.07	6.39
5300					wind cols.	1.38	.32	1.70
5400		30	20			2.67	2.92	5.59
5500					wind cols.	2.09	.49	2.58
5600		30	25			2.96	2.98	5.94
5700					wind cols.	1.99	.47	2.46
5800		30	30			3.34	3.07	6.41
5900					wind cols.	1.87	.44	2.31

B2010 Exterior Walls

B2010 160	Pole Barn Exterior Wall	COST PER S.F.		
		MAT.	INST.	TOTAL
2000	Pole barn exterior wall, pressure treated pole in concrete, 8' O.C.			
3000	Steel siding, 8' eave	4.54	9.60	14.14
3050	10' eave	4.36	8.85	13.21
3100	12' eave	4.13	8.05	12.18
3150	14' eave	4.03	7.65	11.68
3200	16' eave	3.93	7.30	11.23
4000	Aluminum siding, 8' eave	4.09	9.60	13.69
4050	10' eave	3.85	8.70	12.55
4100	12' eave	3.68	8.05	11.73
4150	14' eave	3.58	7.65	11.23
4200	16' eave	3.48	7.30	10.78
5000	Wood siding, 8' eave	4.71	8.45	13.16
5050	10' eave	4.47	7.50	11.97
5100	12' eave	4.30	6.90	11.20
5150	14' eave	4.20	6.45	10.65
5200	16' eave	4.10	6.10	10.20
6000	Plywood siding, 8' eave	4.03	8.40	12.43
6050	10' eave	3.79	7.45	11.24
6100	12' eave	3.62	6.85	10.47
6150	14' eave	3.52	6.45	9.97
6200	16' eave	3.42	6.05	9.47

B2020 Exterior Windows

The table below lists window systems by material, type and size. Prices between sizes listed can be interpolated with reasonable accuracy. Prices include frame, hardware, and casing as illustrated in the component block below.

B2020 102		Wood Windows						
	MATERIAL	TYPE	GLAZING	SIZE	DETAIL	COST PER UNIT		
						MAT.	INST.	TOTAL
3000	Wood	double hung	std. glass	2'-8" x 4'-6"		250	245	495
3050				3'-0" x 5'-6"		325	282	607
3100			insul. glass	2'-8" x 4'-6"		265	245	510
3150				3'-0" x 5'-6"		355	282	637
3200		sliding	std. glass	3'-4" x 2'-7"		330	204	534
3250				4'-4" x 3'-3"		345	224	569
3300				5'-4" x 6'-0"		435	269	704
3350			insul. glass	3'-4" x 2'-7"		400	239	639
3400				4'-4" x 3'-3"		415	260	675
3450				5'-4" x 6'-0"		525	305	830
3500		awning	std. glass	2'-10" x 1'-9"		232	123	355
3600				4'-4" x 2'-8"		370	119	489
3700			insul. glass	2'-10" x 1'-9"		282	142	424
3800				4'-4" x 2'-8"		450	130	580
3900		casement	std. glass	1'-10" x 3'-2"	1 lite	335	162	497
3950				4'-2" x 4'-2"	2 lite	595	215	810
4000				5'-11" x 5'-2"	3 lite	900	277	1,177
4050				7'-11" x 6'-3"	4 lite	1,275	330	1,605
4100				9'-11" x 6'-3"	5 lite	1,650	385	2,035
4150			insul. glass	1'-10" x 3'-2"	1 lite	335	162	497
4200				4'-2" x 4'-2"	2 lite	610	215	825
4250				5'-11" x 5'-2"	3 lite	945	277	1,222
4300				7'-11" x 6'-3"	4 lite	1,350	330	1,680
4350				9'-11" x 6'-3"	5 lite	1,750	385	2,135
4400		picture	std. glass	4'-6" x 4'-6"		470	277	747
4450				5'-8" x 4'-6"		530	310	840
4500			insul. glass	4'-6" x 4'-6"		570	320	890
4550				5'-8" x 4'-6"		650	360	1,010
4600		fixed bay	std. glass	8' x 5'		1,625	505	2,130
4650				9'-9" x 5'-4"		1,175	715	1,890
4700			insul. glass	8' x 5'		2,150	505	2,655
4750				9'-9" x 5'-4"		1,275	715	1,990
4800		casement bay	std. glass	8' x 5'		1,625	585	2,210
4850			insul. glass	8' x 5'		1,825	585	2,410
4900		vert. bay	std. glass	8' x 5'		1,825	585	2,410
4950			insul. glass	8' x 5'		1,925	585	2,510

B2020 Exterior Windows

B2020 104 — Steel Windows

	MATERIAL	TYPE	GLAZING	SIZE	DETAIL	COST PER UNIT		
						MAT.	INST.	TOTAL
5000	Steel	double hung	1/4" tempered	2'-8" x 4'-6"		885	194	1,079
5050				3'-4" x 5'-6"		1,350	296	1,646
5100			insul. glass	2'-8" x 4'-6"		900	222	1,122
5150				3'-4" x 5'-6"		1,375	340	1,715
5200		horz. pivoted	std. glass	2' x 2'		270	64.50	334.50
5250				3' x 3'		610	145	755
5300				4' x 4'		1,075	258	1,333
5350				6' x 4'		1,625	390	2,015
5400			insul. glass	2' x 2'		276	74	350
5450				3' x 3'		620	167	787
5500				4' x 4'		1,100	296	1,396
5550				6' x 4'		1,650	445	2,095
5600		picture window	std. glass	3' x 3'		385	145	530
5650				6' x 4'		1,025	390	1,415
5700			insul. glass	3' x 3'		395	167	562
5750				6' x 4'		1,050	445	1,495
5800		industrial security	std. glass	2'-9" x 4'-1"		815	181	996
5850				4'-1" x 5'-5"		1,600	355	1,955
5900			insul. glass	2'-9" x 4'-1"		830	208	1,038
5950				4'-1" x 5'-5"		1,625	410	2,035
6000		comm. projected	std. glass	3'-9" x 5'-5"		1,325	330	1,655
6050				6'-9" x 4'-1"		1,800	445	2,245
6100			insul. glass	3'-9" x 5'-5"		1,350	375	1,725
6150				6'-9" x 4'-1"		1,850	510	2,360
6200		casement	std. glass	4'-2" x 4'-2"	2 lite	1,175	280	1,455
6250			insul. glass	4'-2" x 4'-2"		1,200	320	1,520
6300			std. glass	5'-11" x 5'-2"	3 lite	2,475	495	2,970
6350			insul. glass	5'-11" x 5'-2"		2,525	565	3,090

B2020 106 — Aluminum Windows

	MATERIAL	TYPE	GLAZING	SIZE	DETAIL	COST PER UNIT		
						MAT.	INST.	TOTAL
6400	Aluminum	double hung	insul. glass	3'-0" x 4'-0"		530	144	674
6450				4'-5" x 5'-3"		435	180	615
6500			insul. glass	3'-1" x 3'-2"		460	173	633
6550				4'-5" x 5'-3"		520	216	736
6600		sliding	std. glass	3' x 2'		239	144	383
6650				5' x 3'		365	160	525
6700				8' x 4'		385	241	626
6750				9' x 5'		585	360	945
6800			insul. glass	3' x 2'		255	144	399
6850				5' x 3'		425	160	585
6900				8' x 4'		620	241	861
6950				9' x 5'		935	360	1,295
7000		single hung	std. glass	2' x 3'		226	144	370
7050				2'-8" x 6'-8"		400	180	580
7100				3'-4" x 5'-0"		325	160	485
7150			insul. glass	2' x 3'		274	144	418
7200				2'-8" x 6'-8"		515	180	695
7250				3'-4" x 5'		360	160	520
7300		double hung	std. glass	2' x 3'		315	97	412
7350				2'-8" x 6'-8"		935	287	1,222

B2020 Exterior Windows

B2020 106	Aluminum Windows							
	MATERIAL	TYPE	GLAZING	SIZE	DETAIL	COST PER UNIT		
						MAT.	INST.	TOTAL
7400	Aluminum	double hung		3'-4" x 5'		875	269	1,144
7450			insul. glass	2' x 3'		325	111	436
7500				2'-8" x 6'-8"		960	330	1,290
7550				3'-4" x 5'-0"		900	310	1,210
7600		casement	std. glass	3'-1" x 3'-2"		278	157	435
7650				4'-5" x 5'-3"		675	380	1,055
7700			insul. glass	3'-1" x 3'-2"		292	180	472
7750				4'-5" x 5'-3"		705	435	1,140
7800		hinged swing	std. glass	3' x 4'		575	194	769
7850				4' x 5'		960	325	1,285
7900			insul. glass	3' x 4'		595	222	817
7950				4' x 5'		990	370	1,360
8200		picture unit	std. glass	2'-0" x 3'-0"		177	97	274
8250				2'-8" x 6'-8"		525	287	812
8300				3'-4" x 5'-0"		490	269	759
8350			insul. glass	2'-0" x 3'-0"		186	111	297
8400				2'-8" x 6'-8"		550	330	880
8450				3'-4" x 5'-0"		515	310	825
8500		awning type	std. glass	3'-0" x 3'-0"	2 lite	460	103	563
8550				3'-0" x 4'-0"	3 lite	540	144	684
8600				3'-0" x 5'-4"	4 lite	650	144	794
8650				4'-0" x 5'-4"	4 lite	715	160	875
8700			insul. glass	3'-0" x 3'-0"	2 lite	490	103	593
8750				3'-0" x 4'-0"	3 lite	620	144	764
8800				3'-0" x 5'-4"	4 lite	765	144	909
8850				4'-0" x 5'-4"	4 lite	855	160	1,015
9051								
9052								

B2020 210	Tubular Aluminum Framing	COST/S.F. OPNG.		
		MAT.	INST.	TOTAL
1100	Alum flush tube frame, for 1/4" glass, 1-3/4"x4", 5'x6'opng, no inter horiz	13.95	11.20	25.15
1150	One intermediate horizontal	19.10	13.40	32.50
1200	Two intermediate horizontals	24	15.55	39.55
1250	5' x 20' opening, three intermediate horizontals	12.85	9.60	22.45
1400	1-3/4" x 4-1/2", 5' x 6' opening, no intermediate horizontals	16.15	11.20	27.35
1450	One intermediate horizontal	21.50	13.40	34.90
1500	Two intermediate horizontals	26.50	15.55	42.05
1550	5' x 20' opening, three intermediate horizontals	14.50	9.60	24.10
1700	For insulating glass, 2"x4-1/2", 5'x6' opening, no intermediate horizontals	16.65	11.85	28.50
1750	One intermediate horizontal	21.50	14.20	35.70
1800	Two intermediate horizontals	26.50	16.45	42.95
1850	5' x 20' opening, three intermediate horizontals	14.45	10.15	24.60
2000	Thermal break frame, 2-1/4"x4-1/2", 5'x6'opng, no intermediate horizontals	17.25	12.05	29.30
2050	One intermediate horizontal	23	14.80	37.80
2100	Two intermediate horizontals	29	17.50	46.50
2150	5' x 20' opening, three intermediate horizontals	15.65	10.65	26.30

The table below lists costs of curtain wall and spandrel panels per S.F. Costs do not include structural framing used to hang the panels.

Glazing Panel

Plate Glass

Spandrel Glass

Polycarbonate

Sandwich Panel

B2020 220	Curtain Wall Panels	COST PER S.F.		
		MAT.	INST.	TOTAL
1000	Glazing panel, insulating, 1/2" thick, 2 lites 1/8" float, clear	10.95	11.30	22.25
1100	Tinted	15.20	11.30	26.50
1200	5/8" thick units, 2 lites 3/16" float, clear	15.05	11.90	26.95
1300	Tinted	15.15	11.90	27.05
1400	1" thick units, 2 lites, 1/4" float, clear	18.25	14.30	32.55
1500	Tinted	26	14.30	40.30
1600	Heat reflective film inside	30.50	12.60	43.10
1700	Light and heat reflective glass, tinted	34.50	12.60	47.10
2000	Plate glass, 1/4" thick, clear	6.35	8.95	15.30
2050	Tempered	9.55	8.95	18.50
2100	Tinted	10	8.95	18.95
2200	3/8" thick, clear	11.05	14.30	25.35
2250	Tempered	18.05	14.30	32.35
2300	Tinted	17.25	14.30	31.55
2400	1/2" thick, clear	18.70	19.50	38.20
2450	Tempered	26.50	19.50	46
2500	Tinted	30	19.50	49.50
2600	3/4" thick, clear	39	30.50	69.50
2650	Tempered	45.50	30.50	76
3000	Spandrel glass, panels, 1/4" plate glass insul w/fiberglass, 1" thick	18.55	8.95	27.50
3100	2" thick	22	8.95	30.95
3200	Galvanized steel backing, add	6.45		6.45
3300	3/8" plate glass, 1" thick	31.50	8.95	40.45
3400	2" thick	35	8.95	43.95
4000	Polycarbonate, masked, clear or colored, 1/8" thick	15.40	6.30	21.70
4100	3/16" thick	17.60	6.50	24.10
4200	1/4" thick	18.70	6.90	25.60
4300	3/8" thick	28.50	7.15	35.65
5000	Facing panel, textured alum., 4' x 8' x 5/16" plywood backing, sgl face	4.48	3.57	8.05
5100	Double face	5.80	3.57	9.37
5200	4' x 10' x 5/16" plywood backing, single face	4.69	3.57	8.26
5300	Double face	6.40	3.57	9.97
5400	4' x 12' x 5/16" plywood backing, single face	4.69	3.57	8.26
5500	Sandwich panel, 22 Ga. galv., both sides 2" insulation, enamel exterior	13.40	6.25	19.65
5600	Polyvinylidene fluoride exterior finish	14.10	6.25	20.35
5700	26 Ga., galv. both sides, 1" insulation, colored 1 side	7.05	5.90	12.95
5800	Colored 2 sides	9.05	5.90	14.95

B2030 Exterior Doors

Costs are listed for exterior door systems by material, type and size. Prices between sizes listed can be interpolated with reasonable accuracy. Prices are per opening for a complete door system including frame.

B2030 110				Glazed Doors, Steel or Aluminum				
	MATERIAL	TYPE	DOORS	SPECIFICATION	OPENING	COST PER OPNG.		
						MAT.	INST.	TOTAL
5600	St. Stl. & glass	revolving	stock unit	manual oper.	6'-0" x 7'-0"	44,000	9,550	53,550
5650				auto Cntrls.	6'-10" x 7'-0"	60,500	10,200	70,700
5700	Bronze		stock unit	manual oper.	6'-10" x 7'-0"	52,000	19,200	71,200
5750				auto Cntrls.	6'-10" x 7'-0"	68,500	19,800	88,300
5800	St. Stl. & glass	balanced	standard	economy	3'-0" x 7'-0"	9,825	1,600	11,425
5850				premium	3'-0" x 7'-0"	17,000	2,100	19,100
6300	Alum. & glass	w/o transom	narrow stile	w/panic Hrdwre.	3'-0" x 7'-0"	1,850	1,050	2,900
6350				dbl. door, Hrdwre.	6'-0" x 7'-0"	3,000	1,725	4,725
6400			wide stile	hdwre.	3'-0" x 7'-0"	2,050	1,025	3,075
6450				dbl. door, Hdwre.	6'-0" x 7'-0"	3,950	2,075	6,025
6500			full vision	hdwre.	3'-0" x 7'-0"	2,700	1,650	4,350
6550				dbl. door, Hdwre.	6'-0" x 7'-0"	3,600	2,325	5,925
6600			non-standard	hdwre.	3'-0" x 7'-0"	2,225	1,025	3,250
6650				dbl. door, Hdwre.	6'-0" x 7'-0"	4,425	2,075	6,500
6700			bronze fin.	hdwre.	3'-0" x 7'-0"	1,625	1,025	2,650
6750				dbl. door, Hrdwre.	6'-0" x 7'-0"	3,250	2,075	5,325
6800			black fin.	hdwre.	3'-0" x 7'-0"	2,350	1,025	3,375
6850				dbl. door, Hdwre.	6'-0" x 7'-0"	4,675	2,075	6,750
6900		w/transom	narrow stile	hdwre.	3'-0" x 10'-0"	2,350	1,200	3,550
6950				dbl. door, Hdwre.	6'-0" x 10'-0"	3,625	2,075	5,700
7000			wide stile	hdwre.	3'-0" x 10'-0"	2,675	1,425	4,100
7050				dbl. door, Hdwre.	6'-0" x 10'-0"	3,975	2,475	6,450
7100			full vision	hdwre.	3'-0" x 10'-0"	2,975	1,600	4,575
7150				dbl. door, Hdwre.	6'-0" x 10'-0"	4,325	2,725	7,050
7200	Alum. & glass	W/transom	non-standard	hdwre.	3'-0" x 10'-0"	2,300	1,125	3,425
7250				dbl. door, Hdwre.	6'-0" x 10'-0"	4,600	2,225	6,825
7300			bronze fin.	hdwre.	3'-0" x 10'-0"	1,725	1,125	2,850
7350				dbl. door, Hdwre.	6'-0" x 10'-0"	3,425	2,225	5,650
7400			black fin.	hdwre.	3'-0" x 10'-0"	2,425	1,125	3,550
7450				dbl. door, Hdwre.	6'-0" x 10'-0"	4,850	2,225	7,075
7500		revolving	stock design	minimum	6'-10" x 7'-0"	22,400	3,850	26,250
7550				average	6'-0" x 7'-0"	27,000	4,800	31,800

B2030 Exterior Doors

B2030 110	Glazed Doors, Steel or Aluminum

	MATERIAL	TYPE	DOORS	SPECIFICATION	OPENING	COST PER OPNG.		
						MAT.	INST.	TOTAL
7600				maximum	6'-10" x 7'-0"	46,200	6,425	52,625
7650				min., automatic	6'-10" x 7'-0"	39,000	4,500	43,500
7700				avg., automatic	6'-10" x 7'-0"	43,600	5,450	49,050
7750				max., automatic	6'-10" x 7'-0"	63,000	7,075	70,075
7800		balanced	standard	economy	3'-0" x 7'-0"	7,275	1,600	8,875
7850				premium	3'-0" x 7'-0"	8,725	2,050	10,775
7900		mall front	sliding panels	alum. fin.	16'-0" x 9'-0"	3,700	825	4,525
7950					24'-0" x 9'-0"	5,275	1,525	6,800
8000				bronze fin.	16'-0" x 9'-0"	4,300	960	5,260
8050					24'-0" x 9'-0"	6,150	1,775	7,925
8100			fixed panels	alum. fin.	48'-0" x 9'-0"	9,825	1,200	11,025
8150				bronze fin.	48'-0" x 9'-0"	11,400	1,400	12,800
8200		sliding entrance	5' x 7' door	electric oper.	12'-0" x 7'-6"	9,025	1,525	10,550
8250		sliding patio	temp. glass	economy	6'-0" x 7'-0"	1,825	283	2,108
8300			temp. glass	economy	12'-0" x 7'-0"	4,275	375	4,650
8350				premium	6'-0" x 7'-0"	2,750	425	3,175
8400					12'-0" x 7'-0"	6,425	565	6,990

B2030   Exterior Doors

Exterior Door System

The table below lists exterior door systems by material, type and size. Prices between sizes listed can be interpolated with reasonable accuracy. Prices are per opening for a complete door system including frame and required hardware.

Wood doors in this table are designed with wood frames and metal doors with hollow metal frames. Depending upon quality the total material and installation cost of a wood door frame is about the same as a hollow metal frame.

B2030 210		Wood Doors						
	MATERIAL	TYPE	DOORS	SPECIFICATION	OPENING	COST PER OPNG.		
						MAT.	INST.	TOTAL
2350	Birch	solid core	single door	hinged	2'-6" x 6'-8"	1,150	310	1,460
2400					2'-6" x 7'-0"	1,150	310	1,460
2450					2'-8" x 7'-0"	1,125	310	1,435
2500					3'-0" x 7'-0"	1,150	310	1,460
2550			double door		2'-6" x 6'-8"	2,150	565	2,715
2600					2'-6" x 7'-0"	2,150	565	2,715
2650					2'-8" x 7'-0"	2,125	565	2,690
2700					3'-0" x 7'-0"	2,000	495	2,495
2750	Wood	combination	storm & screen		3'-0" x 6'-8"	335	75.50	410.50
2800					3'-0" x 7'-0"	370	83	453
2850		overhead	panels, H.D.	manual oper.	8'-0" x 8'-0"	1,125	565	1,690
2900					10'-0" x 10'-0"	1,625	630	2,255
2950					12'-0" x 12'-0"	2,225	755	2,980
3000					14'-0" x 14'-0"	3,550	870	4,420
3050					20'-0" x 16'-0"	5,850	1,750	7,600
3100				electric oper.	8'-0" x 8'-0"	2,150	850	3,000
3150					10'-0" x 10'-0"	2,650	915	3,565
3200					12'-0" x 12'-0"	3,250	1,050	4,300
3250					14'-0" x 14'-0"	4,575	1,150	5,725
3300					20'-0" x 16'-0"	7,075	2,325	9,400

B2030 220		Steel Doors						
	MATERIAL	TYPE	DOORS	SPECIFICATION	OPENING	COST PER OPNG.		
						MAT.	INST.	TOTAL
3350	Steel 18 Ga.	hollow metal	1 door w/frame	no label	2'-6" x 7'-0"	1,550	320	1,870
3400					2'-8" x 7'-0"	1,550	320	1,870
3450					3'-0" x 7'-0"	1,550	320	1,870
3500					3'-6" x 7'-0"	1,675	335	2,010
3550					4'-0" x 8'-0"	1,950	335	2,285
3600			2 doors w/frame	no label	5'-0" x 7'-0"	2,975	590	3,565
3650					5'-4" x 7'-0"	2,975	590	3,565
3700					6'-0" x 7'-0"	2,975	590	3,565
3750					7'-0" x 7'-0"	3,250	625	3,875
3800					8'-0" x 8'-0"	3,825	625	4,450

B20 Exterior Enclosure

B2030 Exterior Doors

B2030 220 — Steel Doors

	MATERIAL	TYPE	DOORS	SPECIFICATION	OPENING	COST PER OPNG.		
						MAT.	INST.	TOTAL
3850	Steel 18 Ga.	hollow metal	1 door w/frame	"A" label	2'-6" x 7'-0"	1,950	385	2,335
3900					2'-8" x 7'-0"	1,925	390	2,315
3950					3'-0" x 7'-0"	1,925	390	2,315
4000					3'-6" x 7'-0"	2,100	395	2,495
4050					4'-0" x 8'-0"	2,300	415	2,715
4100			2 doors w/frame		5'-0" x 7'-0"	3,725	715	4,440
4150					5'-4" x 7'-0"	3,750	720	4,470
4200					6'-0" x 7'-0"	3,750	720	4,470
4250					7'-0" x 7'-0"	4,075	740	4,815
4300					8'-0" x 8'-0"	4,075	740	4,815
4350	Steel 24 Ga.	overhead	sectional	manual oper.	8'-0" x 8'-0"	890	565	1,455
4400					10'-0" x 10'-0"	1,200	630	1,830
4450					12'-0" x 12'-0"	1,450	755	2,205
4500					20'-0" x 14'-0"	4,075	1,625	5,700
4550				electric oper.	8'-0" x 8'-0"	1,925	850	2,775
4600					10'-0" x 10'-0"	2,225	915	3,140
4650					12'-0" x 12'-0"	2,475	1,050	3,525
4700					20'-0" x 14'-0"	5,300	2,200	7,500
4750	Steel		rolling	manual oper.	8'-0" x 8'-0"	1,225	900	2,125
4800					10'-0" x 10'-0"	2,050	1,025	3,075
4850					12'-0" x 12'-0"	2,075	1,200	3,275
4900					14'-0" x 14'-0"	3,350	1,800	5,150
4950					20'-0" x 12'-0"	2,350	1,600	3,950
5000					20'-0" x 16'-0"	3,900	2,400	6,300
5050				electric oper.	8'-0" x 8'-0"	2,425	1,200	3,625
5100					10'-0" x 10'-0"	3,250	1,325	4,575
5150					12'-0" x 12'-0"	3,275	1,500	4,775
5200					14'-0" x 14'-0"	4,550	2,100	6,650
5250					20'-0" x 12'-0"	3,500	1,900	5,400
5300					20'-0" x 16'-0"	5,050	2,700	7,750
5350				fire rated	10'-0" x 10'-0"	2,300	1,300	3,600
5400			rolling grille	manual oper.	10'-0" x 10'-0"	2,750	1,450	4,200
5450					15'-0" x 8'-0"	3,175	1,800	4,975
5500		vertical lift	1 door w/frame	motor operator	16'-0" x 16'-0"	23,700	5,600	29,300
5550					32'-0" x 24'-0"	51,000	3,750	54,750

B2030 230 — Aluminum Doors

	MATERIAL	TYPE	DOORS	SPECIFICATION	OPENING	COST PER OPNG.		
						MAT.	INST.	TOTAL
6000	Aluminum	combination	storm & screen	hinged	3'-0" x 6'-8"	335	81	416
6050					3'-0" x 7'-0"	370	89	459
6100		overhead	rolling grille	manual oper.	12'-0" x 12'-0"	4,400	2,525	6,925
6150				motor oper.	12'-0" x 12'-0"	5,775	2,825	8,600
6200	Alum. & Fbrgls.		heavy duty	manual oper.	12'-0" x 12'-0"	2,975	755	3,730
6250				electric oper.	12'-0" x 12'-0"	4,000	1,050	5,050

B3010 Roof Coverings

Built Up Ply

Multiple ply roofing is the most popular covering for minimum pitch roofs.

B3010 105	Built-Up	COST PER S.F.		
		MAT.	INST.	TOTAL
1200	Asphalt flood coat w/gravel; not incl. insul, flash., nailers			
1300				
1400	Asphalt base sheets & 3 plies #15 asphalt felt, mopped	1.09	1.86	2.95
1500	On nailable deck	1.11	1.95	3.06
1600	4 plies #15 asphalt felt, mopped	1.48	2.05	3.53
1700	On nailable deck	1.31	2.16	3.47
1800	Coated glass base sheet, 2 plies glass (type IV), mopped	1.17	1.86	3.03
1900	For 3 plies	1.41	2.05	3.46
2000	On nailable deck	1.33	2.16	3.49
2300	4 plies glass fiber felt (type IV), mopped	1.75	2.05	3.80
2400	On nailable deck	1.58	2.16	3.74
2500	Organic base sheet & 3 plies #15 organic felt, mopped	1.16	2.06	3.22
2600	On nailable deck	1.13	2.16	3.29
2700	4 plies #15 organic felt, mopped	1.42	1.86	3.28
2750				
2800	Asphalt flood coat, smooth surface, not incl. insul, flash., nailers			
2900	Asphalt base sheet & 3 plies #15 asphalt felt, mopped	1.14	1.71	2.85
3000	On nailable deck	1.06	1.79	2.85
3100	Coated glass fiber base sheet & 2 plies glass fiber felt, mopped	1.12	1.64	2.76
3200	On nailable deck	1.06	1.71	2.77
3300	For 3 plies, mopped	1.37	1.79	3.16
3400	On nailable deck	1.28	1.86	3.14
3700	4 plies glass fiber felt (type IV), mopped	1.61	1.79	3.40
3800	On nailable deck	1.53	1.86	3.39
3900	Organic base sheet & 3 plies #15 organic felt, mopped	1.17	1.71	2.88
4000	On nailable decks	1.08	1.79	2.87
4100	4 plies #15 organic felt, mopped	1.37	1.86	3.23
4200	Coal tar pitch with gravel surfacing			
4300	4 plies #15 tarred felt, mopped	2.57	1.95	4.52
4400	3 plies glass fiber felt (type IV), mopped	2.12	2.16	4.28
4500	Coated glass fiber base sheets 2 plies glass fiber felt, mopped	2.16	2.16	4.32
4600	On nailable decks	1.87	2.28	4.15
4800	3 plies glass fiber felt (type IV), mopped	2.91	1.95	4.86
4900	On nailable decks	2.61	2.05	4.66

B3010 Roof Coverings

Full Adhered Single Ply Membrane

Preformed Metal

Flat Seam

Batten Seam

Standing Seam

B3010 120	Single Ply Membrane	COST PER S.F.		
		MAT.	INST.	TOTAL
1000	CSPE (Chlorosulfonated polyethylene), 45 mils, plate attached	3.40	.75	4.15
2000	EPDM (Ethylene propylene diene monomer), 45 mils, fully adhered	1.22	1.01	2.23
4000	Modified bit., SBS modified, granule surface cap sheet, mopped, 150 mils	.72	2.04	2.76
4500	APP modified, granule surface cap sheet, torched, 180 mils	.98	1.32	2.30
6000	Reinforced PVC, 48 mils, loose laid and ballasted with stone	1.28	.52	1.80
6200	Fully adhered with adhesive	1.68	1.01	2.69

B3010 130	Preformed Metal Roofing	COST PER S.F.		
		MAT.	INST.	TOTAL
0200	Corrugated roofing, aluminum, mill finish, .0175″ thick, .272 P.S.F.	1.09	1.87	2.96
0250	.0215″ thick, .334 P.S.F.	1.43	1.87	3.30

B3010 135	Formed Metal	COST PER S.F.		
		MAT.	INST.	TOTAL
1000	Batten seam, formed copper roofing, 3″ min slope, 16 oz., 1.2 P.S.F.	12.10	6.20	18.30
1100	18 oz., 1.35 P.S.F.	13.60	6.80	20.40
2000	Zinc copper alloy, 3″ min slope, .020″ thick, .88 P.S.F.	12.85	5.65	18.50
3000	Flat seam, copper, 1/4″ min. slope, 16 oz., 1.2 P.S.F.	9	5.65	14.65
3100	18 oz., 1.35 P.S.F.	10.05	5.90	15.95
5000	Standing seam, copper, 2-1/2″ min. slope, 16 oz., 1.25 P.S.F.	9.65	5.25	14.90
5100	18 oz., 1.40 P.S.F.	10.85	5.65	16.50
6000	Zinc copper alloy, 2-1/2″ min. slope, .020″ thick, .87 P.S.F.	12.35	5.65	18
6100	.032″ thick, 1.39 P.S.F.	19.60	6.20	25.80

B3010 Roof Coverings

Shingle and Tile

Shingles and tiles are practical in applications where the roof slope is more than 3-1/2" per foot of rise. Lines 1100 through 6000 list the various materials and the weight per square foot.

Roof Edges

The table below lists the costs for various types of roof perimeter edge treatments.

Roof edge systems include the cost per L.F. for a 2" x 8" treated wood nailer fastened at 4'-0" O.C. and a diagonally cut 4" x 6" treated wood cant.

Roof edge and base flashing are assumed to be made from the same material.

B3010 140	Shingle & Tile	COST PER S.F.		
		MAT.	INST.	TOTAL
1095	Asphalt roofing			
1100	Strip shingles, 4" slope, inorganic class A 210-235 lb./sq.	.95	1.12	2.07
1150	Organic, class C, 235-240 lb./sq.	1.12	1.22	2.34
1200	Premium laminated multi-layered, class A, 260-300 lb./sq.	1.87	1.67	3.54
1545	Metal roofing			
1550	Alum., shingles, colors, 3" min slope, .019" thick, 0.4 PSF	2.77	1.22	3.99
1850	Steel, colors, 3" min slope, 26 gauge, 1.0 PSF	4.38	2.52	6.90
2795	Slate roofing			
2800	Slate roofing, 4" min. slope, shingles, 3/16" thick, 8.0 PSF	5.35	3.14	8.49
3495	Wood roofing			
3500	4" min slope, cedar shingles, 16" x 5", 5" exposure 1.6 PSF	3.03	2.44	5.47
4000	Shakes, 18", 8-1/2" exposure, 2.8 PSF	2.09	3.01	5.10
5095	Tile roofing			
5100	Aluminum, mission, 3" min slope, .019" thick, 0.65 PSF	9.05	2.35	11.40
6000	Clay tile, flat shingle, interlocking, 15", 166 pcs/sq, fireflashed blend	5.70	2.77	8.47

B3010 Roof Coverings

B3010 320	Roof Deck Rigid Insulation	COST PER S.F.		
		MAT.	INST.	TOTAL
0100	Fiberboard low density			
0150	1" thick R2.78	.57	.73	1.30
0300	1 1/2" thick R4.17	.88	.73	1.61
0350	2" thick R5.56	1.17	.73	1.90
0370	Fiberboard high density, 1/2" thick R1.3	.32	.63	.95
0380	1" thick R2.5	.66	.73	1.39
0390	1 1/2" thick R3.8	.98	.73	1.71
0410	Fiberglass, 3/4" thick R2.78	.67	.63	1.30
0450	15/16" thick R3.70	.89	.63	1.52
0550	1-5/16" thick R5.26	1.51	.63	2.14
0650	2 7/16" thick R10	1.85	.73	2.58
1510	Polyisocyanurate 2#/CF density, 1" thick	.55	.51	1.06
1550	1 1/2" thick	.69	.55	1.24
1600	2" thick	.87	.59	1.46
1650	2 1/2" thick	1.11	.61	1.72
1700	3" thick	1.34	.63	1.97
1750	3 1/2" thick	2.15	.63	2.78
1800	Tapered for drainage	.63	.51	1.14
1810	Expanded polystyrene, 1#/CF density, 3/4" thick R2.89	.20	.49	.69
1820	2" thick R7.69	.53	.55	1.08
1830	Extruded polystyrene, 15 PSI compressive strength, 1" thick, R5	.58	.49	1.07
1835	2" thick R10	.76	.55	1.31
1840	3" thick R15	1.52	.63	2.15
2550	40 PSI compressive strength, 1" thick R5	.56	.49	1.05
2600	2" thick R10	1.07	.55	1.62
2650	3" thick R15	1.54	.63	2.17
2700	4" thick R20	2.02	.63	2.65
2750	Tapered for drainage	.80	.51	1.31
2810	60 PSI compressive strength, 1" thick R5	.78	.50	1.28
2850	2" thick R10	1.48	.56	2.04
2900	Tapered for drainage	1.02	.51	1.53
3050	Composites with 2" EPS			
3060	1" Fiberboard	1.46	.62	2.08
3070	7/16" oriented strand board	1.18	.73	1.91
3080	1/2" plywood	1.45	.73	2.18
3090	1" perlite	1.20	.73	1.93
4000	Composites with 1-1/2" polyisocyanurate			
4010	1" fiberboard	1.24	.73	1.97
4020	1" perlite	1.11	.70	1.81
4030	7/16" oriented strand board	.98	.73	1.71

B3010 420 Roof Edges

	EDGE TYPE	DESCRIPTION	SPECIFICATION	FACE HEIGHT		COST PER L.F.		
						MAT.	INST.	TOTAL
1000	Aluminum	mill finish	.050" thick	4"		14.60	10.30	24.90
1100				6"		15.10	10.60	25.70
1300		duranodic	.050" thick	4"		15.15	10.30	25.45
1400				6"		15.65	10.60	26.25
1600		painted	.050" thick	4"		15.50	10.30	25.80
1700				6"		16.90	10.60	27.50
2000	Copper	plain	16 oz.	4"		51	10.30	61.30
2100				6"		51	10.60	61.60
2300			20 oz.	4"		65.50	11.80	77.30
2400				6"		57.50	11.40	68.90
2700	Sheet Metal	galvanized	20 Ga.	4"		17.45	12.30	29.75
2800				6"		17.45	12.30	29.75
3000			24 Ga.	4"		14.60	10.30	24.90

B30 Roofing

B3010 Roof Coverings

B3010 420 — Roof Edges

	EDGE TYPE	DESCRIPTION	SPECIFICATION	FACE HEIGHT		COST PER L.F.		
						MAT.	INST.	TOTAL
3100				6"		14.60	10.30	24.90

B3010 430 — Flashing

	MATERIAL	BACKING	SIDES	SPECIFICATION	QUANTITY	COST PER S.F.		
						MAT.	INST.	TOTAL
0040	Aluminum	none		.019"		1.27	3.68	4.95
0050				.032"		1.49	3.68	5.17
0300		fabric	2	.004"		1.69	1.62	3.31
0400		mastic		.004"		1.69	1.62	3.31
0700	Copper	none		16 oz.	<500 lbs.	7.65	4.64	12.29
0800				24 oz.	<500 lbs.	13.35	5.10	18.45
3500	PVC black	none		.010"		.23	1.87	2.10
3700				.030"		.39	1.87	2.26
4200	Neoprene			1/16"		2.45	1.87	4.32
4500	Stainless steel	none		.015"	<500 lbs.	6.40	4.64	11.04
4600	Copper clad				>2000 lbs.	6.10	3.44	9.54
5000	Plain			32 ga.		3.30	3.44	6.74

B3010 Roof Coverings

B3010 610 — Gutters

	SECTION	MATERIAL	THICKNESS	SIZE	FINISH	COST PER L.F.		
						MAT.	INST.	TOTAL
0050	Box	aluminum	.027"	5"	enameled	2.95	5.50	8.45
0100					mill	2.97	5.50	8.47
0200			.032"	5"	enameled	3.29	5.35	8.64
0500		copper	16 Oz.	5"	lead coated	21	5.35	26.35
0600					mill	13.85	5.35	19.20
1000		steel galv.	28 Ga.	5"	enameled	2.34	5.35	7.69
1200			26 Ga.	5"	mill	2.40	5.35	7.75
1800		vinyl		4"	colors	1.31	4.92	6.23
1900				5"	colors	1.71	4.92	6.63
2300		hemlock or fir		4"x5"	treated	21.50	5.65	27.15
3000	Half round	copper	16 Oz.	4"	lead coated	15.20	5.35	20.55
3100					mill	11.55	5.35	16.90
3600		steel galv.	28 Ga.	5"	enameled	2.34	5.35	7.69
4102		stainless steel		5"	mill	9.80	5.35	15.15
5000		vinyl		4"	white	1.41	4.92	6.33

B3010 620 — Downspouts

	MATERIALS	SECTION	SIZE	FINISH	THICKNESS	COST PER V.L.F.		
						MAT.	INST.	TOTAL
0100	Aluminum	rectangular	2"x3"	embossed mill	.020"	1.07	3.52	4.59
0150				enameled	.020"	1.45	3.52	4.97
0250			3"x4"	enameled	.024"	3.17	4.77	7.94
0300		round corrugated	3"	enameled	.020"	1.73	3.52	5.25
0350			4"	enameled	.025"	2.56	4.77	7.33
0500	Copper	rectangular corr.	2"x3"	mill	16 Oz.	9.65	3.52	13.17
0600		smooth		mill	16 Oz.	14.65	3.52	18.17
0700		rectangular corr.	3"x4"	mill	16 Oz.	13.45	4.61	18.06
1300	Steel		2"x3"	galvanized	28 Ga.	2.13	3.52	5.65
1350				epoxy coated	24 Ga.	2.42	3.52	5.94
1400		smooth		galvanized	28 Ga.	3.33	3.52	6.85
1450		rectangular corr.	3"x4"	galvanized	28 Ga.	2	4.61	6.61
1500				epoxy coated	24 Ga.	3.03	4.61	7.64
1550		smooth		galvanized	28 Ga.	3.37	4.61	7.98
1600		round corrugated	2"	galvanized	28 Ga.	2.29	3.52	5.81
1650			3"	galvanized	28 Ga.	2.29	3.52	5.81
1700			4"	galvanized	28 Ga.	2.87	4.61	7.48
1750			5"	galvanized	28 Ga.	3.81	5.15	8.96
2552	S.S. tubing sch.5	rectangular	3"x4"	mill		54	4.61	58.61

B3010 630 — Gravel Stop

	MATERIALS	SECTION	SIZE	FINISH	THICKNESS	COST PER L.F.		
						MAT.	INST.	TOTAL
5100	Aluminum	extruded	4"	mill	.050"	6.60	4.61	11.21
5200			4"	duranodic	.050"	7.15	4.61	11.76
5300			8"	mill	.050"	8	5.35	13.35
5400			8"	duranodic	.050"	8.80	5.35	14.15
6000			12"-2 pc.	duranodic	.050"	11.05	6.70	17.75
6100	Stainless	formed	6"	mill	24 Ga.	10.80	4.95	15.75

B3020   Roof Openings

Roof Hatch

Smoke Hatch

Skylight

B3020 110	Skylights	COST PER S.F.		
		MAT.	INST.	TOTAL
5100	Skylights, plastic domes, insul curbs, nom. size to 10 S.F., single glaze	30	14	44
5200	Double glazing	34.50	17.25	51.75
5300	10 S.F. to 20 S.F., single glazing	30	5.65	35.65
5400	Double glazing	29	7.10	36.10
5500	20 S.F. to 30 S.F., single glazing	22.50	4.82	27.32
5600	Double glazing	27.50	5.65	33.15
5700	30 S.F. to 65 S.F., single glazing	21	3.67	24.67
5800	Double glazing	28.50	4.82	33.32
6000	Sandwich panels fiberglass, 1-9/16" thick, 2 S.F. to 10 S.F.	18.90	11.20	30.10
6100	10 S.F. to 18 S.F.	17.05	8.45	25.50
6200	2-3/4" thick, 25 S.F. to 40 S.F.	27.50	7.60	35.10
6300	40 S.F. to 70 S.F.	22.50	6.80	29.30

B3020 210	Hatches	COST PER OPNG.		
		MAT.	INST.	TOTAL
0200	Roof hatches with curb and 1" fiberglass insulation, 2'-6"x3'-0", aluminum	1,175	224	1,399
0300	Galvanized steel 165 lbs.	705	224	929
0400	Primed steel 164 lbs.	695	224	919
0500	2'-6"x4'-6" aluminum curb and cover, 150 lbs.	1,000	249	1,249
0600	Galvanized steel 220 lbs.	975	249	1,224
0650	Primed steel 218 lbs.	980	249	1,229
0800	2'x6"x8'-0" aluminum curb and cover, 260 lbs.	1,975	340	2,315
0900	Galvanized steel, 360 lbs.	1,975	340	2,315
0950	Primed steel 358 lbs.	1,575	340	1,915
1200	For plexiglass panels, add to the above	485		485
2100	Smoke hatches, unlabeled not incl. hand winch operator, 2'-6"x3', galv	855	271	1,126
2200	Plain steel, 160 lbs.	840	271	1,111
2400	2'-6"x8'-0", galvanized steel, 360 lbs.	2,150	370	2,520
2500	Plain steel, 350 lbs.	1,725	370	2,095
3000	4'-0"x8'-0", double leaf low profile, aluminum cover, 359 lb.	3,075	280	3,355
3100	Galvanized steel 475 lbs.	2,625	280	2,905
3200	High profile, aluminum cover, galvanized curb, 361 lbs.	2,950	280	3,230

The Concrete Block Partition Systems are defined by weight and type of block, thickness, type of finish and number of sides finished. System components include joint reinforcing on alternate courses and vertical control joints.

C1010 102			Concrete Block Partitions - Regular Weight					
	TYPE	THICKNESS (IN.)	TYPE FINISH	SIDES FINISHED		COST PER S.F.		
						MAT.	INST.	TOTAL
1000	Hollow	4	none	0		1.94	6.20	8.14
1010			gyp. plaster 2 coat	1		2.32	9.10	11.42
1020				2		2.70	11.90	14.60
1200			portland - 3 coat	1		2.21	9.45	11.66
1400			5/8" drywall	1		2.53	8.15	10.68
1500		6	none	0		2.53	6.65	9.18
1510			gyp. plaster 2 coat	1		2.91	9.55	12.46
1520				2		3.29	12.35	15.64
1700			portland - 3 coat	1		2.80	9.90	12.70
1900			5/8" drywall	1		3.12	8.60	11.72
1910				2		3.71	10.55	14.26
2000		8	none	0		2.85	7.10	9.95
2010			gyp. plaster 2 coat	1		3.23	9.95	13.18
2020				2		3.61	12.80	16.41
2200			portland - 3 coat	1		3.12	10.35	13.47
2400			5/8" drywall	1		3.44	9.05	12.49
2410				2		4.03	10.95	14.98
2500	Hollow	10	none	0		3.36	7.45	10.81
2510			gyp. plaster 2 coat	1		3.74	10.30	14.04
2520				2		4.12	13.10	17.22
2700			portland - 3 coat	1		3.63	10.70	14.33
2900			5/8" drywall	1		3.95	9.35	13.30
2910				2		4.54	11.30	15.84
3000	Solid	2	none	0		1.69	6.10	7.79
3010			gyp. plaster	1		2.07	9	11.07
3020				2		2.45	11.80	14.25
3200			portland - 3 coat	1		1.96	9.35	11.31
3400			5/8" drywall	1		2.28	8.05	10.33
3410				2		2.87	10	12.87
3500		4	none	0		2.30	6.40	8.70
3510			gyp. plaster	1		2.82	9.30	12.12
3520				2		3.06	12.10	15.16
3700			portland - 3 coat	1		2.57	9.65	12.22
3900			5/8" drywall	1		2.89	8.35	11.24
3910				2		3.48	10.30	13.78

C1010 Partitions

C1010 102	Concrete Block Partitions - Regular Weight

	TYPE	THICKNESS (IN.)	TYPE FINISH	SIDES FINISHED		COST PER S.F.		
						MAT.	INST.	TOTAL
4000	Solid	6	none	0		2.72	6.90	9.62
4010			gyp. plaster	1		3.10	9.80	12.90
4020				2		3.48	12.60	16.08
4200			portland - 3 coat	1		2.99	10.15	13.14
4400			5/8" drywall	1		3.31	8.85	12.16
4410				2		3.90	10.80	14.70

C1010 104	Concrete Block Partitions - Lightweight

	TYPE	THICKNESS (IN.)	TYPE FINISH	SIDES FINISHED		COST PER S.F.		
						MAT.	INST.	TOTAL
5000	Hollow	4	none	0		2.09	6.05	8.14
5010			gyp. plaster	1		2.47	8.95	11.42
5020				2		2.85	11.75	14.60
5200			portland - 3 coat	1		2.36	9.30	11.66
5400			5/8" drywall	1		2.68	8	10.68
5410				2		3.27	9.95	13.22
5500		6	none	0		2.92	6.45	9.37
5520			gyp. plaster	2		3.68	12.15	15.83
5700			portland - 3 coat	1		3.19	9.70	12.89
5900			5/8" drywall	1		3.51	8.40	11.91
5910				2		4.10	10.35	14.45
6000		8	none	0		3.52	6.95	10.47
6010			gyp. plaster	1		3.90	9.80	13.70
6020				2		4.28	12.65	16.93
6200			portland - 3 coat	1		3.79	10.20	13.99
6400			5/8" drywall	1		4.11	8.90	13.01
6410				2		4.70	10.80	15.50
6500		10	none	0		4.18	7.25	11.43
6510			gyp. plaster	1		4.56	10.10	14.66
6520				2		4.94	12.90	17.84
6700			portland - 3 coat	1		4.45	10.50	14.95
6900			5/8" drywall	1		4.77	9.15	13.92
6910				2		5.35	11.10	16.45
7000	Solid	4	none	0		1.96	6.30	8.26
7010			gyp. plaster	1		2.34	9.20	11.54
7020				2		2.72	12	14.72
7200			portland - 3 coat	1		2.23	9.55	11.78
7400			5/8" drywall	1		2.55	8.25	10.80
7410				2		3.14	10.20	13.34
7500		6	none	0		3.38	6.80	10.18
7510			gyp. plaster	1		3.88	9.75	13.63
7520				2		4.14	12.50	16.64
7700			portland - 3 coat	1		3.65	10.05	13.70
7900			5/8" drywall	1		3.97	8.75	12.72
7910				2		4.56	10.70	15.26
8000		8	none	0		4.29	7.30	11.59
8010			gyp. plaster	1		4.67	10.15	14.82
8020				2		5.05	13	18.05
8200			portland - 3 coat	1		4.56	10.55	15.11
8400			5/8" drywall	1		4.88	9.25	14.13
8410				2		5.45	11.15	16.60

C1010 Partitions

Single Wythe

Double Wythe

C1010 120	Tile Partitions	COST PER S.F.		
		MAT.	INST.	TOTAL
1000	8W series 8"x16", 4" thick wall, reinf every 2 courses, glazed 1 side	15.50	7.45	22.95
1100	Glazed 2 sides	18.65	7.90	26.55
1200	Glazed 2 sides, using 2 wythes of 2" thick tile	22.50	14.30	36.80
1300	6" thick wall, horizontal reinf every 2 courses, glazed 1 side	26.50	7.80	34.30
1400	Glazed 2 sides, each face different color, 2" and 4" tile	27	14.60	41.60
1500	8" thick wall, glazed 2 sides using 2 wythes of 4" thick tile	31	14.90	45.90
1600	10" thick wall, glazed 2 sides using 1 wythe of 4" & 1 wythe of 6" tile	42	15.25	57.25
1700	Glazed 2 sides cavity wall, using 2 wythes of 4" thick tile	31	14.90	45.90
1800	12" thick wall, glazed 2 sides using 2 wythes of 6" thick tile	53	15.60	68.60
1900	Glazed 2 sides cavity wall, using 2 wythes of 4" thick tile	31	14.90	45.90
2100	6T series 5-1/3"x12" tile, 4" thick, non load bearing glazed one side	13.15	11.70	24.85
2200	Glazed two sides	17.30	13.20	30.50
2300	Glazed two sides, using two wythes of 2" thick tile	19.40	23	42.40
2400	6" thick, glazed one side	19.65	12.25	31.90
2500	Glazed two sides	23.50	13.90	37.40
2600	Glazed two sides using 2" thick tile and 4" thick tile	23	23	46
2700	8" thick, glazed one side	26	14.30	40.30
2800	Glazed two sides using two wythes of 4" thick tile	26.50	23.50	50
2900	Glazed two sides using 6" thick tile and 2" thick tile	29.50	23.50	53
3000	10" thick cavity wall, glazed two sides using two wythes of 4" tile	26.50	23.50	50
3100	12" thick, glazed two sides using 4" thick tile and 8" thick tile	39	26	65
3200	2" thick facing tile, glazed one side, on 6" concrete block	13.55	13.60	27.15
3300	On 8" concrete block	13.85	14	27.85
3400	On 10" concrete block	14.40	14.30	28.70

C10 Interior Construction

C1010 Partitions

Wood Stud Framing

Metal Stud Framing

The Drywall Partitions/Stud Framing Systems are defined by type of drywall and number of layers, type and spacing of stud framing, and treatment on the opposite face. Components include taping and finishing.

Cost differences between regular and fire resistant drywall are negligible, and terminology is interchangeable. In some cases fiberglass insulation is included for additional sound deadening.

C1010 124	Drywall Partitions/Wood Stud Framing							
	FACE LAYER	BASE LAYER	FRAMING	OPPOSITE FACE	INSULATION	COST PER S.F.		
						MAT.	INST.	TOTAL
1200	5/8" FR drywall	none	2 x 4, @ 16" O.C.	same	0	1.28	3.41	4.69
1250				5/8" reg. drywall	0	1.26	3.41	4.67
1300				nothing	0	.86	2.27	3.13
1400		1/4" SD gypsum	2 x 4 @ 16" O.C.	same	1-1/2" fiberglass	2.60	5.25	7.85
1450				5/8" FR drywall	1-1/2" fiberglass	2.16	4.61	6.77
1500				nothing	1-1/2" fiberglass	1.74	3.47	5.21
1600		resil. channels	2 x 4 @ 16", O.C.	same	1-1/2" fiberglass	2.10	6.65	8.75
1650				5/8" FR drywall	1-1/2" fiberglass	1.91	5.30	7.21
1700				nothing	1-1/2" fiberglass	1.49	4.17	5.66
1800		5/8" FR drywall	2 x 4 @ 24" O.C.	same	0	1.91	4.33	6.24
1850				5/8" FR drywall	0	1.54	3.76	5.30
1900				nothing	0	1.12	2.62	3.74
2200			2 rows-2 x 4	same	2" fiberglass	2.96	6.25	9.21
2250			16"O.C.	5/8" FR drywall	2" fiberglass	2.59	5.70	8.29
2300				nothing	2" fiberglass	2.17	4.54	6.71
2400	5/8" WR drywall	none	2 x 4, @ 16" O.C.	same	0	1.54	3.41	4.95
2450				5/8" FR drywall	0	1.41	3.41	4.82
2500				nothing	0	.99	2.27	3.26
2600		5/8" FR drywall	2 x 4, @ 24" O.C.	same	0	2.17	4.33	6.50
2650				5/8" FR drywall	0	1.67	3.76	5.43
2700				nothing	0	1.25	2.62	3.87
2800	5/8" VF drywall	none	2 x 4, @ 16" O.C.	same	0	2.40	3.65	6.05
2850				5/8" FR drywall	0	1.84	3.53	5.37
2900				nothing	0	1.42	2.39	3.81
3000	5/8" VF drywall	5/8" FR drywall	2 x 4 , 24" O.C.	same	0	3.03	4.57	7.60
3050				5/8" FR drywall	0	2.10	3.88	5.98
3100				nothing	0	1.68	2.74	4.42
3200	1/2" reg drywall	3/8" reg drywall	2 x 4, @ 16" O.C.	same	0	1.88	4.55	6.43
3250				5/8" FR drywall	0	1.58	3.98	5.56
3300				nothing	0	1.16	2.84	4

C1010 Partitions

C1010 126 — Drywall Partitions/Metal Stud Framing

	FACE LAYER	BASE LAYER	FRAMING	OPPOSITE FACE	INSULATION	COST PER S.F.		
						MAT.	INST.	TOTAL
5000	5/8" FR drywall	none	1-5/8" @ 16" O.C.	same	0	1.12	3.42	4.54
5010				5/8" reg. drywall	0	1.10	3.42	4.52
5020				nothing	0	.70	2.28	2.98
5030			2-1/2"" @ 16" O.C.	same	0	1.17	3.44	4.61
5040				5/8" reg. drywall	0	1.15	3.44	4.59
5050				nothing	0	.75	2.30	3.05
5060			3-5/8" @ 16" O.C.	same	0	1.24	3.46	4.70
5070				5/8" reg. drywall	0	1.22	3.46	4.68
5080				nothing	0	.82	2.32	3.14
5200			1-5/8" @ 24" O.C.	same	0	1.05	3.03	4.08
5250				5/8" reg. drywall	0	1.03	3.03	4.06
5300				nothing	0	.63	1.89	2.52
5400			3-5/8" @ 24" O.C.	same	0	1.14	3.04	4.18
5450				5/8" reg. drywall	0	1.12	3.04	4.16
5500				nothing	0	.72	1.90	2.62
5600		1/4" SD gypsum	1-5/8" @ 24" O.C.	same	0	1.93	4.29	6.22
5650				5/8" FR drywall	0	1.49	3.66	5.15
5700				nothing	0	1.07	2.52	3.59
5800			2-1/2" @ 24" O.C.	same	0	1.97	4.29	6.26
5850				5/8" FR drywall	0	1.53	3.66	5.19
5900				nothing	0	1.11	2.52	3.63
6000		5/8" FR drywall	2-1/2" @ 16" O.C.	same	0	2.06	4.87	6.93
6050				5/8" FR drywall	0	1.69	4.30	5.99
6100				nothing	0	1.27	3.16	4.43
6200			3-5/8" @ 24" O.C.	same	0	1.88	4.18	6.06
6250				5/8"FR drywall	3-1/2" fiberglass	1.99	4.03	6.02
6300				nothing	0	1.09	2.47	3.56
6400	5/8" WR drywall	none	1-5/8" @ 24" O.C.	same	0	1.31	3.03	4.34
6450				5/8" FR drywall	0	1.18	3.03	4.21
6500				nothing	0	.76	1.89	2.65
6600			3-5/8" @ 24" O.C.	same	0	1.40	3.04	4.44
6650				5/8" FR drywall	0	1.27	3.04	4.31
6700				nothing	0	.85	1.90	2.75
6800		5/8" FR drywall	2-1/2" @ 16" O.C.	same	0	2.32	4.87	7.19
6850				5/8" FR drywall	0	1.82	4.30	6.12
6900				nothing	0	1.40	3.16	4.56
7000			3-5/8" @ 24" O.C.	same	0	2.14	4.18	6.32
7050				5/8"FR drywall	3-1/2" fiberglass	2.12	4.03	6.15
7100				nothing	0	1.22	2.47	3.69
7200	5/8" VF drywall	none	1-5/8" @ 24" O.C.	same	0	2.17	3.27	5.44
7250				5/8" FR drywall	0	1.61	3.15	4.76
7300				nothing	0	1.19	2.01	3.20
7400			3-5/8" @ 24" O.C.	same	0	2.26	3.28	5.54
7450				5/8" FR drywall	0	1.70	3.16	4.86
7500				nothing	0	1.28	2.02	3.30
7600		5/8" FR drywall	2-1/2" @ 16" O.C.	same	0	3.18	5.10	8.28
7650				5/8" FR drywall	0	2.25	4.42	6.67
7700				nothing	0	1.83	3.28	5.11
7800			3-5/8" @ 24" O.C.	same	0	3	4.42	7.42
7850				5/8"FR drywall	3-1/2" fiberglass	2.55	4.15	6.70
7900				nothing	0	1.65	2.59	4.24

C10 Interior Construction

C1010 Partitions

C1010 128	Drywall Components	COST PER S.F.		
		MAT.	INST.	TOTAL
0060	Metal studs, 24" O.C. including track, load bearing, 20 gage, 2-1/2"	.66	1.06	1.72
0080	3-5/8"	.78	1.08	1.86
0100	4"	.70	1.10	1.80
0120	6"	1.04	1.12	2.16
0140	Metal studs, 24" O.C. including track, load bearing, 18 gage, 2-1/2"	.66	1.06	1.72
0160	3-5/8"	.78	1.08	1.86
0180	4"	.70	1.10	1.80
0200	6"	1.04	1.12	2.16
0220	16 gage, 2-1/2"	.77	1.21	1.98
0240	3-5/8"	.91	1.23	2.14
0260	4"	.96	1.26	2.22
0280	6"	1.20	1.29	2.49
0300	Non load bearing, 25 gage, 1-5/8"	.21	.75	.96
0340	3-5/8"	.30	.76	1.06
0360	4"	.32	.76	1.08
0380	6"	.41	.78	1.19
0400	20 gage, 2-1/2"	.35	.94	1.29
0420	3-5/8"	.38	.96	1.34
0440	4"	.46	.96	1.42
0460	6"	.58	.98	1.56
0540	Wood studs including blocking, shoe and double top plate, 2"x4", 12" O.C.	.54	1.42	1.96
0560	16" O.C.	.44	1.13	1.57
0580	24" O.C.	.33	.91	1.24
0600	2"x6", 12" O.C.	.82	1.62	2.44
0620	16" O.C.	.66	1.26	1.92
0640	24" O.C.	.50	.99	1.49
0642	Furring one side only, steel channels, 3/4", 12" O.C.	.37	2.03	2.40
0644	16" O.C.	.34	1.80	2.14
0646	24" O.C.	.22	1.36	1.58
0647	1-1/2", 12" O.C.	.51	2.27	2.78
0648	16" O.C.	.46	1.99	2.45
0649	24" O.C.	.30	1.57	1.87
0650	Wood strips, 1" x 3", on wood, 12" O.C.	.42	1.03	1.45
0651	16" O.C.	.32	.77	1.09
0652	On masonry, 12" O.C.	.46	1.14	1.60
0653	16" O.C.	.35	.86	1.21
0654	On concrete, 12" O.C.	.46	2.18	2.64
0655	16" O.C.	.35	1.64	1.99
0665	Gypsum board, one face only, exterior sheathing, 1/2"	.48	1.01	1.49
0680	Interior, fire resistant, 1/2"	.35	.57	.92
0700	5/8"	.37	.57	.94
0720	Sound deadening board 1/4"	.44	.63	1.07
0740	Standard drywall 3/8"	.34	.57	.91
0760	1/2"	.33	.57	.90
0780	5/8"	.35	.57	.92
0800	Tongue & groove coreboard 1"	.81	2.36	3.17
0820	Water resistant, 1/2"	.42	.57	.99
0840	5/8"	.50	.57	1.07
0860	Add for the following:, foil backing	.17		.17
0880	Fiberglass insulation, 3-1/2"	.48	.42	.90
0900	6"	.63	.42	1.05
0920	Rigid insulation 1"	.57	.57	1.14
0940	Resilient furring @ 16" O.C.	.25	1.78	2.03
0960	Taping and finishing	.05	.57	.62
0980	Texture spray	.04	.60	.64
1000	Thin coat plaster	.11	.71	.82
1050	Sound wall framing, 2x6 plates, 2x4 staggered studs, 12" O.C.	.65	1.38	2.03

C1010 Partitions

Gypsum plaster and gypsum lath on metal studs.

Gypsum plaster and diamond metal lath on metal studs.

Gypsum plaster and gypsum lath on wood studs.

Gypsum plaster and diamond metal lath on wood studs.

C1010 140	Plaster Partitions/Metal Stud Framing							
	TYPE	FRAMING	LATH	OPPOSITE FACE		COST PER S.F.		
						MAT.	INST.	TOTAL
1000	2 coat gypsum	2-1/2" @ 16"O.C.	3/8" gypsum	same		2.17	8.20	10.37
1010				nothing		1.30	4.76	6.06
1100		3-1/4" @ 24"O.C.	1/2" gypsum	same		2.07	7.90	9.97
1110				nothing		1.24	4.41	5.65
1500	2 coat vermiculite	2-1/2" @ 16"O.C.	3/8" gypsum	same		2	8.90	10.90
1510				nothing		1.21	5.10	6.31
1600		3-1/4" @ 24"O.C.	1/2" gypsum	same		1.90	8.60	10.50
1610				nothing		1.15	4.77	5.92
2000	3 coat gypsum	2-1/2" @ 16"O.C.	3/8" gypsum	same		2	9.25	11.25
2010				nothing		1.21	5.30	6.51
2020			3.4lb. diamond	same		2.39	9.25	11.64
2030				nothing		1.40	5.30	6.70
2040			2.75lb. ribbed	same		2.14	9.25	11.39
2050				nothing		1.28	5.30	6.58
2100		3-1/4" @ 24"O.C.	1/2" gypsum	same		1.90	8.95	10.85
2110				nothing		1.15	4.94	6.09
2120			3.4lb. ribbed	same		2.38	8.95	11.33
2130				nothing		1.39	4.94	6.33
3500	3 coat gypsum	2-1/2" @ 16"O.C.	3/8" gypsum	same		2.46	11.90	14.36
3510	W/med. Keenes			nothing		1.44	6.65	8.09
3520			3.4lb. diamond	same		2.85	11.90	14.75
3530				nothing		1.63	6.65	8.28
3540			2.75lb. ribbed	same		2.60	11.90	14.50
3550				nothing		1.51	6.65	8.16
3600		3-1/4" @ 24"O.C.	1/2" gypsum	same		2.36	11.60	13.96
3610				nothing		1.38	6.30	7.68
3620			3.4lb. ribbed	same		2.84	11.60	14.44
3630				nothing		1.62	6.30	7.92

C10 Interior Construction

C1010 Partitions

C1010 140				Plaster Partitions/Metal Stud Framing				

	TYPE	FRAMING	LATH	OPPOSITE FACE		COST PER S.F.		
						MAT.	INST.	TOTAL
4000	3 coat gypsum	2-1/2" @ 16"O.C.	3/8" gypsum	same		2.46	13.25	15.71
4010	W/hard Keenes			nothing		1.44	7.25	8.69
4020			3.4lb. diamond	same		2.85	13.25	16.10
4030				nothing		1.63	7.25	8.88
4040			2.75lb. ribbed	same		2.60	13.25	15.85
4050				nothing		1.51	7.25	8.76
4100		3-1/4" @ 24"O.C.	1/2" gypsum	same		2.36	12.95	15.31
4110				nothing		1.38	6.90	8.28
4120			3.4lb. ribbed	same		2.84	12.95	15.79
4130				nothing		1.62	6.90	8.52

C1010 142				Plaster Partitions/Wood Stud Framing				

	TYPE	FRAMING	LATH	OPPOSITE FACE		COST PER S.F.		
						MAT.	INST.	TOTAL
5000	2 coat gypsum	2"x4" @ 16"O.C.	3/8" gypsum	same		2.28	8	10.28
5010				nothing		1.41	4.65	6.06
5100		2"x4" @ 24"O.C.	1/2" gypsum	same		2.10	7.85	9.95
5110				nothing		1.27	4.47	5.74
5500	2 coat vermiculite	2"x4" @ 16"O.C.	3/8" gypsum	same		2.11	8.70	10.81
5510				nothing		1.32	5	6.32
5600		2"x4" @ 24"O.C.	1/2" gypsum	same		1.93	8.60	10.53
5610				nothing		1.18	4.83	6.01
6000	3 coat gypsum	2"x4" @ 16"O.C.	3/8" gypsum	same		2.11	9.05	11.16
6010				nothing		1.32	5.20	6.52
6020			3.4lb. diamond	same		2.50	9.15	11.65
6030				nothing		1.51	5.20	6.71
6040			2.75lb. ribbed	same		2.22	9.20	11.42
6050				nothing		1.38	5.25	6.63
6100		2"x4" @ 24"O.C.	1/2" gypsum	same		1.93	8.90	10.83
6110				nothing		1.18	5	6.18
6120			3.4lb. ribbed	same		2.14	9	11.14
6130				nothing		1.28	5.05	6.33
7500	3 coat gypsum	2"x4" @ 16"O.C.	3/8" gypsum	same		2.57	11.70	14.27
7510	W/med Keenes			nothing		1.55	6.50	8.05
7520			3.4lb. diamond	same		2.96	11.80	14.76
7530				nothing		1.74	6.55	8.29
7540			2.75lb. ribbed	same		2.68	11.85	14.53
7550				nothing		1.61	6.60	8.21
7600		2"x4" @ 24"O.C.	1/2" gypsum	same		2.39	11.55	13.94
7610				nothing		1.41	6.35	7.76
7620			3.4lb. ribbed	same		2.87	11.75	14.62
7630				nothing		1.65	6.45	8.10
8000	3 coat gypsum	2"x4" @ 16"O.C.	3/8" gypsum	same		2.57	13.05	15.62
8010	W/hard Keenes			nothing		1.55	7.15	8.70
8020			3.4lb. diamond	same		2.96	13.10	16.06
8030				nothing		1.74	7.20	8.94
8040			2.75lb. ribbed	same		2.68	13.15	15.83
8050				nothing		1.61	7.20	8.81
8100		2"x4" @ 24"O.C.	1/2" gypsum	same		2.39	12.90	15.29
8110				nothing		1.41	6.95	8.36
8120			3.4lb. ribbed	same		2.87	13.10	15.97
8130				nothing		1.65	7.05	8.70

C10 Interior Construction

C1010 Partitions

C1010 144	Plaster Partition Components	COST PER S.F.		
		MAT.	INST.	TOTAL
0060	Metal studs, 16" O.C., including track, non load bearing, 25 gage, 1-5/8"	.33	1.16	1.49
0080	2-1/2"	.33	1.16	1.49
0100	3-1/4"	.40	1.18	1.58
0120	3-5/8"	.40	1.18	1.58
0140	4"	.44	1.19	1.63
0160	6"	.55	1.20	1.75
0180	Load bearing, 20 gage, 2-1/2"	.89	1.47	2.36
0200	3-5/8"	1.05	1.49	2.54
0220	4"	1.11	1.53	2.64
0240	6"	1.40	1.55	2.95
0260	16 gage 2-1/2"	1.05	1.67	2.72
0280	3-5/8"	1.26	1.72	2.98
0300	4"	1.32	1.74	3.06
0320	6"	1.65	1.77	3.42
0340	Wood studs, including blocking, shoe and double plate, 2"x4", 12" O.C.	.54	1.42	1.96
0360	16" O.C.	.44	1.13	1.57
0380	24" O.C.	.33	.91	1.24
0400	2"x6", 12" O.C.	.82	1.62	2.44
0420	16" O.C.	.66	1.26	1.92
0440	24" O.C.	.50	.99	1.49
0460	Furring one face only, steel channels, 3/4", 12" O.C.	.37	2.03	2.40
0480	16" O.C.	.34	1.80	2.14
0500	24" O.C.	.22	1.36	1.58
0520	1-1/2", 12" O.C.	.51	2.27	2.78
0540	16" O.C.	.46	1.99	2.45
0560	24"O.C.	.30	1.57	1.87
0580	Wood strips 1"x3", on wood., 12" O.C.	.42	1.03	1.45
0600	16"O.C.	.32	.77	1.09
0620	On masonry, 12" O.C.	.46	1.14	1.60
0640	16" O.C.	.35	.86	1.21
0660	On concrete, 12" O.C.	.46	2.18	2.64
0680	16" O.C.	.35	1.64	1.99
0700	Gypsum lath. plain or perforated, nailed to studs, 3/8" thick	.33	.62	.95
0720	1/2" thick	.30	.66	.96
0740	Clipped to studs, 3/8" thick	.33	.70	1.03
0760	1/2" thick	.30	.75	1.05
0780	Metal lath, diamond painted, nailed to wood studs, 2.5 lb.	.52	.62	1.14
0800	3.4 lb.	.52	.66	1.18
0820	Screwed to steel studs, 2.5 lb.	.52	.66	1.18
0840	3.4 lb.	.42	.70	1.12
0860	Rib painted, wired to steel, 2.75 lb	.40	.70	1.10
0880	3.4 lb	.54	.75	1.29
0900	4.0 lb	.69	.82	1.51
0910				
0920	Gypsum plaster, 2 coats	.41	2.72	3.13
0940	3 coats	.59	3.25	3.84
0960	Perlite or vermiculite plaster, 2 coats	.46	3.08	3.54
0980	3 coats	.77	3.85	4.62
1000	Stucco, 3 coats, 1" thick, on wood framing	.80	5.40	6.20
1020	On masonry	.31	4.26	4.57
1100	Metal base galvanized and painted 2-1/2" high	.71	1.99	2.70

C1010 Partitions

Folding Accordion

Folding Leaf

Movable and Borrow Lites

C1010 205	Partitions	COST PER S.F.		
		MAT.	INST.	TOTAL
0360	Folding accordion, vinyl covered, acoustical, 3 lb. S.F., 17 ft max. hgt	31.50	11.30	42.80
0380	5 lb. per S.F. 27 ft max height	44	11.90	55.90
0400	5.5 lb. per S.F., 17 ft. max height	51.50	12.60	64.10
0420	Commercial, 1.75 lb per S.F., 8 ft. max height	28.50	5.05	33.55
0440	2.0 Lb per S.F., 17 ft. max height	29.50	7.55	37.05
0460	Industrial, 4.0 lb. per S.F. 27 ft max height	44.50	15.10	59.60
0480	Vinyl clad wood or steel, electric operation 6 psf	63	7.10	70.10
0500	Wood, non acoustic, birch or mahogany	34	3.77	37.77
0560	Folding leaf, aluminum framed acoustical 12 ft.high., 5.5 lb per S.F., min.	45	18.85	63.85
0580	Maximum	54	37.50	91.50
0600	6.5 lb. per S.F., minimum	47	18.85	65.85
0620	Maximum	58.50	37.50	96
0640	Steel acoustical, 7.5 per S.F., vinyl faced, minimum	66.50	18.85	85.35
0660	Maximum	81.50	37.50	119
0680	Wood acoustic type, vinyl faced to 18' high 6 psf, minimum	62.50	18.85	81.35
0700	Average	74.50	25	99.50
0720	Maximum	96.50	37.50	134
0740	Formica or hardwood faced, minimum	64.50	18.85	83.35
0760	Maximum	68.50	37.50	106
0780	Wood, low acoustical type to 12 ft. high 4.5 psf	47	22.50	69.50
0840	Demountable, trackless wall, cork finish, semi acous, 1-5/8" th, min	41.50	3.48	44.98
0860	Maximum	46	5.95	51.95
0880	Acoustic, 2" thick, minimum	39.50	3.71	43.21
0900	Maximum	60	5.05	65.05
0920	In-plant modular office system, w/prehung steel door			
0940	3" thick honeycomb core panels			
0960	12' x 12', 2 wall	13.60	.71	14.31
0970	4 wall	16.05	.95	17
0980	16' x 16', 2 wall	13.60	.50	14.10
0990	4 wall	9.55	.51	10.06
1000	Gypsum, demountable, 3" to 3-3/4" thick x 9' high, vinyl clad	7.20	2.61	9.81
1020	Fabric clad	18	2.83	20.83
1040	1.75 system, vinyl clad hardboard, paper honeycomb core panel			
1060	1-3/4" to 2-1/2" thick x 9' high	12.10	2.61	14.71
1080	Unitized gypsum panel system, 2" to 2-1/2" thick x 9' high			
1100	Vinyl clad gypsum	15.55	2.61	18.16
1120	Fabric clad gypsum	25.50	2.83	28.33
1140	Movable steel walls, modular system			
1160	Unitized panels, 48" wide x 9' high			
1180	Baked enamel, pre-finished	17.55	2.09	19.64
1200	Fabric clad	25.50	2.22	27.72

C1020 Interior Doors

Single Leaf

Sliding Entrance

Rolling Overhead

C1020 102	Special Doors	COST PER OPNG.		
		MAT.	INST.	TOTAL
2500	Single leaf, wood, 3'-0"x7'-0"x1 3/8", birch, solid core	425	211	636
2510	Hollow core	355	202	557
2530	Hollow core, lauan	345	202	547
2540	Louvered pine	490	202	692
2550	Paneled pine	520	202	722
2600	Hollow metal, comm. quality, flush, 3'-0"x7'-0"x1-3/8"	930	222	1,152
2650	3'-0"x10'-0" openings with panel	1,475	288	1,763
2700	Metal fire, comm. quality, 3'-0"x7'-0"x1-3/8"	1,150	231	1,381
2800	Kalamein fire, comm. quality, 3'-0"x7'-0"x1-3/4"	840	425	1,265
3200	Double leaf, wood, hollow core, 2 - 3'-0"x7'-0"x1-3/8"	615	385	1,000
3300	Hollow metal, comm. quality, B label, 2'-3'-0"x7'-0"x1-3/8"	2,225	485	2,710
3400	6'-0"x10'-0" opening, with panel	2,825	600	3,425
3500	Double swing door system, 12'-0"x7'-0", mill finish	9,000	3,150	12,150
3700	Black finish	9,125	3,250	12,375
3800	Sliding entrance door and system mill finish	10,400	2,700	13,100
3900	Bronze finish	11,300	2,925	14,225
4000	Black finish	11,800	3,025	14,825
4100	Sliding panel mall front, 16'x9' opening, mill finish	3,700	825	4,525
4200	Bronze finish	4,800	1,075	5,875
4300	Black finish	5,925	1,325	7,250
4400	24'x9' opening mill finish	5,275	1,525	6,800
4500	Bronze finish	6,850	1,975	8,825
4600	Black finish	8,450	2,450	10,900
4700	48'x9' opening mill finish	9,825	1,200	11,025
4800	Bronze finish	12,800	1,550	14,350
4900	Black finish	15,700	1,925	17,625
5000	Rolling overhead steel door, manual, 8' x 8' high	1,225	900	2,125
5100	10' x 10' high	2,050	1,025	3,075
5200	20' x 10' high	3,375	1,450	4,825
5300	12' x 12' high	2,075	1,200	3,275
5400	Motor operated, 8' x 8' high	2,425	1,200	3,625
5500	10' x 10' high	3,250	1,325	4,575
5600	20' x 10' high	4,575	1,750	6,325
5700	12' x 12' high	3,275	1,500	4,775
5800	Roll up grille, aluminum, manual, 10' x 10' high, mill finish	3,050	1,750	4,800
5900	Bronze anodized	4,900	1,750	6,650
6000	Motor operated, 10' x 10' high, mill finish	4,425	2,050	6,475
6100	Bronze anodized	6,275	2,050	8,325
6200	Steel, manual, 10' x 10' high	2,750	1,450	4,200
6300	15' x 8' high	3,175	1,800	4,975
6400	Motor operated, 10' x 10' high	4,125	1,750	5,875
6500	15' x 8' high	4,550	2,100	6,650

C1030 Fittings

Toilet Units

Entrance Screens

Urinal Screens

C1030 110	Toilet Partitions	COST PER UNIT		
		MAT.	INST.	TOTAL
0380	Toilet partitions, cubicles, ceiling hung, marble	1,775	515	2,290
0400	Painted metal	565	283	848
0420	Plastic laminate	570	283	853
0460	Stainless steel	1,175	283	1,458
0480	Handicap addition	475		475
0520	Floor and ceiling anchored, marble	2,250	410	2,660
0540	Painted metal	645	226	871
0560	Plastic laminate	865	226	1,091
0600	Stainless steel	1,275	226	1,501
0620	Handicap addition	325		325
0660	Floor mounted marble	1,325	345	1,670
0680	Painted metal	640	162	802
0700	Plastic laminate	540	162	702
0740	Stainless steel	1,550	162	1,712
0760	Handicap addition	345		345
0780	Juvenile deduction	45.50		45.50
0820	Floor mounted with headrail marble	1,275	345	1,620
0840	Painted metal	415	189	604
0860	Plastic laminate	825	189	1,014
0900	Stainless steel	1,150	189	1,339
0920	Handicap addition	410		410
0960	Wall hung, painted metal	700	162	862
1020	Stainless steel	1,825	162	1,987
1040	Handicap addition	410		410
1080	Entrance screens, floor mounted, 54" high, marble	830	114	944
1100	Painted metal	266	75.50	341.50
1140	Stainless steel	1,000	75.50	1,075.50
1300	Urinal screens, floor mounted, 24" wide, laminated plastic	209	142	351
1320	Marble	710	168	878
1340	Painted metal	253	142	395
1380	Stainless steel	655	142	797
1428	Wall mounted wedge type, painted metal	148	113	261
1460	Stainless steel	635	113	748
1500	Partitions, shower stall, single wall, painted steel, 2'-8" x 2'-8"	1,125	267	1,392
1510	Fiberglass, 2'-8" x 2'-8"	875	297	1,172
1520	Double wall, enameled steel, 2'-8" x 2'-8"	1,125	267	1,392
1530	Stainless steel, 2'-8" x 2'-8"	2,525	267	2,792
1560	Tub enclosure, sliding panels, tempered glass, aluminum frame	450	335	785
1570	Chrome/brass frame-deluxe	1,325	445	1,770

C10 Interior Construction

C1030 Fittings

C1030 310	Storage Specialties, EACH	COST EACH		
		MAT.	INST.	TOTAL
0200	Lockers, steel, single tier, 5' to 6' high, per opening, min.	170	47.50	217.50
0210	Maximum	310	55.50	365.50
0600	Shelving, metal industrial, braced, 3' wide, 1' deep	24.50	12.35	36.85
0610	2' deep	32.50	13.15	45.65

C1030 510	Identifying/Visual Aid Specialties, EACH	COST EACH		
		MAT.	INST.	TOTAL
0100	Control boards, magnetic, porcelain finish, framed, 24" x 18"	219	142	361
0110	96" x 48"	1,175	226	1,401
0120	Directory boards, outdoor, black plastic, 36" x 24"	840	565	1,405
0130	36" x 36"	970	755	1,725
0140	Indoor, economy, open faced, 18" x 24"	173	162	335
0500	Signs, interior electric exit sign, wall mounted, 6"	95.50	80	175.50
0510	Street, reflective alum., dbl. face, 4 way, w/bracket	254	37.50	291.50
0520	Letters, cast aluminum, 1/2" deep, 4" high	28	31.50	59.50
0530	1" deep, 10" high	53	31.50	84.50
0540	Plaques, cast aluminum, 20" x 30"	1,550	283	1,833
0550	Cast bronze, 36" x 48"	5,075	565	5,640

C1030 520	Identifying/Visual Aid Specialties, S.F.	COST PER S.F.		
		MAT.	INST.	TOTAL
0100	Bulletin board, cork sheets, no frame, 1/4" thick	2.28	3.90	6.18
0120	Aluminum frame, 1/4" thick, 3' x 5'	9.10	4.76	13.86
0200	Chalkboards, wall hung, alum, frame & chalktrough	14.40	2.51	16.91
0210	Wood frame & chalktrough	12.10	2.70	14.80
0220	Sliding board, one board with back panel	57	2.42	59.42
0230	Two boards with back panel	89	2.42	91.42
0240	Liquid chalk type, alum. frame & chalktrough	13	2.51	15.51
0250	Wood frame & chalktrough	33.50	2.51	36.01

C1030 710	Bath and Toilet Accessories, EACH	COST EACH		
		MAT.	INST.	TOTAL
0100	Specialties, bathroom accessories, st. steel, curtain rod, 5' long, 1" diam	29	43.50	72.50
0120	Dispenser, towel, surface mounted	49	35.50	84.50
0140	Grab bar, 1-1/4" diam., 12" long	32	23.50	55.50
0160	Mirror, framed with shelf, 18" x 24"	205	28.50	233.50
0170	72" x 24"	330	94.50	424.50
0180	Toilet tissue dispenser, surface mounted, single roll	19.60	18.85	38.45
0200	Towel bar, 18" long	46	24.50	70.50
0300	Medicine cabinets, sliding mirror doors, 20" x 16" x 4-3/4", unlighted	137	81	218
0310	24" x 19" x 8-1/2", lighted	197	113	310

C1030 730	Bath and Toilet Accessories, L.F.	COST PER L.F.		
		MAT.	INST.	TOTAL
0100	Partitions, hospital curtain, ceiling hung, polyester oxford cloth	23.50	5.50	29
0110	Designer oxford cloth	19.80	7	26.80

C1030 830	Fabricated Cabinets & Counters, L.F.	COST PER L.F.		
		MAT.	INST.	TOTAL
0110	Household, base, hardwood, one top drawer & one door below x 12" wide	279	45.50	324.50
0120	Four drawer x 24" wide	360	51	411
0130	Wall, hardwood, 30" high with one door x 12" wide	227	51.50	278.50
0140	Two doors x 48" wide	530	61.50	591.50
0150	Counter top-laminated plastic, stock, economy	18.35	18.85	37.20
0160	Custom-square edge, 7/8" thick	16.30	42	58.30

C10 Interior Construction

C1030 Fittings

C1030 830	Fabricated Cabinets & Counters, L.F.	COST PER L.F.		
		MAT.	INST.	TOTAL
0170	School, counter, wood, 32" high	258	56.50	314.50
0180	Metal, 84" high	460	75.50	535.50

C1030 910	Other Fittings, EACH	COST EACH		
		MAT.	INST.	TOTAL
0500	Mail boxes, horizontal, rear loaded, aluminum, 5" x 6" x 15" deep	38.50	16.65	55.15
0510	Front loaded, aluminum, 10" x 12" x 15" deep	106	28.50	134.50
0520	Vertical, front loaded, aluminum, 15" x 5" x 6" deep	33	16.65	49.65
0530	Bronze, duranodic finish	44	16.65	60.65
0540	Letter slot, post office	116	71	187
0550	Mail counter, window, post office, with grille	605	283	888
0700	Turnstiles, one way, 4' arm, 46" diam., manual	1,850	226	2,076
0710	Electric	2,250	945	3,195
0720	3 arm, 5'-5" diam. & 7' high, manual	6,400	1,125	7,525
0730	Electric	8,925	1,875	10,800

C2010 Stair Construction

The table below lists the cost per flight for 4'-0" wide stairs. Side walls are not included. Railings are included in the prices.

C2010 110	Stairs	COST PER FLIGHT		
		MAT.	INST.	TOTAL
0470	Stairs, C.I.P. concrete, w/o landing, 12 risers, w/o nosing	1,125	2,375	3,500
0480	With nosing	2,000	2,575	4,575
0550	W/landing, 12 risers, w/o nosing	1,275	2,900	4,175
0560	With nosing	2,150	3,100	5,250
0570	16 risers, w/o nosing	1,550	3,625	5,175
0580	With nosing	2,725	3,900	6,625
0590	20 risers, w/o nosing	1,825	4,400	6,225
0600	With nosing	3,300	4,725	8,025
0610	24 risers, w/o nosing	2,125	5,125	7,250
0620	With nosing	3,875	5,525	9,400
0630	Steel, grate type w/nosing & rails, 12 risers, w/o landing	5,700	1,250	6,950
0640	With landing	7,975	1,675	9,650
0660	16 risers, with landing	9,875	2,100	11,975
0680	20 risers, with landing	11,800	2,500	14,300
0700	24 risers, with landing	13,700	2,925	16,625
0701				
0710	Concrete fill metal pan & picket rail, 12 risers, w/o landing	7,375	1,250	8,625
0720	With landing	9,725	1,850	11,575
0740	16 risers, with landing	12,200	2,250	14,450
0760	20 risers, with landing	14,600	2,650	17,250
0780	24 risers, with landing	17,100	3,050	20,150
0790	Cast iron tread & pipe rail, 12 risers, w/o landing	7,375	1,250	8,625
0800	With landing	9,725	1,850	11,575
1120	Wood, prefab box type, oak treads, wood rails 3'-6" wide, 14 risers	2,200	470	2,670
1150	Prefab basement type, oak treads, wood rails 3'-0" wide, 14 risers	1,050	117	1,167

C3010 Wall Finishes

C3010 230	Paint & Covering	COST PER S.F.		
		MAT.	INST.	TOTAL
0060	Painting, interior on plaster and drywall, brushwork, primer & 1 coat	.14	.73	.87
0080	Primer & 2 coats	.21	.97	1.18
0100	Primer & 3 coats	.29	1.19	1.48
0120	Walls & ceilings, roller work, primer & 1 coat	.14	.49	.63
0140	Primer & 2 coats	.21	.63	.84
0160	Woodwork incl. puttying, brushwork, primer & 1 coat	.14	1.06	1.20
0180	Primer & 2 coats	.21	1.40	1.61
0200	Primer & 3 coats	.29	1.90	2.19
0260	Cabinets and casework, enamel, primer & 1 coat	.15	1.19	1.34
0280	Primer & 2 coats	.22	1.46	1.68
0300	Masonry or concrete, latex, brushwork, primer & 1 coat	.31	.99	1.30
0320	Primer & 2 coats	.41	1.42	1.83
0340	Addition for block filler	.24	1.22	1.46
0380	Fireproof paints, intumescent, 1/8" thick 3/4 hour	2.43	.97	3.40
0400	3/16" thick 1 hour	5.40	1.46	6.86
0420	7/16" thick 2 hour	7	3.40	10.40
0440	1-1/16" thick 3 hour	11.40	6.80	18.20
0500	Gratings, primer & 1 coat	.36	1.49	1.85
0600	Pipes over 12" diameter	.79	4.76	5.55
0700	Structural steel, brushwork, light framing 300-500 S.F./Ton	.11	1.83	1.94
0720	Heavy framing 50-100 S.F./Ton	.11	.91	1.02
0740	Spraywork, light framing 300-500 S.F./Ton	.11	.41	.52
0760	Heavy framing 50-100 S.F./Ton	.11	.45	.56
0800	Varnish, interior wood trim, no sanding sealer & 1 coat	.08	1.19	1.27
0820	Hardwood floor, no sanding 2 coats	.17	.25	.42
0840	Wall coatings, acrylic glazed coatings, minimum	.34	.91	1.25
0860	Maximum	.72	1.56	2.28
0880	Epoxy coatings, minimum	.44	.91	1.35
0900	Maximum	1.32	2.80	4.12
0940	Exposed epoxy aggregate, troweled on, 1/16" to 1/4" aggregate, minimum	.67	2.03	2.70
0960	Maximum	1.44	3.66	5.10
0980	1/2" to 5/8" aggregate, minimum	1.31	3.66	4.97
1000	Maximum	2.27	5.95	8.22
1020	1" aggregate, minimum	2.30	5.30	7.60
1040	Maximum	3.51	8.65	12.16
1060	Sprayed on, minimum	.62	1.61	2.23
1080	Maximum	1.14	3.28	4.42
1100	High build epoxy 50 mil, minimum	.74	1.22	1.96
1120	Maximum	1.25	5	6.25
1140	Laminated epoxy with fiberglass minimum	.79	1.61	2.40
1160	Maximum	1.43	3.28	4.71
1180	Sprayed perlite or vermiculite 1/16" thick, minimum	.30	.16	.46
1200	Maximum	.80	.74	1.54
1260	Wall coatings, vinyl plastic, minimum	.36	.65	1.01
1280	Maximum	.89	1.98	2.87
1300	Urethane on smooth surface, 2 coats, minimum	.30	.42	.72
1320	Maximum	.64	.72	1.36
1340	3 coats, minimum	.39	.57	.96
1360	Maximum	.86	1.01	1.87
1380	Ceramic-like glazed coating, cementitious, minimum	.52	1.08	1.60
1400	Maximum	.88	1.38	2.26
1420	Resin base, minimum	.36	.74	1.10
1440	Maximum	.58	1.44	2.02
1460	Wall coverings, aluminum foil	1.14	1.74	2.88
1500	Vinyl backing	6.10	1.99	8.09
1520	Cork tiles, 12"x12", light or dark, 3/16" thick	5.55	1.99	7.54
1540	5/16" thick	3.25	2.04	5.29
1560	Basketweave, 1/4" thick	3.85	1.99	5.84

C3010 Wall Finishes

C3010 230	Paint & Covering	COST PER S.F.		
		MAT.	INST.	TOTAL
1580	Natural, non-directional, 1/2″ thick	8.40	1.99	10.39
1600	12″x36″, granular, 3/16″ thick	1.42	1.24	2.66
1620	1″ thick	1.83	1.29	3.12
1640	12″x12″, polyurethane coated, 3/16″ thick	4.43	1.99	6.42
1660	5/16″ thick	6.90	2.04	8.94
1661	Paneling, prefinished plywood, birch	.91	2.70	3.61
1662	Mahogany, African	3.19	2.83	6.02
1663	Philippine (lauan)	.66	2.26	2.92
1664	Oak or cherry	2.27	2.83	5.10
1665	Rosewood	3.19	3.54	6.73
1666	Teak	3.19	2.83	6.02
1667	Chestnut	5.35	3.02	8.37
1668	Pecan	2.31	2.83	5.14
1669	Walnut	5.85	2.83	8.68
1670	Wood board, knotty pine, finished	2.44	4.68	7.12
1671	Rough sawn cedar	3.74	4.68	8.42
1672	Redwood	5.80	4.68	10.48
1673	Aromatic cedar	2.56	5.05	7.61
1680	Cork wallpaper, paper backed, natural	2.24	1	3.24
1700	Color	3.12	1	4.12
1720	Gypsum based, fabric backed, minimum	.98	.60	1.58
1740	Average	1.38	.66	2.04
1760	Maximum	1.54	.75	2.29
1780	Vinyl wall covering, fabric back, light weight	1.02	.75	1.77
1800	Medium weight	.99	1	1.99
1820	Heavy weight	1.63	1.10	2.73
1840	Wall paper, double roll, solid pattern, avg. workmanship	.47	.75	1.22
1860	Basic pattern, avg. workmanship	1.08	.89	1.97
1880	Basic pattern, quality workmanship	2.13	1.10	3.23
1900	Grass cloths with lining paper, minimum	.73	1.20	1.93
1920	Maximum	2.93	1.37	4.30
1940	Ceramic tile, thin set, 4-1/4″ x 4-1/4″	2.48	4.67	7.15
1942				
1960	12″ x 12″	4.78	5.55	10.33

C3010 235	Paint Trim	COST PER L.F.		
		MAT.	INST.	TOTAL
2040	Painting, wood trim, to 6″ wide, enamel, primer & 1 coat	.15	.60	.75
2060	Primer & 2 coats	.22	.76	.98
2080	Misc. metal brushwork, ladders	.72	5.95	6.67
2100	Pipes, to 4″ dia.	.10	1.25	1.35
2120	6″ to 8″ dia.	.19	2.51	2.70
2140	10″ to 12″ dia.	.62	3.75	4.37
2160	Railings, 2″ pipe	.26	2.98	3.24
2180	Handrail, single	.18	1.19	1.37
2185	Caulking & Sealants, Polyurethane, In place, 1 or 2 component, 1/2″ X 1/4″	.36	1.93	2.29

C30 Interior Finishes

C3020 Floor Finishes

C3020 410	Tile & Covering	COST PER S.F.		
		MAT.	INST.	TOTAL
0060	Carpet tile, nylon, fusion bonded, 18" x 18" or 24" x 24", 24 oz.	3.55	.69	4.24
0080	35 oz.	4.38	.69	5.07
0100	42 oz.	5.65	.69	6.34
0140	Carpet, tufted, nylon, roll goods, 12' wide, 26 oz.	3.67	1.11	4.78
0160	36 oz.	4.81	1.11	5.92
0180	Woven, wool, 36 oz.	16	.78	16.78
0200	42 oz.	16.55	.78	17.33
0220	Padding, add to above, minimum	.62	.37	.99
0240	Maximum	1.12	.37	1.49
0260	Composition flooring, acrylic, 1/4" thick	1.79	5.55	7.34
0280	3/8" thick	2.27	6.40	8.67
0300	Epoxy, minimum	3.03	4.27	7.30
0320	Maximum	4.37	5.90	10.27
0340	Epoxy terrazzo, minimum	6.50	6.10	12.60
0360	Maximum	9.90	8.15	18.05
0380	Mastic, hot laid, 1-1/2" thick, minimum	4.48	4.18	8.66
0400	Maximum	5.75	5.55	11.30
0420	Neoprene 1/4" thick, minimum	4.41	5.30	9.71
0440	Maximum	6.05	6.70	12.75
0460	Polyacrylate with ground granite 1/4", minimum	3.88	3.92	7.80
0480	Maximum	7	6	13
0500	Polyester with colored quart 2 chips 1/16", minimum	3.45	2.71	6.16
0520	Maximum	5.15	4.27	9.42
0540	Polyurethane with vinyl chips, minimum	8.25	2.71	10.96
0560	Maximum	11.90	3.34	15.24
0600	Concrete topping, granolithic concrete, 1/2" thick	.32	4.60	4.92
0620	1" thick	.64	4.71	5.35
0640	2" thick	1.27	5.40	6.67
0660	Heavy duty 3/4" thick, minimum	.43	7.10	7.53
0680	Maximum	.80	8.50	9.30
0700	For colors, add to above, minimum	.48	1.64	2.12
0720	Maximum	.81	1.81	2.62
0740	Exposed aggregate finish, minimum	.47	.83	1.30
0760	Maximum	.89	1.12	2.01
0780	Abrasives, .25 P.S.F. add to above, minimum	.56	.61	1.17
0800	Maximum	.85	.61	1.46
0820	Dust on coloring, add, minimum	.48	.40	.88
0840	Maximum	.81	.83	1.64
0860	Floor coloring using 0.6 psf powdered color, 1/2" integral, minimum	5.30	4.60	9.90
0880	Maximum	5.60	4.60	10.20
0900	Dustproofing, add, minimum	.19	.27	.46
0920	Maximum	.70	.40	1.10
0930	Paint	.41	1.42	1.83
0940	Hardeners, metallic add, minimum	.56	.61	1.17
0960	Maximum	1.68	.91	2.59
0980	Non-metallic, minimum	.22	.61	.83
1000	Maximum	.67	.91	1.58
1020	Integral topping and finish, 1:1:2 mix, 3/16" thick	.11	2.71	2.82
1040	1/2" thick	.29	2.86	3.15
1060	3/4" thick	.43	3.19	3.62
1080	1" thick	.58	3.62	4.20
1100	Terrazzo, minimum	3.61	16.25	19.86
1120	Maximum	6.70	20.50	27.20
1340	Cork tile, minimum	7.70	1.57	9.27
1360	Maximum	17.35	1.57	18.92
1380	Polyethylene, in rolls, minimum	4.48	1.80	6.28
1400	Maximum	7.50	1.80	9.30
1420	Polyurethane, thermoset, minimum	5.95	4.95	10.90

C3020 Floor Finishes

C3020 410	Tile & Covering	COST PER S.F.		
		MAT.	INST.	TOTAL
1440	Maximum	7.45	9.90	17.35
1460	Rubber, sheet goods, minimum	8.40	4.12	12.52
1480	Maximum	13.50	5.50	19
1500	Tile, minimum	7.95	1.24	9.19
1520	Maximum	15.35	1.80	17.15
1580	Vinyl, composition tile, minimum	.95	.99	1.94
1600	Maximum	2.49	.99	3.48
1620	Vinyl tile, minimum	3.76	.99	4.75
1640	Maximum	4.02	.99	5.01
1660	Sheet goods, minimum	4.51	1.98	6.49
1680	Maximum	8.25	2.47	10.72
1720	Tile, ceramic natural clay	6.45	4.85	11.30
1730	Marble, synthetic 12"x12"x5/8"	9.90	14.80	24.70
1740	Porcelain type, minimum	5.70	4.85	10.55
1760	Maximum	6.35	5.70	12.05
1800	Quarry tile, mud set, minimum	8.05	6.35	14.40
1820	Maximum	9.40	8.05	17.45
1840	Thin set, deduct		1.27	1.27
1850	Tile, natural stone, marble, in mortar bed, 12" x 12" x 3/8" thick	99.50	24.50	124
1860	Terrazzo precast, minimum	5.15	6.60	11.75
1880	Maximum	10.25	6.60	16.85
1900	Non-slip, minimum	21.50	16.80	38.30
1920	Maximum	22.50	22.50	45
1960	Stone flooring, polished marble in mortar bed	9.30	24.50	33.80
2020	Wood block, end grain factory type, natural finish, 2" thick	4.53	4.53	9.06
2040	Fir, vertical grain, 1"x4", no finish, minimum	2.84	2.22	5.06
2060	Maximum	3.01	2.22	5.23
2080	Prefinished white oak, prime grade, 2-1/4" wide	5.15	3.33	8.48
2100	3-1/4" wide	5.60	3.06	8.66
2120	Maple strip, sanded and finished, minimum	5.70	4.86	10.56
2140	Maximum	5.90	4.86	10.76
2160	Oak strip, sanded and finished, minimum	4.25	4.86	9.11
2180	Maximum	5.50	4.86	10.36
2200	Parquetry, sanded and finished, minimum	5.50	5.05	10.55
2220	Maximum	8.65	7.20	15.85
2260	Add for sleepers on concrete, treated, 24" O.C., 1"x2"	1.78	2.90	4.68
2280	1"x3"	2	2.28	4.28
2300	2"x4"	.95	1.15	2.10
2340	Underlayment, plywood, 3/8" thick	1.02	.75	1.77
2350	1/2" thick	1.17	.78	1.95
2360	5/8" thick	1.30	.81	2.11
2370	3/4" thick	1.54	.87	2.41
2380	Particle board, 3/8" thick	.44	.75	1.19
2390	1/2" thick	.46	.78	1.24
2400	5/8" thick	.57	.81	1.38
2410	3/4" thick	.68	.87	1.55
2420	Hardboard, 4' x 4', .215" thick	.63	.75	1.38
9200	Vinyl, composition tile, 12" x 12" x 1/8" thick, recycled content	2.20	.99	3.19

C3030 Ceiling Finishes

2 Coats of Plaster on Gypsum Lath on Wood Furring

Fiberglass Board on Exposed Suspended Grid System

Plaster and Metal Lath on Metal Furring

C3030 105 — Plaster Ceilings

	TYPE	LATH	FURRING	SUPPORT		COST PER S.F. MAT.	INST.	TOTAL
2400	2 coat gypsum	3/8" gypsum	1"x3" wood, 16" O.C.	wood		1.20	5.65	6.85
2500	Painted			masonry		1.23	5.80	7.03
2600				concrete		1.23	6.50	7.73
2700	3 coat gypsum	3.4# metal		wood		1.57	6.15	7.72
2800	Painted			masonry		1.60	6.25	7.85
2900				concrete		1.60	6.95	8.55
3000	2 coat perlite	3/8" gypsum		wood		1.25	5.90	7.15
3100	Painted			masonry		1.28	6.05	7.33
3200				concrete		1.28	6.75	8.03
3300	3 coat perlite	3.4# metal		wood		1.44	6.05	7.49
3400	Painted			masonry		1.47	6.15	7.62
3500				concrete		1.47	6.85	8.32
3600	2 coat gypsum	3/8" gypsum	3/4" CRC, 12" O.C.	1-1/2" CRC, 48"O.C.		1.25	6.70	7.95
3700	Painted		3/4" CRC, 16" O.C.	1-1/2" CRC, 48"O.C.		1.22	6.10	7.32
3800			3/4" CRC, 24" O.C.	1-1/2" CRC, 48"O.C.		1.10	5.60	6.70
3900	2 coat perlite		3/4" CRC, 12" O.C.	1-1/2" CRC, 48"O.C		1.30	7.20	8.50
4000	Painted		3/4" CRC, 16" O.C.	1-1/2" CRC, 48"O.C.		1.27	6.60	7.87
4100			3/4" CRC, 24" O.C.	1-1/2" CRC, 48"O.C.		1.15	6.10	7.25
4200	3 coat gypsum	3.4# metal	3/4" CRC, 12" O.C.	1-1/2" CRC, 36" O.C.		1.78	8.90	10.68
4300	Painted		3/4" CRC, 16" O.C.	1-1/2" CRC, 36" O.C.		1.75	8.25	10
4400			3/4" CRC, 24" O.C.	1-1/2" CRC, 36" O.C.		1.63	7.75	9.38
4500	3 coat perlite		3/4" CRC, 12" O.C.	1-1/2" CRC, 36" O.C.		1.96	9.75	11.71
4600	Painted		3/4" CRC, 16" O.C.	1-1/2" CRC, 36" O.C.		1.93	9.15	11.08
4700			3/4" CRC, 24" O.C.	1-1/2" CRC, 36" O.C.		1.81	8.65	10.46

C3030 110 — Drywall Ceilings

	TYPE	FINISH	FURRING	SUPPORT		COST PER S.F. MAT.	INST.	TOTAL
4800	1/2" F.R. drywall	painted and textured	1"x3" wood, 16" O.C.	wood		.91	3.48	4.39
4900				masonry		.94	3.59	4.53
5000				concrete		.94	4.29	5.23
5100	5/8" F.R. drywall			wood		.93	3.48	4.41
5200				masonry		.96	3.59	4.55
5300				concrete		.96	4.29	5.25
5400	1/2" F.R. drywall		7/8" resil. channels	24" O.C.		.75	3.37	4.12

C3030 Ceiling Finishes

C3030 110   Drywall Ceilings

	TYPE	FINISH	FURRING	SUPPORT		COST PER S.F.		
						MAT.	INST.	TOTAL
5500	1/2" F.R. drywall	painted and textured	1"x2" wood	stud clips		.91	3.23	4.14
5602		painted	1-5/8" metal studs	24" O.C.		.80	3.01	3.81
5700	5/8" F.R. drywall	painted and textured				.82	3.01	3.83
5702								

C3030 140   Plaster Ceiling Components

		COST PER S.F.		
		MAT.	INST.	TOTAL
0060	Plaster, gypsum incl. finish			
0080	3 coats	.59	3.67	4.26
0100	Perlite, incl. finish, 2 coats	.46	3.61	4.07
0120	3 coats	.77	4.55	5.32
0140	Thin coat on drywall	.11	.71	.82
0200	Lath, gypsum, 3/8" thick	.33	.87	1.20
0220	1/2" thick	.30	.91	1.21
0240	5/8" thick	.33	1.07	1.40
0260	Metal, diamond, 2.5 lb.	.52	.70	1.22
0280	3.4 lb.	.52	.75	1.27
0300	Flat rib, 2.75 lb.	.40	.70	1.10
0320	3.4 lb.	.54	.75	1.29
0440	Furring, steel channels, 3/4" galvanized , 12" O.C.	.37	2.27	2.64
0460	16" O.C.	.34	1.65	1.99
0480	24" O.C.	.22	1.14	1.36
0500	1-1/2" galvanized , 12" O.C.	.51	2.51	3.02
0520	16" O.C.	.46	1.84	2.30
0540	24" O.C.	.30	1.22	1.52
0560	Wood strips, 1"x3", on wood, 12" O.C.	.42	1.62	2.04
0580	16" O.C.	.32	1.22	1.54
0600	24" O.C.	.21	.81	1.02
0620	On masonry, 12" O.C.	.46	1.77	2.23
0640	16" O.C.	.35	1.33	1.68
0660	24" O.C.	.23	.89	1.12
0680	On concrete, 12" O.C.	.46	2.70	3.16
0700	16" O.C.	.35	2.03	2.38
0720	24" O.C.	.23	1.35	1.58
0940	Paint on plaster or drywall, roller work, primer + 1 coat	.14	.49	.63
0960	Primer + 2 coats	.21	.63	.84

C3030 210   Acoustical Ceilings

	TYPE	TILE	GRID	SUPPORT		COST PER S.F.		
						MAT.	INST.	TOTAL
5800	5/8" fiberglass board	24" x 48"	tee	suspended		2.12	1.70	3.82
5900		24" x 24"	tee	suspended		2.35	1.86	4.21
6000	3/4" fiberglass board	24" x 48"	tee	suspended		2.84	1.73	4.57
6100		24" x 24"	tee	suspended		3.07	1.89	4.96
6500	5/8" mineral fiber	12" x 12"	1"x3" wood, 12" O.C.	wood		2.48	3.51	5.99
6600				masonry		2.52	3.66	6.18
6700				concrete		2.52	4.59	7.11
6800	3/4" mineral fiber			wood		2.38	3.51	5.89
6900				masonry		2.38	3.51	5.89
7000				concrete		2.38	3.51	5.89
7100	3/4"mineral fiber on		25 ga. channels	runners		2.79	4.31	7.10
7102	5/8" F.R. drywall							

C30 Interior Finishes

C3030 Ceiling Finishes

C3030 210 — Acoustical Ceilings

	TYPE	TILE	GRID	SUPPORT		COST PER S.F.		
						MAT.	INST.	TOTAL
7200 7201 7202	5/8" plastic coated Mineral fiber	12" x 12"	25 ga. channels	adhesive backed		2.48	1.89	4.37
7300 7301 7302	3/4" plastic coated Mineral fiber	12" x 12"		adhesive backed		2.38	1.89	4.27
7400 7401 7402	3/4" mineral fiber	12" x 12"	conceal 2" bar & channels	suspended		2.63	4.26	6.89

C3030 240 — Acoustical Ceiling Components

		COST PER S.F.		
		MAT.	INST.	TOTAL
2480	Ceiling boards, eggcrate, acrylic, 1/2" x 1/2" x 1/2" cubes	2.05	1.13	3.18
2500	Polystyrene, 3/8" x 3/8" x 1/2" cubes	1.72	1.11	2.83
2520	1/2" x 1/2" x 1/2" cubes	1.91	1.13	3.04
2540	Fiberglass boards, plain, 5/8" thick	1.12	.91	2.03
2560	3/4" thick	1.84	.94	2.78
2580	Grass cloth faced, 3/4" thick	2.21	1.13	3.34
2600	1" thick	3.01	1.17	4.18
2620	Luminous panels, prismatic, acrylic	2.49	1.42	3.91
2640	Polystyrene	1.28	1.42	2.70
2660	Flat or ribbed, acrylic	4.33	1.42	5.75
2680	Polystyrene	2.97	1.42	4.39
2700	Drop pan, white, acrylic	6.35	1.42	7.77
2720	Polystyrene	5.30	1.42	6.72
2740	Mineral fiber boards, 5/8" thick, standard	.79	.84	1.63
2760	Plastic faced	1.21	1.42	2.63
2780	2 hour rating	1.05	.84	1.89
2800	Perforated aluminum sheets, .024 thick, corrugated painted	2.57	1.16	3.73
2820	Plain	4.31	1.13	5.44
3080	Mineral fiber, plastic coated, 12" x 12" or 12" x 24", 5/8" thick	2.06	1.89	3.95
3100	3/4" thick	1.96	1.89	3.85
3120	Fire rated, 3/4" thick, plain faced	1.42	1.89	3.31
3140	Mylar faced	1.42	1.89	3.31
3160	Add for ceiling primer	.14		.14
3180	Add for ceiling cement	.42		.42
3240	Suspension system, furring, 1" x 3" wood 12" O.C.	.42	1.62	2.04
3260	T bar suspension system, 2' x 4' grid	.77	.71	1.48
3280	2' x 2' grid	1	.87	1.87
3300	Concealed Z bar suspension system 12" module	.86	1.09	1.95
3320	Add to above for 1-1/2" carrier channels 4' O.C.	.12	1.20	1.32
3340	Add to above for carrier channels for recessed lighting	.22	1.23	1.45

D10 Conveying

D1010 Elevators and Lifts

Hydraulic

Traction Geared

Traction Gearless

D1010 110	Hydraulic	COST EACH		
		MAT.	INST.	TOTAL
1300	Pass. elev., 1500 lb., 2 Floors, 100 FPM	47,900	18,200	66,100
1400	5 Floors, 100 FPM	88,500	48,500	137,000
1600	2000 lb., 2 Floors, 100 FPM	49,400	18,200	67,600
1700	5 floors, 100 FPM	90,000	48,500	138,500
1900	2500 lb., 2 Floors, 100 FPM	51,000	18,200	69,200
2000	5 floors, 100 FPM	91,500	48,500	140,000
2200	3000 lb., 2 Floors, 100 FPM	52,000	18,200	70,200
2300	5 floors, 100 FPM	92,500	48,500	141,000
2500	3500 lb., 2 Floors, 100 FPM	55,000	18,200	73,200
2600	5 floors, 100 FPM	95,500	48,500	144,000
2800	4000 lb., 2 Floors, 100 FPM	56,500	18,200	74,700
2900	5 floors, 100 FPM	97,000	48,500	145,500
3100	4500 lb., 2 Floors, 100 FPM	59,000	18,200	77,200
3200	5 floors, 100 FPM	99,500	48,500	148,000
4000	Hospital elevators, 3500 lb., 2 Floors, 100 FPM	76,500	18,200	94,700
4100	5 floors, 100 FPM	126,000	48,500	174,500
4300	4000 lb., 2 Floors, 100 FPM	76,500	18,200	94,700
4400	5 floors, 100 FPM	126,000	48,500	174,500
4600	4500 lb., 2 Floors, 100 FPM	83,500	18,200	101,700
4800	5 floors, 100 FPM	133,000	48,500	181,500
4900	5000 lb., 2 Floors, 100 FPM	87,000	18,200	105,200
5000	5 floors, 100 FPM	136,000	48,500	184,500
6700	Freight elevators (Class "B"), 3000 lb., 2 Floors, 50 FPM	118,500	23,200	141,700
6800	5 floors, 100 FPM	212,000	61,000	273,000
7000	4000 lb., 2 Floors, 50 FPM	125,500	23,200	148,700
7100	5 floors, 100 FPM	218,500	61,000	279,500
7500	10,000 lb., 2 Floors, 50 FPM	154,500	23,200	177,700
7600	5 floors, 100 FPM	247,500	61,000	308,500
8100	20,000 lb., 2 Floors, 50 FPM	203,500	23,200	226,700
8200	5 Floors, 100 FPM	296,500	61,000	357,500

D1010 140	Traction Geared Elevators	COST EACH		
		MAT.	INST.	TOTAL
1300	Passenger, 2000 Lb., 5 floors, 200 FPM	121,500	45,700	167,200
1500	15 floors, 350 FPM	286,500	138,000	424,500
1600	2500 Lb., 5 floors, 200 FPM	125,500	45,700	171,200
2100	15 floors, 350 FPM	291,000	138,000	429,000
2200	3500 Lb., 5 floors, 200 FPM	127,500	45,700	173,200
2400	15 floors, 350 FPM	292,500	138,000	430,500
2500	4000 Lb., 5 floors, 200 FPM	129,000	45,700	174,700
2700	15 floors, 350 FPM	293,500	138,000	431,500

D20 Plumbing

D2010 Plumbing Fixtures

D1010 140	Traction Geared Elevators	COST EACH		
		MAT.	INST.	TOTAL
2800	4500 Lb., 5 floors, 200 FPM	131,000	45,700	176,700
3000	15 floors, 350 FPM	296,000	138,000	434,000
3100	5000 Lb., 5 floors, 200 FPM	133,500	45,700	179,200
3300	15 floors, 350 FPM	298,500	138,000	436,500
4000	Hospital, 3500 Lb., 5 floors, 200 FPM	122,500	45,700	168,200
4200	15 floors, 350 FPM	305,000	138,000	443,000
4300	4000 Lb., 5 floors, 200 FPM	122,500	45,700	168,200
4500	15 floors, 350 FPM	305,000	138,000	443,000
4600	4500 Lb., 5 floors, 200 FPM	128,500	45,700	174,200
4800	15 floors, 350 FPM	311,000	138,000	449,000
4900	5000 Lb., 5 floors, 200 FPM	130,000	45,700	175,700
5100	15 floors, 350 FPM	313,000	138,000	451,000
6000	Freight, 4000 Lb., 5 floors, 50 FPM class 'B'	146,500	47,300	193,800
6200	15 floors, 200 FPM class 'B'	346,500	164,500	511,000
6300	8000 Lb., 5 floors, 50 FPM class 'B'	186,000	47,300	233,300
6500	15 floors, 200 FPM class 'B'	386,000	164,500	550,500
7000	10,000 Lb., 5 floors, 50 FPM class 'B'	197,500	47,300	244,800
7200	15 floors, 200 FPM class 'B'	575,000	164,500	739,500
8000	20,000 Lb., 5 floors, 50 FPM class 'B'	218,500	47,300	265,800
8200	15 floors, 200 FPM class 'B'	596,000	164,500	760,500

D1010 150	Traction Gearless Elevators	COST EACH		
		MAT.	INST.	TOTAL
1700	Passenger, 2500 Lb., 10 floors, 200 FPM	300,000	119,000	419,000
1900	30 floors, 600 FPM	657,500	304,000	961,500
2000	3000 Lb., 10 floors, 200 FPM	301,000	119,000	420,000
2200	30 floors, 600 FPM	658,000	304,000	962,000
2300	3500 Lb., 10 floors, 200 FPM	302,000	119,000	421,000
2500	30 floors, 600 FPM	659,500	304,000	963,500
2700	50 floors, 800 FPM	981,000	489,000	1,470,000
2800	4000 Lb., 10 floors, 200 FPM	303,500	119,000	422,500
3000	30 floors, 600 FPM	660,500	304,000	964,500
3200	50 floors, 800 FPM	982,000	489,000	1,471,000
3300	4500 Lb., 10 floors, 200 FPM	305,500	119,000	424,500
3500	30 floors, 600 FPM	663,000	304,000	967,000
3700	50 floors, 800 FPM	984,500	489,000	1,473,500
3800	5000 Lb., 10 floors, 200 FPM	308,500	119,000	427,500
4000	30 floors, 600 FPM	665,500	304,000	969,500
4200	50 floors, 800 FPM	987,000	489,000	1,476,000
6000	Hospital, 3500 Lb., 10 floors, 200 FPM	306,000	119,000	425,000
6200	30 floors, 600 FPM	701,500	304,000	1,005,500
6400	4000 Lb., 10 floors, 200 FPM	306,000	119,000	425,000
6600	30 floors, 600 FPM	701,500	304,000	1,005,500
6800	4500 Lb., 10 floors, 200 FPM	312,000	119,000	431,000
7000	30 floors, 600 FPM	707,000	304,000	1,011,000
7200	5000 Lb., 10 floors, 200 FPM	313,500	119,000	432,500
7400	30 floors, 600 FPM	709,000	304,000	1,013,000

Minimum Plumbing Fixture Requirements

Type of Building or Occupancy (2)	Water Closets (14) (Fixtures per Person)		Urinals (5,10) (Fixtures per Person)		Lavatories (Fixtures per Person)		Bathtubs or Showers (Fixtures per Person)	Drinking Fountains (Fixtures per Person) (3, 13)
	Male	Female	Male	Female	Male	Female		
Assembly Places- Theatres, Auditoriums, Convention Halls, etc.-for permanent employee use	1: 1 - 15 2: 16 - 35 3: 36 - 55 Over 55, add 1 fixture for each additional 40 persons	1: 1 - 15 2: 16 - 35 3: 36 - 55	0: 1 - 9 1: 10 - 50 Add one fixture for each additional 50 males		1 per 40	1 per 40		
Assembly Places- Theatres, Auditoriums, Convention Halls, etc. - for public use	1: 1 - 100 2: 101 - 200 3: 201 - 400 Over 400, add 1 fixture for each additional 500 males and 1 for each additional 125 females	3: 1 - 50 4: 51 - 100 8: 101 - 200 11: 201 - 400	1: 1 - 100 2: 101 - 200 3: 201 - 400 4: 401 - 600 Over 600, add 1 fixture for each additional 300 males		1: 1 - 200 2: 201 - 400 3: 401 - 750 Over 750, add 1 fixture for each additional 500 persons	1: 1 - 200 2: 201 - 400 3: 401 - 750		1: 1 - 150 2: 151 - 400 3: 401 - 750 Over 750, add one fixture for each additional 500 persons
Dormitories (9) School or Labor	1 per 10 Add 1 fixture for each additional 25 males (over 10) and 1 for each additional 20 females (over 8)	1 per 8	1 per 25 Over 150, add 1 fixture for each additional 50 males		1 per 12 Over 12 add 1 fixture for each additional 20 males and 1 for each 15 additional females	1 per 12	1 per 8 For females add 1 bathtub per 30. Over 150, add 1 per 20	1 per 150 (12)
Dormitories- for Staff Use	1: 1 - 15 2: 16 - 35 3: 36 - 55 Over 55, add 1 fixture for each additional 40 persons	1: 1 - 15 3: 16 - 35 4: 36 - 55	1 per 50		1 per 40	1 per 40	1 per 8	
Dwellings: Single Dwelling Multiple Dwelling or Apartment House	1 per dwelling 1 per dwelling or apartment unit				1 per dwelling 1 per dwelling or apartment unit		1 per dwelling 1 per dwelling or apartment unit	
Hospital Waiting rooms	1 per room				1 per room			1 per 150 (12)
Hospitals- for employee use	1: 1 - 15 2: 16 - 35 3: 36 - 55 Over 55, add 1 fixture for each additional 40 persons	1: 1 - 15 3: 16 - 35 4: 36 - 55	0: 1 - 9 1: 10 - 50 Add 1 fixture for each additional 50 males		1 per 40	1 per 40		
Hospitals: Individual Room Ward Room	1 per room 1 per 8 patients				1 per room 1 per 10 patients		1 per room 1 per 20 patients	1 per 150 (12)
Industrial (6) Warehouses Workshops, Foundries and similar establishments- for employee use	1: 1 -10 2: 11 - 25 3: 26 - 50 4: 51 - 75 5: 76 - 100 Over 100, add 1 fixture for each additional 30 persons	1: 1 -10 2: 11 - 25 3: 26 - 50 4: 51 - 75 5: 76 - 100			Up to 100, per 10 persons Over 100, 1 per 15 persons (7, 8)		1 shower for each 15 persons exposed to excessive heat or to skin contamination with poisonous, infectious or irritating material	1 per 150 (12)
Institutional - Other than Hospitals or Penal Institutions (on each occupied floor)	1 per 25	1 per 20	0: 1 - 9 1: 10 - 50 Add 1 fixture for each additional 50 males		1 per 10	1 per 10	1 per 8	1 per 150 (12)
Institutional - Other than Hospitals or Penal Institutions (on each occupied floor)- for employee use	1: 1 - 15 2: 16 - 35 3: 36 - 55 Over 55, add 1 fixture for each additional 40 persons	1: 1 - 15 3: 16 - 35 4: 36 - 55	0: 1 - 9 1: 10 - 50 Add 1 fixture for each additional 50 males		1 per 40	1 per 40	1 per 8	1 per 150 (12)
Office or Public Buildings	1: 1 - 100 2: 101 - 200 3: 201 - 400 Over 400, add 1 fixture for each additional 500 males and 1 for each additional 150 females	3: 1 - 50 4: 51 - 100 8: 101 - 200 11: 201 - 400	1: 1 - 100 2: 101 - 200 3: 201 - 400 4: 401 - 600 Over 600, add 1 fixture for each additional 300 males		1: 1 - 200 2: 201 - 400 3: 401 - 750 Over 750, add 1 fixture for each additional 500 persons	1: 1 - 200 2: 201 - 400 3: 401 - 750		1 per 150 (12)
Office or Public Buildings - for employee use	1: 1 - 15 2: 16 - 35 3: 36 - 55 Over 55, add 1 fixture for each additional 40 persons	1: 1 - 15 3: 16 - 35 4: 36 - 55	0: 1 - 9 1: 10 - 50 Add 1 fixture for each additional 50 males		1 per 40	1 per 40		

D20 Plumbing

D2010 Plumbing Fixtures

Minimum Plumbing Fixture Requirements

Type of Building or Occupancy	Water Closets (14) (Fixtures per Person)		Urinals (5, 10) (Fixtures per Person)		Lavatories (Fixtures per Person)		Bathtubs or Showers (Fixtures per Person)	Drinking Fountains (Fixtures per Person) (3, 13)
	Male	Female	Male	Female	Male	Female		
Penal Institutions - for employee use	1: 1 - 15 2: 16 - 35 3: 36 - 55 Over 55, add 1 fixture for each additional 40 persons	1: 1 - 15 3: 16 - 35 4: 36 - 55	0: 1 - 9 1: 10 - 50 Add 1 fixture for each additional 50 males		1 per 40	1 per 40		1 per 150 (12)
Penal Institutions - for prison use								
Cell	1 per cell				1 per cell			1 per cellblock floor
Exercise room	1 per exercise room		1 per exercise room		1 per exercise room			1 per exercise room
Restaurants, Pubs and Lounges (11)	1: 1 - 50 2: 51 - 150 3: 151 - 300 Over 300, add 1 fixture for each additional 200 persons	1: 1 - 50 2: 51 - 150 4: 151 - 300	1: 1 - 150 Over 150, add 1 fixture for each additional 150 males		1: 1 - 150 2: 151 - 200 3: 201 - 400 Over 400, add 1 fixture for each additional 400 persons	1: 1 - 150 2: 151 - 200 3: 201 - 400		
Schools - for staff use All Schools	1: 1 - 15 2: 16 - 35 3: 36 - 55 Over 55, add 1 fixture for each additional 40 persons	1: 1 - 15 3: 16 - 35 4: 36 - 55	1 per 50		1 per 40	1 per 40		
Schools - for student use: Nursery	1: 1 - 20 2: 21 - 50 Over 50, add 1 fixture for each additional 50 persons	1: 1 - 20 2: 21 - 50			1: 1 - 25 2: 26 - 50 Over 50, add 1 fixture for each additional 50 persons	1: 1 - 25 2: 26 - 50		1 per 150 (12)
Elementary	1 per 30	1 per 25	1 per 75		1 per 35	1 per 35		1 per 150 (12)
Secondary	1 per 40	1 per 30	1 per 35		1 per 40	1 per 40		1 per 150 (12)
Others (Colleges, Universities, Adult Centers, etc.	1 per 40	1 per 30	1 per 35		1 per 40	1 per 40		1 per 150 (12)
Worship Places Educational and Activities Unit	1 per 150	1 per 75	1 per 150		1 per 2 water closets			1 per 150 (12)
Worship Places Principal Assembly Place	1 per 150	1 per 75	1 per 150		1 per 2 water closets			1 per 150 (12)

Notes:
1. The figures shown are based upon one (1) fixture being the minimum required for the number of persons indicated or any fraction thereof.
2. Building categories not shown on this table shall be considered separately by the Administrative Authority.
3. Drinking fountains shall not be installed in toilet rooms.
4. Laundry trays. One (1) laundry tray or one (1) automatic washer standpipe for each dwelling unit or one (1) laundry trays or one (1) automatic washer standpipes, or combination thereof, for each twelve (12) apartments. Kitchen sinks, one (1) for each dwelling or apartment unit.
5. For each urinal added in excess of the minimum required, one water closet may be deducted. The number of water closets shall not be reduced to less than two-thirds (2/3) of the minimum requirement.
6. As required by ANSI Z4.1-1968, Sanitation in Places of Employment.
7. Where there is exposure to skin contamination with poisonous, infectious, or irritating materials, provide one (1) lavatory for each five (5) persons.
8. Twenty-four (24) lineal inches of wash sink or eighteen (18) inches of a circular basin, when provided with water outlets for such space shall be considered equivalent to one (1) lavatory.
9. Laundry trays, one (1) for each fifty (50) persons. Service sinks, one (1) for each hundred (100) persons.
10. General. In applying this schedule of facilities, consideration shall be given to the accessibility of the fixtures. Conformity purely on a numerical basis may not result in an installation suited to the need of the individual establishment. For example, schools should be provided with toilet facilities on each floor having classrooms.
  a. Surrounding materials, wall and floor space to a point two (2) feet in front of urinal lip and four (4) feet above the floor, and at least two (2) feet to each side of the urinal shall be lined with non-absorbent materials.
  b. Trough urinals shall be prohibited.
11. A restaurant is defined as a business which sells food to be consumed on the premises.
  a. The number of occupants for a drive-in restaurant shall be considered as equal to the number of parking stalls.
  b. Employee toilet facilities shall not to be included in the above restaurant requirements. Hand washing facilities shall be available in the kitchen for employees.
12. Where food is consumed indoors, water stations may be substituted for drinking fountains. Offices, or public buildings for use by more than six (6) persons shall have one (1) drinking fountain for the first one hundred fifty (150) persons and one additional fountain for each three hundred (300) persons thereafter.
13. There shall be a minimum of one (1) drinking fountain per occupied floor in schools, theaters, auditoriums, dormitories, offices of public building.
14. The total number of water closets for females shall be at least equal to the total number of water closets and urinals required for males.

423

D2010 Plumbing Fixtures

One Piece Wall Hung Water Closet

Wall Hung Urinal

Side By Side Water Closet Group

Floor Mount Water Closet

Stall Type Urinal

Back to Back Water Closet Group

D2010 110	Water Closet Systems	COST EACH		
		MAT.	INST.	TOTAL
1800	Water closet, vitreous china			
1840	Tank type, wall hung			
1880	Close coupled two piece	1,575	740	2,315
1920	Floor mount, one piece	1,550	785	2,335
1960	One piece low profile	1,600	785	2,385
2000	Two piece close coupled	660	785	1,445
2040	Bowl only with flush valve			
2080	Wall hung	1,925	835	2,760
2120	Floor mount	885	800	1,685
2122				
2160	Floor mount, ADA compliant with 18" high bowl	880	820	1,700

D2010 120	Water Closets, Group	COST EACH		
		MAT.	INST.	TOTAL
1760	Water closets, battery mount, wall hung, side by side, first closet	2,025	860	2,885
1800	Each additional water closet, add	1,925	815	2,740
3000	Back to back, first pair of closets	3,525	1,150	4,675
3100	Each additional pair of closets, back to back	3,475	1,125	4,600

D2010 210	Urinal Systems	COST EACH		
		MAT.	INST.	TOTAL
2000	Urinal, vitreous china, wall hung	620	825	1,445
2040	Stall type	1,425	990	2,415

D2010 Plumbing Fixtures

Systems are complete with trim and rough-in (supply, waste and vent) to connect to supply branches and waste mains.

Vanity Top

Wall Hung

Counter Top Single Bowl

Counter Top Double Bowl

D2010 310	Lavatory Systems	COST EACH		
		MAT.	INST.	TOTAL
1560	Lavatory w/trim, vanity top, PE on CI, 20" x 18", Vanity top by others.	820	740	1,560
1600	19" x 16" oval	650	740	1,390
1640	18" round	930	740	1,670
1680	Cultured marble, 19" x 17"	650	740	1,390
1720	25" x 19"	685	740	1,425
1760	Stainless, self-rimming, 25" x 22"	865	740	1,605
1800	17" x 22"	850	740	1,590
1840	Steel enameled, 20" x 17"	675	760	1,435
1880	19" round	645	760	1,405
1920	Vitreous china, 20" x 16"	745	775	1,520
1960	19" x 16"	750	775	1,525
2000	22" x 13"	750	775	1,525
2040	Wall hung, PE on CI, 18" x 15"	960	815	1,775
2080	19" x 17"	1,050	815	1,865
2120	20" x 18"	825	815	1,640
2160	Vitreous china, 18" x 15"	775	840	1,615
2200	19" x 17"	730	840	1,570
2240	24" x 20"	820	840	1,660
2300	20" x 27", handicap	1,500	905	2,405

D2010 410	Kitchen Sink Systems	COST EACH		
		MAT.	INST.	TOTAL
1720	Kitchen sink w/trim, countertop, PE on CI, 24"x21", single bowl	805	810	1,615
1760	30" x 21" single bowl	1,125	810	1,935
1800	32" x 21" double bowl	910	875	1,785
1880	Stainless steel, 19" x 18" single bowl	1,150	810	1,960
1920	25" x 22" single bowl	1,225	810	2,035
1960	33" x 22" double bowl	1,575	875	2,450
2000	43" x 22" double bowl	1,775	885	2,660
2040	44" x 22" triple bowl	2,025	925	2,950
2080	44" x 24" corner double bowl	1,450	885	2,335
2120	Steel, enameled, 24" x 21" single bowl	1,050	810	1,860
2160	32" x 21" double bowl	1,075	875	1,950
2240	Raised deck, PE on CI, 32" x 21", dual level, double bowl	995	1,100	2,095
2280	42" x 21" dual level, triple bowl	1,850	1,200	3,050

D2010 Plumbing Fixtures

Laboratory Sink

Service Sink

Systems are complete with trim and rough-in (supply, waste and vent) to connect to supply branches and waste mains.

Single Compartment Sink

Double Compartment Sink

D2010 420	Laundry Sink Systems	COST EACH		
		MAT.	INST.	TOTAL
1740	Laundry sink w/trim, PE on CI, black iron frame			
1760	24" x 20", single compartment	1,150	795	1,945
1840	48" x 21" double compartment	1,450	865	2,315
1920	Molded stone, on wall, 22" x 21" single compartment	655	795	1,450
1960	45"x 21" double compartment	900	865	1,765
2040	Plastic, on wall or legs, 18" x 23" single compartment	655	780	1,435
2080	20" x 24" single compartment	675	780	1,455
2120	36" x 23" double compartment	735	840	1,575
2160	40" x 24" double compartment	840	840	1,680

D2010 430	Laboratory Sink Systems	COST EACH		
		MAT.	INST.	TOTAL
1580	Laboratory sink w/trim, stainless steel, single bowl,			
1590	Stainless steel, single bowl,			
1600	Double drainboard, 54" x 24" O.D.	2,125	1,025	3,150
1640	Single drainboard, 47" x 24"O.D.	1,550	1,025	2,575
1670	Stainless steel, double bowl,			
1680	70" x 24" O.D.	2,325	1,025	3,350
1750	Polyethylene, single bowl,			
1760	Flanged, 14-1/2" x 14-1/2" O.D.	555	935	1,490
1800	18-1/2" x 18-1/2" O.D.	655	935	1,590
1840	23-1/2" x 20-1/2" O.D.	700	935	1,635
1920	Polypropylene, cup sink, oval, 7" x 4" O.D.	375	825	1,200
1960	10" x 4-1/2" O.D.	400	825	1,225
1961				

D20 Plumbing

D2010 Plumbing Fixtures

D2010 440	Service Sink Systems	COST EACH		
		MAT.	**INST.**	**TOTAL**
4260	Service sink w/trim, PE on CI, corner floor, 28" x 28", w/rim guard	2,725	1,050	3,775
4300	Wall hung w/rim guard, 22" x 18"	2,900	1,225	4,125
4340	24" x 20"	2,975	1,225	4,200
4380	Vitreous china, wall hung 22" x 20"	2,725	1,225	3,950
4383				

D2010 Plumbing Fixtures

Recessed Bathtub

Corner Bathtub

Systems are complete with trim and rough-in (supply, waste and vent) to connect to supply branches and waste mains.

Circular Wash Fountain

Semi-Circular Wash Fountain

D2010 510	Bathtub Systems	COST EACH		
		MAT.	INST.	TOTAL
2000	Bathtub, recessed, P.E. on Cl., 48" x 42"	3,525	920	4,445
2040	72" x 36"	3,625	1,025	4,650
2080	Mat bottom, 5' long	1,850	890	2,740
2120	5'-6" long	2,575	920	3,495
2160	Corner, 48" x 42"	3,525	890	4,415
2200	Formed steel, enameled, 4'-6" long	1,175	820	1,995

D2010 610	Group Wash Fountain Systems	COST EACH		
		MAT.	INST.	TOTAL
1740	Group wash fountain, precast terrazzo			
1760	Circular, 36" diameter	7,100	1,350	8,450
1800	54" diameter	10,600	1,475	12,075
1840	Semi-circular, 36" diameter	5,975	1,350	7,325
1880	54" diameter	8,175	1,475	9,650
1960	Stainless steel, circular, 36" diameter	6,050	1,250	7,300
2000	54" diameter	8,475	1,375	9,850
2040	Semi-circular, 36" diameter	6,000	1,250	7,250
2080	54" diameter	6,675	1,375	8,050
2160	Thermoplastic, circular, 36" diameter	4,975	1,025	6,000
2200	54" diameter	5,950	1,175	7,125
2240	Semi-circular, 36" diameter	4,975	1,025	6,000
2280	54" diameter	5,825	1,175	7,000

D2010 Plumbing Fixtures

Square Shower Stall

Corner Angle Shower Stall

Systems are complete with trim and rough-in (supply, waste and vent) to connect to supply branches and waste mains.

Wall Mounted, Low Back

Wall Mounted, No Back

D2010 710	Shower Systems	COST EACH		
		MAT.	INST.	TOTAL
1560	Shower, stall, baked enamel, molded stone receptor, 30" square	1,775	855	2,630
1600	32" square	1,775	865	2,640
1640	Terrazzo receptor, 32" square	1,975	865	2,840
1680	36" square	2,125	875	3,000
1720	36" corner angle	2,400	875	3,275
1800	Fiberglass one piece, three walls, 32" square	1,025	840	1,865
1840	36" square	1,050	840	1,890
1880	Polypropylene, molded stone receptor, 30" square	1,200	1,250	2,450
1920	32" square	1,200	1,250	2,450
1960	Built-in head, arm, bypass, stops and handles	117	320	437
2050	Shower, stainless steel panels, handicap			
2100	w/fixed and handheld head, control valves, grab bar, and seat	5,650	3,825	9,475
2500	Shower, group with six heads, thermostatic mix valves & balancing valve	5,450	935	6,385
2520	Five heads	4,525	850	5,375

D2010 810	Drinking Fountain Systems	COST EACH		
		MAT.	INST.	TOTAL
1740	Drinking fountain, one bubbler, wall mounted			
1760	Non recessed			
1800	Bronze, no back	1,500	485	1,985
1840	Cast iron, enameled, low back	1,400	485	1,885
1880	Fiberglass, 12" back	2,450	485	2,935
1920	Stainless steel, no back	1,550	485	2,035
1960	Semi-recessed, poly marble	1,450	485	1,935
2040	Stainless steel	1,650	485	2,135
2080	Vitreous china	1,375	485	1,860
2120	Full recessed, poly marble	2,150	485	2,635
2200	Stainless steel	2,075	485	2,560
2240	Floor mounted, pedestal type, aluminum	2,875	665	3,540
2320	Bronze	2,525	665	3,190
2360	Stainless steel	2,325	665	2,990

D2010 Plumbing Fixtures

Wall Hung Water Cooler

Floor Mounted Water Cooler

Systems are complete with trim and rough-in (supply, waste and vent) to connect to supply branches and waste mains.

D2010 820	Water Cooler Systems	COST EACH		
		MAT.	INST.	TOTAL
1840	Water cooler, electric, wall hung, 8.2 G.P.H.	1,200	630	1,830
1880	Dual height, 14.3 G.P.H.	1,475	645	2,120
1920	Wheelchair type, 7.5 G.P.H.	1,400	630	2,030
1960	Semi recessed, 8.1 G.P.H.	1,175	630	1,805
2000	Full recessed, 8 G.P.H.	2,525	675	3,200
2040	Floor mounted, 14.3 G.P.H.	1,325	545	1,870
2080	Dual height, 14.3 G.P.H.	1,675	665	2,340
2120	Refrigerated compartment type, 1.5 G.P.H.	1,950	545	2,495

D2010 Plumbing Fixtures

Two Fixture   Three Fixture

*Common wall is with adjacent bathrom.

D2010 920	Two Fixture Bathroom, Two Wall Plumbing	COST EACH		
		MAT.	INST.	TOTAL
1180	Bathroom, lavatory & water closet, 2 wall plumbing, stand alone	1,775	2,050	3,825
1200	Share common plumbing wall*	1,600	1,750	3,350

D2010 922	Two Fixture Bathroom, One Wall Plumbing	COST EACH		
		MAT.	INST.	TOTAL
2220	Bathroom, lavatory & water closet, one wall plumbing, stand alone	1,650	1,825	3,475
2240	Share common plumbing wall*	1,450	1,550	3,000

D2010 924	Three Fixture Bathroom, One Wall Plumbing	COST EACH		
		MAT.	INST.	TOTAL
1150	Bathroom, three fixture, one wall plumbing			
1160	Lavatory, water closet & bathtub			
1170	Stand alone	3,150	2,375	5,525
1180	Share common plumbing wall *	2,700	1,725	4,425

D2010 926	Three Fixture Bathroom, Two Wall Plumbing	COST EACH		
		MAT.	INST.	TOTAL
2130	Bathroom, three fixture, two wall plumbing			
2140	Lavatory, water closet & bathtub			
2160	Stand alone	3,175	2,425	5,600
2180	Long plumbing wall common *	2,850	1,925	4,775
3610	Lavatory, bathtub & water closet			
3620	Stand alone	3,425	2,750	6,175
3640	Long plumbing wall common *	3,225	2,475	5,700
4660	Water closet, corner bathtub & lavatory			
4680	Stand alone	4,875	2,450	7,325
4700	Long plumbing wall common *	4,350	1,850	6,200
6100	Water closet, stall shower & lavatory			
6120	Stand alone	3,575	2,750	6,325
6140	Long plumbing wall common *	3,400	2,525	5,925
7060	Lavatory, corner stall shower & water closet			
7080	Stand alone	3,925	2,425	6,350
7100	Short plumbing wall common *	3,225	1,625	4,850

D2010 Plumbing Fixtures

Four Fixture   Five Fixture

*Common wall is with adjacent bathroom.

D2010 928	Four Fixture Bathroom, Two Wall Plumbing	COST EACH		
		MAT.	INST.	TOTAL
1140	Bathroom, four fixture, two wall plumbing			
1150	Bathtub, water closet, stall shower & lavatory			
1160	Stand alone	4,600	2,625	7,225
1180	Long plumbing wall common *	4,075	2,025	6,100
2260	Bathtub, lavatory, corner stall shower & water closet			
2280	Stand alone	5,225	2,650	7,875
2320	Long plumbing wall common *	4,700	2,025	6,725
3620	Bathtub, stall shower, lavatory & water closet			
3640	Stand alone	5,075	3,300	8,375
3660	Long plumbing wall (opp. door) common *	4,525	2,700	7,225
4680	Bathroom, four fixture, three wall plumbing			
4700	Bathtub, stall shower, lavatory & water closet			
4720	Stand alone	5,900	3,650	9,550
4760	Long plumbing wall (opposite door) common *	5,725	3,350	9,075

D2010 932	Five Fixture Bathroom, Two Wall Plumbing	COST EACH		
		MAT.	INST.	TOTAL
1320	Bathroom, five fixture, two wall plumbing			
1340	Bathtub, water closet, stall shower & two lavatories			
1360	Stand alone	5,900	4,225	10,125
1400	One short plumbing wall common *	5,350	3,600	8,950
2360	Bathroom, five fixture, three wall plumbing			
2380	Water closet, bathtub, two lavatories & stall shower			
2400	Stand alone	6,525	4,225	10,750
2440	One short plumbing wall common *	5,975	3,625	9,600
4080	Bathroom, five fixture, one wall plumbing			
4100	Bathtub, two lavatories, corner stall shower & water closet			
4120	Stand alone	6,200	3,775	9,975
4160	Share common wall *	5,225	2,450	7,675

D20 Plumbing

D2020 Domestic Water Distribution

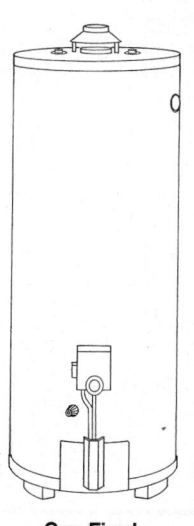

Gas Fired

Installation includes piping and fittings within 10' of heater. Gas and oil fired heaters require vent piping (not included with these units).

Oil Fired

D2020 220	Gas Fired Water Heaters - Residential Systems	COST EACH		
		MAT.	INST.	TOTAL
2200	Gas fired water heater, residential, 100°F rise			
2260	30 gallon tank, 32 GPH	1,825	1,450	3,275
2300	40 gallon tank, 32 GPH	2,150	1,625	3,775
2340	50 gallon tank, 63 GPH	2,200	1,625	3,825
2380	75 gallon tank, 63 GPH	3,075	1,800	4,875
2420	100 gallon tank, 63 GPH	3,250	1,900	5,150
2422				

D2020 230	Oil Fired Water Heaters - Residential Systems	COST EACH		
		MAT.	INST.	TOTAL
2200	Oil fired water heater, residential, 100°F rise			
2220	30 gallon tank, 103 GPH	2,100	1,350	3,450
2260	50 gallon tank, 145 GPH	2,675	1,500	4,175
2300	70 gallon tank, 164 GPH	3,750	1,700	5,450
2340	85 gallon tank, 181 GPH	11,200	1,725	12,925

D20 Plumbing

D2020 Domestic Water Distribution

Electric

Gas Fired

Systems below include piping and fittings within 10' of heater. Electric water heaters do not require venting. Gas fired heaters require vent piping (not included in these prices).

D2020 240	Electric Water Heaters - Commercial Systems	COST EACH		
		MAT.	INST.	TOTAL
1800	Electric water heater, commercial, 100°F rise			
1820	50 gallon tank, 9 KW 37 GPH	5,375	1,200	6,575
1860	80 gal, 12 KW 49 GPH	7,150	1,500	8,650
1900	36 KW 147 GPH	9,400	1,625	11,025
1940	120 gal, 36 KW 147 GPH	10,300	1,750	12,050
1980	150 gal, 120 KW 490 GPH	29,900	1,875	31,775
2020	200 gal, 120 KW 490 GPH	31,400	1,925	33,325
2060	250 gal, 150 KW 615 GPH	38,700	2,250	40,950
2100	300 gal, 180 KW 738 GPH	44,300	2,350	46,650
2140	350 gal, 30 KW 123 GPH	29,000	2,550	31,550
2180	180 KW 738 GPH	39,700	2,550	42,250
2220	500 gal, 30 KW 123 GPH	37,400	3,000	40,400
2260	240 KW 984 GPH	53,500	3,000	56,500
2300	700 gal, 30 KW 123 GPH	31,100	3,425	34,525
2340	300 KW 1230 GPH	45,000	3,425	48,425
2380	1000 gal, 60 KW 245 GPH	39,200	4,750	43,950
2420	480 KW 1970 GPH	60,500	4,750	65,250
2460	1500 gal, 60 KW 245 GPH	79,500	5,875	85,375
2500	480 KW 1970 GPH	108,000	5,875	113,875

D2020 250	Gas Fired Water Heaters - Commercial Systems	COST EACH		
		MAT.	INST.	TOTAL
1760	Gas fired water heater, commercial, 100°F rise			
1780	75.5 MBH input, 63 GPH	5,425	1,850	7,275
1820	95 MBH input, 86 GPH	7,400	1,850	9,250
1860	100 MBH input, 91 GPH	7,600	1,950	9,550
1900	115 MBH input, 110 GPH	8,900	2,000	10,900
1980	155 MBH input, 150 GPH	10,600	2,250	12,850
2020	175 MBH input, 168 GPH	11,400	2,400	13,800
2060	200 MBH input, 192 GPH	12,000	2,725	14,725
2100	240 MBH input, 230 GPH	12,500	2,975	15,475
2140	300 MBH input, 278 GPH	14,100	3,400	17,500
2180	390 MBH input, 374 GPH	16,700	3,425	20,125
2220	500 MBH input, 480 GPH	21,900	3,700	25,600
2260	600 MBH input, 576 GPH	25,000	3,975	28,975

D2020 Domestic Water Distribution

Oil Fired

Oil fired water heater systems include piping and fittings within 10′ of heater. Oil fired heaters require vent piping (not included in these systems).

D2020 260	Oil Fired Water Heaters - Commercial Systems	COST EACH		
		MAT.	INST.	TOTAL
1800	Oil fired water heater, commercial, 100°F rise			
1820	140 gal., 140 MBH input, 134 GPH	22,700	1,600	24,300
1900	140 gal., 255 MBH input, 247 GPH	24,900	1,975	26,875
1940	140 gal., 270 MBH input, 259 GPH	30,400	2,275	32,675
1980	140 gal., 400 MBH input, 384 GPH	31,900	2,625	34,525
2060	140 gal., 720 MBH input, 691 GPH	33,600	2,725	36,325
2100	221 gal., 300 MBH input, 288 GPH	44,700	3,000	47,700
2140	221 gal., 600 MBH input, 576 GPH	49,500	3,025	52,525
2180	221 gal., 800 MBH input, 768 GPH	50,500	3,150	53,650
2220	201 gal., 1000 MBH input, 960 GPH	51,500	3,175	54,675
2260	201 gal., 1250 MBH input, 1200 GPH	52,500	3,250	55,750
2300	201 gal., 1500 MBH input, 1441 GPH	56,500	3,325	59,825
2340	411 gal., 600 MBH input, 576 GPH	57,000	3,425	60,425
2380	411 gal., 800 MBH input, 768 GPH	57,500	3,500	61,000
2420	411 gal., 1000 MBH input, 960 GPH	63,000	4,025	67,025
2460	411 gal., 1250 MBH input, 1200 GPH	64,500	4,125	68,625
2500	397 gal., 1500 MBH input, 1441 GPH	65,000	4,275	69,275
2540	397 gal., 1750 MBH input, 1681 GPH	70,000	4,425	74,425

D2040 Rain Water Drainage

Design Assumptions: Vertical conductor size is based on a maximum rate of rainfall of 4″ per hour. To convert roof area to other rates multiply "Max. S.F. Roof Area" shown by four and divide the result by desired local rate. The answer is the local roof area that may be handled by the indicated pipe diameter.

Basic cost is for roof drain, 10′ of vertical leader and 10′ of horizontal, plus connection to the main.

Pipe Dia.	Max. S.F. Roof Area	Gallons per Min.
2″	544	23
3″	1610	67
4″	3460	144
5″	6280	261
6″	10,200	424
8″	22,000	913

D2040 210	Roof Drain Systems	COST EACH		
		MAT.	INST.	TOTAL
1880	Roof drain, DWV PVC, 2″ diam., piping, 10′ high	265	695	960
1920	For each additional foot add	3.73	21	24.73
1960	3″ diam., 10′ high	355	810	1,165
2000	For each additional foot add	6.65	23.50	30.15
2040	4″ diam., 10′ high	445	915	1,360
2080	For each additional foot add	9.15	26	35.15
2120	5″ diam., 10′ high	1,400	1,050	2,450
2160	For each additional foot add	31	29	60
2200	6″ diam., 10′ high	1,350	1,175	2,525
2240	For each additional foot add	18.95	32	50.95
2280	8″ diam., 10′ high	3,025	1,975	5,000
2320	For each additional foot add	46.50	40.50	87
3940	C.I., soil, single hub, service wt., 2″ diam. piping, 10′ high	565	760	1,325
3980	For each additional foot add	10.25	19.85	30.10
4120	3″ diam., 10′ high	790	830	1,620
4160	For each additional foot add	14.25	21	35.25
4200	4″ diam., 10′ high	925	905	1,830
4240	For each additional foot add	18.55	23	41.55
4280	5″ diam., 10′ high	1,300	990	2,290
4320	For each additional foot add	25.50	25.50	51
4360	6″ diam., 10′ high	1,650	1,050	2,700
4400	For each additional foot add	32	26.50	58.50
4440	8″ diam., 10′ high	3,200	2,175	5,375
4480	For each additional foot add	48.50	45	93.50
6040	Steel galv. sch 40 threaded, 2″ diam. piping, 10′ high	720	740	1,460
6080	For each additional foot add	13.35	19.55	32.90
6120	3″ diam., 10′ high	1,450	1,050	2,500
6160	For each additional foot add	28.50	29	57.50
6200	4″ diam., 10′ high	2,075	1,375	3,450
6240	For each additional foot add	41.50	35	76.50
6280	5″ diam., 10′ high	2,400	1,125	3,525
6320	For each additional foot add	64.50	34	98.50
6360	6″ diam, 10′ high	2,825	1,475	4,300
6400	For each additional foot add	70	46.50	116.50
6440	8″ diam., 10′ high	4,475	2,125	6,600
6480	For each additional foot add	82	52.50	134.50

D2090 Other Plumbing Systems

D2090 810	Piping - Installed - Unit Costs	COST PER L.F.		
		MAT.	INST.	TOTAL
0840	Cast iron, soil, B & S, service weight, 2" diameter	10.25	19.85	30.10
0860	3" diameter	14.25	21	35.25
0880	4" diameter	18.55	23	41.55
0900	5" diameter	25.50	25.50	51
0920	6" diameter	32	26.50	58.50
0940	8" diameter	48.50	45	93.50
0960	10" diameter	78	49	127
0980	12" diameter	111	55	166
1040	No hub, 1-1/2" diameter	10.05	17.65	27.70
1060	2" diameter	10.35	18.70	29.05
1080	3" diameter	14.65	19.55	34.20
1100	4" diameter	18.65	21.50	40.15
1120	5" diameter	25.50	23.50	49
1140	6" diameter	33	24.50	57.50
1160	8" diameter	57.50	38.50	96
1180	10" diameter	93.50	43.50	137
1220	Copper tubing, hard temper, solder, type K, 1/2" diameter	4.92	8.90	13.82
1260	3/4" diameter	8.60	9.40	18
1280	1" diameter	11.65	10.55	22.20
1300	1-1/4" diameter	14.55	12.40	26.95
1320	1-1/2" diameter	18.90	13.90	32.80
1340	2" diameter	29	17.40	46.40
1360	2-1/2" diameter	45.50	21	66.50
1380	3" diameter	63.50	23	86.50
1400	4" diameter	111	33	144
1480	5" diameter	223	39	262
1500	6" diameter	335	51	386
1520	8" diameter	530	57.50	587.50
1560	Type L, 1/2" diameter	3.71	8.60	12.31
1600	3/4" diameter	5.65	9.15	14.80
1620	1" diameter	8.65	10.20	18.85
1640	1-1/4" diameter	12.35	12	24.35
1660	1-1/2" diameter	15.80	13.35	29.15
1680	2" diameter	24	16.55	40.55
1700	2-1/2" diameter	39	20	59
1720	3" diameter	53.50	22.50	76
1740	4" diameter	94	32	126
1760	5" diameter	185	37	222
1780	6" diameter	268	48.50	316.50
1800	8" diameter	410	54	464
1840	Type M, 1/2" diameter	2.91	8.30	11.21
1880	3/4" diameter	4.38	8.90	13.28
1900	1" diameter	7.15	9.95	17.10
1920	1-1/4" diameter	10.50	11.60	22.10
1940	1-1/2" diameter	14.15	12.85	27
1960	2" diameter	22	15.80	37.80
1980	2-1/2" diameter	34.50	19.55	54.05
2000	3" diameter	47.50	21.50	69
2020	4" diameter	87	31.50	118.50
2060	6" diameter	268	46.50	314.50
2080	8" diameter	410	51	461
2120	Type DWV, 1-1/4" diameter	10.90	11.60	22.50
2160	1-1/2" diameter	13.70	12.85	26.55
2180	2" diameter	18.75	15.80	34.55
2200	3" diameter	38.50	21.50	60
2220	4" diameter	68	31.50	99.50
2240	5" diameter	170	35	205
2260	6" diameter	253	46.50	299.50

D2090 Other Plumbing Systems

D2090 810	Piping - Installed - Unit Costs	COST PER L.F.		
		MAT.	INST.	TOTAL
2280	8″ diameter	590	51	641
2800	Plastic,PVC, DWV, schedule 40, 1-1/4″ diameter	3.75	16.55	20.30
2820	1-1/2″ diameter	3.28	19.30	22.58
2830	2″ diameter	3.73	21	24.73
2840	3″ diameter	6.65	23.50	30.15
2850	4″ diameter	9.15	26	35.15
2890	6″ diameter	18.95	32	50.95
3010	Pressure pipe 200 PSI, 1/2″ diameter	2.86	12.85	15.71
3030	3/4″ diameter	3.21	13.65	16.86
3040	1″ diameter	3.49	15.10	18.59
3050	1-1/4″ diameter	4.34	16.55	20.89
3060	1-1/2″ diameter	4.71	19.30	24.01
3070	2″ diameter	5.70	21	26.70
3080	2-1/2″ diameter	10.20	22.50	32.70
3090	3″ diameter	11.45	23.50	34.95
3100	4″ diameter	18.95	26	44.95
3110	6″ diameter	34.50	32	66.50
3120	8″ diameter	51.50	40.50	92
4000	Steel, schedule 40, black, threaded, 1/2″ diameter	3	11.05	14.05
4020	3/4″ diameter	3.49	11.40	14.89
4030	1″ diameter	5.10	13.10	18.20
4040	1-1/4″ diameter	6.30	14.05	20.35
4050	1-1/2″ diameter	7.35	15.65	23
4060	2″ diameter	9.85	19.55	29.40
4070	2-1/2″ diameter	15.45	25	40.45
4080	3″ diameter	19.80	29	48.80
4090	4″ diameter	30	35	65
4100	Grooved, 5″ diameter	40.50	34	74.50
4110	6″ diameter	52	46.50	98.50
4120	8″ diameter	84.50	52.50	137
4130	10″ diameter	114	63	177
4140	12″ diameter	128	72	200
4200	Galvanized, threaded, 1/2″ diameter	4.13	11.05	15.18
4220	3/4″ diameter	4.89	11.40	16.29
4230	1″ diameter	6.70	13.10	19.80
4240	1-1/4″ diameter	8.50	14.05	22.55
4250	1-1/2″ diameter	9.95	15.65	25.60
4260	2″ diameter	13.35	19.55	32.90
4270	2-1/2″ diameter	22	25	47
4280	3″ diameter	28.50	29	57.50
4290	4″ diameter	41.50	35	76.50
4300	Grooved, 5″ diameter	64.50	34	98.50
4310	6″ diameter	70	46.50	116.50
4320	8″ diameter	82	52.50	134.50
4330	10″ diameter	131	63	194
4340	12″ diameter	161	72	233
5010	Flanged, black, 1″ diameter	10	18.75	28.75
5020	1-1/4″ diameter	11.30	20.50	31.80
5030	1-1/2″ diameter	11.95	22.50	34.45
5040	2″ diameter	14.30	29.50	43.80
5050	2-1/2″ diameter	21.50	36.50	58
5060	3″ diameter	25	41	66
5070	4″ diameter	33	50.50	83.50
5080	5″ diameter	53	62.50	115.50
5090	6″ diameter	63.50	80.50	144
5100	8″ diameter	105	105	210
5110	10″ diameter	149	126	275
5120	12″ diameter	180	143	323

D2090 Other Plumbing Systems

D2090 810	Piping - Installed - Unit Costs	COST PER L.F.		
		MAT.	INST.	TOTAL
5720	Grooved joints, black, 3/4" diameter	5.10	9.80	14.90
5730	1" diameter	4.86	11.05	15.91
5740	1-1/4" diameter	6.25	12	18.25
5750	1-1/2" diameter	7.15	13.65	20.80
5760	2" diameter	8.60	17.40	26
5770	2-1/2" diameter	14.80	22	36.80
5900	3" diameter	18.20	25	43.20
5910	4" diameter	25	28	53
5920	5" diameter	40.50	34	74.50
5930	6" diameter	52	46.50	98.50
5940	8" diameter	84.50	52.50	137
5950	10" diameter	114	63	177
5960	12" diameter	128	72	200

D3010 Energy Supply

Forced Hot Water Heating System

Fin Tube Radiation

Terminal Unit Heater

D3010 510	Apartment Building Heating - Fin Tube Radiation	COST PER S.F.		
		MAT.	INST.	TOTAL
1740	Heating systems, fin tube radiation, forced hot water			
1760	1,000 S.F. area, 10,000 C.F. volume	7.08	6.75	13.83
1800	10,000 S.F. area, 100,000 C.F. volume	3.33	4.06	7.39
1840	20,000 S.F. area, 200,000 C.F. volume	3.64	4.55	8.19
1880	30,000 S.F. area, 300,000 C.F. volume	3.52	4.40	7.92

D3010 520	Commercial Building Heating - Fin Tube Radiation	COST PER S.F.		
		MAT.	INST.	TOTAL
1940	Heating systems, fin tube radiation, forced hot water			
1960	1,000 S.F. bldg, one floor	17.10	15.20	32.30
2000	10,000 S.F., 100,000 C.F., total two floors	4.59	5.75	10.34
2040	100,000 S.F., 1,000,000 C.F., total three floors	1.85	2.58	4.43
2080	1,000,000 S.F., 10,000,000 C.F., total five floors	1.03	1.35	2.38

D3010 530	Commercial Bldg. Heating - Terminal Unit Heaters	COST PER S.F.		
		MAT.	INST.	TOTAL
1860	Heating systems, terminal unit heaters, forced hot water			
1880	1,000 S.F. bldg., one floor	16.80	13.90	30.70
1920	10,000 S.F. bldg., 100,000 C.F. total two floors	4.14	4.76	8.90
1960	100,000 S.F. bldg., 1,000,000 C.F. total three floors	1.89	2.36	4.25
2000	1,000,000 S.F. bldg., 10,000,000 C.F. total five floors	1.31	1.51	2.82

D3020 Heat Generating Systems

Small Electric Boiler Systems Considerations:

1. Terminal units are fin tube baseboard radiation rated at 720 BTU/hr with 200° water temperature or 820 BTU/hr steam.
2. Primary use being for residential or smaller supplementary areas, the floor levels are based on 7-1/2″ ceiling heights.
3. All distribution piping is copper for boilers through 205 MBH. All piping for larger systems is steel pipe.

Large Electric Boiler System Considerations:

1. Terminal units are all unit heaters of the same size. Quantities are varied to accommodate total requirements.
2. All air is circulated through the heaters a minimum of three times per hour.
3. As the capacities are adequate for commercial use, gross output rating by floor levels are based on 10′ ceiling height.
4. All distribution piping is black steel pipe.

D3020 102	Small Heating Systems, Hydronic, Electric Boilers	COST PER S.F.		
		MAT.	INST.	TOTAL
1100	Small heating systems, hydronic, electric boilers			
1120	Steam, 1 floor, 1480 S.F., 61 M.B.H.	8.04	8.65	16.69
1160	3,000 S.F., 123 M.B.H.	6.30	7.60	13.90
1200	5,000 S.F., 205 M.B.H.	5.55	7	12.55
1240	2 floors, 12,400 S.F., 512 M.B.H.	4.47	6.95	11.42
1280	3 floors, 24,800 S.F., 1023 M.B.H.	4.96	6.90	11.86
1320	34,750 S.F., 1,433 M.B.H.	4.63	6.70	11.33
1360	Hot water, 1 floor, 1,000 S.F., 41 M.B.H.	12.55	4.82	17.37
1400	2,500 S.F., 103 M.B.H.	9.55	8.65	18.20
1440	2 floors, 4,850 S.F., 205 M.B.H.	9.30	10.35	19.65
1480	3 floors, 9,700 S.F., 410 M.B.H.	9.90	10.70	20.60

D3020 104	Large Heating Systems, Hydronic, Electric Boilers	COST PER S.F.		
		MAT.	INST.	TOTAL
1230	Large heating systems, hydronic, electric boilers			
1240	9,280 S.F., 135 K.W., 461 M.B.H., 1 floor	4.05	3.22	7.27
1280	14,900 S.F., 240 K.W., 820 M.B.H., 2 floors	5.40	5.20	10.60
1320	18,600 S.F., 296 K.W., 1,010 M.B.H., 3 floors	5.30	5.65	10.95
1360	26,100 S.F., 420 K.W., 1,432 M.B.H., 4 floors	5.20	5.55	10.75
1400	39,100 S.F., 666 K.W., 2,273 M.B.H., 4 floors	4.45	4.64	9.09
1440	57,700 S.F., 900 K.W., 3,071 M.B.H., 5 floors	4.25	4.56	8.81
1480	111,700 S.F., 1,800 K.W., 6,148 M.B.H., 6 floors	3.79	3.93	7.72
1520	149,000 S.F., 2,400 K.W., 8,191 M.B.H., 8 floors	3.74	3.93	7.67
1560	223,300 S.F., 3,600 K.W., 12,283 M.B.H., 14 floors	3.98	4.44	8.42

D3020 Heat Generating Systems

Boiler Selection: The maximum allowable working pressures are limited by ASME "Code for Heating Boilers" to 15 PSI for steam and 160 PSI for hot water heating boilers, with a maximum temperature limitation of 250° F. Hot water boilers are generally rated for a working pressure of 30 PSI. High pressure boilers are governed by the ASME "Code for Power Boilers" which is used almost universally for boilers operating over 15 PSIG. High pressure boilers used for a combination of heating/process loads are usually designed for 150 PSIG.

Boiler ratings are usually indicated as either Gross or Net Output. The Gross Load is equal to the Net Load plus a piping and pickup allowance. When this allowance cannot be determined, divide the gross output rating by 1.25 for a value equal to or greater than the next heat loss requirement of the building.

Table below lists installed cost per boiler and includes insulating jacket, standard controls, burner and safety controls. Costs do not include piping or boiler base pad. Outputs are Gross.

D3020 106	Boilers, Hot Water & Steam	COST EACH		
		MAT.	INST.	TOTAL
0600	Boiler, electric, steel, hot water, 12 K.W., 41 M.B.H.	5,475	1,475	6,950
0620	30 K.W., 103 M.B.H.	5,950	1,600	7,550
0640	60 K.W., 205 M.B.H.	6,600	1,725	8,325
0660	120 K.W., 410 M.B.H.	7,025	2,125	9,150
0680	210 K.W., 716 M.B.H.	8,375	3,175	11,550
0700	510 K.W., 1,739 M.B.H.	25,400	5,950	31,350
0720	720 K.W., 2,452 M.B.H.	31,300	6,700	38,000
0740	1,200 K.W., 4,095 M.B.H.	39,100	7,700	46,800
0760	2,100 K.W., 7,167 M.B.H.	65,500	9,700	75,200
0780	3,600 K.W., 12,283 M.B.H.	103,500	16,400	119,900
0820	Steam, 6 K.W., 20.5 M.B.H.	4,350	1,600	5,950
0840	24 K.W., 81.8 M.B.H.	5,300	1,725	7,025
0860	60 K.W., 205 M.B.H.	7,325	1,900	9,225
0880	150 K.W., 512 M.B.H.	10,600	2,950	13,550
0900	510 K.W., 1,740 M.B.H.	35,900	7,275	43,175
0920	1,080 K.W., 3,685 M.B.H.	44,700	10,500	55,200
0940	2,340 K.W., 7,984 M.B.H.	95,000	16,400	111,400
0980	Gas, cast iron, hot water, 80 M.B.H.	2,375	1,850	4,225
1000	100 M.B.H.	2,525	2,000	4,525
1020	163 M.B.H.	3,300	2,700	6,000
1040	280 M.B.H.	4,575	3,000	7,575
1060	544 M.B.H.	9,875	5,300	15,175
1080	1,088 M.B.H.	14,900	6,725	21,625
1100	2,000 M.B.H.	21,600	10,500	32,100
1120	2,856 M.B.H.	31,100	13,500	44,600
1140	4,720 M.B.H.	100,500	18,600	119,100
1160	6,970 M.B.H.	121,500	30,200	151,700
1180	For steam systems under 2,856 M.B.H., add 8%			
1520	Oil, cast iron, hot water, 109 M.B.H.	2,400	2,250	4,650
1540	173 M.B.H.	3,050	2,700	5,750
1560	236 M.B.H.	3,875	3,175	7,050
1580	1,084 M.B.H.	11,600	7,150	18,750
1600	1,600 M.B.H.	14,900	10,300	25,200
1620	2,480 M.B.H.	21,700	13,100	34,800
1640	3,550 M.B.H.	29,000	15,700	44,700
1660	Steam systems same price as hot water			

D3020 Heat Generating Systems

Unit Heater

Fossil Fuel Boiler System Considerations:

1. Terminal units are horizontal unit heaters. Quantities are varied to accommodate total heat loss per building.
2. Unit heater selection was determined by their capacity to circulate the building volume a minimum of three times per hour in addition to the BTU output.
3. Systems shown are forced hot water. Steam boilers cost slightly more than hot water boilers. However, this is compensated for by the smaller size or fewer terminal units required with steam.
4. Floor levels are based on 10' story heights.
5. MBH requirements are gross boiler output.

D3020 108	Heating Systems, Unit Heaters	COST PER S.F.		
		MAT.	INST.	TOTAL
1260	Heating systems, hydronic, fossil fuel, terminal unit heaters,			
1280	Cast iron boiler, gas, 80 M.B.H., 1,070 S.F. bldg.	10.84	10.37	21.21
1320	163 M.B.H., 2,140 S.F. bldg.	7.10	7	14.10
1360	544 M.B.H., 7,250 S.F. bldg.	5.25	4.94	10.19
1400	1,088 M.B.H., 14,500 S.F. bldg.	4.43	4.67	9.10
1440	3,264 M.B.H., 43,500 S.F. bldg.	3.56	3.54	7.10
1480	5,032 M.B.H., 67,100 S.F. bldg.	4.50	3.63	8.13
1520	Oil, 109 M.B.H., 1,420 S.F. bldg.	11.40	9.20	20.60
1560	235 M.B.H., 3,150 S.F. bldg.	7.35	6.50	13.85
1600	940 M.B.H., 12,500 S.F. bldg.	5.30	4.29	9.59
1640	1,600 M.B.H., 21,300 S.F. bldg.	4.90	4.09	8.99
1680	2,480 M.B.H., 33,100 S.F. bldg.	4.90	3.70	8.60
1720	3,350 M.B.H., 44,500 S.F. bldg.	4.56	3.77	8.33
1760	Coal, 148 M.B.H., 1,975 S.F. bldg.	9.95	6	15.95
1800	300 M.B.H., 4,000 S.F. bldg.	7.90	4.70	12.60
1840	2,360 M.B.H., 31,500 S.F. bldg.	5.45	3.77	9.22

D3020 Heat Generating Systems

Fin Tube Radiator

Fossil Fuel Boiler System Considerations:

1. Terminal units are commercial steel fin tube radiation. Quantities are varied to accommodate total heat loss per building.
2. Systems shown are forced hot water. Steam boilers cost slightly more than hot water boilers. However, this is compensated for by the smaller size or fewer terminal units required with steam.
3. Floor levels are based on 10' story heights.
4. MBH requirements are gross boiler output.

D3020 110	Heating System, Fin Tube Radiation	COST PER S.F.		
		MAT.	INST.	TOTAL
3230	Heating systems, hydronic, fossil fuel, fin tube radiation			
3240	Cast iron boiler, gas, 80 MBH, 1,070 S.F. bldg.	13.27	15.51	28.78
3280	169 M.B.H., 2,140 S.F. bldg.	8.20	9.85	18.05
3320	544 M.B.H., 7,250 S.F. bldg.	7	8.45	15.45
3360	1,088 M.B.H., 14,500 S.F. bldg.	6.30	8.25	14.55
3400	3,264 M.B.H., 43,500 S.F. bldg.	5.60	7.25	12.85
3440	5,032 M.B.H., 67,100 S.F. bldg.	6.50	7.40	13.90
3480	Oil, 109 M.B.H., 1,420 S.F. bldg.	15.65	17	32.65
3520	235 M.B.H., 3,150 S.F. bldg.	9.10	9.90	19
3560	940 M.B.H., 12,500 S.F. bldg.	7.20	7.90	15.10
3600	1,600 M.B.H., 21,300 S.F. bldg.	6.90	7.85	14.75
3640	2,480 M.B.H., 33,100 S.F. bldg.	6.90	7.45	14.35
3680	3,350 M.B.H., 44,500 S.F. bldg.	6.55	7.50	14.05
3720	Coal, 148 M.B.H., 1,975 S.F. bldg.	11.60	9.40	21
3760	300 M.B.H., 4,000 S.F. bldg.	9.55	8.10	17.65
3800	2,360 M.B.H., 31,500 S.F. bldg.	7.40	7.45	14.85
4080	Steel boiler, oil, 97 M.B.H., 1,300 S.F. bldg.	12.40	13.95	26.35
4120	315 M.B.H., 4,550 S.F. bldg.	6.20	7.05	13.25
4160	525 M.B.H., 7,000 S.F. bldg.	8.80	8.15	16.95
4200	1,050 M.B.H., 14,000 S.F. bldg.	7.90	8.10	16
4240	2,310 M.B.H., 30,800 S.F. bldg.	7.60	7.50	15.10
4280	3,150 M.B.H., 42,000 S.F. bldg.	7.10	7.60	14.70

D3030 Cooling Generating Systems

Chilled Water Supply & Return Piping

Air Cooled Water Chiller Unit

Roof

Insulate

Return

Fan Coil Unit

Supply

Finish Ceiling

*Cooling requirements would lead to a choice of multiple chillers.

D3030 110	Chilled Water, Air Cooled Condenser Systems	COST PER S.F.		
		MAT.	INST.	TOTAL
1180	Packaged chiller, air cooled, with fan coil unit			
1200	Apartment corridors, 3,000 S.F., 5.50 ton	7.90	8.63	16.53
1240	6,000 S.F., 11.00 ton	6.75	6.85	13.60
1280	10,000 S.F., 18.33 ton	5.90	5.20	11.10
1320	20,000 S.F., 36.66 ton	4.32	3.76	8.08
1360	40,000 S.F., 73.33 ton	5.10	3.77	8.87
1440	Banks and libraries, 3,000 S.F., 12.50 ton	12.65	10.05	22.70
1480	6,000 S.F., 25.00 ton	11.65	8.15	19.80
1520	10,000 S.F., 41.66 ton	8.50	5.65	14.15
1560	20,000 S.F., 83.33 ton	8.70	5.10	13.80
1600	40,000 S.F., 167 ton*			
1680	Bars and taverns, 3,000 S.F., 33.25 ton	21	11.75	32.75
1720	6,000 S.F., 66.50 ton	17.50	8.90	26.40
1760	10,000 S.F., 110.83 ton	14.85	2.66	17.51
1800	20,000 S.F., 220 ton*			
1840	40,000 S.F., 440 ton*			
1920	Bowling alleys, 3,000 S.F., 17.00 ton	16	11.25	27.25
1960	6,000 S.F., 34.00 ton	11.55	7.85	19.40
2000	10,000 S.F., 56.66 ton	9.40	5.60	15
2040	20,000 S.F., 113.33 ton	10.30	5.10	15.40
2080	40,000 S.F., 227 ton*			
2160	Department stores, 3,000 S.F., 8.75 ton	11.05	9.60	20.65
2200	6,000 S.F., 17.50 ton	8.90	7.35	16.25
2240	10,000 S.F., 29.17 ton	6.75	5.30	12.05
2280	20,000 S.F., 58.33 ton	5.35	3.87	9.22
2320	40,000 S.F., 116.66 ton	6.70	3.88	10.58
2400	Drug stores, 3,000 S.F., 20.00 ton	18.20	11.60	29.80
2440	6,000 S.F., 40.00 ton	13.65	8.55	22.20
2480	10,000 S.F., 66.66 ton	13.35	7.25	20.60
2520	20,000 S.F., 133.33 ton	12.50	5.40	17.90
2560	40,000 S.F., 267 ton*			
2640	Factories, 2,000 S.F., 10.00 ton	11	9.65	20.65
2680	6,000 S.F., 20.00 ton	10.05	7.75	17.80
2720	10,000 S.F., 33.33 ton	7.30	5.40	12.70
2760	20,000 S.F., 66.66 ton	7.65	4.85	12.50
2800	40,000 S.F., 133.33 ton	7.30	3.97	11.27
2880	Food supermarkets, 3,000 S.F., 8.50 ton	10.85	9.55	20.40
2920	6,000 S.F., 17.00 ton	8.70	7.30	16
2960	10,000 S.F., 28.33 ton	6.40	5.15	11.55
3000	20,000 S.F., 56.66 ton	5.15	3.78	8.93

D30 HVAC

D3030 Cooling Generating Systems

D3030 110	Chilled Water, Air Cooled Condenser Systems	COST PER S.F.		
		MAT.	INST.	TOTAL
3040	40,000 S.F., 113.33 ton	6.40	3.88	10.28
3120	Medical centers, 3,000 S.F., 7.00 ton	9.70	9.30	19
3160	6,000 S.F., 14.00 ton	7.75	7.10	14.85
3200	10,000 S.F., 23.33 ton	6.95	5.40	12.35
3240	20,000 S.F., 46.66 ton	5.15	3.94	9.09
3280	40,000 S.F., 93.33 ton	5.85	3.81	9.66
3360	Offices, 3,000 S.F., 9.50 ton	10.05	9.50	19.55
3400	6,000 S.F., 19.00 ton	9.70	7.70	17.40
3440	10,000 S.F., 31.66 ton	7.10	5.35	12.45
3480	20,000 S.F., 63.33 ton	7.65	4.94	12.59
3520	40,000 S.F., 126.66 ton	7.20	4.01	11.21
3600	Restaurants, 3,000 S.F., 15.00 ton	14.25	10.40	24.65
3640	6,000 S.F., 30.00 ton	10.95	7.90	18.85
3680	10,000 S.F., 50.00 ton	9	5.75	14.75
3720	20,000 S.F., 100.00 ton	10.40	5.40	15.80
3760	40,000 S.F., 200 ton*			
3840	Schools and colleges, 3,000 S.F., 11.50 ton	12	9.90	21.90
3880	6,000 S.F., 23.00 ton	11	8	19
3920	10,000 S.F., 38.33 ton	8	5.55	13.55
3960	20,000 S.F., 76.66 ton	8.55	5.15	13.70
4000	40,000 S.F., 153 ton*			

D3030 Cooling Generating Systems

*Cooling requirements would lead to a choice of multiple chillers.

D3030 115	Chilled Water, Cooling Tower Systems	COST PER S.F.		
		MAT.	INST.	TOTAL
1300	Packaged chiller, water cooled, with fan coil unit			
1320	Apartment corridors, 4,000 S.F., 7.33 ton	7	8.45	15.45
1360	6,000 S.F., 11.00 ton	6	7.25	13.25
1400	10,000 S.F., 18.33 ton	5.90	5.35	11.25
1440	20,000 S.F., 26.66 ton	4.82	3.98	8.80
1480	40,000 S.F., 73.33 ton	5.05	4.08	9.13
1520	60,000 S.F., 110.00 ton	5.30	4.20	9.50
1600	Banks and libraries, 4,000 S.F., 16.66 ton	12.90	9.15	22.05
1640	6,000 S.F., 25.00 ton	10.90	8.05	18.95
1680	10,000 S.F., 41.66 ton	9.45	5.95	15.40
1720	20,000 S.F., 83.33 ton	8.45	5.70	14.15
1760	40,000 S.F., 166.66 ton	9.30	6.85	16.15
1800	60,000 S.F., 250.00 ton	9.50	7.30	16.80
1880	Bars and taverns, 4,000 S.F., 44.33 ton	22.50	11.40	33.90
1920	6,000 S.F., 66.50 ton	23.50	11.80	35.30
1960	10,000 S.F., 110.83 ton	18.95	9.25	28.20
2000	20,000 S.F., 221.66 ton	22	9.35	31.35
2040	40,000 S.F., 440 ton*			
2080	60,000 S.F., 660 ton*			
2160	Bowling alleys, 4,000 S.F., 22.66 ton	14.80	10	24.80
2200	6,000 S.F., 34.00 ton	13.30	8.80	22.10
2240	10,000 S.F., 56.66 ton	11.60	6.40	18
2280	20,000 S.F., 113.33 ton	10.65	5.95	16.60
2320	40,000 S.F., 226.66 ton	12.60	6.80	19.40
2360	60,000 S.F., 340 ton			
2440	Department stores, 4,000 S.F., 11.66 ton	8.15	9.10	17.25
2480	6,000 S.F., 17.50 ton	9.50	7.45	16.95
2520	10,000 S.F., 29.17 ton	7.25	5.55	12.80
2560	20,000 S.F., 58.33 ton	6	4.11	10.11
2600	40,000 S.F., 116.66 ton	6.45	4.25	10.70
2640	60,000 S.F., 175.00 ton	8.50	6.70	15.20
2720	Drug stores, 4,000 S.F., 26.66 ton	16.15	10.30	26.45
2760	6,000 S.F., 40.00 ton	14.95	8.80	23.75
2800	10,000 S.F., 66.66 ton	15	8	23
2840	20,000 S.F., 133.33 ton	12.20	6.25	18.45
2880	40,000 S.F., 266.67 ton	12.80	7.75	20.55
2920	60,000 S.F., 400 ton*			
3000	Factories, 4,000 S.F., 13.33 ton	11.05	8.70	19.75
3040	6,000 S.F., 20.00 ton	9.45	7.50	16.95
3080	10,000 S.F., 33.33 ton	7.95	5.70	13.65
3120	20,000 S.F., 66.66 ton	8.35	5.15	13.50
3160	40,000 S.F., 133.33 ton	7.15	4.38	11.53

D3030 Cooling Generating Systems

D3030 115	Chilled Water, Cooling Tower Systems	COST PER S.F.		
		MAT.	INST.	TOTAL
3200	60,000 S.F., 200.00 ton	8.55	7	15.55
3280	Food supermarkets, 4,000 S.F., 11.33 ton	8.05	9	17.05
3320	6,000 S.F., 17.00 ton	8.40	7.35	15.75
3360	10,000 S.F., 28.33 ton	7.10	5.50	12.60
3400	20,000 S.F., 56.66 ton	6.20	4.12	10.32
3440	40,000 S.F., 113.33 ton	6.35	4.26	10.61
3480	60,000 S.F., 170.00 ton	8.40	6.70	15.10
3560	Medical centers, 4.000 S.F., 9.33 ton	6.95	8.30	15.25
3600	6,000 S.F., 14.00 ton	8.25	7.15	15.40
3640	10,000 S.F., 23.33 ton	6.50	5.35	11.85
3680	20,000 S.F., 46.66 ton	5.50	4.03	9.53
3720	40,000 S.F., 93.33 ton	5.75	4.18	9.93
3760	60,000 S.F., 140.00 ton	7.05	6.75	13.80
3840	Offices, 4,000 S.F., 12.66 ton	10.70	8.65	19.35
3880	6,000 S.F., 19.00 ton	9.35	7.70	17.05
3920	10,000 S.F., 31.66 ton	7.85	5.75	13.60
3960	20,000 S.F., 63.33 ton	8.20	5.15	13.35
4000	40,000 S.F., 126.66 ton	7.70	6.60	14.30
4040	60,000 S.F., 190.00 ton	8.30	6.95	15.25
4120	Restaurants, 4,000 S.F., 20.00 ton	13.25	9.30	22.55
4160	6,000 S.F., 30.00 ton	11.95	8.30	20.25
4200	10,000 S.F., 50.00 ton	10.65	6.20	16.85
4240	20,000 S.F., 100.00 ton	9.95	5.95	15.90
4280	40,000 S.F., 200.00 ton	9.90	6.65	16.55
4320	60,000 S.F., 300.00 ton	10.60	7.55	18.15
4400	Schools and colleges, 4,000 S.F., 15.33 ton	12.15	9	21.15
4440	6,000 S.F., 23.00 ton	10.30	7.90	18.20
4480	10,000 S.F., 38.33 ton	8.90	5.85	14.75
4520	20,000 S.F., 76.66 ton	8.20	5.65	13.85
4560	40,000 S.F., 153.33 ton	8.75	6.70	15.45
4600	60,000 S.F., 230.00 ton	8.80	7.05	15.85

D3050 Terminal & Package Units

Rooftop, Single Zone System

*Above normal capacity

D3050 150	Rooftop Single Zone Unit Systems	COST PER S.F.		
		MAT.	INST.	TOTAL
1260	Rooftop, single zone, air conditioner			
1280	Apartment corridors, 500 S.F., .92 ton	4.25	4	8.25
1320	1,000 S.F., 1.83 ton	4.22	3.96	8.18
1360	1500 S.F., 2.75 ton	2.63	3.25	5.88
1400	3,000 S.F., 5.50 ton	2.48	3.12	5.60
1440	5,000 S.F., 9.17 ton	2.70	2.84	5.54
1480	10,000 S.F., 18.33 ton	2.74	2.66	5.40
1560	Banks or libraries, 500 S.F., 2.08 ton	9.60	9	18.60
1600	1,000 S.F., 4.17 ton	6	7.40	13.40
1640	1,500 S.F., 6.25 ton	5.65	7.10	12.75
1680	3,000 S.F., 12.50 ton	6.15	6.45	12.60
1720	5,000 S.F., 20.80 ton	6.25	6.05	12.30
1760	10,000 S.F., 41.67 ton	5.05	6	11.05
1840	Bars and taverns, 500 S.F. 5.54 ton	13.90	11.95	25.85
1880	1,000 S.F., 11.08 ton	15.25	10.25	25.50
1920	1,500 S.F., 16.62 ton	14.90	9.50	24.40
1960	3,000 S.F., 33.25 ton	12.70	9.05	21.75
2000	5,000 S.F., 55.42 ton	11.40	9.05	20.45
2040	10,000 S.F., 110.83 ton*			
2080	Bowling alleys, 500 S.F., 2.83 ton	8.15	10.05	18.20
2120	1,000 S.F., 5.67 ton	7.65	9.65	17.30
2160	1,500 S.F., 8.50 ton	8.35	8.75	17.10
2200	3,000 S.F., 17.00 ton	8.15	8.40	16.55
2240	5,000 S.F., 28.33 ton	7.05	8.15	15.20
2280	10,000 S.F., 56.67 ton	6.40	8.15	14.55
2360	Department stores, 500 S.F., 1.46 ton	6.70	6.30	13
2400	1,000 S.F., 2.92 ton	4.19	5.20	9.39
2480	3,000 S.F., 8.75 ton	4.29	4.52	8.81
2520	5,000 S.F., 14.58 ton	4.20	4.33	8.53
2560	10,000 S.F., 29.17 ton	3.62	4.21	7.83
2640	Drug stores, 500 S.F., 3.33 ton	9.60	11.85	21.45
2680	1,000 S.F., 6.67 ton	9	11.35	20.35
2720	1,500 S.F., 10.00 ton	9.80	10.30	20.10
2760	3,000 S.F., 20.00 ton	10	9.65	19.65
2800	5,000 S.F., 33.33 ton	8.30	9.60	17.90
2840	10,000 S.F., 66.67 ton	7.50	9.60	17.10
2920	Factories, 500 S.F., 1.67 ton	7.65	7.20	14.85
3000	1,500 S.F., 5.00 ton	4.51	5.70	10.21
3040	3,000 S.F., 10.00 ton	4.91	5.15	10.06
3080	5,000 S.F., 16.67 ton	4.80	4.94	9.74
3120	10,000 S.F., 33.33 ton	4.14	4.81	8.95
3200	Food supermarkets, 500 S.F., 1.42 ton	6.55	6.15	12.70

D3050 Terminal & Package Units

D3050 150	Rooftop Single Zone Unit Systems	COST PER S.F.		
		MAT.	INST.	TOTAL
3240	1,000 S.F., 2.83 ton	4.03	5	9.03
3280	1,500 S.F., 4.25 ton	3.84	4.83	8.67
3320	3,000 S.F., 8.50 ton	4.18	4.38	8.56
3360	5,000 S.F., 14.17 ton	4.08	4.20	8.28
3400	10,000 S.F., 28.33 ton	3.52	4.08	7.60
3480	Medical centers, 500 S.F., 1.17 ton	5.40	5.05	10.45
3520	1,000 S.F., 2.33 ton	5.40	5.05	10.45
3560	1,500 S.F., 3.50 ton	3.35	4.15	7.50
3640	5,000 S.F., 11.67 ton	3.43	3.61	7.04
3680	10,000 S.F., 23.33 ton	3.50	3.39	6.89
3760	Offices, 500 S.F., 1.58 ton	7.30	6.85	14.15
3800	1,000 S.F., 3.17 ton	4.55	5.60	10.15
3840	1,500 S.F., 4.75 ton	4.28	5.40	9.68
3880	3,000 S.F., 9.50 ton	4.66	4.90	9.56
3920	5,000 S.F., 15.83 ton	4.56	4.69	9.25
3960	10,000 S.F., 31.67 ton	3.94	4.57	8.51
4000	Restaurants, 500 S.F., 2.50 ton	11.55	10.80	22.35
4040	1,000 S.F., 5.00 ton	6.75	8.55	15.30
4080	1,500 S.F., 7.50 ton	7.35	7.75	15.10
4120	3,000 S.F., 15.00 ton	7.20	7.40	14.60
4160	5,000 S.F., 25.00 ton	7.50	7.25	14.75
4200	10,000 S.F., 50.00 ton	5.65	7.20	12.85
4240	Schools and colleges, 500 S.F., 1.92 ton	8.85	8.30	17.15
4280	1,000 S.F., 3.83 ton	5.50	6.80	12.30
4360	3,000 S.F., 11.50 ton	5.65	5.95	11.60
4400	5,000 S.F., 19.17 ton	5.75	5.55	11.30

D3050 Terminal & Package Units

*Note A: Small single zone unit recommended.

*Note B: A combination of multizone units recommended.

D3050 155	Rooftop Multizone Unit Systems	COST PER S.F.		
		MAT.	INST.	TOTAL
1240	Rooftop, multizone, air conditioner			
1260	Apartment corridors, 1,500 S.F., 2.75 ton. See Note A.			
1280	3,000 S.F., 5.50 ton	11.03	5.03	16.06
1320	10,000 S.F., 18.30 ton	7.60	4.85	12.45
1360	15,000 S.F., 27.50 ton	7.40	4.84	12.24
1400	20,000 S.F., 36.70 ton	7.70	4.84	12.54
1440	25,000 S.F., 45.80 ton	7.20	4.87	12.07
1520	Banks or libraries, 1,500 S.F., 6.25 ton	25	11.50	36.50
1560	3,000 S.F., 12.50 ton	21	11.25	32.25
1600	10,000 S.F., 41.67 ton	16.35	11.10	27.45
1640	15,000 S.F., 62.50 ton	12	11	23
1680	20,000 S.F., 83.33 ton	12	11	23
1720	25,000 S.F., 104.00 ton	10.65	10.95	21.60
1800	Bars and taverns, 1,500 S.F., 16.62 ton	54.50	16.55	71.05
1840	3,000 S.F., 33.24 ton	45	15.95	60.95
1880	10,000 S.F., 110.83 ton	27	15.90	42.90
1920	15,000 S.F., 165 ton, See Note B.			
1960	20,000 S.F., 220 ton, See Note B.			
2000	25,000 S.F., 275 ton, See Note B.			
2080	Bowling alleys, 1,500 S.F., 8.50 ton	34	15.60	49.60
2120	3,000 S.F., 17.00 ton	28.50	15.25	43.75
2160	10,000 S.F., 56.70 ton	22.50	15.10	37.60
2200	15,000 S.F., 85.00 ton	16.30	14.95	31.25
2240	20,000 S.F., 113.00 ton	14.50	14.90	29.40
2280	25,000 S.F., 140.00 ton see Note B.			
2360	Department stores, 1,500 S.F., 4.37 ton, See Note A.			
2400	3,000 S.F., 8.75 ton	17.55	8.05	25.60
2440	10,000 S.F., 29.17 ton	12.25	7.70	19.95
2520	20,000 S.F., 58.33 ton	8.40	7.70	16.10
2560	25,000 S.F., 72.92 ton	8.40	7.70	16.10
2640	Drug stores, 1,500 S.F., 10.00 ton	40	18.35	58.35
2680	3,000 S.F., 20.00 ton	27.50	17.70	45.20
2720	10,000 S.F., 66.66 ton	19.15	17.60	36.75
2760	15,000 S.F., 100.00 ton	17.10	17.55	34.65
2800	20,000 S.F., 135 ton, See Note B.			
2840	25,000 S.F., 165 ton, See Note B.			
2920	Factories, 1,500 S.F., 5 ton, See Note A.			
3000	10,000 S.F., 33.33 ton	14	8.80	22.80

D3050 Terminal & Package Units

D3050 155	Rooftop Multizone Unit Systems	COST PER S.F.		
		MAT.	INST.	TOTAL
3040	15,000 S.F., 50.00 ton	13.10	8.85	21.95
3080	20,000 S.F., 66.66 ton	9.60	8.80	18.40
3120	25,000 S.F., 83.33 ton	9.60	8.80	18.40
3200	Food supermarkets, 1,500 S.F., 4.25 ton, See Note A.			
3240	3,000 S.F., 8.50 ton	17.05	7.80	24.85
3280	10,000 S.F., 28.33 ton	11.45	7.45	18.90
3320	15,000 S.F., 42.50 ton	11.10	7.55	18.65
3360	20,000 S.F., 56.67 ton	8.15	7.50	15.65
3400	25,000 S.F., 70.83 ton	8.15	7.50	15.65
3480	Medical centers, 1,500 S.F., 3.5 ton, See Note A.			
3520	3,000 S.F., 7.00 ton	14.05	6.45	20.50
3560	10,000 S.F., 23.33 ton	9.25	6.15	15.40
3600	15,000 S.F., 35.00 ton	9.80	6.15	15.95
3640	20,000 S.F., 46.66 ton	9.15	6.20	15.35
3680	25,000 S.F., 58.33 ton	6.70	6.15	12.85
3760	Offices, 1,500 S.F., 4.75 ton, See Note A.			
3800	3,000 S.F., 9.50 ton	19.05	8.70	27.75
3840	10,000 S.F., 31.66 ton	13.35	8.35	21.70
3920	20,000 S.F., 63.33 ton	9.10	8.35	17.45
3960	25,000 S.F., 79.16 ton	9.10	8.35	17.45
4000	Restaurants, 1,500 S.F., 7.50 ton	30	13.75	43.75
4040	3,000 S.F., 15.00 ton	25.50	13.50	39
4080	10,000 S.F., 50.00 ton	19.60	13.30	32.90
4120	15,000 S.F., 75.00 ton	14.35	13.20	27.55
4160	20,000 S.F., 100.00 ton	12.85	13.15	26
4200	25,000 S.F., 125 ton, See Note B.			
4240	Schools and colleges, 1,500 S.F., 5.75 ton	23	10.55	33.55
4320	10,000 S.F., 38.33 ton	15.05	10.20	25.25
4360	15,000 S.F., 57.50 ton	11	10.10	21.10
4400	20,000 S.F.,76.66 ton	11.05	10.10	21.15
4440	25,000 S.F., 95.83 ton	10.35	10.10	20.45

D3050 Terminal & Package Units

Self-Contained Water Cooled System

D3050 160	Self-contained, Water Cooled Unit Systems	COST PER S.F.		
		MAT.	INST.	TOTAL
1280	Self-contained, water cooled unit	3.52	3.23	6.75
1300	Apartment corridors, 500 S.F., .92 ton	3.50	3.20	6.70
1320	1,000 S.F., 1.83 ton	3.49	3.22	6.71
1360	3,000 S.F., 5.50 ton	2.93	2.69	5.62
1400	5,000 S.F., 9.17 ton	2.78	2.50	5.28
1440	10,000 S.F., 18.33 ton	3.94	2.23	6.17
1520	Banks or libraries, 500 S.F., 2.08 ton	7.65	3.32	10.97
1560	1,000 S.F., 4.17 ton	6.65	6.10	12.75
1600	3,000 S.F., 12.50 ton	6.35	5.65	12
1640	5,000 S.F., 20.80 ton	8.95	5.05	14
1680	10,000 S.F., 41.66 ton	7.80	5.05	12.85
1760	Bars and taverns, 500 S.F., 5.54 ton	16.80	5.60	22.40
1800	1,000 S.F., 11.08 ton	16.35	9.75	26.10
1840	3,000 S.F., 33.25 ton	21	7.65	28.65
1880	5,000 S.F., 55.42 ton	19.80	8	27.80
1920	10,000 S.F., 110.00 ton	19.25	7.90	27.15
2000	Bowling alleys, 500 S.F., 2.83 ton	10.45	4.51	14.96
2040	1,000 S.F., 5.66 ton	9.05	8.30	17.35
2080	3,000 S.F., 17.00 ton	12.20	6.85	19.05
2120	5,000 S.F., 28.33 ton	11.05	6.60	17.65
2160	10,000 S.F., 56.66 ton	10.35	6.75	17.10
2200	Department stores, 500 S.F., 1.46 ton	5.40	2.32	7.72
2240	1,000 S.F., 2.92 ton	4.66	4.27	8.93
2280	3,000 S.F., 8.75 ton	4.43	3.96	8.39
2320	5,000 S.F., 14.58 ton	6.25	3.54	9.79
2360	10,000 S.F., 29.17 ton	5.70	3.41	9.11
2440	Drug stores, 500 S.F., 3.33 ton	12.30	5.35	17.65
2480	1,000 S.F., 6.66 ton	10.65	9.75	20.40
2520	3,000 S.F., 20.00 ton	14.30	8.10	22.40
2560	5,000 S.F., 33.33 ton	15.05	8	23.05
2600	10,000 S.F., 66.66 ton	12.15	7.95	20.10
2680	Factories, 500 S.F., 1.66 ton	6.15	2.65	8.80
2720	1,000 S.F. 3.37 ton	5.40	4.93	10.33
2760	3,000 S.F., 10.00 ton	5.05	4.52	9.57
2800	5,000 S.F., 16.66 ton	7.15	4.04	11.19
2840	10,000 S.F., 33.33 ton	6.50	3.89	10.39

D3050 Terminal & Package Units

D3050 160	Self-contained, Water Cooled Unit Systems	COST PER S.F.		
		MAT.	INST.	TOTAL
2920	Food supermarkets, 500 S.F., 1.42 ton	5.20	2.26	7.46
2960	1,000 S.F., 2.83 ton	5.45	4.97	10.42
3000	3,000 S.F., 8.50 ton	4.53	4.15	8.68
3040	5,000 S.F., 14.17 ton	4.31	3.85	8.16
3080	10,000 S.F., 28.33 ton	5.55	3.32	8.87
3160	Medical centers, 500 S.F., 1.17 ton	4.29	1.86	6.15
3200	1,000 S.F., 2.33 ton	4.46	4.09	8.55
3240	3,000 S.F., 7.00 ton	3.73	3.41	7.14
3280	5,000 S.F., 11.66 ton	3.54	3.17	6.71
3320	10,000 S.F., 23.33 ton	5	2.83	7.83
3400	Offices, 500 S.F., 1.58 ton	5.85	2.52	8.37
3440	1,000 S.F., 3.17 ton	6.05	5.55	11.60
3480	3,000 S.F., 9.50 ton	4.80	4.30	9.10
3520	5,000 S.F., 15.83 ton	6.80	3.84	10.64
3560	10,000 S.F., 31.67 ton	6.15	3.70	9.85
3640	Restaurants, 500 S.F., 2.50 ton	9.20	3.99	13.19
3680	1,000 S.F., 5.00 ton	8	7.30	15.30
3720	3,000 S.F., 15.00 ton	7.60	6.80	14.40
3760	5,000 S.F., 25.00 ton	10.75	6.10	16.85
3800	10,000 S.F., 50.00 ton	6.70	5.55	12.25
3880	Schools and colleges, 500 S.F., 1.92 ton	7.05	3.05	10.10
3920	1,000 S.F., 3.83 ton	6.10	5.60	11.70
3960	3,000 S.F., 11.50 ton	5.80	5.20	11
4000	5,000 S.F., 19.17 ton	8.25	4.65	12.90
4040	10,000 S.F., 38.33 ton	7.20	4.65	11.85

D3050 Terminal & Package Units

Self-Contained Air Cooled System

D3050 165	Self-contained, Air Cooled Unit Systems	COST PER S.F.		
		MAT.	INST.	TOTAL
1300	Self-contained, air cooled unit			
1320	Apartment corridors, 500 S.F., .92 ton	4.55	4.10	8.65
1360	1,000 S.F., 1.83 ton	4.49	4.08	8.57
1400	3,000 S.F., 5.50 ton	3.78	3.81	7.59
1440	5,000 S.F., 9.17 ton	3.26	3.63	6.89
1480	10,000 S.F., 18.33 ton	3.40	3.32	6.72
1560	Banks or libraries, 500 S.F., 2.08 ton	9.85	5.30	15.15
1600	1,000 S.F., 4.17 ton	8.55	8.65	17.20
1640	3,000 S.F., 12.50 ton	7.45	8.25	15.70
1680	5,000 S.F., 20.80 ton	7.75	7.55	15.30
1720	10,000 S.F., 41.66 ton	8.05	7.40	15.45
1800	Bars and taverns, 500 S.F., 5.54 ton	20	11.55	31.55
1840	1,000 S.F., 11.08 ton	19.30	16.65	35.95
1880	3,000 S.F., 33.25 ton	21	14.35	35.35
1920	5,000 S.F., 55.42 ton	21.50	14.40	35.90
1960	10,000 S.F., 110.00 ton	21.50	14.30	35.80
2040	Bowling alleys, 500 S.F., 2.83 ton	13.50	7.25	20.75
2080	1,000 S.F., 5.66 ton	11.70	11.80	23.50
2120	3,000 S.F., 17.00 ton	10.55	10.30	20.85
2160	5,000 S.F., 28.33 ton	10.90	10.05	20.95
2200	10,000 S.F., 56.66 ton	11.15	10.05	21.20
2240	Department stores, 500 S.F., 1.46 ton	6.95	3.73	10.68
2280	1,000 S.F., 2.92 ton	6	6.05	12.05
2320	3,000 S.F., 8.75 ton	5.20	5.80	11
2360	5,000 S.F., 14.58 ton	5.20	5.80	11
2400	10,000 S.F., 29.17 ton	5.60	5.15	10.75
2480	Drug stores, 500 S.F., 3.33 ton	15.85	8.50	24.35
2520	1,000 S.F., 6.66 ton	13.70	13.85	27.55
2560	3,000 S.F., 20.00 ton	12.45	12.15	24.60
2600	5,000 S.F., 33.33 ton	12.75	11.80	24.55
2640	10,000 S.F., 66.66 ton	13.20	11.80	25
2720	Factories, 500 S.F., 1.66 ton	8.05	4.30	12.35
2760	1,000 S.F., 3.33 ton	6.90	6.95	13.85
2800	3,000 S.F., 10.00 ton	5.95	6.60	12.55
2840	5,000 S.F., 16.66 ton	6.15	6.05	12.20
2880	10,000 S.F., 33.33 ton	6.40	5.90	12.30
2960	Food supermarkets, 500 S.F., 1.42 ton	6.75	3.63	10.38
3000	1,000 S.F., 2.83 ton	6.90	6.30	13.20
3040	3,000 S.F., 8.50 ton	5.85	5.90	11.75
3080	5,000 S.F., 14.17 ton	5.05	5.60	10.65

D3050 Terminal & Package Units

D3050 165	Self-contained, Air Cooled Unit Systems	COST PER S.F.		
		MAT.	INST.	TOTAL
3120	10,000 S.F., 28.33 ton	5.45	5.05	10.50
3200	Medical centers, 500 S.F., 1.17 ton	5.60	2.99	8.59
3240	1,000 S.F., 2.33 ton	5.75	5.20	10.95
3280	3,000 S.F., 7.00 ton	4.81	4.86	9.67
3320	5,000 S.F., 16.66 ton	4.16	4.62	8.78
3360	10,000 S.F., 23.33 ton	4.33	4.24	8.57
3440	Offices, 500 S.F., 1.58 ton	7.55	4.05	11.60
3480	1,000 S.F., 3.16 ton	7.80	7.10	14.90
3520	3,000 S.F., 9.50 ton	5.65	6.25	11.90
3560	5,000 S.F., 15.83 ton	5.90	5.75	11.65
3600	10,000 S.F., 31.66 ton	6.10	5.60	11.70
3680	Restaurants, 500 S.F., 2.50 ton	11.85	6.40	18.25
3720	1,000 S.F., 5.00 ton	10.30	10.40	20.70
3760	3,000 S.F., 15.00 ton	8.90	9.90	18.80
3800	5,000 S.F., 25.00 ton	9.55	8.85	18.40
3840	10,000 S.F., 50.00 ton	10.05	8.85	18.90
3920	Schools and colleges, 500 S.F., 1.92 ton	9.10	4.90	14
3960	1,000 S.F., 3.83 ton	7.95	8	15.95
4000	3,000 S.F., 11.50 ton	6.85	7.60	14.45
4040	5,000 S.F., 19.17 ton	7.10	6.95	14.05
4080	10,000 S.F., 38.33 ton	7.40	6.80	14.20

D3050 Terminal & Package Units

Refrigerant Piping — Air Cooled Condensing Unit — Roof — Supply Duct — Finish Ceiling — Return Grille — DX Air Handling Unit — Supply Diffuser

*Cooling requirements would lead to more than one system.

D3050 170	Split Systems With Air Cooled Condensing Units	COST PER S.F.		
		MAT.	INST.	TOTAL
1260	Split system, air cooled condensing unit			
1280	Apartment corridors, 1,000 S.F., 1.83 ton	2.75	2.58	5.33
1320	2,000 S.F., 3.66 ton	2.02	2.61	4.63
1360	5,000 S.F., 9.17 ton	2.21	3.25	5.46
1400	10,000 S.F., 18.33 ton	2.53	3.54	6.07
1440	20,000 S.F., 36.66 ton	2.78	3.61	6.39
1520	Banks and libraries, 1,000 S.F., 4.17 ton	4.58	5.95	10.53
1560	2,000 S.F., 8.33 ton	5.05	7.40	12.45
1600	5,000 S.F., 20.80 ton	5.75	8.05	13.80
1640	10,000 S.F., 41.66 ton	6.30	8.20	14.50
1680	20,000 S.F., 83.32 ton	7.35	8.55	15.90
1760	Bars and taverns, 1,000 S.F., 11.08 ton	11.85	11.65	23.50
1800	2,000 S.F., 22.16 ton	16	13.95	29.95
1840	5,000 S.F., 55.42 ton	14.15	13.05	27.20
1880	10,000 S.F., 110.84 ton	16.25	13.60	29.85
1920	20,000 S.F., 220 ton*			
2000	Bowling alleys, 1,000 S.F., 5.66 ton	6.40	11.05	17.45
2040	2,000 S.F., 11.33 ton	6.80	10.05	16.85
2080	5,000 S.F., 28.33 ton	7.80	10.95	18.75
2120	10,000 S.F., 56.66 ton	8.60	11.15	19.75
2160	20,000 S.F., 113.32 ton	10.90	12.10	23
2320	Department stores, 1,000 S.F., 2.92 ton	3.25	4.08	7.33
2360	2,000 S.F., 5.83 ton	3.30	5.70	9
2400	5,000 S.F., 14.58 ton	3.52	5.15	8.67
2440	10,000 S.F., 29.17 ton	4.01	5.65	9.66
2480	20,000 S.F., 58.33 ton	4.41	5.75	10.16
2560	Drug stores, 1,000 S.F., 6.66 ton	7.55	13	20.55
2600	2,000 S.F., 13.32 ton	8.05	11.80	19.85
2640	5,000 S.F., 33.33 ton	10.10	13.15	23.25
2680	10,000 S.F., 66.66 ton	10.75	13.70	24.45
2720	20,000 S.F., 133.32 ton*			
2800	Factories, 1,000 S.F., 3.33 ton	3.71	4.64	8.35
2840	2,000 S.F., 6.66 ton	3.77	6.50	10.27
2880	5,000 S.F., 16.66 ton	4.60	6.45	11.05
2920	10,000 S.F., 33.33 ton	5.05	6.55	11.60
2960	20,000 S.F., 66.66 ton	5.40	6.85	12.25
3040	Food supermarkets, 1,000 S.F., 2.83 ton	3.16	3.96	7.12
3080	2,000 S.F., 5.66 ton	3.21	5.50	8.71
3120	5,000 S.F., 14.66 ton	3.42	5	8.42
3160	10,000 S.F., 28.33 ton	3.90	5.50	9.40
3200	20,000 S.F., 56.66 ton	4.30	5.60	9.90
3280	Medical centers, 1,000 S.F., 2.33 ton	2.86	3.20	6.06

D30 HVAC

D3050 Terminal & Package Units

D3050 170	Split Systems With Air Cooled Condensing Units	COST PER S.F.		
		MAT.	INST.	TOTAL
3320	2,000 S.F., 4.66 ton	2.64	4.55	7.19
3360	5,000 S.F., 11.66 ton	2.82	4.14	6.96
3400	10,000 S.F., 23.33 ton	3.21	4.51	7.72
3440	20,000 S.F., 46.66 ton	3.53	4.59	8.12
3520	Offices, 1,000 S.F., 3.17 ton	3.53	4.42	7.95
3560	2,000 S.F., 6.33 ton	3.58	6.20	9.78
3600	5,000 S.F., 15.83 ton	3.82	5.60	9.42
3640	10,000 S.F., 31.66 ton	4.37	6.10	10.47
3680	20,000 S.F., 63.32 ton	5.10	6.50	11.60
3760	Restaurants, 1,000 S.F., 5.00 ton	5.65	9.75	15.40
3800	2,000 S.F., 10.00 ton	6.05	8.85	14.90
3840	5,000 S.F., 25.00 ton	6.90	9.70	16.60
3880	10,000 S.F., 50.00 ton	7.60	9.85	17.45
3920	20,000 S.F., 100.00 ton	9.65	10.65	20.30
4000	Schools and colleges, 1,000 S.F., 3.83 ton	4.21	5.45	9.66
4040	2,000 S.F., 7.66 ton	4.61	6.80	11.41
4080	5,000 S.F., 19.17 ton	5.30	7.40	12.70
4120	10,000 S.F., 38.33 ton	5.80	7.55	13.35

D3090 Other HVAC Systems/Equip

Cast Iron Garage Exhaust System

Dual Exhaust System

D3090 320	Garage Exhaust Systems	COST PER BAY		
		MAT.	INST.	TOTAL
1040	Garage, single 3" exhaust outlet, cars & light trucks, one bay	4,250	1,900	6,150
1060	Additional bays up to seven bays	995	510	1,505
1500	4" outlet, trucks, one bay	4,275	1,900	6,175
1520	Additional bays up to six bays	1,025	510	1,535
1600	5" outlet, diesel trucks, one bay	4,600	1,900	6,500
1650	Additional single bays up to six	1,450	605	2,055
1700	Two adjoining bays	4,600	1,900	6,500
2000	Dual exhaust, 3" outlets, pair of adjoining bays	5,325	2,375	7,700
2100	Additional pairs of adjoining bays	1,625	605	2,230

Reference - System Classification

System Classification
Rules for installation of sprinkler systems vary depending on the classification of occupancy falling into one of three categories as follows:

Light Hazard Occupancy
The protection area allotted per sprinkler should not exceed 225 S.F., with the maximum distance between lines and sprinklers on lines being 15'. The sprinklers do not need to be staggered. Branch lines should not exceed eight sprinklers on either side of a cross main. Each large area requiring more than 100 sprinklers and without a sub-dividing partition should be supplied by feed mains or risers sized for ordinary hazard occupancy.
Maximum system area = 52,000 S.F.

Included in this group are:

Churches	Nursing Homes
Clubs	Offices
Educational	Residential
Hospitals	Restaurants
Institutional	Theaters and Auditoriums
Libraries	(except stages and prosceniums)
(except large stack rooms)	Unused Attics
Museums	

Ordinary Hazard Occupancy
The protection area allotted per sprinkler shall not exceed 130 S.F. of noncombustible ceiling and 130 S.F. of combustible ceiling. The maximum allowable distance between sprinkler lines and sprinklers on line is 15'. Sprinklers shall be staggered if the distance between heads exceeds 12'. Branch lines should not exceed eight sprinklers on either side of a cross main.
Maximum system area = 52,000 S.F.

Included in this group are:

Group 1	Group 2
Automotive Parking and Showrooms	Cereal Mills
Bakeries	Chemical Plants—Ordinary
Beverage manufacturing	Confectionery Products
Canneries	Distilleries
Dairy Products Manufacturing/Processing	Dry Cleaners
Electronic Plans	Feed Mills
Glass and Glass Products Manufacturing	Horse Stables
Laundries	Leather Goods Manufacturing
Restaurant Service Areas	Libraries—Large Stack Room Areas
	Machine Shops
	Metal Working
	Mercantile
	Paper and Pulp Mills
	Paper Process Plants
	Piers and Wharves
	Post Offices
	Printing and Publishing
	Repair Garages
	Stages
	Textile Manufacturing
	Tire Manufacturing
	Tobacco Products Manufacturing
	Wood Machining
	Wood Product Assembly

Extra Hazard Occupancy
The protection area allotted per sprinkler shall not exceed 100 S.F. of noncombustible ceiling and 100 S.F. of combustible ceiling. The maximum allowable distance between lines and between sprinklers on lines is 12'. Sprinklers on alternate lines shall be staggered if the distance between sprinklers on lines exceeds 8'. Branch lines should not exceed six sprinklers on either side of a cross main.
Maximum system area:
   Design by pipe schedule = 25,000 S.F.
   Design by hydraulic calculation = 40,000 S.F.

Included in this group are:

Group 1	Group 2
Aircraft hangars	Asphalt Saturating
Combustible Hydraulic Fluid Use Area	Flammable Liquids Spraying
Die Casting	Flow Coating
Metal Extruding	Manufactured/Modular Home
Plywood/Particle Board Manufacturing	Building Assemblies (where
Printing (inkls with flash points < 100	finished enclosure is present
degrees F	and has combustible interiors)
Rubber Reclaiming, Compounding,	Open Oil Quenching
Drying, Milling, Vulcanizing	Plastics Processing
Saw Mills	Solvent Cleaning
Textile Picking, Opening, Blending,	Varnish and Paint Dipping
Garnetting, Carding, Combing of	
Cotton, Synthetics, Wood Shoddy,	
or Burlap	
Upholstering with Plastic Foams	

Reference - Sprinkler Systems (Automatic)

Sprinkler systems may be classified by type as follows:

1. **Wet Pipe System.** A system employing automatic sprinklers attached to a piping system containing water and connected to a water supply so that water discharges immediately from sprinklers opened by a fire.

2. **Dry Pipe System.** A system employing automatic sprinklers attached to a piping system containing air under pressure, the release of which as from the opening of sprinklers permits the water pressure to open a valve known as a "dry pipe valve". The water then flows into the piping system and out the opened sprinklers.

3. **Pre-Action System.** A system employing automatic sprinklers attached to a piping system containing air that may or may not be under pressure, with a supplemental heat responsive system of generally more sensitive characteristics than the automatic sprinklers themselves, installed in the same areas as the sprinklers; actuation of the heat responsive system, as from a fire, opens a valve which permits water to flow into the sprinkler piping system and to be discharged from any sprinklers which may be open.

4. **Deluge System.** A system employing open sprinklers attached to a piping system connected to a water supply through a valve which is opened by the operation of a heat responsive system installed in the same areas as the sprinklers. When this valve opens, water flows into the piping system and discharges from all sprinklers attached thereto.

5. **Combined Dry Pipe and Pre-Action Sprinkler System.** A system employing automatic sprinklers attached to a piping system containing air under pressure with a supplemental heat responsive system of generally more sensitive characteristics than the automatic sprinklers themselves, installed in the same areas as the sprinklers; operation of the heat responsive system, as from a fire, actuates tripping devices which open dry pipe valves simultaneously and without loss of air pressure in the system. Operation of the heat responsive system also opens approved air exhaust valves at the end of the feed main which facilitates the filling of the system with water which usually precedes the opening of sprinklers. The heat responsive system also serves as an automatic fire alarm system.

6. **Limited Water Supply System.** A system employing automatic sprinklers and conforming to these standards but supplied by a pressure tank of limited capacity.

7. **Chemical Systems.** Systems using halon, carbon dioxide, dry chemical or high expansion foam as selected for special requirements. Agent may extinguish flames by chemically inhibiting flame propagation, suffocate flames by excluding oxygen, interrupting chemical action of oxygen uniting with fuel or sealing and cooling the combustion center.

8. **Firecycle System.** Firecycle is a fixed fire protection sprinkler system utilizing water as its extinguishing agent. It is a time delayed, recycling, preaction type which automatically shuts the water off when heat is reduced below the detector operating temperature and turns the water back on when that temperature is exceeded. The system senses a fire condition through a closed circuit electrical detector system which controls water flow to the fire automatically. Batteries supply up to 90 hour emergency power supply for system operation. The piping system is dry (until water is required) and is monitored with pressurized air. Should any leak in the system piping occur, an alarm will sound, but water will not enter the system until heat is sensed by a firecycle detector.

Area coverage sprinkler systems may be laid out and fed from the supply in any one of several patterns as shown below. It is desirable, if possible, to utilize a central feed and achieve a shorter flow path from the riser to the furthest sprinkler. This permits use of the smallest sizes of pipe possible with resulting savings.

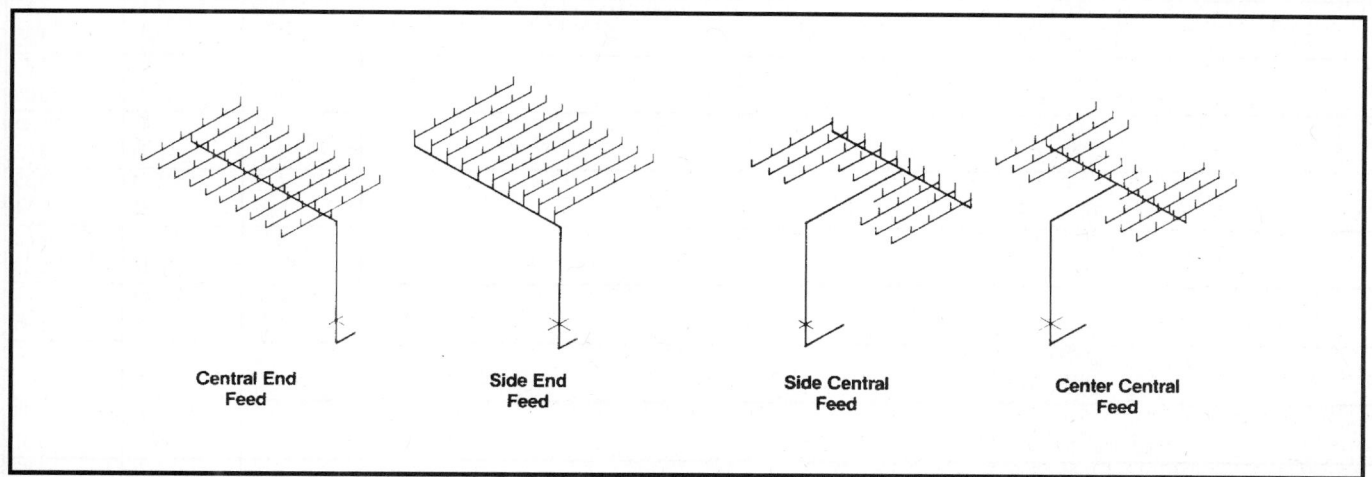

| Central End Feed | Side End Feed | Side Central Feed | Center Central Feed |

Dry Pipe System: A system employing automatic sprinklers attached to a piping system containing air under pressure, the release of which from the opening of sprinklers permits the water pressure to open a valve known as a "dry pipe valve". The water then flows into the piping system and out the opened sprinklers.

All areas are assumed to be open.

D4010 310	Dry Pipe Sprinkler Systems	COST PER S.F.		
		MAT.	INST.	TOTAL
0520	Dry pipe sprinkler systems, steel, black, sch. 40 pipe			
0530	Light hazard, one floor, 500 S.F.	9.30	6.10	15.40
0560	1000 S.F.	5.35	3.58	8.93
0580	2000 S.F.	5.10	3.60	8.70
0600	5000 S.F.	2.68	2.44	5.12
0620	10,000 S.F.	1.92	2.04	3.96
0640	50,000 S.F.	1.48	1.82	3.30
0660	Each additional floor, 500 S.F.	2.05	3	5.05
0680	1000 S.F.	1.79	2.46	4.25
0700	2000 S.F.	1.73	2.29	4.02
0720	5000 S.F.	1.41	1.94	3.35
0740	10,000 S.F.	1.33	1.81	3.14
0760	50,000 S.F.	1.20	1.62	2.82
1000	Ordinary hazard, one floor, 500 S.F.	9.50	6.15	15.65
1020	1000 S.F.	5.50	3.61	9.11
1040	2000 S.F.	5.20	3.75	8.95
1060	5000 S.F.	3.11	2.63	5.74
1080	10,000 S.F.	2.47	2.70	5.17
1100	50,000 S.F.	2.23	2.52	4.75
1140	Each additional floor, 500 S.F.	2.24	3.07	5.31
1160	1000 S.F.	2.07	2.75	4.82
1180	2000 S.F.	2.04	2.50	4.54
1200	5000 S.F.	1.92	2.16	4.08
1220	10,000 S.F.	1.71	2.14	3.85
1240	50,000 S.F.	1.64	1.83	3.47
1500	Extra hazard, one floor, 500 S.F.	13.15	7.65	20.80
1520	1000 S.F.	8.05	5.55	13.60
1540	2000 S.F.	5.80	4.85	10.65
1560	5000 S.F.	3.60	3.69	7.29
1580	10,000 S.F.	3.76	3.50	7.26
1600	50,000 S.F.	4.10	3.38	7.48
1660	Each additional floor, 500 S.F.	3.12	3.80	6.92
1680	1000 S.F.	3.07	3.62	6.69
1700	2000 S.F.	2.82	3.63	6.45
1720	5000 S.F.	2.42	3.18	5.60
1740	10,000 S.F.	2.87	2.87	5.74
1760	50,000 S.F.	2.92	2.76	5.68
2020	Grooved steel, black, sch. 40 pipe, light hazard, one floor, 2000 S.F.	4.87	3.08	7.95

D4010 Sprinklers

D4010 310	Dry Pipe Sprinkler Systems	COST PER S.F.		
		MAT.	INST.	TOTAL
2060	10,000 S.F.	1.87	1.75	3.62
2100	Each additional floor, 2000 S.F.	1.72	1.83	3.55
2150	10,000 S.F.	1.28	1.52	2.80
2200	Ordinary hazard, one floor, 2000 S.F.	5.10	3.28	8.38
2250	10,000 S.F.	2.30	2.28	4.58
2300	Each additional floor, 2000 S.F.	1.97	2.03	4
2350	10,000 S.F.	1.71	2.05	3.76
2400	Extra hazard, one floor, 2000 S.F.	5.75	4.13	9.88
2450	10,000 S.F.	3.28	2.91	6.19
2500	Each additional floor, 2000 S.F.	2.78	2.98	5.76
2550	10,000 S.F.	2.53	2.53	5.06
3050	Grooved steel, black, sch. 10 pipe, light hazard, one floor, 2000 S.F.	4.77	3.07	7.84
3100	10,000 S.F.	1.80	1.73	3.53
3150	Each additional floor, 2000 S.F.	1.62	1.82	3.44
3200	10,000 S.F.	1.21	1.50	2.71
3250	Ordinary hazard, one floor, 2000 S.F.	5.05	3.27	8.32
3300	10,000 S.F.	2.20	2.25	4.45
3350	Each additional floor, 2000 S.F.	1.88	2.02	3.90
3400	10,000 S.F.	1.61	2.02	3.63
3450	Extra hazard, one floor, 2000 S.F.	5.70	4.12	9.82
3500	10,000 S.F.	3.07	2.86	5.93
3550	Each additional floor, 2000 S.F.	2.72	2.97	5.69
3600	10,000 S.F.	2.42	2.49	4.91
4050	Copper tubing, type M, light hazard, one floor, 2000 S.F.	6.15	3.07	9.22
4100	10,000 S.F.	2.89	1.75	4.64
4150	Each additional floor, 2000 S.F.	3	1.86	4.86
4200	10,000 S.F.	2.30	1.53	3.83
4250	Ordinary hazard, one floor, 2000 S.F.	6.55	3.41	9.96
4300	10,000 S.F.	3.54	2.08	5.62
4350	Each additional floor, 2000 S.F.	3.86	2.12	5.98
4400	10,000 S.F.	2.79	1.81	4.60
4450	Extra hazard, one floor, 2000 S.F.	7.80	4.15	11.95
4500	10,000 S.F.	7.90	3.18	11.08
4550	Each additional floor, 2000 S.F.	4.81	3	7.81
4600	10,000 S.F.	6.15	2.77	8.92
5050	Copper tubing, type M, T-drill system, light hazard, one floor			
5060	2000 S.F.	5.95	2.86	8.81
5100	10,000 S.F.	2.47	1.46	3.93
5150	Each additional floor, 2000 S.F.	2.83	1.65	4.48
5200	10,000 S.F.	1.88	1.24	3.12
5250	Ordinary hazard, one floor, 2000 S.F.	5.90	2.92	8.82
5300	10,000 S.F.	3.18	1.86	5.04
5350	Each additional floor, 2000 S.F.	2.74	1.67	4.41
5400	10,000 S.F.	2.48	1.54	4.02
5450	Extra hazard, one floor, 2000 S.F.	6.65	3.44	10.09
5500	10,000 S.F.	5.45	2.34	7.79
5550	Each additional floor, 2000 S.F.	3.70	2.29	5.99
5600	10,000 S.F.	3.70	1.93	5.63

Preaction System: A system employing automatic sprinklers attached to a piping system containing air that may or may not be under pressure, with a supplemental heat responsive system of generally more sensitive characteristics than the automatic sprinklers themselves, installed in the same areas as the sprinklers. Actuation of the heat responsive system, as from a fire, opens a valve which permits water to flow into the sprinkler piping system and to be discharged from those sprinklers which were opened by heat from the fire.

All areas are assumed to be opened.

D4010 350	Preaction Sprinkler Systems	COST PER S.F.		
		MAT.	INST.	TOTAL
0520	Preaction sprinkler systems, steel, black, sch. 40 pipe			
0530	Light hazard, one floor, 500 S.F.	9.20	4.87	14.07
0560	1000 S.F.	5.40	3.67	9.07
0580	2000 S.F.	4.94	3.59	8.53
0600	5000 S.F.	2.56	2.43	4.99
0620	10,000 S.F.	1.81	2.04	3.85
0640	50,000 S.F.	1.38	1.81	3.19
0660	Each additional floor, 500 S.F.	2.29	2.67	4.96
0680	1000 S.F.	1.81	2.46	4.27
0700	2000 S.F.	1.74	2.29	4.03
0720	5000 S.F.	1.29	1.93	3.22
0740	10,000 S.F.	1.22	1.81	3.03
0760	50,000 S.F.	1.18	1.66	2.84
1000	Ordinary hazard, one floor, 500 S.F.	9.50	5.30	14.80
1020	1000 S.F.	5.35	3.60	8.95
1040	2000 S.F.	5.30	3.75	9.05
1060	5000 S.F.	2.85	2.61	5.46
1080	10,000 S.F.	2.16	2.68	4.84
1100	50,000 S.F.	1.92	2.51	4.43
1140	Each additional floor, 500 S.F.	2.61	3.08	5.69
1160	1000 S.F.	1.79	2.48	4.27
1180	2000 S.F.	1.62	2.47	4.09
1200	5000 S.F.	1.78	2.32	4.10
1220	10,000 S.F.	1.57	2.45	4.02
1240	50,000 S.F.	1.48	2.17	3.65
1500	Extra hazard, one floor, 500 S.F.	12.80	6.75	19.55
1520	1000 S.F.	7.40	5.10	12.50
1540	2000 S.F.	5.30	4.83	10.13

D4010 Sprinklers

D4010 350	Preaction Sprinkler Systems	COST PER S.F.		
		MAT.	**INST.**	**TOTAL**
1560	5000 S.F.	3.36	3.98	7.34
1580	10,000 S.F.	3.30	3.88	7.18
1600	50,000 S.F.	3.57	3.77	7.34
1660	Each additional floor, 500 S.F.	3.16	3.80	6.96
1680	1000 S.F.	2.59	3.60	6.19
1700	2000 S.F.	2.33	3.61	5.94
1720	5000 S.F.	1.95	3.19	5.14
1740	10,000 S.F.	2.25	2.90	5.15
1760	50,000 S.F.	2.19	2.73	4.92
2020	Grooved steel, black, sch. 40 pipe, light hazard, one floor, 2000 S.F.	4.88	3.08	7.96
2060	10,000 S.F.	1.76	1.75	3.51
2100	Each additional floor of 2000 S.F.	1.73	1.83	3.56
2150	10,000 S.F.	1.17	1.52	2.69
2200	Ordinary hazard, one floor, 2000 S.F.	4.96	3.27	8.23
2250	10,000 S.F.	1.99	2.26	4.25
2300	Each additional floor, 2000 S.F.	1.81	2.02	3.83
2350	10,000 S.F.	1.40	2.03	3.43
2400	Extra hazard, one floor, 2000 S.F.	5.25	4.11	9.36
2450	10,000 S.F.	2.66	2.88	5.54
2500	Each additional floor, 2000 S.F.	2.29	2.96	5.25
2550	10,000 S.F.	1.88	2.49	4.37
3050	Grooved steel, black, sch. 10 pipe light hazard, one floor, 2000 S.F.	4.78	3.07	7.85
3100	10,000 S.F.	1.69	1.73	3.42
3150	Each additional floor, 2000 S.F.	1.63	1.82	3.45
3200	10,000 S.F.	1.10	1.50	2.60
3250	Ordinary hazard, one floor, 2000 S.F.	4.80	3.06	7.86
3300	10,000 S.F.	1.63	2.22	3.85
3350	Each additional floor, 2000 S.F.	1.72	2.01	3.73
3400	10,000 S.F.	1.30	2	3.30
3450	Extra hazard, one floor, 2000 S.F.	5.20	4.10	9.30
3500	10,000 S.F.	2.42	2.82	5.24
3550	Each additional floor, 2000 S.F.	2.23	2.95	5.18
3600	10,000 S.F.	1.77	2.45	4.22
4050	Copper tubing, type M, light hazard, one floor, 2000 S.F.	6.15	3.07	9.22
4100	10,000 S.F.	2.78	1.75	4.53
4150	Each additional floor, 2000 S.F.	3.02	1.86	4.88
4200	10,000 S.F.	1.93	1.52	3.45
4250	Ordinary hazard, one floor, 2000 S.F.	6.40	3.40	9.80
4300	10,000 S.F.	3.23	2.06	5.29
4350	Each additional floor, 2000 S.F.	3.05	1.88	4.93
4400	10,000 S.F.	2.28	1.65	3.93
4450	Extra hazard, one floor, 2000 S.F.	7.30	4.13	11.43
4500	10,000 S.F.	7.20	3.13	10.33
4550	Each additional floor, 2000 S.F.	4.32	2.98	7.30
4600	10,000 S.F.	5.50	2.73	8.23
5050	Copper tubing, type M, T-drill system, light hazard, one floor			
5060	2000 S.F.	5.95	2.86	8.81
5100	10,000 S.F.	2.36	1.46	3.82
5150	Each additional floor, 2000 S.F.	2.84	1.65	4.49
5200	10,000 S.F.	1.77	1.24	3.01
5250	Ordinary hazard, one floor, 2000 S.F.	5.75	2.91	8.66
5300	10,000 S.F.	2.87	1.84	4.71
5350	Each additional floor, 2000 S.F.	2.60	1.67	4.27
5400	10,000 S.F.	2.28	1.61	3.89
5450	Extra hazard, one floor, 2000 S.F.	6.20	3.42	9.62
5500	10,000 S.F.	4.76	2.29	7.05
5550	Each additional floor, 2000 S.F.	3.21	2.27	5.48
5600	10,000 S.F.	3.05	1.89	4.94

Deluge System: A system employing open sprinklers attached to a piping system connected to a water supply through a valve which is opened by the operation of a heat responsive system installed in the same areas as the sprinklers. When this valve opens, water flows into the piping system and discharges from all sprinklers attached thereto.

D4010 370	Deluge Sprinkler Systems	COST PER S.F.		
		MAT.	INST.	TOTAL
0520	Deluge sprinkler systems, steel, black, sch. 40 pipe			
0530	Light hazard, one floor, 500 S.F.	28	4.93	32.93
0560	1000 S.F.	14.65	3.53	18.18
0580	2000 S.F.	9.90	3.60	13.50
0600	5000 S.F.	4.54	2.44	6.98
0620	10,000 S.F.	2.80	2.04	4.84
0640	50,000 S.F.	1.58	1.81	3.39
0660	Each additional floor, 500 S.F.	2.29	2.67	4.96
0680	1000 S.F.	1.81	2.46	4.27
0700	2000 S.F.	1.74	2.29	4.03
0720	5000 S.F.	1.29	1.93	3.22
0740	10,000 S.F.	1.22	1.81	3.03
0760	50,000 S.F.	1.18	1.66	2.84
1000	Ordinary hazard, one floor, 500 S.F.	29	5.65	34.65
1020	1000 S.F.	14.65	3.63	18.28
1040	2000 S.F.	10.25	3.76	14.01
1060	5000 S.F.	4.83	2.62	7.45
1080	10,000 S.F.	3.15	2.68	5.83
1100	50,000 S.F.	2.17	2.55	4.72
1140	Each additional floor, 500 S.F.	2.61	3.08	5.69
1160	1000 S.F.	1.79	2.48	4.27
1180	2000 S.F.	1.62	2.47	4.09
1200	5000 S.F.	1.66	2.14	3.80
1220	10,000 S.F.	1.53	2.17	3.70
1240	50,000 S.F.	1.40	1.98	3.38
1500	Extra hazard, one floor, 500 S.F.	31.50	6.85	38.35
1520	1000 S.F.	17.10	5.30	22.40
1540	2000 S.F.	10.30	4.84	15.14
1560	5000 S.F.	5.05	3.67	8.72
1580	10,000 S.F.	4.16	3.54	7.70
1600	50,000 S.F.	4.24	3.46	7.70
1660	Each additional floor, 500 S.F.	3.16	3.80	6.96

D40 Fire Protection

D4010 Sprinklers

D4010 370	Deluge Sprinkler Systems	COST PER S.F.		
		MAT.	INST.	TOTAL
1680	1000 S.F.	2.59	3.60	6.19
1700	2000 S.F.	2.33	3.61	5.94
1720	5000 S.F.	1.95	3.19	5.14
1740	10,000 S.F.	2.30	3.01	5.31
1760	50,000 S.F.	2.31	2.91	5.22
2000	Grooved steel, black, sch. 40 pipe, light hazard, one floor			
2020	2000 S.F.	9.85	3.09	12.94
2060	10,000 S.F.	2.77	1.77	4.54
2100	Each additional floor, 2,000 S.F.	1.73	1.83	3.56
2150	10,000 S.F.	1.17	1.52	2.69
2200	Ordinary hazard, one floor, 2000 S.F.	4.96	3.27	8.23
2250	10,000 S.F.	2.98	2.26	5.24
2300	Each additional floor, 2000 S.F.	1.81	2.02	3.83
2350	10,000 S.F.	1.40	2.03	3.43
2400	Extra hazard, one floor, 2000 S.F.	10.25	4.12	14.37
2450	10,000 S.F.	3.68	2.89	6.57
2500	Each additional floor, 2000 S.F.	2.29	2.96	5.25
2550	10,000 S.F.	1.88	2.49	4.37
3000	Grooved steel, black, sch. 10 pipe, light hazard, one floor			
3050	2000 S.F.	9.15	2.94	12.09
3100	10,000 S.F.	2.68	1.73	4.41
3150	Each additional floor, 2000 S.F.	1.63	1.82	3.45
3200	10,000 S.F.	1.10	1.50	2.60
3250	Ordinary hazard, one floor, 2000 S.F.	9.85	3.27	13.12
3300	10,000 S.F.	2.62	2.22	4.84
3350	Each additional floor, 2000 S.F.	1.72	2.01	3.73
3400	10,000 S.F.	1.30	2	3.30
3450	Extra hazard, one floor, 2000 S.F.	10.15	4.11	14.26
3500	10,000 S.F.	3.41	2.82	6.23
3550	Each additional floor, 2000 S.F.	2.23	2.95	5.18
3600	10,000 S.F.	1.77	2.45	4.22
4000	Copper tubing, type M, light hazard, one floor			
4050	2000 S.F.	11.10	3.08	14.18
4100	10,000 S.F.	3.77	1.75	5.52
4150	Each additional floor, 2000 S.F.	3.01	1.85	4.86
4200	10,000 S.F.	1.93	1.52	3.45
4250	Ordinary hazard, one floor, 2000 S.F.	11.35	3.41	14.76
4300	10,000 S.F.	4.22	2.06	6.28
4350	Each additional floor, 2000 S.F.	3.05	1.88	4.93
4400	10,000 S.F.	2.28	1.65	3.93
4450	Extra hazard, one floor, 2000 S.F.	12.25	4.14	16.39
4500	10,000 S.F.	8.25	3.15	11.40
4550	Each additional floor, 2000 S.F.	4.32	2.98	7.30
4600	10,000 S.F.	5.50	2.73	8.23
5000	Copper tubing, type M, T-drill system, light hazard, one floor			
5050	2000 S.F.	10.95	2.87	13.82
5100	10,000 S.F.	3.35	1.46	4.81
5150	Each additional floor, 2000 S.F.	2.44	1.68	4.12
5200	10,000 S.F.	1.77	1.24	3.01
5250	Ordinary hazard, one floor, 2000 S.F.	10.70	2.92	13.62
5300	10,000 S.F.	3.86	1.84	5.70
5350	Each additional floor, 2000 S.F.	2.58	1.66	4.24
5400	10,000 S.F.	2.28	1.61	3.89
5450	Extra hazard, one floor, 2000 S.F.	11.15	3.43	14.58
5500	10,000 S.F.	5.75	2.29	8.04
5550	Each additional floor, 2000 S.F.	3.21	2.27	5.48
5600	10,000 S.F.	3.05	1.89	4.94

Firecycle is a fixed fire protection sprinkler system utilizing water as its extinguishing agent. It is a time delayed, recycling, preaction type which automatically shuts the water off when heat is reduced below the detector operating temperature and turns the water back on when that temperature is exceeded.

The system senses a fire condition through a closed circuit electrical detector system which controls water flow to the fire automatically. Batteries supply up to 90 hours emergency power supply for system operation. The piping system is dry (until water is required) and is monitored with pressurized air. Should any leak in the system piping occur, an alarm will sound, but water will not enter the system until heat is sensed by a Firecycle detector.

D4010 390	Firecycle Sprinkler Systems	COST PER S.F.		
		MAT.	INST.	TOTAL
0520	Firecycle sprinkler systems, steel black sch. 40 pipe			
0530	Light hazard, one floor, 500 S.F.	46	9.50	55.50
0560	1000 S.F.	24	6	30
0580	2000 S.F.	14.05	4.40	18.45
0600	5000 S.F.	6.25	2.76	9.01
0620	10,000 S.F.	3.70	2.21	5.91
0640	50,000 S.F.	1.81	1.84	3.65
0660	Each additional floor of 500 S.F.	2.36	2.68	5.04
0680	1000 S.F.	1.84	2.46	4.30
0700	2000 S.F.	1.50	2.28	3.78
0720	5000 S.F.	1.32	1.94	3.26
0740	10,000 S.F.	1.30	1.82	3.12
0760	50,000 S.F.	1.23	1.65	2.88
1000	Ordinary hazard, one floor, 500 S.F.	46.50	9.90	56.40
1020	1000 S.F.	23.50	5.90	29.40
1040	2000 S.F.	14.15	4.55	18.70
1060	5000 S.F.	6.50	2.94	9.44
1080	10,000 S.F.	4.05	2.85	6.90
1100	50,000 S.F.	2.59	2.84	5.43
1140	Each additional floor, 500 S.F.	2.68	3.09	5.77
1160	1000 S.F.	1.82	2.48	4.30
1180	2000 S.F.	1.84	2.27	4.11
1200	5000 S.F.	1.69	2.15	3.84
1220	10,000 S.F.	1.48	2.13	3.61
1240	50,000 S.F.	1.43	1.88	3.31
1500	Extra hazard, one floor, 500 S.F.	49.50	11.40	60.90
1520	1000 S.F.	25.50	7.40	32.90
1540	2000 S.F.	14.45	5.65	20.10
1560	5000 S.F.	6.75	3.99	10.74
1580	10,000 S.F.	5.15	4.02	9.17

D40 Fire Protection

D4010 Sprinklers

		MAT.	INST.	TOTAL
1600	50,000 S.F.	4.37	4.45	8.82
1660	Each additional floor, 500 S.F.	3.23	3.81	7.04
1680	1000 S.F.	2.62	3.60	6.22
1700	2000 S.F.	2.37	3.61	5.98
1720	5000 S.F.	1.98	3.20	5.18
1740	10,000 S.F.	2.33	2.91	5.24
1760	50,000 S.F.	2.32	2.80	5.12
2020	Grooved steel, black, sch. 40 pipe, light hazard, one floor			
2030	2000 S.F.	14	3.89	17.89
2060	10,000 S.F.	3.94	2.65	6.59
2100	Each additional floor, 2000 S.F.	1.77	1.83	3.60
2150	10,000 S.F.	1.25	1.53	2.78
2200	Ordinary hazard, one floor, 2000 S.F.	14.10	4.08	18.18
2250	10,000 S.F.	4.16	2.56	6.72
2300	Each additional floor, 2000 S.F.	1.85	2.02	3.87
2350	10,000 S.F.	1.48	2.04	3.52
2400	Extra hazard, one floor, 2000 S.F.	14.40	4.92	19.32
2450	10,000 S.F.	4.50	3.02	7.52
2500	Each additional floor, 2000 S.F.	2.33	2.96	5.29
2550	10,000 S.F.	1.96	2.50	4.46
3050	Grooved steel, black, sch. 10 pipe light hazard, one floor,			
3060	2000 S.F.	13.90	3.88	17.78
3100	10,000 S.F.	3.58	1.90	5.48
3150	Each additional floor, 2000 S.F.	1.67	1.82	3.49
3200	10,000 S.F.	1.18	1.51	2.69
3250	Ordinary hazard, one floor, 2000 S.F.	14	4.07	18.07
3300	10,000 S.F.	3.78	2.40	6.18
3350	Each additional floor, 2000 S.F.	1.76	2.01	3.77
3400	10,000 S.F.	1.38	2.01	3.39
3450	Extra hazard, one floor, 2000 S.F.	14.35	4.91	19.26
3500	10,000 S.F.	4.29	2.97	7.26
3550	Each additional floor, 2000 S.F.	2.27	2.95	5.22
3600	10,000 S.F.	1.85	2.46	4.31
4060	Copper tubing, type M, light hazard, one floor, 2000 S.F.	15.30	3.88	19.18
4100	10,000 S.F.	4.67	1.92	6.59
4150	Each additional floor, 2000 S.F.	3.05	1.86	4.91
4200	10,000 S.F.	2.27	1.54	3.81
4250	Ordinary hazard, one floor, 2000 S.F.	15.55	4.21	19.76
4300	10,000 S.F.	5.10	2.23	7.33
4350	Each additional floor, 2000 S.F.	3.09	1.88	4.97
4400	10,000 S.F.	2.33	1.63	3.96
4450	Extra hazard, one floor, 2000 S.F.	16.45	4.94	21.39
4500	10,000 S.F.	9.15	3.33	12.48
4550	Each additional floor, 2000 S.F.	4.36	2.98	7.34
4600	10,000 S.F.	5.55	2.74	8.29
5060	Copper tubing, type M, T-drill system, light hazard, one floor 2000 S.F.	15.10	3.67	18.77
5100	10,000 S.F.	4.25	1.63	5.88
5150	Each additional floor, 2000 S.F.	3.06	1.75	4.81
5200	10,000 S.F.	1.85	1.25	3.10
5250	Ordinary hazard, one floor, 2000 S.F.	14.85	3.72	18.57
5300	10,000 S.F.	4.76	2.01	6.77
5350	Each additional floor, 2000 S.F.	2.62	1.66	4.28
5400	10,000 S.F.	2.36	1.62	3.98
5450	Extra hazard, one floor, 2000 S.F.	15.30	4.23	19.53
5500	10,000 S.F.	6.65	2.44	9.09
5550	Each additional floor, 2000 S.F.	3.25	2.27	5.52
5600	10,000 S.F.	3.13	1.90	5.03

D40 Fire Protection

D4010 Sprinklers

Wet Pipe System. A system employing automatic sprinklers attached to a piping system containing water and connected to a water supply so that water discharges immediately from sprinklers opened by heat from a fire.

All areas are assumed to be open.

D4010 410	Wet Pipe Sprinkler Systems	COST PER S.F.		
		MAT.	INST.	TOTAL
0520	Wet pipe sprinkler systems, steel, black, sch. 40 pipe			
0530	Light hazard, one floor, 500 S.F.	2.80	3.14	5.94
0560	1000 S.F.	5.85	3.25	9.10
0580	2000 S.F.	5.25	3.26	8.51
0600	5000 S.F.	2.47	2.29	4.76
0620	10,000 S.F.	1.60	1.96	3.56
0640	50,000 S.F.	1.08	1.77	2.85
0660	Each additional floor, 500 S.F.	1.26	2.68	3.94
0680	1000 S.F.	1.30	2.49	3.79
0700	2000 S.F.	1.22	2.26	3.48
0720	5000 S.F.	.87	1.91	2.78
0740	10,000 S.F.	.85	1.79	2.64
0760	50,000 S.F.	.70	1.40	2.10
1000	Ordinary hazard, one floor, 500 S.F.	3.08	3.35	6.43
1020	1000 S.F.	5.80	3.18	8.98
1040	2000 S.F.	5.35	3.41	8.76
1060	5000 S.F.	2.76	2.47	5.23
1080	10,000 S.F.	1.95	2.60	4.55
1100	50,000 S.F.	1.58	2.44	4.02
1140	Each additional floor, 500 S.F.	1.56	3.03	4.59
1160	1000 S.F.	1.26	2.45	3.71
1180	2000 S.F.	1.36	2.46	3.82
1200	5000 S.F.	1.38	2.34	3.72
1220	10,000 S.F.	1.20	2.43	3.63
1240	50,000 S.F.	1.14	2.15	3.29
1500	Extra hazard, one floor, 500 S.F.	11.20	5.20	16.40
1520	1000 S.F.	7	4.53	11.53
1540	2000 S.F.	5.65	4.64	10.29
1560	5000 S.F.	3.47	4.07	7.54
1580	10,000 S.F.	3.03	3.84	6.87
1600	50,000 S.F.	3.39	3.71	7.10
1660	Each additional floor, 500 S.F.	2.11	3.75	5.86
1680	1000 S.F.	2.06	3.57	5.63
1700	2000 S.F.	1.81	3.58	5.39
1720	5000 S.F.	1.53	3.17	4.70
1740	10,000 S.F.	1.88	2.88	4.76
1760	50,000 S.F.	1.87	2.76	4.63
2020	Grooved steel, black sch. 40 pipe, light hazard, one floor, 2000 S.F.	5.20	2.75	7.95

D4010 Sprinklers

D4010 410	Wet Pipe Sprinkler Systems	COST PER S.F.		
		MAT.	INST.	TOTAL
2060	10,000 S.F.	2	1.74	3.74
2100	Each additional floor, 2000 S.F.	1.21	1.80	3.01
2150	10,000 S.F.	.80	1.50	2.30
2200	Ordinary hazard, one floor, 2000 S.F.	5.25	2.94	8.19
2250	10,000 S.F.	1.78	2.18	3.96
2300	Each additional floor, 2000 S.F.	1.29	1.99	3.28
2350	10,000 S.F.	1.03	2.01	3.04
2400	Extra hazard, one floor, 2000 S.F.	5.55	3.78	9.33
2450	10,000 S.F.	2.42	2.79	5.21
2500	Each additional floor, 2000 S.F.	1.77	2.93	4.70
2550	10,000 S.F.	1.51	2.47	3.98
3050	Grooved steel, black sch. 10 pipe, light hazard, one floor, 2000 S.F.	5.10	2.74	7.84
3100	10,000 S.F.	1.48	1.65	3.13
3150	Each additional floor, 2000 S.F.	1.11	1.79	2.90
3200	10,000 S.F.	.73	1.48	2.21
3250	Ordinary hazard, one floor, 2000 S.F.	5.20	2.93	8.13
3300	10,000 S.F.	1.68	2.15	3.83
3350	Each additional floor, 2000 S.F.	1.20	1.98	3.18
3400	10,000 S.F.	.93	1.98	2.91
3450	Extra hazard, one floor, 2000 S.F.	5.50	3.77	9.27
3500	10,000 S.F.	2.21	2.74	4.95
3550	Each additional floor, 2000 S.F.	1.71	2.92	4.63
3600	10,000 S.F.	1.40	2.43	3.83
4050	Copper tubing, type M, light hazard, one floor, 2000 S.F.	6.45	2.74	9.19
4100	10,000 S.F.	2.57	1.67	4.24
4150	Each additional floor, 2000 S.F.	2.49	1.83	4.32
4200	10,000 S.F.	1.82	1.51	3.33
4250	Ordinary hazard, one floor, 2000 S.F.	6.70	3.07	9.77
4300	10,000 S.F.	3.02	1.98	5
4350	Each additional floor, 2000 S.F.	2.82	2.01	4.83
4400	10,000 S.F.	2.11	1.77	3.88
4450	Extra hazard, one floor, 2000 S.F.	7.60	3.80	11.40
4500	10,000 S.F.	7	3.05	10.05
4550	Each additional floor, 2000 S.F.	3.80	2.95	6.75
4600	10,000 S.F.	5.10	2.71	7.81
5050	Copper tubing, type M, T-drill system, light hazard, one floor			
5060	2000 S.F.	6.30	2.53	8.83
5100	10,000 S.F.	2.15	1.38	3.53
5150	Each additional floor, 2000 S.F.	2.32	1.62	3.94
5200	10,000 S.F.	1.40	1.22	2.62
5250	Ordinary hazard, one floor, 2000 S.F.	6.05	2.58	8.63
5300	10,000 S.F.	2.66	1.76	4.42
5350	Each additional floor, 2000 S.F.	2.06	1.63	3.69
5400	10,000 S.F.	1.91	1.59	3.50
5450	Extra hazard, one floor, 2000 S.F.	6.50	3.09	9.59
5500	10,000 S.F.	4.55	2.21	6.76
5550	Each additional floor, 2000 S.F.	2.79	2.28	5.07
5600	10,000 S.F.	2.68	1.87	4.55

D4020 Standpipes

Roof

Roof connections with hose gate valves (for combustible roof)

Hose connections on each floor (size based on class of service)

Check Valve

Siamese inlet connections (for fire department use)

D4020 310	Wet Standpipe Risers, Class I	COST PER FLOOR		
		MAT.	INST.	TOTAL
0550	Wet standpipe risers, Class I, steel, black sch. 40, 10' height			
0560	4" diameter pipe, one floor	4,750	3,425	8,175
0580	Additional floors	1,075	1,075	2,150
0600	6" diameter pipe, one floor	8,075	6,025	14,100
0620	Additional floors	1,950	1,675	3,625
0640	8" diameter pipe, one floor	12,500	7,250	19,750
0660	Additional floors	2,950	2,050	5,000

D4020 310	Wet Standpipe Risers, Class II	COST PER FLOOR		
		MAT.	INST.	TOTAL
1030	Wet standpipe risers, Class II, steel, black sch. 40, 10' height			
1040	2" diameter pipe, one floor	1,875	1,250	3,125
1060	Additional floors	550	480	1,030
1080	2-1/2" diameter pipe, one floor	2,750	1,800	4,550
1100	Additional floors	635	555	1,190

D4020 310	Wet Standpipe Risers, Class III	COST PER FLOOR		
		MAT.	INST.	TOTAL
1530	Wet standpipe risers, Class III, steel, black sch. 40, 10' height			
1540	4" diameter pipe, one floor	4,850	3,425	8,275
1560	Additional floors	915	895	1,810
1580	6" diameter pipe, one floor	8,175	6,025	14,200
1600	Additional floors	2,000	1,675	3,675
1620	8" diameter pipe, one floor	12,600	7,250	19,850
1640	Additional floors	3,000	2,050	5,050

D4020 Standpipes

| Roof | | Roof connections with hose gate valves (for combustible roof) |
| Hose connections on each floor (size based on class of service) |
| Check valve | | Siamese inlet connections (for fire department use) |

D4020 330	Dry Standpipe Risers, Class I	COST PER FLOOR		
		MAT.	INST.	TOTAL
0530	Dry standpipe riser, Class I, steel, black sch. 40, 10' height			
0540	4" diameter pipe, one floor	2,850	2,775	5,625
0560	Additional floors	990	1,000	1,990
0580	6" diameter pipe, one floor	5,775	4,775	10,550
0600	Additional floors	1,875	1,625	3,500
0620	8" diameter pipe, one floor	9,225	5,775	15,000
0640	Additional floors	2,875	1,975	4,850

D4020 330	Dry Standpipe Risers, Class II	COST PER FLOOR		
		MAT.	INST.	TOTAL
1030	Dry standpipe risers, Class II, steel, black sch. 40, 10' height			
1040	2" diameter pipe, one floor	1,525	1,275	2,800
1060	Additional floor	475	420	895
1080	2-1/2" diameter pipe, one floor	2,175	1,500	3,675
1100	Additional floors	560	500	1,060

D4020 330	Dry Standpipe Risers, Class III	COST PER FLOOR		
		MAT.	INST.	TOTAL
1530	Dry standpipe risers, Class III, steel, black sch. 40, 10' height			
1540	4" diameter pipe, one floor	2,900	2,725	5,625
1560	Additional floors	850	915	1,765
1580	6" diameter pipe, one floor	5,850	4,775	10,625
1600	Additional floors	1,925	1,625	3,550
1620	8" diameter pipe, one floor	9,275	5,775	15,050
1640	Additional floor	2,925	1,975	4,900

D40 Fire Protection

D4020 Standpipes

D4020 410	Fire Hose Equipment	COST EACH		
		MAT.	INST.	TOTAL
0100	Adapters, reducing, 1 piece, FxM, hexagon, cast brass, 2-1/2" x 1-1/2"	58		58
0200	Pin lug, 1-1/2" x 1"	50		50
0250	3" x 2-1/2"	131		131
0300	For polished chrome, add 75% mat.			
0400	Cabinets, D.S. glass in door, recessed, steel box, not equipped			
0500	Single extinguisher, steel door & frame	115	151	266
0550	Stainless steel door & frame	215	151	366
0600	Valve, 2-1/2" angle, steel door & frame	142	100	242
0650	Aluminum door & frame	172	100	272
0700	Stainless steel door & frame	231	100	331
0750	Hose rack assy, 2-1/2" x 1-1/2" valve & 100' hose, steel door & frame	265	201	466
0800	Aluminum door & frame	390	201	591
0850	Stainless steel door & frame	520	201	721
0900	Hose rack assy & extinguisher,2-1/2"x1-1/2" valve & hose,steel door & frame	330	241	571
0950	Aluminum	500	241	741
1000	Stainless steel	605	241	846
1550	Compressor, air, dry pipe system, automatic, 200 gal., 3/4 H.P.	810	515	1,325
1600	520 gal., 1 H.P.	835	515	1,350
1650	Alarm, electric pressure switch (circuit closer)	92.50	26	118.50
2500	Couplings, hose, rocker lug, cast brass, 1-1/2"	56		56
2550	2-1/2"	73		73
3000	Escutcheon plate, for angle valves, polished brass, 1-1/2"	16.70		16.70
3050	2-1/2"	27		27
3500	Fire pump, electric, w/controller, fittings, relief valve			
3550	4" pump, 30 H.P., 500 G.P.M.	17,100	3,750	20,850
3600	5" pump, 40 H.P., 1000 G.P.M.	18,800	4,250	23,050
3650	5" pump, 100 H.P., 1000 G.P.M.	25,900	4,725	30,625
3700	For jockey pump system, add	2,775	605	3,380
5000	Hose, per linear foot, synthetic jacket, lined,			
5100	300 lb. test, 1-1/2" diameter	3.40	.46	3.86
5150	2-1/2" diameter	5.85	.55	6.40
5200	500 lb. test, 1-1/2" diameter	3.50	.46	3.96
5250	2-1/2" diameter	6.20	.55	6.75
5500	Nozzle, plain stream, polished brass, 1-1/2" x 10"	50		50
5550	2-1/2" x 15" x 13/16" or 1-1/2"	105		105
5600	Heavy duty combination adjustable fog and straight stream w/handle 1-1/2"	465		465
5650	2-1/2" direct connection	575		575
6000	Rack, for 1-1/2" diameter hose 100 ft. long, steel	64	60.50	124.50
6050	Brass	109	60.50	169.50
6500	Reel, steel, for 50 ft. long 1-1/2" diameter hose	137	86	223
6550	For 75 ft. long 2-1/2" diameter hose	222	86	308
7050	Siamese, w/plugs & chains, polished brass, sidewalk, 4" x 2-1/2" x 2-1/2"	665	480	1,145
7100	6" x 2-1/2" x 2-1/2"	810	605	1,415
7200	Wall type, flush, 4" x 2-1/2" x 2-1/2"	545	241	786
7250	6" x 2-1/2" x 2-1/2"	755	262	1,017
7300	Projecting, 4" x 2-1/2" x 2-1/2"	495	241	736
7350	6" x 2-1/2" x 2-1/2"	840	262	1,102
7400	For chrome plate, add 15% mat.			
8000	Valves, angle, wheel handle, 300 Lb., rough brass, 1-1/2"	94.50	56	150.50
8050	2-1/2"	183	95.50	278.50
8100	Combination pressure restricting, 1-1/2"	89.50	56	145.50
8150	2-1/2"	183	95.50	278.50
8200	Pressure restricting, adjustable, satin brass, 1-1/2"	125	56	181
8250	2-1/2"	176	95.50	271.50
8300	Hydrolator, vent and drain, rough brass, 1-1/2"	74.50	56	130.50
8350	2-1/2"	74.50	56	130.50
8400	Cabinet assy, incls. adapter, rack, hose, and nozzle	820	365	1,185

D4090 Other Fire Protection Systems

General: Automatic fire protection (suppression) systems other than water sprinklers may be desired for special environments, high risk areas, isolated locations or unusual hazards. Some typical applications would include:

1. Paint dip tanks
2. Securities vaults
3. Electronic data processing
4. Tape and data storage
5. Transformer rooms
6. Spray booths
7. Petroleum storage
8. High rack storage

Piping and wiring costs are highly variable and are not included.

D4090 910	Fire Suppression Unit Components	COST EACH		
		MAT.	INST.	TOTAL
0020	Detectors with brackets			
0040	Fixed temperature heat detector	55.50	80	135.50
0060	Rate of temperature rise detector	55.50	80	135.50
0080	Ion detector (smoke) detector	120	103	223
0200	Extinguisher agent			
0240	200 lb FM200, container	8,300	315	8,615
0280	75 lb carbon dioxide cylinder	1,350	209	1,559
0320	Dispersion nozzle			
0340	FM200 1-1/2" dispersion nozzle	71.50	49.50	121
0380	Carbon dioxide 3" x 5" dispersion nozzle	71.50	38.50	110
0420	Control station			
0440	Single zone control station with batteries	1,850	640	2,490
0470	Multizone (4) control station with batteries	3,500	1,275	4,775
0500	Electric mechanical release	179	335	514
0550	Manual pull station	64.50	116	180.50
0640	Battery standby power 10" x 10" x 17"	450	160	610
0740	Bell signalling device	85.50	80	165.50
0900	Standard low-rise sprinkler accessory package, 3 story	2,650	1,800	4,450
1000	Standard mid-rise sprinkler accessory package, 8 story	5,700	3,425	9,125
1100	Standard high-rise sprinkler accessory package, 16 story	12,300	6,700	19,000

D4090 920	FM200 Systems	COST PER C.F.		
		MAT.	INST.	TOTAL
0820	Average FM200 system, minimum			1.88
0840	Maximum			3.74

D5010 Electrical Service/Distribution

D5010 120	Overhead Electric Service, 3 Phase - 4 Wire	COST EACH		
		MAT.	INST.	TOTAL
0200	Service installation, includes breakers, metering, 20' conduit & wire			
0220	3 phase, 4 wire, 120/208 volts, 60 A	615	1,050	1,665
0240	3 phase, 4 wire, 120/208 volts, 100 A	840	1,175	2,015
0245	100 A w/circuit breaker	1,600	1,450	3,050
0280	200 A	1,600	1,625	3,225
0285	200 A w/circuit breaker	3,225	2,050	5,275
0320	400 A	3,225	3,250	6,475
0325	400 A w/circuit breaker	6,250	4,050	10,300
0360	600 A	5,400	4,775	10,175
0365	600 A, w/switchboard	9,775	6,050	15,825
0400	800 A	7,725	5,725	13,450
0405	800 A, w/switchboard	12,100	7,175	19,275
0440	1000 A	9,375	7,050	16,425
0445	1000 A, w/switchboard	14,600	8,650	23,250
0480	1200 A	12,500	8,050	20,550
0485	1200 A, w/groundfault switchboard	35,200	9,975	45,175
0520	1600 A	15,500	10,500	26,000
0525	1600 A, w/groundfault switchboard	40,100	12,600	52,700
0560	2000 A	20,600	12,800	33,400
0565	2000 A, w/groundfault switchboard	49,000	15,700	64,700
0610	1 phase, 3 wire, 120/240 volts, 100 A (no safety switch)	193	575	768
0615	100 A w/load center	555	1,100	1,655
0620	200 A	460	790	1,250
0625	200 A w/load center	1,250	1,600	2,850

D5010   Electrical Service/Distribution

D5010 130	Underground Electric Service	COST EACH		
		MAT.	INST.	TOTAL
0950	Underground electric service including excavation, backfill, and compaction			
1000	3 phase, 4 wire, 277/480 volts, 2000 A	41,600	20,400	62,000
1050	2000 A w/groundfault switch	68,000	22,800	90,800
1100	1600 A	33,000	16,500	49,500
1150	1600 A w/groundfault switchboard	57,500	18,500	76,000
1200	1200 A	25,200	13,100	38,300
1250	1200 A w/groundfault switchboard	47,900	15,000	62,900
1400	800 A	18,300	10,900	29,200
1450	800 A w/ switchboard	22,600	12,300	34,900
1500	600 A	11,600	10,000	21,600
1550	600 A w/ switchboard	16,000	11,300	27,300
1600	1 phase, 3 wire, 120/240 volts, 200 A	3,325	3,475	6,800
1650	200 A w/load center	4,100	4,275	8,375
1700	100 A	2,250	2,825	5,075
1750	100 A w/load center	3,025	3,650	6,675

D5010 230	Feeder Installation	COST PER L.F.		
		MAT.	INST.	TOTAL
0200	Feeder installation 600 V, including RGS conduit and XHHW wire, 60 A	5.75	11.75	17.50
0240	100 A	10.50	15.30	25.80
0280	200 A	25	23	48
0320	400 A	50	46	96
0360	600 A	91	75	166
0400	800 A	119	89	208
0440	1000 A	147	117	264
0480	1200 A	182	150	332
0520	1600 A	238	178	416
0560	2000 A	293	234	527
1200	Branch installation 600 V, including EMT conduit and THW wire, 15 A	1.03	5.70	6.73
1240	20 A	1.26	6.10	7.36
1280	30 A	1.62	6.30	7.92
1320	50 A	3.29	8.75	12.04
1360	65 A	4.17	9.30	13.47
1400	85 A	6.45	10.85	17.30
1440	100 A	7.30	11.05	18.35
1480	130 A	10.85	12.90	23.75
1520	150 A	13.45	14.80	28.25
1560	200 A	18.60	16.90	35.50

D5010 Electrical Service/Distribution

D5010 240	Switchgear	COST EACH		
		MAT.	INST.	TOTAL
0190	Switchgear installation, including switchboard, panels, & circuit breaker			
0200	120/208 V, 1 phase, 400 A	8,075	2,700	10,775
0240	600 A	10,600	3,025	13,625
0280	800 A	13,500	3,500	17,000
0300	1000 A	16,500	3,900	20,400
0320	1200 A	17,300	4,400	21,700
0360	1600 A	26,800	5,050	31,850
0400	2000 A	31,900	5,500	37,400
0500	277/480 V, 3 phase, 400 A	10,900	5,000	15,900
0520	600 A	15,500	5,775	21,275
0540	800 A	18,100	6,400	24,500
0560	1000 A	22,500	7,100	29,600
0580	1200 A	24,400	7,950	32,350
0600	1600 A	33,500	8,700	42,200
0620	2000 A	41,000	9,600	50,600

D5010 250	Panelboard	COST EACH		
		MAT.	INST.	TOTAL
0900	Panelboards, NQOD, 4 wire, 120/208 volts w/conductor & conduit			
1000	100 A, 0 stories, 0' horizontal	1,275	1,350	2,625
1020	1 stories, 25' horizontal	1,675	1,925	3,600
1040	5 stories, 50' horizontal	2,475	3,075	5,550
1060	10 stories, 75' horizontal	3,400	4,425	7,825
1080	225A, 0 stories, 0' horizontal	2,400	1,775	4,175
2000	1 stories, 25' horizontal	3,625	2,825	6,450
2020	5 stories, 50' horizontal	6,025	4,900	10,925
2040	10 stories, 75' horizontal	8,825	7,300	16,125
2060	400A, 0 stories, 0' horizontal	3,550	2,650	6,200
2080	1 stories, 25' horizontal	5,200	4,350	9,550
3000	5 stories, 50' horizontal	8,475	7,725	16,200
3020	10 stories, 75' horizontal	17,800	15,100	32,900
3040	600 A, 0 stories, 0' horizontal	5,250	3,200	8,450
3060	1 stories, 25' horizontal	8,750	5,975	14,725
3080	5 stories, 50' horizontal	15,600	11,500	27,100
4000	10 stories, 75' horizontal	35,400	22,600	58,000
4010	Panelboards, NEHB, 4 wire, 277/480 volts w/conductor, conduit, & safety switch			
4020	100 A, 0 stories, 0' horizontal, includes safety switch	3,000	1,850	4,850
4040	1 stories, 25' horizontal	3,400	2,450	5,850
4060	5 stories, 50' horizontal	4,200	3,600	7,800
4080	10 stories, 75' horizontal	5,125	4,925	10,050
5000	225 A, 0 stories, 0' horizontal	4,500	2,275	6,775
5020	1 stories, 25' horizontal	5,725	3,325	9,050
5040	5 stories, 50' horizontal	8,125	5,375	13,500
5060	10 stories, 75' horizontal	10,900	7,800	18,700
5080	400 A, 0 stories, 0' horizontal	7,425	3,475	10,900
6000	1 stories, 25' horizontal	9,075	5,200	14,275
6020	5 stories, 50' horizontal	12,300	8,575	20,875
6040	10 stories, 75' horizontal	21,700	16,000	37,700
6060	600 A, 0 stories, 0' horizontal	11,100	4,425	15,525
6080	1 stories, 25' horizontal	14,500	7,200	21,700
7000	5 stories, 50' horizontal	21,400	12,700	34,100
7020	10 stories, 75' horizontal	41,200	23,800	65,000

D5020 Lighting and Branch Wiring

Duplex Wall Receptacle

Undercarpet Receptacle System

D5020 110	Receptacle (by Wattage)	COST PER S.F.		
		MAT.	INST.	TOTAL
0190	Receptacles include plate, box, conduit, wire & transformer when required			
0200	2.5 per 1000 S.F., .3 watts per S.F.	.39	1.43	1.82
0240	With transformer	.46	1.50	1.96
0280	4 per 1000 S.F., .5 watts per S.F.	.44	1.65	2.09
0320	With transformer	.55	1.76	2.31
0360	5 per 1000 S.F., .6 watts per S.F.	.51	1.96	2.47
0400	With transformer	.65	2.10	2.75
0440	8 per 1000 S.F., .9 watts per S.F.	.52	2.18	2.70
0480	With transformer	.74	2.41	3.15
0520	10 per 1000 S.F., 1.2 watts per S.F.	.56	2.36	2.92
0560	With transformer	.84	2.64	3.48
0600	16.5 per 1000 S.F., 2.0 watts per S.F.	.65	2.95	3.60
0640	With transformer	1.11	3.42	4.53
0680	20 per 1000 S.F., 2.4 watts per S.F.	.69	3.21	3.90
0720	With transformer	1.25	3.78	5.03

D5020 115	Receptacles, Floor	COST PER S.F.		
		MAT.	INST.	TOTAL
0200	Receptacle systems, underfloor duct, 5' on center, low density	7.15	3.14	10.29
0240	High density	7.70	4.04	11.74
0280	7' on center, low density	5.65	2.70	8.35
0320	High density	6.20	3.60	9.80
0400	Poke thru fittings, low density	1.23	1.54	2.77
0440	High density	2.47	3.07	5.54
0520	Telepoles, using Romex, low density	1.19	.95	2.14
0560	High density	2.39	1.89	4.28
0600	Using EMT, low density	1.25	1.26	2.51
0640	High density	2.51	2.50	5.01
0720	Conduit system with floor boxes, low density	1.15	1.08	2.23
0760	High density	2.31	2.15	4.46
0840	Undercarpet power system, 3 conductor with 5 conductor feeder, low density	1.52	.38	1.90
0880	High density	2.99	.79	3.78

D5020 Lighting and Branch Wiring

Description: Table D5020 130 includes the cost for switch, plate, box, conduit in slab or EMT exposed and copper wire. Add 20% for exposed conduit.

No power required for switches.

Federal energy guidelines recommend the maximum lighting area controlled per switch shall not exceed 1000 S.F. and that areas over 500 S.F. shall be so controlled that total illumination can be reduced by at least 50%.

D5020 130	Wall Switch by Sq. Ft.	COST PER S.F.		
		MAT.	INST.	TOTAL
0200	Wall switches, 1.0 per 1000 S.F.	.06	.23	.29
0240	1.2 per 1000 S.F.	.06	.26	.32
0280	2.0 per 1000 S.F.	.09	.37	.46
0320	2.5 per 1000 S.F.	.12	.47	.59
0360	5.0 per 1000 S.F.	.26	.99	1.25
0400	10.0 per 1000 S.F.	.50	2.01	2.51

D5020 135	Miscellaneous Power	COST PER S.F.		
		MAT.	INST.	TOTAL
0200	Miscellaneous power, to .5 watts	.03	.12	.15
0240	.8 watts	.05	.16	.21
0280	1 watt	.06	.22	.28
0320	1.2 watts	.07	.25	.32
0360	1.5 watts	.09	.30	.39
0400	1.8 watts	.10	.34	.44
0440	2 watts	.12	.41	.53
0480	2.5 watts	.15	.51	.66
0520	3 watts	.17	.60	.77

D5020 140	Central A. C. Power (by Wattage)	COST PER S.F.		
		MAT.	INST.	TOTAL
0200	Central air conditioning power, 1 watt	.07	.25	.32
0220	2 watts	.08	.29	.37
0240	3 watts	.11	.32	.43
0280	4 watts	.18	.43	.61
0320	6 watts	.34	.57	.91
0360	8 watts	.41	.62	1.03
0400	10 watts	.60	.72	1.32

D50 Electrical

D5020 Lighting and Branch Wiring

Power System   **Switch**   **Motor Starter**   **Switch**   **Motor Connection**   **Motor**

Motor Installation

D5020 145	Motor Installation	COST EACH		
		MAT.	INST.	TOTAL
0200	Motor installation, single phase, 115V, 1/3 HP motor size	580	975	1,555
0240	1 HP motor size	600	975	1,575
0280	2 HP motor size	650	1,025	1,675
0320	3 HP motor size	730	1,050	1,780
0360	230V, 1 HP motor size	580	985	1,565
0400	2 HP motor size	615	985	1,600
0440	3 HP motor size	695	1,050	1,745
0520	Three phase, 200V, 1-1/2 HP motor size	680	1,075	1,755
0560	3 HP motor size	725	1,175	1,900
0600	5 HP motor size	795	1,325	2,120
0640	7-1/2 HP motor size	825	1,350	2,175
0680	10 HP motor size	1,275	1,675	2,950
0720	15 HP motor size	1,675	1,875	3,550
0760	20 HP motor size	2,150	2,150	4,300
0800	25 HP motor size	2,200	2,150	4,350
0840	30 HP motor size	3,400	2,550	5,950
0880	40 HP motor size	4,300	3,025	7,325
0920	50 HP motor size	7,350	3,500	10,850
0960	60 HP motor size	7,675	3,700	11,375
1000	75 HP motor size	9,875	4,225	14,100
1040	100 HP motor size	26,900	5,000	31,900
1080	125 HP motor size	27,400	5,475	32,875
1120	150 HP motor size	31,900	6,450	38,350
1160	200 HP motor size	32,700	7,650	40,350
1240	230V, 1-1/2 HP motor size	650	1,075	1,725
1280	3 HP motor size	695	1,175	1,870
1320	5 HP motor size	760	1,300	2,060
1360	7-1/2 HP motor size	760	1,300	2,060
1400	10 HP motor size	1,175	1,575	2,750
1440	15 HP motor size	1,325	1,750	3,075
1480	20 HP motor size	2,025	2,100	4,125
1520	25 HP motor size	2,150	2,150	4,300
1560	30 HP motor size	2,225	2,150	4,375
1600	40 HP motor size	4,100	2,950	7,050
1640	50 HP motor size	4,400	3,100	7,500
1680	60 HP motor size	7,350	3,525	10,875
1720	75 HP motor size	8,975	4,000	12,975
1760	100 HP motor size	10,500	4,450	14,950
1800	125 HP motor size	27,400	5,150	32,550
1840	150 HP motor size	29,100	5,875	34,975
1880	200 HP motor size	31,200	6,525	37,725
1960	460V, 2 HP motor size	800	1,075	1,875
2000	5 HP motor size	845	1,175	2,020
2040	10 HP motor size	875	1,300	2,175
2080	15 HP motor size	1,150	1,500	2,650
2120	20 HP motor size	1,225	1,600	2,825

D5020 Lighting and Branch Wiring

D5020 145	Motor Installation	COST EACH		
		MAT.	INST.	TOTAL
2160	25 HP motor size	1,300	1,675	2,975
2200	30 HP motor size	1,650	1,800	3,450
2240	40 HP motor size	2,150	1,925	4,075
2280	50 HP motor size	2,425	2,150	4,575
2320	60 HP motor size	3,575	2,525	6,100
2360	75 HP motor size	4,200	2,800	7,000
2400	100 HP motor size	4,700	3,125	7,825
2440	125 HP motor size	7,675	3,525	11,200
2480	150 HP motor size	9,525	3,950	13,475
2520	200 HP motor size	11,300	4,450	15,750
2600	575V, 2 HP motor size	800	1,075	1,875
2640	5 HP motor size	845	1,175	2,020
2680	10 HP motor size	875	1,300	2,175
2720	20 HP motor size	1,150	1,500	2,650
2760	25 HP motor size	1,225	1,600	2,825
2800	30 HP motor size	1,650	1,800	3,450
2840	50 HP motor size	1,800	1,875	3,675
2880	60 HP motor size	3,500	2,525	6,025
2920	75 HP motor size	3,575	2,525	6,100
2960	100 HP motor size	4,200	2,800	7,000
3000	125 HP motor size	7,350	3,475	10,825
3040	150 HP motor size	7,675	3,525	11,200
3080	200 HP motor size	9,725	4,000	13,725

D5020 155	Motor Feeder	COST PER L.F.		
		MAT.	INST.	TOTAL
0200	Motor feeder systems, single phase, feed up to 115V 1HP or 230V 2 HP	2.19	7.55	9.74
0240	115V 2HP, 230V 3HP	2.36	7.70	10.06
0280	115V 3HP	2.72	8	10.72
0360	Three phase, feed to 200V 3HP, 230V 5HP, 460V 10HP, 575V 10HP	2.34	8.15	10.49
0440	200V 5HP, 230V 7.5HP, 460V 15HP, 575V 20HP	2.60	8.30	10.90
0520	200V 10HP, 230V 10HP, 460V 30HP, 575V 30HP	3.14	8.80	11.94
0600	200V 15HP, 230V 15HP, 460V 40HP, 575V 50HP	4.42	10.05	14.47
0680	200V 20HP, 230V 25HP, 460V 50HP, 575V 60HP	6.75	12.80	19.55
0760	200V 25HP, 230V 30HP, 460V 60HP, 575V 75HP	7.60	13	20.60
0840	200V 30HP	8.65	13.40	22.05
0920	230V 40HP, 460V 75HP, 575V 100HP	11.10	14.65	25.75
1000	200V 40HP	12.50	15.65	28.15
1080	230V 50HP, 460V 100HP, 575V 125HP	15.90	17.25	33.15
1160	200V 50HP, 230V 60HP, 460V 125HP, 575V 150HP	18.60	18.35	36.95
1240	200V 60HP, 460V 150HP	23	21.50	44.50
1320	230V 75HP, 575V 200HP	26.50	22.50	49
1400	200V 75HP	30.50	23	53.50
1480	230V 100HP, 460V 200HP	40	26.50	66.50
1560	200V 100HP	55	33.50	88.50
1640	230V 125HP	55	33.50	88.50
1720	200V 125HP, 230V 150HP	64.50	41.50	106
1800	200V 150HP	77.50	45	122.50
1880	200V 200HP	99	47.50	146.50
1960	230V 200HP	101	49.50	150.50

Fluorescent Fixture

Incandescent Fixture

D5020 210	Fluorescent Fixtures (by Wattage)	COST PER S.F.		
		MAT.	INST.	TOTAL
0190	Fluorescent fixtures recess mounted in ceiling			
0195	T12, standard 40 watt lamps			
0200	1 watt per S.F., 20 FC, 5 fixtures @40 watts per 1000 S.F.	.73	1.87	2.60
0240	2 watt per S.F., 40 FC, 10 fixtures @40 watt per 1000 S.F.	1.46	3.69	5.15
0280	3 watt per S.F., 60 FC, 15 fixtures @40 watt per 1000 S.F	2.19	5.55	7.74
0320	4 watt per S.F., 80 FC, 20 fixtures @40 watt per 1000 S.F.	2.91	7.40	10.31
0400	5 watt per S.F., 100 FC, 25 fixtures @40 watt per 1000 S.F.	3.65	9.25	12.90
0450	T8, energy saver 32 watt lamps			
0500	0.8 watt per S.F., 20 FC, 5 fixtures @32 watt per 1000 S.F.	.76	1.87	2.63
0520	1.6 watt per S.F., 40 FC, 10 fixtures @32 watt per 1000 S.F.	1.53	3.69	5.22
0540	2.4 watt per S.F., 60 FC, 15 fixtures @ 32 watt per 1000 S.F	2.31	5.55	7.86
0560	3.2 watt per S.F., 80 FC, 20 fixtures @32 watt per 1000 S.F.	3.06	7.40	10.46
0580	4 watt per S.F., 100 FC, 25 fixtures @32 watt per 1000 S.F.	3.82	9.25	13.07

D5020 216	Incandescent Fixture (by Wattage)	COST PER S.F.		
		MAT.	INST.	TOTAL
0190	Incandescent fixture recess mounted, type A			
0200	1 watt per S.F., 8 FC, 6 fixtures per 1000 S.F.	1	1.51	2.51
0240	2 watt per S.F., 16 FC, 12 fixtures per 1000 S.F.	1.99	3.02	5.01
0280	3 watt per S.F., 24 FC, 18 fixtures, per 1000 S.F.	2.98	4.48	7.46
0320	4 watt per S.F., 32 FC, 24 fixtures per 1000 S.F.	3.96	6	9.96
0400	5 watt per S.F., 40 FC, 30 fixtures per 1000 S.F.	4.97	7.50	12.47

D5020 Lighting and Branch Wiring

High Bay Fixture

Low Bay Fixture

D5020 226	H.I.D. Fixture, High Bay, 16′ (by Wattage)	COST PER S.F.		
		MAT.	INST.	TOTAL
0190	High intensity discharge fixture, 16′ above work plane			
0240	1 watt/S.F., type E, 42 FC, 1 fixture/1000 S.F.	1.05	1.57	2.62
0280	Type G, 52 FC, 1 fixture/1000 S.F.	1.05	1.57	2.62
0320	Type C, 54 FC, 2 fixture/1000 S.F.	1.23	1.76	2.99
0440	2 watt/S.F., type E, 84 FC, 2 fixture/1000 S.F.	2.10	3.22	5.32
0480	Type G, 105 FC, 2 fixture/1000 S.F.	2.10	3.22	5.32
0520	Type C, 108 FC, 4 fixture/1000 S.F.	2.45	3.52	5.97
0640	3 watt/S.F., type E, 126 FC, 3 fixture/1000 S.F.	3.17	4.79	7.96
0680	Type G, 157 FC, 3 fixture/1000 S.F.	3.17	4.79	7.96
0720	Type C, 162 FC, 6 fixture/1000 S.F.	3.69	5.30	8.99
0840	4 watt/S.F., type E, 168 FC, 4 fixture/1000 S.F.	4.22	6.45	10.67
0880	Type G, 210 FC, 4 fixture/1000 S.F.	4.22	6.45	10.67
0920	Type C, 243 FC, 9 fixture/1000 S.F.	5.35	7.35	12.70
1040	5 watt/S.F., type E, 210 FC, 5 fixture/1000 S.F.	5.25	8	13.25
1080	Type G, 262 FC, 5 fixture/1000 S.F.	5.25	8	13.25
1120	Type C, 297 FC, 11 fixture/1000 S.F.	6.60	9.15	15.75

D5020 234	H.I.D. Fixture, High Bay, 30′ (by Wattage)	COST PER S.F.		
		MAT.	INST.	TOTAL
0190	High intensity discharge fixture, 30′ above work plane			
0240	1 watt/S.F., type E, 37 FC, 1 fixture/1000 S.F.	1.19	1.99	3.18
0280	Type G, 45 FC., 1 fixture/1000 S.F.	1.19	1.99	3.18
0320	Type F, 50 FC, 1 fixture/1000 S.F.	1	1.57	2.57
0440	2 watt/S.F., type E, 74 FC, 2 fixtures/1000 S.F.	2.36	4	6.36
0480	Type G, 92 FC, 2 fixtures/1000 S.F.	2.36	4	6.36
0520	Type F, 100 FC, 2 fixtures/1000 S.F.	2.01	3.19	5.20
0640	3 watt/S.F., type E, 110 FC, 3 fixtures/1000 S.F.	3.58	6.05	9.63
0680	Type G, 138 FC, 3 fixtures/1000 S.F.	3.58	6.05	9.63
0720	Type F, 150 FC, 3 fixtures/1000 S.F.	3.02	4.75	7.77
0840	4 watt/S.F., type E, 148 FC, 4 fixtures/1000 S.F.	4.75	8.05	12.80
0880	Type G, 185 FC, 4 fixtures/1000 S.F.	4.75	8.05	12.80
0920	Type F, 200 FC, 4 fixtures/1000 S.F.	4.02	6.40	10.42
1040	5 watt/S.F., type E, 185 FC, 5 fixtures/1000 S.F.	5.95	10.05	16
1080	Type G, 230 FC, 5 fixtures/1000 S.F.	5.95	10.05	16
1120	Type F, 250 FC, 5 fixtures/1000 S.F.	5.05	7.95	13

D5020 238	H.I.D. Fixture, Low Bay, 8′-10′ (by Wattage)	COST PER S.F.		
		MAT.	INST.	TOTAL
0190	High intensity discharge fixture, 8′-10′ above work plane			
0240	1 watt/S.F., type J, 30 FC, 4 fixtures/1000 S.F.	2.40	3.26	5.66
0280	Type K, 29 FC, 5 fixtures/1000 S.F.	2.45	2.92	5.37
0400	2 watt/S.F., type J, 52 FC, 7 fixtures/1000 S.F.	4.30	6	10.30
0440	Type K, 63 FC, 11 fixtures/1000 S.F.	5.30	6.15	11.45
0560	3 watt/S.F., type J, 81 FC, 11 fixtures/1000 S.F.	6.65	9.05	15.70

D50 Electrical

D5020 Lighting and Branch Wiring

D5020 238	H.I.D. Fixture, Low Bay, 8'-10' (by Wattage)	COST PER S.F.		
		MAT.	INST.	TOTAL
0600	Type K, 92 FC, 16 fixtures/1000 S.F.	7.75	9.10	16.85
0720	4 watt/S.F., type J, 103 FC, 14 fixtures/1000 S.F.	8.55	11.90	20.45
0760	Type K, 127 FC, 22 fixtures/1000 S.F.	10.60	12.30	22.90
0880	5 watt/S.F., type J, 133 FC, 18 fixtures/1000 S.F.	10.95	15	25.95
0920	Type K, 155 FC, 27 fixtures/1000 S.F.	13.05	15.25	28.30

D5020 242	H.I.D. Fixture, Low Bay, 16' (by Wattage)	COST PER S.F.		
		MAT.	INST.	TOTAL
0190	High intensity discharge fixture, mounted 16' above work plane			
0240	1 watt/S.F., type J, 28 FC, 4 fixt./1000 S.F.	2.54	3.70	6.24
0280	Type K, 27 FC, 5 fixt./1000 S.F.	2.83	4.14	6.97
0400	2 watt/S.F., type J, 48 FC, 7 fixt/1000 S.F.	4.66	7.15	11.81
0440	Type K, 58 FC, 11 fixt/1000 S.F.	6	8.45	14.45
0560	3 watt/S.F., type J, 75 FC, 11 fixt/1000 S.F.	7.20	10.85	18.05
0600	Type K, 85 FC, 16 fixt/1000 S.F.	8.85	12.60	21.45
0720	4 watt/S.F., type J, 95 FC, 14 fixt/1000 S.F.	9.30	14.30	23.60
0760	Type K, 117 FC, 22 fixt/1000 S.F.	12.05	16.95	29
0880	5 watt/S.F., type J, 122 FC, 18 fixt/1000 S.F.	11.85	18	29.85
0920	Type K, 143 FC, 27 fixt/1000 S.F.	14.85	21	35.85

D50 Electrical

D5030 Communications and Security

D5030 910	Communication & Alarm Systems	COST EACH		
		MAT.	INST.	TOTAL
0200	Communication & alarm systems, includes outlets, boxes, conduit & wire			
0210	Sound system, 6 outlets	5,700	8,100	13,800
0220	12 outlets	8,175	12,900	21,075
0240	30 outlets	14,600	24,500	39,100
0280	100 outlets	44,200	82,000	126,200
0320	Fire detection systems, non-addressable, 12 detectors	3,275	6,700	9,975
0360	25 detectors	5,725	11,300	17,025
0400	50 detectors	11,200	22,500	33,700
0440	100 detectors	21,000	40,900	61,900
0450	Addressable type, 12 detectors	4,925	6,750	11,675
0452	25 detectors	8,975	11,400	20,375
0454	50 detectors	17,300	22,400	39,700
0456	100 detectors	33,500	41,200	74,700
0458	Fire alarm control panel, 8 zone, excluding wire and conduit	850	1,275	2,125
0459	12 zone	2,600	1,925	4,525
0460	Fire alarm command center, addressable without voice, excl. wire & conduit	4,875	1,125	6,000
0462	Addressable with voice	10,300	1,750	12,050
0480	Intercom systems, 6 stations	3,875	5,525	9,400
0560	25 stations	12,500	21,200	33,700
0640	100 stations	47,800	78,000	125,800
0680	Master clock systems, 6 rooms	5,100	9,025	14,125
0720	12 rooms	7,975	15,400	23,375
0760	20 rooms	11,100	21,700	32,800
0800	30 rooms	18,000	40,100	58,100
0840	50 rooms	29,200	67,500	96,700
0920	Master TV antenna systems, 6 outlets	2,550	5,700	8,250
0960	12 outlets	4,800	10,600	15,400
1000	30 outlets	11,100	24,600	35,700
1040	100 outlets	36,800	80,500	117,300

D50 Electrical

D5090 Other Electrical Systems

Generator System

A: Engine
B: Battery
C: Charger
D: Transfer Switch
E: Muffler

D5090 210	Generators (by kW)	COST PER kW		
		MAT.	INST.	TOTAL
0190	Generator sets, include battery, charger, muffler & transfer switch			
0200	Gas/gasoline operated, 3 phase, 4 wire, 277/480 volt, 7.5 kW	1,075	282	1,357
0240	11.5 kW	985	212	1,197
0280	20 kW	670	138	808
0320	35 kW	455	91	546
0360	80 kW	325	54.50	379.50
0400	100 kW	286	53	339
0440	125 kW	470	50	520
0480	185 kW	420	38	458
0560	Diesel engine with fuel tank, 30 kW	600	106	706
0600	50 kW	430	83	513
0640	75 kW	370	66.50	436.50
0680	100 kW	310	56.50	366.50
0760	150 kW	249	44.50	293.50
0840	200 kW	210	36	246
0880	250 kW	197	30	227
0960	350 kW	173	24.50	197.50
1040	500 kW	188	19.35	207.35

E1010 Commercial Equipment

E1010 110	Security/Vault, EACH	COST EACH		
		MAT.	INST.	TOTAL
0100	Bank equipment, drive up window, drawer & mike, no glazing, economy	7,500	1,450	8,950
0110	Deluxe	10,000	2,875	12,875
0120	Night depository, economy	8,200	1,450	9,650
0130	Deluxe	11,700	2,875	14,575
0140	Pneumatic tube systems, 2 station, standard	28,400	4,875	33,275
0150	Teller, automated, 24 hour, single unit	48,700	4,875	53,575
0160	Teller window, bullet proof glazing, 44" x 60"	4,200	895	5,095
0170	Pass through, painted steel, 72" x 40"	4,625	1,800	6,425
0300	Safe, office type, 1 hr. rating, 34" x 20" x 20"	2,500		2,500
0310	4 hr. rating, 62" x 33" x 20"	9,700		9,700
0320	Data storage, 4 hr. rating, 63" x 44" x 16"	14,700		14,700
0330	Jewelers, 63" x 44" x 16"	15,700		15,700
0340	Money, "B" label, 9" x 14" x 14"	595		595
0350	Tool and torch resistive, 24" x 24" x 20"	8,625	226	8,851
0500	Security gates-scissors type, painted steel, single, 6' high, 5-1/2' wide	245	360	605
0510	Double gate, 7-1/2' high, 14' wide	770	720	1,490

E1010 510	Mercantile Equipment, EACH	COST EACH		
		MAT.	INST.	TOTAL
0015	Barber equipment, chair, hydraulic, economy	610	23.50	633.50
0020	Deluxe	3,775	35.50	3,810.50
0100	Checkout counter, single belt	3,450	90.50	3,540.50
0110	Double belt, power take-away	4,975	101	5,076
0200	Display cases, freestanding, glass and aluminum, 3'-6" x 3' x 1'-0" deep	1,325	142	1,467
0220	Wall mounted, glass and aluminum, 3' x 4' x 1'-4" deep	2,350	226	2,576
0320	Frozen food, chest type, 12 ft. long	8,925	385	9,310

E1010 610	Laundry/Dry Cleaning, EACH	COST EACH		
		MAT.	INST.	TOTAL
0100	Laundry equipment, dryers, gas fired, residential, 16 lb. capacity	735	232	967
0110	Commercial, 30 lb. capacity, single	3,575	232	3,807
0120	Dry cleaners, electric, 20 lb. capacity	36,600	6,675	43,275
0130	30 lb. capacity	55,500	8,900	64,400
0140	Ironers, commercial, 120" with canopy, 8 roll	192,000	19,100	211,100
0150	Institutional, 110", single roll	34,900	3,200	38,100
0160	Washers, residential, 4 cycle	955	232	1,187
0170	Commercial, coin operated, deluxe	3,650	232	3,882

E10 Equipment

E1020 Institutional Equipment

E1020 110	Ecclesiastical Equipment, EACH	COST EACH		
		MAT.	INST.	TOTAL
0090	Church equipment, altar, wood, custom, plain	2,775	405	3,180
0100	Granite, custom, deluxe	41,300	5,150	46,450
0110	Baptistry, fiberglass, economy	6,225	1,475	7,700
0120	Bells & carillons, keyboard operation	19,800	8,625	28,425
0130	Confessional, wood, single, economy	3,450	945	4,395
0140	Double, deluxe	20,600	2,825	23,425
0150	Steeples, translucent fiberglas, 30" square, 15' high	9,100	1,800	10,900

E1020 130	Ecclesiastical Equipment, L.F.	COST PER L.F.		
		MAT.	INST.	TOTAL
0100	Arch. equip., church equip. pews, bench type, hardwood, economy	103	28.50	131.50
0110	Deluxe	204	37.50	241.50

E1020 210	Library Equipment, EACH	COST EACH		
		MAT.	INST.	TOTAL
0110	Library equipment, carrels, metal, economy	280	113	393
0120	Hardwood, deluxe	2,150	142	2,292

E1020 230	Library Equipment, L.F.	COST PER L.F.		
		MAT.	INST.	TOTAL
0100	Library equipment, book shelf, metal, single face, 90" high x 10" shelf	133	47	180
0110	Double face, 90" high x 10" shelf	345	102	447
0120	Charging desk, built-in, with counter, plastic laminate	330	81	411

E1020 310	Theater and Stage Equipment, EACH	COST EACH		
		MAT.	INST.	TOTAL
0200	Movie equipment, changeover, economy	510		510
0210	Film transport, incl. platters and autowind, economy	5,525		5,525
0220	Lamphouses, incl. rectifiers, xenon, 1000W	7,300	320	7,620
0230	4000W	10,400	425	10,825
0240	Projector mechanisms, 35 mm, economy	12,200		12,200
0250	Deluxe	16,700		16,700
0260	Sound systems, incl. amplifier, single, economy	3,625	710	4,335
0270	Dual, Dolby/super sound	18,200	1,600	19,800
0280	Projection screens, wall hung, manual operation, 50 S.F., economy	325	113	438
0290	Electric operation, 100 S.F., deluxe	2,175	565	2,740

E1020 320	Theater and Stage Equipment, S.F.	COST PER S.F.		
		MAT.	INST.	TOTAL
0090	Movie equipment, projection screens, rigid in wall, acrylic, 1/4" thick	46	5.50	51.50
0100	1/2" thick	53.50	8.25	61.75
0110	Stage equipment, curtains, velour, medium weight	8.70	1.89	10.59
0120	Silica based yarn, fireproof	16.70	22.50	39.20
0130	Stages, portable with steps, folding legs, 8" high	35.50		35.50
0140	Telescoping platforms, aluminum, deluxe	52	29.50	81.50

E1020 330	Theater and Stage Equipment, L.F.	COST PER L.F.		
		MAT.	INST.	TOTAL
0100	Stage equipment, curtain track, heavy duty	67.50	63	130.50
0110	Lights, border, quartz, colored	190	32	222

E1020 610	Detention Equipment, EACH	COST EACH		
		MAT.	INST.	TOTAL
0110	Detention equipment, cell front rolling door, 7/8" bars, 5' x 7' high	5,800	1,525	7,325
0120	Cells, prefab., including front, 5' x 7' x 7' deep	10,600	2,050	12,650

E10 Equipment

E1020 Institutional Equipment

E1020 610	Detention Equipment, EACH	COST EACH		
		MAT.	INST.	TOTAL
0130	Doors and frames, 3' x 7', single plate	5,050	770	5,820
0140	Double plate	6,150	770	6,920
0150	Toilet apparatus, incl wash basin	3,700	985	4,685
0160	Visitor cubicle, vision panel, no intercom	3,525	1,525	5,050

E1020 710	Laboratory Equipment, EACH	COST EACH		
		MAT.	INST.	TOTAL
0110	Laboratory equipment, glassware washer, distilled water, economy	6,875	740	7,615
0120	Deluxe	14,400	1,325	15,725
0140	Radio isotope	18,600		18,600

E1020 720	Laboratory Equipment, S.F.	COST PER S.F.		
		MAT.	INST.	TOTAL
0100	Arch. equip., lab equip., counter tops, acid proof, economy	44	13.80	57.80
0110	Stainless steel	142	13.80	155.80

E1020 730	Laboratory Equipment, L.F.	COST PER L.F.		
		MAT.	INST.	TOTAL
0110	Laboratory equipment, cabinets, wall, open	181	56.50	237.50
0120	Base, drawer units	560	63	623
0130	Fume hoods, not incl. HVAC, economy	540	210	750
0140	Deluxe incl. fixtures	875	470	1,345

E1020 810	Medical Equipment, EACH	COST EACH		
		MAT.	INST.	TOTAL
0100	Dental equipment, central suction system, economy	1,700	580	2,280
0110	Compressor-air, deluxe	9,725	1,175	10,900
0120	Chair, hydraulic, economy	2,450	1,175	3,625
0130	Deluxe	8,500	2,350	10,850
0140	Drill console with accessories, economy	2,275	365	2,640
0150	Deluxe	5,325	365	5,690
0160	X-ray unit, portable	2,550	147	2,697
0170	Panoramic unit	17,100	975	18,075
0300	Medical equipment, autopsy table, standard	10,600	695	11,295
0310	Deluxe	16,400	1,150	17,550
0320	Incubators, economy	3,300		3,300
0330	Deluxe	12,800		12,800
0700	Station, scrub-surgical, single, economy	4,675	232	4,907
0710	Dietary, medium, with ice	18,200		18,200
0720	Sterilizers, general purpose, single door, 20" x 20" x 28"	14,200		14,200
0730	Floor loading, double door, 28" x 67" x 52"	224,000		224,000
0740	Surgery tables, standard	13,200	1,025	14,225
0750	Deluxe	28,600	1,450	30,050
0770	Tables, standard, with base cabinets, economy	1,100	375	1,475
0780	Deluxe	6,100	565	6,665
0790	X-ray, mobile, economy	18,300		18,300
0800	Stationary, deluxe	244,000		244,000

E10 Equipment

E1030   Vehicular Equipment

E1030 110	Vehicular Service Equipment, EACH	COST EACH		
		MAT.	INST.	TOTAL
0110	Automotive equipment, compressors, electric, 1-1/2 H.P., std. controls	490	1,075	1,565
0120	5 H.P., dual controls	3,400	1,600	5,000
0130	Hoists, single post, 4 ton capacity, swivel arms	6,050	4,000	10,050
0140	Dual post, 12 ton capacity, adjustable frame	10,400	845	11,245
0150	Lube equipment, 3 reel type, with pumps	9,550	3,200	12,750
0160	Product dispenser, 6 nozzles, w/vapor recovery, not incl. piping, installed	26,900		26,900
0800	Scales, dial type, built in floor, 5 ton capacity, 8' x 6' platform	8,250	3,400	11,650
0810	10 ton capacity, 9' x 7' platform	11,800	4,850	16,650
0820	Truck (including weigh bridge), 20 ton capacity, 24' x 10'	12,600	5,650	18,250

E1030 210	Parking Control Equipment, EACH	COST EACH		
		MAT.	INST.	TOTAL
0110	Parking equipment, automatic gates, 8 ft. arm, one way	4,700	1,150	5,850
0120	Traffic detectors, single treadle	2,000	530	2,530
0130	Booth for attendant, economy	8,225		8,225
0140	Deluxe	30,800		30,800
0150	Ticket printer/dispenser, rate computing	9,750	915	10,665
0160	Key station on pedestal	880	310	1,190

E1030 310	Loading Dock Equipment, EACH	COST EACH		
		MAT.	INST.	TOTAL
0110	Dock bumpers, rubber blocks, 4-1/2" thick, 10" high, 14" long	69.50	22	91.50
0120	6" thick, 20" high, 11" long	161	43.50	204.50
0130	Dock boards, H.D., 5' x 5', aluminum, 5000 lb. capacity	1,600		1,600
0140	16,000 lb. capacity	1,900		1,900
0150	Dock levelers, hydraulic, 7' x 8', 10 ton capacity	10,200	1,500	11,700
0160	Dock lifters, platform, 6' x 6', portable, 3000 lb. capacity	10,100		10,100
0170	Dock shelters, truck, scissor arms, economy	1,925	565	2,490
0180	Deluxe	2,650	1,125	3,775

E10 Equipment

E1090 Other Equipment

E1090 210	Solid Waste Handling Equipment, EACH	COST EACH		
		MAT.	INST.	TOTAL
0110	Waste handling, compactors, single bag, 250 lbs./hr., hand fed	16,400	665	17,065
0120	Heavy duty industrial, 5 C.Y. capacity	35,400	3,200	38,600
0130	Incinerator, electric, 100 lbs./hr., economy	70,500	3,200	73,700
0140	Gas, 2000 lbs./hr., deluxe	440,000	26,500	466,500
0150	Shredder, no baling, 35 tons/hr.	331,000		331,000
0160	Incl. baling, 50 tons/day	661,000		661,000

E1090 350	Food Service Equipment, EACH	COST EACH		
		MAT.	INST.	TOTAL
0110	Kitchen equipment, bake oven, single deck	6,100	156	6,256
0120	Broiler, without oven	3,850	156	4,006
0130	Commercial dish washer, semiautomatic, 50 racks/hr.	8,350	965	9,315
0140	Automatic, 275 racks/hr.	34,200	4,050	38,250
0150	Cooler, beverage, reach-in, 6 ft. long	3,900	209	4,109
0160	Food warmer, counter, 1.65 kw	725		725
0170	Fryers, with submerger, single	1,375	179	1,554
0180	Double	2,650	250	2,900
0185	Ice maker, 1000 lb. per day, with bin	5,375	1,250	6,625
0190	Kettles, steam jacketed, 20 gallons	8,950	272	9,222
0200	Range, restaurant type, burners, 2 ovens and 24" griddle	4,975	209	5,184
0210	Range hood, incl. carbon dioxide system, economy	5,750	415	6,165
0220	Deluxe	42,000	1,250	43,250

E1090 360	Food Service Equipment, S.F.	COST PER S.F.		
		MAT.	INST.	TOTAL
0110	Refrigerators, prefab, walk-in, 7'-6" high, 6' x 6'	174	20.50	194.50
0120	12' x 20'	109	10.35	119.35

E1090 410	Residential Equipment, EACH	COST EACH		
		MAT.	INST.	TOTAL
0110	Arch. equip., appliances, range, cook top, 4 burner, economy	320	106	426
0120	Built in, single oven 30" wide, economy	740	106	846
0130	Standing, single oven-21" wide, economy	495	90.50	585.50
0140	Double oven-30" wide, deluxe	2,775	90.50	2,865.50
0150	Compactor, residential, economy	705	113	818
0160	Deluxe	1,100	189	1,289
0170	Dish washer, built-in, 2 cycles, economy	258	335	593
0180	4 or more cycles, deluxe	1,200	665	1,865
0190	Garbage disposer, sink type, economy	95	133	228
0200	Deluxe	239	133	372
0210	Refrigerator, no frost, 10 to 12 C.F., economy	460	90.50	550.50
0220	21 to 29 C.F., deluxe	3,675	300	3,975
0300	Washing machine, automatic	1,650	695	2,345

E1090 610	School Equipment, EACH	COST EACH		
		MAT.	INST.	TOTAL
0110	School equipment, basketball backstops, wall mounted, wood, fixed	1,500	995	2,495
0120	Suspended type, electrically operated	6,950	1,925	8,875
0130	Bleachers-telescoping, manual operation, 15 tier, economy (per seat)	99.50	35	134.50
0140	Power operation, 30 tier, deluxe (per seat)	410	62	472
0150	Weight lifting gym, universal, economy	365	905	1,270
0160	Deluxe	16,200	1,800	18,000
0170	Scoreboards, basketball, 1 side, economy	2,625	840	3,465
0180	4 sides, deluxe	6,250	11,600	17,850
0800	Vocational shop equipment, benches, metal	595	226	821
0810	Wood	690	226	916

E10 Equipment

E1090 Other Equipment

E1090 610	School Equipment, EACH	COST EACH		
		MAT.	INST.	TOTAL
0820	Dust collector, not incl. ductwork, 6' diam.	5,075	610	5,685
0830	Planer, 13" x 6"	1,200	283	1,483

E1090 620	School Equipment, S.F.	COST PER S.F.		
		MAT.	INST.	TOTAL
0110	School equipment, gym mats, naugahyde cover, 2" thick	4.04		4.04
0120	Wrestling, 1" thick, heavy duty	6.10		6.10

E1090 810	Athletic, Recreational, and Therapeutic Equipment, EACH	COST EACH		
		MAT.	INST.	TOTAL
0050	Bowling alley with gutters	50,500	11,900	62,400
0060	Combo. table and ball rack	1,250		1,250
0070	Bowling alley automatic scorer	10,900		10,900
0110	Sauna, prefabricated, incl. heater and controls, 7' high, 6' x 4'	5,925	865	6,790
0120	10' x 12'	13,500	1,900	15,400
0130	Heaters, wall mounted, to 200 C.F.	745		745
0140	Floor standing, to 1000 C.F., 12500 W	4,075	213	4,288
0610	Shooting range incl. bullet traps, controls, separators, ceilings, economy	38,500	7,525	46,025
0620	Deluxe	57,000	12,700	69,700
0650	Sport court, squash, regulation, in existing building, economy			40,400
0660	Deluxe			45,000
0670	Racketball, regulation, in existing building, economy	43,800	10,800	54,600
0680	Deluxe	47,400	21,500	68,900
0700	Swimming pool equipment, diving stand, stainless steel, 1 meter	9,725	420	10,145
0710	3 meter	15,900	2,825	18,725
0720	Diving boards, 16 ft. long, aluminum	4,350	420	4,770
0730	Fiberglass	3,525	420	3,945
0740	Filter system, sand, incl. pump, 6000 gal./hr.	2,125	770	2,895
0750	Lights, underwater, 12 volt with transformer, 300W	370	640	1,010
0760	Slides, fiberglass with aluminum handrails & ladder, 6' high, straight	3,750	710	4,460
0780	12' high, straight with platform	14,700	945	15,645

E1090 820	Athletic, Recreational, and Therapeutic Equipment, S.F.	COST PER S.F.		
		MAT.	INST.	TOTAL
0110	Swimming pools, residential, vinyl liner, metal sides	19.55	7.95	27.50
0120	Concrete sides	23.50	14.35	37.85
0130	Gunite shell, plaster finish, 350 S.F.	43.50	29.50	73
0140	800 S.F.	35	17.20	52.20
0150	Motel, gunite shell, plaster finish	53.50	37	90.50
0160	Municipal, gunite shell, tile finish, formed gutters	206	65	271

E20 Furnishings

E2010 Fixed Furnishings

E2010 310	Window Treatment, EACH	COST EACH		
		MAT.	INST.	TOTAL
0110	Furnishings, blinds, exterior, aluminum, louvered, 1'-4" wide x 3'-0" long	82.50	56.50	139
0120	1'-4" wide x 6'-8" long	166	63	229
0130	Hemlock, solid raised, 1'-4" wide x 3'-0" long	79	56.50	135.50
0140	1'-4" wide x 6'-9" long	177	63	240
0150	Polystyrene, louvered, 1'-3" wide x 3'-3" long	71.50	56.50	128
0160	1'-3" wide x 6'-8" long	139	63	202
0200	Interior, wood folding panels, louvered, 7" x 20" (per pair)	86	33.50	119.50
0210	18" x 40" (per pair)	145	33.50	178.50

E2010 320	Window Treatment, S.F.	COST PER S.F.		
		MAT.	INST.	TOTAL
0110	Furnishings, blinds-interior, venetian-aluminum, stock, 2" slats	8.40	.96	9.36
0120	Custom, 1" slats, deluxe	5.30	.96	6.26
0130	Vertical, PVC or cloth, T&B track, economy	8.55	1.23	9.78
0140	Deluxe	25.50	1.42	26.92
0150	Draperies, unlined, economy	3.38		3.38
0160	Lightproof, deluxe	9.70		9.70
0510	Shades, mylar, wood roller, single layer, non-reflective	5.45	.83	6.28
0520	Metal roller, triple layer, heat reflective	7.25	.83	8.08
0530	Vinyl, light weight, 4 ga.	.66	.83	1.49
0540	Heavyweight, 6 ga.	2.01	.83	2.84
0550	Vinyl coated cotton, lightproof decorator shades	3.23	.83	4.06
0560	Woven aluminum, 3/8" thick, light and fireproof	6.35	1.62	7.97

E2010 420	Fixed Floor Grilles and Mats, S.F.	COST PER S.F.		
		MAT.	INST.	TOTAL
0110	Floor mats, recessed, inlaid black rubber, 3/8" thick, solid	28	2.92	30.92
0120	Colors, 1/2" thick, perforated	30	2.92	32.92
0130	Link-including nosings, steel-galvanized, 3/8" thick	25.50	2.92	28.42
0140	Vinyl, in colors	26.50	2.92	29.42

E2010 510	Fixed Multiple Seating, EACH	COST EACH		
		MAT.	INST.	TOTAL
0110	Seating, painted steel, upholstered, economy	145	32.50	177.50
0120	Deluxe	465	40.50	505.50
0400	Seating, lecture hall, pedestal type, economy	206	51.50	257.50
0410	Deluxe	530	78	608
0500	Auditorium chair, veneer construction	250	51.50	301.50
0510	Fully upholstered, spring seat	261	51.50	312.50

E2020 Moveable Furnishings

E2020 210	Furnishings/EACH	COST EACH		
		MAT.	INST.	TOTAL
0200	Hospital furniture, beds, manual, economy	865		865
0210	Deluxe	2,750		2,750
0220	All electric, economy	1,775		1,775
0230	Deluxe	4,850		4,850
0240	Patient wall systems, no utilities, economy, per room	1,550		1,550
0250	Deluxe, per room	2,100		2,100
0300	Hotel furnishings, standard room set, economy, per room	2,600		2,600
0310	Deluxe, per room	9,275		9,275
0500	Office furniture, standard employee set, economy, per person	670		670
0510	Deluxe, per person	2,600		2,600
0550	Posts, portable, pedestrian traffic control, economy	146		146
0560	Deluxe	460		460
0700	Restaurant furniture, booth, molded plastic, stub wall and 2 seats, economy	400	283	683
0710	Deluxe	1,550	375	1,925
0720	Upholstered seats, foursome, single-economy	835	113	948
0730	Foursome, double-deluxe	1,925	189	2,114

E2020 220	Furniture and Accessories, L.F.	COST PER L.F.		
		MAT.	INST.	TOTAL
0210	Dormitory furniture, desk top (built-in),laminated plastc, 24"deep, economy	47.50	22.50	70
0220	30" deep, deluxe	267	28.50	295.50
0230	Dressing unit, built-in, economy	188	94.50	282.50
0240	Deluxe	565	142	707
0310	Furnishings, cabinets, hospital, base, laminated plastic	296	113	409
0320	Stainless steel	545	113	658
0330	Countertop, laminated plastic, no backsplash	51	28.50	79.50
0340	Stainless steel	165	28.50	193.50
0350	Nurses station, door type, laminated plastic	345	113	458
0360	Stainless steel	655	113	768
0710	Restaurant furniture, bars, built-in, back bar	219	113	332
0720	Front bar	300	113	413
0910	Wardrobes & coatracks, standing, steel, single pedestal, 30" x 18" x 63"	116		116
0920	Double face rack, 39" x 26" x 70"	125		125
0930	Wall mounted rack, steel frame & shelves, 12" x 15" x 26"	77.50	8.05	85.55
0940	12" x 15" x 50"	47.50	4.21	51.71

F1010 Special Structures

F1010 120	Air-Supported Structures, S.F.	COST PER S.F.		
		MAT.	INST.	TOTAL
0110	Air supported struc., polyester vinyl fabric, 24oz., warehouse, 5000 S.F.	27.50	.36	27.86
0120	50,000 S.F.	12.90	.29	13.19
0130	Tennis, 7,200 S.F.	26	.30	26.30
0140	24,000 S.F.	18.05	.30	18.35
0150	Woven polyethylene, 6 oz., shelter, 3,000 S.F.	7.25	.60	7.85
0160	24,000 S.F.	6.15	.30	6.45
0170	Teflon coated fiberglass, stadium cover, economy	63	.16	63.16
0180	Deluxe	75	.21	75.21
0190	Air supported storage tank covers, reinf. vinyl fabric, 12 oz., 400 S.F.	25.50	.51	26.01
0200	18,000 S.F.	8.10	.46	8.56

F1010 210	Pre-Engineered Structures, EACH	COST EACH		
		MAT.	INST.	TOTAL
0600	Radio towers, guyed, 40 lb. section, 50' high, 70 MPH basic wind speed	3,025	1,450	4,475
0610	90 lb. section, 400' high, wind load 70 MPH basic wind speed	41,900	16,300	58,200
0620	Self supporting, 60' high, 70 MPH basic wind speed	4,950	2,850	7,800
0630	190' high, wind load 90 MPH basic wind speed	31,100	11,400	42,500
0700	Shelters, aluminum frame, acrylic glazing, 8' high, 3' x 9'	2,625	1,275	3,900
0710	9' x 12'	6,250	1,975	8,225

F1010 320	Other Special Structures, S.F.	COST PER S.F.		
		MAT.	INST.	TOTAL
0110	Swimming pool enclosure, transluscent, freestanding, economy	66	5.65	71.65
0120	Deluxe	102	16.15	118.15
0510	Tension structures, steel frame, polyester vinyl fabric, 12,000 S.F.	14.55	2.63	17.18
0520	20,800 S.F.	14.30	2.38	16.68

F1010 330	Special Structures, EACH	COST EACH		
		MAT.	INST.	TOTAL
0110	Kiosks, round, 5' diam., 7' high, aluminum wall, illuminated	25,800		25,800
0120	Rectangular, 5' x 9', 1" insulated dbl. wall fiberglass, 7'-6" high	26,400		26,400
0220	Silos, steel prefab, 30,000 gal., painted, economy	24,300	5,800	30,100
0230	Epoxy-lined, deluxe	50,500	11,600	62,100

F1010 340	Special Structures, S.F.	COST PER S.F.		
		MAT.	INST.	TOTAL
0110	Comfort stations, prefab, mobile on steel frame, economy	215		215
0120	Permanent on concrete slab, deluxe	211	47	258
0210	Domes, bulk storage, wood framing, wood decking, 50' diam.	79.50	1.80	81.30
0220	116' diam.	38.50	2.08	40.58
0230	Steel framing, metal decking, 150' diam.	30.50	11.75	42.25
0240	400' diam.	25	9	34
0250	Geodesic, wood framing, wood panels, 30' diam.	36	2.04	38.04
0260	60' diam.	23.50	1.28	24.78
0270	Aluminum framing, acrylic panels, 40' diam.			83
0280	Aluminum panels, 400' diam.			26
0310	Garden house, prefab, wood, shell only, 48 S.F.	52	5.65	57.65
0320	200 S.F.	31	23.50	54.50
0410	Greenhouse, shell-stock, residential, lean-to, 8'-6" long x 3'-10" wide	40.50	33.50	74
0420	Freestanding, 8'-6" long x 13'-6" wide	26	10.50	36.50
0430	Commercial-truss frame, under 2000 S.F., deluxe			19.10
0440	Over 5,000 S.F., economy			17.25
0450	Institutional-rigid frame, under 500 S.F., deluxe			39
0460	Over 2,000 S.F., economy			12.90
0510	Hangar, prefab, galv. roof and walls, bottom rolling doors, economy	12.65	4.65	17.30
0520	Electric bifolding doors, deluxe	12.45	6.05	18.50

F10 Special Construction

F1020 Integrated Construction

F1020 110 — Integrated Construction, EACH

	Integrated Construction, EACH	COST EACH		
		MAT.	INST.	TOTAL
0110	Integrated ceilings, radiant electric, 2' x 4' panel, manila finish	99	25.50	124.50
0120	ABS plastic finish	112	49	161

F1020 120 — Integrated Construction, S.F.

	Integrated Construction, S.F.	COST PER S.F.		
		MAT.	INST.	TOTAL
0110	Integrated ceilings, Luminaire, suspended, 5' x 5' modules, 50% lighted	4.32	13.55	17.87
0120	100% lighted	6.45	24.50	30.95
0130	Dimensionaire, 2' x 4' module tile system, no air bar	2.61	2.26	4.87
0140	With air bar, deluxe	3.83	2.26	6.09
0220	Pedestal access floors, stl pnls, no stringers, vinyl covering, >6000 S.F.	13.50	1.77	15.27
0230	With stringers, high pressure laminate covering, under 6000 S.F.	12.40	1.89	14.29
0240	Carpet covering, under 6000 S.F.	13.80	1.89	15.69
0250	Aluminum panels, no stringers, no covering	36	2.26	38.26

F1020 250 — Special Purpose Room, EACH

	Special Purpose Room, EACH	COST EACH		
		MAT.	INST.	TOTAL
0110	Portable booth, acoustical, 27 db 1000 hz., 15 S.F. floor	3,925		3,925
0120	55 S.F. flr.	8,050		8,050

F1020 260 — Special Purpose Room, S.F.

	Special Purpose Room, S.F.	COST PER S.F.		
		MAT.	INST.	TOTAL
0110	Anechoic chambers, 7' high, 100 cps cutoff, 25 S.F.			2,600
0120	200 cps cutoff, 100 S.F.			1,350
0130	Audiometric rooms, under 500 S.F.	57.50	23	80.50
0140	Over 500 S.F.	55	18.85	73.85
0300	Darkrooms, shell, not including door, 240 S.F., 8' high	22.50	9.45	31.95
0310	64 S.F., 12' high	54	17.70	71.70
0510	Music practice room, modular, perforated steel, under 500 S.F.	35.50	16.15	51.65
0520	Over 500 S.F.	30	14.15	44.15

F1020 330 — Special Construction, L.F.

	Special Construction, L.F.	COST PER L.F.		
		MAT.	INST.	TOTAL
0110	Spec. const., air curtains, shipping & receiving, 8' high x 5' wide, economy	750	134	884
0120	20' high x 8' wide, heated, deluxe	3,200	335	3,535
0130	Customer entrance, 10' high x 5' wide, economy	1,125	134	1,259
0140	12' high x 4' wide, heated, deluxe	2,025	167	2,192

F10 Special Construction

F1030 Special Construction Systems

F1030 120	Sound, Vibration, and Seismic Construction, S.F.	COST PER S.F.		
		MAT.	INST.	TOTAL
0020	Special construction, acoustical, enclosure, 4" thick, 8 psf panels	36	23.50	59.50
0030	Reverb chamber, 4" thick, parallel walls	51	28.50	79.50
0110	Sound absorbing panels, 2'-6" x 8', painted metal	13.55	7.90	21.45
0120	Vinyl faced	10.60	7.10	17.70
0130	Flexible transparent curtain, clear	8.20	9.35	17.55
0140	With absorbing foam, 75% coverage	11.40	9.35	20.75
0150	Strip entrance, 2/3 overlap	8.35	14.85	23.20
0160	Full overlap	10.55	17.45	28
0200	Audio masking system, plenum mounted, over 10,000 S.F.	.80	.29	1.09
0210	Ceiling mounted, under 5,000 S.F.	1.39	.53	1.92

F1030 210	Radiation Protection, EACH	COST EACH		
		MAT.	INST.	TOTAL
0110	Shielding, lead x-ray protection, radiography room, 1/16" lead, economy	11,100	3,825	14,925
0120	Deluxe	13,400	6,375	19,775
0210	Deep therapy x-ray, 1/4" lead, economy	31,100	11,900	43,000
0220	Deluxe	38,400	15,900	54,300

F1030 220	Radiation Protection, S.F.	COST PER S.F.		
		MAT.	INST.	TOTAL
0110	Shielding, lead, gypsum board, 5/8" thick, 1/16" lead	11.15	6.70	17.85
0120	1/8" lead	24	7.65	31.65
0130	Lath, 1/16" thick	11.05	7.10	18.15
0140	1/8" thick	22	7.95	29.95
0150	Radio frequency, galvanized steel, prefab type, economy	4.91	3.02	7.93
0160	Radio frequency, door, copper/wood laminate, 4" x 7'	8.65	8.10	16.75

F1030 910	Other Special Construction Systems, EACH	COST EACH		
		MAT.	INST.	TOTAL
0110	Disappearing stairways, folding, pine, 8'-6" ceiling	191	142	333
0220	Automatic electric, wood, 8' to 9' ceiling	9,275	1,125	10,400
0300	Fireplace prefabricated, freestanding or wall hung, economy	1,325	435	1,760
0310	Deluxe	3,000	630	3,630
0320	Woodburning stoves, cast iron, economy	1,075	870	1,945
0330	Deluxe	2,775	1,425	4,200

F10 Special Construction

F1040 Special Facilities

F1040 210	Ice Rinks, EACH	COAT EACH		
		MAT.	INST.	TOTAL
0100	Ice skating rink, 85' x 200', 55° system, 5 mos., 100 ton			632,500
0110	90° system, 12 mos., 135 ton			715,000
0120	Dash boards, acrylic screens, polyethylene coated plywood	148,500	38,100	186,600
0130	Fiberglass and aluminum construction	170,500	38,100	208,600

F1040 510	Liquid & Gas Storage Tanks, EACH	COST EACH		
		MAT.	INST.	TOTAL
0100	Tanks, steel, ground level, 100,000 gal.			226,500
0110	10,000,000 gal.			5,151,500
0120	Elevated water, 50,000 gal.		191,000	463,000
0130	1,000,000 gal.		890,500	2,050,500
0150	Cypress wood, ground level, 3,000 gal.	10,300	11,300	21,600
0160	Redwood, ground level, 45,000 gal.	78,000	30,700	108,700

F1040 Special Facilities

F1040 910	Special Construction, EACH	COST EACH		
		MAT.	INST.	TOTAL
0110	Special construction, bowling alley incl. pinsetter, scorer etc., economy	45,900	11,300	57,200
0120	Deluxe	58,000	12,600	70,600
0130	For automatic scorer, economy, add	9,050		9,050
0140	Deluxe, add	10,900		10,900
0300	Control tower, modular, 12' x 10', incl. instrumentation, economy			891,000
0310	Deluxe			1,540,000
0400	Garage costs, residential, prefab, wood, single car economy	5,750	1,125	6,875
0410	Two car deluxe	12,800	2,275	15,075
0500	Hangars, prefab, galv. steel, bottom rolling doors, economy (per plane)	16,800	5,175	21,975
0510	Electrical bi-folding doors, deluxe (per plane)	14,900	7,100	22,000

G1030 Site Earthwork

G1030 805	Trenching Common Earth	COST PER L.F.		
		MAT.	INST.	TOTAL
1310	Trenching, common earth, no slope, 2' wide, 2' deep, 3/8 C.Y. bucket		2.57	2.57
1330	4' deep, 3/8 C.Y. bucket		5.07	5.07
1360	10' deep, 1 C.Y. bucket		11.23	11.23
1400	4' wide, 2' deep, 3/8 C.Y. bucket		5.31	5.31
1420	4' deep, 1/2 C.Y. bucket		8.87	8.87
1450	10' deep, 1 C.Y. bucket		24.25	24.25
1480	18' deep, 2-1/2 C.Y. bucket		39.05	39.05
1520	6' wide, 6' deep, 5/8 C.Y. bucket w/trench box		23.55	23.55
1540	10' deep, 1 C.Y. bucket		32.05	32.05
1570	20' deep, 3-1/2 C.Y. bucket		55	55
1640	8' wide, 12' deep, 1-1/2 C.Y. bucket w/trench box		45.40	45.40
1680	24' deep, 3-1/2 C.Y. bucket		86.50	86.50
1730	10' wide, 20' deep, 3-1/2 C.Y. bucket w/trench box		77	77
1740	24' deep, 3-1/2 C.Y. bucket		101	101
3500	1 to 1 slope, 2' wide, 2' deep, 3/8 C.Y. bucket		5.07	5.07
3540	4' deep, 3/8 C.Y. bucket		15.08	15.08
3600	10' deep, 1 C.Y. bucket		67.50	67.50
3800	4' wide, 2' deep, 3/8 C.Y. bucket		7.81	7.81
3840	4' deep, 1/2 C.Y. bucket		17.57	17.57
3900	10' deep, 1 C.Y. bucket		85.50	85.50
4030	6' wide, 6' deep, 5/8 C.Y. bucket w/trench box		46.60	46.60
4050	10' deep, 1 C.Y. bucket		77	77
4080	20' deep, 3-1/2 C.Y. bucket		232.50	232.50
4500	8' wide, 12' deep, 1-1/2 C.Y. bucket w/trench box		115	115
4650	24' deep, 3-1/2 C.Y. bucket		353	353
4800	10' wide, 20' deep, 3-1/2 C.Y. bucket w/trench box		238	238
4850	24' deep, 3-1/2 C.Y. bucket		374	374

G1030 806	Trenching Loam & Sandy Clay	COST PER L.F.		
		MAT.	INST.	TOTAL
1310	Trenching, loam & sandy clay, no slope, 2' wide, 2' deep, 3/8 C.Y. bucket		2.52	2.52

G1030 807	Trenching Sand & Gravel	COST PER L.F.		
		MAT.	INST.	TOTAL
1310	Trenching, sand & gravel, no slope, 2' wide, 2' deep, 3/8 C.Y. bucket		2.39	2.39
1320	3' deep, 3/8 C.Y. bucket		3.95	3.95
1330	4' deep, 3/8 C.Y. bucket		4.70	4.70
1340	6' deep, 3/8 C.Y. bucket		5.90	5.90
1350	8' deep, 1/2 C.Y. bucket		7.80	7.80
1360	10' deep, 1 C.Y. bucket		8.40	8.40
1400	4' wide, 2' deep, 3/8 C.Y. bucket		4.88	4.88
1410	3' deep, 3/8 C.Y. bucket		7.20	7.20
1420	4' deep, 1/2 C.Y. bucket		8.20	8.20
1430	6' deep, 1/2 C.Y. bucket		12.85	12.85
1440	8' deep, 1/2 C.Y. bucket		18.35	18.35
1450	10' deep, 1 C.Y. bucket		18.55	18.55
1460	12' deep, 1 C.Y. bucket		23	23
1470	15' deep, 1-1/2 C.Y. bucket		27.50	27.50
1480	18' deep, 2-1/2 C.Y. bucket		30.50	30.50
1520	6' wide, 6' deep, 5/8 C.Y. bucket w/trench box		22	22
1530	8' deep, 3/4 C.Y. bucket		29	29
1540	10' deep, 1 C.Y. bucket		28.50	28.50
1550	12' deep, 1-1/2 C.Y. bucket		32.50	32.50
1560	16' deep, 2 C.Y. bucket		42	42
1570	20' deep, 3-1/2 C.Y. bucket		50	50
1580	24' deep, 3-1/2 C.Y. bucket		61.50	61.50

G10 Site Preparation

G1030 Site Earthwork

G1030 807	Trenching Sand & Gravel	COST PER L.F.		
		MAT.	INST.	TOTAL
1640	8' wide, 12' deep, 1-1/2 C.Y. bucket w/trench box		42.50	42.50
1650	15' deep, 1-1/2 C.Y. bucket		53	53
1660	18' deep, 2-1/2 C.Y. bucket		61.50	61.50
1680	24' deep, 3-1/2 C.Y. bucket		81	81
1730	10' wide, 20' deep, 3-1/2 C.Y. bucket w/trench box		81	81
1740	24' deep, 3-1/2 C.Y. bucket		101	101
1780	12' wide, 20' deep, 3-1/2 C.Y. bucket w/trench box		97	97
1790	25' deep, 3-1/2 C.Y. bucket		126	126
1800	1/2:1 slope, 2' wide, 2' deep, 3/8 C.Y. bucket		3.54	3.54
1810	3' deep, 3/8 C.Y. bucket		6.15	6.15
1820	4' deep, 3/8 C.Y. bucket		9.40	9.40
1840	6' deep, 3/8 C.Y. bucket		14.65	14.65
1860	8' deep, 1/2 C.Y. bucket		23.50	23.50
1880	10' deep, 1 C.Y. bucket		29.50	29.50
2300	4' wide, 2' deep, 3/8 C.Y. bucket		6.05	6.05
2310	3' deep, 3/8 C.Y. bucket		9.80	9.80
2320	4' deep, 1/2 C.Y. bucket		12.25	12.25
2340	6' deep, 1/2 C.Y. bucket		22.50	22.50
2360	8' deep, 1/2 C.Y. bucket		36.50	36.50
2380	10' deep, 1 C.Y. bucket		42	42
2400	12' deep, 1 C.Y. bucket		70	70
2430	15' deep, 1-1/2 C.Y. bucket		78.50	78.50
2460	18' deep, 2-1/2 C.Y. bucket		124	124
2840	6' wide, 6' deep, 5/8 C.Y. bucket w/trench box		32.50	32.50
2860	8' deep, 3/4 C.Y. bucket		48	48
2880	10' deep, 1 C.Y. bucket		53	53
2900	12' deep, 1-1/2 C.Y. bucket		65	65
2940	16' deep, 2 C.Y. bucket		99	99
2980	20' deep, 3-1/2 C.Y. bucket		135	135
3020	24' deep, 3-1/2 C.Y. bucket		187	187
3100	8' wide, 12' deep, 1-1/4 C.Y. bucket w/trench box		75.50	75.50
3120	15' deep, 1-1/2 C.Y. bucket		104	104
3140	18' deep, 2-1/2 C.Y. bucket		134	134
3180	24' deep, 3-1/2 C.Y. bucket		206	206
3270	10' wide, 20' deep, 3-1/2 C.Y. bucket w/trench box		166	166
3280	24' deep, 3-1/2 C.Y. bucket		227	227
3370	12' wide, 20' deep, 3-1/2 C.Y. bucket w/trench box		185	185
3380	25' deep, 3-1/2 C.Y. bucket		262	262
3500	1:1 slope, 2' wide, 2' deep, 3/8 C.Y. bucket		6.35	6.35
3520	3' deep, 3/8 C.Y. bucket		8.80	8.80
3540	4' deep, 3/8 C.Y. bucket		14	14
3560	6' deep, 3/8 C.Y. bucket		14.65	14.65
3580	8' deep, 1/2 C.Y. bucket		39	39
3600	10' deep, 1 C.Y. bucket		50	50
3800	4' wide, 2' deep, 3/8 C.Y. bucket		7.20	7.20
3820	3' deep, 3/8 C.Y. bucket		12.45	12.45
3840	4' deep, 1/2 C.Y. bucket		16.25	16.25
3860	6' deep, 1/2 C.Y. bucket		32	32
3880	8' deep, 1/2 C.Y. bucket		55	55
3900	10' deep, 1 C.Y. bucket		66	66
3920	12' deep, 1 C.Y. bucket		93.50	93.50
3940	15' deep, 1-1/2 C.Y. bucket		131	131
3960	18' deep, 2-1/2 C.Y. bucket		171	171
4030	6' wide, 6' deep, 5/8 C.Y. bucket w/trench box		43.50	43.50
4040	8' deep, 3/4 C.Y. bucket		67	67
4050	10' deep, 1 C.Y. bucket		77.50	77.50
4060	12' deep, 1-1/2 C.Y. bucket		97.50	97.50
4070	16' deep, 2 C.Y. bucket		156	156

G10 Site Preparation

G1030 Site Earthwork

G1030 807	Trenching Sand & Gravel	COST PER L.F.		
		MAT.	INST.	TOTAL
4080	20' deep, 3-1/2 C.Y. bucket		219	219
4090	24' deep, 3-1/2 C.Y. bucket		310	310
4500	8' wide, 12' deep, 1-1/2 C.Y. bucket w/trench box		108	108
4550	15' deep, 1-1/2 C.Y. bucket		156	156
4600	18' deep, 2-1/2 C.Y. bucket		205	205
4650	24' deep, 3-1/2 C.Y. bucket		330	330
4800	10' wide, 20' deep, 3-1/2 C.Y. bucket w/trench box		251	251
4850	24' deep, 3-1/2 C.Y. bucket		350	350
4950	12' wide, 20' deep, 3-1/2 C.Y. bucket w/trench box		266	266
4980	25' deep, 3-1/2 C.Y. bucket		395	395

G1030 815	Pipe Bedding	COST PER L.F.		
		MAT.	INST.	TOTAL
1440	Pipe bedding, side slope 0 to 1, 1' wide, pipe size 6" diameter	1.65	.88	2.53
1460	2' wide, pipe size 8" diameter	3.57	1.91	5.48
1500	Pipe size 12" diameter	3.72	2	5.72
1600	4' wide, pipe size 20" diameter	8.90	4.77	13.67
1660	Pipe size 30" diameter	9.35	5	14.35
1680	6' wide, pipe size 32" diameter	16	8.60	24.60
1740	8' wide, pipe size 60" diameter	31.50	16.95	48.45
1780	12' wide, pipe size 84" diameter	58.50	31	89.50

G2010 Roadways

The Bituminous Roadway Systems are listed for pavement thicknesses between 3-1/2" and 7" and crushed stone bases from 3" to 22" in depth. Systems costs are expressed per linear foot for varying widths of two and multi-lane roads. Earth moving is not included. Granite curbs and line painting are added as required system components.

G2010 232	Bituminous Roadways Crushed Stone	COST PER L.F.		
		MAT.	INST.	TOTAL
1050	Bitum. roadway, two lanes, 3-1/2" th. pvmt., 3" th. crushed stone, 24' wide	74.50	52.50	127
1100	28' wide	82	53	135
1150	32' wide	90	61	151
1200	4" thick crushed stone, 24' wide	77	50.50	127.50
1210	28' wide	85	54	139
1220	32' wide	93	58	151
1222	36' wide	101	61.50	162.50
1224	40' wide	110	65	175
1230	6" thick crushed stone, 24' wide	82.50	52	134.50
1240	28' wide	91.50	56	147.50
1250	32' wide	101	60	161
1252	36' wide	110	64	174
1254	40' wide	119	68	187
1256	8" thick crushed stone, 24' wide	88	53.50	141.50
1258	28' wide	98	58	156
1260	32' wide	108	62	170
1262	36' wide	118	66.50	184.50
1264	40' wide	128	70.50	198.50
1300	9" thick crushed stone, 24' wide	91	55	146
1350	28' wide	101	59.50	160.50
1400	32' wide	112	64	176
1410	10" thick crushed stone, 24' wide	93.50	55.50	149
1412	28' wide	104	60	164
1414	32' wide	115	64.50	179.50
1416	36' wide	126	69	195
1418	40' wide	137	73.50	210.50
1420	12" thick crushed stone, 24' wide	99	57.50	156.50
1422	28' wide	110	61.50	171.50
1424	32' wide	122	66.50	188.50
1426	36' wide	134	71.50	205.50
1428	40' wide	146	76	222
1430	15" thick crushed stone, 24' wide	107	59.50	166.50
1432	28' wide	120	65	185
1434	32' wide	133	70	203
1436	36' wide	146	75.50	221.50
1438	40' wide	159	80.50	239.50
1440	18" thick crushed stone, 24' wide	115	62	177
1442	28' wide	129	68	197
1444	32' wide	144	73.50	217.50
1446	36' wide	158	79.50	237.50
1448	40' wide	173	84.50	257.50
1550	4" thick pavement., 4" thick crushed stone, 24' wide	83	51.50	134.50

G2010 Roadways

G2010 232	Bituminous Roadways Crushed Stone	COST PER L.F.		
		MAT.	INST.	TOTAL
1600	28' wide	92	55	147
1650	32' wide	101	58.50	159.50
1652	36' wide	110	62	172
1654	40' wide	119	66	185
1700	6" thick crushed stone , 24' wide	88	53	141
1710	28' wide	98	56.50	154.50
1720	32' wide	108	61	169
1722	36' wide	118	65	183
1724	40' wide	128	68.50	196.50
1726	8" thick crushed stone , 24' wide	93.50	54.50	148
1728	28' wide	104	59	163
1730	32' wide	115	63	178
1732	36' wide	126	67.50	193.50
1734	40' wide	137	71.50	208.50
1800	10" thick crushed stone , 24' wide	99.50	56	155.50
1850	28' wide	111	59.50	170.50
1900	32' wide	123	65.50	188.50
1902	36' wide	134	70	204
1904	40' wide	139	72.50	211.50

G2020 Parking Lots

G2020 210	Parking Lots Gravel Base	COST PER CAR		
		MAT.	INST.	TOTAL
1500	Parking lot, 90° angle parking, 3″ bituminous paving, 6″ gravel base	810	430	1,240
1540	10″ gravel base	925	500	1,425
1560	4″ bituminous paving, 6″ gravel base	1,025	455	1,480
1600	10″ gravel base	1,150	525	1,675
1620	6″ bituminous paving, 6″ gravel base	1,375	485	1,860
1660	10″ gravel base	1,500	555	2,055
1800	60° angle parking, 3″ bituminous paving, 6″ gravel base	810	430	1,240
1840	10″ gravel base	925	500	1,425
1860	4″ bituminous paving, 6″ gravel base	1,025	455	1,480
1900	10″ gravel base	1,150	525	1,675
1920	6″ bituminous paving, 6″ gravel base	1,375	485	1,860
1960	10″ gravel base	1,500	555	2,055
2200	45° angle parking, 3″ bituminous paving, 6″ gravel base	830	445	1,275
2240	10″ gravel base	950	510	1,460
2260	4″ bituminous paving, 6″ gravel base	1,050	465	1,515
2300	10″ gravel base	1,175	540	1,715
2320	6″ bituminous paving, 6″ gravel base	1,425	500	1,925
2360	10″ gravel base	1,525	570	2,095

G2040 Site Development

G2040 810	Flagpoles	COST EACH		
		MAT.	INST.	TOTAL
0110	Flagpoles, on grade, aluminum, tapered, 20' high	1,075	690	1,765
0120	70' high	9,075	1,725	10,800
0130	Fiberglass, tapered, 23' high	635	690	1,325
0140	59' high	5,750	1,525	7,275
0150	Concrete, internal halyard, 20' high	1,425	550	1,975
0160	100' high	17,100	1,375	18,475

G2040 950	Other Site Development, EACH	COST EACH		
		MAT.	INST.	TOTAL
0110	Grandstands, permanent, closed deck, steel, economy (per seat)			19.90
0120	Deluxe (per seat)			22.50
0130	Composite design, economy (per seat)			38.50
0140	Deluxe (per seat)			68.50

G3030 Storm Sewer

G3030 210	Manholes & Catch Basins	COST PER EACH		
		MAT.	INST.	TOTAL
1920	Manhole/catch basin, brick, 4' I.D. riser, 4' deep	1,275	1,750	3,025
1980	10' deep	2,875	4,150	7,025
3200	Block, 4' I.D. riser, 4' deep	1,125	1,425	2,550
3260	10' deep	2,475	3,425	5,900
4620	Concrete, cast-in-place, 4' I.D. riser, 4' deep	1,275	2,450	3,725
4680	10' deep	3,075	5,825	8,900
5820	Concrete, precast, 4' I.D. riser, 4' deep	1,575	1,300	2,875
5880	10' deep	3,150	3,000	6,150
6200	6' I.D. riser, 4' deep	3,250	1,950	5,200
6260	10' deep	6,625	4,550	11,175

G4020 Site Lighting

Light Pole

G4020 210	Light Pole (Installed)	COST EACH		
		MAT.	INST.	TOTAL
0200	Light pole, aluminum, 20' high, 1 arm bracket	1,250	1,150	2,400
0240	2 arm brackets	1,375	1,150	2,525
0280	3 arm brackets	1,500	1,200	2,700
0320	4 arm brackets	1,650	1,200	2,850
0360	30' high, 1 arm bracket	2,150	1,450	3,600
0400	2 arm brackets	2,300	1,450	3,750
0440	3 arm brackets	2,425	1,500	3,925
0480	4 arm brackets	2,550	1,500	4,050
0680	40' high, 1 arm bracket	2,650	1,950	4,600
0720	2 arm brackets	2,800	1,950	4,750
0760	3 arm brackets	2,925	2,000	4,925
0800	4 arm brackets	3,050	2,000	5,050
0840	Steel, 20' high, 1 arm bracket	1,475	1,225	2,700
0880	2 arm brackets	1,600	1,225	2,825
0920	3 arm brackets	1,625	1,250	2,875
0960	4 arm brackets	1,750	1,250	3,000
1000	30' high, 1 arm bracket	1,725	1,575	3,300
1040	2 arm brackets	1,825	1,575	3,400
1080	3 arm brackets	1,850	1,600	3,450
1120	4 arm brackets	2,000	1,600	3,600
1320	40' high, 1 arm bracket	2,250	2,125	4,375
1360	2 arm brackets	2,350	2,125	4,475
1400	3 arm brackets	2,375	2,150	4,525
1440	4 arm brackets	2,500	2,150	4,650

Reference Section

All the reference information is in one section making it easy to find what you need to know ... and easy to use the book on a daily basis. This section is visually identified by a vertical gray bar on the edge of pages.

In this Reference Section, we've included General Conditions; Location Factors for adjusting costs to the region you are in; Historical Cost Indexes for cost comparisons over time; a Glossary; an explanation of all Abbreviations used in the book; and sample Estimating Forms.

Table of Contents

General Conditions 518
Location Factors 519
Historical Cost Indexes 525
Square Foot Costs 533
Glossary 542
Abbreviations 546
Forms 550

General Conditions, Overhead & Profit

The total building costs in the Commercial/Industrial/Institutional section include a 10% allowance for general conditions and a 15% allowance for the general contractor's overhead and profit and contingencies.

General contractor overhead includes indirect costs such as permits, Workers' Compensation, insurances, supervision and bonding fees. Overhead will vary with the size of project, the contractor's operating procedures and location. Profits will vary with economic activity and local conditions.

Contingencies provide for unforeseen construction difficulties which include material shortages and weather. In all situations, the appraiser should give consideration to possible adjustment of the 25% factor used in developing the Commercial/Industrial/Institutional models.

Architectural Fees

Tabulated below are typical percentage fees by project size, for good professional architectural service. Fees may vary from those listed depending upon degree of design difficulty and economic conditions in any particular area.

Rates can be interpolated horizontally and vertically. Various portions of the same project requiring different rates should be adjusted proportionately. For alterations, add 50% to the fee for the first $500,000 of project cost and add 25% to the fee for project cost over $500,000.

Architectural fees tabulated below include Engineering fees.

Insurance Exclusions

Many insurance companies exclude from coverage such items as architect's fees, excavation, foundations below grade, underground piping and site preparation. Since exclusions vary among insurance companies, it is recommended that for greatest accuracy each exclusion be priced separately using the unit-in-place section.

As a rule of thumb, exclusions can be calculated at 9% of total building cost plus the appropriate allowance for architect's fees.

Building Types	Total Project Size in Thousands of Dollars						
	100	250	500	1,000	5,000	10,000	50,000
Factories, garages, warehouses, repetitive housing	9.0%	8.0%	7.0%	6.2%	5.3%	4.9%	4.5%
Apartments, banks, schools, libraries, offices, municipal buildings	12.2	12.3	9.2	8.0	7.0	6.6	6.2
Churches, hospitals, homes, laboratories, museums, research	15.0	13.6	12.7	11.9	9.5	8.8	8.0
Memorials, monumental work, decorative furnishings	—	16.0	14.5	13.1	10.0	9.0	8.3

Location Factors

Costs shown in *RSMeans Square Foot Costs* are based on national averages for materials and installation. To adjust these costs to a specific location, simply multiply the base cost by the factor for that city.

The data is arranged alphabetically by state and postal zip code numbers. For a city not listed, use the factor for a nearby city with similar economic characteristics.

STATE/ZIP	CITY	Residential	Commercial
ALABAMA			
350-352	Birmingham	.86	.87
354	Tuscaloosa	.78	.82
355	Jasper	.72	.79
356	Decatur	.76	.80
357-358	Huntsville	.85	.85
359	Gadsden	.75	.81
360-361	Montgomery	.76	.81
362	Anniston	.76	.82
363	Dothan	.74	.77
364	Evergreen	.72	.77
365-366	Mobile	.81	.84
367	Selma	.72	.77
368	Phenix City	.73	.79
369	Butler	.72	.77
ALASKA			
995-996	Anchorage	1.22	1.18
997	Fairbanks	1.24	1.18
998	Juneau	1.22	1.18
999	Ketchikan	1.26	1.24
ARIZONA			
850,853	Phoenix	.86	.89
851,852	Mesa/Tempe	.85	.88
855	Globe	.82	.87
856-857	Tucson	.84	.87
859	Show Low	.86	.88
860	Flagstaff	.86	.89
863	Prescott	.81	.86
864	Kingman	.83	.87
865	Chambers	.83	.86
ARKANSAS			
716	Pine Bluff	.78	.82
717	Camden	.69	.75
718	Texarkana	.73	.76
719	Hot Springs	.69	.76
720-722	Little Rock	.80	.83
723	West Memphis	.77	.81
724	Jonesboro	.75	.80
725	Batesville	.72	.77
726	Harrison	.73	.76
727	Fayetteville	.69	.76
728	Russellville	.75	.77
729	Fort Smith	.80	.82
CALIFORNIA			
900-902	Los Angeles	1.09	1.07
903-905	Inglewood	1.06	1.03
906-908	Long Beach	1.05	1.04
910-912	Pasadena	1.04	1.04
913-916	Van Nuys	1.07	1.06
917-918	Alhambra	1.08	1.05
919-921	San Diego	1.03	1.04
922	Palm Springs	1.04	1.03
923-924	San Bernardino	1.05	1.02
925	Riverside	1.07	1.06
926-927	Santa Ana	1.05	1.03
928	Anaheim	1.06	1.06
930	Oxnard	1.08	1.06
931	Santa Barbara	1.07	1.06
932-933	Bakersfield	1.06	1.05
934	San Luis Obispo	1.07	1.05
935	Mojave	1.05	1.02
936-938	Fresno	1.10	1.06
939	Salinas	1.13	1.09
940-941	San Francisco	1.24	1.23
942,956-958	Sacramento	1.11	1.09
943	Palo Alto	1.18	1.14
944	San Mateo	1.22	1.15
945	Vallejo	1.16	1.12
946	Oakland	1.21	1.17
947	Berkeley	1.23	1.16
948	Richmond	1.23	1.15
949	San Rafael	1.22	1.17
950	Santa Cruz	1.15	1.11
951	San Jose	1.21	1.16
952	Stockton	1.11	1.07
953	Modesto	1.10	1.07

STATE/ZIP	CITY	Residential	Commercial
CALIFORNIA (CONT'D)			
954	Santa Rosa	1.19	1.15
955	Eureka	1.11	1.06
959	Marysville	1.11	1.07
960	Redding	1.11	1.08
961	Susanville	1.11	1.08
COLORADO			
800-802	Denver	.89	.93
803	Boulder	.91	.91
804	Golden	.87	.91
805	Fort Collins	.88	.92
806	Greeley	.85	.89
807	Fort Morgan	.89	.91
808-809	Colorado Springs	.86	.92
810	Pueblo	.88	.91
811	Alamosa	.84	.90
812	Salida	.87	.91
813	Durango	.88	.91
814	Montrose	.86	.91
815	Grand Junction	.91	.92
816	Glenwood Springs	.88	.92
CONNECTICUT			
060	New Britain	1.11	1.09
061	Hartford	1.10	1.10
062	Willimantic	1.11	1.10
063	New London	1.10	1.08
064	Meriden	1.10	1.09
065	New Haven	1.11	1.10
066	Bridgeport	1.11	1.10
067	Waterbury	1.11	1.10
068	Norwalk	1.12	1.13
069	Stamford	1.12	1.13
D.C.			
200-205	Washington	.94	.97
DELAWARE			
197	Newark	1.02	1.03
198	Wilmington	1.02	1.03
199	Dover	1.01	1.03
FLORIDA			
320,322	Jacksonville	.82	.84
321	Daytona Beach	.87	.87
323	Tallahassee	.78	.81
324	Panama City	.77	.81
325	Pensacola	.81	.84
326,344	Gainesville	.80	.85
327-328,347	Orlando	.87	.87
329	Melbourne	.87	.90
330-332,340	Miami	.86	.88
333	Fort Lauderdale	.86	.87
334,349	West Palm Beach	.86	.85
335-336,346	Tampa	.90	.90
337	St. Petersburg	.80	.85
338	Lakeland	.87	.89
339,341	Fort Myers	.86	.87
342	Sarasota	.89	.89
GEORGIA			
300-303,399	Atlanta	.87	.88
304	Statesboro	.73	.79
305	Gainesville	.77	.81
306	Athens	.76	.82
307	Dalton	.75	.81
308-309	Augusta	.81	.82
310-312	Macon	.79	.83
313-314	Savannah	.80	.83
315	Waycross	.79	.81
316	Valdosta	.74	.82
317,398	Albany	.77	.82
318-319	Columbus	.80	.84
HAWAII			
967	Hilo	1.18	1.15
968	Honolulu	1.22	1.18

Location Factors

STATE/ZIP	CITY	Residential	Commercial
STATES & POSS.			
969	Guam	.93	1.00
IDAHO			
832	Pocatello	.87	.91
833	Twin Falls	.81	.87
834	Idaho Falls	.85	.89
835	Lewiston	.99	.98
836-837	Boise	.88	.91
838	Coeur d'Alene	.97	.97
ILLINOIS			
600-603	North Suburban	1.19	1.15
604	Joliet	1.22	1.17
605	South Suburban	1.19	1.15
606-608	Chicago	1.22	1.18
609	Kankakee	1.13	1.11
610-611	Rockford	1.11	1.10
612	Rock Island	.98	.98
613	La Salle	1.12	1.10
614	Galesburg	1.04	1.02
615-616	Peoria	1.07	1.05
617	Bloomington	1.04	1.03
618-619	Champaign	1.05	1.04
620-622	East St. Louis	1.04	1.02
623	Quincy	1.03	.99
624	Effingham	1.05	1.01
625	Decatur	1.05	1.02
626-627	Springfield	1.05	1.03
628	Centralia	1.04	1.00
629	Carbondale	1.02	.99
INDIANA			
460	Anderson	.91	.90
461-462	Indianapolis	.93	.93
463-464	Gary	1.06	1.03
465-466	South Bend	.91	.91
467-468	Fort Wayne	.90	.89
469	Kokomo	.92	.88
470	Lawrenceburg	.88	.87
471	New Albany	.88	.87
472	Columbus	.92	.90
473	Muncie	.92	.91
474	Bloomington	.94	.91
475	Washington	.91	.90
476-477	Evansville	.91	.92
478	Terre Haute	.90	.92
479	Lafayette	.93	.91
IOWA			
500-503,509	Des Moines	.91	.93
504	Mason City	.77	.84
505	Fort Dodge	.75	.80
506-507	Waterloo	.82	.86
508	Creston	.84	.89
510-511	Sioux City	.87	.88
512	Sibley	.74	.80
513	Spencer	.76	.81
514	Carroll	.80	.86
515	Council Bluffs	.86	.91
516	Shenandoah	.81	.86
520	Dubuque	.86	.91
521	Decorah	.78	.84
522-524	Cedar Rapids	.93	.92
525	Ottumwa	.86	.87
526	Burlington	.88	.88
527-528	Davenport	.97	.96
KANSAS			
660-662	Kansas City	.98	.98
664-666	Topeka	.78	.85
667	Fort Scott	.89	.88
668	Emporia	.83	.86
669	Belleville	.81	.85
670-672	Wichita	.79	.85
673	Independence	.89	.87
674	Salina	.80	.86
675	Hutchinson	.79	.83
676	Hays	.82	.85
677	Colby	.83	.85
678	Dodge City	.81	.86
679	Liberal	.80	.85
KENTUCKY			
400-402	Louisville	.92	.92
403-405	Lexington	.90	.91

STATE/ZIP	CITY	Residential	Commercial
KENTUCKY (CONT'D)			
406	Frankfort	.89	.91
407-409	Corbin	.83	.85
410	Covington	.94	.94
411-412	Ashland	.95	.97
413-414	Campton	.88	.89
415-416	Pikeville	.92	.94
417-418	Hazard	.87	.88
420	Paducah	.89	.90
421-422	Bowling Green	.90	.91
423	Owensboro	.91	.93
424	Henderson	.92	.91
425-426	Somerset	.85	.88
427	Elizabethtown	.88	.89
LOUISIANA			
700-701	New Orleans	.86	.88
703	Thibodaux	.82	.84
704	Hammond	.75	.78
705	Lafayette	.83	.83
706	Lake Charles	.83	.84
707-708	Baton Rouge	.82	.84
710-711	Shreveport	.78	.82
712	Monroe	.74	.79
713-714	Alexandria	.76	.80
MAINE			
039	Kittery	.92	.91
040-041	Portland	.97	.97
042	Lewiston	.97	.95
043	Augusta	.93	.92
044	Bangor	.96	.95
045	Bath	.92	.90
046	Machias	.96	.92
047	Houlton	.97	.92
048	Rockland	.96	.91
049	Waterville	.91	.90
MARYLAND			
206	Waldorf	.90	.91
207-208	College Park	.88	.92
209	Silver Spring	.90	.91
210-212	Baltimore	.90	.93
214	Annapolis	.89	.92
215	Cumberland	.88	.90
216	Easton	.83	.85
217	Hagerstown	.87	.91
218	Salisbury	.82	.83
219	Elkton	.89	.89
MASSACHUSETTS			
010-011	Springfield	1.07	1.04
012	Pittsfield	1.07	1.04
013	Greenfield	1.05	1.03
014	Fitchburg	1.13	1.09
015-016	Worcester	1.14	1.11
017	Framingham	1.16	1.11
018	Lowell	1.16	1.13
019	Lawrence	1.17	1.14
020-022, 024	Boston	1.21	1.18
023	Brockton	1.16	1.12
025	Buzzards Bay	1.14	1.09
026	Hyannis	1.13	1.10
027	New Bedford	1.16	1.11
MICHIGAN			
480,483	Royal Oak	1.02	1.00
481	Ann Arbor	1.03	1.01
482	Detroit	1.05	1.03
484-485	Flint	.96	.96
486	Saginaw	.93	.94
487	Bay City	.93	.94
488-489	Lansing	.94	.96
490	Battle Creek	.93	.93
491	Kalamazoo	.92	.92
492	Jackson	.94	.95
493,495	Grand Rapids	.91	.92
494	Muskegon	.90	.91
496	Traverse City	.86	.89
497	Gaylord	.89	.91
498-499	Iron mountain	.91	.93
MINNESOTA			
550-551	Saint Paul	1.11	1.08
553-555	Minneapolis	1.13	1.09
556-558	Duluth	1.06	1.03

Location Factors

STATE/ZIP	CITY	Residential	Commercial
MINNESOTA (CONT'd)			
559	Rochester	1.04	1.02
560	Mankato	1.00	.99
561	Windom	.93	.94
562	Willmar	.97	.98
563	St. Cloud	1.05	1.06
564	Brainerd	.96	.99
565	Detroit Lakes	.95	.98
566	Bemidji	.94	.99
567	Thief River Falls	.94	.96
MISSISSIPPI			
386	Clarksdale	.74	.78
387	Greenville	.81	.84
388	Tupelo	.76	.79
389	Greenwood	.78	.78
390-392	Jackson	.82	.84
393	Meridian	.81	.83
394	Laurel	.77	.80
395	Biloxi	.80	.81
396	Mccomb	.75	.77
397	Columbus	.76	.79
MISSOURI			
630-631	St. Louis	1.03	1.03
633	Bowling Green	.96	.97
634	Hannibal	.93	.95
635	Kirksville	.90	.96
636	Flat River	.96	.98
637	Cape Girardeau	.89	.95
638	Sikeston	.88	.95
639	Poplar Bluff	.87	.94
640-641	Kansas City	1.05	1.04
644-645	St. Joseph	.98	.98
646	Chillicothe	.97	.97
647	Harrisonville	.99	1.00
648	Joplin	.90	.92
650-651	Jefferson City	.93	.96
652	Columbia	.92	.96
653	Sedalia	.92	.96
654-655	Rolla	.97	.96
656-658	Springfield	.89	.92
MONTANA			
590-591	Billings	.90	.92
592	Wolf Point	.87	.90
593	Miles City	.88	.89
594	Great Falls	.91	.92
595	Havre	.84	.89
596	Helena	.88	.90
597	Butte	.88	.91
598	Missoula	.88	.89
599	Kalispell	.87	.89
NEBRASKA			
680-681	Omaha	.90	.91
683-685	Lincoln	.87	.89
686	Columbus	.87	.89
687	Norfolk	.89	.90
688	Grand Island	.88	.90
689	Hastings	.90	.91
690	Mccook	.83	.87
691	North Platte	.89	.90
692	Valentine	.84	.89
693	Alliance	.84	.88
NEVADA			
889-891	Las Vegas	1.03	1.04
893	Ely	1.02	1.01
894-895	Reno	.95	.97
897	Carson City	.96	.97
898	Elko	.93	.93
NEW HAMPSHIRE			
030	Nashua	.98	.98
031	Manchester	.98	.98
032-033	Concord	.97	.97
034	Keene	.88	.87
035	Littleton	.92	.88
036	Charleston	.86	.85
037	Claremont	.87	.85
038	Portsmouth	.97	.96

STATE/ZIP	CITY	Residential	Commercial
NEW JERSEY			
070-071	Newark	1.14	1.12
072	Elizabeth	1.16	1.11
073	Jersey City	1.13	1.10
074-075	Paterson	1.14	1.11
076	Hackensack	1.13	1.10
077	Long Branch	1.13	1.09
078	Dover	1.13	1.10
079	Summit	1.14	1.10
080,083	Vineland	1.11	1.09
081	Camden	1.12	1.10
082,084	Atlantic City	1.15	1.09
085-086	Trenton	1.13	1.11
087	Point Pleasant	1.10	1.09
088-089	New Brunswick	1.15	1.11
NEW MEXICO			
870-872	Albuquerque	.83	.88
873	Gallup	.83	.88
874	Farmington	.83	.88
875	Santa Fe	.85	.89
877	Las Vegas	.83	.87
878	Socorro	.83	.87
879	Truth/Consequences	.82	.85
880	Las Cruces	.81	.85
881	Clovis	.83	.87
882	Roswell	.83	.88
883	Carrizozo	.83	.89
884	Tucumcari	.83	.88
NEW YORK			
100-102	New York	1.34	1.31
103	Staten Island	1.28	1.28
104	Bronx	1.30	1.27
105	Mount Vernon	1.12	1.13
106	White Plains	1.15	1.13
107	Yonkers	1.16	1.16
108	New Rochelle	1.16	1.14
109	Suffern	1.13	1.10
110	Queens	1.30	1.28
111	Long Island City	1.33	1.29
112	Brooklyn	1.34	1.29
113	Flushing	1.32	1.29
114	Jamaica	1.31	1.28
115,117,118	Hicksville	1.20	1.21
116	Far Rockaway	1.31	1.29
119	Riverhead	1.21	1.21
120-122	Albany	.98	.99
123	Schenectady	.99	.99
124	Kingston	1.05	1.08
125-126	Poughkeepsie	1.16	1.12
127	Monticello	1.05	1.07
128	Glens Falls	.91	.94
129	Plattsburgh	.95	.93
130-132	Syracuse	.98	.98
133-135	Utica	.94	.95
136	Watertown	.92	.95
137-139	Binghamton	.97	.99
140-142	Buffalo	1.06	1.02
143	Niagara Falls	1.02	1.00
144-146	Rochester	.99	.98
147	Jamestown	.90	.92
148-149	Elmira	.92	.95
NORTH CAROLINA			
270,272-274	Greensboro	.85	.80
271	Winston-Salem	.86	.81
275-276	Raleigh	.86	.79
277	Durham	.85	.80
278	Rocky Mount	.81	.77
279	Elizabeth City	.80	.77
280	Gastonia	.85	.80
281-282	Charlotte	.86	.81
283	Fayetteville	.89	.83
284	Wilmington	.86	.80
285	Kinston	.81	.77
286	Hickory	.80	.78
287-288	Asheville	.83	.79
289	Murphy	.82	.76
NORTH DAKOTA			
580-581	Fargo	.79	.87
582	Grand Forks	.73	.80
583	Devils Lake	.77	.83
584	Jamestown	.71	.77
585	Bismarck	.78	.86

STATE/ZIP	CITY	Residential	Commercial
NORTH DAKOTA (CONT'D)			
586	Dickinson	.75	.83
587	Minot	.82	.88
588	Williston	.75	.82
OHIO			
430-432	Columbus	.95	.95
433	Marion	.90	.90
434-436	Toledo	.98	.98
437-438	Zanesville	.90	.91
439	Steubenville	.95	.96
440	Lorain	.96	.95
441	Cleveland	1.00	.99
442-443	Akron	.98	.97
444-445	Youngstown	.95	.94
446-447	Canton	.93	.93
448-449	Mansfield	.91	.92
450	Hamilton	.92	.92
451-452	Cincinnati	.92	.92
453-454	Dayton	.92	.91
455	Springfield	.93	.92
456	Chillicothe	.96	.95
457	Athens	.90	.91
458	Lima	.91	.93
OKLAHOMA			
730-731	Oklahoma City	.82	.83
734	Ardmore	.78	.81
735	Lawton	.80	.83
736	Clinton	.80	.82
737	Enid	.76	.81
738	Woodward	.79	.82
739	Guymon	.79	.81
740-741	Tulsa	.78	.82
743	Miami	.85	.83
744	Muskogee	.74	.79
745	Mcalester	.75	.80
746	Ponca City	.78	.81
747	Durant	.77	.81
748	Shawnee	.76	.81
749	Poteau	.76	.80
OREGON			
970-972	Portland	.99	.99
973	Salem	.98	1.00
974	Eugene	.99	.99
975	Medford	.97	.98
976	Klamath Falls	.97	.98
977	Bend	1.00	.99
978	Pendleton	.98	.97
979	Vale	.96	.91
PENNSYLVANIA			
150-152	Pittsburgh	1.01	1.02
153	Washington	.96	1.00
154	Uniontown	.95	.99
155	Bedford	.91	.96
156	Greensburg	.97	1.00
157	Indiana	.94	.98
158	Dubois	.92	.98
159	Johnstown	.92	.98
160	Butler	.94	.97
161	New Castle	.93	.94
162	Kittanning	.94	.97
163	Oil City	.91	.94
164-165	Erie	.94	.95
166	Altoona	.88	.94
167	Bradford	.91	.96
168	State College	.91	.94
169	Wellsboro	.92	.94
170-171	Harrisburg	.97	.98
172	Chambersburg	.90	.93
173-174	York	.93	.96
175-176	Lancaster	.92	.92
177	Williamsport	.85	.87
178	Sunbury	.94	.96
179	Pottsville	.94	.96
180	Lehigh Valley	1.02	1.03
181	Allentown	1.04	1.02
182	Hazleton	.93	.97
183	Stroudsburg	.92	.98
184-185	Scranton	.98	.99
186-187	Wilkes-Barre	.95	.97
188	Montrose	.92	.96
189	Doylestown	1.06	1.06

STATE/ZIP	CITY	Residential	Commercial
PENNSYLVANIA (CONT'D)			
190-191	Philadelphia	1.16	1.14
193	Westchester	1.10	1.07
194	Norristown	1.10	1.10
195-196	Reading	.98	.99
PUERTO RICO			
009	San Juan	.75	.80
RHODE ISLAND			
028	Newport	1.09	1.07
029	Providence	1.10	1.08
SOUTH CAROLINA			
290-292	Columbia	.86	.80
293	Spartanburg	.86	.80
294	Charleston	.94	.84
295	Florence	.82	.79
296	Greenville	.85	.79
297	Rock Hill	.80	.76
298	Aiken	.97	.85
299	Beaufort	.79	.75
SOUTH DAKOTA			
570-571	Sioux Falls	.76	.82
572	Watertown	.73	.78
573	Mitchell	.74	.77
574	Aberdeen	.75	.79
575	Pierre	.77	.83
576	Mobridge	.73	.77
577	Rapid City	.78	.83
TENNESSEE			
370-372	Nashville	.85	.88
373-374	Chattanooga	.83	.85
375,380-381	Memphis	.84	.87
376	Johnson City	.72	.81
377-379	Knoxville	.75	.81
382	Mckenzie	.73	.81
383	Jackson	.77	.83
384	Columbia	.78	.83
385	Cookeville	.71	.81
TEXAS			
750	Mckinney	.72	.77
751	Waxahackie	.78	.81
752-753	Dallas	.84	.85
754	Greenville	.70	.75
755	Texarkana	.73	.77
756	Longview	.68	.74
757	Tyler	.74	.80
758	Palestine	.75	.78
759	Lufkin	.78	.80
760-761	Fort Worth	.83	.84
762	Denton	.75	.76
763	Wichita Falls	.78	.79
764	Eastland	.75	.76
765	Temple	.77	.77
766-767	Waco	.78	.80
768	Brownwood	.72	.77
769	San Angelo	.73	.77
770-772	Houston	.85	.87
773	Huntsville	.77	.80
774	Wharton	.72	.79
775	Galveston	.83	.85
776-777	Beaumont	.81	.81
778	Bryan	.74	.81
779	Victoria	.71	.74
780	Laredo	.75	.78
781-782	San Antonio	.80	.83
783-784	Corpus Christi	.79	.80
785	Mc Allen	.76	.77
786-787	Austin	.78	.81
788	Del Rio	.73	.76
789	Giddings	.78	.79
790-791	Amarillo	.79	.82
792	Childress	.80	.80
793-794	Lubbock	.80	.81
795-796	Abilene	.76	.79
797	Midland	.80	.80
798-799,885	El Paso	.74	.77
UTAH			
840-841	Salt Lake City	.80	.87
842,844	Ogden	.79	.85
843	Logan	.79	.86

Location Factors

STATE/ZIP	CITY	Residential	Commercial
UTAH (CONT'd)			
845	Price	.77	.85
846-847	Provo	.79	.86
VERMONT			
050	White River Jct.	.90	.90
051	Bellows Falls	.97	.96
052	Bennington	1.01	.96
053	Brattleboro	.96	.96
054	Burlington	.95	.94
056	Montpelier	.94	.93
057	Rutland	.94	.93
058	St. Johnsbury	.91	.90
059	Guildhall	.91	.89
VIRGINIA			
220-221	Fairfax	1.02	.93
222	Arlington	1.04	.94
223	Alexandria	1.06	.94
224-225	Fredericksburg	1.02	.92
226	Winchester	1.01	.92
227	Culpeper	1.02	.91
228	Harrisonburg	.87	.86
229	Charlottesville	.90	.85
230-232	Richmond	.96	.87
233-235	Norfolk	.98	.86
236	Newport News	.97	.86
237	Portsmouth	.91	.85
238	Petersburg	.94	.86
239	Farmville	.85	.79
240-241	Roanoke	.96	.85
242	Bristol	.84	.80
243	Pulaski	.84	.81
244	Staunton	.87	.83
245	Lynchburg	.93	.85
246	Grundy	.81	.79
WASHINGTON			
980-981,987	Seattle	1.02	1.04
982	Everett	1.04	1.01
983-984	Tacoma	1.01	1.01
985	Olympia	.99	1.01
986	Vancouver	.97	.99
988	Wenatchee	.94	.96
989	Yakima	.98	.99
990-992	Spokane	.97	.94
993	Richland	.97	.97
994	Clarkston	.92	.92
WEST VIRGINIA			
247-248	Bluefield	.94	.95
249	Lewisburg	.93	.95
250-253	Charleston	.97	.97
254	Martinsburg	.89	.93
255-257	Huntington	.98	.98
258-259	Beckley	.93	.95
260	Wheeling	.95	.97
261	Parkersburg	.93	.96
262	Buckhannon	.94	.96
263-264	Clarksburg	.94	.97
265	Morgantown	.94	.96
266	Gassaway	.94	.96
267	Romney	.93	.95
268	Petersburg	.94	.95
WISCONSIN			
530,532	Milwaukee	1.08	1.04
531	Kenosha	1.03	1.01
534	Racine	1.02	1.01
535	Beloit	1.01	1.01
537	Madison	.99	1.00
538	Lancaster	.97	.96
539	Portage	.97	.97
540	New Richmond	.99	.96
541-543	Green Bay	1.02	.98
544	Wausau	.96	.95
545	Rhinelander	.96	.96
546	La Crosse	.96	.96
547	Eau Claire	.99	.98
548	Superior	.97	.97
549	Oshkosh	.96	.95
WYOMING			
820	Cheyenne	.80	.85
821	Yellowstone Nat. Pk.	.80	.84
822	Wheatland	.77	.84

STATE/ZIP	CITY	Residential	Commercial
WYOMING (CONT'd)			
823	Rawlins	.81	.86
824	Worland	.80	.83
825	Riverton	.80	.84
826	Casper	.75	.83
827	Newcastle	.81	.85
828	Sheridan	.80	.85
829-831	Rock Springs	.84	.86
CANADIAN FACTORS (reflect Canadian currency)			
ALBERTA			
	Calgary	1.13	1.12
	Edmonton	1.12	1.12
	Fort McMurray	1.14	1.11
	Lethbridge	1.12	1.08
	Lloydminster	1.07	1.04
	Medicine Hat	1.07	1.03
	Red Deer	1.07	1.04
BRITISH COLUMBIA			
	Kamloops	1.05	1.05
	Prince George	1.05	1.05
	Vancouver	1.07	1.09
	Victoria	1.05	1.04
MANITOBA			
	Brandon	1.06	1.01
	Portage la Prairie	1.02	.97
	Winnipeg	1.00	1.01
NEW BRUNSWICK			
	Bathurst	.95	.93
	Dalhousie	.95	.93
	Fredericton	1.00	.99
	Moncton	.96	.95
	Newcastle	.95	.94
	St. John	1.03	.99
NEWFOUNDLAND			
	Corner Brook	.99	.99
	St Johns	1.04	1.04
NORTHWEST TERRITORIES			
	Yellowknife	1.09	1.10
NOVA SCOTIA			
	Bridgewater	.98	.97
	Dartmouth	1.00	1.01
	Halifax	1.01	1.03
	New Glasgow	1.00	1.00
	Sydney	.99	.98
	Truro	.97	.97
	Yarmouth	1.00	1.00
ONTARIO			
	Barrie	1.14	1.08
	Brantford	1.15	1.08
	Cornwall	1.14	1.07
	Hamilton	1.12	1.09
	Kingston	1.14	1.07
	Kitchener	1.07	1.03
	London	1.10	1.08
	North Bay	1.15	1.09
	Oshawa	1.13	1.07
	Ottawa	1.11	1.08
	Owen Sound	1.13	1.07
	Peterborough	1.12	1.07
	Sarnia	1.15	1.08
	Sault Ste Marie	1.07	1.03
	St. Catharines	1.09	1.02
	Sudbury	1.06	1.02
	Thunder Bay	1.11	1.03
	Timmins	1.11	1.06
	Toronto	1.13	1.11
	Windsor	1.10	1.02
PRINCE EDWARD ISLAND			
	Charlottetown	.92	.96
	Summerside	.94	.95
QUEBEC			
	Cap-de-la-Madeleine	1.13	1.03
	Charlesbourg	1.13	1.03
	Chicoutimi	1.15	1.04
	Gatineau	1.13	1.02

Location Factors

STATE/ZIP	CITY	Residential	Commercial
QUEBEC (CONT'D)			
	Granby	1.13	
	Hull	1.13	1.02
	Joliette	1.13	1.03
	Laval	1.13	1.02
	Montreal	1.14	1.08
	Quebec	1.13	1.07
	Rimouski	1.15	1.04
	Rouyn-Noranda	1.13	1.02
	Saint Hyacinthe	1.13	1.02
	Sherbrooke	1.13	1.03
	Sorel	1.13	1.03
	St Jerome	1.13	1.02
	Trois Rivieres	1.17	1.06
SASKATCHEWAN			
	Moose Jaw	.95	.94
	Prince Albert	.93	.92
	Regina	1.07	1.06
	Saskatoon	1.05	1.01
YUKON			
	Whitehorse	.98	1.02

Historical Cost Indexes

The following tables are the estimated Historical Cost Indexes based on a 30-city national average with a base of 100 on January 1, 1993.

The indexes may be used to:

1. Estimate and compare construction costs for different years in the same city.

2. Estimate and compare construction costs in different cities for the same year.

3. Estimate and compare construction costs in different cities for different years.

4. Compare construction trends in any city with the national average.

EXAMPLES

1. Estimate and compare construction costs for different years in the same city.

A. To estimate the construction cost of a building in Lexington, KY in 1970, knowing that it cost $915,000 in 2014.

Index Lexington, KY in 1970 = 26.9
Index Lexington, KY in 2014 = 183.7

$$\frac{Index\ 1970}{Index\ 2014} \quad x \quad Cost\ 2014 \quad = \quad Cost\ 1970$$

$$\frac{26.9}{183.7} \quad x \quad \$915,000 \quad = \quad \$134,000$$

Construction Cost in Lexington, KY in 1970 = $134,000

B. To estimate the current construction cost of a building in Boston, MA that was built in 1980 for $900,000.

Index Boston, MA in 1980 = 64.0
Index Boston, MA in 2014 = 238.0

$$\frac{Index\ 2014}{Index\ 1980} \quad x \quad Cost\ 1980 \quad = \quad Cost\ 2014$$

$$\frac{238.0}{64.0} \quad x \quad \$900,000 \quad = \quad \$3,347,000$$

Construction Cost in Boston in 2014 = $3,347,000

2. Estimate and compare construction costs in different cities for the same year.

To compare the construction cost of a building in Topeka, KS in 2014 with the known cost of $800,000 in Baltimore, MD in 2014

Index Topeka, KS in 2014 = 172.4
Index Baltimore, MD in 2014 = 187.8

$$\frac{Index\ Topeka}{Index\ Baltimore} \quad x \quad Cost\ Baltimore \quad = \quad Cost\ Topeka$$

$$\frac{172.4}{187.8} \quad x \quad \$800,000 \quad = \quad \$734,500$$

Construction Cost in Topeka in 2014 = $734,500

3. Estimate and compare construction costs in different cities for different years.

To compare the construction cost of a building in Detroit, MI in 2014 with the known construction cost of $5,000,000 for the same building in San Francisco, CA in 1980.

Index Detroit, MI in 2014 = 208.0
Index San Francisco, CA in 1980 = 75.2

$$\frac{Index\ Detroit\ 2014}{Index\ San\ Francisco\ 1980} \quad x \quad Cost\ San\ Francisco\ 1980 = Cost\ Detroit\ 2014$$

$$\frac{208.0}{75.2} \quad x \quad \$5,000,000 \quad = \quad \$13,830,000$$

Construction Cost in Detroit in 2014 = $13,830,000

4. Compare construction trends in any city with the national average.

To compare the construction cost in Las Vegas, NV from 1975 to 2014 with the increase in the National Average during the same time period.

Index Las Vegas, NV for 1975 = 42.8   For 2014 = 211.1
Index 30 City Average for 1975 = 43.7   For 2014 = 202.7

A. National Average escalation = $\frac{Index\ -\ 30\ City\ 2014}{Index\ -\ 30\ City\ 1975}$
From 1975 to 2014

$$= \frac{202.7}{43.7}$$

National Average escalation
From 1975 to 2014 = 4.64 or increased by 464%

B. Escalation for Las Vegas, NV = $\frac{Index\ Las\ Vegas,\ NV\ 2014}{Index\ Las\ Vegas,\ NV\ 1975}$
From 1975 to 2014

$$= \frac{211.1}{42.8}$$

Las Vegas escalation
From 1975 to 2014 = 4.93 or increased by 493%

Conclusion: Construction costs in Las Vegas are higher than National average costs and increased at a greater rate from 1975 to 2014 than the National Average.

Historical Cost Indexes

Year	National 30 City Average	Alabama Birming-ham	Hunts-ville	Mobile	Mont-gomery	Tusca-loosa	Alaska Anchor-age	Arizona Phoenix	Tuscon	Arkansas Fort Smith	Little Rock	California Anaheim	Bakers-field	Fresno	Los Angeles	Oxnard
Jan 2014	202.7E	177.0E	173.2E	170.1E	163.2E	165.3E	239.7E	179.7E	176.3E	165.1E	168.4E	212.4E	212.4E	214.9E	216.9E	214.1E
2013	196.9	173.3	168.7	165.7	158.7	161.6	235.3	174.1	169.2	161.2	163.2	207.0	205.6	210.3	210.7	207.8
2012	194.0	169.1	162.7	163.2	153.8	154.6	232.5	172.2	166.4	158.7	161.0	204.1	202.9	207.3	207.2	204.7
2011	185.7	163.0	156.3	156.9	147.6	148.3	225.1	163.8	159.5	152.0	154.1	196.1	194.6	199.8	199.2	197.0
2010	181.6	159.6	152.9	153.1	144.4	144.9	218.3	160.7	157.3	150.3	152.5	192.8	190.8	195.0	194.9	192.8
2009	182.5	162.7	157.2	155.6	148.8	149.4	222.9	161.3	156.8	149.2	156.3	194.5	192.3	195.0	196.6	194.5
2008	171.0	150.3	146.9	143.7	138.4	138.8	210.8	152.2	148.4	138.6	145.4	182.7	179.8	183.2	184.7	182.6
2007	165.0	146.9	143.3	140.3	134.8	135.4	206.8	147.7	143.1	134.8	141.7	175.1	173.7	176.7	177.5	176.2
2006	156.2	135.7	133.6	126.7	124.0	122.2	196.4	137.9	134.8	123.2	127.2	166.8	164.9	169.8	167.3	167.4
2005	146.7	127.9	125.4	119.3	116.6	114.6	185.6	128.5	124.1	115.4	119.4	156.5	153.0	157.9	157.1	156.4
2004	132.8	115.9	112.9	107.0	104.9	102.9	167.0	116.5	113.6	103.8	108.6	142.1	139.5	143.8	142.0	140.9
2003	129.7	113.1	110.7	104.8E	102.6E	100.8E	163.5E	113.9E	110.6	101.8E	105.8E	139.4	137.2	142.1	139.6	138.7
2002	126.7	110.0	103.4	103.6	101.7	99.7	159.5	113.3	110.2	100.4	102.1	136.5	133.4	136.0	136.4	136.3
2001	122.2	106.0	100.5	100.6	98.3	95.9	152.6	109.0	106.4	97.3	98.7	132.5	129.3	132.8	132.4	132.4
2000	118.9	104.1	98.9	99.1	94.2	94.6	148.3	106.9	104.9	94.4	95.7	129.4	125.2	129.4	129.9	129.7
1999	116.6	101.2	97.4	97.7	92.5	92.8	145.9	105.5	103.3	93.1	94.4	127.9	123.6	126.9	128.7	128.2
1998	113.6	96.2	94.0	94.8	90.3	89.8	143.8	102.1	101.0	90.6	91.4	125.2	120.3	123.9	125.8	124.7
1997	111.5	94.6	92.4	93.3	88.8	88.3	142.0	101.8	100.7	89.3	90.1	124.0	119.1	122.3	124.6	123.5
1996	108.9	90.9	91.4	92.3	87.5	86.5	140.4	98.3	97.4	86.5	86.7	121.7	117.2	120.2	122.4	121.5
1995	105.6	87.8	88.0	88.8	84.5	83.5	138.0	96.1	95.5	85.0	85.6	120.1	115.7	117.5	120.9	120.0
1994	103.0	85.9	86.1	86.8	82.6	81.7	134.0	93.7	93.1	82.4	83.9	118.1	113.6	114.5	119.0	117.5
1990	93.2	79.4	77.6	82.7	78.4	75.2	125.8	86.4	87.0	77.1	77.9	107.7	102.7	103.3	107.5	107.4
1985	81.8	71.1	70.5	72.7	70.9	67.9	116.0	78.1	77.7	69.6	71.0	95.4	92.2	92.6	94.6	96.6
1980	60.7	55.2	54.1	56.8	56.8	54.0	91.4	63.7	62.4	53.1	55.8	68.7	69.4	68.7	67.4	69.9
1975	43.7	40.0	40.9	41.8	40.1	37.8	57.3	44.5	45.2	39.0	38.7	47.6	46.6	47.7	48.3	47.0
1970	27.8	24.1	25.1	25.8	25.4	24.2	43.0	27.2	28.5	24.3	22.3	31.0	30.8	31.1	29.0	31.0
1965	21.5	19.6	19.3	19.6	19.5	18.7	34.9	21.8	22.0	18.7	18.5	23.9	23.7	24.0	22.7	23.9
1960	19.5	17.9	17.5	17.8	17.7	16.9	31.7	19.9	20.0	17.0	16.8	21.7	21.5	21.8	20.6	21.7
1955	16.3	14.8	14.7	14.9	14.9	14.2	26.6	16.7	16.7	14.3	14.5	18.2	18.1	18.3	17.3	18.2
1950	13.5	12.2	12.1	12.3	12.3	11.7	21.9	13.8	13.8	11.8	11.6	15.1	15.0	15.1	14.3	15.1
1945	8.6	7.8	7.7	7.8	7.8	7.5	14.0	8.8	8.8	7.5	7.4	9.6	9.5	9.6	9.1	9.6
1940	6.6	6.0	6.0	6.1	6.0	5.8	10.8	6.8	6.8	5.8	5.7	7.4	7.4	7.4	7.0	7.4

Year	National 30 City Average	California River-side	Sacra-mento	San Diego	San Francisco	Santa Barbara	Stockton	Vallejo	Colorado Colorado Springs	Denver	Pueblo	Connecticut Bridge-Port	Bristol	Hartford	New Britain	New Haven
Jan 2014	202.7E	213.2E	220.5E	210.3E	247.4E	213.7E	216.9E	226.7E	185.8E	188.8E	184.8E	222.5E	222.0E	223.2E	221.5E	223.3E
2013	196.9	207.0	215.0	203.2	241.0	207.9	211.8	222.2	180.7	183.4	180.0	217.8	217.2	218.4	216.8	218.5
2012	194.0	204.1	211.9	198.9	237.6	204.8	208.8	218.9	179.4	182.2	177.9	213.9	213.3	214.4	212.9	214.7
2011	185.7	195.8	203.1	192.3	227.9	196.2	201.3	210.3	171.7	174.1	170.7	205.2	204.2	205.1	203.9	205.8
2010	181.6	192.7	196.7	188.2	223.0	192.9	195.9	204.6	170.5	172.6	168.1	198.8	199.1	199.8	198.8	200.7
2009	182.5	193.1	198.1	191.6	224.9	193.6	194.5	202.7	168.4	172.0	166.7	199.0	197.7	198.7	197.4	199.3
2008	171.0	181.3	186.0	179.9	210.6	181.5	183.2	191.6	158.8	161.9	157.9	185.8	184.8	185.7	184.5	186.1
2007	165.0	174.7	179.1	173.6	201.1	175.2	178.2	185.9	152.6	155.9	152.3	179.6	178.3	179.6	178.0	179.5
2006	156.2	166.0	172.2	164.0	191.2	166.4	171.0	177.9	146.1	149.2	145.0	169.5	168.0	169.5	167.7	169.8
2005	146.7	155.4	161.1	153.8	179.7	155.7	160.0	167.2	138.3	141.1	136.4	160.8	159.4	159.6	159.1	160.8
2004	132.8	141.0	147.2	139.0	163.6	141.4	144.2	148.6	125.6	127.2	123.5	143.6	142.9	142.4	142.7	144.3
2003	129.7	138.7	144.9	136.6	162.1	139.2	141.8	146.4	123.1	123.7	120.7	141.3	140.2	140.3	140.0	141.6
2002	126.7	135.3	138.4	134.2	157.9	135.9	136.9	143.8	118.7	121.3	116.7	133.8	133.6	133.1	133.3	134.8
2001	122.2	131.4	135.5	129.7	151.8	131.5	134.1	140.2	113.3	117.2	113.1	128.6	128.5	128.5	128.3	128.6
2000	118.9	128.0	131.5	127.1	146.9	128.7	130.7	137.1	109.8	111.8	108.8	122.7	122.6	122.9	122.4	122.7
1999	116.6	126.5	129.4	124.9	145.1	127.2	127.9	135.3	107.0	109.1	107.1	121.1	121.3	121.2	121.1	121.3
1998	113.6	123.7	125.9	121.3	141.9	123.7	124.7	132.5	103.3	106.5	103.7	119.1	119.4	120.0	119.7	120.0
1997	111.5	122.6	124.7	120.3	139.2	122.4	123.3	130.6	101.1	104.4	102.0	119.2	119.5	119.9	119.7	120.0
1996	108.9	120.6	122.4	118.4	136.8	120.5	121.4	128.1	98.5	101.4	99.7	117.4	117.6	117.9	117.8	118.1
1995	105.6	119.2	119.5	115.4	133.8	119.0	119.0	122.5	96.1	98.9	96.8	116.0	116.5	116.9	116.3	116.5
1994	103.0	116.6	114.8	113.4	131.4	116.4	115.5	119.7	94.2	95.9	94.6	114.3	115.0	115.3	114.7	114.8
1990	93.2	107.0	104.9	105.6	121.8	106.4	105.4	111.4	86.9	88.8	88.8	96.3	95.9	96.6	95.9	96.5
1985	81.8	94.8	92.2	94.2	106.2	93.2	93.7	97.0	79.6	81.0	80.4	86.1	86.2	87.2	86.1	86.3
1980	60.7	68.7	71.3	68.1	75.2	71.1	71.2	71.9	60.7	60.9	59.5	61.5	60.7	61.9	60.7	61.4
1975	43.7	47.3	49.1	47.7	49.8	46.1	47.6	46.5	43.1	42.7	42.5	45.2	45.5	46.0	45.2	46.0
1970	27.8	31.0	32.1	30.7	31.6	31.3	31.8	31.8	27.6	26.1	27.3	29.2	28.2	29.6	28.2	29.3
1965	21.5	23.9	24.8	24.0	23.7	24.1	24.5	24.5	21.3	20.9	21.0	22.4	21.7	22.6	21.7	23.2
1960	19.5	21.7	22.5	21.7	21.5	21.9	22.3	22.2	19.3	19.0	19.1	20.0	19.8	20.0	19.8	20.0
1955	16.3	18.2	18.9	18.2	18.0	18.4	18.7	18.6	16.2	15.9	16.0	16.8	16.6	16.8	16.6	16.8
1950	13.5	15.0	15.0	15.0	14.9	15.2	15.4	15.4	13.4	13.2	13.2	13.9	13.7	13.8	13.7	13.9
1945	8.6	9.6	10.0	9.6	9.5	9.7	9.9	9.8	8.5	8.4	8.4	8.8	8.7	8.8	8.7	8.9
1940	6.6	7.4	7.7	7.4	7.3	7.5	7.6	7.6	6.6	6.5	6.5	6.8	6.8	6.8	6.8	6.8

Historical Cost Indexes

Year	National 30 City Average	Connecticut			Delaware	D.C.	Florida						Georgia			
		Norwalk	Stamford	Water-bury	Wilming-ton	Washing-ton	Fort Lau-derdale	Jackson-ville	Miami	Orlando	Talla-hassee	Tampa	Albany	Atlanta	Colum-bus	Macon
Jan 2014	202.7E	228.0E	229.0E	222.0E	208.6E	196.6E	175.8E	171.0E	178.1E	177.2E	164.1E	183.6E	166.7E	177.3E	170.2E	168.2E
2013	196.9	223.1	224.2	217.3	203.6	191.7	173.2	168.4	175.8	174.8	160.8	180.2	163.2	173.3	166.7	164.9
2012	194.0	219.8	220.0	213.4	201.0	189.6	170.9	165.8	173.7	172.8	158.5	177.8	158.3	170.7	160.6	159.3
2011	185.7	211.0	211.2	204.6	193.3	182.3	164.4	159.4	167.0	166.1	151.7	171.4	151.8	164.0	154.3	152.7
2010	181.6	198.3	203.8	199.4	187.7	179.0	160.3	155.4	163.3	162.5	148.1	167.5	148.3	160.1	150.9	149.4
2009	182.5	198.8	204.3	198.4	188.9	181.4	160.7	152.0	165.2	163.9	145.1	165.1	152.0	164.5	155.6	153.5
2008	171.0	185.2	189.2	185.3	177.5	170.4	149.6	142.5	152.9	153.0	135.3	155.6	140.4	153.2	143.9	142.5
2007	165.0	178.6	183.3	179.1	173.4	163.1	145.6	139.0	148.9	148.1	131.7	152.0	135.8	148.0	140.1	138.1
2006	156.2	169.7	173.7	169.1	158.3	153.0	136.0	126.5	136.7	134.3	118.4	136.6	123.6	139.9	126.3	124.3
2005	146.7	160.9	164.1	160.5	149.6	142.7	126.0	119.2	127.1	126.0	110.7	127.7	115.7	131.7	118.9	116.1
2004	132.8	143.6	146.5	143.2	136.1	126.8	114.8	107.8	115.6	113.2	100.6	116.6	102.8	119.6	102.0	105.0
2003	129.7	140.6	145.1	140.8	133.0	124.6	109.0	105.6	110.5	107.8	98.0	103.5	100.5	115.8	99.1	102.7
2002	126.7	133.5	136.2	133.9	129.4	120.3	107.1	104.6	107.4	106.7	97.3	102.8	99.7	113.0	98.3	101.9
2001	122.2	128.2	131.5	128.8	124.8	115.9	104.3	100.8	104.6	103.8	94.8	100.3	96.4	109.1	95.5	99.0
2000	118.9	121.5	126.4	123.2	117.4	113.8	102.4	99.0	101.8	101.2	93.6	98.9	94.9	106.1	94.1	97.0
1999	116.6	120.0	122.0	121.2	116.6	111.5	101.4	98.0	100.8	100.1	92.5	97.9	93.5	102.9	92.8	95.8
1998	113.6	118.8	120.8	120.1	112.3	109.6	99.4	96.2	99.0	98.4	90.9	96.3	91.4	100.8	90.4	93.3
1997	111.5	118.9	120.9	120.2	110.7	106.4	98.6	95.4	98.2	97.2	89.9	95.5	89.9	98.5	88.7	91.6
1996	108.9	117.0	119.0	118.4	108.6	105.4	95.9	92.6	95.9	95.1	88.0	93.6	86.6	94.3	83.9	88.3
1995	105.6	115.5	117.9	117.3	106.1	102.3	94.0	90.9	93.7	93.5	86.5	92.2	85.0	92.0	82.6	86.8
1994	103.0	113.9	116.4	115.8	105.0	99.6	92.2	88.9	91.8	91.5	84.5	90.2	82.3	89.6	80.6	83.7
1990	93.2	96.3	98.9	95.1	92.5	90.4	83.9	81.1	84.0	82.9	78.4	85.0	75.0	80.4	74.0	76.9
1985	81.8	85.3	86.8	85.6	81.1	78.8	76.7	73.4	78.3	73.9	70.6	77.3	66.9	70.3	66.1	68.1
1980	60.7	60.7	60.9	62.3	58.5	59.6	55.3	55.8	56.5	56.7	53.5	57.2	51.7	54.0	51.1	51.3
1975	43.7	44.7	45.0	46.3	42.9	43.7	42.1	40.3	43.2	41.5	38.1	41.3	37.5	38.4	36.2	36.5
1970	27.8	28.1	28.2	28.9	27.0	26.3	25.7	22.8	27.0	26.2	24.5	24.2	23.8	25.2	22.8	23.4
1965	21.5	21.6	21.7	22.2	20.9	21.8	19.8	17.4	19.3	20.2	18.9	18.6	18.3	19.8	17.6	18.0
1960	19.5	19.7	19.7	20.2	18.9	19.4	18.0	15.8	17.6	18.3	17.2	16.9	16.7	17.1	16.0	16.4
1955	16.3	16.5	16.5	17.0	15.9	16.3	15.1	13.2	14.7	15.4	14.4	14.1	14.0	14.4	13.4	13.7
1950	13.5	13.6	13.7	14.0	13.1	13.4	12.5	11.0	12.2	12.7	11.9	11.7	11.5	11.9	11.0	11.3
1945	8.6	8.7	8.7	8.9	8.4	8.6	7.9	7.0	7.8	8.1	7.6	7.5	7.4	7.6	7.0	7.2
1940	6.6	6.7	6.7	6.9	6.4	6.6	6.1	5.4	6.0	6.2	5.8	5.7	5.7	5.8	5.5	5.6

Year	National 30 City Average	Georgia Savan-nah	Hawaii Hono-lulu	Idaho		Illinois						Indiana				
				Boise	Poca-tello	Chicago	Decatur	Joliet	Peoria	Rock-ford	Spring-field	Ander-son	Evans-ville	Fort Wayne	Gary	Indian-apolis
Jan 2014	202.7E	167.3E	237.6E	183.9E	184.5E	237.8E	205.8E	236.3E	211.7E	221.7E	207.8E	182.3E	186.7E	179.7E	207.8E	187.3E
2013	196.9	163.5	231.5	179.6	179.9	231.1	200.8	228.7	207.2	217.2	203.2	177.8	182.5	175.9	203.6	182.7
2012	194.0	158.9	227.9	170.4	171.5	226.2	195.7	222.7	199.7	211.8	197.2	175.2	177.8	171.8	197.9	180.6
2011	185.7	151.7	219.0	162.8	163.6	217.6	187.9	216.8	193.4	205.8	189.4	168.4	169.7	165.0	191.0	173.0
2010	181.6	147.9	214.6	161.7	162.4	210.6	181.2	208.3	186.2	197.6	182.2	162.8	165.9	160.0	183.7	168.1
2009	182.5	152.8	218.6	162.6	163.4	209.0	182.2	205.9	186.2	196.5	184.0	164.9	166.9	163.0	185.2	170.3
2008	171.0	141.1	205.5	153.2	152.8	195.7	168.7	185.5	172.2	180.2	168.5	152.4	155.8	151.0	169.0	159.2
2007	165.0	136.9	200.4	148.0	148.1	186.5	160.5	177.7	166.0	175.0	159.2	149.0	152.6	147.7	165.4	154.1
2006	156.2	124.0	191.9	141.6	141.2	177.8	153.8	168.7	155.2	163.3	152.8	139.8	144.4	139.1	154.5	144.6
2005	146.7	116.9	181.2	133.8	132.5	164.4	145.0	158.3	146.5	151.2	145.4	131.4	136.2	131.0	146.4	137.4
2004	132.8	105.6	161.2	122.0	120.5	149.3	129.3	145.1	133.9	138.1	130.3	120.9	123.5	120.1	132.2	125.0
2003	129.7	103.0	159.4	120.2	118.7	146.2	127.4	143.5	132.4	137.3	128.4	119.7	121.4	118.2	131.4	122.5
2002	126.7	102.0	157.2	118.3	117.1	141.2	123.8	138.5	129.6	132.9	125.3	117.5	119.0	116.4	129.1	120.5
2001	122.2	99.0	150.0	114.3	113.4	135.8	120.1	133.7	124.3	127.8	119.8	113.4	115.6	112.1	123.4	116.4
2000	118.9	97.5	144.8	112.9	112.1	131.2	115.1	124.6	119.0	122.2	116.2	109.8	111.5	108.4	117.8	113.2
1999	116.6	96.0	143.0	110.2	109.6	129.6	113.0	122.6	116.4	120.7	113.8	107.1	109.3	106.8	112.8	110.6
1998	113.6	93.7	140.4	107.4	107.0	125.2	110.1	119.8	113.8	115.5	111.1	105.0	107.2	104.5	111.1	108.0
1997	111.5	92.0	139.8	104.6	104.7	121.3	107.8	117.5	111.5	113.1	108.9	101.9	104.4	101.8	110.3	105.2
1996	108.9	88.6	134.5	102.2	102.1	118.8	106.6	116.2	109.3	111.5	106.5	100.0	102.1	99.9	107.5	102.7
1995	105.6	87.4	130.3	99.5	98.2	114.2	98.5	110.5	102.3	103.6	98.1	96.4	97.2	95.0	100.7	100.1
1994	103.0	85.3	124.0	94.8	95.0	111.3	97.3	108.9	100.9	102.2	97.0	93.6	95.8	93.6	99.1	97.1
1990	93.2	77.9	104.7	88.2	88.1	98.4	90.9	98.4	93.7	94.0	90.1	84.6	89.3	83.4	88.4	87.1
1985	81.8	68.9	94.7	78.0	78.0	82.4	81.9	83.4	83.7	83.0	81.5	75.2	79.8	75.0	77.8	77.1
1980	60.7	52.2	68.9	60.3	59.5	62.8	62.3	63.4	64.5	61.6	61.1	56.5	59.0	56.7	59.8	57.9
1975	43.7	36.9	44.6	40.8	40.5	45.7	43.1	44.5	44.7	42.7	42.4	39.5	41.7	39.9	41.9	40.6
1970	27.8	21.0	30.4	26.7	26.6	29.1	28.0	28.6	29.0	27.5	27.6	25.4	26.4	25.5	27.1	26.2
1965	21.5	16.4	21.8	20.6	20.5	22.7	21.5	22.1	22.4	21.2	21.3	19.5	20.4	19.7	20.8	20.7
1960	19.5	14.9	19.8	18.7	18.6	20.2	19.6	20.0	20.3	19.2	19.3	17.7	18.7	17.9	18.9	18.4
1955	16.3	12.5	16.6	15.7	15.6	16.9	16.4	16.8	17.0	16.1	16.2	14.9	15.7	15.0	15.9	15.5
1950	13.5	10.3	13.7	13.0	12.9	14.0	13.6	13.9	14.0	13.3	13.4	12.3	12.9	12.4	13.1	12.8
1945	8.6	6.6	8.8	8.3	8.2	8.9	8.6	8.9	9.0	8.5	8.6	7.8	8.3	7.9	8.4	8.1
1940	6.6	5.1	6.8	6.4	6.3	6.9	6.7	6.8	6.9	6.5	6.6	6.0	6.4	6.1	6.5	6.3

Historical Cost Indexes

Year	National 30 City Average	Indiana			Iowa					Kansas		Kentucky		Louisiana		
		Muncie	South Bend	Terre Haute	Cedar Rapids	Daven-port	Des Moines	Sioux City	Water-loo	Topeka	Wichita	Lexing-ton	Louis-ville	Baton Rouge	Lake Charles	New Orleans
Jan 2014	202.7E	183.6E	183.7E	186.9E	187.3E	195.0E	187.3E	178.2E	175.1E	172.4E	171.8E	183.7E	186.2E	171.0E	170.2E	177.3E
2013	196.9	179.3	179.3	182.6	183.4	190.8	181.8	173.2	171.3	168.8	167.3	179.1	182.4	166.3	166.2	173.1
2012	194.0	175.8	174.3	178.9	180.3	184.6	179.2	168.8	169.2	162.3	161.4	174.8	177.5	164.4	163.8	171.7
2011	185.7	169.2	168.1	171.3	173.8	178.1	172.7	162.3	162.8	156.3	155.3	167.8	170.8	156.9	156.5	162.1
2010	181.6	163.1	163.5	167.8	170.4	175.6	170.2	159.0	160.2	152.8	151.3	158.7	166.9	153.7	153.4	160.3
2009	182.5	164.5	167.1	168.0	165.9	172.0	162.1	156.3	147.6	154.5	152.4	160.7	167.5	156.9	154.4	161.9
2008	171.0	153.0	153.1	155.9	157.3	163.4	152.4	147.8	139.2	144.9	143.1	152.0	156.8	144.0	141.5	149.3
2007	165.0	149.7	149.5	152.7	152.4	157.6	148.9	144.0	135.0	141.0	138.7	147.6	150.9	139.4	138.0	145.2
2006	156.2	141.2	141.3	144.0	145.8	151.1	142.9	137.3	128.4	134.7	132.9	129.0	143.0	129.4	129.8	135.8
2005	146.7	131.0	133.8	135.2	135.7	142.1	133.5	129.4	120.0	125.9	125.6	121.5	135.1	120.8	117.7	126.2
2004	132.8	120.0	120.6	123.0	122.7	128.6	121.6	116.2	108.3	112.6	113.4	110.1	120.3	105.6	109.0	115.3
2003	129.7	118.7	119.2	121.7	120.9	126.4	120.2	114.6	105.9	109.4	111.3	107.8	118.7	103.3	106.1	112.4
2002	126.7	116.7	117.1	119.9	116.0	122.1	116.7	111.4	103.7	107.8	109.6	106.2	116.4	102.5	105.0	110.6
2001	122.2	112.8	111.6	115.5	112.5	117.5	113.2	107.7	100.6	104.3	105.2	103.3	112.7	99.4	101.3	104.6
2000	118.9	109.1	106.9	110.8	108.8	112.6	108.9	99.0	98.1	101.0	101.1	101.4	109.3	97.8	99.7	102.1
1999	116.6	105.7	103.7	107.9	104.1	109.2	107.6	96.7	96.4	98.7	99.3	99.7	106.6	96.1	97.6	99.5
1998	113.6	103.6	102.3	106.0	102.5	106.8	103.8	95.1	94.8	97.4	97.4	97.4	101.5	94.7	96.1	97.7
1997	111.5	101.3	101.2	104.6	101.2	105.6	102.5	93.8	93.5	96.3	96.2	96.1	99.9	93.3	96.8	96.2
1996	108.9	99.4	99.1	102.1	99.1	102.0	99.1	90.9	90.7	93.6	93.8	94.4	98.3	91.5	94.9	94.3
1995	105.6	95.6	94.6	97.2	95.4	96.6	94.4	88.2	88.9	91.1	91.0	91.6	94.6	89.6	92.7	91.6
1994	103.0	93.2	93.0	95.8	93.0	92.3	92.4	85.9	86.8	89.4	88.1	89.6	92.2	87.7	89.9	89.5
1990	93.2	83.9	85.1	89.1	87.1	86.5	86.9	80.4	80.3	83.2	82.6	82.8	82.6	82.0	84.1	84.5
1985	81.8	75.2	76.0	79.2	75.9	77.6	77.1	72.1	72.3	75.0	74.7	75.5	74.5	74.9	78.5	78.2
1980	60.7	56.1	58.3	59.7	62.7	59.6	61.8	59.3	57.7	58.9	58.0	59.3	59.8	59.1	60.0	57.2
1975	43.7	39.2	40.3	41.9	43.1	41.0	43.1	41.0	40.0	42.0	43.1	42.7	42.5	40.4	40.6	41.5
1970	27.8	25.3	26.2	27.0	28.2	26.9	27.6	26.6	25.9	27.0	25.5	26.9	25.9	25.0	26.7	27.2
1965	21.5	19.5	20.2	20.9	21.7	20.8	21.7	20.5	20.0	20.8	19.6	20.7	20.3	19.4	20.6	20.4
1960	19.5	17.8	18.3	18.9	19.7	18.8	19.5	18.6	18.2	18.9	17.8	18.8	18.4	17.6	18.7	18.5
1955	16.3	14.9	15.4	15.9	16.6	15.8	16.3	15.6	15.2	15.8	15.0	15.8	15.4	14.8	15.7	15.6
1950	13.5	12.3	12.7	13.1	13.7	13.1	13.5	12.9	12.6	13.1	12.4	13.0	12.8	12.2	13.0	12.8
1945	8.6	7.8	8.1	8.4	8.7	8.3	8.6	8.2	8.0	8.3	7.9	8.3	8.1	7.8	8.3	8.2
1940	6.6	6.0	6.3	6.5	6.7	6.4	6.6	6.3	6.2	6.4	6.1	6.4	6.3	6.0	6.4	6.3

Year	National 30 City Average	Louisiana Shreve-port	Maine		Maryland Balti-more	Massachusetts									Wor-cester	Michigan	
			Lewis-ton	Portland		Boston	Brockton	Fall River	Law-rence	Lowell	New Bedford	Pitts-field	Spring-field			Ann Arbor	Dear-born
Jan 2014	202.7E	165.0E	192.9E	195.0E	187.8E	238.0E	226.2E	226.5E	230.0E	228.0E	225.4E	210.6E	211.3E	224.0E	207.7E	207.1E
2013	196.9	159.0	187.9	189.5	183.2	232.9	221.6	221.8	225.3	223.4	221.1	205.9	206.5	219.3	201.2	202.4
2012	194.0	153.2	180.7	182.4	180.8	229.3	217.2	217.8	221.6	219.3	217.0	200.2	201.9	215.2	196.1	199.2
2011	185.7	146.7	167.4	169.1	173.6	219.3	208.2	206.0	211.6	210.1	205.2	191.2	194.5	206.6	186.7	189.4
2010	181.6	145.1	162.1	163.7	168.3	214.3	202.7	200.7	204.9	204.7	200.0	185.9	189.4	201.1	183.3	186.8
2009	182.5	147.6	159.4	161.8	169.1	211.8	199.2	197.6	201.9	201.9	196.9	185.1	187.1	198.2	179.2	186.9
2008	171.0	135.9	149.1	150.9	157.7	198.6	186.4	185.1	188.7	189.1	184.5	171.3	173.7	184.5	169.6	176.4
2007	165.0	132.4	146.4	148.2	152.5	191.8	180.4	179.7	182.0	181.7	179.1	166.8	169.1	180.4	166.8	172.5
2006	156.2	125.2	140.2	139.8	144.9	180.4	171.6	170.4	172.3	173.5	170.4	157.3	159.7	171.6	161.1	165.5
2005	146.7	117.4	131.7	131.4	135.8	169.6	161.3	159.6	162.2	162.3	159.6	147.6	150.7	158.8	147.5	155.8
2004	132.8	105.7	119.8	119.4	121.4	154.1	144.4	143.6	146.4	146.7	143.6	131.9	136.5	143.2	135.9	142.1
2003	129.7	103.9	117.7	117.3	118.1	150.2	139.6	140.6	143.3	143.6	140.5	128.9	133.8	139.0	134.1	139.0
2002	126.7	102.1	117.5	117.1	115.6	145.6	136.0	135.0	136.9	137.3	134.9	124.7	128.3	134.9	131.4	134.3
2001	122.2	98.3	114.6	114.3	111.7	140.9	132.1	131.4	133.1	132.9	131.3	120.3	124.5	130.1	126.8	129.8
2000	118.9	96.2	105.7	105.4	107.7	138.9	129.4	128.4	129.7	130.3	128.3	116.7	121.0	127.3	124.3	125.8
1999	116.6	94.8	105.0	104.7	106.4	136.2	126.7	126.3	127.3	127.4	126.2	115.0	118.8	123.8	117.5	122.7
1998	113.6	92.0	102.8	102.5	104.1	132.8	125.0	124.7	125.0	125.3	124.6	114.2	117.1	122.6	116.0	119.7
1997	111.5	90.1	101.7	101.4	102.2	132.1	124.4	124.7	125.1	125.6	124.7	114.6	117.4	122.9	113.5	117.9
1996	108.9	88.5	99.5	99.2	99.6	128.7	121.6	122.2	121.7	122.1	122.2	112.7	115.0	120.2	112.9	116.2
1995	105.6	86.7	96.8	96.5	96.1	128.6	119.6	117.7	120.5	119.6	117.2	110.7	112.7	114.8	106.1	110.5
1994	103.0	85.0	95.2	94.9	94.4	124.9	114.2	113.7	116.8	116.9	111.6	109.2	111.1	112.9	105.0	109.0
1990	93.2	80.3	88.5	88.6	85.6	110.9	103.7	102.9	105.2	102.8	102.6	98.7	101.4	103.2	93.2	96.5
1985	81.8	73.6	76.7	77.0	72.7	92.8	88.8	88.7	89.4	88.2	88.6	85.0	85.6	86.7	80.1	82.7
1980	60.7	58.7	57.3	58.5	53.6	64.0	63.7	64.1	63.4	62.7	63.1	61.8	62.0	62.3	62.9	64.0
1975	43.7	40.5	41.9	42.1	39.8	46.6	45.8	45.7	46.2	45.7	46.1	45.5	45.8	46.0	44.1	44.9
1970	27.8	26.4	26.5	25.8	25.1	29.2	29.1	29.2	29.1	28.9	29.0	28.6	28.5	28.7	28.5	28.9
1965	21.5	20.3	20.4	19.4	20.2	23.0	22.5	22.5	22.5	22.2	22.4	22.0	22.4	22.1	22.0	22.3
1960	19.5	18.5	18.6	17.6	17.5	20.5	20.4	20.4	20.4	20.2	20.3	20.0	20.1	20.1	20.0	20.2
1955	16.3	15.5	15.6	14.7	14.7	17.2	17.1	17.1	17.1	16.9	17.1	16.8	16.9	16.8	16.7	16.9
1950	13.5	12.8	12.9	12.2	12.1	14.2	14.1	14.1	14.1	14.0	14.1	13.8	14.0	13.9	13.8	14.0
1945	8.6	8.1	8.2	7.8	7.7	9.1	9.0	9.0	9.0	8.9	9.0	8.9	8.9	8.9	8.8	8.9
1940	6.6	6.3	6.3	6.0	6.0	7.0	6.9	7.0	7.0	6.9	6.9	6.8	6.9	6.8	6.8	6.9

Year	National 30 City Average	Michigan						Minnesota			Mississippi		Missouri			
		Detroit	Flint	Grand Rapids	Kala-mazoo	Lansing	Sagi-naw	Duluth	Minne-apolis	Roches-ter	Biloxi	Jackson	Kansas City	St. Joseph	St. Louis	Spring-field
Jan 2014	202.7E	208.0E	195.3E	186.7E	186.6E	194.6E	190.9E	209.0E	220.7E	205.6E	163.9E	169.0E	210.0E	197.6E	208.9E	186.3E
2013	196.9	203.1	190.6	182.4	182.4	190.2	186.5	205.1	216.3	201.4	160.9	164.3	204.7	193.1	202.4	181.6
2012	194.0	200.2	186.3	176.4	178.9	185.9	182.8	203.1	214.7	199.7	157.6	160.5	200.8	189.0	198.0	177.7
2011	185.7	190.3	178.5	169.9	171.9	178.0	174.6	195.7	208.1	193.8	151.4	154.3	191.1	178.8	190.6	168.3
2010	181.6	187.5	176.2	160.6	167.3	175.8	171.9	193.1	203.8	188.9	148.0	151.0	186.1	174.2	185.9	164.3
2009	182.5	187.8	176.0	156.7	166.3	173.7	168.6	191.8	203.1	188.0	152.8	156.6	185.6	172.3	187.2	163.7
2008	171.0	177.0	164.4	140.2	155.7	161.6	158.7	177.4	190.6	175.0	141.8	147.1	175.5	164.2	176.2	152.9
2007	165.0	172.9	161.7	137.2	152.6	158.7	156.1	174.2	184.5	171.4	137.7	131.2	169.0	157.8	170.6	145.3
2006	156.2	165.8	153.8	131.1	146.0	152.5	150.6	166.2	173.9	161.9	123.3	117.1	162.0	152.4	159.3	139.4
2005	146.7	156.2	145.1	123.1	134.9	142.0	140.6	157.3	164.6	152.8	116.0	109.9	151.3	143.1	149.4	131.7
2004	132.8	141.9	129.6	112.8	122.5	129.7	127.6	139.1	150.1	137.0	105.3	99.3	135.1	126.9	135.5	116.3
2003	129.7	138.7	127.9	110.9	120.8	127.7	126.0	136.7	146.5	134.5	101.4	96.7	131.9	124.8	133.3	113.9
2002	126.7	134.2	126.9	107.4	119.9	125.3	124.4	131.9	139.5	130.0	101.0	96.3	128.4	122.7	129.6	112.5
2001	122.2	129.4	122.4	104.3	115.2	120.1	119.7	131.4	136.1	124.9	98.7	93.9	121.8	114.7	125.5	106.7
2000	118.9	125.3	119.8	102.7	111.6	117.6	115.9	124.1	131.1	120.1	97.2	92.9	118.2	111.9	122.4	104.3
1999	116.6	122.6	113.7	100.9	106.1	111.5	110.1	120.3	126.5	117.1	95.7	91.8	114.9	106.1	119.8	101.1
1998	113.6	119.5	112.3	99.7	104.9	110.1	108.7	117.7	124.6	115.5	92.1	89.5	108.2	104.2	115.9	98.9
1997	111.5	117.6	110.8	98.9	104.2	108.7	107.5	115.9	121.9	114.1	90.9	88.3	106.4	102.4	113.2	97.3
1996	108.9	116.0	109.7	93.9	103.5	107.8	106.9	115.0	120.4	113.5	87.1	85.4	103.2	99.9	110.1	94.6
1995	105.6	110.1	104.1	91.1	96.4	98.3	102.3	100.3	111.9	102.5	84.2	83.5	99.7	96.1	106.3	89.5
1994	103.0	108.5	102.9	89.7	95.0	97.1	101.1	99.1	109.3	101.1	82.4	81.7	97.3	92.8	103.2	88.2
1990	93.2	96.0	91.7	84.0	87.4	90.2	88.9	94.3	100.5	95.6	76.4	75.6	89.5	86.8	94.0	82.6
1985	81.8	81.6	80.7	75.8	79.4	80.0	80.5	85.2	87.9	86.5	69.4	68.5	78.2	77.3	80.8	73.2
1980	60.7	62.5	63.1	59.8	61.7	60.3	63.3	63.4	64.1	64.8	54.3	54.3	59.1	60.4	59.7	56.7
1975	43.7	45.8	44.9	41.8	43.7	44.1	44.8	45.2	46.0	45.3	37.9	37.7	42.7	45.4	44.8	41.1
1970	27.8	29.7	28.5	26.7	28.1	27.8	28.7	28.9	29.5	28.9	24.4	21.3	25.3	28.3	28.4	26.0
1965	21.5	22.1	21.9	20.6	21.7	21.5	22.2	22.3	23.4	22.3	18.8	16.4	20.6	21.8	21.8	20.0
1960	19.5	20.1	20.0	18.7	19.7	19.5	20.1	20.3	20.5	20.2	17.1	14.9	19.0	19.8	19.5	18.2
1955	16.3	16.8	16.7	15.7	16.5	16.3	16.9	17.0	17.2	17.0	14.3	12.5	16.0	16.6	16.3	15.2
1950	13.5	13.9	13.8	13.0	13.6	13.5	13.9	14.0	14.2	14.0	11.8	10.3	13.2	13.7	13.5	12.6
1945	8.6	8.9	8.8	8.3	8.7	8.6	8.9	8.9	9.0	8.9	7.6	6.6	8.4	8.8	8.6	8.0
1940	6.6	6.8	6.8	6.4	6.7	6.6	6.9	6.9	7.0	6.9	5.8	5.1	6.5	6.7	6.7	6.2

Year	National 30 City Average	Montana		Nebraska		Nevada		New Hampshire		New Jersey					NM	NY
		Billings	Great Falls	Lincoln	Omaha	Las Vegas	Reno	Man-chester	Nashua	Camden	Jersey City	Newark	Pater-son	Trenton	Albu-querque	Albany
Jan 2014	202.7E	185.3E	186.0E	180.1E	183.8E	211.1E	195.5E	198.9E	197.3E	222.3E	223.3E	227.3E	225.2E	224.2E	178.3E	200.7E
2013	196.9	180.5	181.1	175.5	180.6	206.8	190.4	193.8	192.5	217.7	219.3	223.6	221.2	218.7	173.6	195.3
2012	194.0	178.6	179.5	169.3	177.1	202.6	186.8	189.2	188.3	213.6	215.2	219.2	217.5	213.7	171.0	191.2
2011	185.7	168.8	170.8	162.8	169.6	195.7	179.8	176.8	176.1	205.5	207.0	210.3	209.2	206.4	163.3	180.9
2010	181.6	166.5	168.6	159.3	165.8	193.7	175.6	172.5	172.0	201.2	203.3	206.3	205.3	200.8	162.5	177.8
2009	182.5	165.3	166.0	161.7	165.0	191.5	176.5	174.0	173.5	196.8	200.5	203.6	202.0	198.6	163.0	178.1
2008	171.0	153.1	154.6	152.0	154.8	176.2	167.0	162.5	161.9	184.0	187.3	189.6	188.7	185.6	152.6	166.0
2007	165.0	147.7	147.8	147.7	150.3	166.7	161.4	159.3	158.7	179.3	183.3	185.2	184.6	181.7	146.7	159.4
2006	156.2	140.5	140.8	132.4	140.7	160.0	154.5	146.7	146.4	167.7	171.0	173.6	172.2	169.9	140.1	151.6
2005	146.7	131.9	132.4	124.1	132.8	149.5	145.4	136.8	136.5	159.0	162.4	163.9	163.0	161.5	130.4	142.2
2004	132.8	118.2	117.9	112.1	119.4	137.1	130.5	124.2	123.9	143.4	145.4	147.2	146.6	146.0	118.3	128.6
2003	129.7	115.8	115.8	110.2	117.3	133.8	128.3	122.4	122.2	142.0	144.3	145.7	145.0	143.0	116.4	126.8
2002	126.7	114.6	114.5	108.2	115.0	131.9	126.4	119.9	119.6	135.9	138.5	140.2	140.1	137.6	114.6	122.6
2001	122.2	117.5	117.7	101.3	111.6	127.8	122.5	116.2	116.2	133.4	136.7	136.9	136.8	136.0	111.4	119.2
2000	118.9	113.7	113.9	98.8	107.0	125.8	118.2	111.9	111.9	128.4	130.5	132.6	132.4	130.6	109.0	116.5
1999	116.6	112.1	112.7	96.6	104.8	121.9	114.4	109.6	109.6	125.3	128.8	131.6	129.5	129.6	106.7	114.6
1998	113.6	109.7	109.1	94.9	101.2	118.1	111.4	110.1	110.0	124.3	127.7	128.9	128.5	127.9	103.8	113.0
1997	111.5	107.4	107.6	93.3	99.5	114.6	109.8	108.6	108.6	121.9	125.1	126.4	126.4	125.2	100.8	110.0
1996	108.9	108.0	107.5	91.4	97.4	111.8	108.9	106.5	106.4	119.1	122.5	122.5	123.8	121.8	98.6	108.3
1995	105.6	104.7	104.9	85.6	93.4	108.5	105.0	100.9	100.8	107.0	112.2	111.9	112.1	111.2	96.3	103.6
1994	103.0	100.2	100.7	84.3	91.0	105.3	102.2	97.8	97.7	105.4	110.6	110.1	110.6	108.2	93.4	102.4
1990	93.2	92.9	93.8	78.8	85.0	96.3	94.5	86.3	86.3	93.0	93.5	93.8	97.2	94.5	84.9	93.2
1985	81.8	83.9	84.3	71.5	77.5	87.6	85.0	78.1	78.1	81.3	83.3	83.5	84.5	82.8	76.7	79.5
1980	60.7	63.9	64.6	58.5	63.5	64.6	63.0	56.6	56.0	58.6	60.6	60.1	60.0	58.9	59.0	59.5
1975	43.7	43.1	43.8	40.9	43.2	42.8	41.9	41.3	40.8	42.3	43.4	44.2	43.9	43.8	40.3	43.9
1970	27.8	28.5	28.9	26.4	26.8	29.4	28.0	26.2	25.6	27.2	27.8	29.0	27.8	27.4	26.4	28.3
1965	21.5	22.0	22.3	20.3	20.6	22.4	21.6	20.6	19.7	20.9	21.4	23.8	21.4	21.3	20.6	22.3
1960	19.5	20.0	20.3	18.5	18.7	20.2	19.6	18.0	17.9	19.0	19.4	19.4	19.4	19.2	18.5	19.3
1955	16.3	16.7	17.0	15.5	15.7	16.9	16.4	15.1	15.0	16.0	16.3	16.3	16.3	16.1	15.6	16.2
1950	13.5	13.9	14.0	12.8	13.0	14.0	13.6	12.5	12.4	13.2	13.5	13.5	13.5	13.3	12.9	13.4
1945	8.6	8.8	9.0	8.1	8.3	8.9	8.7	8.0	7.9	8.4	8.6	8.6	8.6	8.5	8.2	8.5
1940	6.6	6.8	6.9	6.3	6.4	6.9	6.7	6.2	6.1	6.5	6.6	6.6	6.6	6.6	6.3	6.6

Year	National 30 City Average	New York								North Carolina					N. Dakota Fargo	Ohio Akron
		Bing-hamton	Buffalo	New York	Roches-ter	Schen-ectady	Syracuse	Utica	Yonkers	Charlotte	Durham	Greens-boro	Raleigh	Winston-Salem		
Jan 2014	202.7E	199.9E	206.0E	265.1E	199.1E	200.1E	198.2E	192.8E	234.9E	163.8E	162.6E	162.7E	161.0E	163.1E	175.7E	196.2E
2013	196.9	195.5	200.7	259.4	194.3	195.5	193.6	188.5	230.0	159.6	158.4	158.7	157.5	159.1	169.6	191.8
2012	194.0	192.9	198.1	256.3	191.2	191.4	189.6	185.2	227.1	156.4	155.6	156.3	155.4	157.2	167.3	187.7
2011	185.7	176.1	188.1	245.6	181.9	181.5	180.8	173.5	218.9	142.6	143.8	142.2	142.8	140.9	160.3	180.8
2010	181.6	173.8	184.0	241.4	179.6	179.0	176.7	170.5	217.1	140.5	141.6	140.0	140.6	138.8	156.2	174.5
2009	182.5	172.9	184.4	239.9	179.6	178.8	176.9	171.3	217.5	145.1	145.8	144.0	145.1	142.7	154.3	175.7
2008	171.0	160.7	173.9	226.8	168.0	167.2	165.9	161.6	202.1	135.8	136.6	134.6	135.3	133.8	145.0	165.4
2007	165.0	155.7	168.6	215.2	163.5	159.8	159.8	155.0	196.5	132.8	133.7	131.7	132.1	131.0	139.8	159.0
2006	156.2	147.5	159.2	204.5	155.2	151.1	150.9	146.4	186.0	125.1	124.6	123.8	124.2	123.0	133.2	152.8
2005	146.7	137.5	149.4	194.0	147.3	142.2	141.9	136.9	176.1	110.5	112.1	112.1	112.1	111.1	125.3	144.4
2004	132.8	123.5	136.1	177.7	132.0	128.4	127.3	124.4	161.8	98.9	100.0	100.1	100.3	99.4	113.0	131.9
2003	129.7	121.8	132.8	173.4	130.3	126.7	124.7	121.7	160.0	96.2	97.5	97.5	97.8	96.8	110.6	129.6
2002	126.7	119.0	128.5	170.1	127.1	123.0	121.8	118.4	154.8	94.8	96.1	96.1	96.3	95.5	106.3	127.2
2001	122.2	116.0	125.2	164.4	123.1	120.1	118.6	115.3	151.4	91.5	92.9	92.9	93.3	92.3	103.1	123.5
2000	118.9	112.4	122.3	159.2	120.0	117.5	115.1	112.4	144.8	90.3	91.6	91.6	91.9	91.0	97.9	117.8
1999	116.6	108.6	120.2	155.9	116.8	114.7	113.7	108.5	140.6	89.3	90.2	90.3	90.5	90.1	96.8	116.0
1998	113.6	109.0	119.1	154.4	117.2	114.2	113.6	108.6	141.4	88.2	89.1	89.2	89.4	89.0	95.2	113.1
1997	111.5	107.2	115.7	150.3	115.2	111.2	110.6	107.0	138.8	86.8	87.7	87.8	87.9	87.6	93.5	110.6
1996	108.9	105.5	114.0	148.0	113.3	109.5	108.2	105.2	137.2	85.0	85.9	86.0	86.1	85.8	91.7	107.9
1995	105.6	99.3	110.1	140.7	106.6	104.6	104.0	97.7	129.4	81.8	82.6	82.6	82.7	82.6	88.4	103.4
1994	103.0	98.1	107.2	137.1	105.2	103.5	102.3	96.5	128.1	80.3	81.1	81.0	81.2	81.1	87.0	102.2
1990	93.2	87.0	94.1	118.1	94.6	93.9	91.0	85.6	111.4	74.8	75.4	75.5	75.5	75.3	81.3	94.6
1985	81.8	77.5	83.2	94.9	81.6	80.1	81.0	77.0	92.8	66.9	67.6	67.7	67.6	67.5	73.4	86.8
1980	60.7	58.0	60.6	66.0	60.5	60.3	61.6	58.5	65.9	51.1	52.2	52.5	51.7	50.8	57.4	62.3
1975	43.7	42.5	45.1	49.5	44.8	43.7	44.8	42.7	47.1	36.1	37.0	37.0	37.3	36.1	39.3	44.7
1970	27.8	27.0	28.9	32.8	29.2	27.8	28.5	26.9	30.0	20.9	23.7	23.6	23.4	23.0	25.8	28.3
1965	21.5	20.8	22.2	25.5	22.8	21.4	21.9	20.7	23.1	16.0	18.2	18.2	18.0	17.7	19.9	21.8
1960	19.5	18.9	19.9	21.5	19.7	19.5	19.9	18.8	21.0	14.4	16.6	16.6	16.4	16.1	18.1	19.9
1955	16.3	15.8	16.7	18.1	16.5	16.3	16.7	15.8	17.6	12.1	13.9	13.9	13.7	13.5	15.2	16.6
1950	13.5	13.1	13.8	14.9	13.6	13.5	13.8	13.0	14.5	10.0	11.5	11.5	11.4	11.2	12.5	13.7
1945	8.6	8.3	8.8	9.5	8.7	8.6	8.8	8.3	9.3	6.4	7.3	7.3	7.2	7.1	8.0	8.8
1940	6.6	6.4	6.8	7.4	6.7	6.7	6.8	6.4	7.2	4.9	5.6	5.6	5.6	5.5	6.2	6.8

Year	National 30 City Average	Ohio									Oklahoma			Oregon		PA
		Canton	Cincin-nati	Cleve-land	Colum-bus	Dayton	Lorain	Spring-field	Toledo	Youngs-town	Lawton	Oklahoma City	Tulsa	Eugene	Port-land	Allen-town
Jan 2014	202.7E	188.2E	186.6E	200.9E	191.9E	184.9E	192.6E	185.8E	198.0E	190.9E	167.2E	169.0E	166.2E	199.2E	200.4E	207.6E
2013	196.9	183.9	181.9	195.5	187.1	180.7	187.6	181.5	193.5	186.5	162.7	165.5	161.7	194.7	195.6	203.2
2012	194.0	180.2	178.6	191.4	183.5	177.6	184.1	178.0	190.4	183.3	158.1	158.0	151.3	190.1	191.8	199.3
2011	185.7	172.1	171.3	184.0	175.7	168.4	176.8	168.4	183.1	176.5	151.7	151.6	144.8	184.9	186.6	192.2
2010	181.6	167.5	166.5	180.2	170.3	163.4	173.0	164.6	176.5	171.7	149.5	149.4	143.1	181.5	182.9	187.9
2009	182.5	168.4	168.1	181.6	171.2	165.3	174.0	166.0	178.5	172.8	152.5	153.3	146.8	181.3	183.6	188.3
2008	171.0	158.4	159.0	170.6	160.2	157.5	163.9	157.5	168.2	161.5	141.3	140.6	136.2	172.3	174.7	175.7
2007	165.0	153.2	152.4	164.9	155.1	149.4	158.1	150.3	161.6	156.7	136.2	135.6	132.5	168.5	169.5	169.4
2006	156.2	147.0	144.9	156.9	146.9	142.9	151.8	143.4	154.5	150.3	129.5	129.5	125.7	160.5	161.7	160.1
2005	146.7	137.7	136.8	147.9	138.0	134.5	143.3	134.8	145.5	141.1	121.6	121.6	117.8	150.9	152.2	150.2
2004	132.8	125.6	124.3	135.6	126.2	121.1	131.5	122.0	132.8	129.3	109.3	109.4	107.3	136.8	137.8	133.9
2003	129.7	123.7	121.3	132.7	123.7	119.4	126.1	120.0	130.4	126.2	107.5	107.8	105.0	134.2	135.9	130.3
2002	126.7	120.9	119.2	130.0	120.9	117.5	124.3	118.0	128.4	123.6	106.3	106.0	104.1	132.2	133.9	128.1
2001	122.2	117.7	115.9	125.9	117.1	114.0	120.4	114.7	123.8	119.9	102.0	102.1	99.7	129.8	131.2	123.5
2000	118.9	112.7	110.1	121.3	112.5	109.0	115.0	109.2	115.7	114.1	98.7	98.9	97.5	126.3	127.4	119.9
1999	116.6	110.6	107.9	118.7	109.5	107.1	112.0	106.4	113.6	111.9	97.5	97.4	96.2	120.9	124.3	117.8
1998	113.6	108.5	105.0	114.8	106.8	104.5	109.4	104.1	111.2	109.0	94.3	94.5	94.5	120.0	122.2	115.7
1997	111.5	106.4	102.9	112.9	104.7	102.6	107.4	102.2	108.5	107.2	92.9	93.2	93.0	118.1	119.6	113.9
1996	108.9	103.2	100.2	110.1	101.1	98.8	103.8	98.4	105.1	104.1	90.9	91.3	91.2	114.4	116.1	112.0
1995	105.6	98.8	97.1	106.4	99.1	94.6	97.1	92.0	100.6	100.1	85.3	88.0	89.0	112.2	114.3	108.3
1994	103.0	97.7	95.0	104.8	95.4	93.0	96.0	90.1	99.3	98.9	84.0	86.5	87.6	107.6	109.2	106.4
1990	93.2	92.1	86.7	95.1	88.1	85.9	89.4	83.4	92.9	91.8	77.1	79.9	80.0	98.0	99.4	95.0
1985	81.8	83.7	78.2	86.2	77.7	76.3	80.7	74.3	84.7	82.7	71.2	73.9	73.8	88.7	90.1	81.9
1980	60.7	60.6	59.8	61.0	58.6	56.6	60.8	56.2	64.0	61.5	52.2	55.5	57.2	68.9	68.4	58.7
1975	43.7	44.0	43.7	44.6	42.2	40.5	42.7	40.0	44.9	44.5	38.6	38.6	39.2	44.6	44.9	42.3
1970	27.8	27.8	28.2	29.6	26.7	27.0	27.5	25.4	29.1	29.6	24.1	23.4	24.1	30.4	30.0	27.3
1965	21.5	21.5	20.7	21.1	20.2	20.0	21.1	19.6	21.3	21.0	18.5	17.8	20.6	23.4	22.6	21.0
1960	19.5	19.5	19.3	19.6	18.7	18.1	19.2	17.8	19.4	19.1	16.9	16.1	18.1	21.2	21.1	19.1
1955	16.3	16.3	16.2	16.5	15.7	15.2	16.1	14.9	16.2	16.0	14.1	13.5	15.1	17.8	17.7	16.0
1950	13.5	13.5	13.3	13.6	13.0	12.5	13.3	12.3	13.4	13.2	11.7	11.2	12.5	14.7	14.6	13.2
1945	8.6	8.6	8.5	8.7	8.3	8.0	8.5	7.8	8.6	8.4	7.4	7.1	8.0	9.4	9.3	8.4
1940	6.6	6.7	6.5	6.7	6.4	6.2	6.5	6.1	6.6	6.5	5.7	5.5	6.1	7.2	7.2	6.5

Historical Cost Indexes

Year	National 30 City Average	Pennsylvania						RI	South Carolina		South Dakota		Tennessee			
		Erie	Harris-burg	Phila-delphia	Pitts-burgh	Reading	Scranton	Provi-dence	Charles-ton	Colum-bia	Rapid City	Sioux Falls	Chatta-nooga	Knox-ville	Memphis	Nash-ville
Jan 2014	202.7E	191.5E	198.1E	230.1E	206.8E	200.3E	199.4E	218.4E	170.4E	161.7E	167.4E	166.1E	171.6E	163.4E	175.5E	177.4E
2013	196.9	187.2	192.5	223.6	201.4	196.1	196.0	213.4	166.3	157.9	159.6	161.2	167.4	159.3	169.3	172.8
2012	194.0	182.0	187.9	221.8	196.8	190.8	191.5	209.3	155.3	148.1	156.7	158.8	163.8	155.8	166.3	167.5
2011	185.7	176.0	180.9	212.8	187.7	184.3	185.3	196.8	149.4	142.3	149.5	151.3	157.3	149.3	158.4	160.7
2010	181.6	171.0	175.2	209.3	182.3	179.8	180.8	192.8	147.4	140.2	147.3	149.0	152.4	144.7	154.2	156.7
2009	182.5	171.9	176.5	209.5	181.7	180.7	181.3	192.9	150.8	144.3	148.2	151.1	155.7	148.0	157.2	159.8
2008	171.0	161.0	165.7	196.2	169.2	169.3	167.9	178.2	142.1	134.8	138.4	141.3	136.7	133.4	146.0	147.5
2007	165.0	156.0	159.4	188.4	163.2	164.9	163.1	174.4	139.3	131.7	129.5	133.0	133.7	130.6	143.1	144.4
2006	156.2	148.7	150.7	177.8	155.5	155.0	153.9	163.6	122.4	118.7	122.8	126.6	127.0	123.9	136.5	135.5
2005	146.7	140.6	141.5	166.4	146.6	145.5	142.9	155.6	110.2	109.6	115.2	118.5	116.0	115.1	128.6	127.9
2004	132.8	127.0	126.2	148.4	133.1	128.7	129.0	138.8	98.9	98.4	103.9	107.3	105.0	104.5	115.6	115.8
2003	129.7	124.5	123.8	145.5	130.5	126.3	126.0	135.9	96.1	95.7	101.3	104.0	102.8	102.3	111.1	110.9
2002	126.7	122.1	121.1	142.0	127.8	123.4	124.2	131.1	94.8	93.9	100.2	103.2	102.2	101.2	107.6	109.2
2001	122.2	118.9	118.4	136.9	124.1	120.4	121.1	127.8	92.1	91.3	96.8	99.7	98.2	96.5	102.6	104.3
2000	118.9	114.6	114.0	132.1	120.9	115.9	117.7	122.8	89.9	89.1	94.2	98.0	96.9	95.0	100.8	100.8
1999	116.6	113.8	112.8	129.8	119.6	114.8	116.3	121.6	89.0	88.1	92.4	95.8	95.9	93.4	99.7	98.6
1998	113.6	109.8	110.5	126.6	117.1	112.5	113.7	120.3	88.0	87.2	90.7	93.6	94.9	92.4	97.2	96.8
1997	111.5	108.5	108.8	123.3	113.9	110.8	112.3	118.9	86.5	85.6	89.3	92.1	93.6	90.8	96.1	94.9
1996	108.9	106.8	105.7	120.3	110.8	108.7	109.9	117.2	84.9	84.1	87.2	90.0	91.6	88.8	94.0	91.9
1995	105.6	99.8	100.6	117.1	106.3	103.6	103.8	111.1	82.7	82.2	84.0	84.7	89.2	86.0	91.2	87.6
1994	103.0	98.2	99.4	115.2	103.7	102.2	102.6	109.6	81.2	80.6	82.7	83.1	87.4	84.1	89.0	84.8
1990	93.2	88.5	89.5	98.5	91.2	90.8	91.3	94.1	73.7	74.5	77.2	78.4	79.9	75.1	81.3	77.1
1985	81.8	79.6	77.2	82.2	81.5	77.7	80.0	83.0	65.9	66.9	69.7	71.2	72.5	67.7	74.3	66.7
1980	60.7	59.4	56.9	58.7	61.3	57.7	58.4	59.2	50.6	51.1	54.8	57.1	55.0	51.6	55.9	53.1
1975	43.7	43.4	42.2	44.5	44.5	43.6	41.9	42.7	35.0	36.4	37.7	39.6	39.1	37.3	40.7	37.0
1970	27.8	27.5	25.8	27.5	28.7	27.1	27.0	27.3	22.8	22.9	24.8	25.8	24.9	22.0	23.0	22.8
1965	21.5	21.1	20.1	21.7	22.4	20.9	20.8	21.9	17.6	17.6	19.1	19.9	19.2	17.1	18.3	17.4
1960	19.5	19.1	18.6	19.4	19.7	19.0	18.9	19.1	16.0	16.0	17.3	18.1	17.4	15.5	16.6	15.8
1955	16.3	16.1	15.6	16.3	16.5	15.9	15.9	16.0	13.4	13.4	14.5	15.1	14.6	13.0	13.9	13.3
1950	13.5	13.3	12.9	13.5	13.6	13.2	13.1	13.2	11.1	11.1	12.0	12.5	12.1	10.7	11.5	10.9
1945	8.6	8.5	8.2	8.6	8.7	8.4	8.3	8.4	7.1	7.1	7.7	8.0	7.7	6.8	7.3	7.0
1940	6.6	6.5	6.3	6.6	6.7	6.4	6.5	6.5	5.4	5.5	5.9	6.2	6.0	5.3	5.6	5.4

Year	National 30 City Average	Texas														Utah
		Abi-lene	Ama-rillo	Austin	Beau-mont	Corpus Christi	Dallas	El Paso	Fort Worth	Houston	Lubbock	Odessa	San Antonio	Waco	Wichita Falls	Ogden
Jan 2014	202.7E	159.7E	165.2E	164.1E	164.6E	161.4E	171.2E	155.8E	168.9E	175.2E	163.8E	158.5E	168.4E	161.6E	160.3E	172.4E
2013	196.9	155.2	161.7	158.7	160.2	157.7	167.4	151.2	161.7	169.4	159.3	151.5	164.3	156.1	155.9	167.7
2012	194.0	152.5	158.6	154.3	158.2	151.8	165.2	149.1	159.4	167.8	156.6	149.1	160.7	153.8	152.9	165.6
2011	185.7	145.9	151.9	147.6	152.4	145.0	157.9	142.5	152.8	160.8	150.0	142.5	152.6	147.3	146.6	158.7
2010	181.6	144.2	150.1	144.7	150.5	142.1	155.1	140.8	149.6	157.3	148.1	140.7	147.9	145.8	145.0	157.5
2009	182.5	143.5	147.3	146.4	149.8	141.7	155.5	141.1	150.1	160.9	144.6	139.1	150.8	146.7	146.1	155.1
2008	171.0	132.4	137.0	137.5	140.3	133.2	144.1	130.7	138.3	149.1	134.7	128.9	141.0	136.1	136.1	144.8
2007	165.0	128.5	132.2	131.6	137.1	128.8	138.6	126.2	134.8	146.0	130.2	125.0	136.4	132.1	132.1	140.0
2006	156.2	121.6	125.7	125.5	130.1	122.0	131.1	120.3	127.6	138.2	123.2	118.3	129.8	125.2	125.3	133.4
2005	146.7	113.8	117.3	117.9	121.3	114.4	123.7	112.5	119.4	129.0	115.5	110.5	121.3	116.1	117.3	126.0
2004	132.8	102.9	106.3	105.7	108.5	102.9	112.0	101.5	108.4	115.9	104.7	99.9	108.4	104.8	105.1	115.2
2003	129.7	100.5	104.4	103.9	106.1	100.4	109.3	99.5	105.5	113.4	102.3	97.6	104.8	102.7	103.0	112.7
2002	126.7	99.9	101.9	102.4	104.5	98.9	107.9	98.7	104.6	111.5	100.5	95.9	103.7	100.5	101.4	110.8
2001	122.2	93.4	98.4	99.8	102.3	96.6	103.8	95.5	100.9	107.8	97.6	93.4	100.5	97.8	97.3	107.7
2000	118.9	93.4	98.1	99.1	101.6	96.9	102.7	92.4	99.9	106.0	97.6	93.4	99.4	97.3	96.9	104.6
1999	116.6	91.8	94.5	96.0	99.7	94.0	101.0	90.7	97.6	104.6	96.0	92.1	98.0	94.8	95.5	103.3
1998	113.6	89.8	92.7	94.2	97.9	91.8	97.9	88.4	94.5	101.3	93.3	90.1	94.8	92.7	92.9	98.5
1997	111.5	88.4	91.3	92.8	96.8	90.3	96.1	87.0	93.3	100.1	91.9	88.8	93.4	91.4	91.5	96.1
1996	108.9	86.8	89.6	90.9	95.3	88.5	94.1	86.7	91.5	97.9	90.2	87.1	92.3	89.7	89.9	94.1
1995	105.6	85.2	87.4	89.3	93.7	87.4	91.4	85.2	89.5	95.9	88.4	85.6	88.9	86.4	86.8	92.2
1994	103.0	83.3	85.5	87.0	91.8	86.4	89.6	82.2	87.4	93.4	87.0	83.9	87.0	84.9	85.4	89.4
1990	93.2	78.0	80.1	81.3	86.5	79.3	84.5	76.7	82.1	85.4	81.5	78.6	80.7	79.6	80.3	83.4
1985	81.8	71.1	72.5	74.5	79.3	72.3	77.6	69.4	75.1	79.6	74.0	71.2	73.9	71.7	73.3	75.2
1980	60.7	53.4	55.2	54.5	57.6	54.5	57.9	53.1	57.0	59.4	55.6	57.2	55.0	54.9	55.4	62.2
1975	43.7	37.6	39.0	39.0	39.6	38.1	40.7	38.0	40.4	41.2	38.9	37.9	39.0	38.6	38.0	40.0
1970	27.8	24.5	24.9	24.9	25.7	24.5	25.5	23.7	25.9	25.4	25.1	24.6	23.3	24.8	24.5	26.8
1965	21.5	18.9	19.2	19.2	19.9	18.9	19.9	19.0	19.9	20.0	19.4	19.0	18.5	19.2	18.9	20.6
1960	19.5	17.1	17.4	17.4	18.1	17.1	18.2	17.0	18.1	18.2	17.6	17.3	16.8	17.4	17.2	18.8
1955	16.3	14.4	14.6	14.6	15.1	14.4	15.3	14.3	15.2	15.2	14.8	14.5	14.1	14.6	14.4	15.7
1950	13.5	11.9	12.1	12.1	12.5	11.9	12.6	11.8	12.5	12.6	12.2	12.0	11.6	12.1	11.9	13.0
1945	8.6	7.6	7.7	7.7	8.0	7.6	8.0	7.5	8.0	8.0	7.8	7.6	7.4	7.7	7.6	8.3
1940	6.6	5.9	5.9	5.9	6.1	5.8	6.2	5.8	6.2	6.2	6.0	5.9	5.7	5.9	5.8	6.4

531

Historical Cost Indexes

Year	National 30 City Average	Utah Salt Lake City	Vermont Burlington	Vermont Rutland	Virginia Alexandria	Virginia Newport News	Virginia Norfolk	Virginia Richmond	Virginia Roanoke	Washington Seattle	Washington Spokane	Washington Tacoma	West Virginia Charleston	West Virginia Huntington	Wisconsin Green Bay	Wisconsin Kenosha
Jan 2014	202.7E	175.8E	190.9E	188.2E	189.6E	173.7E	175.1E	175.7E	172.7E	209.2E	189.8E	204.8E	195.8E	197.8E	198.0E	205.4E
2013	196.9	171.1	178.7	176.6	185.0	170.0	171.5	170.4	168.3	203.4	184.3	199.1	187.2	193.2	193.9	201.2
2012	194.0	168.8	172.4	170.5	182.4	168.3	169.7	169.4	166.4	201.9	181.6	194.3	183.4	186.4	190.0	195.5
2011	185.7	161.8	158.8	157.1	174.5	159.8	161.1	159.0	154.2	194.1	175.5	187.6	177.5	180.3	181.4	187.6
2010	181.6	160.9	156.3	154.6	170.9	156.7	158.0	156.6	151.8	191.8	171.5	186.0	171.6	176.1	179.0	185.1
2009	182.5	160.4	158.3	156.7	172.5	160.0	161.9	160.7	155.6	188.5	173.0	186.3	174.6	177.4	175.5	182.5
2008	171.0	149.7	147.2	145.8	161.8	150.8	150.8	150.9	145.9	176.9	162.4	174.9	162.8	165.7	165.6	172.2
2007	165.0	144.6	144.4	143.2	155.0	146.2	146.1	147.3	142.9	171.4	156.7	168.7	158.7	160.1	159.4	164.8
2006	156.2	137.7	131.7	130.7	146.2	133.7	134.6	134.8	129.7	162.9	150.1	160.7	149.4	151.4	152.7	157.1
2005	146.7	129.4	124.6	123.8	136.5	123.5	124.4	125.4	112.2	153.9	141.9	151.5	140.8	141.0	144.4	148.3
2004	132.8	117.8	113.0	112.3	121.5	108.9	110.2	110.9	99.7	138.0	127.6	134.5	124.8	125.6	128.9	132.4
2003	129.7	116.0	110.7	110.1	119.5	104.8	106.2	108.6	97.0	134.9	125.9	133.0	123.3	123.6	127.4	130.9
2002	126.7	113.7	109.0	108.4	115.1	102.9	104.1	106.6	95.2	132.7	123.9	131.4	121.2	120.9	123.0	127.3
2001	122.2	109.1	105.7	105.2	110.8	99.8	100.3	102.9	92.1	127.9	120.3	125.7	114.6	117.5	119.1	123.6
2000	118.9	106.5	98.9	98.3	108.1	96.5	97.6	100.2	90.7	124.6	118.3	122.9	111.5	114.4	114.6	119.1
1999	116.6	104.5	98.2	97.7	106.1	95.6	96.5	98.8	89.8	123.3	116.7	121.6	110.6	113.4	112.1	115.8
1998	113.6	99.5	97.8	97.3	104.1	93.7	93.9	97.0	88.3	119.4	114.3	118.3	106.7	109.0	109.5	112.9
1997	111.5	97.2	96.6	96.3	101.2	91.6	91.7	92.9	86.9	118.1	111.7	117.2	105.3	107.7	105.6	109.1
1996	108.9	94.9	95.1	94.8	99.7	90.2	90.4	91.6	85.5	115.2	109.2	114.3	103.1	104.8	103.8	106.4
1995	105.6	93.1	91.1	90.8	96.3	86.0	86.4	87.8	82.8	113.7	107.4	112.8	95.8	97.2	97.6	97.9
1994	103.0	90.2	89.5	89.3	93.9	84.6	84.8	86.3	81.4	109.9	104.0	108.3	94.3	95.3	96.3	96.2
1990	93.2	84.3	83.0	82.9	86.1	76.3	76.7	77.6	76.1	100.1	98.5	100.5	86.1	86.8	86.7	87.8
1985	81.8	75.9	74.8	74.9	75.1	68.7	68.8	69.5	67.2	88.3	89.0	91.2	77.7	77.7	76.7	77.4
1980	60.7	57.0	55.3	58.3	57.3	52.5	52.4	54.3	51.3	67.9	66.3	66.7	57.7	58.3	58.6	58.3
1975	43.7	40.1	41.8	43.9	41.7	37.2	36.9	37.1	37.1	44.9	44.4	44.5	41.0	40.0	40.9	40.5
1970	27.8	26.1	25.4	26.8	26.2	23.9	21.5	22.0	23.7	28.8	29.3	29.6	26.1	25.8	26.4	26.5
1965	21.5	20.0	19.8	20.6	20.2	18.4	17.1	17.2	18.3	22.4	22.5	22.8	20.1	19.9	20.3	20.4
1960	19.5	18.4	18.0	18.8	18.4	16.7	15.4	15.6	16.6	20.4	20.8	20.8	18.3	18.1	18.4	18.6
1955	16.3	15.4	15.1	15.7	15.4	14.0	12.9	13.1	13.9	17.1	17.4	17.4	15.4	15.2	15.5	15.6
1950	13.5	12.7	12.4	13.0	12.7	11.6	10.7	10.8	11.5	14.1	14.4	14.4	12.7	12.5	12.8	12.9
1945	8.6	8.1	7.9	8.3	8.1	7.4	6.8	6.9	7.3	9.0	9.2	9.2	8.1	8.0	8.1	8.2
1940	6.6	6.3	6.1	6.4	6.2	5.7	5.3	5.3	5.7	7.0	7.1	7.1	6.2	6.2	6.3	6.3

Year	National 30 City Average	Washington Madison	Washington Milwaukee	Washington Racine	Wyoming Cheyenne	Canada Calgary	Canada Edmonton	Canada Hamilton	Canada London	Canada Montreal	Canada Ottawa	Canada Quebec	Canada Toronto	Canada Vancouver	Canada Winnipeg
Jan 2014	202.7E	201.9E	210.1E	204.6E	172.3E	226.9E	227.3E	220.5E	217.8E	218.7E	217.9E	216.6E	224.9E	220.4E	203.8E
2013	196.9	197.8	204.6	200.5	167.6	222.7	223.3	216.0	213.7	214.5	214.1	212.6	220.9	216.2	200.2
2012	194.0	191.2	202.2	194.9	165.0	219.1	219.6	211.1	208.2	209.6	209.7	207.5	216.6	214.0	200.7
2011	185.7	183.4	191.9	187.0	155.3	212.6	212.4	204.2	200.1	202.1	202.0	200.6	209.6	207.1	192.6
2010	181.6	181.3	187.1	184.4	154.4	200.6	200.7	197.7	193.7	193.9	195.6	192.7	200.7	192.7	182.9
2009	182.5	180.0	187.3	182.8	155.2	205.4	206.6	203.0	198.9	198.8	200.1	197.4	205.6	199.6	188.5
2008	171.0	168.4	176.3	173.0	146.5	190.2	191.0	194.3	188.6	186.7	188.0	186.8	194.6	184.9	174.4
2007	165.0	160.7	168.9	164.7	141.3	183.1	184.4	186.8	182.4	181.7	182.4	182.0	187.7	180.6	170.1
2006	156.2	152.8	158.8	157.2	128.0	163.6	164.8	169.0	164.9	158.6	163.7	159.0	170.6	169.3	155.9
2005	146.7	145.2	148.4	147.9	118.9	154.4	155.7	160.0	156.2	149.2	155.1	150.1	162.6	159.4	146.9
2004	132.8	129.7	134.2	132.7	104.7	138.8	139.4	142.6	140.4	134.5	141.0	135.7	146.0	141.7	129.7
2003	129.7	128.4	131.1	131.5	102.6	133.6	134.2	139.1	137.0	130.2	137.4	131.4	142.3	137.0	124.4
2002	126.7	124.5	128.2	126.5	101.7	122.5	122.2	136.3	134.1	127.2	134.9	128.4	139.8	134.6	121.4
2001	122.2	120.6	123.9	123.3	99.0	117.5	117.4	131.5	129.1	124.4	130.2	125.5	134.7	130.2	117.2
2000	118.9	116.6	120.5	118.7	98.1	115.9	115.8	130.0	127.5	122.8	128.8	124.1	133.1	128.4	115.6
1999	116.6	115.9	117.4	115.5	96.9	115.3	115.2	128.1	125.6	120.8	126.8	121.9	131.2	127.1	115.2
1998	113.6	110.8	113.4	112.7	95.4	112.5	112.4	126.3	123.9	119.0	124.7	119.6	128.5	123.8	113.7
1997	111.5	106.1	110.1	109.3	93.2	110.7	110.6	124.4	121.9	114.6	122.8	115.4	125.7	121.9	111.4
1996	108.9	104.4	107.1	106.5	91.1	109.1	109.0	122.6	120.2	112.9	121.0	113.6	123.9	119.0	109.7
1995	105.6	96.5	103.9	97.8	87.6	107.4	107.4	119.9	117.5	110.8	118.2	111.5	121.6	116.2	107.6
1994	103.0	94.5	100.6	96.1	85.4	106.7	106.6	116.5	114.2	109.5	115.0	110.2	117.8	115.1	105.5
1990	93.2	84.3	88.9	87.3	79.1	98.0	97.1	103.8	101.4	99.0	102.7	96.8	104.6	103.2	95.1
1985	81.8	74.3	77.4	77.0	72.3	90.2	89.1	85.8	84.9	82.4	83.9	79.9	86.5	89.8	83.4
1980	60.7	56.8	58.8	58.1	56.9	64.9	63.3	63.7	61.9	59.2	60.9	59.3	60.9	65.0	61.7
1975	43.7	40.7	43.3	40.7	40.6	42.2	41.6	42.9	41.6	39.7	41.5	39.0	42.2	42.4	39.2
1970	27.8	26.5	29.4	26.5	26.0	28.9	28.6	28.5	27.8	25.6	27.6	26.0	25.6	26.0	23.1
1965	21.5	20.6	21.8	20.4	20.0	22.3	22.0	22.0	21.4	18.7	21.2	20.1	19.4	20.5	17.5
1960	19.5	18.1	19.0	18.6	18.2	20.2	20.0	20.0	19.5	17.0	19.3	18.2	17.6	18.6	15.8
1955	16.3	15.2	15.9	15.6	15.2	17.0	16.8	16.7	16.3	14.3	16.2	15.3	14.8	15.5	13.3
1950	13.5	12.5	13.2	12.9	12.6	14.0	13.9	13.8	13.5	11.8	13.4	12.6	12.2	12.8	10.9
1945	8.6	8.0	8.4	8.2	8.0	9.0	8.8	8.8	8.6	7.5	8.5	8.0	7.8	8.2	7.0
1940	6.6	6.2	6.5	6.3	6.2	6.9	6.8	6.8	6.6	5.8	6.6	6.2	6.0	6.3	5.4

Estimating Tips

- The cost figures in this Square Foot Cost section were derived from approximately 11,000 projects contained in the RSMeans database of completed construction projects. They include the contractor's overhead and profit, but do not generally include architectural fees or land costs. The figures have been adjusted to January of the current year. New projects are added to our files each year, and outdated projects are discarded. For this reason, certain costs may not show a uniform annual progression. In no case are all subdivisions of a project listed.

- These projects were located throughout the U.S. and reflect a tremendous variation in square foot (S.F.) and cubic foot (C.F.) costs. This is due to differences, not only in labor and material costs, but also in individual owners' requirements. For instance, a bank in a large city would have different features than one in a rural area. This is true of all the different types of buildings analyzed. Therefore, caution should be exercised when using these square foot costs. For example, for courthouses, costs in the database are local courthouse costs and will not apply to the larger, more elaborate federal courthouses. As a general rule, the projects in the 1/4 column do not include any site work or equipment, while the projects in the 3/4 column may include both equipment and site work. The median figures do not generally include site work.

- None of the figures "go with" any others. All individual cost items were computed and tabulated separately. Thus, the sum of the median figures for plumbing, HVAC and electrical will not normally total up to the total mechanical and electrical costs arrived at by separate analysis and tabulation of the projects.

- Each building was analyzed as to total and component costs and percentages. The figures were arranged in ascending order with the results tabulated as shown. The 1/4 column shows that 25% of the projects had lower costs and 75% had higher. The 3/4 column shows that 75% of the projects had lower costs and 25% had higher. The median column shows that 50% of the projects had lower costs and 50% had higher.

- There are two times when square foot costs are useful. The first is in the conceptual stage when no details are available. Then square foot costs make a useful starting point. The second is after the bids are in and the costs can be worked back into their appropriate categories for information purposes. As soon as details become available in the project design, the square foot approach should be discontinued and the project priced as to its particular components. When more precision is required, or for estimating the replacement cost of specific buildings, the current edition of *RSMeans Square Foot Costs* should be used.

- In using the figures in this section, it is recommended that the median column be used for preliminary figures if no additional information is available. The median figures, when multiplied by the total city construction cost index figures (see city cost indexes) and then multiplied by the project size modifier at the end of this section, should present a fairly accurate base figure, which would then have to be adjusted in view of the estimator's experience, local economic conditions, code requirements, and the owner's particular requirements. There is no need to factor the percentage figures, as these should remain constant from city to city. All tabulations mentioning air conditioning had at least partial air conditioning.

- The editors of this book would greatly appreciate receiving cost figures on one or more of your recent projects, which would then be included in the averages for next year. All cost figures received will be kept confidential, except that they will be averaged with other similar projects to arrive at square foot cost figures for next year's book. See the last page of the book for details and the discount available for submitting one or more of your projects.

50 17 00 | S.F. Costs		UNIT	UNIT COSTS			% OF TOTAL		
			1/4	MEDIAN	3/4	1/4	MEDIAN	3/4
01	**0010** **APARTMENTS Low Rise (1 to 3 story)**	S.F.	73	92.50	123				**01**
	0020 Total project cost	C.F.	6.55	8.70	10.75			
	0100 Site work	S.F.	5.35	8.55	15	6.05%	10.55%	13.95%
	0500 Masonry		1.44	3.55	5.80	1.54%	3.92%	6.50%
	1500 Finishes		7.75	10.65	13.15	9.05%	10.75%	12.85%
	1800 Equipment		2.40	3.63	5.40	2.71%	3.99%	5.95%
	2720 Plumbing		5.70	7.30	9.30	6.65%	8.95%	10.05%
	2770 Heating, ventilating, air conditioning		3.63	4.47	6.55	4.20%	5.60%	7.60%
	2900 Electrical		4.25	5.65	7.65	5.20%	6.65%	8.35%
	3100 Total: Mechanical & Electrical		15.10	19.60	24	16.05%	18.20%	23%
	9000 Per apartment unit, total cost	Apt.	68,000	104,000	153,500			
	9500 Total: Mechanical & Electrical	"	12,900	20,300	26,500			
02	**0010** **APARTMENTS Mid Rise (4 to 7 story)**	S.F.	97	117	144				**02**
	0020 Total project costs	C.F.	7.55	10.45	14.30			
	0100 Site work	S.F.	3.88	7.85	15.15	5.25%	6.70%	9.20%
	0500 Masonry		4.05	8.90	12.15	5.10%	7.25%	10.50%
	1500 Finishes		12.70	17	20	10.70%	13.50%	17.70%
	1800 Equipment		2.71	4.22	5.55	2.54%	3.47%	4.31%
	2500 Conveying equipment		2.20	2.70	3.26	2.05%	2.27%	2.69%
	2720 Plumbing		5.70	9.10	9.65	5.70%	7.20%	8.95%
	2900 Electrical		6.40	8.70	10.55	6.35%	7.20%	8.95%
	3100 Total: Mechanical & Electrical		20.50	25.50	31	18.25%	21%	23%
	9000 Per apartment unit, total cost	Apt.	109,500	129,500	214,000			
	9500 Total: Mechanical & Electrical	"	20,700	24,000	25,100			
03	**0010** **APARTMENTS High Rise (8 to 24 story)**	S.F.	110	127	152				**03**
	0020 Total project costs	C.F.	10.70	12.45	14.65			
	0100 Site work	S.F.	3.99	6.45	9	2.58%	4.84%	6.15%
	0500 Masonry		6.35	11.55	14.40	4.74%	9.65%	11.05%
	1500 Finishes		12.20	15.25	18	9.75%	11.80%	13.70%
	1800 Equipment		3.54	4.35	5.75	2.78%	3.49%	4.35%
	2500 Conveying equipment		2.50	3.79	5.15	2.23%	2.78%	3.37%
	2720 Plumbing		7.05	9.55	11.70	6.80%	7.20%	10.45%
	2900 Electrical		7.55	9.55	12.90	6.45%	7.65%	8.80%
	3100 Total: Mechanical & Electrical		22.50	29	35	17.95%	22.50%	24.50%
	9000 Per apartment unit, total cost	Apt.	114,000	126,000	174,500			
	9500 Total: Mechanical & Electrical	"	22,700	28,200	29,900			
04	**0010** **AUDITORIUMS**	S.F.	115	158	230				**04**
	0020 Total project costs	C.F.	7.15	9.95	14.30			
	2720 Plumbing	S.F.	6.80	10	11.95	5.85%	7.20%	8.70%
	2900 Electrical		9.20	13.30	22	6.85%	9.50%	11.40%
	3100 Total: Mechanical & Electrical		61	81.50	99	24.50%	27.50%	31%
05	**0010** **AUTOMOTIVE SALES**	S.F.	84.50	115	143				**05**
	0020 Total project costs	C.F.	5.55	6.70	8.65			
	2720 Plumbing	S.F.	3.86	6.70	7.30	2.89%	6.05%	6.50%
	2770 Heating, ventilating, air conditioning		5.95	9.10	9.80	4.61%	10%	10.35%
	2900 Electrical		6.80	10.70	15.70	7.25%	8.80%	12.15%
	3100 Total: Mechanical & Electrical		19	30.50	36.50	17.30%	20.50%	22%
06	**0010** **BANKS**	S.F.	166	207	263				**06**
	0020 Total project costs	C.F.	11.85	16.10	21			
	0100 Site work	S.F.	19	30	42.50	7.90%	12.95%	17%
	0500 Masonry		7.55	16.15	29	3.36%	6.90%	10.05%
	1500 Finishes		14.85	22.50	28	5.85%	8.65%	11.70%
	1800 Equipment		6.25	13.75	28	1.34%	5.55%	10.50%
	2720 Plumbing		5.20	7.45	10.85	2.82%	3.90%	4.93%
	2770 Heating, ventilating, air conditioning		9.85	13.20	17.60	4.86%	7.15%	8.50%
	2900 Electrical		15.75	21	27.50	8.25%	10.20%	12.20%
	3100 Total: Mechanical & Electrical		38	50.50	61	16.55%	19.45%	24%
	3500 See also division 11020 & 11030 (MF2004 11 16 00 & 11 17 00)							

50 17 00 | S.F. Costs

		UNIT	UNIT COSTS			% OF TOTAL		
			1/4	MEDIAN	3/4	1/4	MEDIAN	3/4
13	0010	**CHURCHES**	S.F.	112	143	185			
	0020	Total project costs	C.F.	6.90	8.75	11.50			
	1800	Equipment	S.F.	1.21	3.17	6.80	.93%	2.11%	4.31%
	2720	Plumbing		4.35	6.10	8.95	3.51%	4.96%	6.25%
	2770	Heating, ventilating, air conditioning		10.15	13.25	18.75	7.50%	10%	12%
	2900	Electrical		9.55	12.95	17.65	7.30%	8.80%	10.90%
	3100	Total: Mechanical & Electrical	↓	29.50	39	51.50	18.30%	22%	24.50%
	3500	See also division 11040 (MF2004 11 91 00)							
15	0010	**CLUBS, COUNTRY**	S.F.	120	144	182			
	0020	Total project costs	C.F.	9.65	11.75	16.25			
	2720	Plumbing	S.F.	7.25	10.75	24.50	5.60%	7.90%	10%
	2900	Electrical		9.40	12.90	16.80	7%	8.95%	11%
	3100	Total: Mechanical & Electrical	↓	50	62.50	66	19%	26.50%	29.50%
17	0010	**CLUBS, SOCIAL Fraternal**	S.F.	101	138	184			
	0020	Total project costs	C.F.	5.95	9.05	10.80			
	2720	Plumbing	S.F.	6	7.50	11.30	5.60%	6.90%	8.55%
	2770	Heating, ventilating, air conditioning		7.05	10.50	13.45	8.20%	9.25%	14.40%
	2900	Electrical		6.85	11.80	13.55	5.95%	9.30%	10.55%
	3100	Total: Mechanical & Electrical	↓	37	40	51	21%	23%	23.50%
18	0010	**CLUBS, Y.M.C.A.**	S.F.	132	164	247			
	0020	Total project costs	C.F.	5.55	9.25	13.80			
	2720	Plumbing	S.F.	7.60	15.10	16.95	5.65%	7.60%	10.85%
	2900	Electrical		9.85	12.75	22	6.45%	8%	9.20%
	3100	Total: Mechanical & Electrical	↓	40	45.50	74.50	20.50%	21.50%	28.50%
19	0010	**COLLEGES Classrooms & Administration**	S.F.	116	164	212			
	0020	Total project costs	C.F.	6.95	12.35	19.85			
	0500	Masonry	S.F.	9.15	16.85	20.50	5.10%	8.05%	10.50%
	2720	Plumbing		5.20	12.65	23.50	5.10%	6.60%	8.95%
	2900	Electrical		9.85	15.55	21.50	7.70%	9.85%	12%
	3100	Total: Mechanical & Electrical	↓	41.50	57	76	23%	28%	31.50%
21	0010	**COLLEGES Science, Engineering, Laboratories**	S.F.	225	264	305			
	0020	Total project costs	C.F.	12.95	18.85	21.50			
	1800	Equipment	S.F.	6.10	28.50	31	2%	6.45%	12.65%
	2900	Electrical		18.60	26.50	40.50	7.10%	9.40%	12.10%
	3100	Total: Mechanical & Electrical	↓	69	82	127	28.50%	31.50%	41%
	3500	See also division 11600 (MF2004 11 53 00)							
23	0010	**COLLEGES Student Unions**	S.F.	144	195	236			
	0020	Total project costs	C.F.	8	10.50	13			
	3100	Total: Mechanical & Electrical	S.F.	54	58.50	69	23.50%	26%	29%
25	0010	**COMMUNITY CENTERS**	S.F.	120	147	199			
	0020	Total project costs	C.F.	7.75	11.05	14.35			
	1800	Equipment	S.F.	2.40	4.70	7.75	1.47%	3.01%	5.30%
	2720	Plumbing		5.60	9.85	13.45	4.85%	7%	8.95%
	2770	Heating, ventilating, air conditioning		8.45	13.10	18.80	6.80%	10.35%	12.90%
	2900	Electrical		10.05	13.25	19.50	7.15%	8.90%	10.40%
	3100	Total: Mechanical & Electrical	↓	33	42	60	18.80%	23%	30%
28	0010	**COURT HOUSES**	S.F.	171	202	278			
	0020	Total project costs	C.F.	13.15	15.70	19.80			
	2720	Plumbing	S.F.	8.15	11.35	12.90	5.95%	7.45%	8.20%
	2900	Electrical		18.20	20.50	30	9.05%	10.65%	12.15%
	3100	Total: Mechanical & Electrical	↓	51	66.50	73	22.50%	26.50%	30%
30	0010	**DEPARTMENT STORES**	S.F.	63.50	85.50	108			
	0020	Total project costs	C.F.	3.39	4.40	5.95			
	2720	Plumbing	S.F.	1.97	2.49	3.78	1.82%	4.21%	5.90%
	2770	Heating, ventilating, air conditioning	↓	4.79	8.90	13.35	8.20%	9.10%	14.80%

		50 17 00 | S.F. Costs	UNIT	UNIT COSTS			% OF TOTAL			
				1/4	MEDIAN	3/4	1/4	MEDIAN	3/4	
30	2900	Electrical	S.F.	7.25	9.95	11.75	9.05%	12.15%	14.95%	30
	3100	Total: Mechanical & Electrical	↓	12.80	16.35	28.50	13.20%	21.50%	50%	
31	0010	**DORMITORIES Low Rise (1 to 3 story)**	S.F.	120	166	208				31
	0020	Total project costs	C.F.	6.80	10.95	16.45				
	2720	Plumbing	S.F.	7.20	9.65	12.20	8.05%	9%	9.65%	
	2770	Heating, ventilating, air conditioning		7.65	9.15	12.20	4.61%	8.05%	10%	
	2900	Electrical		7.95	12.10	16.55	6.40%	8.65%	9.50%	
	3100	Total: Mechanical & Electrical	↓	41.50	44.50	69	22%	25%	27%	
	9000	Per bed, total cost	Bed	51,000	56,500	121,000				
32	0010	**DORMITORIES Mid Rise (4 to 8 story)**	S.F.	147	192	237				32
	0020	Total project costs	C.F.	16.25	17.85	21.50				
	2900	Electrical	S.F.	15.65	17.80	24	8.20%	10.20%	11.95%	
	3100	Total: Mechanical & Electrical	"	44	87.50	88.50	25%	30.50%	35.50%	
	9000	Per bed, total cost	Bed	21,000	47,900	277,000				
34	0010	**FACTORIES**	S.F.	55.50	83	128				34
	0020	Total project costs	C.F.	3.58	5.35	8.85				
	0100	Site work	S.F.	6.35	11.60	18.40	6.95%	11.45%	17.95%	
	2720	Plumbing		3.01	5.60	9.25	3.73%	6.05%	8.10%	
	2770	Heating, ventilating, air conditioning		5.85	8.40	11.35	5.25%	8.45%	11.35%	
	2900	Electrical		6.95	10.95	16.75	8.10%	10.50%	14.20%	
	3100	Total: Mechanical & Electrical	↓	19.80	30.50	40	21%	28.50%	35.50%	
36	0010	**FIRE STATIONS**	S.F.	111	153	209				36
	0020	Total project costs	C.F.	6.45	8.90	11.85				
	0500	Masonry	S.F.	15.10	29	37.50	7.50%	10.95%	15.55%	
	1140	Roofing		3.61	9.75	11.10	1.90%	4.94%	5.05%	
	1580	Painting		2.80	4.18	4.28	1.37%	1.57%	2.07%	
	1800	Equipment		1.38	2.64	4.87	.62%	1.63%	3.42%	
	2720	Plumbing		6.20	9.85	13.95	5.85%	7.35%	9.45%	
	2770	Heating, ventilating, air conditioning		6.15	9.95	15.35	5.15%	7.40%	9.40%	
	2900	Electrical		7.95	14.10	19	6.90%	8.60%	10.60%	
	3100	Total: Mechanical & Electrical	↓	40.50	52	59	18.40%	23%	27%	
37	0010	**FRATERNITY HOUSES & Sorority Houses**	S.F.	111	142	195				37
	0020	Total project costs	C.F.	11	11.50	13.85				
	2720	Plumbing	S.F.	8.35	9.60	17.55	6.80%	8%	10.85%	
	2900	Electrical	↓	7.30	15.80	19.35	6.60%	9.90%	10.65%	
38	0010	**FUNERAL HOMES**	S.F.	117	159	289				38
	0020	Total project costs	C.F.	11.90	13.25	25.50				
	2900	Electrical	S.F.	5.15	9.45	10.35	3.58%	4.44%	5.95%	
39	0010	**GARAGES, COMMERCIAL (Service)**	S.F.	66	102	141				39
	0020	Total project costs	C.F.	4.35	6.40	9.35				
	1800	Equipment	S.F.	3.73	8.40	13.05	2.21%	4.62%	6.80%	
	2720	Plumbing		4.58	7.05	12.85	5.45%	7.85%	10.65%	
	2730	Heating & ventilating		4.51	7.80	9.95	5.25%	6.85%	8.20%	
	2900	Electrical		6.30	9.60	13.80	7.15%	9.25%	10.85%	
	3100	Total: Mechanical & Electrical	↓	11.85	26.50	39	12.35%	17.40%	26%	
40	0010	**GARAGES, MUNICIPAL (Repair)**	S.F.	97	129	182				40
	0020	Total project costs	C.F.	6.05	7.70	13.25				
	0500	Masonry	S.F.	5.10	17.85	27.50	4.03%	9.15%	12.50%	
	2720	Plumbing		4.36	8.35	15.75	3.59%	6.70%	7.95%	
	2730	Heating & ventilating		7.45	10.80	21	6.15%	7.45%	13.50%	
	2900	Electrical		7.15	11.30	16.40	6.65%	8.15%	11.15%	
	3100	Total: Mechanical & Electrical	↓	33	46	66.50	21.50%	23%	28.50%	
41	0010	**GARAGES, PARKING**	S.F.	38.50	55	95				41
	0020	Total project costs	C.F.	3.55	4.82	7				

50 17 00 | S.F. Costs

			UNIT	UNIT COSTS			% OF TOTAL		
				1/4	MEDIAN	3/4	1/4	MEDIAN	3/4
41	2720	Plumbing	S.F.	.65	1.66	2.56	1.72%	2.70%	3.85%
	2900	Electrical		2.08	2.74	4	4.52%	5.40%	6.35%
	3100	Total: Mechanical & Electrical	↓	4.03	5.90	7.35	7%	8.90%	11.05%
	3200								
	9000	Per car, total cost	Car	16,000	20,000	25,500			
43	0010	**GYMNASIUMS**	S.F.	105	140	193			
	0020	Total project costs	C.F.	5.25	7.10	8.75			
	1800	Equipment	S.F.	2.50	4.68	8.45	1.76%	3.26%	6.70%
	2720	Plumbing		5.75	7.75	10.20	4.65%	6.40%	7.75%
	2770	Heating, ventilating, air conditioning		6.25	10.90	22	5.15%	9.05%	11.10%
	2900	Electrical		8.35	11	14.65	6.75%	8.50%	10.30%
	3100	Total: Mechanical & Electrical	↓	28.50	40	48.50	19.75%	23.50%	29%
	3500	See also division 11480 (MF2004 11 67 00)							
46	0010	**HOSPITALS**	S.F.	202	253	350			
	0020	Total project costs	C.F.	15.30	19.05	27			
	1800	Equipment	S.F.	5.10	9.85	17	.80%	2.53%	4.80%
	2720	Plumbing		17.40	24.50	31.50	7.60%	9.10%	10.85%
	2770	Heating, ventilating, air conditioning		25.50	32.50	45.50	7.80%	12.95%	16.65%
	2900	Electrical		22.50	30	44.50	10%	11.75%	14.10%
	3100	Total: Mechanical & Electrical	↓	65	90.50	134	28%	33.50%	37%
	9000	Per bed or person, total cost	Bed	233,500	322,000	371,000			
	9900	See also division 11700 (MF2004 11 71 00)							
48	0010	**HOUSING For the Elderly**	S.F.	99	126	154			
	0020	Total project costs	C.F.	7.10	9.85	12.55			
	0100	Site work	S.F.	6.90	10.75	15.75	5.05%	7.90%	12.10%
	0500	Masonry		1.87	11.30	16.50	1.30%	6.05%	11%
	1800	Equipment		2.40	3.30	5.25	1.88%	3.23%	4.43%
	2510	Conveying systems		2.24	3.24	4.40	1.78%	2.20%	2.81%
	2720	Plumbing		7.40	9.40	11.85	8.15%	9.55%	10.50%
	2730	Heating, ventilating, air conditioning		3.78	5.35	8	3.30%	5.60%	7.25%
	2900	Electrical		7.40	10.05	12.85	7.30%	8.50%	10.25%
	3100	Total: Mechanical & Electrical	↓	25.50	31.50	40.50	18.10%	22.50%	29%
	9000	Per rental unit, total cost	Unit	92,500	108,000	120,000			
	9500	Total: Mechanical & Electrical	"	20,600	23,600	27,600			
50	0010	**HOUSING Public (Low Rise)**	S.F.	83.50	116	151			
	0020	Total project costs	C.F.	6.60	9.25	11.50			
	0100	Site work	S.F.	10.60	15.30	25	8.35%	11.75%	16.50%
	1800	Equipment		2.27	3.70	5.65	2.26%	3.03%	4.24%
	2720	Plumbing		6	7.95	10.05	7.15%	9.05%	11.60%
	2730	Heating, ventilating, air conditioning		3.02	5.85	6.40	4.26%	6.05%	6.45%
	2900	Electrical		5.05	7.50	10.45	5.10%	6.55%	8.25%
	3100	Total: Mechanical & Electrical	↓	24	31	34.50	14.50%	17.55%	26.50%
	9000	Per apartment, total cost	Apt.	91,500	104,000	131,000			
	9500	Total: Mechanical & Electrical	"	19,500	24,100	26,700			
51	0010	**ICE SKATING RINKS**	S.F.	71.50	167	183			
	0020	Total project costs	C.F.	5.25	5.35	6.20			
	2720	Plumbing	S.F.	2.66	5	5.10	3.12%	3.23%	5.65%
	2900	Electrical	↓	7.65	11.70	12.40	6.30%	10.15%	15.05%
52	0010	**JAILS**	S.F.	185	280	360			
	0020	Total project costs	C.F.	19.60	27.50	32			
	1800	Equipment	S.F.	8.45	25	42.50	2.80%	6.95%	9.80%
	2720	Plumbing		21	28	37	7%	8.90%	13.35%
	2770	Heating, ventilating, air conditioning		19.60	26	50.50	7.50%	9.45%	17.75%
	2900	Electrical		23	31	39	9.40%	11.70%	15.25%
	3100	Total: Mechanical & Electrical	↓	61	108	128	28%	30%	34%
53	0010	**LIBRARIES**	S.F.	140	186	243			
	0020	Total project costs	C.F.	9.40	11.75	15			

		50 17 00 | S.F. Costs	UNIT	UNIT COSTS			% OF TOTAL			
				1/4	MEDIAN	3/4	1/4	MEDIAN	3/4	
53	0500	Masonry	S.F.	9.30	19	31.50	5.60%	7.15%	10.95%	53
	1800	Equipment		1.88	5.05	7.60	.28%	1.39%	4.07%	
	2720	Plumbing		5.05	7.20	10	3.38%	4.60%	5.70%	
	2770	Heating, ventilating, air conditioning		11.20	19	23	7.80%	10.95%	12.80%	
	2900	Electrical		14.10	18.65	25	8.40%	10.55%	12%	
	3100	Total: Mechanical & Electrical		46	56	65.50	21%	24%	28%	
54	0010	**LIVING, ASSISTED**	S.F.	127	151	176				54
	0020	Total project costs	C.F.	10.70	12.50	14.20				
	0500	Masonry	S.F.	3.68	4.44	5.45	2.36%	3.16%	3.86%	
	1800	Equipment		2.81	3.35	4.30	2.12%	2.45%	2.87%	
	2720	Plumbing		10.65	14.25	14.75	6.05%	8.15%	10.60%	
	2770	Heating, ventilating, air conditioning		12.65	13.20	14.45	7.95%	9.35%	9.70%	
	2900	Electrical		12.45	14	16.15	9%	9.95%	10.65%	
	3100	Total: Mechanical & Electrical		34	40.50	47	24%	28.50%	31.50%	
55	0010	**MEDICAL CLINICS**	S.F.	129	159	203				55
	0020	Total project costs	C.F.	9.45	12.25	16.30				
	1800	Equipment	S.F.	1.65	7.35	11.40	1.05%	2.94%	6.35%	
	2720	Plumbing		8.60	12.10	16.15	6.15%	8.40%	10.10%	
	2770	Heating, ventilating, air conditioning		10.25	13.40	19.70	6.65%	8.85%	11.35%	
	2900	Electrical		11.10	15.75	20.50	8.10%	10%	12.20%	
	3100	Total: Mechanical & Electrical		35.50	48	66	22%	27%	33.50%	
	3500	See also division 11700 (MF2004 11 71 00)								
57	0010	**MEDICAL OFFICES**	S.F.	121	151	185				57
	0020	Total project costs	C.F.	9.05	12.30	16.60				
	1800	Equipment	S.F.	4.01	7.95	11.15	.66%	4.87%	6.50%	
	2720	Plumbing		6.70	10.35	13.95	5.60%	6.80%	8.50%	
	2770	Heating, ventilating, air conditioning		8.10	11.70	15.45	6.10%	8%	9.70%	
	2900	Electrical		9.70	14.20	19.75	7.50%	9.80%	11.70%	
	3100	Total: Mechanical & Electrical		26.50	38.50	55	19.30%	23%	28.50%	
59	0010	**MOTELS**	S.F.	76.50	111	145				59
	0020	Total project costs	C.F.	6.80	9.15	14.95				
	2720	Plumbing	S.F.	7.75	9.90	11.80	9.45%	10.60%	12.55%	
	2770	Heating, ventilating, air conditioning		4.74	7.05	12.65	5.60%	5.60%	10%	
	2900	Electrical		7.25	9.15	11.40	7.45%	9.05%	10.45%	
	3100	Total: Mechanical & Electrical		21.50	31	53	18.50%	24%	25.50%	
	5000									
	9000	Per rental unit, total cost	Unit	39,000	74,000	80,000				
	9500	Total: Mechanical & Electrical	"	7,600	11,500	13,400				
60	0010	**NURSING HOMES**	S.F.	120	155	193				60
	0020	Total project costs	C.F.	9.45	11.80	16.15				
	1800	Equipment	S.F.	3.28	5	8.40	2%	3.62%	4.99%	
	2720	Plumbing		10.30	15.60	18.80	8.75%	10.10%	12.70%	
	2770	Heating, ventilating, air conditioning		10.85	16.45	22	9.70%	11.45%	11.80%	
	2900	Electrical		11.90	14.95	20.50	9.40%	10.60%	12.50%	
	3100	Total: Mechanical & Electrical		28.50	39.50	66.50	26%	28%	30%	
	9000	Per bed or person, total cost	Bed	53,500	67,000	86,000				
61	0010	**OFFICES Low Rise (1 to 4 story)**	S.F.	101	132	172				61
	0020	Total project costs	C.F.	7.25	9.95	13.10				
	0100	Site work	S.F.	8.15	14.20	21	5.95%	9.70%	13.55%	
	0500	Masonry		3.92	7.90	14.40	2.61%	5.40%	8.45%	
	1800	Equipment		.91	2.11	5.75	.57%	1.50%	3.42%	
	2720	Plumbing		3.62	5.60	8.20	3.66%	4.50%	6.10%	
	2770	Heating, ventilating, air conditioning		8	11.15	16.35	7.20%	10.30%	11.70%	
	2900	Electrical		8.30	11.85	16.85	7.45%	9.65%	11.40%	
	3100	Total: Mechanical & Electrical		23	31.50	48	18.20%	22%	27%	
62	0010	**OFFICES Mid Rise (5 to 10 story)**	S.F.	107	130	176				62
	0020	Total project costs	C.F.	7.60	9.70	13.75				

50 17 00 | S.F. Costs

			UNIT	UNIT COSTS			% OF TOTAL		
				1/4	MEDIAN	3/4	1/4	MEDIAN	3/4
62	2720	Plumbing	S.F.	3.24	5	7.20	2.83%	3.74%	4.50%	62
	2770	Heating, ventilating, air conditioning		8.15	11.65	18.60	7.65%	9.40%	11%	
	2900	Electrical		7.95	10.20	15.40	6.35%	7.80%	10%	
	3100	Total: Mechanical & Electrical		20.50	26.50	50.50	18.95%	21%	27.50%	
63	0010	OFFICES High Rise (11 to 20 story)	S.F.	132	166	204				63
	0020	Total project costs	C.F.	9.20	11.50	16.50				
	2900	Electrical	S.F.	8	9.75	14.50	5.80%	7.85%	10.50%	
	3100	Total: Mechanical & Electrical		26	34.50	58.50	16.90%	23.50%	34%	
64	0010	POLICE STATIONS	S.F.	158	208	265				64
	0020	Total project costs	C.F.	12.60	15.40	21				
	0500	Masonry	S.F.	15.80	26	33	7.80%	9.10%	11.35%	
	1800	Equipment		2.27	11.05	17.50	.98%	3.35%	6.70%	
	2720	Plumbing		8.85	17.60	22	5.65%	6.90%	10.75%	
	2770	Heating, ventilating, air conditioning		12.95	18.35	26	5.85%	10.55%	11.70%	
	2900	Electrical		17.25	25	32.50	9.80%	11.70%	14.50%	
	3100	Total: Mechanical & Electrical		65.50	69	92	28.50%	31.50%	32.50%	
65	0010	POST OFFICES	S.F.	125	154	196				65
	0020	Total project costs	C.F.	7.50	9.50	10.80				
	2720	Plumbing	S.F.	5.05	6.95	8.80	4.24%	5.30%	5.60%	
	2770	Heating, ventilating, air conditioning		7.85	10.85	12.05	6.65%	7.15%	9.35%	
	2900	Electrical		10.30	14.50	17.20	7.25%	9%	11%	
	3100	Total: Mechanical & Electrical		29.50	39	44	16.25%	18.80%	22%	
66	0010	POWER PLANTS	S.F.	865	1,150	2,100				66
	0020	Total project costs	C.F.	24	52	111				
	2900	Electrical	S.F.	61	130	193	9.30%	12.75%	21.50%	
	8100	Total: Mechanical & Electrical		152	495	1,100	32.50%	32.50%	52.50%	
67	0010	RELIGIOUS EDUCATION	S.F.	101	131	161				67
	0020	Total project costs	C.F.	5.60	8	10				
	2720	Plumbing	S.F.	4.20	5.95	8.40	4.40%	5.30%	7.10%	
	2770	Heating, ventilating, air conditioning		10.60	12	16.95	10.05%	11.45%	12.35%	
	2900	Electrical		7.40	11.25	14.85	7.60%	9.05%	10.35%	
	3100	Total: Mechanical & Electrical		32.50	42.50	52	22%	23%	27%	
69	0010	RESEARCH Laboratories & Facilities	S.F.	154	217	315				69
	0020	Total project costs	C.F.	11.20	22	26.50				
	1800	Equipment	S.F.	6.70	13.15	32	.94%	4.58%	9.10%	
	2720	Plumbing		10.95	19.30	31	6.15%	8.30%	10.80%	
	2770	Heating, ventilating, air conditioning		13.55	45.50	54	7.25%	16.50%	17.50%	
	2900	Electrical		18.10	29	47.50	9.55%	11.15%	14.60%	
	3100	Total: Mechanical & Electrical		57.50	102	144	29.50%	37%	41%	
70	0010	RESTAURANTS	S.F.	146	188	245				70
	0020	Total project costs	C.F.	12.25	16.10	21				
	1800	Equipment	S.F.	8.65	23	35	6.10%	13%	15.65%	
	2720	Plumbing		11.55	14	18.40	6.10%	8.15%	9%	
	2770	Heating, ventilating, air conditioning		14.70	20.50	24.50	9.20%	12%	12.40%	
	2900	Electrical		15.40	19	24.50	8.35%	10.55%	11.55%	
	3100	Total: Mechanical & Electrical		47.50	51	66	21%	25%	29.50%	
	9000	Per seat unit, total cost	Seat	5,350	7,125	8,450				
	9500	Total: Mechanical & Electrical	"	1,350	1,775	2,100				
72	0010	RETAIL STORES	S.F.	68	91.50	121				72
	0020	Total project costs	C.F.	4.62	6.60	9.15				
	2720	Plumbing	S.F.	2.47	4.12	7.05	3.26%	4.60%	6.80%	
	2770	Heating, ventilating, air conditioning		5.35	7.30	10.95	6.75%	8.75%	10.15%	
	2900	Electrical		6.15	8.40	12.10	7.25%	9.90%	11.60%	
	3100	Total: Mechanical & Electrical		16.30	21	28	17.05%	21%	23.50%	
74	0010	SCHOOLS Elementary	S.F.	111	138	169				74
	0020	Total project costs	C.F.	7.25	9.30	12.05				
	0500	Masonry	S.F.	7.85	16.95	25	4.89%	10.50%	14%	
	1800	Equipment		2.58	4.93	9.30	1.83%	3.13%	4.61%	

50 17 | Square Foot Costs

50 17 00 | S.F. Costs

			UNIT	1/4	MEDIAN	3/4	1/4	MEDIAN	3/4	
				UNIT COSTS			**% OF TOTAL**			
74	2720	Plumbing	S.F.	6.40	9.05	12.05	5.70%	7.15%	9.35%	**74**
	2730	Heating, ventilating, air conditioning		9.60	15.25	21.50	8.15%	10.80%	14.90%	
	2900	Electrical	↓	10.50	14	17.85	8.45%	10.05%	11.85%	
	3100	Total: Mechanical & Electrical		38	46.50	59	25%	27.50%	30%	
	9000	Per pupil, total cost	Ea.	12,800	19,000	42,500				
	9500	Total: Mechanical & Electrical	"	3,600	4,550	11,500				
76	0010	**SCHOOLS Junior High & Middle**	S.F.	115	142	173				**76**
	0020	Total project costs	C.F.	7.30	9.40	10.55				
	0500	Masonry	S.F.	12.30	18.40	22.50	7.55%	11.10%	14.30%	
	1800	Equipment		3.14	5.90	8.65	1.80%	3.03%	4.80%	
	2720	Plumbing		6.70	8.25	10.20	5.30%	6.80%	7.25%	
	2770	Heating, ventilating, air conditioning		13.35	16.20	28.50	8.90%	11.55%	14.20%	
	2900	Electrical		11.70	14.45	18.25	8.05%	9.55%	10.60%	
	3100	Total: Mechanical & Electrical	↓	36.50	47	58.50	23%	25.50%	29.50%	
	9000	Per pupil, total cost	Ea.	14,500	19,100	25,600				
78	0010	**SCHOOLS Senior High**	S.F.	120	147	184				**78**
	0020	Total project costs	C.F.	7.20	10.10	17.05				
	1800	Equipment	S.F.	3.17	7.40	10.25	1.88%	2.67%	4.30%	
	2720	Plumbing		6.70	10.05	18.35	5.60%	6.90%	8.30%	
	2770	Heating, ventilating, air conditioning		11.50	15.65	24	8.95%	11.60%	15%	
	2900	Electrical		12.05	16.05	23.50	8.70%	10.35%	12.50%	
	3100	Total: Mechanical & Electrical	↓	39.50	47	76	24%	26.50%	28.50%	
	9000	Per pupil, total cost	Ea.	11,200	22,900	28,600				
80	0010	**SCHOOLS Vocational**	S.F.	96.50	140	173				**80**
	0020	Total project costs	C.F.	6	8.60	11.90				
	0500	Masonry	S.F.	4.24	14	21.50	3.20%	4.61%	10.95%	
	1800	Equipment		3.02	7.50	10.35	1.24%	3.10%	4.26%	
	2720	Plumbing		6.15	9.20	13.55	5.40%	6.90%	8.55%	
	2770	Heating, ventilating, air conditioning		8.65	16.05	27	8.60%	11.90%	14.65%	
	2900	Electrical		10.05	13.75	18.80	8.45%	11%	13.20%	
	3100	Total: Mechanical & Electrical	↓	38	66.50	85	27.50%	29.50%	31%	
	9000	Per pupil, total cost	Ea.	13,400	36,000	53,500				
83	0010	**SPORTS ARENAS**	S.F.	84.50	113	174				**83**
	0020	Total project costs	C.F.	4.58	8.20	10.60				
	2720	Plumbing	S.F.	4.22	7.40	15.65	4.35%	6.35%	9.40%	
	2770	Heating, ventilating, air conditioning		10.55	12.45	17.30	8.80%	10.20%	13.55%	
	2900	Electrical	↓	7.80	11.90	15.40	7.65%	9.75%	11.90%	
85	0010	**SUPERMARKETS**	S.F.	78	90	106				**85**
	0020	Total project costs	C.F.	4.34	5.25	7.95				
	2720	Plumbing	S.F.	4.35	5.50	6.40	5.40%	6%	7.45%	
	2770	Heating, ventilating, air conditioning		6.40	8.50	10.35	8.60%	8.65%	9.60%	
	2900	Electrical		9.15	11.15	13.25	10.40%	12.45%	13.60%	
	3100	Total: Mechanical & Electrical	↓	25	26.50	35.50	23.50%	27.50%	28.50%	
86	0010	**SWIMMING POOLS**	S.F.	126	295	450				**86**
	0020	Total project costs	C.F.	10.10	12.60	13.75				
	2720	Plumbing	S.F.	11.65	13.35	17.90	4.80%	9.70%	20.50%	
	2900	Electrical		9.60	15.35	34	6.05%	6.95%	7.60%	
	3100	Total: Mechanical & Electrical	↓	60	79	104	11.15%	14.10%	23.50%	
87	0010	**TELEPHONE EXCHANGES**	S.F.	157	238	310				**87**
	0020	Total project costs	C.F.	10.40	16.75	23				
	2720	Plumbing	S.F.	7.05	10.90	16	4.52%	5.80%	6.90%	
	2770	Heating, ventilating, air conditioning		16.40	33	41	11.80%	16.05%	18.40%	
	2900	Electrical		17.05	27	48	10.90%	14%	17.85%	
	3100	Total: Mechanical & Electrical	↓	50.50	95.50	135	29.50%	33.50%	44.50%	
91	0010	**THEATERS**	S.F.	99.50	135	199				**91**
	0020	Total project costs	C.F.	4.87	7.20	10.55				

540

		50 17 00 | S.F. Costs	UNIT	UNIT COSTS			% OF TOTAL		
				1/4	MEDIAN	3/4	1/4	MEDIAN	3/4
91	2720	Plumbing	S.F.	3.28	3.80	15.55	2.92%	4.70%	6.80%
	2770	Heating, ventilating, air conditioning		10.25	12.40	15.35	8%	12.25%	13.40%
	2900	Electrical		9.20	12.45	25.50	8.05%	9.35%	12.25%
	3100	Total: Mechanical & Electrical	↓	23.50	32	37.50	21.50%	25.50%	27.50%
94	0010	**TOWN HALLS City Halls & Municipal Buildings**	S.F.	110	149	195			
	0020	Total project costs	C.F.	7.95	12.40	18.10			
	2720	Plumbing	S.F.	4.91	9.20	16.10	4.31%	5.95%	7.95%
	2770	Heating, ventilating, air conditioning		8.85	17.60	26	7.05%	9.05%	13.45%
	2900	Electrical		11.15	15.40	21	8.05%	9.45%	11.65%
	3100	Total: Mechanical & Electrical	↓	38.50	49	75	22%	26.50%	31%
97	0010	**WAREHOUSES & Storage Buildings**	S.F.	44	63	93			
	0020	Total project costs	C.F.	2.30	3.60	5.95			
	0100	Site work	S.F.	4.53	9	13.55	6.05%	12.95%	19.55%
	0500	Masonry		2.49	6.25	13.45	3.60%	7.35%	12%
	1800	Equipment		.67	1.52	8.55	.72%	1.69%	5.55%
	2720	Plumbing		1.46	2.62	4.91	2.90%	4.80%	6.55%
	2730	Heating, ventilating, air conditioning		1.67	4.71	6.30	2.41%	5%	8.90%
	2900	Electrical		2.60	4.89	8	5.15%	7.20%	10.05%
	3100	Total: Mechanical & Electrical	↓	7.25	11.10	22	13.30%	18.90%	26%
99	0010	**WAREHOUSE & OFFICES Combination**	S.F.	54	72	99			
	0020	Total project costs	C.F.	2.76	4.01	5.90			
	1800	Equipment	S.F.	.93	1.81	2.69	.42%	1.19%	2.40%
	2720	Plumbing		2.08	3.63	5.40	3.74%	4.76%	6.30%
	2770	Heating, ventilating, air conditioning		3.29	5.15	7.20	5%	5.65%	10.05%
	2900	Electrical		3.68	5.45	8.50	5.85%	8%	10%
	3100	Total: Mechanical & Electrical	↓	10.25	15.55	24.50	14.55%	19.95%	24.50%

Glossary

Accent lighting–Fixtures or directional beams of light arranged to bring attention to an object or area.

Acoustical material–A material fabricated for the sole purpose of absorbing sound.

Addition–An expansion to an existing structure generally in the form of a room, floor(s) or wing(s). An increase in the floor area or volume of a structure.

Aggregate–Materials such as sand, gravel, stone, vermiculite, perlite and fly ash (slag) which are essential components in the production of concrete, mortar or plaster.

Air conditioning system–An air treatment to control the temperature, humidity and cleanliness of air and to provide for its distribution throughout the structure.

Air curtain–A stream of air directed downward to prevent the loss of hot or cool air from the structure and inhibit the entrance of dust and insects. Generally installed at loading platforms.

Anodized aluminum–Aluminum treated by an electrolytic process to produce an oxide film that is corrosion resistant.

Arcade–A covered passageway between buildings often with shops and offices on one or both sides.

Ashlar–A square-cut building stone or a wall constructed of cut stone.

Asphalt paper–A sheet paper material either coated or saturated with asphalt to increase its strength and resistance to water.

Asphalt shingles–Shingles manufactured from saturated roofing felts, coated with asphalt and topped with mineral granules to prevent weathering.

Assessment ratio–The ratio between the market value and assessed valuation of a property.

Back-up–That portion of a masonry wall behind the exterior facing-usually load bearing.

Balcony–A platform projecting from a building either supported from below or cantilevered. Usually protected by railing.

Bay–Structural component consisting of beams and columns occurring consistently throughout the structure.

Beam–A horizontal structural framing member that transfers loads to vertical members (columns) or bearing walls.

Bid–An offer to perform work described in a contract at a specified price.

Board foot–A unit or measure equal in volume to a board one foot long, one foot wide and one inch thick.

Booster pump–A supplemental pump installed to increase or maintain adequate pressure in the system.

Bowstring roof–A roof supported by trusses fabricated in the shape of a bow and tied together by a straight member.

Brick veneer–A facing of brick laid against, but not bonded to, a wall.

Bridging–A method of bracing joists for stiffness, stability and load distribution.

Broom finish–A method of finishing concrete by lightly dragging a broom over freshly placed concrete.

Built-up roofing–Installed on flat or extremely low-pitched roofs, a roof covering composed of plies or laminations of saturated roofing felts alternated with layers of coal tar pitch or asphalt and surfaced with a layer of gravel or slag in a thick coat of asphalt and finished with a capping sheet.

Caisson–A watertight chamber to expedite work on foundations or structure below water level.

Cantilever–A structural member supported only at one end.

Carport–An automobile shelter having one or more sides open to the weather.

Casement window–A vertical opening window having one side fixed.

Caulking–A resilient compound generally having a silicone or rubber base used to prevent infiltration of water or outside air.

Cavity wall–An exterior wall usually of masonry having an inner and outer wall separated by a continuous air space for thermal insulation.

Cellular concrete–A lightweight concrete consisting of cement mixed with gas-producing materials which, in turn, forms bubbles resulting in good insulating qualities.

Chattel mortgage–A secured interest in a property as collateral for payment of a note.

Clapboard–A wood siding used as exterior covering in frame construction. It is applied horizontally with grain running lengthwise. The thickest section of the board is on the bottom.

Clean room–An environmentally controlled room usually found in medical facilities or precision manufacturing spaces where it is essential to eliminate dust, lint or pathogens.

Close studding–A method of construction whereby studs are spaced close together and the intervening spaces are plastered.

Cluster housing–A closely grouped series of houses resulting in a high density land use.

Cofferdam–A watertight enclosure used for foundation construction in waterfront areas. Water is pumped out of the cofferdam allowing free access to the work area.

Collar joint–Joint between the collar beam and roof rafters.

Column–A vertical structural member supporting horizontal members (beams) along the direction of its longitudinal axis.

Combination door (windows)–Door (windows) having interchangeable screens and glass for seasonal use.

Common area–Spaces either inside or outside the building designated for use by the occupant of the building but not the general public.

Common wall–A wall used jointly by two dwelling units.

Compound wall–A wall constructed of more than one material.

Concrete–A composite material consisting of sand, coarse aggregate (gravel, stone or slag), cement and water that when mixed and allowed to harden forms a hard stone-like material.

Concrete floor hardener–A mixture of chemicals applied to the surface of concrete to produce a dense, wear-resistant bearing surface.

Conduit–A tube or pipe used to protect electric wiring.

Coping–The top cover or capping on a wall.

Craneway–Steel or concrete column and beam supports and rails on which a crane travels.

Curtain wall–A non-bearing exterior wall not supported by beams or girders of the steel frame.

Dampproofing–Coating of a surface to prevent the passage of water or moisture.

Dead load–Total weight of all structural components plus permanently attached fixtures and equipment.

Decibel–Unit of acoustical measurement.

Decorative block–A concrete masonry unit having a special treatment on its face.

Deed restriction–A restriction on the use of a property as set forth in the deed.

Depreciation–A loss in property value caused by physical aging, functional or economic obsolescence.

Direct heating–Heating of spaces by means of exposed heated surfaces (stove, fire, radiators, etc.).

Distributed load–A load that acts evenly over a structural member.

Dock bumper–A resilient material attached to a loading dock to absorb the impact of trucks backing in.

Dome–A curved roof shape spanning an area.

Dormer–A structure projecting from a sloping roof.

Double-hung window–A window having two vertical sliding sashes-one covering the upper section and one covering the lower.

Downspout–A vertical pipe for carrying rain water from the roof to the ground.

Drain tile–A hollow tile used to drain water-soaked soil.

Dressed size–In lumber about 3/8" - 1/2" less than nominal size after planing and sawing.

Drop panel–The depressed surface on the bottom side of a flat concrete slab which surrounds a column.

Dry pipe sprinkler system–A sprinkler system that is activated with water only in case of fire. Used in areas susceptible to freezing or to avoid the hazards of leaking pipes.

Drywall–An interior wall constructed of gypsum board, plywood or wood paneling. No water is required for application.

Duct–Pipe for transmitting warm or cold air. A pipe containing electrical cable or wires.

Dwelling–A structure designed as living quarters for one or more families.

Easement–A right of way or free access over land owned by another.

Eave–The lower edge of a sloping roof that overhangs the side wall of the structure.

Economic rent–That rent on a property sufficient to pay all operating costs exclusive of services and utilities.

Economic life–The term during which a structure is expected to be profitable. Generally shorter than the physical life of the structure.

Economic obsolescence–Loss in value due to unfavorable economic influences occurring from outside the structure itself.

Effective age–The age a structure appears to be based on observed physical condition determined by degree of maintenance and repair.

Elevator–A mechanism for vertical transport of personnel or freight equipped with car or platform.

Ell–A secondary wing or addition to a structure at right angles to the main structure.

Eminent domain–The right of the state to take private property for public use.

Envelope–The shape of a building indicating volume.

Equity–Value of an owner's interest calculated by subtracting outstanding mortgages and expenses from the value of the property.

Escheat–The assumption of ownership by the state, of property whose owner cannot be determined.

Facade–The exterior face of a building sometimes decorated with elaborate detail.

Face brick–Brick manufactured to present an attractive appearance.

Facing block–A concrete masonry unit having a decorative exterior finish.

Feasibility study–A detailed evaluation of a proposed project to determine its financial potential.

Felt paper–Paper sheathing used on walls as an insulator and to prevent infiltration of moisture.

Fenestration–Pertaining to the density and arrangement of windows in a structure.

Fiberboard–A building material composed of wood fiber compressed with a binding agent, produced in sheet form.

Fiberglass–Fine spun filaments of glass processed into various densities to produce thermal and acoustical insulation.

Field house–A long structure used for indoor athletic events.

Finish floor–The top or wearing surface of the floor system.

Fireproofing–The use of fire-resistant materials for the protection of structural members to ensure structural integrity in the event of fire.

Fire stop–A material or member used to seal an opening to prevent the spread of fire.

Flashing–A thin, impervious material such as copper or sheet metal used to prevent air or water penetration.

Float finish–A concrete finish accomplished by using a flat tool with a handle on the back.

Floor drain–An opening installed in a floor for removing excess water into a plumbing system.

Floor load–The live load the floor system has been designed for and which may be applied safely.

Flue–A heat-resistant enclosed passage in a chimney to remove gaseous products of combustion from a fireplace or boiler.

Footing–The lowest portion of the foundation wall that transmits the load directly to the soil.

Foundation–Below grade wall system that supports the structure.

Foyer–A portion of the structure that serves as a transitional space between the interior and exterior.

Frontage–That portion of a lot that is placed facing a street, public way or body of water.

Frost action–The effects of freezing and thawing on materials and the resultant structural damage.

Functional obsolescence–An inadequacy caused by outmoded design, dated construction materials or over or undersized areas, all of which cause excessive operating costs.

Furring strips–Wood or metal channels used for attaching gypsum or metal lath to masonry walls as a finish or for leveling purposes.

Gambrel roof (mansard)–A roof system having two pitches on each side.

Garden apartment–Two or three story apartment building with common outside areas.

General contractor–The prime contractor responsible for work on the construction site.

Girder–A principal horizontal supporting member.

Girt–A horizontal framing member for adding rigid support to columns which also acts as a support for sheathing or siding.

Grade beam–That portion of the foundation system that directly supports the exterior walls of the building.

Gross area–The total enclosed floor area of a building.

Ground area–The area computed by the exterior dimensions of the structure.

Ground floor–The floor of a building in closest proximity to the ground.

Grout–A mortar containing a high water content used to fill joints and cavities in masonry work.

Gutter–A wood or sheet metal conduit set along the building eaves used to channel rainwater to leaders or downspouts.

Gunite–A concrete mix placed pneumatically.

Gypsum–Hydrated calcium sulphate used as both a retarder in Portland cement and as a major ingredient in plaster of Paris. Used in sheets as a substitute for plaster.

Hall–A passageway providing access to various parts of a building–a large room for entertainment or assembly.

Hangar–A structure for the storage or repair of aircraft.

Head room–The distance between the top of the finished floor to the bottom of the finished ceiling.

Hearth–The floor of a fireplace and the adjacent area of fireproof material.

Heat pump–A mechanical device for providing either heating or air conditioning.

Hip roof–A roof whose four sides meet at a common point with no gabled ends.

I-beam–A structural member having a cross-section resembling the letter "I".

Insulation–Material used to reduce the effects of heat, cold or sound.

Jack rafter–An unusually short rafter generally found in hip roofs.

Jalousie–Adjustable glass louvers which pivot simultaneously in a common frame.

Jamb–The vertical member on either side of a door frame or window frame.

Joist–Parallel beams of timber, concrete or steel used to support floor and ceiling.

Junction box–A box that protects splices or joints in electrical wiring.

Kalamein door–Solid core wood doors clad with galvanized sheet metal.

Kip–A unit of weight equal to 1,000 pounds.

Lally column–A concrete-filled steel pipe used as a vertical support.

Laminated beam–A beam built up by gluing together several pieces of timber.

Landing–A platform between flights of stairs.

Lath–Strips of wood or metal used as a base for plaster.

Lead-lined door, sheetrock–Doors or sheetrock internally lined with sheet lead to provide protection from X-ray radiation.

Lean-to–A small shed or building addition with a single pitched roof attached to the exterior wall of the main building.

Lintel–A horizontal framing member used to carry a load over a wall opening.

Live load–The moving or movable load on a structure composed of furnishings, equipment or personnel weight.

Load bearing partition–A partition that supports a load in addition to its own weight.

Loading dock leveler–An adjustable platform for handling off-on loading of trucks.

Loft building–A commercial/industrial type building containing large, open unpartitioned floor areas.

Louver window–A window composed of a series of sloping, overlapping blades or slats that may be adjusted to admit varying degrees of air or light.

Main beam–The principal load bearing beam used to transmit loads directly to columns.

Mansard roof–A roof having a double pitch on all four sides, the lower level having the steeper pitch.

Mansion–An extremely large and imposing residence.

Masonry–The utilization of brick, stone, concrete or block for walls and other building components.

Mastic–A sealant or adhesive compound generally used as either a binding agent or floor finish.

Membrane fireproofing–A coating of metal lath and plaster to provide resistance to fire and heat.

Mesh reinforcement–An arrangement of wire tied or welded at their intersection to provide strength and resistance to cracking.

Metal lath–A diamond-shaped metallic base for plaster.

Mezzanine–A low story situated between two main floors.

Mill construction–A heavy timber construction that achieves fire resistance by using large wood structural members, noncombustible bearing and non-bearing walls and omitting concealed spaces under floors and roof.

Mixed occupancy–Two or more classes of occupancy in a single structure.

Molded brick–A specially shaped brick used for decorative purposes.

Monolithic concrete–Concrete poured in a continuous process so there are no joints.

Movable partition–A non-load bearing demountable partition that can be relocated and can be either ceiling height or partial height.

Moving walk–A continually moving horizontal passenger carrying device.

Multi-zone system–An air conditioning system that is capable of handling several individual zones simultaneously.

Net floor area–The usable, occupied area of a structure excluding stairwells, elevator shafts and wall thicknesses.

Non-combustible construction–Construction in which the walls, partitions and the structural members are of non-combustible materials.

Nurses call system–An electrically operated system for use by patients or personnel for summoning a nurse.

Occupancy rate–The number of persons per room, per dwelling unit, etc.

One-way joist connection–A framing system for floors and roofs in a concrete building consisting of a series of parallel joists supported by girders between columns.

Open web joist–A lightweight prefabricated metal chord truss.

Parapet–A low guarding wall at the point of a drop. That portion of the exterior wall that extends above the roof line.

Parging–A thin coat of mortar applied to a masonry wall used primarily for waterproofing purposes.

Parquet–Inlaid wood flooring set in a simple design.

Peaked roof–A roof of two or more slopes that rises to a peak.

Penthouse–A structure occupying usually half the roof area and used to house elevator, HVAC equipment, or other mechanical or electrical systems.

Pier–A column designed to support a concentrated load.

Pilaster–A column usually formed of the same material and integral with, but projecting from, a wall.

Pile–A concrete, wood or steel column usually less than 2′ in diameter which is driven or otherwise introduced into the soil to carry a vertical load or provide vertical support.

Pitched roof–A roof having one or more surfaces with a pitch greater than 10°.

Plenum–The space between the suspended ceiling and the floor above.

Plywood–Structural wood made of three or more layers of veneer and bonded together with glue.

Porch–A structure attached to a building to provide shelter for an entranceway or to serve as a semi-enclosed space.

Post and beam framing–A structural framing system where beams rest on posts rather than bearing walls.

Post-tensioned concrete–Concrete that has the reinforcing tendons tensioned after the concrete has set.

Pre-cast concrete–Concrete structural components fabricated at a location other than in-place.

Pre-stressed concrete–Concrete that has the reinforcing tendons tensioned prior to the concrete setting.

Purlins–A horizontal structural member supporting the roof deck and resting on the trusses, girders, beams or rafters.

Rafters–Structural members supporting the roof deck and covering.

Resilient flooring–A manufactured interior floor covering material in either sheet or tile form, that is resilient.

Ridge–The horizontal line at the junction of two sloping roof edges.

Rigid frame–A structural framing system in which all columns and beams are rigidly connected; there are no hinged joints.

Roof drain–A drain designed to accept rainwater and discharge it into a leader or downspout.

Rough floor–A layer of boards or plywood nailed to the floor joists that serves as a base for the finished floor.

Sanitary sewer–A sewer line designed to carry only liquid or waterborne waste from the structure to a central treatment plant.

Sawtooth roof–Roof shape found primarily in industrial roofs that creates the appearance of the teeth of a saw.

Semi-rigid frame–A structural system wherein the columns and beams are so attached that there is some flexibility at the joints.

Septic tank–A covered tank in which waste matter is decomposed by natural bacterial action.

Service elevator–A combination passenger and freight elevator.

Sheathing–The first covering of exterior studs by boards, plywood or particle board.

Shoring–Temporary bracing for structural components during construction.

Span–The horizontal distance between supports.

Specification–A detailed list of materials and requirements for construction of a building.

Storm sewer–A system of pipes used to carry rainwater or surface waters.

Stucco–A cement plaster used to cover exterior wall surfaces usually applied over a wood or metal lath base.

Stud–A vertical wooden structural component.

Subfloor–A system of boards, plywood or particle board laid over the floor joists to form a base.

Superstructure–That portion of the structure above the foundation or ground level.

Terrazzo–A durable floor finish made of small chips of colored stone or marble, embedded in concrete, then polished to a high sheen.

Tile–A thin piece of fired clay, stone or concrete used for floor, roof or wall finishes.

Unit cost–The cost per unit of measurement.

Vault–A room especially designed for storage.

Veneer–A thin surface layer covering a base of common material.

Vent–An opening serving as an outlet for air.

Wainscot–The lower portion of an interior wall whose surface differs from that of the upper wall.

Wall bearing construction–A structural system where the weight of the floors and roof are carried directly by the masonry walls rather than the structural framing system.

Waterproofing–Any of a number of materials applied to various surfaces to prevent the infiltration of water.

Weatherstrip–A thin strip of metal, wood or felt used to cover the joint between the door or window sash and the jamb, casing or sill to keep out air, dust, rain, etc.

Wing–A building section or addition projecting from the main structure.

X-ray protection–Lead encased in sheetrock or plaster to prevent the escape of radiation.

A	Area Square Feet; Ampere	Brk., brk	Brick
AAFES	Army and Air Force Exchange Service	brkt	Bracket
		Brng.	Bearing
ABS	Acrylonitrile Butadiene Stryrene; Asbestos Bonded Steel	Brs.	Brass
		Brz.	Bronze
A.C., AC	Alternating Current; Air-Conditioning; Asbestos Cement; Plywood Grade A & C	Bsn.	Basin
		Btr.	Better
		Btu	British Thermal Unit
		BTUH	BTU per Hour
ACI	American Concrete Institute	Bu.	bushels
ACR	Air Conditioning Refrigeration	BUR	Built-up Roofing
ADA	Americans with Disabilities Act	BX	Interlocked Armored Cable
AD	Plywood, Grade A & D	°C	degree centegrade
Addit.	Additional	c	Conductivity, Copper Sweat
Adj.	Adjustable	C	Hundred; Centigrade
af	Audio-frequency	C/C	Center to Center, Cedar on Cedar
AFUE	Annual Fuel Utilization Efficiency	C-C	Center to Center
AGA	American Gas Association	Cab	Cabinet
Agg.	Aggregate	Cair.	Air Tool Laborer
A.H., Ah	Ampere Hours	Cal.	caliper
A hr.	Ampere-hour	Calc	Calculated
A.H.U., AHU	Air Handling Unit	Cap.	Capacity
A.I.A.	American Institute of Architects	Carp.	Carpenter
AIC	Ampere Interrupting Capacity	C.B.	Circuit Breaker
Allow.	Allowance	C.C.A.	Chromate Copper Arsenate
alt., alt	Alternate	C.C.F.	Hundred Cubic Feet
Alum.	Aluminum	cd	Candela
a.m.	Ante Meridiem	cd/sf	Candela per Square Foot
Amp.	Ampere	CD	Grade of Plywood Face & Back
Anod.	Anodized	CDX	Plywood, Grade C & D, exterior glue
ANSI	American National Standards Institute	Cefi.	Cement Finisher
		Cem.	Cement
APA	American Plywood Association	CF	Hundred Feet
Approx.	Approximate	C.F.	Cubic Feet
Apt.	Apartment	CFM	Cubic Feet per Minute
Asb.	Asbestos	CFRP	Carbon Fiber Reinforced Plastic
A.S.B.C.	American Standard Building Code	c.g.	Center of Gravity
Asbe.	Asbestos Worker	CHW	Chilled Water; Commercial Hot Water
ASCE.	American Society of Civil Engineers		
A.S.H.R.A.E.	American Society of Heating, Refrig. & AC Engineers	C.I., CI	Cast Iron
		C.I.P., CIP	Cast in Place
ASME	American Society of Mechanical Engineers	Circ.	Circuit
		C.L.	Carload Lot
ASTM	American Society for Testing and Materials	CL	Chain Link
		Clab.	Common Laborer
Attchmt.	Attachment	Clam	Common maintenance laborer
Avg., Ave.	Average	C.L.F.	Hundred Linear Feet
AWG	American Wire Gauge	CLF	Current Limiting Fuse
AWWA	American Water Works Assoc.	CLP	Cross Linked Polyethylene
Bbl.	Barrel	cm	Centimeter
B&B, BB	Grade B and Better; Balled & Burlapped	CMP	Corr. Metal Pipe
		CMU	Concrete Masonry Unit
B&S	Bell and Spigot	CN	Change Notice
B.&W.	Black and White	Col.	Column
b.c.c.	Body-centered Cubic	CO₂	Carbon Dioxide
B.C.Y.	Bank Cubic Yards	Comb.	Combination
BE	Bevel End	comm.	Commercial, Communication
B.F.	Board Feet	Compr.	Compressor
Bg. cem.	Bag of Cement	Conc.	Concrete
BHP	Boiler Horsepower; Brake Horsepower	Cont., cont	Continuous; Continued, Container
		Corr.	Corrugated
B.I.	Black Iron	Cos	Cosine
bidir.	bidirectional	Cot	Cotangent
Bit., Bitum.	Bituminous	Cov.	Cover
Bit., Conc.	Bituminous Concrete	C/P	Cedar on Paneling
Bk.	Backed	CPA	Control Point Adjustment
Bkrs.	Breakers	Cplg.	Coupling
Bldg., bldg	Building	CPM	Critical Path Method
Blk.	Block	CPVC	Chlorinated Polyvinyl Chloride
Bm.	Beam	C.Pr.	Hundred Pair
Boil.	Boilermaker	CRC	Cold Rolled Channel
bpm	Blows per Minute	Creos.	Creosote
BR	Bedroom	Crpt.	Carpet & Linoleum Layer
Brg.	Bearing	CRT	Cathode-ray Tube
Brhe.	Bricklayer Helper	CS	Carbon Steel, Constant Shear Bar Joist
Bric.	Bricklayer		

Csc	Cosecant
C.S.F.	Hundred Square Feet
CSI	Construction Specifications Institute
CT	Current Transformer
CTS	Copper Tube Size
Cu	Copper, Cubic
Cu. Ft.	Cubic Foot
cw	Continuous Wave
C.W.	Cool White; Cold Water
Cwt.	100 Pounds
C.W.X.	Cool White Deluxe
C.Y.	Cubic Yard (27 cubic feet)
C.Y./Hr.	Cubic Yard per Hour
Cyl.	Cylinder
d	Penny (nail size)
D	Deep; Depth; Discharge
Dis., Disch.	Discharge
Db	Decibel
Dbl.	Double
DC	Direct Current
DDC	Direct Digital Control
Demob.	Demobilization
d.f.t.	Dry Film Thickness
d.f.u.	Drainage Fixture Units
D.H.	Double Hung
DHW	Domestic Hot Water
DI	Ductile Iron
Diag.	Diagonal
Diam., Dia	Diameter
Distrib.	Distribution
Div.	Division
Dk.	Deck
D.L.	Dead Load; Diesel
DLH	Deep Long Span Bar Joist
dlx	Deluxe
Do.	Ditto
DOP	Dioctyl Phthalate Penetration Test (Air Filters)
Dp., dp	Depth
D.P.S.T.	Double Pole, Single Throw
Dr.	Drive
DR	Dimension Ratio
Drink.	Drinking
D.S.	Double Strength
D.S.A.	Double Strength A Grade
D.S.B.	Double Strength B Grade
Dty.	Duty
DWV	Drain Waste Vent
DX	Deluxe White, Direct Expansion
dyn	Dyne
e	Eccentricity
E	Equipment Only; East; emissivity
Ea.	Each
EB	Encased Burial
Econ.	Economy
E.C.Y	Embankment Cubic Yards
EDP	Electronic Data Processing
EIFS	Exterior Insulation Finish System
E.D.R.	Equiv. Direct Radiation
Eq.	Equation
EL	elevation
Elec.	Electrician; Electrical
Elev.	Elevator; Elevating
EMT	Electrical Metallic Conduit; Thin Wall Conduit
Eng.	Engine, Engineered
EPDM	Ethylene Propylene Diene Monomer
EPS	Expanded Polystyrene
Eqhv.	Equip. Oper., Heavy
Eqlt.	Equip. Oper., Light
Eqmd.	Equip. Oper., Medium
Eqmm.	Equip. Oper., Master Mechanic
Eqol.	Equip. Oper., Oilers
Equip.	Equipment
ERW	Electric Resistance Welded

Abbreviation	Meaning
E.S.	Energy Saver
Est.	Estimated
esu	Electrostatic Units
E.W.	Each Way
EWT	Entering Water Temperature
Excav.	Excavation
excl	Excluding
Exp., exp	Expansion, Exposure
Ext., ext	Exterior; Extension
Extru.	Extrusion
f.	Fiber stress
F	Fahrenheit; Female; Fill
Fab., fab	Fabricated; fabric
FBGS	Fiberglass
F.C.	Footcandles
f.c.c.	Face-centered Cubic
f'c.	Compressive Stress in Concrete; Extreme Compressive Stress
F.E.	Front End
FEP	Fluorinated Ethylene Propylene (Teflon)
F.G.	Flat Grain
F.H.A.	Federal Housing Administration
Fig.	Figure
Fin.	Finished
FIPS	Female Iron Pipe Size
Fixt.	Fixture
FJP	Finger jointed and primed
Fl. Oz.	Fluid Ounces
Flr.	Floor
FM	Frequency Modulation; Factory Mutual
Fmg.	Framing
FM/UL	Factory Mutual/Underwriters Labs
Fdn.	Foundation
FNPT	Female National Pipe Thread
Fori.	Foreman, Inside
Foro.	Foreman, Outside
Fount.	Fountain
fpm	Feet per Minute
FPT	Female Pipe Thread
Fr	Frame
F.R.	Fire Rating
FRK	Foil Reinforced Kraft
FSK	Foil/scrim/kraft
FRP	Fiberglass Reinforced Plastic
FS	Forged Steel
FSC	Cast Body; Cast Switch Box
Ft., ft	Foot; Feet
Ftng.	Fitting
Ftg.	Footing
Ft lb.	Foot Pound
Furn.	Furniture
FVNR	Full Voltage Non-Reversing
FVR	Full Voltage Reversing
FXM	Female by Male
Fy.	Minimum Yield Stress of Steel
g	Gram
G	Gauss
Ga.	Gauge
Gal., gal.	Gallon
gpm, GPM	Gallon per Minute
Galv., galv	Galvanized
GC/MS	Gas Chromatograph/Mass Spectrometer
Gen.	General
GFI	Ground Fault Interrupter
GFRC	Glass Fiber Reinforced Concrete
Glaz.	Glazier
GPD	Gallons per Day
gpf	Gallon per flush
GPH	Gallons per Hour
GPM	Gallons per Minute
GR	Grade
Gran.	Granular
Grnd.	Ground
GVW	Gross Vehicle Weight
GWB	Gypsum wall board
H	High Henry
HC	High Capacity
H.D., HD	Heavy Duty; High Density
H.D.O.	High Density Overlaid
HDPE	High density polyethelene plastic
Hdr.	Header
Hdwe.	Hardware
H.I.D., HID	High Intensity Discharge
Help.	Helper Average
HEPA	High Efficiency Particulate Air Filter
Hg	Mercury
HIC	High Interrupting Capacity
HM	Hollow Metal
HMWPE	high molecular weight polyethylene
HO	High Output
Horiz.	Horizontal
H.P., HP	Horsepower; High Pressure
H.P.F.	High Power Factor
Hr.	Hour
Hrs./Day	Hours per Day
HSC	High Short Circuit
Ht.	Height
Htg.	Heating
Htrs.	Heaters
HVAC	Heating, Ventilation & Air-Conditioning
Hvy.	Heavy
HW	Hot Water
Hyd.; Hydr.	Hydraulic
Hz	Hertz (cycles)
I.	Moment of Inertia
IBC	International Building Code
I.C.	Interrupting Capacity
ID	Inside Diameter
I.D.	Inside Dimension; Identification
I.F.	Inside Frosted
I.M.C.	Intermediate Metal Conduit
In.	Inch
Incan.	Incandescent
Incl.	Included; Including
Int.	Interior
Inst.	Installation
Insul., insul	Insulation/Insulated
I.P.	Iron Pipe
I.P.S., IPS	Iron Pipe Size
IPT	Iron Pipe Threaded
I.W.	Indirect Waste
J	Joule
J.I.C.	Joint Industrial Council
K	Thousand; Thousand Pounds; Heavy Wall Copper Tubing, Kelvin
K.A.H.	Thousand Amp. Hours
kcmil	Thousand Circular Mils
KD	Knock Down
K.D.A.T.	Kiln Dried After Treatment
kg	Kilogram
kG	Kilogauss
kgf	Kilogram Force
kHz	Kilohertz
Kip	1000 Pounds
KJ	Kiljoule
K.L.	Effective Length Factor
K.L.F.	Kips per Linear Foot
Km	Kilometer
KO	Knock Out
K.S.F.	Kips per Square Foot
K.S.I.	Kips per Square Inch
kV	Kilovolt
kVA	Kilovolt Ampere
kVAR	Kilovar (Reactance)
KW	Kilowatt
KWh	Kilowatt-hour
L	Labor Only; Length; Long; Medium Wall Copper Tubing
Lab.	Labor
lat	Latitude
Lath.	Lather
Lav.	Lavatory
lb.; #	Pound
L.B., LB	Load Bearing; L Conduit Body
L. & E.	Labor & Equipment
lb./hr.	Pounds per Hour
lb./L.F.	Pounds per Linear Foot
lbf/sq.in.	Pound-force per Square Inch
L.C.L.	Less than Carload Lot
L.C.Y.	Loose Cubic Yard
Ld.	Load
LE	Lead Equivalent
LED	Light Emitting Diode
L.F.	Linear Foot
L.F. Nose	Linear Foot of Stair Nosing
L.F. Rsr	Linear Foot of Stair Riser
Lg.	Long; Length; Large
L & H	Light and Heat
LH	Long Span Bar Joist
L.H.	Labor Hours
L.L., LL	Live Load
L.L.D.	Lamp Lumen Depreciation
lm	Lumen
lm/sf	Lumen per Square Foot
lm/W	Lumen per Watt
LOA	Length Over All
log	Logarithm
L-O-L	Lateralolet
long.	longitude
L.P., LP	Liquefied Petroleum; Low Pressure
L.P.F.	Low Power Factor
LR	Long Radius
L.S.	Lump Sum
Lt.	Light
Lt. Ga.	Light Gauge
L.T.L.	Less than Truckload Lot
Lt. Wt.	Lightweight
L.V.	Low Voltage
M	Thousand; Material; Male; Light Wall Copper Tubing
M²CA	Meters Squared Contact Area
m/hr.; M.H.	Man-hour
mA	Milliampere
Mach.	Machine
Mag. Str.	Magnetic Starter
Maint.	Maintenance
Marb.	Marble Setter
Mat; Mat'l.	Material
Max.	Maximum
MBF	Thousand Board Feet
MBH	Thousand BTU's per hr.
MC	Metal Clad Cable
MCC	Motor Control Center
M.C.F.	Thousand Cubic Feet
MCFM	Thousand Cubic Feet per Minute
M.C.M.	Thousand Circular Mils
MCP	Motor Circuit Protector
MD	Medium Duty
MDF	Medium-density fibreboard
M.D.O.	Medium Density Overlaid
Med.	Medium
MF	Thousand Feet
M.F.B.M.	Thousand Feet Board Measure
Mfg.	Manufacturing
Mfrs.	Manufacturers
mg	Milligram
MGD	Million Gallons per Day
MGPH	Thousand Gallons per Hour
MH, M.H.	Manhole; Metal Halide; Man-Hour
MHz	Megahertz
Mi.	Mile
MI	Malleable Iron; Mineral Insulated
MIPS	Male Iron Pipe Size
mj	Mechanical Joint
m	Meter
mm	Millimeter
Mill.	Millwright
Min., min.	Minimum, minute

547

Abbreviations

Abbreviation	Meaning
Misc.	Miscellaneous
ml	Milliliter, Mainline
M.L.F.	Thousand Linear Feet
Mo.	Month
Mobil.	Mobilization
Mog.	Mogul Base
MPH	Miles per Hour
MPT	Male Pipe Thread
MRGWB	Moisture Resistant Gypsum Wallboard
MRT	Mile Round Trip
ms	Millisecond
M.S.F.	Thousand Square Feet
Mstz.	Mosaic & Terrazzo Worker
M.S.Y.	Thousand Square Yards
Mtd., mtd., mtd	Mounted
Mthe.	Mosaic & Terrazzo Helper
Mtng.	Mounting
Mult.	Multi; Multiply
M.V.A.	Million Volt Amperes
M.V.A.R.	Million Volt Amperes Reactance
MV	Megavolt
MW	Megawatt
MXM	Male by Male
MYD	Thousand Yards
N	Natural; North
nA	Nanoampere
NA	Not Available; Not Applicable
N.B.C.	National Building Code
NC	Normally Closed
NEMA	National Electrical Manufacturers Assoc.
NEHB	Bolted Circuit Breaker to 600V.
NFPA	National Fire Protection Association
NLB	Non-Load-Bearing
NM	Non-Metallic Cable
nm	Nanometer
No.	Number
NO	Normally Open
N.O.C.	Not Otherwise Classified
Nose.	Nosing
NPT	National Pipe Thread
NQOD	Combination Plug-on/Bolt on Circuit Breaker to 240V.
N.R.C., NRC	Noise Reduction Coefficient/ Nuclear Regulator Commission
N.R.S.	Non Rising Stem
ns	Nanosecond
nW	Nanowatt
OB	Opposing Blade
OC	On Center
OD	Outside Diameter
O.D.	Outside Dimension
ODS	Overhead Distribution System
O.G.	Ogee
O.H.	Overhead
O&P	Overhead and Profit
Oper.	Operator
Opng.	Opening
Orna.	Ornamental
OSB	Oriented Strand Board
OS&Y	Outside Screw and Yoke
OSHA	Occupational Safety and Health Act
Ovhd.	Overhead
OWG	Oil, Water or Gas
Oz.	Ounce
P.	Pole; Applied Load; Projection
p.	Page
Pape.	Paperhanger
P.A.P.R.	Powered Air Purifying Respirator
PAR	Parabolic Reflector
P.B., PB	Push Button
Pc., Pcs.	Piece, Pieces
P.C.	Portland Cement; Power Connector
P.C.F.	Pounds per Cubic Foot
PCM	Phase Contrast Microscopy
PDCA	Painting and Decorating Contractors of America
P.E., PE	Professional Engineer; Porcelain Enamel; Polyethylene; Plain End
P.E.C.I.	Porcelain Enamel on Cast Iron
Perf.	Perforated
PEX	Cross linked polyethylene
Ph.	Phase
P.I.	Pressure Injected
Pile.	Pile Driver
Pkg.	Package
Pl.	Plate
Plah.	Plasterer Helper
Plas.	Plasterer
plf	Pounds Per Linear Foot
Pluh.	Plumbers Helper
Plum.	Plumber
Ply.	Plywood
p.m.	Post Meridiem
Pntd.	Painted
Pord.	Painter, Ordinary
pp	Pages
PP, PPL	Polypropylene
P.P.M.	Parts per Million
Pr.	Pair
P.E.S.B.	Pre-engineered Steel Building
Prefab.	Prefabricated
Prefin.	Prefinished
Prop.	Propelled
PSF, psf	Pounds per Square Foot
PSI, psi	Pounds per Square Inch
PSIG	Pounds per Square Inch Gauge
PSP	Plastic Sewer Pipe
Pspr.	Painter, Spray
Psst.	Painter, Structural Steel
P.T.	Potential Transformer
P. & T.	Pressure & Temperature
Ptd.	Painted
Ptns.	Partitions
Pu	Ultimate Load
PVC	Polyvinyl Chloride
Pvmt.	Pavement
PRV	Pressure Relief Valve
Pwr.	Power
Q	Quantity Heat Flow
Qt.	Quart
Quan., Qty.	Quantity
Q.C.	Quick Coupling
r	Radius of Gyration
R	Resistance
R.C.P.	Reinforced Concrete Pipe
Rect.	Rectangle
recpt.	receptacle
Reg.	Regular
Reinf.	Reinforced
Req'd.	Required
Res.	Resistant
Resi.	Residential
RF	Radio Frequency
RFID	Radio-frequency identification
Rgh.	Rough
RGS	Rigid Galvanized Steel
RHW	Rubber, Heat & Water Resistant; Residential Hot Water
rms	Root Mean Square
Rnd.	Round
Rodm.	Rodman
Rofc.	Roofer, Composition
Rofp.	Roofer, Precast
Rohe.	Roofer Helpers (Composition)
Rots.	Roofer, Tile & Slate
R.O.W.	Right of Way
RPM	Revolutions per Minute
R.S.	Rapid Start
Rsr	Riser
RT	Round Trip
S.	Suction; Single Entrance; South
SBS	Styrene Butadiere Styrene
SC	Screw Cover
SCFM	Standard Cubic Feet per Minute
Scaf.	Scaffold
Sch., Sched.	Schedule
S.C.R.	Modular Brick
S.D.	Sound Deadening
SDR	Standard Dimension Ratio
S.E.	Surfaced Edge
Sel.	Select
SER, SEU	Service Entrance Cable
S.F.	Square Foot
S.F.C.A.	Square Foot Contact Area
S.F. Flr.	Square Foot of Floor
S.F.G.	Square Foot of Ground
S.F. Hor.	Square Foot Horizontal
SFR	Square Feet of Radiation
S.F. Shlf.	Square Foot of Shelf
S4S	Surface 4 Sides
Shee.	Sheet Metal Worker
Sin.	Sine
Skwk.	Skilled Worker
SL	Saran Lined
S.L.	Slimline
Sldr.	Solder
SLH	Super Long Span Bar Joist
S.N.	Solid Neutral
SO	Stranded with oil resistant inside insulation
S-O-L	Socketolet
sp	Standpipe
S.P.	Static Pressure; Single Pole; Self-Propelled
Spri.	Sprinkler Installer
spwg	Static Pressure Water Gauge
S.P.D.T.	Single Pole, Double Throw
SPF	Spruce Pine Fir; Sprayed Polyurethane Foam
S.P.S.T.	Single Pole, Single Throw
SPT	Standard Pipe Thread
Sq.	Square; 100 Square Feet
Sq. Hd.	Square Head
Sq. In.	Square Inch
S.S.	Single Strength; Stainless Steel
S.S.B.	Single Strength B Grade
sst, ss	Stainless Steel
Sswk.	Structural Steel Worker
Sswl.	Structural Steel Welder
St.; Stl.	Steel
STC	Sound Transmission Coefficient
Std.	Standard
Stg.	Staging
STK	Select Tight Knot
STP	Standard Temperature & Pressure
Stpi.	Steamfitter, Pipefitter
Str.	Strength; Starter; Straight
Strd.	Stranded
Struct.	Structural
Sty.	Story
Subj.	Subject
Subs.	Subcontractors
Surf.	Surface
Sw.	Switch
Swbd.	Switchboard
S.Y.	Square Yard
Syn.	Synthetic
S.Y.P.	Southern Yellow Pine
Sys.	System
t.	Thickness
T	Temperature; Ton
Tan	Tangent
T.C.	Terra Cotta
T & C	Threaded and Coupled
T.D.	Temperature Difference
Tdd	Telecommunications Device for the Deaf
T.E.M.	Transmission Electron Microscopy
temp	Temperature, Tempered, Temporary
TFFN	Nylon Jacketed Wire

TFE	Tetrafluoroethylene (Teflon)	U.L., UL	Underwriters Laboratory	w/	With
T. & G.	Tongue & Groove;	Uld.	unloading	W.C., WC	Water Column; Water Closet
	Tar & Gravel	Unfin.	Unfinished	W.F.	Wide Flange
Th., Thk.	Thick	UPS	Uninterruptible Power Supply	W.G.	Water Gauge
Thn.	Thin	URD	Underground Residential	Wldg.	Welding
Thrded	Threaded		Distribution	W. Mile	Wire Mile
Tilf.	Tile Layer, Floor	US	United States	W-O-L	Weldolet
Tilh.	Tile Layer, Helper	USGBC	U.S. Green Building Council	W.R.	Water Resistant
THHN	Nylon Jacketed Wire	USP	United States Primed	Wrck.	Wrecker
THW.	Insulated Strand Wire	UTMCD	Uniform Traffic Manual For Control	W.S.P.	Water, Steam, Petroleum
THWN	Nylon Jacketed Wire		Devices	WT., Wt.	Weight
T.L., TL	Truckload	UTP	Unshielded Twisted Pair	WWF	Welded Wire Fabric
T.M.	Track Mounted	V	Volt	XFER	Transfer
Tot.	Total	VA	Volt Amperes	XFMR	Transformer
T-O-L	Threadolet	V.C.T.	Vinyl Composition Tile	XHD	Extra Heavy Duty
tmpd	Tempered	VAV	Variable Air Volume	XHHW,	Cross-Linked Polyethylene Wire
TPO	Thermoplastic Polyolefin	VC	Veneer Core	XLPE	Insulation
T.S.	Trigger Start	VDC	Volts Direct Current	XLP	Cross-linked Polyethylene
Tr.	Trade	Vent.	Ventilation	Xport	Transport
Transf.	Transformer	Vert.	Vertical	Y	Wye
Trhv.	Truck Driver, Heavy	V.F.	Vinyl Faced	yd	Yard
Trlr	Trailer	V.G.	Vertical Grain	yr	Year
Trlt.	Truck Driver, Light	VHF	Very High Frequency	Δ	Delta
TTY	Teletypewriter	VHO	Very High Output	%	Percent
TV	Television	Vib.	Vibrating	~	Approximately
T.W.	Thermoplastic Water Resistant	VLF	Vertical Linear Foot	Ø	Phase; diameter
	Wire	VOC	Volitile Organic Compound	@	At
UCI	Uniform Construction Index	Vol.	Volume	#	Pound; Number
UF	Underground Feeder	VRP	Vinyl Reinforced Polyester	<	Less Than
UGND	Underground Feeder	W	Wire; Watt; Wide; West	>	Greater Than
UHF	Ultra High Frequency			Z	zone
U.I.	United Inch				

FORMS

RESIDENTIAL COST ESTIMATE

OWNER'S NAME: _____ APPRAISER: _____

RESIDENCE ADDRESS: _____ PROJECT: _____

CITY, STATE, ZIP CODE: _____ DATE: _____

CLASS OF CONSTRUCTION
- ☐ ECONOMY
- ☐ AVERAGE
- ☐ CUSTOM
- ☐ LUXURY

RESIDENCE TYPE
- ☐ 1 STORY
- ☐ 1-1/2 STORY
- ☐ 2 STORY
- ☐ 2-1/2 STORY
- ☐ 3 STORY
- ☐ BI-LEVEL
- ☐ TRI-LEVEL

CONFIGURATION
- ☐ DETACHED
- ☐ TOWN/ROW HOUSE
- ☐ SEMI-DETACHED

OCCUPANCY
- ☐ ONE STORY
- ☐ TWO FAMILY
- ☐ THREE FAMILY
- ☐ OTHER _____

EXTERIOR WALL SYSTEM
- ☐ WOOD SIDING—WOOD FRAME
- ☐ BRICK VENEER—WOOD FRAME
- ☐ STUCCO ON WOOD FRAME
- ☐ PAINTED CONCRETE BLOCK
- ☐ SOLID MASONRY (AVERAGE & CUSTOM)
- ☐ STONE VENEER—WOOD FRAME
- ☐ SOLID BRICK (LUXURY)
- ☐ SOLID STONE (LUXURY)

*LIVING AREA (Main Building)

First Level _____ S.F.
Second Level _____ S.F.
Third Level _____ S.F.
Total _____ S.F.

*LIVING AREA (Wing or Ell) ( )

First Level _____ S.F.
Second Level _____ S.F.
Third Level _____ S.F.
Total _____ S.F.

*LIVING AREA (Wing or Ell) ( )

First Level _____ S.F.
Second Level _____ S.F.
Third Level _____ S.F.
Total _____ S.F.

*Basement Area is not part of living area.

MAIN BUILDING	COSTS PER S.F. LIVING AREA
Cost per Square Foot of Living Area, from Page _____	$
Basement Addition: _____ % Finished, _____ % Unfinished	+
Roof Cover Adjustment: _____ Type, Page _____ (Add or Deduct)	( )
Central Air Conditioning: ☐ Separate Ducts ☐ Heating Ducts, Page _____	+
Heating System Adjustment: _____ Type, Page _____ (Add or Deduct)	( )
Main Building: Adjusted Cost per S.F. of Living Area	$

MAIN BUILDING TOTAL COST: $ _____ /S.F. (Cost per S.F. Living Area) x _____ S.F. (Living Area) x _____ Town/Row House Multiplier (Use 1 for Detached) = $ _____ TOTAL COST

WING OR ELL ( ) _____ STORY	COSTS PER S.F. LIVING AREA
Cost per Square Foot of Living Area, from Page _____	$
Basement Addition: _____ % Finished, _____ % Unfinished	+
Roof Cover Adjustment: _____ Type, Page _____ (Add or Deduct)	( )
Central Air Conditioning: ☐ Separate Ducts ☐ Heating Ducts, Page _____	+
Heating System Adjustment: _____ Type, Page _____ (Add or Deduct)	( )
Wing or Ell ( ): Adjusted Cost per S.F. of Living Area	$

WING OR ELL ( ) TOTAL COST: $ _____ /S.F. (Cost per S.F. Living Area) x _____ S.F. (Living Area) = $ _____ TOTAL COST

WING OR ELL ( ) _____ STORY	COSTS PER S.F. LIVING AREA
Cost per Square Foot of Living Area, from Page _____	$
Basement Addition: _____ % Finished, _____ % Unfinished	+
Roof Cover Adjustment: _____ Type, Page _____ (Add or Deduct)	( )
Central Air Conditioning: ☐ Separate Ducts ☐ Heating Ducts, Page _____	+
Heating System Adjustment: _____ Type, Page _____ (Add or Deduct)	( )
Wing or Ell ( ): Adjusted Cost per S.F. of Living Area	$

WING OR ELL ( ) TOTAL COST: $ _____ /S.F. (Cost per S.F. Living Area) x _____ S.F. (Living Area) = $ _____ TOTAL COST

TOTAL THIS PAGE [_____]

**RESIDENTIAL
COST ESTIMATE**

Total Page 1				$
		QUANTITY	UNIT COST	
Additional Bathrooms: _____ Full, _____ Half				
Finished Attic: _____ Ft. x _____ Ft.		S.F.		+
Breezeway: ☐ Open ☐ Enclosed _____ Ft. x _____ Ft.		S.F.		+
Covered Porch: ☐ Open ☐ Enclosed _____ Ft. x _____ Ft.		S.F.		+
Fireplace: ☐ Interior Chimney ☐ Exterior Chimney ☐ No. of Flues ☐ Additional Fireplaces				+
Appliances:				+
Kitchen Cabinets Adjustment: (+/−)				
☐ Garage ☐ Carport: _____ Car(s) Description _____ (+/−)				
Miscellaneous:				+

ADJUSTED TOTAL BUILDING COST | $ |

REPLACEMENT COST	
ADJUSTED TOTAL BUILDING COST	$ _____
Site Improvements	
(A) Paving & Sidewalks	$ _____
(B) Landscaping	$ _____
(C) Fences	$ _____
(D) Swimming Pool	$ _____
(E) Miscellaneous	$ _____
TOTAL	$ _____
Location Factor	x _____
Location Replacement Cost	$ _____
Depreciation	−$ _____
LOCAL DEPRECIATED COST	$ _____

INSURANCE COST	
ADJUSTED TOTAL BUILDING COST	$ _____
Insurance Exclusions	
(A) Footings, Site Work, Underground Piping	−$ _____
(B) Architects' Fees	−$ _____
Total Building Cost Less Exclusion	$ _____
Location Factor	x _____
LOCAL INSURABLE REPLACEMENT COST	$ _____

SKETCH AND ADDITIONAL CALCULATIONS

CII APPRAISAL

1. SUBJECT PROPERTY: _____
2. BUILDING: _____
3. ADDRESS: _____
4. BUILDING USE: _____

5. DATE: _____
6. APPRAISER: _____

7. YEAR BUILT: _____

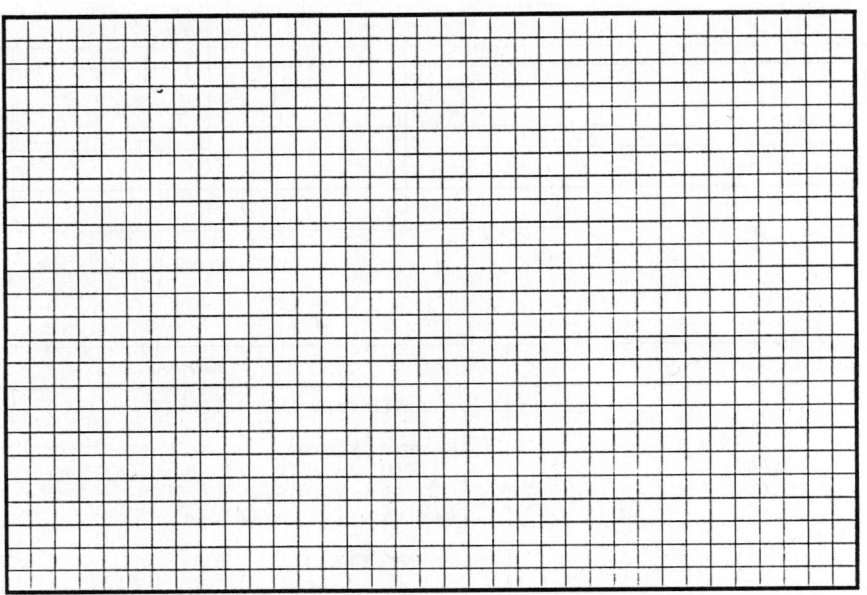

8. EXTERIOR WALL CONSTRUCTION: _____
9. FRAME: _____
10. GROUND FLOOR AREA: _____ S.F.   11. GROSS FLOOR AREA (EXCL. BASEMENT): _____ S.F.
12. NUMBER OF STORIES: _____   13. STORY HEIGHT: _____
14. PERIMETER: _____ L.F.   15. BASEMENT AREA: _____ S.F.
16. GENERAL COMMENTS: _____
_____
_____
_____
_____
_____
_____

NO.		DESCRIPTION		UNIT	UNIT COST	NEW SF COST	MODEL SF COST	+/- CHANGE
A SUBSTRUCTURE								
A	1010	Standard Foundations	Bay size:	S.F. Gnd.				
A	1030	Slab on Grade Material:	Thickness:	S.F. Slab				
A	2010	Basement Excavation Depth:	Area:	S.F. Gnd.				
A	2020	Basement Walls		L.F. Walls				
B SHELL								
	B10 Superstructure							
B	1010	Floor Construction Elevated floors:		S.F. Floor				
				S.F. Floor				
B	1020	Roof Construction		S.F. Roof				
	B20 Exterior Enclosure							
B	2010	Exterior walls Material:	Thickness: % of wall	S.F. Walls				
		Material:	Thickness: % of wall	S.F. Walls				
B	2020	Exterior Windows Type:	% of wall	S.F. Wind.				
		Type:	% of wall Each	S.F. Wind.				
B	2030	Exterior Doors Type:	Number:	Each				
		Type:	Number:	Each				
	B30 Roofing							
B	3010	Roof Coverings Material:		S.F. Roof				
		Material:		S.F. Roof				
B	3020	Roof Openings		S.F. Opng.				
C INTERIORS								
C	1010	Partitions: Material:	Density:	S.F. Part.				
		Material:	Density:					
C	1020	Interior Doors Type:	Number:	Each				
C	1030	Fittings		Each				
C	2010	Stair Construction		Flight				
C	3010	Wall Finishes Material:	% of Wall	S.F. Walls				
		Material:		S.F. Walls				
C	3020	Floor Finishes Material:		S.F. Floor				
		Material:		S.F. Floor				
		Material:		S.F. Floor				
C	3030	Ceiling Finishes Material:		S.F. Ceil.				

	NO.	SYSTEM/COMPONENT	DESCRIPTION	UNIT	UNIT COST	NEW S.F. COST	MODEL S.F. COST	+/- CHANGE
D SERVICES								
	D10 Conveying							
D	1010	Elevators & Lifts	Type: Capacity: Stops:	Each				
D	1020	Escalators & Moving Walks	Type:	Each				
	D20 Plumbing							
D	2010	Plumbing		Each				
D	2020	Domestic Water Distribution		S.F. Floor				
D	2040	Rain Water Drainage		S.F. Roof				
	D30 HVAC							
D	3010	Energy Supply		Each				
D	3020	Heat Generating Systems	Type:	S.F. Floor				
D	3030	Cooling Generating Systems	Type:	S.F. Floor				
D	3090	Other HVAC Sys. & Equipment		Each				
	D40 Fire Protection							
D	4010	Sprinklers		S.F. Floor				
D	4020	Standpipes		S.F. Floor				
	D50 Electrical							
D	5010	Electrical Service/Distribution		S.F. Floor				
D	5020	Lighting & Branch Wiring		S.F. Floor				
D	5030	Communications & Security		S.F. Floor				
D	5090	Other Electrical Systems		S.F. Floor				
E EQUIPMENT & FURNISHINGS								
E	1010	Commercial Equipment		Each				
E	1020	Institutional Equipment		Each				
E	1030	Vehicular Equipment		Each				
E	1090	Other Equipment		Each				
F SPECIAL CONSTRUCTION								
F	1020	Integrated Construction		S.F.				
F	1040	Special Facilities		S.F.				
G BUILDING SITEWORK								

Total Change

ITEM		
17	Model 020 total ____ $ _____	
18	Adjusted S.F. cost____ $ _____ item 17 +/- changes	
19	Building area - from item 11 _____ S.F. x adjusted S.F. cost..	$...
20	Basement area - from item 15 _____ S.F. x S.F. cost $	$..
21	Base building sub-total - item 20 + item 19	$.....
22	Miscellaneous addition (quality, etc.)	$......
23	Sub-total - item 22 + 21	$.......
24	General conditions -25 % of item 23	$......
25	Sub-total - item 24 + item 23..	$.......
26	Architects fees _____ % of item 25	$
27	Sub-total - item 26 + item 27	$......
28	Location modifier	x....
29	Local replacement cost - item 28 x item 27	$.....
30	Depreciation _____ % of item 29	$
31	Depreciated local replacement cost - item 29 less item 30	$.....
32	Exclusions	$........
33	Net depreciated replacement cost - item 31 less item 32	$....

Base Cost per square foot floor area: *(from square foot table)*

Specify source:

> Page: _____ , Model # _____ , Area _____ S.F.,
> Exterior wall _____ , Frame _____

Adjustments for exterior wall variation:

Size Adjustment:
  (Interpolate)

Height Adjustment: _____ + _____ = _____

Adjusted Base Cost per square foot:

Building Cost $ _____ x _____ = _____
                   Adjusted Base Cost   *Floor Area*
                   per square foot

Basement Cost $ _____ x _____ = _____
                      Basement Cost   *Basement Area*

Lump Sum Additions

TOTAL BUILDING COST *(Sum of above costs)*   _____

Modifications: *(complexity, workmanship, size)*   +/- _____ %   _____

Location Modifier: City _____ Date _____   x   _____

       Local cost of replacement   _____

Less depreciation: _____   -   _____

       Local cost of replacement less depreciation $ _____

Notes

560

Reed Construction Data/RSMeans—
a tradition of excellence in construction cost
information and services since 1942

For more information visit the RSMeans website at **www.rsmeans.com**

Table of Contents
Annual Cost Guides
Seminars
New Titles
Reference Books
Order Form

Unit prices according to the latest MasterFormat!

Book Selection Guide

The following table provides definitive information on the content of each cost data publication. The number of lines of data provided in each unit price or assemblies division, as well as the number of reference tables and crews, is listed for each book. The presence of other elements such as equipment rental costs, historical cost indexes, city cost indexes, square foot models, or cross-referenced indexes is also indicated. You can use the table to help select the RSMeans book that has the quantity and type of information you most need in your work.

Unit Cost Divisions	Building Construction	Mechanical	Electrical	Commercial Renovation	Square Foot	Site Work Landsc.	Green Building	Interior	Concrete Masonry	Open Shop	Heavy Construction	Light Commercial	Facilities Construction	Plumbing	Residential
1	582	395	411	508	521	196	319	463	581	511	244	1054	411	180
2	789	279	85	741	1005	180	399	222	788	746	481	1233	289	257
3	1689	347	231	1087	1477	995	329	2040	1688	1685	479	1787	317	385
4	963	21	0	932	729	179	620	1159	931	621	521	1176	0	435
5	1873	158	155	1068	811	1779	1073	716	1873	1034	954	1874	204	723
6	2404	18	18	2062	110	560	1523	278	2400	126	2085	2076	22	2612
7	1531	215	128	1569	584	747	516	509	1528	26	1282	1633	227	1018
8	2107	81	45	2530	268	1140	1768	112	2093	0	2109	2842	0	1511
9	1929	72	26	1726	313	449	2014	387	1870	15	1644	2179	54	1430
10	1006	17	10	623	215	27	818	158	1006	29	511	1098	235	224
11	1026	208	165	489	126	54	878	28	1010	0	230	1046	169	110
12	557	0	2	327	248	151	1669	12	545	19	364	1718	23	317
13	729	117	114	246	347	128	253	66	728	253	82	756	71	80
14	277	36	0	224	0	0	261	0	277	0	12	297	16	6
21	90	0	16	37	0	0	250	0	87	0	68	427	432	220
22	1159	7329	156	1170	1578	1099	849	20	1123	1687	861	7171	9082	712
23	1182	6901	586	886	160	898	741	38	1106	111	759	5013	1830	434
26	1379	499	10134	1039	816	661	1142	55	1351	562	1305	10083	444	621
27	72	0	298	34	13	0	60	0	72	39	52	280	0	4
28	97	58	137	72	0	21	79	0	100	0	41	152	44	26
31	1498	735	610	803	3206	289	7	1208	1443	3285	600	1560	660	611
32	782	54	8	859	4396	352	362	286	753	1824	407	1660	166	455
33	509	1020	542	209	2036	41	0	231	508	2024	120	1585	1211	118
34	109	0	47	4	192	0	0	31	64	195	0	130	0	0
35	18	0	0	0	327	0	0	0	18	442	0	83	0	0
41	60	0	0	32	0	0	22	0	60	30	0	67	14	0
44	75	83	0	0	0	0	0	0	0	0	0	75	75	0
46	23	16	0	0	274	151	0	0	23	264	0	33	33	0
48	12	0	27	0	0	27	0	0	12	19	12	12	0	12
Totals	**24527**	**18659**	**13951**	**19277**	**19752**	**10124**	**15952**	**8019**	**24038**	**15547**	**15223**	**49100**	**16029**	**12501**

Assem Div	Building Construction	Mechanical	Electrical	Commercial Renovation	Square Foot	Site Work Landscape	Assemblies	Green Building	Interior	Concrete Masonry	Heavy Construction	Light Commercial	Facilities Construction	Plumbing	Asm Div	Residential
A		15	0	188	150	577	598	0	0	536	571	154	24	0	1	368
B		0	0	848	2498	0	5658	56	329	1975	368	2089	174	0	2	211
C		0	0	647	872	0	1251	0	1576	146	0	762	249	0	3	588
D		1067	943	712	1856	72	2532	330	822	0	0	1342	1106	1081	4	851
E		0	0	86	260	0	300	0	5	0	0	257	5	0	5	392
F		0	0	0	114	0	114	0	0	0	0	114	3	0	6	357
G		522	442	318	262	3740	663	0	0	534	1558	199	288	758	7	307
															8	760
															9	80
															10	0
															11	0
															12	0
Totals		**1604**	**1385**	**2799**	**6012**	**4389**	**11116**	**386**	**2732**	**3191**	**2497**	**4917**	**1849**	**1839**		**3914**

Reference Section	Building Construction Costs	Mechanical	Electrical	Commercial Renovation	Square Foot	Site Work Landscape	Assem.	Green Building	Interior	Concrete Masonry	Open Shop	Heavy Construction	Light Commercial	Facilities Construction	Plumbing	Resi.
Reference Tables	yes	yes	yes	yes	no	yes	yes	yes	yes	yes	yes	yes	yes	yes	yes	yes
Models					111			25					50			28
Crews	561	561	561	540		561		558	561	561	538	561	538	540	561	538
Equipment Rental Costs	yes	yes	yes	yes		yes		yes	yes	yes	yes	yes	yes	yes	yes	yes
Historical Cost Indexes	yes	yes	yes	yes	yes	yes	yes	yes	yes	yes	yes	yes	yes	yes	yes	no
City Cost Indexes	yes	yes	yes	yes	yes	yes	yes	yes	yes	yes	yes	yes	yes	yes	yes	yes

RSMeans Building Construction Cost Data 2014

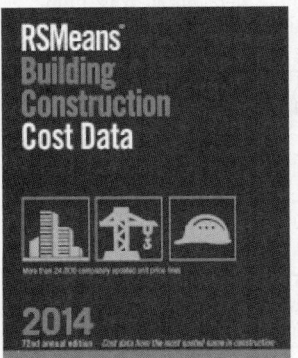

Offers you unchallenged unit price reliability in an easy-to-use format. Whether used for verifying complete, finished estimates or for periodic checks, it supplies more cost facts better and faster than any comparable source. More than 24,000 unit prices have been updated for 2014. The City Cost Indexes and Location Factors cover more than 930 areas, for indexing to any project location in North America. Order and get *RSMeans Quarterly Update Service* FREE.

$194.95 | Available Sept. 2013 | Catalog no. 60014

RSMeans Green Building Cost Data 2014

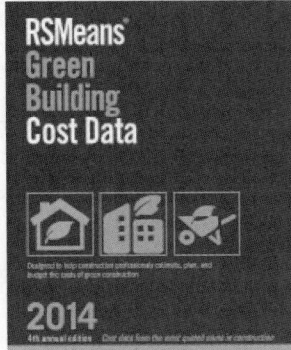

Estimate, plan, and budget the costs of green building for both new commercial construction and renovation work with this fourth edition of *RSMeans Green Building Cost Data*. More than 10,000 unit costs for a wide array of green building products plus assemblies costs. Easily identified cross references to LEED and Green Globes building rating systems criteria.

$160.95 | Available Nov. 2013 | Catalog no. 60554

RSMeans Mechanical Cost Data 2014

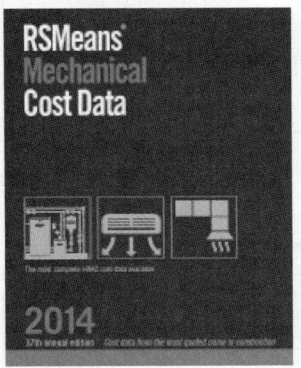

Total unit and systems price guidance for mechanical construction . . . materials, parts, fittings, and complete labor cost information. Includes prices for piping, heating, air conditioning, ventilation, and all related construction.

Plus new 2014 unit costs for:

- Thousands of installed HVAC/controls assemblies components
- "On-site" Location Factors for more than 930 cities and towns in the U.S. and Canada
- Crews, labor, and equipment

$191.95 | Available Oct. 2013 | Catalog no. 60024

RSMeans Facilities Construction Cost Data 2014

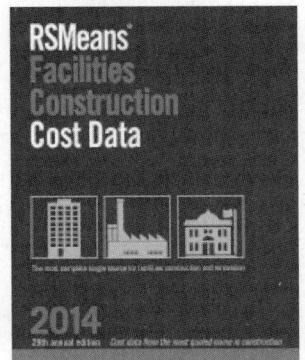

For the maintenance and construction of commercial, industrial, municipal, and institutional properties. Costs are shown for new and remodeling construction and are broken down into materials, labor, equipment, and overhead and profit. Special emphasis is given to sections on mechanical, electrical, furnishings, site work, building maintenance, finish work, and demolition.

More than 49,000 unit costs, plus assemblies costs and a comprehensive Reference Section are included.

$496.95 | Available Nov. 2013 | Catalog no. 60204

RSMeans Square Foot Costs 2014
Accurate and Easy-to-Use

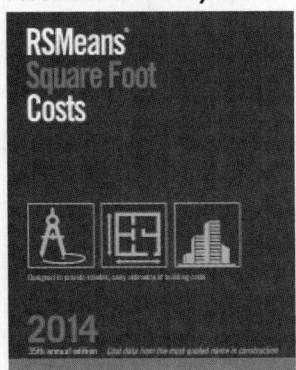

- **Updated price information** based on nationwide figures from suppliers, estimators, labor experts, and contractors
- New green building models
- Realistic graphics, offering true-to-life illustrations of building projects
- Extensive information on using square foot cost data, including sample estimates and alternate pricing methods

$205.95 | Available Oct. 2013 | Catalog no. 60054

RSMeans Commercial Renovation Cost Data 2014
Commercial/Multifamily Residential

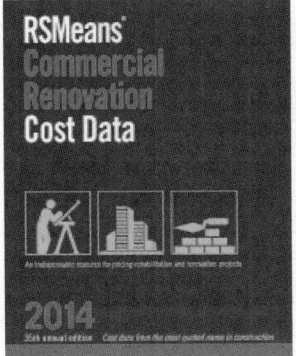

Use this valuable tool to estimate commercial and multifamily residential renovation and remodeling.

Includes: New costs for hundreds of unique methods, materials, and conditions that only come up in repair and remodeling, PLUS:

- Unit costs for more than 19,000 construction components
- Installed costs for more than 2,000 assemblies
- More than 930 "on-site" localization factors for the U.S. and Canada

$156.95 | Available Oct. 2013 | Catalog no. 60044

RSMeans Electrical Cost Data 2014

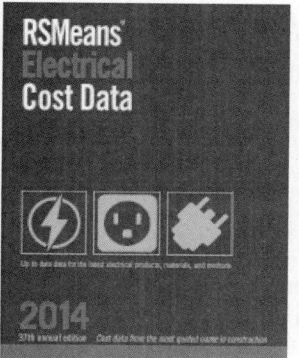

Pricing information for every part of electrical cost planning. More than 13,000 unit and systems costs with design tables; clear specifications and drawings; engineering guides; illustrated estimating procedures; complete labor-hour and materials costs for better scheduling and procurement; and the latest electrical products and construction methods.

- A variety of special electrical systems, including cathodic protection
- Costs for maintenance, demolition, HVAC/mechanical, specialties, equipment, and more

$196.95 | Available Oct. 2013 | Catalog no. 60034

RSMeans Assemblies Cost Data 2014

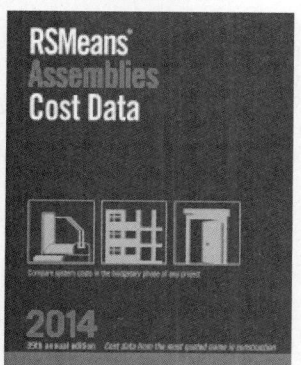

RSMeans Assemblies Cost Data takes the guesswork out of preliminary or conceptual estimates. Now you don't have to try to calculate the assembled cost by working up individual component costs. We've done all the work for you.

Presents detailed illustrations, descriptions, specifications, and costs for every conceivable building assembly—over 350 types in all—arranged in the easy-to-use UNIFORMAT II system. Each illustrated "assembled" cost includes a complete grouping of materials and associated installation costs, including the installing contractor's overhead and profit.

$315.95 | Available Sept. 2013 | Catalog no. 60064

RSMeans Residential Cost Data 2014

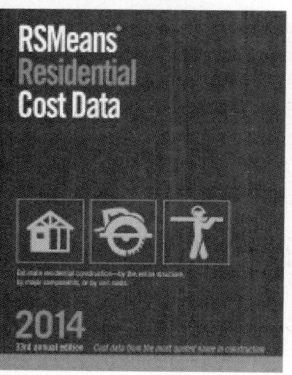

Contains square foot costs for 28 basic home models with the look of today, plus hundreds of custom additions and modifications you can quote right off the page. Includes costs for more than 700 residential systems. Complete with blank estimating forms, sample estimates, and step-by-step instructions.

Contains line items for cultured stone and brick, PVC trim lumber, and TPO roofing.

$139.95 | Available Oct. 2013 | Catalog no. 60174

RSMeans Electrical Change Order Cost Data 2014

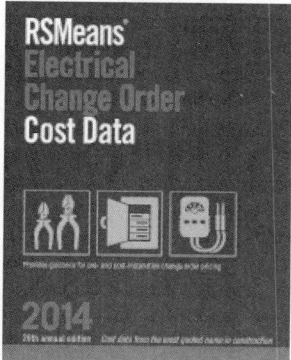

RSMeans Electrical Change Order Cost Data provides you with electrical unit prices exclusively for pricing change orders—based on the recent, direct experience of contractors and suppliers. Analyze and check your own change order estimates against the experience others have had doing the same work. It also covers productivity analysis and change order cost justifications. With useful information for calculating the effects of change orders and dealing with their administration.

$187.95 | Available Dec. 2013 | Catalog no. 60234

RSMeans Open Shop Building Construction Cost Data 2014

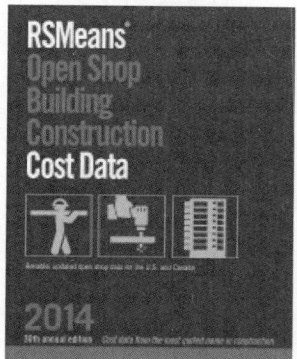

The latest costs for accurate budgeting and estimating of new commercial and residential construction . . . renovation work . . . change orders . . . cost engineering.

RSMeans Open Shop "BCCD" will assist you to:

- Develop benchmark prices for change orders
- Plug gaps in preliminary estimates and budgets
- Estimate complex projects
- Substantiate invoices on contracts
- Price ADA-related renovations

$165.95 | Available Dec. 2013 | Catalog no. 60154

RSMeans Site Work & Landscape Cost Data 2014

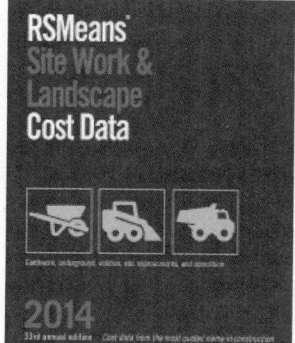

Includes unit and assemblies costs for earthwork, sewerage, piped utilities, site improvements, drainage, paving, trees and shrubs, street openings/repairs, underground tanks, and more. Contains 78 types of assemblies costs for accurate conceptual estimates.

Includes:

- Estimating for infrastructure improvements
- Environmentally-oriented construction
- ADA-mandated handicapped access
- Hazardous waste line items

$187.95 | Available Dec. 2013 | Catalog no. 60284

RSMeans Facilities Maintenance & Repair Cost Data 2014

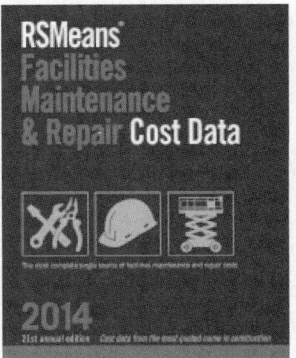

RSMeans Facilities Maintenance & Repair Cost Data gives you a complete system to manage and plan your facility repair and maintenance costs and budget efficiently. Guidelines for auditing a facility and developing an annual maintenance plan. Budgeting is included, along with reference tables on cost and management, and information on frequency and productivity of maintenance operations.

The only nationally recognized source of maintenance and repair costs. Developed in cooperation with the Civil Engineering Research Laboratory (CERL) of the Army Corps of Engineers.

$434.95 | Available Nov. 2013 | Catalog no. 60304

RSMeans Concrete & Masonry Cost Data 2014

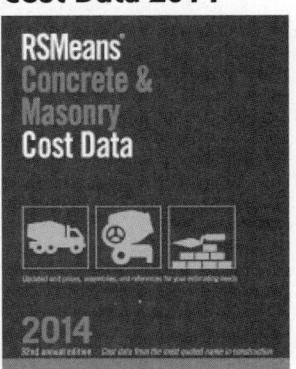

Provides you with cost facts for virtually all concrete/masonry estimating needs, from complicated formwork to various sizes and face finishes of brick and block—all in great detail. The comprehensive Unit Price Section contains more than 8,000 selected entries. Also contains an Assemblies [Cost] Section, and a detailed Reference Section that supplements the cost data.

$177.95 | Available Dec. 2013 | Catalog no. 60114

RSMeans Construction Cost Indexes 2014

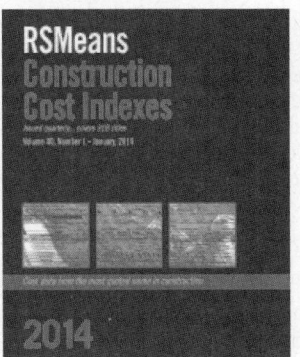

What materials and labor costs will change unexpectedly this year? By how much?

- Breakdowns for 318 major cities
- National averages for 30 key cities
- Expanded five major city indexes
- Historical construction cost indexes

$362.00 per year (subscription) | Catalog no. 50144
$93.50 individual quarters | Catalog no. 60144 A,B,C,D

RSMeans Light Commercial Cost Data 2014

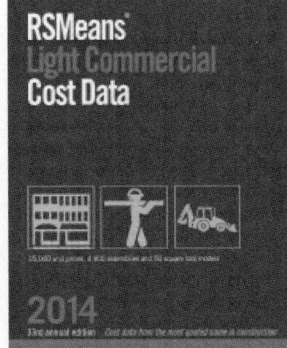

Specifically addresses the light commercial market, which is a specialized niche in the construction industry. Aids you, the owner/designer/contractor, in preparing all types of estimates—from budgets to detailed bids. Includes new advances in methods and materials.

Assemblies Section allows you to evaluate alternatives in the early stages of design/planning.

More than 15,000 unit costs ensure that you have the prices you need . . . when you need them.

$144.95 | Available Nov. 2013 | Catalog no. 60184

RSMeans Labor Rates for the Construction Industry 2014

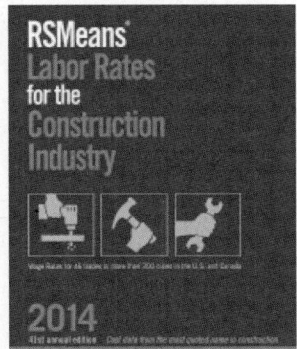

Complete information for estimating labor costs, making comparisons, and negotiating wage rates by trade for more than 300 U.S. and Canadian cities. With 46 construction trades listed by local union number in each city, and historical wage rates included for comparison. Each city chart lists the county and is alphabetically arranged with handy visual flip tabs for quick reference.

$424.95 | Available Dec. 2013 | Catalog no. 60124

RSMeans Interior Cost Data 2014

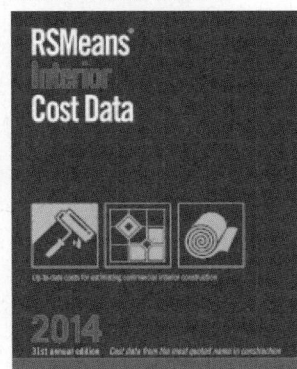

Provides you with prices and guidance needed to make accurate interior work estimates. Contains costs on materials, equipment, hardware, custom installations, furnishings, and labor costs . . . for new and remodel commercial and industrial interior construction, including updated information on office furnishings, and reference information.

$196.95 | Available Nov. 2013 | Catalog no. 60094

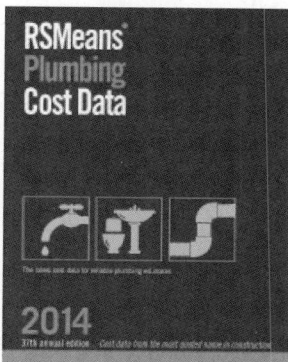

Professional Development

RSMeans Online™ Training

Construction estimating is vital to the decision-making process at each state of every project. RSMeansOnline works the way you do. It's systematic, flexible and intuitive. In this one day class you will see how you can estimate any phase of any project faster and better.

Some of what you'll learn:
- Customizing RSMeansOnline
- Making the most of RSMeans "Circle Reference" numbers
- How to integrate your cost data
- Generate reports, exporting estimates to MS Excel, sharing, collaborating and more

Also available: RSMeans Online™ training webinar

Facilities Construction Estimating

In this *two-day* course, professionals working in facilities management can get help with their daily challenges to establish budgets for all phases of a project.

Some of what you'll learn:
- Determining the full scope of a project
- Identifying the scope of risks and opportunities
- Creative solutions to estimating issues
- Organizing estimates for presentation and discussion
- Special techniques for repair/remodel and maintenance projects
- Negotiating project change orders

Who should attend: facility managers, engineers, contractors, facility tradespeople, planners, and project managers.

Scheduling with Microsoft Project

Two days of hands-on training gives you a look at the basics to putting it all together with MS Project to create a complete project schedule. Learn to work better and faster, manage changes and updates, enhance tracking, generate actionable reports, and boost control of your time and budget.

Some of what you'll learn:
- Defining task/activity relationships: link tasks, establish predecessor/successor relationships and create logs
- Baseline scheduling: the essential what/when
- Using MS Project to determine the critical path
- Integrate RSMeans data with MS Project
- The dollar-loaded schedule: enhance the reliability of this "must-know" technique for scheduling public projects.

Who should attend: contractors' project-management teams, architects and engineers, project owners and their representatives, and those interested in improving their project planning and scheduling and management skills.

Maintenance & Repair Estimating for Facilities

This *two-day* course teaches attendees how to plan, budget, and estimate the cost of ongoing and preventive maintenance and repair for existing buildings and grounds.

Some of what you'll learn:
- The most financially favorable maintenance, repair, and replacement scheduling and estimating
- Auditing and value engineering facilities
- Preventive planning and facilities upgrading
- Determining both in-house and contract-out service costs
- Annual, asset-protecting M&R plan

Who should attend: facility managers, maintenance supervisors, buildings and grounds superintendents, plant managers, planners, estimators, and others involved in facilities planning and budgeting.

Practical Project Management for Construction Professionals

In this *two-day* course, acquire the essential knowledge and develop the skills to effectively and efficiently execute the day-to-day responsibilities of the construction project manager.

Covers:
- General conditions of the construction contract
- Contract modifications: change orders and construction change directives
- Negotiations with subcontractors and vendors
- Effective writing: notification and communications
- Dispute resolution: claims and liens

Who should attend: architects, engineers, owner's representatives, project managers.

Mechanical & Electrical Estimating

This *two-day* course teaches attendees how to prepare more accurate and complete mechanical/electrical estimates, avoiding the pitfalls of omission and double-counting, while understanding the composition and rationale within the RSMeans mechanical/electrical database.

Some of what you'll learn:
- The unique way mechanical and electrical systems are interrelated
- M&E estimates—conceptual, planning, budgeting, and bidding stages
- Order of magnitude, square foot, assemblies, and unit price estimating
- Comparative cost analysis of equipment and design alternatives

Who should attend: architects, engineers, facilities managers, mechanical and electrical contractors, and others who need a highly reliable method for developing, understanding, and evaluating mechanical and electrical contracts.

Professional Development

Unit Price Estimating

This interactive *two-day* seminar teaches attendees how to interpret project information and process it into final, detailed estimates with the greatest accuracy level.

The most important credential an estimator can take to the job is the ability to visualize construction and estimate accurately.

Some of what you'll learn:
- Interpreting the design in terms of cost
- The most detailed, time-tested methodology for accurate pricing
- Key cost drivers—material, labor, equipment, staging, and subcontracts
- Understanding direct and indirect costs for accurate job cost accounting and change order management

Who should attend: corporate and government estimators and purchasers, architects, engineers, and others who need to produce accurate project estimates.

RSMeans CostWorks® CD Training

This one-day course helps users become more familiar with the functionality of *RSMeans CostWork*s program. Each menu, icon, screen, and function found in the program is explained in depth. Time is devoted to hands-on estimating exercises.

Some of what you'll learn:
- Searching the database using all navigation methods
- Exporting RSMeans data to your preferred spreadsheet format
- Viewing crews, assembly components, and much more
- Automatically regionalizing the database

This training session requires you to bring a laptop computer to class.

When you register for this course you will receive an outline for your laptop requirements.

Also offering web training for CostWorks CD!

Facilities Est. Using RSMeans CostWorks® CD

Combines hands-on skill building with best estimating practices and real-life problems. Brings you up-to-date with key concepts, and provides tips, pointers, and guidelines to save time and avoid cost oversights and errors.

Some of what you'll learn:
- Estimating process concepts
- Customizing and adapting RSMeans cost data
- Establishing scope of work to account for all known variables
- Budget estimating: when, why, and how
- Site visits: what to look for—what you can't afford to overlook
- How to estimate repair and remodeling variables

This training session requires you to bring a laptop computer to class.

Who should attend: facility managers, architects, engineers, contractors, facility tradespeople, planners, project managers and anyone involved with JOC, SABRE, or IDIQ.

Conceptual Estimating Using RSMeans CostWorks® CD

This *two day* class uses the leading industry data and a powerful software package to develop highly accurate conceptual estimates for your construction projects. All attendees must bring a laptop computer loaded with the current year *Square Foot Model Costs* and the *Assemblies Cost Data* CostWorks titles.

Some of what you'll learn:
- Introduction to conceptual estimating
- Types of conceptual estimates
- Helpful hints
- Order of magnitude estimating
- Square foot estimating
- Assemblies estimating

Who should attend: architects, engineers, contractors, construction estimators, owner's representatives, and anyone looking for an electronic method for performing square foot estimating.

Assessing Scope of Work for Facility Construction Estimating

This *two-day* practical training program addresses the vital importance of understanding the SCOPE of projects in order to produce accurate cost estimates for facility repair and remodeling.

Some of what you'll learn:
- Discussions of site visits, plans/specs, record drawings of facilities, and site-specific lists
- Review of CSI divisions, including means, methods, materials, and the challenges of scoping each topic
- Exercises in SCOPE identification and SCOPE writing for accurate estimating of projects
- Hands-on exercises that require SCOPE, take-off, and pricing

Who should attend: corporate and government estimators, planners, facility managers, and others who need to produce accurate project estimates.

Unit Price Est. Using RSMeans CostWorks® CD

Step-by-step instruction and practice problems to identify and track key cost drivers—material, labor, equipment, staging, and subcontractors—for each specific task. Learn the most detailed, time-tested methodology for accurately "pricing" these variables, their impact on each other and on total cost.

Some of what you'll learn:
- Unit price cost estimating
- Order of magnitude, square foot, and assemblies estimating
- Quantity takeoff
- Direct and indirect construction costs
- Development of contractor's bill rates
- How to use *RSMeans Building Construction Cost Data*

This training session requires you to bring a laptop computer to class.

Who should attend: architects, engineers, corporate and government estimators, facility managers, and government procurement staff.

Professional Development

For more information visit the RSMeans website at **www.rsmeans.com**

Registration Information

Register early . . . Save up to $100! Register 30 days before the start date of a seminar and save $100 off your total fee. *Note: This discount can be applied only once per order. It cannot be applied to team discount registrations or any other special offer.*

How to register Register by phone today! The RSMeans toll-free number for making reservations is **1-800-334-3509, Press 1.**

Two day seminar registration fee - $935. One-day *RSMeans CostWorks*® **training registration fee - $375.** To register by mail, complete the registration form and return, with your full fee, to: RSMeans Seminars, 700 Longwater Drive, Norwell, MA 02061.

Government pricing All federal government employees save off the regular seminar price. Other promotional discounts cannot be combined with the government discount.

Team discount program for two to four seminar registrations. Call for pricing: 1-800-334-3509, Press 1

Multiple course discounts When signing up for two or more courses, call for pricing.

Refund policy Cancellations will be accepted up to ten business days prior to the seminar start. There are no refunds for cancellations received later than ten working days prior to the first day of the seminar. A $150 processing fee will be applied for all cancellations. Written notice of cancellation is required. Substitutions can be made at any time before the session starts. **No-shows are subject to the full seminar fee.**

AACE approved courses Many seminars described and offered here have been approved for 14 hours (1.4 recertification credits) of credit by the AACE

International Certification Board toward meeting the continuing education requirements for recertification as a Certified Cost Engineer/Certified Cost Consultant.

AIA Continuing Education We are registered with the AIA Continuing Education System (AIA/CES) and are committed to developing quality learning activities in accordance with the CES criteria. Many seminars meet the AIA/CES criteria for Quality Level 2. AIA members may receive (14) learning units (LUs) for each two-day RSMeans course.

Daily course schedule The first day of each seminar session begins at 8:30 a.m. and ends at 4:30 p.m. The second day begins at 8:00 a.m. and ends at 4:00 p.m. Participants are urged to bring a hand-held calculator, since many actual problems will be worked out in each session.

Continental breakfast Your registration includes the cost of a continental breakfast, and a morning and afternoon refreshment break. These informal segments allow you to discuss topics of mutual interest with other seminar attendees. (You are free to make your own lunch and dinner arrangements.)

Hotel/transportation arrangements RSMeans arranges to hold a block of rooms at most host hotels. To take advantage of special group rates when making your reservation, be sure to mention that you are attending the RSMeans seminar. You are, of course, free to stay at the lodging place of your choice. (**Hotel reservations and transportation arrangements should be made directly by seminar attendees.**)

Important Class sizes are limited, so please register as soon as possible.

Note: Pricing subject to change.

Registration Form

ADDS-1000

Call 1-800-334-3509, Press 1 to register or FAX this form 1-800-632-6732. Visit our website: www.rsmeans.com

Please register the following people for the RSMeans construction seminars as shown here. We understand that we must make our own hotel reservations if overnight stays are necessary.

☐ Full payment of $_____enclosed.

☐ Bill me.

Please print name of registrant(s).

(To appear on certificate of completion)

_____

_____

_____

_____

P.O. #: _____
GOVERNMENT AGENCIES MUST SUPPLY PURCHASE ORDER NUMBER OR TRAINING FORM.

Please mail check to: RSMeans Seminars, 700 Longwater Drive, Norwell, MA 02061 USA

Firm name_____

Address_____

City/State/Zip_____

Telephone no._____ Fax no._____

E-mail address_____

Charge registration(s) to: ☐ MasterCard ☐ VISA ☐ American Express

Account no._____ Exp. date_____

Cardholder's signature_____

Seminar name_____

Seminar City _____

Solar Energy: Technologies & Project Delivery for Buildings

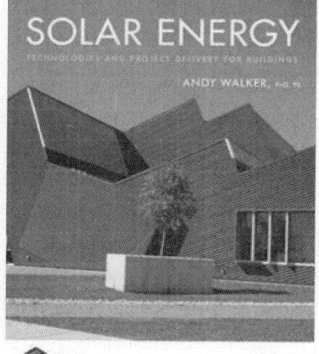

by Andy Walker

An authoritative reference on the design of solar energy systems in building projects, with applications, operating principles, and simple tools for the construction, engineering, and design professionals, the book simplifies the solar design and engineering process and provides sample documentation for the complete design of a solar energy system for buildings.

$85.00 | 320 pages, hardover | Catalog no. 67365

Project Scheduling & Management for Construction, 4th Edition

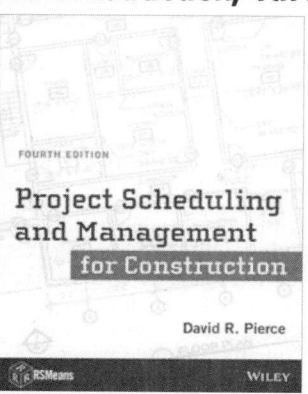

by David R. Pierce

First published in 1988 by RSMeans, the new edition of *Project Scheduling and Management for Construction* has been substantially revised for both professionals and students enrolled in construction management and civil engineering programs. While retaining its emphasis on developing practical, professional-level scheduling skills, the new edition is a relatable, real world case study.

$95.00 | 272 pages, softcover | Catalog no. 67367

Estimating Building Costs, 2nd Edition

For the Residential & Light Commercial Construction Professional

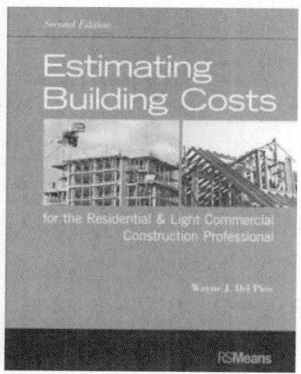

by Wayne J. Del Pico

This book guides readers through the entire estimating process, explaining in detail how to put together a reliable estimate that can be used not only for budgeting, but also for developing a schedule, managing a project, dealing with contingencies, and ultimately making a profit.

Completely revised and updated to reflect the CSI MasterFormat 2010 system, this practical guide describes estimating techniques for each building system and how to apply them according to the latest industry standards.

$75.00 | 398 pages, softcover | Catalog no. 67343A

Project Control: Integrating Cost & Schedule in Construction

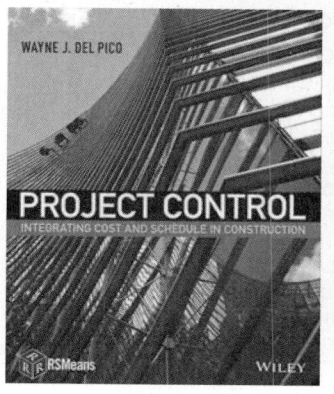

by Wayne J. Del Pico

Written by a seasoned professional in the field, *Project Control: Integrating Cost and Schedule in Construction* fills a void in the area of project control as applied in the construction industry today. It demonstrates how productivity models for an individual project are created, monitored, and controlled, and how corrective actions are implemented as deviations from the baseline occur.

$95.00 | 240 pages, softcover | Catalog no. 67366

How to Estimate with Means Data & CostWorks, 4th Edition

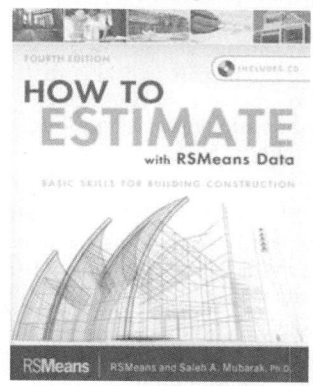

by RSMeans and Saleh A. Mubarak, Ph.D.

This step-by-step guide takes you through all the major construction items with extensive coverage of site work, concrete and masonry, wood and metal framing, doors and windows, and other divisions. The only construction cost estimating handbook that uses the most popular source of construction data, RSMeans, this indispensible guide features access to the instructional version of CostWorks in electronic form, enabling you to practice techniques to solve real-world estimating problems.

$75.00 | 292 pages, softcover | Includes CostWorks CD
Catalog no. 67324C

RSMeans Cost Data, Student Edition

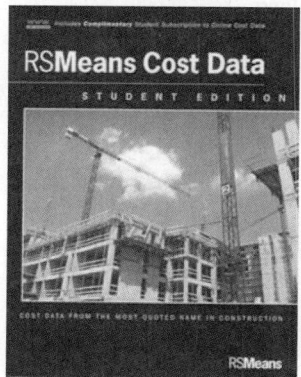

This book provides a thorough introduction to cost estimating in a self-contained print and online package. With clear explanations and a hands-on, example-driven approach, it is the ideal reference for students and new professionals.

Features include:

- Commercial and residential construction cost data in print and online formats
- Complete how-to guidance on the essentials of cost estimating
- A supplemental website with plans, problem sets, and a full sample estimate

$99.00 | 512 pages, softcover | Catalog no. 67363

Reference Books

For more information visit the RSMeans website at **www.rsmeans.com**

Value Engineering: Practical Applications

For Design, Construction, Maintenance & Operations

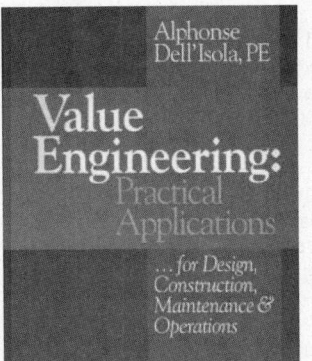

by Alphonse Dell'Isola, PE

A tool for immediate application—for engineers, architects, facility managers, owners, and contractors. Includes making the case for VE—the management briefing; integrating VE into planning, budgeting, and design; conducting life cycle costing; using VE methodology in design review and consultant selection; case studies; VE workbook; and a life cycle costing program on disk.

$85.00 | Over 450 pages, illustrated, softcover | Catalog no. 67319A

Risk Management for Design & Construction

Introduces risk as a central pillar of project management and shows how a project manager can prepare to deal with uncertainty. Experts in the field use clear, straightforward terminology to demystify the concepts of project uncertainty and risk. Includes:

• Integrated cost and schedule risk analysis

• An introduction to a ready-to-use system of analyzing a project's risks and tools to proactively manage risks

• A methodology that was developed and used by the Washington State Department of Transportation

• Case studies and examples on the proper application of principles
• Information about combining value analysis with risk analysis

$125.00 | Over 250 pages, softcover | Catalog no. 67359

How Your House Works, 2nd Edition

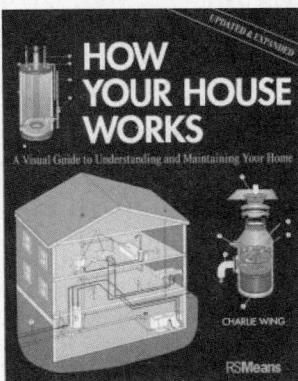

by Charlie Wing

Knowledge of your home's systems helps you control repair and construction costs and makes sure the correct elements are being installed or replaced. This book uncovers the mysteries behind just about every major appliance and building element in your house. See-through, cross-section drawings in full color show you exactly how these things should be put together and how they function, including what to check if they don't work. It just might save you having to call in a professional.

$22.95 | 192 pages, softcover | Catalog no. 67351A

Complete Book of Framing, 2nd Edition

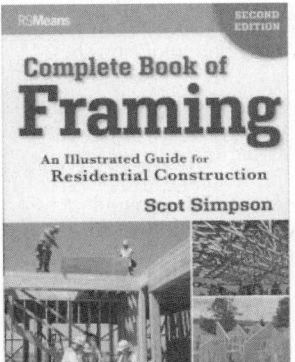

by Scot Simpson

This updated, easy-to-learn guide to rough carpentry and framing is written by an expert with more than thirty years of framing experience. Starting with the basics, this book begins with types of lumber, nails, and what tools are needed, followed by detailed, fully illustrated steps for framing each building element. Framer-Friendly Tips throughout the book show how to get a task done right—and more easily.

$29.95 | 352 pages, softcover | Catalog no. 67353A

Green Home Improvement

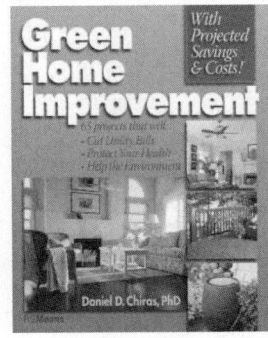

by Daniel D. Chiras, PhD

With energy costs rising and environmental awareness increasing, people are looking to make their homes greener. This book, with 65 projects and actual costs and projected savings help homeowners prioritize their green improvements.

Projects range from simple water savers that cost only a few dollars, to bigger-ticket items such as HVAC systems. With color photos and cost estimates, each project compares options and describes the work involved, the benefits, and the savings.

$34.95 | 320 pages, illustrated, softcover | Catalog no. 67355

Life Cycle Costing for Facilities

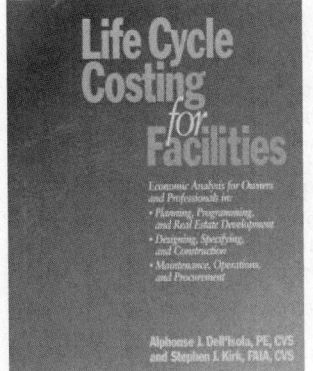

by Alphonse Dell'Isola and Dr. Steven Kirk

Guidance for achieving higher quality design and construction projects at lower costs! Cost-cutting efforts often sacrifice quality to yield the cheapest product. Life cycle costing enables building designers and owners to achieve both. The authors of this book show how LCC can work for a variety of projects — from roads to HVAC upgrades to different types of buildings.

$99.95 | 396 pages, hardcover | Catalog no. 67341

For more information visit the RSMeans website at **www.rsmeans.com**

Builder's Essentials: Plan Reading & Material Takeoff
For Residential and Light Commercial Construction

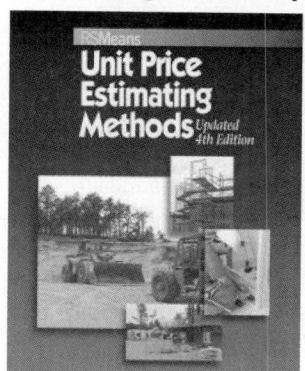

by Wayne J. DelPico

A valuable tool for understanding plans and specs, and accurately calculating material quantities. Step-by-step instructions and takeoff procedures based on a full set of working drawings.

$45.00 | Over 420 pages, softcover | Catalog no. 67307

Means Unit Price Estimating Methods, 4th Edition

Includes cost data and estimating examples, updated to reflect changes to the CSI numbering system and new features of RSMeans cost data. It describes the most productive, universally accepted ways to estimate, and uses checklists and forms to illustrate shortcuts and timesavers. A model estimate demonstrates procedures. A new chapter explores computer estimating alternatives.

$75.00 | Over 350 pages, illustrated, softcover | Catalog no. 67303B

Concrete Repair & Maintenance Illustrated

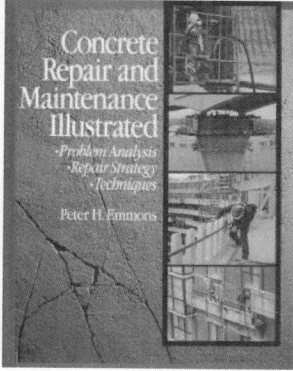

by Peter Emmons

Hundreds of illustrations show users how to analyze, repair, clean, and maintain concrete structures for optimal performance and cost effectiveness. From parking garages to roads and bridges to structural concrete, this comprehensive book describes the causes, effects, and remedies for concrete wear and failure. Invaluable for planning jobs, selecting materials, and training employees, this book is a must-have for concrete specialists, general contractors, facility managers, civil and structural engineers, and architects.

$75.00 | 300 pages, illustrated, softcover | Catalog no. 67146

Square Foot & UNIFORMAT Assemblies Estimating Methods, 3rd Edition

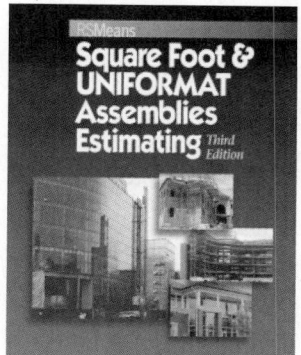

Develop realistic square foot and assemblies costs for budgeting and construction funding. The new edition features updated guidance on square foot and assemblies estimating using UNIFORMAT II. An essential reference for anyone who performs conceptual estimates.

$75.00 | Over 300 pages, illustrated, softcover | Catalog no. 67145B

Electrical Estimating Methods, 3rd Edition

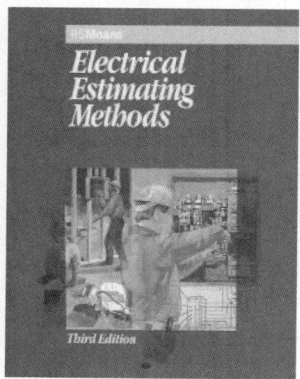

Expanded edition includes sample estimates and cost information in keeping with the latest version of the CSI MasterFormat and UNIFORMAT II. Complete coverage of fiber optic and uninterruptible power supply electrical systems, broken down by components, and explained in detail. Includes a new chapter on computerized estimating methods. A practical companion to *RSMeans Electrical Cost Data.*

$75.00 | Over 325 pages, hardcover | Catalog no. 67230B

Residential & Light Commercial Construction Standards, 3rd Edition

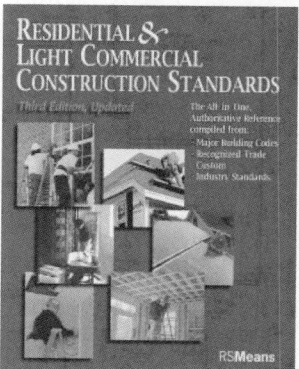

Updated by RSMeans and contributing authors

This book provides authoritative requirements and recommendations compiled from leading professional associations, industry publications, and building code organizations. This all-in-one reference helps establish a standard for workmanship, quickly resolve disputes, and avoid defect claims. Updated third edition includes new coverage of green building, seismic, hurricane, and mold-resistant construction.

$65.00 | Over 550 pages, illustrated, softcover | Catalog no. 67322B

Reference Books

For more information visit the RSMeans website at **www.rsmeans.com**

Construction Business Management

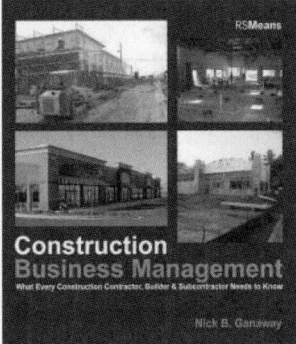

by Nick Ganaway

Only 43% of construction firms stay in business after four years. Make sure your company thrives with valuable guidance from a pro with 25 years of success as a commercial contractor. Find out what it takes to build all aspects of a business that is profitable, enjoyable, and enduring. With a bonus chapter on retail construction.

$55.00 | 200 pages, softcover | Catalog no. 67352

The Practice of Cost Segregation Analysis

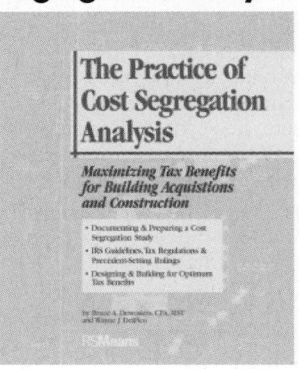

by Bruce A. Desrosiers and Wayne J. DelPico

This expert guide walks you through the practice of cost segregation analysis, which enables property owners to defer taxes and benefit from "accelerated cost recovery" through depreciation deductions on assets that are properly identified and classified.

With a glossary of terms, sample cost segregation estimates for various building types, key information resources, and updates via a dedicated website, this book is a critical resource for anyone involved in cost segregation analysis.

$105.00 | Over 225 pages | Catalog no. 67345

Green Building: Project Planning & Cost Estimating, 3rd Edition

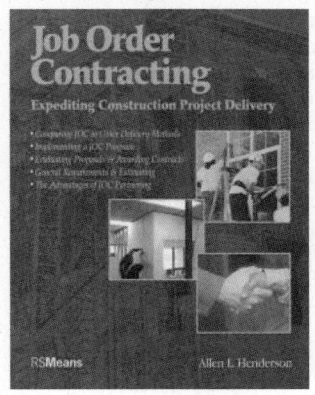

Since the widely read first edition of this book, green building has gone from a growing trend to a major force in design and construction.

This new edition has been updated with the latest in green building technologies, design concepts, standards, and costs. Full-color with all new case studies—plus a new chapter on commercial real estate.

$110.00 | Over 450 pages, softcover | Catalog no. 67338B

Project Scheduling & Management for Construction, 3rd Edition

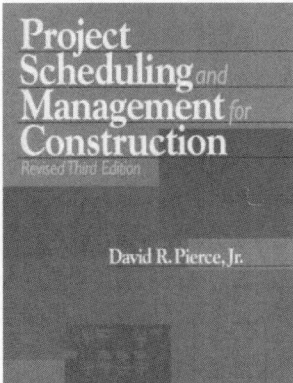

by David R. Pierce, Jr.

A comprehensive yet easy-to-follow guide to construction project scheduling and control—from vital project management principles through the latest scheduling, tracking, and controlling techniques. The author is a leading authority on scheduling, with years of field and teaching experience at leading academic institutions. Spend a few hours with this book and come away with a solid understanding of this essential management topic.

$64.95 | Over 300 pages, illustrated, hardcover | Catalog no. 67247B

Preventive Maintenance for Multi-Family Housing

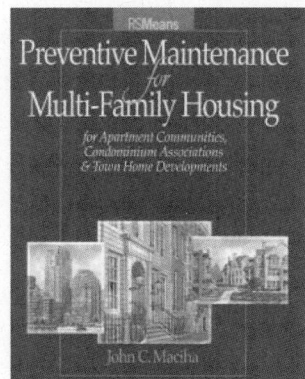

by John C. Maciha

Prepared by one of the nation's leading experts on multi-family housing.

This complete PM system for apartment and condominium communities features expert guidance, checklists for buildings and grounds maintenance tasks and their frequencies, a reusable wall chart to track maintenance, and a dedicated website featuring customizable electronic forms. A must-have for anyone involved with multi-family housing maintenance and upkeep.

$95.00 | 225 pages | Catalog no. 67346

Job Order Contracting: Expediting Construction Project Delivery

by Allen L. Henderson

Expert guidance to help you implement JOC—fast becoming the preferred project delivery method for repair and renovation, minor new construction, and maintenance projects in the public sector and in many states and municipalities. The author, a leading JOC expert and practitioner, shows how to:

- Establish a JOC program
- Evaluate proposals & award contracts
- Handle general requirements and estimating
- Partner for maximum benefits

$89.95 | 192 pages, illustrated, hardcover | Catalog no. 67348

Reference Books

For more information visit the RSMeans website at **www.rsmeans.com**

Construction Supervision

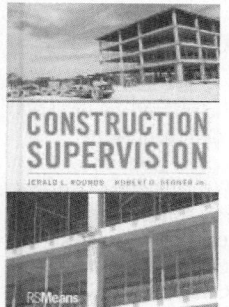

This brand new title inspires supervisory excellence with proven tactics and techniques applied by thousands of construction supervisors over the past decade. Recognizing the unique and critical role the supervisor plays in project success, the book's leadership guidelines carve out a practical blueprint for motivating work performance and increasing productivity through effective communication.

Features:

- A unique focus on field supervision and crew management

- Coverage of supervision from the foreman to the superintendent level

- An overview of technical skills whose mastery will build confidence and success for the supervisor

- A detailed view of "soft" management and communication skills

$95.00 | Over 450 pages, softcover | Catalog no. 67358

Building & Renovating Schools

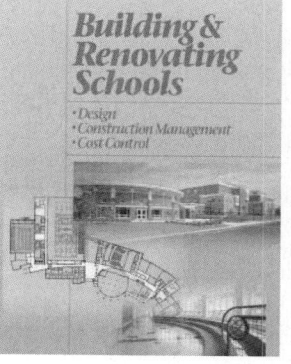

This all-inclusive guide covers every step of the school construction process—from initial planning, needs assessment, and design, right through moving into the new facility. A must-have resource for anyone concerned with new school construction or renovation. With square foot cost models for elementary, middle, and high school facilities, and real-life case studies of recently completed school projects.

The contributors to this book—architects, construction project managers, contractors, and estimators who specialize in school construction—provide start-to-finish, expert guidance on the process.

$99.95 | Over 425 pages, hardcover | Catalog no. 67342

The Homeowner's Guide to Mold

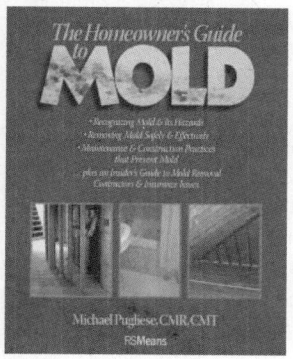

By Michael Pugliese

Expert guidance to protect your health and your home.

Mold, whether caused by leaks, humidity or flooding, is a real health and financial issue—for homeowners and contractors.

This full-color book explains:

- Construction and maintenance practices to prevent mold

- How to inspect for and remove mold

- Mold remediation procedures and costs

- What to do after a flood

- How to deal with insurance companies

$21.95 | 144 pages, softcover | Catalog no. 67344

Universal Design Ideas for Style, Comfort & Safety

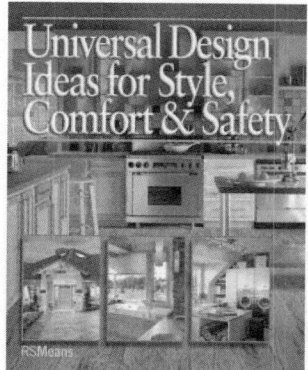

by RSMeans and Lexicon Consulting, Inc.

Incorporating universal design when building or remodeling helps people of any age and physical ability more fully and safely enjoy their living spaces. This book shows how universal design can be artfully blended into the most attractive homes. It discusses specialized products like adjustable countertops and chair lifts, as well as simple ways to enhance a home's safety and comfort. With color photos and expert guidance, every area of the home is covered. Includes budget estimates that give an idea how much projects will cost.

$21.95 | 160 pages, illustrated, softcover | Catalog no. 67354

Landscape Estimating Methods, 5th Edition

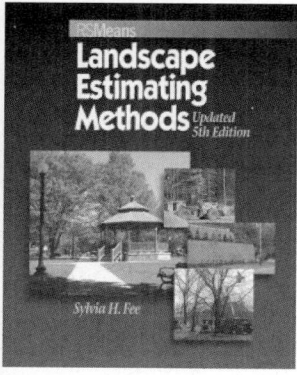

Answers questions about preparing competitive landscape construction estimates, with up-to-date cost estimates and the new MasterFormat classification system. Expanded and revised to address the latest materials and methods, including new coverage on approaches to green building. Includes:

- Step-by-step explanation of the estimating process

- Sample forms and worksheets that save time and prevent errors

$75.00 | Over 350 pages, softcover | Catalog no. 67295C

Plumbing Estimating Methods, 3rd Edition

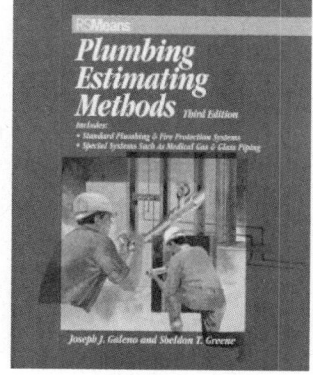

by Joseph J. Galeno and Sheldon T. Greene

Updated and revised! This practical guide walks you through a plumbing estimate, from basic materials and installation methods through change order analysis. *Plumbing Estimating Methods* covers residential, commercial, industrial, and medical systems, and features sample takeoff and estimate forms and detailed illustrations of systems and components.

$65.00 | 330+ pages, softcover | Catalog no. 67283B

Reference Books

For more information visit the RSMeans website at **www.rsmeans.com**

Understanding & Negotiating Construction Contracts

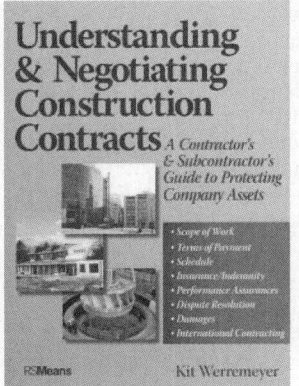

by Kit Werremeyer

Take advantage of the author's 30 years' experience in small-to-large (including international) construction projects. Learn how to identify, understand, and evaluate high risk terms and conditions typically found in all construction contracts—then negotiate to lower or eliminate the risk, improve terms of payment, and reduce exposure to claims and disputes. The author avoids "legalese" and gives real-life examples from actual projects.

$80.00 | 300 pages, softcover | Catalog no. 67350

The Gypsum Construction Handbook

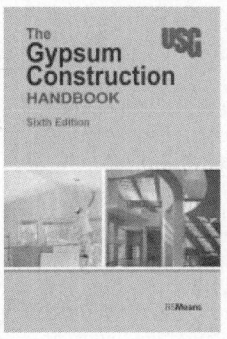

by USG

An invaluable reference of construction procedures for gypsum drywall, cement board, veneer plaster, and conventional plaster. This new edition includes the newest product developments, installation methods, fire- and sound-rated construction information, illustrated framing-to-finish application instructions, estimating and planning information, and more. Great for architects and engineers; contractors, builders, and dealers; apprentices and training programs; building inspectors and code officials; and anyone interested in gypsum construction. Features information on tools and safety practices, a glossary of construction terms, and a list of important agencies and associations. Also available in Spanish.

$40.00 | Over 575 pages, illustrated, softcover | Catalog no. 67357A

Mechanical Estimating Methods, 4th Edition

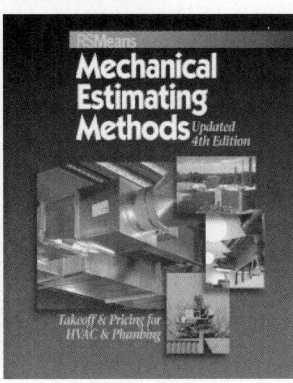

Completely updated, this guide assists you in making a review of plans, specs, and bid packages, with suggestions for takeoff procedures, listings, substitutions, and pre-bid scheduling for all components of HVAC. Includes suggestions for budgeting labor and equipment usage. Compares materials and construction methods to allow you to select the best option.

$70.00 per copy | Over 350 pages, illustrated, softcover | Catalog no. 67294B

Means Illustrated Construction Dictionary

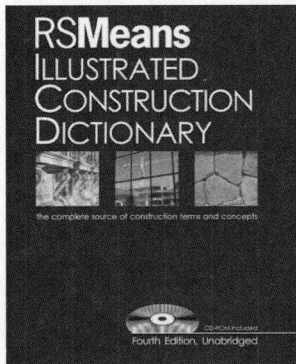

Unabridged 4th Edition, with CD-ROM

Long regarded as the industry's finest, *Means Illustrated Construction Dictionary* is now even better. With nearly 20,000 terms and more than 1,400 illustrations and photos, it is the clear choice for the most comprehensive and current information. The companion CD-ROM that comes with this new edition adds extra features such as: larger graphics and expanded definitions.

$99.95 | Over 790 pages, illust., hardcover | Catalog no. 67292B

RSMeans Estimating Handbook, 3rd Edition

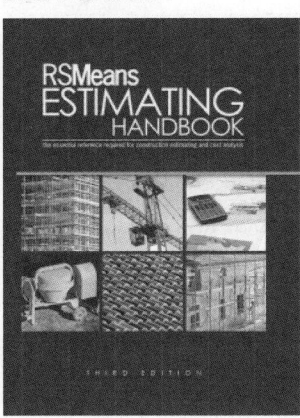

Widely used in the industry for tasks ranging from routine estimates to special cost analysis projects, this handbook has been completely updated and reorganized with new and expanded technical information.

RSMeans Estimating Handbook will help construction professionals:

- Evaluate architectural plans and specifications
- Prepare accurate quantity takeoffs
- Compare design alternatives and costs
- Perform value engineering
- Double-check estimates and quotes
- Estimate change orders

$110.00 | Over 900 pages, hardcover | Catalog No. 67276B